9. Inform editors if you're submitting simultaneous or previously published poems. (Note: Some editors will not consider such submissions.)

10. Enclose a SASE or, for reply from outside your country, a SAE with IRCs (from the post office) with every query, submission and/or follow-up letter.

11. Weigh your manuscript before mailing to be sure you include sufficient postage and an appropriate size envelope for its return.

12. Always keep copies of your work as well as detailed records of where and when you submitted your poems.

For more information about submitting your poetry for publication, read:

How to Use Your Poet's Market, page 3

The Business of Poetry, page 6

The Publishers of Poetry introduction, page 29

1994
Poet's Market

*Where & How to Publish
Your Poetry*

Edited by

*Michael J. Bugeja
and
Christine Martin*

WRITER'S DIGEST BOOKS
CINCINNATI, OHIO

If you are a poetry publisher and would like to be considered for a listing in the next edition of Poet's Market, *please request a questionnaire from* Poet's Market, *1507 Dana Ave., Cincinnati, Ohio 45207.*

Distributed in Canada by McGraw-Hill,
300 Water Street
Whitby Ontario L1N 9B6.
Also distributed in Australia by Kirby Books, Private Bag No. 19, P.O. Alexandria NSW 2015.

Managing Editor, Market Books Department:
Constance J. Achabal
Supervising Editor: Michael Willins

This 1994 hardcover edition of Poet's Market *features a "self-jacket" that eliminates the need for a separate dust jacket. It provides sturdy protection for your book while it saves paper, trees and energy.*

International Standard Serial Number
0883-5470
International Standard Book Number
0-89879-611-3

Contents

The Markets

Resources

Indexes

From the Editors

While writing poetry is a solitary affair, marketing poetry does not need to be! At **Poet's Market**, we strive to draw the poetry community together, to put you, the poet, in direct touch with editors and publishers.

To accomplish our task, we've expanded this year's directory—literally. In fact, you'll find 24 more pages in this edition than in our previous one. The book's growth is the result of more than 300 *new* listings as well as more detailed information and increased editorial commentary.

And, for the first time, we've included a section on Conferences and Workshops. These events not only provide opportunities for you to learn more about writing poetry, but they also serve as a forum where you can meet poets, editors and publishers face-to-face.

Of course, the Publishers of Poetry section remains the largest and most important part of **Poet's Market**. All told, this section lists 1,700 poetry markets, including mass circulation and literary magazines, trade book publishers, small presses and university quarterlies.

Whether a tried-and-true market or brand new one, each listing contains up-to-date details about the publisher's policies. And we're constantly adding and/or refining information to reflect changes in the marketplace. This year, for instance, we've noted if editors require cover letters with submissions and whether they are open to unsolicited book reviews.

In addition, coeditor, poet Michael J. Bugeja, continues to personally review publications and add comments to listings to let you know exactly what editors are publishing—whether they favor lyric free verse or formal pieces, for example. And, beginning with this edition, we've included information about the awards or honors a publication has received. Together, these comments will help you better evaluate possible markets.

You'll also find special codes within the listings and indexes at the back of the book to help you determine which publishers are potential markets for your work. (See How to Use Your **Poet's Market** and the introduction to the Publishers of Poetry section for details.)

Yet, we do more than simply provide listings of poetry publishers. Once again, Michael covers the many aspects of properly preparing and marketing poetry submissions in The Business of Poetry. This article discusses the supplies you will need and explains exactly how you should type and mail your manuscript. Other topics include recordkeeping, simultaneous/multiple submissions, rights, anthologies, readings and book publishing.

Like the information within the listings, the material in The Business of Poetry is updated and expanded. This year, Michael pays particular attention to the question of using cover letters, offers more tips on selecting poetry contests and includes an entirely new section on marketing book reviews.

This edition also features 11 Close-up interviews with poets and editors who offer insight and advice on breaking into the field.

A few of this year's Close-up editors are primarily interested in a certain region. Tom Trusky of Ahsahta Press, for example, seeks poets writing about the American West. Janice Townley Moore, poetry editor of _Georgia Journal_, largely publishes writers living in the Southern United States. And though he publishes folks from around the world, Dennis Haskell, coeditor of _Westerly_, says his literary magazine is known for its interest in Australia and the Indian Ocean region.

Some of our featured poets, while not necessarily regional in their focus, draw ideas for their work from their environments. Both William Stafford and George Whipple seem inspired by nature. And Toi Derricotte and Charlene Blue Horse often write about their backgrounds.

Besides gaining ideas from the world around them, many of this year's poets gather support from their local writing community. Derricotte meets monthly with five women writer friends in her area. Poet Judy Klare believes belonging to two writers' groups is a key to her success. And Whipple specifically suggests you befriend other poets for "mutual encouragement." On a larger scale, those providing support to poets include editors Peter Davison, Leslie Mellichamp and Neal Bowers, all of whom offer advice in this edition.

But that's not all **Poet's Market** contains! We also include contact information for U.S. and Canadian art agencies (where you can inquire about the availability of grants) as well as listings of various contests and awards.

In addition to our new Conferences and Workshops section, there are sections devoted to Writing Colonies, where you can spend time solely on your work; Organizations, whose membership benefits include that "mutual encouragement"; and Publications, which offer articles and market information.

Finally, whether this is your first edition of **Poet's Market** or your ninth, Michael and I are always ready and willing to listen, to answer your questions or consider your suggestions. After all, we want you to have plenty of company in the marketing process . . . so the community of published poets expands.

Michael J. Bugeja

Christine Martin

Michael J. Bugeja

Christine Martin

How to Use Your Poet's Market

Poet's Market not only provides listings of poetry publishers, it is also designed to help you determine which ones are the best markets for your work. All you need to know is how to use it.

The first step is to examine your poetry. Do you write poetry that makes a political statement? Poetry about wildlife? religious symbols? other poets? Do you write sonnets? prose poems? About a certain area? In a language other than English?

Maybe you don't write any specific type of poetry. Maybe the answer depends on which one of your works we're talking about. No matter. If you've put craft into your poems, you'll find a place for them.

Start with the indexes

All Publishers of Poetry listings are coded by the category of poetry they are seeking. Publishers that desire poetry within certain realms — that is, on certain subjects, in certain forms or from certain areas — may be quickly identified by a **IV** and word(s) denoting the specialization(s). For example, *Tails of Wonder* is coded **IV-Science fiction/fantasy** because this quarterly seeks material with some connection to those genres.

Once you've considered your own poetry, you don't have to comb each page for compatible listings. Turn to the Subject Index. Here you will find all publishers with **IV** codes divided according to their specialization.

Glance through the boldface headings to locate the specialization that matches your work. If you write haiku, for instance, check under **Form/Style**. If you don't immediately find a matching specialization, look under **Themes**. If you're an older adult who writes about the animals and the lake near your home, check under both **Senior Citizen** and **Nature/Rural/Ecology** and write down those publishers that sound interesting.

Publishers may classify themselves as **Regional** in the Subject Index, but checking the Geographical Index is also helpful. Here you'll find a list of the publishers located in your state or country. While some publishers don't consider themselves explicitly "regional" in terms of the poetry they accept, they are often more open to writers from their own area.

Another useful resource, particularly if you're trying to publish a small collection of poems, is the Chapbook Publishers Index. This lists those publishers who consider chapbook manuscripts, typically 20-25 pages of poetry connected by a theme. You'll also find more information about chapbook and book publishing in The Business of Poetry.

Finally, all imprints and/or publications located at the same address are grouped together. If you've heard about a particular publisher, but can't seem to find its listing, check the General Index. The General Index lists *all* titles in the book and includes cross references where necessary.

Check market codes

Once you have a list of possible markets for your work—because of specialization or location or an interest in chapbooks—look up their listings and check the market category codes following their titles to discover how open they are to submissions.

Besides the **IV** code already discussed, publishers may also have **I, II, III** or **V**. Those with **I** are open to beginners' submissions, so if you're just starting out, try submitting to them. Publishers with **II** codes are general markets which expect poets to be familiar with literary journals and magazines. Those coded **III** are limited as to the number of submissions they accept, so chances of publishing with these folks are limited too. Finally, those with **V** are not accepting unsolicited manuscripts. Although you may have picked such a publisher out of the Geographical Index, you can't submit your poetry to it at this time. That's okay. Cross it off your list and move on to the next one.

When you discover publishers with more than one code, read their listings carefully to determine if they're still possible markets for your work. For instance, a publisher may be **I, IV-Religious**, which means it either wants religious material as well as poetry from beginners or religious material only, including poetry from beginners. For more information about market category codes, see the introduction to the Publishers of Poetry section.

Also, as you read the listings based on the indexes, others will attract your eye. Don't feel limited by those on your list. Many publications don't want to be noted for a specialization and are open to ALL types of work.

Read carefully

When you've narrowed your list of possible markets by using the indexes and checking market categories, read each listing *carefully*. Look for the general purpose of the publisher and statements about its interests in poetry. For example, *Hellas*, a semiannual journal, accepts any kind of poetry but especially welcomes poems in meter. In their listing, they say, "We prize elegance and formality in verse, but specifically encourage poetry of the utmost boldness and innovation, so long as it is not willfully obscurantist."

Also, the names of poets recently published and the sample lines of poetry will give you insight into what level of writing an editor is looking for and indicate editorial preferences.

Consider the date a publisher was founded as well. Older publishers have more stability, and sometimes more prestige. However, newer publishers, especially those new to this edition (designated by a ‡), are often more receptive to submissions.

Carefully reading the description of a publication's format will help you visualize how your poetry will appear in its pages. Better yet, review sample copies. This is the best way for you to determine whether your poetry is right for a publication. Sample copies can be ordered from publishers or often found on the shelves of your library or local bookstore.

However, don't just locate a sample copy, decide your work is appropriate and submit to that market without knowing submission procedures. Inappropriate submissions will not only leave a bad impression of your work, they can also affect a publisher's willingness to accept unsolicited manuscripts from others as well.

If you haven't already done so, read The Business of Poetry. It explains how you should submit your work, including what a manuscript should look like, how it should be mailed and how to keep records of where it was sent. Most publishers also include specific submission procedures in their listings. Finally, many publishers offer guidelines, usually for a self-addressed, stamped envelope (SASE). Send for them. The goal, after all, is to increase — not decrease — your chances of acceptance.

Other resources

As you begin submitting your poetry, you may want to consider other markets for your work, such as Contests and Awards. Preceding that section is a list of art agencies in the United States and Canada. After you've collected a number of publishing credits, contact the agency in your area to inquire about the availability of grants for creative artists.

While developing your craft, however, take advantage of the various resources for poets. For support services and feedback from others, for example, consider joining one of the groups listed under Organizations Useful to Poets. If you're looking for a place to get away and write, check Writing Colonies. On the other hand, if you're seeking instruction and marketing tips, attend one of the events in the Conferences and Workshops section or consult one of the magazines listed under Publications Useful to Poets.

Finally, if you don't recognize a symbol or an abbreviation being used, refer to the Key to Symbols on page 28 or the Glossary on page 502. And, for easy reference, you will find a list of U.S. and Canadian Postal Codes on page 27.

The Business of Poetry

by Michael J. Bugeja

Successful poets know that you need more than talent, craft and insight to make art, if you want to share it with an audience. You must market your verse—process it in a standard format, research contests and magazines, keep records, buy postage and supplies, invest in equipment and deal with editors and others involved in the creative world.

At first, though, many poets resist the business of poetry. It seems unpleasant, complex or inconvenient. They would rather compose poems than market them.

We agree. The more time you can devote to writing, the more poems you will be able to submit to editors. That's why we have simplified the business aspects of poetry in one comprehensive article, from equipment and supplies to book publishing options, and all the phases in between.

As in any business, however, editorial practices change with the times and require poets to change along with them. For instance, the policy regarding cover letters has evolved somewhat since last year, and a new section on book reviewing has been included—both reflecting supply and demand in the marketplace. (As for other changes in this year's **Poet's Market**, see From the Editors on page 1.)

Our objective remains the same: To provide you with the latest information about the poetry publishing world and how you can break into it or expand therein.

Supplies and equipment

Several options exist, but in any case, you'll have to spend money to market your poems. First of all, you'll need to purchase stamps to send your poems

Michael J. Bugeja is an internationally published writer and poet with more than 500 credits in literary magazines, including TriQuarterly, The Formalist, The Georgia Review, and New England Review. He has won a National Endowment for the Arts Fellowship and the 1992 Strousse Prize from Prairie Schooner. He has five book-length collections of poetry. His most recent three are: Platonic Love (Orchises Press, 1991); After Oz (Orchises Press, 1993) and Flight From Valhalla (Livingston University Press, 1993). In addition, he has written a book of social criticism titled Culture's Sleeping Beauty: Essays on Poetry, Prejudice, and Belief (Whitston, 1992) and a poetry text titled The Art and Craft of Poetry (Writer's Digest Books, 1994). He writes a monthly poetry column for Writer's Digest and frequently keynotes writing conferences and workshops across the country. He is also a full professor at the E.W. Scripps School of Journalism, Ohio University, Athens, Ohio, where he teaches ethics and writing.

to magazines and to have them returned in self-addressed, stamped envelopes (SASEs).

If you plan to market poems abroad, invest in International Reply Coupons (IRCs). These work in lieu of an individual country's stamps and can be used by editors to return your work. (One IRC equals one ounce of surface mail.) Some post offices don't carry IRCs, but that shouldn't sway you. If you still want to send work abroad, send the editor a letter, noting that you're sending a disposable manuscript and if you don't hear back in six months, you will assume that your manuscript has been rejected. Never send cash in lieu of stamps. (Foreign editors must wait until they receive several dollars from U.S. writers to meet foreign exchange minimums.)

As for supplies, purchase a ream of bond paper (no onionskin), a box of #10 (4½×9½) business envelopes in which to send poems, a box of #9 (4×9) business envelopes (or #10 envelopes folded into thirds) in which poems will be returned, a few pads of paper for early drafts of poems, pens and pencils for signing letters and copyediting, and file folders in which to keep poems and records. You should anticipate total costs of about $60-80 every four months (depending on how much you write or how often you submit, of course).

For poets without typewriters

Invest in pads and pencils. You cannot send handwritten work to editors because most will reject it outright. Instead, work diligently on poems until you have about a dozen in final form, then take the poems to a photocopying center or library and ask to rent a typewriter. Type the poems in standard format (see The Standard Submission on page 9), then photocopy them on white bond paper (25% cotton rag), making about 10 copies of each poem so you have extras. Send out copies of those extras when your poems are returned soiled; this way, you won't have to retype them.

If you cannot rent a typewriter, hire a typist. Talk the typist out of the usual per page rate (why pay $2 for a 14-line poem?) and into an hourly one.

Though the process without a typewriter is complicated, once you have pristine originals and plenty of clear copies (there is no need to type envelopes), marketing work without a typewriter is quite easy.

Initial equipment costs: $0.

Occasional supplies and/or services: $25-80 for copies, typing and other services.

For those with typewriters

Invest in ribbons. Use cloth or film, but be sure the type is dark and clear. You'll also want to buy correction paper, tape or fluid to type final drafts without mistakes. (Some electric units have built-in correction tape.) Unless your typewriter has a built-in memory, you may want to take final drafts to a copying center to make extras of the poems (on white 25% cotton bond) you intend to submit. This saves you from having to retype when you receive soiled poems back from magazines.

Of course, keep your typewriter in good shape by servicing it regularly, using cotton swabs after heavy use to clean the font and covering it to prevent dust from gumming up the mechanism or slowing the tension of the keys.

Initial equipment costs: $20-500 (from secondhand manuals to memory electronic units).

Occasional supplies and/or services: $15-50 for ribbons and correction materials, $10-20 for photocopying, $25 and up for service/repairs.

For those with word processors or computers

Invest in memory disks and ribbons designed for your unit. If you have a typical word processor, the type should be crisp. If you have a computer, you'll need a printer. Spring for letter-quality instead of dot-matrix (even "near letter quality" is too faint to read on some models). Using dot-matrix with a modern computer system is like mounting used tires on a Rolls Royce. You might as well go the extra mile and purchase a letter-quality unit and, while you're at it, an extra font in the same style as the one in your printer.

Keep in mind that word processors and computers, though wonderful, also malfunction, leaving you with no way to conduct business during the interim. That's why you should print several copies of finished poems while your unit is in operation. (Keep those copies in folders for use when your unit is down.) A more expensive option is to have another compatible unit—a typewriter using the same font or a laptop with the same software—in case your main unit fails.

Finally, cover your unit when it is not in use and service as recommended. Also, make back-up copies of your disks.

Initial equipment costs: $200 and up (for secondhand units to the state-of-the-art computer models with appropriate software).

Occasional supplies and/or services: $20-80 for ribbons, disks and other supplies, $80 and up for computer service and repair.

Reference materials

Obviously, you have found this directory. If you haven't done so already, read How to Use Your **Poet's Market**, beginning on page 3. The several categories of markets (coded I, II, III, IV, V) will help you determine which magazines publish poems similar to yours.

Serious poets, however, seldom rely solely on directories for tips about markets. They either subscribe to several magazines, study them at the local library or send away for sample copies (always a good investment). For instance, publications such as *Epoch* and *The New Criterion* are open, generally, to all forms of poetry. Yet, anyone who reads these magazines knows that *Epoch* tends to publish free verse, much of it lyric, emphasizing poetic diction and leaning occasionally toward the avant-garde, while *The New Criterion* favors a more structured free verse and an occasional formal piece. So it's always best to review sample copies before submitting your work. (If you are unfamiliar with such terms as "lyric," "diction," "structured free verse," etc., consult a poetry text in your library or order one from Writer's Digest Books.)

In addition to consulting directories or studying sample copies, consult magazines like *Writer's Digest* or *AWP Chronicle* to keep abreast of new markets or to record changes with old ones. If you cannot afford subscriptions to writing magazines, again, go to the library and read them.

In your study, den or work area at home, you'll also want some general reference books. A good home library might consist of a dictionary (I use the 2,500-page Random House second edition unabridged, but Webster's New World editions also are excellent), a thesaurus (nothing beats the Penguin Roget's), a rhyming dictionary (again, I use Random's), **Princeton Encyclopedia of Poetry & Poetics** (to look up forms and categories of poems and/or poetic techniques and terms), a poetry text (try my **The Art and Craft of Poetry** or John Drury's **Creating Poetry**, both available from Writer's Digest Books) and access to encyclopedias (I use the Britannica). You can buy the above (sans the Britannica) for about $175. Encyclopedias can cost up to $1,000 or more. Again, however, there is absolutely nothing wrong with checking out such books in the library. A personal library, though, is a great convenience.

The standard submission

Once you have studied the markets and perfected your poems, it's time to prepare a manuscript. Generally you should send three to five poems, with or without a cover letter (see Cover Letters on page 11).

Here are some typing rules:
- Use good bond paper (20-25% cotton) and dark cloth or film ribbons on typewriters and printers.
- Leave at least one-inch margins on all sides of the page.
- Type your name, address and telephone number in the upper right-hand corner.
- Type the title of your poem flush left or centered in all caps or initial caps. (I use all caps to distinguish my title from my first line and flush left to create an attractive white space.) After you type the title, drop down two lines.
- Type or print poems single-spaced, one poem to a page. (Single-spacing

saves paper, eliminates irregular spacing between stanzas and helps the editor visualize the shape of the poem.)

- Drop down two lines to indicate stanzas.
- Indicate if your poem is longer than a page. Type your name (address is optional) at the top left margin of each additional page and underneath that, in parentheses, a key word from the title of the poem along with the page number and stanza information.

This is how it should appear:

> Jane Doe
> ("The Ultimate Poem," page 2, begin new stanza)
>
> or
>
> Jane Doe
> ("The Ultimate Poem," page 2, continue stanza)

Putting such information on additional pages helps editors assemble poems if they get shuffled during handling. Stanza information also helps editors visualize poems on the page. After providing the information, drop down six spaces and continue typing the poem.

- Proofread your poem, especially if you are going to make photocopies of the original. Nothing turns off editors more than misspellings, typos and grammatical and punctuation errors.

Finally, arrange the poems in an order that will entice an editor to continue reading. Some editors like several poems on a theme. Others like to see the range of your work, formal to free verse. Some editors want your best poem first and perhaps a light one at the end to leave an upbeat impression. In the end, the choice is yours, but it helps to discover what editors prefer.

Fold the entire manuscript in thirds. Do not fold each poem individually because editors hate to expend the extra energy to unravel each work. (Multiply that energy times thousands of submissions in a month and you will sympathize with the beleaguered editor.) Also, save the cost of paper clips. You don't need them, even though some editorial assistants prefer them. Using paper clips soils poems quicker, and then you'll have to retype.

The question of copyrights

Copyright notices on poems, even on book-length manuscripts, usually are unnecessary. Some editors believe that those who use the symbol are amateurs overly concerned about literary theft. (Plagiarists will steal with or without the copyright, thank you, and few, if any, editors will "borrow" your ideas.) Most editors realize that you own the copyright and won't mind if you put "Copyright 1994 by Jane Doe" on your poems. For instance, Stanley W. Lindberg, editor of *The Georgia Review*, says, "You own the copyright at the moment of creation, and as an editor, I know that. If a poet feels better using the notice, okay: Use the notice. It shouldn't influence the editor one way or another."

Keep in mind that most magazines are copyrighted, and book publishers usually take out copyrights in your name.

If you want to bone up on origins of copyright law, you might want to order **The Nature of Copyright** by L. Ray Patterson and Stanley W. Lindberg (University of Georgia Press, 1991).

If you want to take out copyrights on your work, you can solicit forms by writing the Copyright Office, Library of Congress, Washington DC 20559.

Cover letters

Increasingly editors are requesting that manuscripts be accompanied by cover letters, business-style letters in which you share information about yourself along with any publishing credits.

More and more editors prefer cover letters because of the insight they provide into the skills and backgrounds of submitting writers. Many editors, particularly those with space for contributor's notes, specifically require poets to include brief biographical information with their manuscripts. Other editors ask poets to indicate whether they are sending previously published poems or simultaneous submissions (see Simultaneous/Multiple Submissions on page 15).

For poets, a cover letter serves as a means to personally present yourself—and your work—to specific editors. It's also your chance to develop a connection with an editor. And your publishing history (or lack thereof) may impress editors or encourage them to give you your first publication.

While a few editors still find cover letters unnecessary, some small press editors feel slighted when poets submit without a word or two about themselves. So check each listing to see which editors desire cover letters.

If an editor requires a cover letter, or if you prefer to use one, keep your cover letter brief (no longer than a page). Compose letters in an accepted business-style format free of misspellings and grammatical and punctuation errors (don't doom your manuscript before an editor even reads it). And share information about yourself and/or your work in a professional manner. In particular, avoid praising your work (remember, that's the editor's job) or including inappropriate personal information.

Finally, research the publication in question. Poets who send letters without knowledge of markets may embarrass themselves, for example, by telling an editor with no interest in politics why they love protest poems (or an activist why they hate them). Also some editors dislike magazines associated with certain styles.

Here are typing rules and composition guidelines (also refer to the Sample Cover Letter on page 13):

- Use plain white paper or tastefully designed personal letterhead (no seemingly self-absorbed letterhead proclaiming that you are "Jane Doe, Poet At Large" or "John Doe, Published Poet").
- Type the date in the upper left corner. Drop down two lines.
- Type your address *only* (no name), single-spaced, flush left. Drop down two lines.
- Type the name and title of the editor (consult the listings or sample copies and, if you still can't find a specific name, use "Poetry Editor") and then type the name and address of the magazine, all flush left. Drop down two more lines.
- Type the salutation and the editor's full name. Don't guess at courtesy titles—Mr., Mrs. or Ms.—or appear informal by using first names: "Dear John" or "Jane." Drop down two lines.
- In the first paragraph, tell the editor that you are sending a manuscript for consideration. List titles of enclosed poems.
- In the second paragraph, share your publishing credits or writing interests. If you have read the particular magazine, you may want to mention that first. In any case, make sure to note if any of the enclosed poems have been previously published.
- In the third paragraph, add some personal data about your job or hobbies, particularly if it relates to the enclosed poems.
- In the last paragraph, thank the editor for his or her time. Drop down two lines.
- Type "Sincerely" or "Cordially" as the closing salutation or "Yours" or "Best Wishes" if you have had contact before with the editor. Drop down four more lines.
- Type your full name and include your telephone number (optional).

After you have composed your cover letter, you are ready to send your work to market.

Mailing the manuscript

If you are using a cover letter, fold it in thirds and put it atop your folded manuscript. Make sure your outer envelope and the inner self-addressed one are stamped. Typically, one first class stamp on a #10 envelope will pay for three pages of poetry, a cover letter and SASE. If you are not using a letter, you can send four pages of poetry.

Don't overstuff the envelope. You don't want to risk delaying the mail or paying additional postage on your returned work, especially since many editors will include subscription material in your SASE. If you want to be safe, invest in a postal scale (one-pound maximum units are available at most supply shops for about $10-15).

SAMPLE COVER LETTER

January 1, 1994

1507 Dana Avenue
Cincinnati, OH 45701

Lucia Cordell Getsi, Editor
The Spoon River Poetry Review
English Department
Illinois State University
Normal, IL 61761

Dear Lucia Cordell Getsi:

Please consider the enclosed poems: "Cafe Figaro,"
"Pomp and Circumstance" and "The Mozarteum."

I enjoyed reading your magazine when it was titled
Spoon River Quarterly but like the new name because it
reflects the many fine poems you publish each year. I
have followed with interest the careers of several recent
contributors, especially Marcia Hurlow and James
Plath, whose poems I first encountered in the Summer/
Fall 1991 issue.

As for me, I have new poems forthcoming in *Poet &
Critic, Poetpourri* and *The Hampden-Sydney Poetry Review*. I enjoy photography and travel and have recently
visited Austria, Germany and Italy. (In fact, the enclosed
poems in part document my European experience.) Otherwise I work as a reporter for a local Cincinnati newspaper, covering education and entertainment.

Thanks for your time and consideration.

Sincerely,

Jane Doe

Jane Doe
(513)555-2222

Once your manuscript is in the mail, don't worry about it. Instead, concentrate on composing more poems and keep records of ones making the rounds.

Recordkeeping

Keep a folder containing originals of your poems so that if your manuscript is lost in the mail or at the magazine, you will have a backup. Also keep a business log. (Note: If you use a computer, keep a set of printed originals and business logs. While it's easy to keep business files on disk, and even to make backups of those disks, you never know when the next power outage is going to strike or when your computer will require a service call.)

A business log is a record of when, where and what happened to a manuscript. It contains the title of each poem, the name of the targeted magazine and the date sent. You may have to refer to the date if tracking down a lost or late manuscript. You also should record the date of the magazine's response. Finally, you can keep notes about the submission, especially if you have written the editor to check the status of a late manuscript.

You can use 3×5 file cards to keep these records. Simply mark the name of the poem at the top and use each line of the card to indicate where and when a manuscript was sent (and the outcome). If you use file cards, keep them in a gray metal container for easy access. I prefer keeping records on plain sheets of paper in a file folder along with poems so that I have records and originals in the same place.

This is how a sample entry looks:

POMP AND CIRCUMSTANCE:

    1. *New England Review*, sent 9-1-92, no response as of 2-3-93, inquiry sent 2-3-93, rejected 2-15-93.

    2. *Iowa Review*, sent 2-15-93, rejected 5-19-93.

    3. *Georgia Review*, sent 6-1-93, rejected 6-21-93, (not reading June-August).

    4. *American Poetry Review*, sent 6-21-93, rejected 9-6-93.

    5. *Field*, sent 9-10-93, rejected 9-25-93.

    6. *Ohio Review*, sent 10-9-93, rejected 12-27-93.

    7. *Spoon River Poetry Review*, sent 1-1-94, accepted 2-2-94.

As you can see, such records not only help poets keep track of manuscripts but also provide marketing information—response times, reading cycles—about specific publications.

Response times

As poets, we want the best of both worlds. We would like our poems read closely—no scanning one or two lines and then rejecting the entire batch, please—and then we would like to know, preferably within a month, the status of our manuscript. Some magazines with adequate staff fulfill these goals. Most do not. Typically, virtuous editors who read every poem closely also are the slowest to respond because, well, they are reading manuscripts! Many small press publishers operate at a loss and many editors at literary magazines donate their time.

That said, editors have an obligation to process your work in a timely manner. Please check each listing for the stated response times. What seems like a quick response at one magazine can seem like a delay at another, and vice versa. For instance, *Field* is known as having one of the quickest turn-around times for a literary magazine: usually within two weeks. *South Carolina Review*, on the other hand, lists a response time of "6-9 months" and does not read in the months of "June, July, August or December."

If a listing does not include response times, the general rule is three to four months. Allow your manuscript to languish two weeks longer than the stated or general response time and then send an inquiry.

An inquiry is a brief business letter with SASE or return postcard, addressed to a specific editor, requesting information about the status of a manuscript. Consult your logs and name the poems sent and the date of submission. Ask when the editor anticipates making a decision. Don't press the staff to act quickly or vent your frustrations in a personal letter. Simply send the inquiry, wait another month and if the magazine still does not contact you, cut your losses. Send a postcard withdrawing the poems.

There are plenty of listings in **Poet's Market**. Eventually your work will find a home.

Simultaneous/multiple submissions

Unless you tell them otherwise, editors assume that all submitted work is original and not previously published elsewhere. (Plagiarism—which can lead to civil, criminal and federal lawsuits—is on the rise, so more editors are requiring writers to sign contracts documenting originality.) They also assume that the work is not being considered at another magazine. If it is, you are engaging in "simultaneous" submissions.

Some editors have no qualms about considering poems that are also being considered by other editors. Others consider this an insult. The jury is still out on the issue, but many more poets these days are sending manuscripts to more than one editor at a time. They believe, rightly so, that many editors are too slow to respond and that the market for poems is limited at best. So a submission of three to five poems sent to two or more editors stands a better chance of acceptance.

But there are risks, too. When an editor accepts a poem that is out at two or more places, the poet must telephone or write the other editors immediately, withdrawing his work. Don't tell the editors that one particular poem has been accepted and others rejected at a rival's magazine, so they should consider the remaining "rejected" ones. Withdraw *all* poems at once. If asked to explain, you are obligated to do so only if the editor has already typeset or processed the work in question. In such a case, tell the truth and suffer the consequences. (Typically, your work no longer will be welcome at the magazine.)

On the other hand, if you tell the editors in question that you are simultaneously submitting your work when you send it to them, you may not only receive a more prompt response, but you may also eliminate the risk of leaving a bad impression (provided, of course, that the editors will consider such work).

For the record, I do not promote simultaneous submissions (although occasionally I practice it with select publications). First, recordkeeping becomes more complicated. Second, if you are not publishing regularly as a poet, you'll only collect rejections quicker while still perfecting your craft. That can be discouraging. Third, if you *are* publishing regularly as a poet, you're more likely to end up with poems being accepted at several places at once. Why taint your name?

On the other hand, your chances at some prestigious magazines are slim at best, and thus you have little to lose by sending your work to such publications while submitting simultaneously to another, more realistic market. The prestigious market is usually going to reject you anyway, eliminating the worry about being *accepted* simultaneously. And if you are accepted, say, at *Poets On:* and *The New Yorker*, I'm sure that *Poets On:* Editor Ruth Daigon will understand and release any claim on your poem.

The term "multiple" submissions is often used interchangeably with "simultaneous." Some editors, however, define "multiple" as more than one poem in a submission (send three to five) and others as more than one submission by the same poet sent to the same publication. (In other words, you send five poems to *Bellowing Ark*, for example, and then compose five more and send those before the editor has responded to your first submission.) Unless you are submitting to different contests sponsored by a magazine, this also is considered taboo.

Rights

If your work is accepted for publication, you'll receive a formal or an informal contract. A formal contract is a legal document. An informal agreement is a letter from the editor telling you that she has accepted your poem(s). In the latter case, the editor is buying or, more commonly, acquiring first rights. (Most magazines do not pay for poetry beyond copies of the issue containing your work.)

If you receive an informal contract, it usually means that the editor is acquiring the right to publish your work before anyone else in a U.S. or Canadian periodical. (British publishers who send acceptance letters without formal contracts are usually acquiring first British serial rights, which means you can still publish your work in the United States or Canada.)

In such cases, copyright reverts to you on publication. (You must sign a legal document — or formal contract — to assign copyright ownership to an editor or publisher.) Nonetheless, if you use your poem in a subsequent book (or send it to a journal that accepts previously published poems), you should mention that the work appeared originally in a certain magazine.

If you receive a formal contract, terms should be spelled out. Many formal contracts for first rights include the right to reprint the work in a future edition or anthology of the magazine, or in any form or medium ordained by the publisher. Contracts from European and Australian outlets may demand other stipulations.

Some formal contracts, however, are for all rights. Now you ought to be wary. Selling all rights essentially means that you no longer own the poem. It's tantamount to selling a car, with this difference: *35 years* after the assignment of such rights to a publisher, the original author has a five-year window to reclaim copyright ownership. (This is known as your "termination right," but you must wait a long time to claim it!) When you sell all rights, you need the publisher's permission to reprint your own work in a future collection.

You don't have to sign contracts relinquishing all rights. Write the editor and offer first rights, and if the editor refuses, ask how you can go about regaining the right to reprint your work. If the editor responds explaining how, and you agree to those terms, ask him to include the terms in the contract and initial them. You add your initials and send back a copy of the contract to the publisher.

Typically, however, a formal contract will contain a clause explaining how you can reclaim rights to reprint your own work. Some agreements grant reprint rights only in books in which you are the sole author. In general, only a few publishers purchase all rights and usually will let you reprint work or will reassign copyright to you upon written request.

Anthologies

The term anthology has become confusing. It used to mean a respected publisher like Morrow or Norton would feature exceptional poems in a collection that universities and libraries across the country would acquire for classes or reference rooms.

Such anthologies are still being published today, of course. For instance, the University of Illinois Press recently released a volume of verse titled **Working**

Classics, featuring poems that originally appeared in magazines about the service industry. To be included in such a work is a high honor. Poets get copies of such anthologies for free and, depending on the press run, may be paid for their contributions.

Increasingly, however, companies are promoting another type of anthology. These companies do not misrepresent their services and are essentially correct when they dispute others who label them "vanity" presses (see Book Publishing Options on page 24). You don't have to buy these anthologies for your work to appear therein. But if you want a copy featuring your work, expect to pay $35-45 (or more). And while it is true that a few prestigious anthologies — purchased regularly by hundreds of libraries — also charge similar fees for authors who wish to purchase their annuals, there exists one key difference: the latter *reprint* poems from dozens of prestigious magazines. Conversely, the anthologies in question accept almost everything they receive, providing it is not profane or offensive.

Again, this is a legitimate service. Some people simply don't want to spend the $35-45 it might take to invest in supplies, postage, etc., to submit to small press and literary magazines. (It probably will cost you that much or more to be accepted in a modest-looking magazine when you are just starting out.) The issue here, however, is whether having your work accepted by these anthology companies will enhance your literary career.

In truth, such credits have little value. Editors of literary and small press magazines will discount your anthology publication because they know it was easy to place your work there.

Here's a better option: Send your work to magazines listed under the I category for beginners. A market like *Mobius* is an excellent credit, and the editor often comments on rejected work. *Poet* is another exceptional outlet because it has a section, titled "Poetic Feelings," that showcases beginning work; moreover, your verse will appear alongside that of more experienced poets, highlighted in other sections of the magazine.

Other listings for beginners are annuals requiring you to buy anthologies or subscriptions. While we recommend you submit to markets that provide at least one free copy of the issue including your work, we feel these listings may encourage you or enhance your career. Our questionnaires allow us to exclude listings that we believe might take advantage of poets. Nonetheless, if you have a problem with any listing, write us and we'll reconsider that entry.

Contests

Many poets like to submit to poetry contests. Some contests, however, are not geared to celebrate poets or their work but to generate start-up funds for new publications and to increase readership or revenue for others. Nonetheless, a few contests do pay substantial sums for poems and that is enough to tempt many writers.

Here are 10 tips to help you select contests for your work:

1. *Study the market.* Small press and university competitions usually have a prestige factor, offering publication and modest to generous prizes. If a magazine sponsors a contest, request a sample copy to determine whether you would want your work to appear therein. At least check the listing to get a feel for editorial tastes or policies. You might want to ascertain when a publication was founded (because some new magazines host contests to generate start-up funds). Generally, if a magazine isn't listed, can't be located in the library and is less than a year old with a circulation under 250, think twice about entering.

2. *Identify anthology presses.* Contests offering magnificent prizes for poetry often require, or at least strongly promote, the purchase of anthologies to cover costs. If your motivation is to claim a prize, by all means enter. If you win (or are selected for inclusion in the anthology), you may buy or refuse to buy the book.

3. *Consider club contests.* Many states have poetry societies and writers' federations that host contests in conjunction with conventions. Prizes are modest because dues are limited. Such competitions inspire writers by offering several awards in numerous categories, increasing your chances. Some provide individual critiques by outside judges who suggest ways to improve your work, increasing your chances in the future.

4. *Investigate sponsors.* Some organizations unaffiliated with magazines or poetry societies host annual competitions because money has been deposited in a trust for such purposes. These include contests sponsored by universities, corporations and individuals and usually are reputable, especially those with nonprofit/tax-exempt status. In any case, before you enter, ask for lists of previous winners and/or biographies of past judges. (Always include a SASE.) If such information is refused, think twice before entering.

5. *Evaluate entry fees.* Many magazines charge entry fees to break even, covering such costs as judging, handling and prizes. Some want a profit. Typical entry fees range between $2-10 per poem. Anything higher is suspect. After all, you should get something for your money, too. As prestige counts in the making of a literary career, you might want to pay $5 for a certificate or honorable mention. A safe bet, though, is to enter competitions that provide a free copy of the award issue or a year's subscription.

6. *Send for guidelines.* Contests are usually advertised in literary journals or publications for writers. If the ad or promotion is small, guidelines won't be spelled out, so send for them in order to honor submission and eligibility requirements. (Again, enclose a SASE.) If officials don't provide guidelines or publish an address for rules—including how much a poet has to pay, if anything, for a copy of the award issue—avoid the contest.

7. *Solicit winning entries.* Sponsors of competitions will be glad to sell you previous award issues. Or you can look them up in the library. Some officials provide booklets of winners, also for a fee. If you decide to enter a contest, you might want to spring for the additional cost. The information contained in an award issue or booklet is invaluable. You'll get to see the type and style of the winning poem. And while it is true that many contests feature different judges of varied tastes each year, the staff typically screens entries. If you know its taste beforehand, you can usually decide which poem is appropriate for a given contest.

8. *Research judges.* Some contests announce final judges in advertisements or promotions. Others keep such information secret, fearing friends of the judge will enter and hinder objectivity. Some judges see all entries without prior in-house screening. If judges are named, look up their work in the library to assess what styles, themes or topics might appeal to them. Then check your inventory and make the appropriate selections.

9. *Obey all rules.* Serious contests have strict rules that must be obeyed. Otherwise, your entry will be eliminated and your fee deposited. Every contest has different rules and submission requirements. For instance, some ask you to submit 3×5 file cards listing individual titles. Others want a separate cover sheet. Read each rule and check it off as you prepare your submission. Don't fudge. If the contest specifies word length or calls for a certain style or form, honor it. When your manuscript is ready for mailing, read each rule again for a final check.

10. *Submit elsewhere at risk.* Generally, reputable contests require that your submission be unpublished and not under consideration elsewhere. Occasionally, the latter requirement is omitted. Some contests have a reading cycle of six months to a year, so tying up a poem that long may be costly. If you decide you can't wait, submit elsewhere. Should your work be accepted by a magazine while under consideration at a competition, notify contest officials immediately and offer to withdraw it. Usually they will be happy to keep your entry fee and remove your name from consideration.

Readings

The quickest way to sate the need to publish or win contests is to read your poems before an audience. When you do, you share your love of verse and, in the process, meet other poetry lovers, writers, editors, teachers, bookstore operators, librarians and arts council executives. All these people are important in building a literary career. Moreover, when you are just starting out, reaction to your poems is part of the learning experience.

You can schedule readings through these groups and agencies:

1. *Local clubs.* Ask club officers if their group would be interested in hearing appropriate poetry on a specific occasion (a selection of war poems for Amvets on Veteran's Day, for example).

2. *Local churches.* Ask pastors if you may read for a group affiliated with the denomination (a youth or recreation committee, perhaps) or recite appropriate poetry on a specific occasion (a selection of Christmas verse in mid-December).

3. *Area institutions.* Ask administrators at convalescence homes, hospitals and soup kitchens if you may read your poems as part of an outreach or recreation program.

4. *Libraries.* Librarians often will help arrange readings as part of their community calendars. (If you write children's poems, in particular, the library is a great resource and children a greater audience.)

5. *Area schools.* Gear your poetry to a specific club at an area school. (If you write science fiction poems, for instance, ask the adviser of the high school Science Club if you can read verse at the next meeting.)

6. *Cafes.* Many cafes still sponsor readings and poetry "slams," in which poets square off against each other in competition. Check with cafe owners.

7. *Bookstores.* Some bookstores sponsor readings to bring in customers. Check with managers.

8. *Open-mike sessions.* More and more colleges and universities are drawing crowds at literary functions by scheduling 5-minute poetry readings for anyone who signs up. Check with English departments or sponsoring groups.

9. *Radio stations.* Broadcast owners have an obligation to cover community events or interests, and your poetry reading may qualify as such. Check with station managers.

10. *Access TV.* Cable stations reserve a channel for local programming. Contact cable management for details in your area.

Finally, review the arts and entertainment section of your newspaper to get a feel for the type of events in your neighborhood.

There is no end to the possibilities, but it takes initiative and drive. After you have found a place to read, design and photocopy some fliers announcing the event and post them in strategic places. Local shopper tabloids usually offer free space in the classifieds where you can list readings. Church and/or club bulletins and library newsletters also provide space. Write a news release in the concise style of your community newspaper and send it to the managing editor. And don't forget family members and friends. Write a personal note on each flier and mail or deliver it in person, asking for their support.

Finally, it's always courteous (not to mention good public relations) to offer refreshments afterward. The casual atmosphere will allow you to mingle and make new contacts with those in attendance.

Book reviews

The typical editor receives hundreds of poems in any given week, but only a few book reviews. Poets generally don't buy as many poetry collections as they should or are too busy trying to promote their own work, flooding the market. So good reviews are always in demand.

When you write them, you promote poetry and make contacts with editors who will treat you henceforth as a past contributor.

Editors usually are interested in reviews of books by poets whose verse originally appeared in their magazines. For instance, Eve Shelnutt often publishes in *Cream City Review* and *Prairie Schooner*, so when her collection **First, a Long Hesitation** was published by Carnegie-Mellon Press, I put these two prestigious journals high on my list of magazines that might want a critique of her latest work. I sent the review to *CCR* first and it was promptly accepted.

So pick a collection by an author whose work you have followed and check the acknowledgments section to determine which magazines have previously published individual poems. That will help you locate markets, but it should not dictate whether a book gets a positive or negative critique. By no means should you review a bad or mediocre collection favorably just to get a byline in a journal; editors want objective criticism. Neither should you review the works of friends to promote their careers. In fact, some journals — *The Georgia Review* is one — will reject your work outright if editors discover you are engaging in such practices.

The best bet, simply, is to purchase a collection off the shelf of a bookstore. The best months to do this are January and February when collections are marketed with the current copyright year. (For instance, in January 1994, you should purchase a book with a 1994 copyright.) Because reviews are timely, a book bought in January 1994 and reviewed by February allows you to submit the manuscript for a minimum of 11 months.

Editors usually have a backlog, so a review of a 1994 book probably will appear in print in 1995. (That's why a 1993 copyright date decreases your chances for a sale.) When you factor in the response times required with each submission of a review to an editor, you'll appreciate your 11 months even more. Typically you'll get three to five chances to place a review before editors will start to lose interest.

Because of timeliness, you may want to consider simultaneous submissions of your review if you have yet to place it after the first six to eight months. (As soon as the review is accepted, be sure to withdraw it immediately from other publications.)

Finally, be sure to send the type of review that the magazine normally publishes. Scan sample copies to ascertain which of the following formats is preferred by specific editors:

1. *The Essay Review* (also known as an omnibus or multi-book review) is about 8-10 manuscript pages and features several books by the same author or by several authors. If the latter, the collections should have something in common—a review of ecology books, say, or rhymed collections. The review should carry a title, just like an essay.

2. *The Standard Review* is about 3-5 manuscript pages and concentrates on a single book (perhaps briefly mentioning other books by the same author). A title is optional.

3. *The Book Brief* is 1-2 manuscript pages and critiques one book as concisely as possible. No title is required.

By far, the book brief is the easiest to place because length is so short. The standard review requires more technical expertise but also is moderately easy to place. The essay review, however, not only requires great technical skill but is difficult to place because of space considerations. It might be worth your while, if considering this type, to query the editor of a magazine first to see if she would be interested in your books and author(s). As always, include a SASE.

Book manuscripts

After you have done several readings and published extensively, it is time to start thinking about assembling a chapbook or book. A chapbook is a slim volume of about 20-25 pages (although some editors want no more than a dozen and others as many as 40). A book-length collection usually consists of 48-80 pages. Research listings (see the Chapbook Publishers Index on page 503) to familiarize yourself with length and submission requirements.

Here are standard manuscript specifications for poetry collections:

- Type a title page containing your name, address and telephone number.
- Type another title page without your name, address and telephone number. (This way you can submit your collection to presses and competitions that require anonymity during the selection process.) Do not number this page.
- Type an acknowledgments page stating the names of magazines where individual poems have previously appeared. Do not number this page.
- Type poems according to the style mentioned earlier for individual poems (without the address in the upper right corner). Do not number these pages yet.
- Assemble your poems in the order you think best represents your work. Now number pages consecutively.
- Type a contents page containing page numbers for individual poems. Do

not number this page but place it after the acknowledgments page and before the first poem in your collection.

As for mailing, poetry collections require manila envelopes (9 × 12) for the manuscript and the SASE. Because weights vary, take your manuscript to the post office or purchase a standard postal scale. Weigh the two envelopes, manuscript and any other contents (checks for reading fees, entry forms, cover letters) to determine what it will cost to mail the collection. Take away the outer envelope and any checks, forms or letters to determine the cost of the SASE.

Book publishing options

The road to book publication is lengthy. Usually you will have to wait years before publishing your first chapbook or book, gaining recognition by placing 100 or more poems in magazines and journals. The surest route is to write excellent poems and to collect so many magazine acceptances that editors, sooner or later, take note.

Books are more difficult to place than chapbooks, chiefly because production costs are higher and because the market for poetry is not good. Thus, many houses (especially university-affiliated ones) will require reading fees to recover costs. Many small press and chapbook publishers also require fees.

Start the process by knowing your publishing options:

1. *Standard publishing.* A commercial, literary or small press publisher considers submissions or conducts competitions. If your work is chosen — and again, competition is extraordinarily keen (with one or two books chosen out of hundreds each year) — the publisher pays all production costs and you usually get a 10% royalty on the wholesale price. Sometimes you get no royalties but receive 10% of the press run.

2. *Cooperative publishing.* You work with the publisher in some capacity and share the burdens. Arrangements vary, so be wary. Make sure you can fulfill your end of the bargain before signing agreements. Some will require you to pay certain costs of production. Others will require you to participate in printing or marketing phases. In any case, cooperative publishing is respected in the literary and small press world, and you should look into it if you cannot place your collections with publishers offering standard contracts.

3. *Self-publishing.* Many good poets have self-published, unconcerned about status within the literary world and hoping simply to share their verse with others. Many impatient poets have self-published, too. Decide which type of poet you are, as the practice of self-publishing can easily be overlooked by reviewers. If you decide to take this option, you'll work with printers, invent a name for your "press," publish your book, own all copies, advertise to sell

them and collect all proceeds. But mostly you will foot the bill, so schedule modest press runs of 100 to 300 copies.

Also look into cheaper ways to make books, especially if you own or have access to a computer with design programs. Design pages on the screen, print out typeset galleys, assemble the book and take it to a photocopying center. Representatives there will help you choose a cover and explain ways to bind your book. You can save hundreds of dollars.

Before you decide to self-publish, check out **The Complete Guide To Self-Publishing** by Tom and Marilyn Ross ($18.95 from Writer's Digest Books).

4. *Vanity/subsidy presses.* Avoid these. Nobody respects them. Under these arrangements you pay a "press" to manufacture and advertise your book. Ads are usually collective — 20 books getting one blurb line apiece — and placed in the general media (as opposed to specific markets). Sometimes you own all the copies, sometimes you don't. Some agreements are less offensive than others, but all bank on your general ignorance of publishing.

Submitting book manuscripts

Now that you know your options, the next step is to know the market if you plan to submit your chapbook or book to commercial, literary, small press or cooperative publishers. Begin by reviewing such listings and isolating a dozen potential presses for your collection. You'll need at least that many to have a shot. The typical publisher accepts one or two collections each year, with press runs of 500 to 1,000, and receives that many unsolicited manuscripts in the usual 30-day reading cycle.

To increase your odds:

1. *Avoid big-time houses.* These are Madison Avenue presses (Norton, Random House, etc.) that usually only publish a few books a year by top-name authors — often by special invitation. You stand virtually no chance of being accepted here unless you are already a celebrated writer.

2. *Research authors and presses.* Within listings you'll find names of poets previously published by each press. Make a list of authors cited in listings that intrigue you. Take the list to your local or nearest university library to see if their books are available for loan. If not, use a comprehensive library computer system (InfoTrak, for example) and input each author's name. You'll see where he has published poems. This publishing history will help you gauge the type of verse a select author usually publishes. You'll also discover whether anyone has reviewed the book in question.

It's always a plus for a press if a book is reviewed in a reputable magazine, indicating that the publisher promotes the work of his or her authors. Such information will help you decide whether you should send your manuscript to the press for consideration.

In any case, never send out a chapbook or book without having inspected the press' product. Whenever possible, we provide information about the quality of production. (Some chapbooks and a few books are nothing more than photocopied verse stapled with card covers and should be used as a last resort.) But you don't want to rely solely on any listing—even ours—without having done prior research.

If you can't locate one of the publisher's books in the library or bookstore, send for a sample copy of the most recently published chapbook or book. (With any luck, you can review it.)

3. *Request guidelines.* Before mailing a manuscript, be sure to request submission guidelines. (As always, include a SASE.) Such guidelines spell out reading cycles, fees (avoid any over $15) and manuscript requirements. For instance, some publishers prefer queries and sample poems before inviting you to submit collections. Follow requirements to the letter, and keep a file of guidelines as a future marketing tool.

4. *Simultaneously submit.* When you have found a dozen potential book markets, submit to all of them during the requisite reading cycles. Most publishers understand the difficulty poets face in trying to place a collection. If your work is accepted elsewhere, notify other editors immediately. They will appreciate your professionalism and will be glad to consider your next volume.

5. *Update or recycle markets.* After exhausting your dozen markets, search for new ones or try old ones again. (University publishers feature different judges each year, so submit to them in the next cycle.)

There are few greater joys than learning your collection will be published by a reputable press. Although no one can promise that you will publish a chapbook or book, you can feel confident that if you follow suggestions here and elsewhere in **Poet's Market**, you will gain an edge over the competition.

U.S. and Canadian Postal Codes

United States

AL	Alabama	MD	Maryland	TX	Texas
AK	Alaska	MA	Massachusetts	UT	Utah
AZ	Arizona	MI	Michigan	VT	Vermont
AR	Arkansas	MN	Minnesota	VI	Virgin Islands
CA	California	MS	Mississippi	VA	Virginia
CO	Colorado	MO	Missouri	WA	Washington
CT	Connecticut	MT	Montana	WV	West Virginia
DE	Delaware	NE	Nebraska	WI	Wisconsin
DC	District of Columbia	NV	Nevada	WY	Wyoming
FL	Florida	NH	New Hampshire		
GA	Georgia	NJ	New Jersey	**Canada**	
GU	Guam	NM	New Mexico	AB	Alberta
HI	Hawaii	NY	New York	BC	British Columbia
ID	Idaho	NC	North Carolina	LB	Labrador
IL	Illinois	ND	North Dakota	MB	Manitoba
IN	Indiana	OH	Ohio	NB	New Brunswick
IA	Iowa	OK	Oklahoma	NF	Newfoundland
KS	Kansas	OR	Oregon	NT	Northwest Territories
KY	Kentucky	PA	Pennsylvania	NS	Nova Scotia
LA	Louisiana	PR	Puerto Rico	ON	Ontario
ME	Maine	RI	Rhode Island	PEI	Prince Edward Island
		SC	South Carolina	PQ	Quebec
		SD	South Dakota	SK	Sasketchewan
		TN	Tennessee	YT	Yukon

ALWAYS include a self-addressed, stamped envelope (SASE) when sending a ms or query to a publisher within your own country. When sending material to other countries, include a self-addressed envelope and International Reply Coupons (IRCs), available for purchase at most post offices.

Key to Symbols and Abbreviations

‡ *New listing*
ms — *manuscript;* mss — *manuscripts*
b&w — *black-and-white (photo or illustration)*
SASE — *self-addressed, stamped envelope*
SAE — *self-addressed envelope*
IRC — *International Reply Coupon, for reply mail from countries outside your own.*

Important Market Listing Information

• *Listings are based on questionnaires and verified copy. They are not advertisements nor are markets reported here necessarily endorsed by the editors of this book.*
• *Information in the listings comes directly from the publishers and is as accurate as possible, but publications and editors come and go, and poetry needs fluctuate between the publication date of this directory and the time you use it.*
• **Poet's Market** reserves the right to exclude any listing that does not meet its requirements.

The Markets

Publishers of Poetry

It takes just one glance at this directory to discover that this section, Publishers of Poetry, is the largest and by far the most important section of **Poet's Market**. After all, it is here that we list those folks who publish poetry in everything from small, stapled newsletters to hardcover books. It should come as little surprise then that this section experiences the most change from year to year, and 1994 is no exception.

As in years past, the most noticeable, and perhaps the most interesting change, is the inclusion of new listings. You'll find approximately 300 new markets in this edition. Some of them, such as *Apalachee Quarterly*, *Cincinnati Poetry Review* and *Oxalis* were listed in previous editions of **Poet's Market** but not the 1993 edition. When we went to press last year, for example, *Cincinnati Poetry Review* was between editors. Now, with editor Jeffrey Hillard in place, the review is seeking submissions once again.

Most new listings, however, have never been previously listed. Some are, in fact, new publications just getting off the ground. *The Bacon Press* and *The Illinois Review* are two such examples. *The Northern Centinel*, on the other hand, is a newspaper which was founded in 1788 and used poetry in its earlier years. The current publisher has decided to return to that tradition and now plans to use two poems in each issue. This market and all other new listings are preceded by a double dagger (‡).

Locating specific publishers

If you're looking for a specific publisher or publication, check the General Index at the end of this book. Some publishers are listed in this section but have simply changed names, thus changing alphabetical order. In such a case, you will find both titles included in the General Index. For example, if you were looking for Caravan Press, you would find it cross-referenced in the General Index to Center Press, its new name. The same holds true for *The Belladonna Review*, which is now just *The Review*.

Also, to provide a detailed picture of each publisher, **Poet's Market** lists all of a publisher's related activities in one listing. Most market listings include a magazine or a magazine and a press, but some are more extensive. The best example is the listing for *Amelia*. If you were looking for *Cicada*, another of Frederick Raborg's publications, you would find *Cicada* cross-referenced to *Amelia* in the General Index. Once you look up the listing for *Amelia*, you will find all the information for not only *Amelia* and *Cicada*, but also *SPSM&H*, Raborg's quarterly sonnet magazine. In addition, there is a complete list of all the awards this publisher offers.

Of course, once you begin browsing pages and discovering new listings, you may also notice that some of the publications that *were* in last year's edition are no longer included. *Bold Print*, which was new last year, is not listed this year because the editor has been overwhelmed with submissions. *The Gamut*, *The Poetry Peddler* and *Sideshow Magazine* have all, unfortunately, ceased publication. You'll find a list of these and other publishers who no longer have market listings under Publishers of Poetry/'93-'94 Changes at the end of this section. Wherever possible, we have noted the reason a publisher is not presently included.

Including cover letters

Each year, we refine information within the listings. Besides providing a detailed picture of each publisher, we also want to reflect changes in the marketplace. Over the past few years we have noticed an increase in the number of publishers who desire cover letters with submissions. Consequently, this year we specifically asked editors and publishers if they require cover letters and, if so, what information they would like included in them.

As expected, many publishers do indeed want to see cover letters, and most prefer cover letters containing brief bios and/or lists of publishing credits. Where appropriate, we have added this information (in bold) to individual listings. It is important to note, however, that most editors have a definite stance on this issue—they either want a cover letter or don't want one. So read listings carefully. In addition, those who *do* want cover letters usually have strong opinions about what should be included. Generally speaking, use a cover letter as a way to introduce yourself, not as a vehicle for your life story. Also, it's best not to explain your poems in your cover letter; most editors expect the poetry to speak for itself. For more information about cover letters (and a sample), see page 11 of The Business of Poetry by Michael J. Bugeja.

Sending book reviews

Other questions we asked editors and publishers this year concerned their use of book reviews. Last year we asked editors if they published reviews of poetry books and, if so, to indicate the length and type. What we discovered, however, is that just because editors said their publications included book reviews did not mean editors were necessarily open to reviews written by folks other than staff members. To clarify matters this year, we asked editors to indicate whether they only publish staff-written reviews or are open to unsolicited reviews. We also asked if a poet might send his or her book for review consideration. Again, you will find this information added to listings.

While no editor is obligated to review any of the books he or she receives, you will stand a better chance of having your book reviewed if you know the subject matter an editor prefers. For example, send your book of science fiction poetry to an editor of a science fiction publication. Likewise, if you've written a book of haiku, send it to a editor that primarily publishes haiku and related forms.

When submitting reviews, put as much time into finding the best market for your review of someone else's poetry as you do in trying to find the best market for your own poetry. For example, *Fireweed: Poetry of Western Oregon* is open to unsolicited reviews of books by Oregon poets. If you send the editor your review of a book by a New Mexico poet, you would be doing a disservice to yourself and the poet whose work you reviewed. This topic is covered in further detail on page 22 of The Business of Poetry.

Including reply envelopes

This year we also asked editors and publishers to tell us their "complaints" about poetry submissions, essentially what poets are doing incorrectly when they submit. Without a doubt, the foremost response was failure to include a self-addressed, stamped envelope (SASE) with correspondence. Whether you are requesting guidelines, submitting a batch of poems or querying an editor about your book manuscript, *always* include a SASE for a reply.

If you want your poems returned (particularly if the editor chooses not to publish them), include a SASE that is large enough to contain your work and has the proper postage. When sending poetry to an editor or publisher outside your own country, include a self-addressed envelope (SAE) and International Reply Coupons (IRCs), which can be purchased at the post office. This information is generally not included in individual listings but is repeated at the bottom of various pages within this section.

Submitting properly

Ranking behind complaints about missing SASEs are complaints about messy submissions, inappropriate submissions and lengthy submissions (those that include too many poems at one time). You should be aware that the way your poetry is presented can often be as important as the quality of your work when an editor decides to accept or reject it. If you have not done so already, read (or reread) The Business of Poetry. This article explains how to properly prepare, and mail, your manuscript, whether it contains five poems or 15.

Inappropriate submissions are often sent by poets who have not taken the time to research the market in question. One of the best ways to understand the market to which you are submitting is to read a copy of the magazine, or a few of the books published by a press. You can find some of these magazines at your local newsstand or library. College and university libraries carry many of the literary journals listed here. And bookstores are a good place to examine the poetry titles released by a press. However, when you are unable to locate a sample, order one directly from the publisher. Editors appreciate purchases of their publications, and listings contain the price of sample copies. Read How to Use Your **Poet's Market** on page 3 for more information on finding the best markets for your work and avoiding inappropriate submissions.

Even if your poetry manuscript is targeted to the right market, and presented properly, editors still may be annoyed if you include too many poems in one package. Five or six poems are usually enough for an editor to review at any one time. However, like many aspects of poetry publishing, this, too, is subjective. Some editors only want to see three poems at a time; others prefer to see 10. If an editor or publisher has indicated a specific number, we have included this information within the listing.

Reading listings carefully

In addition to our specific questions, each year we ask editors and publishers to make any necessary changes or additions to the information already present in their listings. As you may suspect, some publications have new editors. Others have changed locations. A few, such as *Dialogue: A Journal of Mormon Thought*, *Inky Blue* and *Rural Heritage*, have both a new editor and a new address.

Another change made by editors this year is their frequency of publication. Perhaps in response to increasing costs of publication and/or increasing demands on their time, many publishers are releasing fewer issues of a magazine (but often more pages in each issue) or fewer books of poetry. Not all publishers have cut back, however. Some have launched additional publications or have begun to release chapbooks in addition to their magazines. Others now offer poetry contests. The listing for *Magic Realism*, for example, now includes information for *A Theater of Blood*, another publication of Pyx Press, and the listing for *Poetic Page* includes information for *Opus Literary Review*. Read listings carefully to notice such changes.

Continuing commentary

We have also continued to add editorial comments to help you evaluate markets for your work. Last year, Michael Bugeja provided comments about editors, the type of poetry generally found in a magazine and/or occasionally the magazine's appearance. This year he has not only updated many comments but provided comments for other listings as well.

Approximately 120 listings contain new information—primarily about the type of poetry included—based upon Bugeja's reviews of recent issues. For example, here's what you'll find added to the listing for *Boulevard*: "Poetry herein—mostly free verse but wide-ranging in content, length and tone—is accessible and exciting. Poems have one thing in common: careful attention to craft (particularly line, stanza and voice)." Look for these types of comments either at the end of a listing or following the description of the magazine itself.

We have also noted which publications had poetry selected for inclusion in the 1992 volume of **The Best American Poetry**, an annual anthology which highlights the best poetry published in periodicals during the previous year. (The 1993 edition was not available at the time we went to press.) Thirty-eight publications had poetry selected for the 1992 volume, including *American Poetry Review*, *The New Yorker* and *The Yale Review*. You'll find such comments near the end of listings for these publications. This anthology (published by Collier Books, Macmillan Publishing Company, 866 Third Ave., New York NY 10022) indicates what certain publications are including within their pages and may also help you develop an understanding of current trends within the field.

Including awards

This year we also added information about awards and honors received by editors and publishers or their magazines and books. While such information can help you determine the quality of a publication or press, it is important to note that we included only the most recent awards and, with few exceptions, only that information which the editor or publisher has supplied. For example, if you write children's poetry, it may be helpful to know that *Cricket, The Magazine for Children* has received Parents' Choice Awards every year since 1986 and its related publication, *Ladybug, The Magazine for Young Children*, which was launched in 1990, received Parents' Choice Awards in 1991 and 1992.

Occasionally editors and publishers volunteered information about other editions of **The Best American Poetry**, and some also noted that they have had work included in the **Pushcart Prize** anthologies (published by Pushcart Press, Box 380, Wainscott NY 11975), which showcase the "Best of the Small Presses." Again, you will find such comments near the end of listings. If you are unfamiliar with any of the awards or anthologies listed, you may want to check your library for further information.

As part of our continuing editorial commentary, we have also included the results of the 1993 Poetry 60 list compiled by *Writer's Digest* magazine. The list includes six categories of poetry and ranks the top 10 publications in each category, based upon various surveys. The categories are as follows: Nontraditional Verse, Traditional Verse, Open Markets (those most open to both free and formal verse), Top Pay, New Poets (those who often publish poets whose work is new to them) and Poets' Pick (those in which poets would most like to see their work published). Again, you'll find comments indicating where publications ranked in these categories near the end of relevant listings. If you are interested in knowing more about how the Poetry 60 list was compiled, locate the June 1993 issue of *Writer's Digest* in your library or write *Writer's Digest* directly at 1507 Dana Ave., Cincinnati OH 45207.

Understanding market categories

Finally, all of the listings in this section include one or more Roman numerals in their heading. These "codes," selected by editors and/or publishers, may help you determine the most appropriate markets for your poetry. (For more information, see How to Use Your **Poet's Market** on page 3.) The market category codes and their explanation are as follows:

I. **Publishers very open to beginners' submissions.** For acceptance, some may require fees, purchase of the publication or membership in an organization, but they are not, so far as we can determine, exploitative of poets. They publish much of the material received and frequently respond with criticism and suggestions.

II. **The general market to which most poets familiar with literary journals and magazines should submit.** Typically they accept 10% or less of poems received and usually reject others without comment. They pay at least one copy. A poet developing a list of publication credits will find many of these to be respected names in the literary world.

III. **Limited markets,** typically overstocked. This code is most often used by many prestigious magazines and publishers to discourage widespread submissions from poets who have not published elsewhere—although many do on occasion publish relatively new and/or little-known poets.

IV. **Specialized publications** encourage contributors from a specific geographical area, age-group, sex, sexual orientation or ethnic background or accept poems in specific forms (such as haiku) or on specific themes. In most **IV** listings we also state the specialty (e.g., **IV-Nature/rural/ecology**). Often a listing emphasizes more than one subject area; these listings are marked with two codes.

V. **Listings which do not accept unsolicited manuscripts.** You cannot submit to these without specific permission to do so. If the press or magazine for some reason seems especially appropriate for you, query with SASE. But, in general, these folks prefer to locate poets themselves. Sometimes they are just temporarily overstocked or have projects lined up for the next few years.

We have included these listings because it is important to know not only where to send your poetry but also where NOT to send it. Also, many are interesting publishers, and this book is widely used as a reference by librarians, researchers, publishers, suppliers and others who need to have as complete a listing of poetry publishers as possible.

AARDVARK ENTERPRISES (I), (formerly listed under *Breakthrough!*), 204 Millbank Dr. SW, Calgary, Alberta T2Y 2H9 Canada, phone (403)256-4639, founded 1982, poetry editor J. Alvin Speers. Aardvark publishes chapbooks on subsidy arrangements. They have published poetry by Ellen Sandry, Edna Janes Kayser, Susan Davidson and W. Ray Lundy. As a sample the editor selected these lines from his poem "Called":

> *I am called by the light of*
> *the morning,*
> *By water lapping the sand;*
> *By moonlight on the horizon,*
> *And the touch of a loved*
> *one's hand*

For subsidized chapbook publication, query with 3-5 samples, bio, previous publications. "We publish for hire—quoting price with full particulars. We do not market these except by special arrangement. Prefer poet does that. We strongly recommend seeing our books first. Send SASE for catalog to buy book samples. Please note US stamps cannot be used in Canada." The editor says *Breakthrough!* magazine was discontinued "to concentrate on books, which include **How To Do-It-Yourself, Publish For Low Cost**, and consulting for 'Do-It-Selfers.' Our sound, economical methods have proven successful."

ABBEY; ABBEY CHEAPOCHAPBOOKS (II), Dept. PM, 5360 Fallriver Row Court, Columbia MD 21044, phone (301)730-4272, founded 1970, editor David Greisman. They want **"poetry that does for the mind what that first sip of Molson Ale does for the palate. No pornography or politics."** They have published poetry by Richard Peabody, Vera Bergstrom, Margot Treitel, Harry Calhoun, Wayne Hogan and Tom Bilicke. *Abbey*, a quarterly, aims "to be a journal but to do it so informally that one wonders about my intent." It is magazine-sized, 20-26 pgs., photocopied. They publish about 150 of 1,000 poems received/year. Press run is 200. Subscription: $2. **Sample postpaid: 50¢. Guidelines available for SASE. Reports in 1 month. Pays 1-2 copies.** *Abbey Cheapochapbooks* come out 1-2 times a year averaging 10-15 pgs. **For chapbook consideration query with 4-6 samples, bio and list of publications. Reports in 2 months. Pays 25-50 copies.** The editor says he is "definitely seeing poetry from 2 schools—the nit'n'grit school and the textured/reflective school. I much prefer the latter."

ABIKO QUARTERLY LITTER-ARY RAG (II, IV-Translations), 8-1-8 Namiki, Abiko, Chiba Japan 270-11, phone 011-81-471-84-7904, founded 1988, poetry editor Jesse Glass, is a literary-style quarterly journal **"heavily influenced by James Joyce's** Finnegan's Wake**. We publish all kinds, with an emphasis on the innovative and eclectic. We sometimes include originals and translations. No 'light verse,' and no religious verse, please! Include two international reply coupons with SAE for response. Originals will not be returned."** They have published poetry by Kenji Miyazawa, Murray Thompson, Cid Corman, Lew Turco, Yonah Wollach and Fumiaki Den. It is magazine-sized, desktop published with Macintosh laser printer. Press run 350 for 150 subscribers of which 10 are libraries, 100 shelf sales. **Sample postpaid: 900 yen. Editors always comment on rejections. Pays 1 copy.** Open to unsolicited reviews. Poets may also send books for review consideration. The editor says, "Poets are in a hurry to publish. Poets, educate yourselves! Read contemporary poetry. In fact, read all poetry! Work at your craft before you attempt to publish."

ABORIGINAL SF (IV-Science fiction), Box 2449, Woburn MA 01888-0849, founded 1986, editor Charles C. Ryan, appears quarterly. **"Poetry should be 1-2 pgs., double-spaced. Subject matter must be science fiction, science or space-related. No long poems, no fantasy."** The magazine is 116 pgs., with 12 illustrations. Press run is 23,000, mostly subscriptions. Subscriptions for "special" writer's rate: $15/4 issues. **Sample postpaid: $3.50. No simultaneous submissions. Send SASE for guidelines. Reports in 2-3 months, has no backlog. Pays $25/poem and 2 copies. Buys first North American serial rights.** Reviews related books of poetry in 100-300 words.

‡**ABOVE THE BRIDGE MAGAZINE (IV-Regional, humor),** P.O. Box 416, Marquette MI 49855-0416, founded 1985, editor Lynn DeLoughary St. Arnaud, is a quarterly magazine, circulation 1,500, for Upper Peninsula readers. They buy about 20 poems/year—**free verse, light verse and traditional. "No abstractions such as Life, Love, etc. Be specific, preferably specific about the Upper Peninsula of Michigan—humor is our first choice."** As a sample the editor selected the opening stanza of "April Storm" by Mary B. Knapp:

> *placid, gray*
> *lukewarm day*
> *abruptly metamorphic*
> *horizon blackness, breezy air . . .*

Above the Bridge is magazine-sized, 48 pgs., saddle-stapled, typeset with glossy cover, using b&w graphics and local ads. Single copy: $3.50; subscription: $13. **Sample postpaid: $3. Submit maximum of 3 poems, typed, 20 lines each. Considers simultaneous submissions. Send SASE for guidelines. Pays $5. Buys one-time rights.** Reviews books of poetry "about the area or by authors from the area." Open to unsolicited reviews. Poets may also send books for review consideration.

ABRAXAS MAGAZINE (V); GHOST PONY PRESS (III), 2518 Gregory St., Madison WI 53711, phone (608)238-0175, *Abraxas* founded 1968, Ghost Pony Press in 1980, by editor/publisher Ingrid Swanberg, who says "Ghost Pony Press is a small press publisher of poetry books; *Abraxas* is a literary journal (irregular) publishing contemporary poetry, criticism, translations and reviews of small press books. *Do not confuse these separate presses!*" *Abraxas* **no longer considers unsolicited material, except as announced as projects arise.** She is interested in poetry that is **"contemporary lyric, concrete, experimental." Does not want to see "political posing; academic regurgitations."** They have published poetry by William Stafford, Ivan Argüelles, Denise Levertov, César Vallejo and Andrea Moorhead. As a sample the editor selected the final lines of an untitled poem by próspero saíz:

> *the beautiful grief of the moon is my beam of silence*
> *Dawn*
> *the splendor of the moon dies*
> *my lips open to a gentle breeze*
> *she rides a silken yellow scarf into the vanishing clouds*
> *i am still here.*

The magazine is 80 pgs. (160 pgs., double issues), flat-spined, 6×9, litho offset, with original art on its matte card cover, using "unusual graphics in text, original art and collages, concrete poetry, exchange ads only, letters from contributors, essays." It appears "irregularly, 4-9 month intervals." Press run 600, 550 circulation, 300 subscriptions of which 150 are libraries. Subscription: $16/4 issues, $20/4 issues overseas. **Sample postpaid: $4 ($6 double issues).** *Abraxas* **will announce submission guidelines as projects arise. Pays 1 copy plus 40% discount on additional copies.** To submit to Ghost Pony Press, **inquire with SASE plus 5-10 poems and cover letter. Previously published material OK for book publication by Ghost Pony Press. Reports on queries in 1-3 months, mss in 3 months. Payment varies per project. Send SASE for catalog to buy samples.** Editor sometimes comments briefly on rejections. They have recently published **Zen Concrete & Etc.,** a "definitive collection" of poetry by d.a. levy. That book is a 245-page, 8½×11, perfect-bound paperback available for $27.50 (plus $2 shipping and handling).

‡**ABSOLUTE INTERZONE BIZARRE (I, IV-Subscribers),** P.O. Box 354, Hatboro PA 19040, founded 1992, editor Bob Lennon (who also edits *Alternative Press Magazine*). *AIB*, published 3 times a year, is a subscribers only magazine **"open to most anything but will shy away from very traditional styles, religious and love poems."** The editor says *AIB* is approximately 30 pgs., 8½×11, photocopied and side-stapled, with cover art and 40-80 poems and drawings inside. Press run is 500 for about that many subscribers. Subscription: $15, outside US $18. **Sample postpaid: $5, outside US $6. Checks payable to Bob Lennon. You must subscribe to submit. Previously published poems and simultaneous submissions OK. Submit up to 5 poems. "Please send in clean copy as it may very well appear exactly as received." Seldom comments on rejections. Send SASE for guidelines. Reports in 1 week to 3 months. Pays 1 copy. Acquires first North American serial or reprint rights.** Reviews chapbooks, books and music. **They also publish 2-3 chapbooks/year but are not presently accepting unsolicited chapbook mss. Send $4 for sample and information.** As for the magazine, the editor says they "will not 'criticize' submissions because we want you to do your own thing and isn't that what art is all about? We will encourage writers and work with them until they have something we can use. If you subscribe, you are almost guaranteed a place in our pages once. Subscription is a prerequisite absolutely needed to meet

our goals which are: to keep this zine afloat so that we can continue to publish a fantastic amount of poetry and still maintain a level of quality which is consistent and desirable to the writing world. Send us your best, your tired, wary, your most sarcastic, funny and downright irreverent. This mag will work like a democratic institution where YOU help to determine not only the look but the feel of the end product. Interaction from writers is highly encouraged. Please send in b&w drawings, photos and cartoons. We are accepting submissions for cover art. All art intended for front or back cover should reflect what YOU feel the title of the magazine means."

ACM (ANOTHER CHICAGO MAGAZINE) (II); LEFT FIELD PRESS (V), 3709 N. Kenmore, Chicago IL 60613, founded 1976, poetry editor Barry Silesky. *ACM* is a literary biannual, **emphasis on quality, experimental, politically aware** prose, fiction, poetry, reviews, cross-genre work and essays. The editor wants **no religious verse.** They have published prose and poetry by Albert Goldbarth, Michael McClure, Jack Anderson, Jerome Sala, Nance VanWinkel, Nadja Tesich, Wanda Coleman, Thomas McGrath and Marilyn Krysl. As a sample, the editor selected these lines (poet unidentified):

> *The black trunk of the ancient tree splits*
> *into two branches at eye level.*
> *Thus Lopo Gonclaveo crossed*
> *the equator. No boiling waters. No harm*

The editor says *ACM* is digest-sized, 220 pgs., offset with b&w art and ads. Editors appreciate traditional to experimental verse with an emphasis on message, especially poems with strong voices articulating social or political concerns. Circulation 1,500, for 500 subscriptions of which 100 are libraries. **Sample postpaid: $7. Submit 3-8 pgs. typed. Simultaneous submissions OK. Reports in 2-3 months, has 3- to 6-month backlog. Pays $5/page and 1 copy. Buys first serial rights.** Reviews books of poetry in 250-500 words. Open to unsolicited reviews. Poets may also send books for review consideration. **They do not accept freelance submissions for chapbook publication.** Work published in *ACM* has been included in **Best American Poetry 1992** and **Pushcart Prize** anthologies.

ACUMEN MAGAZINE; EMBER PRESS (I, II), 6 The Mount, Higher Furzeham, Brixham, S. Devon TQ5 8QY England, phone (0803)851098, press founded 1971, *Acumen* founded 1984, poetry editor Patricia Oxley, is a "small press publisher of a general literary magazine with emphasis on good poetry." They want **"well-crafted, high quality, imaginative poems showing a sense of form. No experimental verse of an obscene type."** They have published poetry by Elizabeth Jennings, William Oxley, Gavin Ewart, D.J. Enright, Peter Porter, Kathleen Raine and R.S. Thomas. As a sample Mrs. Oxley selected these lines from "The Green Field" by Dannie Abse:

> *As soft-eyed lovers for the very first time,*
> *turning out the light for the first time,*
> *blot out all detail, all colours,*
> *and whisper the old code-words, 'Love you.'*

Acumen appears in April and October of each year and is 100 pgs, digest-sized, flat-spined, professionally printed with illustrations and ads. Of about 12,000 poems received they accept about 90. Press run is 650 for 400 subscriptions (15 libraries). Subscription: $25. **Sample postpaid: $10. No previously published poems; simultaneous submissions OK, if not to UK magazines. Reports in one month. Pays "by negotiation" and one copy.** Staff reviews books of poetry in up to 300 words, single format or 600 words, multi-book. Send books for review consideration to Glyn Pursglove, 25 St. Albans Rd., Brynmill, Swansea, Wales. Patricia Oxley advises, "Read *Acumen* carefully to see what kind of poetry we publish. Also read widely in many poetry magazines, and don't forget the poets of the past—they can still teach us a great deal."

ADASTRA PRESS (II), Dept. PM, 101 Strong St., Easthampton MA 01027, phone (413)527-3324, founded 1980 by Gary Metras, who says, "I publish poetry because I love poetry. I produce the books on antique equipment using antique methods because I own the equipment and because it's cheaper— I don't pay myself a salary—it's a hobby—it's **a love affair with poetry and printing of fine editions.** I literally sweat making these books and I want the manuscript to show me the author also sweated." All his books and chapbooks are **limited editions, handset, letterpress,** printed with handsewn signatures. "Chances of acceptance are slim. About 1 in 200 submissions is accepted, which means I only take 1 or 2 unsolicited mss a year." The chapbooks are in square-spine paper wrappers, cloth editions also handcrafted. He wants **"no rhyme, no religious. Poetry is communication first, although it is art. Long poems and thematic groups are nice for chapbooks. No subjects are tabu, but topics should be drawn from real life experiences. I include accurate dreams as real life."** Poets published include Thomas Lux, W.D. Ehrhart, Wally Swist and David Chorlton. As a sample the editor selected these lines from "Things We Leave Go" by Greg Joly:

> *tubers of bearded iris*
> *swim dark into the clouded lawn*

> seed heavy weeds
> come the full solstice moon
> grackles wire feet dance
> on empty metal silos

1-4 chapbooks are brought out each year. **Author is paid in copies, usually 10% of the print run.** "I only read chapbook manuscripts in the month of February, picking one or two for the following year. Queries, with a sample of 3-5 poems from a chapbook manuscript, are read throughout the year and if I like what I see in the sample, I'll ask you to submit the ms in February. I prefer a cover letter and a) samples from a completed chapbook ms or b) a completed chapbook ms. Do not submit or query about full-length collections. I will only be accepting chapbook manuscripts of 12-18 double-spaced pages. Any longer collections would be a special invitation to a poet. If you want to see a typical handcrafted Adastra chapbook, send $5 and I'll mail a current title.** If you'd like a fuller look at what, how and why I do what I do, send check for $11.50 ($10 plus $1.50 postage and handling) and I'll mail a copy of **The Adastra Reader: Being the Collected Chapbooks in Facsimile with Author Notes, Bibliography and Comments on Hand Bookmaking,** published in 1987. This is a 247-page anthology covering Adastra publishing from 1979-1986."

ADRIFT (II, IV-Ethnic), 4D, 239 East 5th St., New York NY 10003, founded 1980, editor Thomas McGonigle, who says, "The **orientation of the magazine is Irish, Irish-American. I expect reader-writer knows and goes beyond Yeats, Kavanagh, Joyce, O'Brien." The literary magazine is open to all kinds of submissions, but does not want to see "junk."** They have published poetry by James Liddy, Thomas McCarthy, Francis Stuart and Gilbert Sorrentino. *Adrift* appears twice a year and is magazine-sized, 32 pgs., offset on heavy stock, cover matte card, saddle-stapled. Circulation is 1,000 with 200 subscriptions, 50 of which go to libraries. Single copy: $4; subscription: $8. **Sample postpaid: $5. Simultaneous submissions OK. Magazine pays, rate varies; contributors receive 1 copy.** Reviews books of poetry. Open to unsolicited reviews. Poets may also send books for review consideration.

‡**ADVOCACY PRESS (V, IV-Children)**, P.O. Box 236, Santa Barbara CA 93102, founded 1983, director of operations Carol Terry, publishes children's books. **"Must have rhythm and rhyme."** They have published 3 books of rhymes for children: **Father Gander Nursery Rhymes** (nonsexist, nonviolent, nonracist version of Mother Goose), **Mother Nature Nursery Rhymes,** and **Nature's Wonderful World in Rhyme.** Their books are 32-48 pgs., illustrated in full color. **"No present plans for additional books in the Children's Rhymes series. Publish no other poetry at this time."** Query with description of concept and sample. SASE required for reply.

THE ADVOCATE (I), 301A Rolling Hills Park, Prattsville NY 12468, phone (518)299-3103, editor Remington Wright, founded 1987, is an advertiser-supported tabloid appearing bimonthly, 12,000 copies distributed free, **using "original, previously unpublished works,** such as feature stories, essays, 'think' pieces, letters to the editor, profiles, humor, fiction, poetry, puzzles, cartoons or line drawings." They want **"nearly any kind of poetry, any length, but not religious or pornographic. Poetry ought to speak to people and not be so oblique as to have meaning only to the poet. If I had to be there to understand the poem, don't send it."** As a sample the editor selected the opening lines from "You Brought Me Lilacs" by Tilitha Waicekauskas:

> I was young and slender, and in your eyes
> I was more beautiful than morning skies.
> My hair was as black as a raven's wing
> And the love in your eyes made my spirit sing.
> For I adored you and on my hand
> Was your diamond of promise—a platinum band
> —And you brought me lilacs.

Sample postpaid: $3. No previously published poems or simultaneous submissions. Editor "occasionally" **comments on rejections. Reports in 6-8 weeks; publishes accepted material an average of 4-6 months after acceptance. Pays 2 copies. Acquires first rights only.** Accepts about 25% of poems received. Reviews books of poetry. Open to unsolicited reviews. Poets may also send books to the attention of J.B. Samuels for review consideration. Offers occasional contests. The editor says, "All submissions and correspondence must be accompanied by a self-addressed, stamped envelope with sufficient postage."

The double dagger before a listing indicates that the listing is new in this edition. New markets are often the most receptive to submissions.

AEGINA PRESS, INC.; UNIVERSITY EDITIONS (I, II), 59 Oak Lane, Spring Valley, Huntington WV 25704, founded 1983, publisher Ira Herman, is **primarily subsidy for poetry**, strongly committed to publishing new or established poets. Publishes subsidy titles under the University Editions imprint. Aegina has published non-subsidized poetry as well. **Authors of books accepted on a non-subsidized basis receive a 15% royalty.** "We try to provide a way for talented poets to have their collections published, which otherwise might go unpublished because of commercial, bottom-line considerations. Aegina Press will publish quality poetry that the large publishers will not handle because it is not commercially viable. We believe it is unfair that a poet has to have a 'name' or a following in order to have a book of poems accepted by a publisher. Poetry is the purest form of literary art, and it should be made available to those who appreciate it." Poets published include Kenneth Berry. As a sample the editor selected these lines from **Word Mandalas** by John M. Feagan:

> *The earth draws insouciantly, mutely*
> *Along its ethereal axis,*
> *And winter spins off into space,*
> *Like an old man's lost toupee —*

"**Most poetry books we accept are subsidized by the author (or an institution).** In return, the author receives all sales proceeds from the book, and any unsold copies left from the print run belong to the author. Minimum print run is 500 copies. We can do larger runs as well. Our marketing program includes submission to distributors, agents, other publishers, and bookstores and libraries." **Manuscripts should be typed and no shorter than 40 pages. There is no upper length limit. Simultaneous submissions OK. Reporting time is 1 month for full manuscripts, 7-10 days for queries.** They publish perfect-bound (flat-spined) paperbacks with glossy covers. **Sample books are available for $5 each plus $1.50 postage and handling.**

AERIAL (V), P.O. Box 25642, Washington DC 20007, phone (202)333-1544, founded 1984, editor Rod Smith, editorial assistants Gretchen Johnsen and Wayne Kline, is a yearly publication. Issue #6/7 was the John Cage issue. They have published work by Jackson MacLow, Melanie Neilson, Steve Benson, Phyllis Rosenzweig and Charles Bernstein. Two special issues are in the works, on Barrett Watten and Bruce Andrews, therefore **they're not looking for new work at this time.** As a sample the editor selected these lines from "subtracted words" by P. Inman:

> *still dollar in its pale*
> *mice sight. Parts of knock*
> *in a river of propellor blade.*
> *Wage sand gist. Keyhole*
> *college, its brink on. An*
> *ash stelm of mind ball*

The magazine is 6×9, offset, varies from 180 to 280 pgs. Circulation is 1,000. **Sample postpaid: $7.50. Poets should submit 1-10 pages. Reporting time is 1 week-2 months and time to publication is 3-12 months.** Also looking for critical/political/philosophical writing.

AETHLON: THE JOURNAL OF SPORT LITERATURE (IV-Sports), Dept. PM, English Dept., East Tennessee State University, Johnson City TN 37614-0002, phone (615)929-4339, founded 1983, general editor Don Johnson, Professor of English, ETSU, poetry editor Robert W. Hamblin, Professor of English, Southeast Missouri State University, Cape Girardeau MO 63701. (Submit poetry to this address.) *Aethlon* publishes a variety of sport-related literature, including scholarly articles, fiction, poetry, personal essays and reviews; 6-10 poems/issue; two issues annually, fall and spring. **Subject matter must be sports-related; no restrictions regarding form, length, style or purpose. They do not want to see "doggerel, cliché-ridden or oversentimental" poems.** Poets published include Neal Bowers, Joseph Duemer, Robert Fink, Jan Mordenski, H.R. Stonebeck, Jim Thomas, Stephen Tudor and Don Welch. The magazine is digest-sized, offset printed, flat-spined, with illustrations and some ads, 200 pgs./issue. Circulation is 1,000 of which 750 are subscriptions, 250 to libraries. Subscription is included with membership ($30) in the Sport Literature Association. **Sample postpaid: $12.50. Will accept simultaneous submissions. "Only typed mss with SASE considered."** Submissions are reported on in **6-8 weeks and the backlog time is 6-12 months.** Contributors receive 5 offprints and a copy of the issue in which their poem appears.

AFRICA WORLD PRESS (IV-Ethnic), Box 1892, Trenton NJ 08607, founded 1979, editor Kassahun Checole, publishes **poetry books by Africans, African-Americans, Caribbean and Latin Americans.** Two poetry publications by Africa World Press are: **Under A Soprano Sky** by Sonia Sanchez and **From the Pyramid to the Projects** by Askia Muhammad Toure, winner of an American Book Award for 1989. **Considers simultaneous submissions. Authors receive 7½% royalty; number of copies negotiable. Send SASE for catalog.**

AFRICAN AMERICAN REVIEW (IV-Ethnic), (formerly *Black American Literature Forum*), Dept. of English, Indiana State University, Terre Haute IN 47809, founded 1967 (as *Negro American Literature Forum*), poetry editors Sterling Plumpp, Thadious M. Davis, Pinkie Gordon Lane and E. Ethelbert Miller, is a "magazine primarily devoted to the analysis of African American literature, **although one issue per year focuses on poetry by African Americans.**" No specifications as to form, length, style, subject matter or purpose. They have published poems by Amiri Baraka, Gwendolyn Brooks, Dudley Randall and Owen Dodson. *AAR* is 6×9, 200 pgs. with photo on the cover. They receive about 500 submissions/year, use 50. Individual subscriptions: $20 USA, $27 foreign. **Sample postpaid: $10. Submit maximum of 6 poems to editor Joe Weixlmann. The editors sometimes comment on rejections. Send SASE for guidelines. Pays in copies. Reports in 3-4 months.**

AFRO-HISPANIC REVIEW (IV-Ethnic), Romance Languages, #143 Arts & Sciences, University of Missouri, Columbia MO 65211, founded 1982, editors Marvin A. Lewis and Edward J. Mullen, appears 3 times a year using some **poetry related to Afro-Hispanic life and issues.** They have published poetry by Manuel Zapata Olivella, Melvin E. Lewis and Antar Al Basir. **Sample copy: $5. Reports in 6 weeks. Pays 5 copies.** Reviews books of poetry in "about 500 words."

‡AGASSIZ (II), 207 Lind Hall, 207 Church St. SE, Minneapolis MN 55455, founded 1979, poetry editor changes periodically, is an annual using **"all types of poetry."** *Agassiz* is 240 pgs., 7×9, professionally printed and perfect-bound with 4-color glossy cover. Of "200 manuscript packets received, we accept 30-35 poems." **Mss should be no longer than 3,000 words, typed and double-spaced; include page number and abbreviated title at top of each page. Name only on cover letter, along with title of submission, short bio and phone number. Include SASE. Reports in 6 months. Pays 2 copies.** Staff reviews books of poetry. Send books for review consideration to Will Hermes at the above address.

AGNI (II), Boston University, 236 Bay State Rd., Boston MA 02215, phone (617)353-5389, founded 1972, editor Askold Melnyczuk. *Agni* is a biannual journal of poetry, fiction and essays "by both emerging and established writers." Editors seem to select readable, intelligent poetry—mostly lyric free verse (with some narrative and dramatic, too)—that somehow communicates tension or risk. They have published poetry by Derek Walcott, Patricia Traxler, Thom Gunn, Maxine Scates, Mark Halliday and Ha Jin. As a sample the editor selected these lines from Rafael Campo's poem, "Grandfather's Will":

> *I leave you the plantation, and the pain*
> *Of sugar. I leave you even the scattered sins*
> *Of island life: thirst in spite of water*
> *Everywhere, to not escape, and to think*
> *You rose above the sea on purpose. Tanks*
> *Are crushing my body now—the traitors*
> *In our house have come for me. A word of caution:*
> *Remember me. Bury me in the ocean.*
> *Burn me to brown sugar—drink me, a potion*
> *In your coffee. It grows on your plantation.*

Agni is typeset, printed offset and perfect-bound with about 40 poems featured in each issue. Circulation is 1,500 by subscription, mail order and bookstore sales. Subscription: $12. **Sample: $7. They will consider simultaneous submissions but not previously published poems. Reads submissions October 1 through April 30 only. Mss received at other times will be returned unread. Reports in 1-4 months. Pays $10/page, $150 maximum, plus 2 copies and one-year subscription. Buys first serial rights.** Work published in *Agni* has been included in **Best American Poetry** and **Pushcart Prize** anthologies.

AG-PILOT INTERNATIONAL MAGAZINE (IV-Specialized), P.O. Box 1607, Mt. Vernon WA 98273, phone (206)336-9737, publisher Tom Wood, "is intended to be a fun-to-read, technical, as well as humorous and serious publication for the ag pilot and operator." It appears monthly, 48-64 pgs., circulation 8,400. "Interested in **agricultural aviation (crop dusting) related poetry ONLY.**" Buys 1/ issue. **Pays $10-50.**

THE AGUILAR EXPRESSION (I, II), P.O. Box 304, Webster PA 15087, phone (412)379-8019, founded 1986, editor/publisher Xavier F. Aguilar, appears 2 times/year, and is **"open to all types of poetry, including erotica that is well written."** They have recently published poetry by Laura Albrecht and Rebecca Charry. As a sample the editor selected the poem "Tempo Di Marcia" by George R. Beck:

> *. . .I ride my steed*
> *down forest green paths*
> *cloaked with purple grapes*

The editor describes it as 6-8 pgs., magazine-sized, circulation 150. **Sample postpaid: $5. Cover** letter, including writing background, required with submissions. Reports in 1 month. Pays 1 copy. Open to unsolicited reviews. "We are also now seeking poetry manuscripts as we wish to publish 1 or 2 chapbooks in 1993-1994. Send SASE for details." The editor says, "In publishing poetry, I try to exhibit the unique reality that we too often take for granted and acquaint as mediocre. We encourage poetics that deal with *now*, which our readers can relate to. We also offer a cash prize for an essay relating to the writing of poetics (four typed pages). Guidelines for SASE."

AHSAHTA PRESS; COLD DRILL; COLD-DRILL BOOKS; POETRY IN PUBLIC PLACES (IV-Regional), English Dept., Boise State University, Boise ID 83725, phone (208)385-1246. Ahsahta Press is a project to publish **contemporary poetry of the American West**. But, say editors Tom Trusky, Orv Burmaster and Dale Boyer, "Spare us paens to the pommel, Jesus in the sagebrush, haiku about the Eiffel Tower, 'nice' or 'sweet' poems." The work should "draw on the cultures, history, ecologies of the American West." They publish collections (45 + pgs.) of individual poets in handsome flat-spined paperbacks with plain matte covers, with an appreciative introduction, at most 3/year. Occasionally they bring out an anthology on cassette of their authors. And they have published an anthology (94 pgs.) **Women Poets of the West**, with an introduction by Ann Stanford. Some of their poets are Susan Deal, Leo Romero, David Baker, Linda Bierds, Philip St. Clair and Gretel Ehrlich. As a sample here are lines from Gerrye Payne's "Machines," in the collection **The Year-God**:

> Machines sit to hand, vortices of possibility.
> Under their blank gaze biological life
> Flares and dies, is ashamed.
> The neighbor's tractor hums, clearing brush,
> inventing geometry in random chaparral.

You may submit only during their January 1 through March 31 reading period each year—a sample of 15 of your poems with SASE. They will report in about 2 months. Multiple and simultaneous submissions OK. If they like the sample, they'll ask for a book ms. If it is accepted, you get 25 copies of the 1st and 2nd printings and a 25% royalty commencing with the 3rd. They seldom comment on the samples, frequently on the mss. Send SASE for their catalog and order a few books, if you don't find them in your library. "Old advice but true: read what we publish before submitting. 75% of the submissions we receive should never have been sent to us. Save stamps, spirit and sweat." *Cold Drill* publishes "primarily Boise State University students, faculty and staff, but will consider writings by Idahoans — or writing about Idaho by 'furriners.' " They do some of the most creative publishing in this country today, and it is worth buying a **sample of** *cold-drill* for $9 just to see what they're up to. This annual "has been selected as top undergraduate literary magazine in the U.S. by such important acronyms as CSPA, CCLM and UCDA." It comes in a box stuffed with various pamphlets, postcards, posters, a newspaper, even 3-D comics with glasses to read them by. **No restrictions on types of poetry.** As yet they have published no poets of national note, but Tom Trusky offers these lines as a sample, from Patrick Flanagan, "Postcard From a Freshman":

> The girls here are gorgeous, studying hard,
> many new friends, roommate
> never showers, tried to
> kill myself, doctor says
> i'm getting better

Circulation is 400, including 100 subscribers, of which 20 are libraries. "We read material throughout the year, notifying only those whose work we've accepted December 15 through January 1. Manuscripts should be photocopies with author's name and address on separate sheet. Simultaneous submissions OK. Payment: 1 copy." They also publish two 24-page chapbooks and one 75-page flat-spined paperback/year. **Query about book publication.** "We want to publish a literary magazine that is exciting to read. We want more readers than just our contributors and their mothers. Our format and our content have allowed us to achieve those goals, so far." Poetry in Public Places is a series of 8 monthly posters/year "presenting the poets in Boise State University's creative students series and poets in BSU's Ahsahta Press poetry series." These, like all publications emanating from BSU, are elegantly done, with striking art. The posters are on coated stock.

‡AILERON PRESS; AILERON: A LITERARY JOURNAL; VOWEL MOVEMENT (II), P.O. Box 891, Austin TX 78767-0891, founded 1980, editor Ric Williams. *Aileron* is an annual periodical consisting **of poetry and occasional short fiction, with some art. They want "poetry that moves us, that makes us want to read it again and again. We are especially keen on innovative uses of language — the unexpected word and the unusual cadence. We would like to see more poetic craft displayed, and, though not inimical to rhymed work, feel that few contemporary poets handle rhyme well."** They have published poetry by

CLOSE-UP

Start with Regional Publications

*You know what they say
of country hospitality
how a person, alone, mid-winter,
can go mad
without a diary—
the back of last year's calendar,
4-H flyer, the rude brown almanac
kraft bags
can afford.*

(from "Invitation")

Tom Trusky

Photo by Enver Sulejman

"It makes real sense for a beginning poet to start at home," says Tom Trusky. "Unless you're writing verse entitled 'Truth' or 'Hope' or 'Faith,' you're probably going to write about things you know best, things in your life and territory, and that will be of special interest to people in your region. So begin by establishing a local or regional reputation and then slowly building on it."

As founder and coeditor of Ahsahta Press at Boise State University, Trusky provides a book publishing opportunity for contemporary poets writing about the American West, the 14 states.west of the Mississippi.

In fact, Ahsahta (the name is Mandan Indian and means Rocky Mountain Bighorn Sheep) publishes up to three book-length collections annually. "We see our role as providing a first and a major sort of publication for poets who write about the West," Trusky says. "You don't have to live in the West, by the way. You can live in Tallahassee, but as long as your poetry in some way draws on the ecology, the history, the cultures, whatever it may be in the West, we'll consider it Western."

However, Trusky and his coeditors, Orvis Burmaster and Dale Boyer, seek to publish regional material that is also universal. "We aspire to be regional like Robert Frost is regional," he says. "In some ways Robert Frost is just a New England poet, but he is universal. The human situation, the fate of the land or the fate of a culture, those are universal concerns, and I hope our poets achieve those universals while drawing on the West."

Poets interested in Ahsahta may send a sampler—15 representative poems—with a SASE only in the months of January, February or March. Trusky and his coeditors then read samplers and "if any one of us is smitten, sees a glimmer of something that he is inspired or excited by, we call for a complete manuscript.

"At that time, we like to get more poems than would make a 60-page book, quite frankly, so that gives us some options. For example, a poet may have a complete manuscript of 47 poems, but we may ask her to delete four poems that we don't feel are strong. We try to help define the poet's real strength and vision."

In the end, all three must agree to publish a manuscript "and that has been absolutely brutal at times. But my attitude toward the resulting product then is that three people with strong, independent views about what poetry is, have agreed," says Trusky.

Books chosen are published in paperback and have a series format. The cover, for example, is a flat color with a ram's head logo and the title. "Poets may choose the color of their covers and suggest a poet, critic or historian to write an insightful, yet critical introduction to their work," he says. "But we don't include photographs or line drawings. It's just the words on the acid-free page."

Besides publishing collections, Trusky and company help promote them. From the first printing of 500 copies, they send up to 50 to reviewers and others the authors recommend. Poets themselves receive 25 copies from both the first and second printings. Beginning with the third edition, they receive 25% royalties.

All told, Ahsahta receives about 250 samplers a year, but most should have never been sent, says Trusky. "It's just incredible to me that poets who want to be published by Ahsahta will send us material totally disregarding **Poet's Market** and everything else they read. We get hundreds of manuscripts about New York, about Paris, about Tokyo. Sometimes people will say 'I was born in Portland, Oregon, but I've lived in Paris since 1974,' and all the poems are about Paris.

"I wish people would realize we're just interested in material about the region. I'm sorry to say, though, we're not interested in 'cowboy poetry.' I have nothing against traditional forms of poetry or rhymed poems, but, unfortunately, most practitioners of that sort of thing are not writing interesting, quality poetry in my mind."

Trusky suggests poets preparing to submit a sampler first read what Ahsahta has published. "At the very least, I urge people to write for our free catalog because we always highlight our year's poets by including an abstract of two to three poems."

When poets include photos or drawings in submissions, he can tell they don't know the series. "I don't want drawings that enhance poems, I want poems that are already so wonderful the poet has drawn whatever it was in my mind for me."

He also doesn't want to see cover letters or resumes. "Who you know or where you've published is not of major concern to us. Our first concern is the poetry."

Serving as coeditor of Ahsahta is only one of Trusky's many roles at Boise State. He is an adviser of *cold-drill*, the university's annual magazine, published as a boxed collection. "The magazine primarily features work about Idaho or by Idahoans or of interest to Idahoans," he says. He also publishes *cold-drill* books, works of those who have appeared in the magazine. And he produces Poetry in Public Places, a series of monthly poetry posters, timed for the academic year and distributed free to libraries, school rooms, senior citizen centers and other public places.

Formerly a professor of English, Trusky's newest role is director of the Hemingway Western Studies Center. He recently redefined the center's book series and now sponsors the Rocky Mountain Artists'/Eccentric Book Competition to encourage the creation of inexpensive, multiple edition, artists'/eccentric books dealing with public issues such as race, religion, gender and the environment.

Fascinated by the whole creative process, he finds true joy in having a new work to help produce, publish and promote. "I'm still gripped with that over the transom sort of miracle," he says. The most recent example is a *cold-drill* book, the diary of an Idaho woman that came in totally unsolicited. His enthusiasm for that project shows in his own lines of poetry at the beginning of this interview.

Regarding all his "fiefdoms," Trusky says, "We bring poets, I hope, initial local or regional as well as national notice. Then they may go on to be published by magazines like *The New Yorker* or by major American publishers. We like to see ourselves as stepping stones. Go ahead and use us."

— *Christine Martin*

Anselm Hollo, Simon Perchik, Hal J. Daniel III and Tomaz Salamun. As a sample the editor selected these lines by Elkion Tumbalé:

> Blue cup modal gorges
> Lurk frondly on
> Orchid Zontal
> Obsidian felines

Aileron is digest-sized, saddle-stapled, typeset (in small type), with b&w original line art and stiff cover with art. Circulation is 350, with 25 subscriptions. Subscription: $14 for 4 issues. **Sample postpaid: $4.** Each issue contains 40-60 pages of poetry garnered from 400-600 submissions each year of which 60-100 are used, 6-month backlog. **All formats acceptable; must have name and address on each page; no limitations on form, length or subject matter. Send SASE for guidelines. Reports in 6 weeks. Pays 1 copy.** *Vowel Movement*, "a 'pataphysical journal,' is published occasionally as a special issue of *Aileron*. It contains **avant-garde humor, satire, and work that is outrageous or experimental in nature."**

AIM MAGAZINE (IV-Social issues, ethnic), 7308 S. Eberhart Ave., Chicago IL 60619, phone (312)874-6184, founded 1974, poetry editor Henry Blakely, is a magazine-sized quarterly, circulation 10,000, glossy cover, **"dedicated to racial harmony and peace."** They use 3-4 poems ("poetry with social significance mainly") in each issue. **They ask for 32 lines average length.** They have published poetry by J. Douglas Studer, Wayne Dowdy and Maria DeGuzman. They have 3,000 subscriptions of which 15 are libraries. Single copy: $3.50; subscription: $10. **Sample postpaid: $4. They receive only about 30 submissions/year of which they use half. Simultaneous submissions OK. Reports in 3-6 weeks. Pays $3/poem. You will not receive an acceptance slip: "We simply send payment and magazine copy."** The editor's advice: "Read the work of published poets."

AIREINGS (II, IV-Women), #24, Brudenell Rd., Leeds, West Yorkshire LS6 1BD United Kingdom, phone 0532-785893, founded 1980, editor Jean Barker. "Poems acceptable from all over the world. **Primarily like women's work as we are a Women's Co-op running the mag and like to redress the balance a bit, but we are happy to receive work by men also. Poetry on all subjects. We do draw a line on sexist/racist stuff, but we like a broad spectrum of work as long as it is not too long, as we only run to 40 pgs."** They have recently published poetry by Geoffrey Holloway, Pauline Kirk, Jane Legge, Mary Sheepshanks, C. A de Lomallini and Linda Marshall. As a sample the editor selected these lines (poet unidentified):

> At thirty, weatherbeaten,
> He was old for life; stone
> Pressed into stone, the interface
> of man and nature, bone
> locked into bone; what holds
> the wall held up the builder too.

The magazine appears twice a year, "illustrated by our own artist. No ads yet, but we may have to later, if we are under extreme financial pressure." *Aireings* is digest-sized, 40 pgs., saddle-stapled, photocopied from typescript with matte b&w card cover. They publish about 5% of the poetry received. They print 300-350 copies for 100 subscribers (10 libraries) and shelf sales. It costs £1.50/copy, which includes UK postage (overseas: Payment in sterling £5. Other currencies: check equivalent of £10 or in notes equivalent of £6.50.). **"Work should be typed if possible— just legible if not." Simultaneous submissions and previously published (if not in the North of England) OK. Reports "after our editorial deadlines, which are the 1st of January and July." Pays 2 copies.** Staff reviews books of poetry in 500 words.

ALABAMA LITERARY REVIEW (II), English Dept., Troy State University, Troy AL 36082, phone (205)670-3000, ext. 3286, poetry editor Ed Hicks, a biannual, **wants poetry that is "imagistic—*but* in motion. Will look at anything,"** but does not want to see "lyrics sent as poetry. We want serious craft." They have published poetry by R.T. Smith, Ed Peaco, Joanne M. Riley and Martha Payne. As a sample the editor selected these lines from "Late Fall" by Diane Swan:

> It's hard to tell birds
> from wind-rushed leaves
> as they skirl up in the funnels
> of blinking October light

The beautifully printed 100-page, 6×9 magazine, matte cover with art, b&w art and some colored pages inside, receives 300 submissions/year, uses 30, has a 2-month backlog. **Sample postpaid: $4.50. Will consider simultaneous submissions. Reads submissions September 1 through July 31 only. Sometimes comments on rejections. Reports in 2-3 months. Pays copies. Acquires first rights.** Open to unsolicited reviews. Poets may also send books for review consideration.

ALASKA QUARTERLY REVIEW (II), College of Arts and Sciences, University of Alaska Anchorage, 3221 Providence Dr., Anchorage AK 99508, phone (907)786-4775, founded 1981, executive editor Ronald Spatz, poetry editor Thomas Sexton. "A journal devoted to contemporary literary art. **We publish both traditional and experimental fiction, poetry, essays and criticism on contemporary writing, literature and philosophy of literature.**" Editors seem to welcome all styles and forms of poetry with the most emphasis perhaps on voice and content that displays "risk," or intriguing ideas or situations. They publish two double-issues a year, **each using between 18-25 pgs. of poetry.** They receive up to 2,000 submissions each year, accept about 40. They have a circulation of 1,000; 250 subscribers, of which 32 are libraries. Subscription: $8. **Sample postpaid: $4. Manuscripts are *not* read from May 15 through August 15. They take up to 4 months to report, sometimes longer during peak periods in late winter. Pay depends on funding. Acquires first North American serial rights.**

ALBATROSS; THE ANABIOSIS PRESS (II, IV-Nature), 125 Horton Ave., Englewood FL 34223, founded 1985, editors Richard Smyth and Richard Brobst. *Albatross* appears in the spring and fall. **"We consider the albatross to be a metaphor for an environment that must survive. This is not to say that we publish only environmental or nature poetry, but that we are biased toward such subject matters. We publish mostly free verse 200 lines/poem maximum, and we prefer a narrative style, but again, this is not necessary. We do not want trite rhyming poetry which doesn't convey a deeply felt experience in a mature expression with words."** They have published poetry by Simon Perchik, Michael Jennings, Karen Volkman and Elizabeth Rees. As a sample, the editors selected these lines by Polly Buckingham:

> *Many white birds scatter like*
> *doves in a sand dollar,*
> *and I receive you, my body*
> *a murex, whelk, moonshell.*

The magazine is 32-36 pgs., 5½ × 8½, laser typeset with linen cover, some b&w drawings, and, in addition to the poetry, has an interview with a poet in each issue. Circulation 300 to 75 subscribers of which 10 are libraries. Many complimentary copies are sent out to bookstores, poets and libraries. Subscription: $5/2 issues. **Sample postpaid: $3. "Poems should be typed single-spaced, with name and address in left corner and length in lines in right corner."** No simultaneous submissions. **Cover letter not required; "We do, however, need bio notes if published."** Send SASE for guidelines. **Reports in 4-6 months, has 6- to 12-month backlog. Pays 2 copies. Acquires all rights. Returns rights provided that "previous publication in *Albatross* is mentioned in all subsequent reprintings."** Staff reviews books of poetry. Also holds a chapbook contest. **Submit 16-20 pgs. of poetry, any theme, any style. Deadline is February 15 of each year. Include name, address and phone number on the title page. Charges $5 reading fee (check payable to *Albatross*). Winner receives $50 and 25 copies of his/her published chapbook. All entering receive a free copy of the winning chapbook.** "The Anabiosis Press is now a nonprofit organization. Membership fee is $20 plus $20/year for membership dues." Comments? "We expect a poet to read as much contemporary poetry as possible."

THE ALCHEMIST (II), Box 123, Lasalle, Quebec H8R 3T7 Canada, founded 1974, poetry editor Marco Fraticelli, is an irregularly-issued literary journal using mostly poetry. **No restrictions on form, style or content, though the editor says they are "very receptive to haiku and tanka."** It is 100 pgs., digest-sized, flat-spined, handsomely printed and illustrated with b&w drawings. They have a print run of 500, 200 subscriptions, of which 30 are libraries, and they send out some 200 complimentary copies. Subscription: $12 for 4 issues, $3/issue. **Sample postpaid: $2. Considers simultaneous submissions.** They have a 6-month backlog. **Reports in 1 month. Pays 2 copies.**

ALDEBARAN (II), Roger Williams University, 1 Old Ferry Rd., Bristol RI 02809, editor Quantella Owens, publishes a spring and a fall issue. *"Aldebaran* **publishes both poetry and fiction in traditional, contemporary and experimental forms; we are receptive to nearly all styles and topics.** We would like to see more diversity in our magazine and encourage submissions from writers of all genres, from fantasy to dark fiction, science fiction, comedy, horror and drama, as well as classical and contemporary poetry and fiction." The magazine is 50-100 pgs., side-stapled or perfect-bound, digest-sized. Press run is 300. Subscription: $10 for 2 issues. **Sample postpaid: $5. Submit no more than 5 poems at a time. Reads submissions February 1 through April 1 and September 1 through November 1. Student-run publication. Seldom comments on rejections. Send SASE for guidelines. Reports in 6-12 weeks.**

ALICEJAMESBOOKS; BEATRICE HAWLEY AWARD (IV-Regional, women, ethnic), 33 Richdale Ave., Cambridge MA 02140, phone (617)354-1408, founded 1973, is "an author's collective, which publishes exclusively **poetry, with an emphasis on poetry by women; authors are exclusively from the New England Area.** We strongly encourage submissions by poets of color." They publish flat-spined paperbacks of high quality, both in production and contents, no children's poetry, and their books have won numerous awards and been very respectably reviewed. "Each poet becomes a working member of the co-op with a two-year work commitment." That is, you have to live close enough to attend meetings and participate in the editorial and publishing process. They publish about 4 books, 72 pgs., each year in editions of 1,000, paperbacks—no hardbacks. **Query first, but no need for samples:** simply ask for dates of reading periods, which are in early spring and early fall. **Simultaneous submissions OK, but "we would like to know when a manuscript is being submitted elsewhere." Send two copies of the ms. Reports in 2-3 months. Pays authors 100 paperback copies.** Offers Beatrice Hawley Award for poets who cannot meet the work requirement due to geographical or financial restraints.

ALIVE NOW!; POCKETS; WEAVINGS (IV-Religious, children, themes); THE UPPER ROOM (V), 1908 Grand Ave., P.O. Box 189, Nashville TN 37202, phone (615)340-7200. This publishing company brings out about 20 books a year and four magazines: *The Upper Room, alive now!, Pockets* and *Weavings.* Of these, two use freelance poetry. *Pockets, Devotional Magazine for Children,* which comes out 11 times a year, circulation 68,000-70,000, is for children 6-12, "offers stories, activities, prayers, poems—all geared to giving children a better understanding of themselves as children of God. Some of the material is not overtly religious but deals with situations, special seasons and holidays, ecological concerns from a Christian perspective." It uses 3-4 pgs. of poetry/issue. Sample: free with 7×9 SAE and 4 first class stamps. Ordinarily 24-line limit on poetry. Send SASE for themes and guidelines. Pays $25-50. The other magazine which uses poetry is *alive now!,* a bimonthly, circulation 75,000, for a general Christian audience interested in reflection and meditation. **Guidelines and themes list free (with SASE). They buy 30 poems a year, avant-garde and free verse. Submit 5 poems, 10-45 lines. Pays $10-25.** *The Upper Room* magazine does not accept poetry.

‡ALLARDYCE, BARNETT PUBLISHERS (V), 14 Mount St., Lewes, East Sussex BN7 1HL England, founded 1982, editorial director Anthony Barnett. Allardyce, Barnett publishes "literature, music, art. **We cannot consider unsolicited manuscripts."** They have published books of poetry by J.H. Prynne, Douglas Oliver and Veronica Forrest-Thomson. In the US, their books can be obtained through Small Press Distribution in Berkeley, CA, except for music titles which are distributed by North Country-Cadence, Redwood, NY.

ALLEGHENY REVIEW (I, IV-Students), Dept. PM, Box 32, Allegheny College, Meadville PA 16335, founded 1983, editors Lauren Dyer and Joe Miksch. "Each year *Allegheny Review* compiles and publishes a review of the nation's best **undergraduate literature.** It is entirely composed of and by college undergraduates and is nationally distributed both as a review and as a classroom text, particularly suited to creative writing courses. We will print **poetry of appreciable literary merit on any topic, submitted by college undergraduates. No limitations except excessive length (2-3 pgs.)** as we wish to represent as many authors as possible, although exceptions are made in areas of great quality and interest." They have published poetry by Eric Sanborn, Cheryl Connor, Rick Alley and Kristi Coulter. The *Review* appears in a 6×9, flat-spined, professionally-printed format, b&w photo on glossy card cover. **Sample: $3.50 and 11×18 SASE. Submit 3 to 5 poems, typed.** Submissions should be accompanied by a letter "telling the college poet is attending, year of graduation, any background, goals and philosophies that the author feels are pertinent to the work submitted." Reports 1-2 months following **deadline. Poem judged best in the collection earns $50-75 honorarium.** "Ezra Pound gave the best advice: 'Make it new.' We're seeing far too much imitation; there's already been a Sylvia Plath, a Galway Kinnell. Don't be afraid to try new things. Be innovative. Also, traditional forms are coming 'back in style,' or so we hear. Experiment with them; write a villanelle, a sestina or a sonnet. And when you submit, please take enough pride in your work to do so professionally. Handwritten or poorly-typed and proofed submissions definitely convey an impression, a negative one."

ALLY PRESS CENTER (V), Dept. PM, 524 Orleans St., St. Paul MN 55107, founded 1973, owner Paul Feroe, **publishes and distributes work by Robert Bly, Michael Meade, James Hillman and Robert Moore, including books, cassette tapes and videotapes.** Two to three times a year a complete catalog is mailed out along with information about Bly's reading and workshop schedule. **The press is not accepting unsolicited mss at this time.** Book catalog is free on request.

Market conditions are constantly changing! If you're still using this book and it is 1995 or later, buy the newest edition of Poet's Market *at your favorite bookstore or order directly from* Writer's Digest Books.

ALMS HOUSE PRESS (I), P.O. Box 217, Pearl River NY 10965-0217, founded 1985, poetry editors Lorraine De Gennaro and Alana Sherman, holds an **annual poetry competition with $7 entry fee (contestants receive a copy of a chapbook).** "We have no preferences with regard to style as long as the poetry is high caliber. We like to see previous publication in the small press, but we are open to new writers. We look for variety and excellence and are open to experimental forms as well as traditional forms. Any topics as long as the poems are not whiny or too depressing, pornographic or religious." They have published chapbooks by Martin Anderson and Sandra Marshburn. As a sample they selected these lines by Steven Lautermilch:

> *Fisher, fishwife, hold each to each.*
> *Your children, small fry, grow only to feed*
> *the sighing grave. And your roofs,*
> *like these keels,*
> *are the bed and birth of shells.*

Submit 16- to 24-page chapbook including all front matter, title page and table of contents, between March 1 and May 31. Name, address and phone number should appear on title page only. Winner receives 15 copies. Send SASE for current rules. Sample copy postpaid: $4. They offer a critical and editorial service for $25.

ALOHA, THE MAGAZINE OF HAWAII AND THE PACIFIC (IV-Regional), Suite 309, 49 S. Hotel St., Honolulu HI 96813, editor Cheryl Chee Tsutsumi, is a bimonthly (every 2 months) "consumer magazine with Hawaii and Pacific focus. **Not interested in lengthy poetry. Poems should be limited to 100 words or less. Subject should be focused on Hawaii.**" As a sample we selected these lines by William Beyer:

> *Elusive gulls*
> *ascend,*
> *descend*
> *with perfect grace,*
> *in celebration*
> *above the constant rhythm*
> *of a rising tide.*

Aloha is 64 pgs., magazine-sized, flat-spined, elegantly printed on glossy stock with many full-color pages, glossy card cover in color. They publish 6 of more than 50 poems received/year. Circulation 65,000. **Sample postpaid: $2.95. Ms should be typed, double-spaced, with name, address and phone number included.** Poems are matched to color photos, so it is "difficult to say" how long it will be between acceptance and publication. **Send SASE for guidelines. Reports within 2 months. Pays $30 plus 1 copy (and up to 10 at discount).**

ALPHA BEAT SOUP; ALPHA BEAT PRESS (I, IV-Form/style), 31 A Waterloo St., New Hope PA 18938, founded 1987, poetry editor David Christy, appears twice a year **emulating the Beat literary tradition.** *Alpha Beat Soup* is "an international poetry and arts journal featuring Beat, 'post-Beat independent' and modern writing." Christy says that **25% of each issue is devoted to little known or previously unpublished poets.** They have recently published works by Pradip Choudhuri, Erling Friis-Baastad, Ana Pine, George Dowden and Charles Bukowski. *ABS* is 7 × 8½, 50-75 pgs., photocopied from IBM laser printer, card cover offset, graphics included. They use 50% of poetry received. Press run is 600 for 400 subscribers (11 of them libraries). Single copy: $8; subscription: $15. **Sample postpaid: $10. Simultaneous submissions and previously published poems OK. Cover letter, including "an introduction to the poet's work," required.** Editor comments on rejections "only on request." **Pays 1 copy.** Reviews books of poetry in approximately 700 words, multi-book format. Open to unsolicited reviews. Poets may also send books for review consideration. **Alpha Beat Press publishes chapbooks and supplements as well as a monthly poetry broadside.** *Alpha Beat Soup* ranked #2 in the "Nontraditional Verse" category of the June 1993 *Writer's Digest* Poetry 60 list.

‡ALPHABOX PRESS (V), 41 Mapesbury Rd., London NW2 4HJ England, founded 1971, is a small press publishing small editions, about 2 chapbooks a year averaging 20 pgs., and fine printed editions every two or three years of about the same length. **Publications include experimental and visual poetry. "No submissions wanted."**

ALTERNATIVE PRESS MAGAZINE (II), P.O. Box 205, Hatboro PA 19040, founded 1989, poetry editor Bob Lennon, coeditor Lynne Budnick-Lennon, appears quarterly using "**experimental, philosophical poetry; open to many subjects and styles. No traditional, religious, or worn-out love poems.**" They have published poetry by T.N. Turner, Leslie Parker, Thomas Kretz, Rod Farmer, Robb Allan, Michael Estabrook, Tracy Lyn Rottkamp and Cheryl A. Townsend. As a sample the editor selected these lines from "WELcome 2 my bRAIN" by Lori Steinberg:

> *WATER on the bRAIN*

DUGH!!
BoinK/BoinK!!
where am i??
            KANSAS!?
RUFF! RUFF!

It is photocopied from typescript, digest-sized, 36 pgs. with matte card cover, saddle-stapled. Press run is 500 for about 100 subscribers, and growing. Some shelf sales. Subscription: $10 for 4 issues. **Sample postpaid: $3. Inquire about reduced rates for back issues. "Poets from Canada and overseas should include $1 extra for each issue ordered." Make all checks payable to Bob Lennon.** *"Alternative Press* **will attempt to print many poems submitted unlike some magazines that print trash and reject most poems. Submit up to 5 poems—remember that we publish a digest-sized mag and longer pieces have a harder time finding a place." Simultaneous submissions and previously published poems OK. Guidelines available for SASE. Reports within 2 weeks-2 months. Pays 1-3 copies and "occasionally small sums." Editor comments on submissions "sometimes."** They are "now doing reviews of 'zines, books, chapbooks and music." Open to unsolicited reviews. Poets may also send books for review consideration. *"APM* is currently not accepting unsolicited mss for our chopbook (that's no typo) series but they are available for $3 postage paid." The editor says, "We like to publish new poets, but they should read at least one copy to see what the magazine is about. Send poetry that comes from inside, not works that conform to outdated modes of writing. Response to this listing has been outstanding, but everyone who submits stands a fair chance at being published. This includes our friends in Europe, Australia and Canada too. We are trying to lose our sanity at *APM.* The amount of poetry that we receive adds to this but a lot of normal, bland and unfeeling poetry is no help. Remember, no SASE—no reply! Creative people should avoid creative writing courses. I want to see the '90s on fire. Write poetry that will burn in my fingers when I read it."

AMATEUR WRITERS JOURNAL/FOUR SEASONS POETRY CLUB MAGAZINE (I), 3653 Harrison St., Bellaire OH 43906, founded 1967, editor/publisher Rosalind Gill, appears quarterly. Though **you have to buy a copy to see your work in print,** *AWJ* "accepts all types of articles, essays, short stories and poetry of any theme. No avant-garde or pornographic material accepted. **Prefer material of seasonal nature to be submitted in the season prevalent at the time. Length up to 40 regular lines (no longer than 10 words per line). Rhymed or unrhymed. Also accept haiku, limericks and all types of short poems. Do not want to see pornographic—pertaining to raw sex."** They have published poetry by Robert Lowery, Eleanore M. Barker, Elsie Watkins and Remelda Gibson. As a sample the editor selected the first stanza of "Inspiration" by Donna Dietrich:

In the darkness, words come
prancing across my pillow,
clogging my veins and synapses
tap-dancing across my brain.
I quickly reach for the light switch
blinding my bleary eyes.

AWJ is 38 pgs., magazine-sized, photocopied from typescript, side-stapled with colored paper cover. Press run is 500+. **Subscription: $8. Sample postpaid: $2. Submit more than one poem/ page, single-spaced, camera-ready if writer has typewriter available. Considers simultaneous submissions. Cover letter required; include names of other publications to which ms has been submitted, if any. Send SASE for guidelines. Reports "upon publication." Backlog varies, but seasonal poetry is published immediately.** Certificates of merit are given for "best of issue." Open to unsolicited reviews. Poets may also send books for review consideration. The editor advises: "Always adhere to editor's guidelines; send seasonal poems in correct season; write or print legibly if you can't send typed material."

AMBER (III), #404, 40 Rose St., Dartmouth, Nova Scotia B3A 2T6 Canada, phone (902)461-4934, founded 1967, editor Hazel F. Goddard, appears 4 times/year (in January, April, July and October). *"Amber* and its one-page supplement, *Marsh & Maple,* promote and distribute current work. *Amber* is nonprofit, entirely subscription-supported." They want **"free verse, half page, regular line lengths (not over 56 characters preferred), also haiku and occasional sonnet. Any subject, but must be in good taste,** *not vulgar.* **Original, bright content. No religious verse."** They have published poetry by John D. Engle, Jr., Diana K. Rubin and Tony Cosier. As a sample the editor selected these lines (poet unidentified):

i am a symphony
blazing syllables of light
across each phrase
lengthening like eighth notes
from a phantom violin

to touch the inner ear

The editor says *Amber* is 28 pgs., stapled. They receive about 500 poems a year, use roughly 70%. Press run is 100 for 90 subscribers of which 3 are libraries. Single copy: $2.50; subscription: $10. **Sample postpaid: $1. Previously published poems OK; no simultaneous submissions. Every sheet should bear the poet's name. "Prefer poems to be seasonal, if on nature."** Time between acceptance and publication is 1-6 months. Seldom comments on rejections. **"First acceptance paid for with 1 free copy; continuing submissions expected to be covered by a subscription."** The editor says, "I receive many books of poets' poems. If up to an average standard I select from them for publication in my magazine. Most poems are from well-crafted poets, a few new writers. Need not be professional but *must* be good work. When space allows, I list contests poets may like to enter, comment on books poets send and devote centrefold to personal chatting, poets' successes, etc."

AMBIT (III), 17 Priory Gardens, Highgate, London N6 5QY England, phone 340-3566, editor Martin Bax; poetry editors Edwin Brock, Carol Ann Duffy and Henry Graham; prose editor J.G. Ballard; and art editor Mike Foreman. *Ambit* is a 96-page quarterly which has recently published poetry by Selima Hill. As a sample the editor selected these excerpts from "Two Poems For Two Suicides" by Henry Graham:

1
All right then
who would fardels bare?
Or the world away out of earshot
careless of your one foot in too many graves
every waking hour.

2
It got to seem like a war,
casualties
I used to say,
though no one was shooting at us.
Or were they?

Subscription: £20. **Sample: £5. Pay is "variable plus 2 free copies."** Staff reviews books of poetry. Send books for review consideration, attn. review editor.

AMELIA; CICADA; SPSM&H; THE AMELIA AWARDS (II, IV-Form), 329 "E" St., Bakersfield CA 93304 or P.O. Box 2385, Bakersfield CA 93303, phone (805)323-4064. *Amelia*, founded 1983, poetry editor Frederick A. Raborg, Jr., is a quarterly magazine that publishes chapbooks as well. Central to its operations is a series of contests, most with entry fees, spaced evenly throughout the year, awarding more than $3,500 annually, but they publish many poets who have not entered the contests as well. Among poets published are Pattiann Rogers, Stuart Freibert, John Millett, David Ray, Larry Rubin, Charles Bukowski, Maxine Kumin, Charles Edward Eaton and Shuntaro Tanikawa. As a sample the editor selected these lines by Phyllis K. Collier:

An hour and a half out of Tulsa, June is painting the corn white,
Along the highway the hills exhale their hot breaths,
Their secret grasses whispering in the wind past Sallisaw,
Messages clear and fervent over wildflowers that rush by
And shimmy in the wakes of semis, settle down around us
In the truck cab, back in the camper where tonight we will
Lie somewhere in Arkansas, listening.

They are **"receptive to all forms to 100 lines. We do not want to see the patently-religious or overtly-political. Erotica is fine; pornography, no."** The digest-sized, flat-spined magazine is offset on high-quality paper and usually features an original four-color cover; its circulation is about 1,250, with 522 subscriptions, of which 28 are libraries. Subscription: $25/year. **Sample postpaid: $7.95. Submit 3-5 poems. No simultaneous submissions except for entries to the annual Amelia Chapbook Award. Reports in 2-12 weeks, the latter if under serious consideration. Pays $2-25/poem plus 2 copies. "Almost always I try to comment."** The editor comments, "*Amelia* is not afraid of strong themes, but we do look for professional, polished work even in handwritten submissions. Poets should have something to say about matters other than the moon. We like to see strong **traditional pieces as well as the contemporary and experimental. And neatness *does* count.**" Fred Raborg has done more than most other editors to ensure a wide range of styles and forms, from traditional European to Asian, from lyric to narrative. Typically he is swamped with submissions and so response time can exceed stated parameters. *Amelia* continues to place in outside surveys as a top market for freelancers, because of editorial openness. Brief reviews are also featured. It may be interesting to note that *Amelia* ranked #3 in the "Traditional

Verse" category of the June 1993 *Writer's Digest* Poetry 60 list. As for Raborg's other publications, *Cicada* is a quarterly magazine that publishes **haiku, senryu and other Japanese forms,** plus essays on the form—techniques and history—as well as fiction which in some way incorporates haiku or Japanese poetry in its plot, and reviews of books pertaining to Japan and its poetry or collections of haiku. Among poets published are Roger Ishii, H.F. Noyes, Knute Skinner, Katherine Machan Aal, Ryah Tumarkin Goodman and Ryokufu Ishizaki. These sample lines are by Hugh Finn of Zimbabwe:

> *Its green enquiry*
> *Welcomed, the bean lifts luggage*
> *Into warm summer.*

They are receptive to experimental forms as well as the traditional. "Try to avoid still-life as haiku; strive for the *whole* of an emotion, whether minuscule or panoramic. Erotica is fine; the Japanese are great lovers of the erotic." The magazine is offset on high quality paper, with a circulation of 600, with 432 subscriptions of which 26 are libraries. Subscription: $14/year. **Sample postpaid: $4.50. Submit 3-10 haiku or poems. No simultaneous submissions. Reports in 2 weeks.** No payment, except three "best of issue" poets each receive $10 on publication plus copy. "I try to make some comment on returned poems always." *SPSM&H* is a quarterly magazine that publishes **only sonnets, sonnet sequences,** essays on the form—both technique and history—as well as romantic or Gothic fiction which, in some way, incorporates the form, and reviews of sonnet collections or collections containing a substantial number of sonnets. They are **"receptive to experimental forms as well as the traditional, and appreciate wit when very good."** Among poets published are Margaret Ryan, Harold Witt, Sharon E. Martin, Rhina P. Espaillat and Robert Wolfkill. These sample lines are by Alexandra Peyer Smith:

> *Quick as swallows swooping from a barn goes*
> *Time: aimed like arrowheads against the blue*
> *Or gray of daylight's startling intent.*
> *And where it lands is just as fresh as those*
> *Persistent elements of life that cue*
> *The clocks to slow, as if they would. Time went*
> *Where each new second's flick might hurl it.*

Perhaps it may help to know the editor's favorite Shakespearean sonnet is #29, and he feels John Updike clarified the limits of experimentation with the form in his "Love Sonnet" from **Midpoint.** The magazine is offset on high quality paper, with a circulation of 600, for 432 subscribers and 26 libraries. Subscription: $14/year. **Sample postpaid: $4. Submit 3-5 poems. No simultaneous submissions. Reports in 2 weeks.** No payment, except two "best of issue" poets **each receive $14 on publication plus copy. "I always try to comment on returns."** The following annual contests have various entry fees: The Amelia Awards (six prizes of $200, $100, $50 plus three honorable mentions of $10 each); The Anna B. Janzen Prize for Romantic Poetry ($100, annual deadline January 2); The Bernice Jennings Traditional Poetry Award ($100, annual deadline January 2); The Georgie Starbuck Galbraith Light/Humorous Verse Prizes (six awards of $100, $50, $25 plus three honorable mentions of $5 each, annual deadline March 1); The Charles William Duke Longpoem Award ($100, annual deadline April 1); The Lucille Sandberg Haiku Awards (six awards of $100, $50, $25 plus three honorable mentions of $5 each, annual deadline April 1); The Grace Hines Narrative Poetry Award ($100, annual deadline May 1); The Amelia Chapbook Award ($250, book publication and 50 copies, annual deadline July 1); The Johanna B. Bourgoyne Poetry Prizes (six awards of $100, $50, $25, plus three honorable mentions of $5 each), The Douglas Manning Smith Epic/Heroic Poetry Prize ($100, annual deadline August 1); The Hildegarde Janzen Prize for Oriental Forms of Poetry (six awards of $50, $30, $20 and three honorable mentions of $5 each, annual deadline September 1); The Eugene Smith Prize For Sonnets (six awards of $140, $50, $25 and three honorable mentions of $5 each); The A&C Limerick Prizes (six awards of $50, $30, $20 and three honorable mentions of $5 each); The Montegue Wade Lyric Poetry Prize ($100, annual deadline November 1).

AMERICA; FOLEY POETRY CONTEST (II), 106 W. 56th St., New York NY 10019, phone (212)581-4640, founded 1909, poetry editor Patrick Samway, S.J., is a weekly journal of opinion published by the Jesuits of North America. They primarily publish articles on religious, social, political and cultural themes. **They are "looking for imaginative poetry of all kinds. We have no restrictions on form or subject matter, though we prefer to receive poems of 35 lines or less."** They have published poetry by Howard Nemerov, Fred Chappell, William Heyen and Eve Shelnutt. *America* is 24 pgs., magazine-sized, professionally printed on thin stock with thin paper cover, circulation 35,000. Subscription: $33. **Sample postpaid: $1.25. Send SASE for excellent guidelines. Reports in 2 weeks. Pays $1.40/line plus 2 copies.** The annual Foley Poetry Contest offers a prize of $500, usually in late winter. Send SASE for rules. The editor says, "*America* is committed to publishing quality poetry as it has done for the past 80 years. We would encourage beginning and established poets to submit their poems to us."

AMERICAN ATHEIST PRESS; GUSTAV BROUKAL PRESS; AMERICAN ATHEIST (IV-Theme), P.O. Box 2117, Austin TX 78768-2117, phone (512)458-1244, founded 1958, editor R. Murray-O'Hair, publishes the quarterly magazine with 30,000 circulation, *American Atheist*, and under various imprints some dozen books a year reflecting "concerns of Atheists, such as separation of state and church, civil liberties and atheist news." **Poetry is used primarily in the poetry section of the magazine. It must have "a particular slant to atheism, dealing with subjects such as the atheist lifestyle. Anticlerical poems and puns are more than liable to be rejected. Any form or style is acceptable. Preferred length is under 40 lines."** They have published poetry by Julia Rhodes Pozonzycki, Allan Case and Thomas A. Easton. Of their 17,000 subscriptions, 1,000 are libraries. The magazine-sized format is professionally printed, with art and photos, glossy, color cover. Single copy: $2.95; subscription: $25. **Sample: free.** They receive over 20-30 poetry submissions/week, use about 12/year. **Submit typed, double-spaced mss. Simultaneous submissions OK. Time-dependent poems (such as winter) should be submitted 4 months in advance. Guidelines available for SASE, but a label is preferred to an envelope. Reports within 3-4 months. Pays "first-timers" 10 copies or 6-month subscription or $12 credit voucher for AAP products. Thereafter, $15/poem plus 10 copies. Buys one-time rights. Sometimes comments on rejected mss.** Reviews related books of poetry in 500-1,000 words. They do not normally publish poetry in book form but will consider it.

THE AMERICAN COWBOY POET MAGAZINE (I, IV-Themes), Dept. PM, P.O. Box 326, Eagle ID 83616, phone (208)888-9838, founded 1988 as *The American Cowboy Poet Newspaper,* magazine format in January 1991, publisher Rudy Gonzales, editor Rose Fitzgerald. *ACPM* is a quarterly "about real cowboys" using **"authentic cowboy poetry. Must be clean—entertaining. Submissions should avoid 'like topics.' We will not publish any more poems about Old Blackie dying, this old hat, if this pair of boots could talk, etc. We do not publish free verse poetry. Only traditional cowboy with rhyme and meter."** They also publish articles including "Featured Poet," stories of cowboy poetry gatherings and news of coming events. Subscription: $12/year, $15 Canada, $20 overseas. **Sample postpaid: $3. Cover letter required with submissions. Send SASE for guidelines. Editor always comments on rejections.** Staff reviews related books of poetry. Send books for review consideration.

AMERICAN DANE (IV-Ethnic), 3717 Harney St., Omaha NE 68131-3844, phone (402)341-5049, founded 1916, editor Jennifer Denning-Kock, is the monthly magazine of the Danish Brotherhood in America, circulation 7,000, which uses **poetry with a Danish ethnic flavor.** It is 20-28 pgs., magazine-sized. Subscription: $12. **Sample postpaid: $1.50. Simultaneous submissions OK. Reads submissions June 1 through September 1 only. Send SASE for guidelines. Buys 1-3 poems/year. Reports in 2 weeks, up to 1-year backlog. Pays $35 maximum plus 2 copies. Buys first rights only.**

AMERICAN KNIGHT (I), 4541 W. 36½ St. #14, Minneapolis MN 55416-4857, founded 1989, editor Nancy Morín, is a quarterly publishing **poetry by those who contribute poetry or subscribe. "Open-minded acceptance; we prefer poetry with reflective insight and that which encourages the reader to release the limitations of physical and emotional perception. Nothing trite, no 'mushy-love' rhymes."** They have published poetry by Andy Roman, T.N. Turner and Clebo Rainey. These sample lines are the editor's:

> *In some rites*
> *you can find*
> *the sweat of 'flow'*
> *and the sweat of vanity.*
> *Yes, I'd rather be the initiate;*
> *never, never the mystic slave.*

The editor says, "To make a living in America today is quite a rare thing. *AK* has been developed for poets and poetry. It is here to give those who love the excitement of seeing their work in print and knowing that their poetry is being read by others, a chance to reach and enhance a broader audience. **Never hold back for rhyming reasons. This can be a great blockade when trying to get a point across to readers. This is a nonprofit quarterly written by the writers who contribute poetry or prose. Cost per issue: $2 plus 85¢ loose stamps.** Donations are greatly appreciated however, and can be made to *American Knight*." The editor describes it as 11×17, folded at center, printed on 20 lb. or heavier paper, typed, with art on cover, more than 8 pgs. **Sample postpaid: $2.50. Send SASE for guidelines. Send up to 5 poems. Do not staple. Deadlines: February 20, May 23, August 23, November 20 (yearly). Reports in 3-4 weeks. Pays "at least 1" copy but requests 95¢ postage to receive "pay" copy.**

AMERICAN LITERARY REVIEW, A National Journal of Poems and Stories, University of North Texas, P.O. Box 13615, Denton TX 76203. Prefers not to share information.

AMERICAN POETRY REVIEW (III), Dept. PM, 1704 Walnut St., Philadelphia PA 19103, phone (215)496-0439, founded 1972, is probably the **most widely circulated (20,000 copies bimonthly) and best-known periodical devoted to poetry in the world.** Poetry editors are Stephen Berg, David Bonanno and Arthur Vogelsang, and they have **published most of the leading poets writing in English and many translations.** The poets include Gerald Stern, Brenda Hillman, John Ashbery, Norman Dubie, Marvin Bell, Galway Kinnell, James Dickey, Lucille Clifton and Tess Gallagher. *APR* is a newsprint tabloid with 15,000 subscriptions, of which 1,000 are libraries. They receive about 4,000 submissions/year, use 200. This popular publication contains mostly free verse (some leaning to the avant-garde) with flashes of brilliance in every issue. Editors seem to put an emphasis on language and voice. Because *APR* is a tabloid, it can feature long poems (or ones with long line lengths) in an attractive format. Translations are welcome. In all, this is a difficult market to crack because of the volume of submissions. **Sample and price per issue: $3. No simultaneous submissions. Reports in 3 months, has 1-3 year backlog. Pays $1.25/line.** The magazine is also a major resource for opinion, reviews, theory, news and ads pertaining to poetry. Each year the editors award the Jerome J. Shestack Prizes of $1,000, $500 and $250 for the best poems, in their judgment, published in *APR*. Poetry published here has also been included in **Best American Poetry 1992**.

THE AMERICAN SCHOLAR (III), 1811 Q St. NW, Washington DC 20009, phone (202)265-3808, founded 1932, associate editor Sandra Costich, is an academic quarterly which **uses about 5 poems/issue. "We would like to see poetry that develops an image, a thought or event, without the use of a single cliché or contrived archaism. The most hackneyed subject matter is self-conscious love; the most tired verse is iambic pentameter with rhyming endings. The usual length of our poems is 30 lines. From 1-4 poems may be submitted at one time;** *no more* **for a careful reading."** They have published poetry by Robert Pack, Alan Shapiro and Gregory Djanikian. As a sample we selected these lines from "Art and Worship" by Bruce Bawer:

> *If a sculpture, story, symphony,*
> *or some plain strain played on a violin*
> *seems to articulate a verity*
> *resoundingly, it is because it springs*
> *out of a kindred sensibility,*
> *soaring above the universal din*
> *to remind us all that we are kin*
> *with anyone whom song inspires to sing.*

What little poetry is used in this high-prestige magazine is accomplished, intelligent and open (in terms of style and form). Study before submitting (**sample: $5.75, guidelines available for SASE). Reports in 2 months. Pays $50/poem. Buys first rights only.**

AMERICAN TOLKIEN SOCIETY; MINAS TIRITH EVENING STAR; W.W. PUBLICATIONS (IV-Themes), P.O. Box 373, Highland MI 48357-0373, founded 1967, editor Philip W. Helms. There are special poetry issues. Membership in the ATS is open to all, regardless of country of residence, and entitles one to receive the journal. Dues are $7.50 per annum to addresses in US, $12.50 in Canada and $15 elsewhere. Their magazines and chapbooks use **poetry of fantasy about Middle-Earth and Tolkien.** They have published poetry by Thomas M. Egan, Anne Etkin, Nancy Pope and Martha Benedict. *Minas Tirith Evening Star* is magazine-sized, offset from typescript with cartoon-like b&w graphics. They have a press run of 400 for 350 subscribers of which 10% are libraries. Single copy: $3.50; subscription: $7.50. **Sample postpaid: $1.50.** "Please make checks payable to American Tolkien Society." **No simultaneous submissions; previously published poems "maybe." Cover letter preferred. Editor sometimes comments on rejections. Send SASE for guidelines. Reports in 2 weeks. Pays contributor's copies.** Reviews related books of poetry; length depends on the volume, "a sentence to several pages." Open to unsolicited reviews. Poets may also send books to Paul Ritz, Reviews, P.O. Box 901, Clearwater FL 34617 for review consideration. Under imprint of W.W. Publications they publish collections of poetry 50-100 pgs. **For book or chapbook consideration, submit sample poems. Publishes 2 chapbooks/year.** They sometimes sponsor contests.

THE AMERICAN VOICE (II), 332 W. Broadway, Louisville KY 40202, phone (502)562-0045, founded 1985, editor Frederick Smock, is a literary quarterly publishing North and South American writers. They prefer **free verse, avant-garde, in areas such as ethnic/nationality, gay/lesbian, translation, women/feminism and literary.** They have published poetry by Olga Broumas, Odysseus Elytis, Cheryl Clarke, Marge Piercy and Ernesto Cardenal. As a sample here is one stanza of a long poem, "Mother's Day at the Air Force Museum," by George Ella Lyon:

> *My son loves the machine guns.*
> *He looks through a sight,*
> *he strafes the still air.*
> *At home, his Lego men*

die smiling.

TAV is elegantly printed, flat-spined, 140+ pgs. of high-quality stock with matte card cover. Editors seem to prefer lyric free verse, much of it accessible, by well-known and new writers. Issues we have seen also had room for both long and sequence poems. Circulation is 2,000 with 800 subscriptions of which 100 are libraries. Subscription: $15/year. **Sample postpaid: $5. No simultaneous submissions. Cover letter requested. Occasionally comments on rejections. Reports in 6 weeks, has a 3-month backlog. Pays $150/poem and 2 copies. (They pay $75 to translator of a poem.)** Open to unsolicited reviews. Poets may also send books for review consideration. *The American Voice* has received an **Utne Reader** Alternative Press Award and has had work included in the **Pushcart Prize** anthologies.

AMERICAN WRITING: A MAGAZINE; NIERIKA EDITIONS (IV-Form/style), 4343 Manayunk Ave., Philadelphia PA 19128, phone (215)483-7051, founded 1990, editor Alexandra Grilikhes, appears twice a year using **poetry that is "experimental: voice of the loner, takes risks with form, interested in the powers of intuition and states of being. No cerebral, academic poetry."** They have published poetry by Ivan Argüelles, Nico Vassilakis, Charles Fishman, John M. Bennett and Portia Wright. As a sample the editor selected these lines by Bruce Robinson:

> *let helmet, heart,*
> *head hurl past the line you've always taken,*
> *and then how easy it is, light at last,*
> *to track that release, not unpromising*
> *but promising nothing,*
> *that while it waits for a proper word*
> *is called destination.*

AW is digest-sized, flat-spined, 70+ pgs., professionally printed, with matte card cover. Press run is 1,000 for 100 subscriptions. Subscription: $10. **Sample postpaid: $6. Guidelines on subscription form. Reporting time varies. "If it's a 'possible,' we may keep it 3 months." Pays 2 copies/accepted submission group.** The editor says, "Many magazines print the work of the same authors [the big names] who often publish 'lesser' works that way. *AW* is interested in the work itself, its particular strength and energy, rather than in the long lists of credits. We like to know *something* about the authors, however."

‡AMERICAS REVIEW; AMERICAS REVIEW POETRY COMPETITION (I, IV-Political), Box 7681, Berkeley CA 94707, founded 1985, editor Gerald Gray, is a "literary annual with **emphasis on political content of the poetry** and prose we publish. Only limit is subject matter; it is almost always political in some general sense (though a few items of poetry are not). We do print, for instance, the love poetry of political figures." With that in mind, the editor says he would like to see poetry in the areas of ethnic/nationality, humor (in context), ecology and social issues as well as translations. "We deliberately publish little-known or obscure poets, but we have included works by Nicholis Guillen, Otto Rene Castillo, Julia Vinograd, Dorianne Laux, Sergio Ramirez, Claribel Algeria and Gary Snyder." As a sample Gerald Gray selected these lines by Gioconda Belli:

> *That's why I sit down to brandish these poems;*
> *to build against wind and tide*
> *a small space of happiness*
> *having faith that all this will not end—*

The editor describes the annual as 6×9, flat-spined, about 75 pgs., offset, using b&w graphics. It has a press run of 1,000 for 50 subscriptions (10 of them libraries) and the rest are for shelf sales. Single copy: $5 ($6 to libraries). **Sample postpaid: $4. "Submit September 1 through December 31 for most timely consideration." Pays $10/author, plus 1 copy. Editor "sometimes" comments on rejections.** Their annual contest has a reading fee of $5 for up to five poems. They award three prizes of $100 each for published, unpublished or translated poetry. The contest runs September 1 through December 31. They note, "Our poetry and fiction is usually, but not exclusively, political in nature. All poems submitted will be considered for publication. Poems other than the winners chosen for publication will be paid in cash at our usual rate. Winners and others accepted will appear in the annual issue."

‡THE AMHERST REVIEW (II), Box 1811, Amherst College, P.O. Box 5000, Amherst MA 01002-5000, editor Ismée Bartels, is an annual literary magazine seeking quality submissions in fiction, poetry, nonfiction and photography/artwork. **"All kinds of poetry welcome."** The editor says the review is 50 pgs., 5×8, soft cover with photography, art and graphics. They receive 300-500 poems a year, accept around 10. Most copies are distributed free to Amherst students. **Sample postpaid: $6. No previously published poems; simultaneous submissions OK. Reads submissions from October to February only. Magazine staff makes democratic decision. Seldom comments on rejections. Send SASE for guidelines. Reports in late March. Pays 1 copy.**

THE AMICUS JOURNAL (V), Dept. PM, 40 W. 20th St., New York NY 10011, phone (212)727-2700, poetry editor Francesca Lyman, is the **journal of the Natural Resources Defense Council, a quarterly with a circulation of about 120,000, which pays $25/poem. The poetry is "nature based, but** *not* **'nature poetry.'** " **They are not currently accepting submissions "because our cup runneth over with poetry."** They have used poems by some of the best known poets in the country, including David Wagoner, Gary Snyder, David Ignatow, Marvin Bell and William Stafford. *The Amicus Journal* is finely-printed, saddle-stapled, on high quality paper with glossy cover, using much art, photography and cartoons. **Free sample for SASE.**

ANACONDA PRESS; FUEL (II), P.O. Box 146640, Chicago IL 60614, editor-in-chief Andy Lowry. Currently publishing *fuel*, "a wiry, highly energized mini-magazine using lots of cool poetry, art and fiction." Also publishing 3-4 poetry chapbooks/year. **"We're looking for daring, eccentric works. No academia allowed!" Send SASE for most recent guidelines. Pays 1-2 copies if published in 'zine. Chapbook payment is negotiable. Rights revert to authors.**

ANALECTA (IV-Students), Dept. PM, Liberal Arts Council, FAC 19, University of Texas, Austin TX 78712, phone (512)471-6563, founded 1974, editor Chris Carr, is an annual of literary works and photography by **college/university students and graduate students chosen in an annual contest. No restrictions on type; limited to 5 poems/submission. Deadline is in mid-October; write for specifics. Submissions cannot be returned.** "Our purpose is to provide a forum for excellent student writing. **Works must be previously unpublished."** Of about 800 submissions received, they publish about 40. As a sample, the editor selected this excerpt from "A Car" by Eric Rasmussen:

> *This car is mine.*
>
> *I drive it naked, drive it fat;*
> *Drive it crooked with my shoes off,*
> *Baking my feet on the hot pedals.*

It is a 150-page magazine, glossy plates for interior artwork in b&w, 7×10, flat-spined, soft cover. Press run 800 for 700 subscribers, 100 shelf sales. **Sample postpaid: $7.50. Entries must be typed; name should appear on cover sheet only. Send SASE for guidelines. Prizes in each category. Pays 2 copies and monetary prizes vary.**

ANHINGA PRESS; ANHINGA PRIZE (II), P.O. Box 10595, Tallahassee FL 32302-0595, phone (904)575-5592, founded 1972, poetry editors Rick Campbell and Van Brock, publishes **"books and anthologies of poetry. We also offer the Anhinga Prize for poetry — $500 and publication — for a book-length manuscript each year. We want to see contemporary poetry which respects language. We're inclined toward poetry that is not obscure, that can be understood by any literate audience."** They have published poetry by Sherry Rind, Yvonne Sapia, Judith Kitchen, Ricardo Pau-Llosa, Robert J. Levy, Michael Mott, Rick Lott, Will Wells, Gary Corseri, Julianne Seeman, Nick Bozanic, Jean Monahan and P.V. LeForge. As a sample the editors selected these lines from **The Secret Life of Moles:**

> *The sun migrates across whatever scenes*
> *death can spare:*
> *and we have many of these small reprieves*
> *living within us.*
> *When we die, will life stop again?*
> *And for whom?*

Considers simultaneous submissions. Send a "business size" SASE for catalog. Also send SASE for rules (submissions accepted in January) of the Anhinga Prize for poetry, which requires an entry fee, for which all contestants receive a copy of the winning book. The contest has been judged by such distinguished poets as William Stafford, Louis Simpson, Henry Taylor, Hayden Carruth and Denise Levertov.

ANIMA: THE JOURNAL OF HUMAN EXPERIENCE (II, IV-Women/feminism, spirituality/inspirational), 1053 Wilson Ave., Chambersburg PA 17201, founded 1974, editor Barbara Rotz. *Anima* "celebrates the wholistic vision that emerges from thoughtful and imaginative encounters with the differences between woman and man, East and West, yin and yang—*anima* and *animus*. **Written largely by and about women** who are pondering new experiences of themselves and our world, this

The double dagger before a listing indicates that the listing is new in this edition. New markets are often the most receptive to submissions.

equinoctial journal welcomes contributions, verbal and visual, from the known and unknown. We publish very few poems, but they are carefully selected. **We are not interested in simply private experiences. Poetry must communicate. Advise all would-be poets to study the kinds of things we do publish. No restrictions on length, form, or such matters.**" There are 5-10 pages of poetry in each semiannual issue of the elegantly-printed and illustrated 8½" square, glossy-covered magazine, 1,000 subscriptions of which 150 are libraries. Single copy: $5.95. Sample: $3.95. Slow reporting—sometimes 3-6 months. Payment is offprints with covers.

ANJOU (V), P.O. Box 322 Station P., Toronto, Ontario M5S 2S8 Canada, founded 1980, edited by Richard Lush and Roger Greenwald, publishes broadsides of poetry. **"We do not wish to receive submissions because we publish only by solicitation."**

ANSUDA PUBLICATIONS; ANSUDA MAGAZINE (II), P.O. Box 158JA, Harris IA 51345, founded 1978, "is a small press operation, publishing independently of outside influences, such as grants, donations, awards, etc. Our operating capital comes from magazine and book sales only." Their magazine, *Ansuda* (formerly *The Pub*), "uses some poetry, and we also publish separate chapbooks of individual poets. **We prefer poems with a social slant and originality—we do *not* want love poems, personal poems that can only be understood by the poet, or anything from the haiku family of poem styles. No limits on length, though very short poems lack the depth we seek—no limits on form or style, but rhyme and meter must make sense. Too many poets write senseless rhymes using the first words to pop into their heads. As a result, we prefer blank and free verse."** They have recently published poetry by Ian Lawrence, Paul M. Lamb, Anthony Constantino and Terry Everton. They offer no sample because "most of our poems are at least 25-30 lines long and every line complements all other lines, so it is hard to pick out only four lines to illustrate." *Ansuda*, which appears irregularly (1-3 times a year), is a low-budget publication, digest-sized, mimeographed on inexpensive paper, making it possible to print 80 or more pages and sell copies for **$3.75 (the price of a sample).** Press run is 300 for 130 subscribers, of which 7 are libraries. Each issue has 3-12 pages of poetry, but **"we would publish more if we had it; our readers would like more poetry."** Everything accepted goes into the next issue, so there is no backlog. **Reports immediately to 1 month. Pays 2 copies. Acquires first rights. They also publish 1-2 chapbooks (24-28 pgs.)/year. For these, query with 3-6 sample poems.** "We are *not* interested in past credits, who you studied under, etc. Names mean nothing to us and we have found that small press is so large that big names in one circle are unknown in another circle. In fact, **we get better material from the unknowns who have nothing to brag about (usually)." Replies to queries immediately, to mss in 1-2 months. Simultaneous submissions OK only if clearly indicated. Pays royalties plus 5 copies for chapbooks.** Daniel Betz adds, "About all I have left to say is to tell the novice to keep sending his work out. It won't get published in a desk drawer. There are so many little mags out there that eventually you'll find homes for your poems. Yes, some poets get published on their first few tries, but I've made first acceptances to some who have been submitting for 5 to 10 years with no luck, until their poem and my mag just seemed to click. It just takes time and lots of patience."

ANTAEUS; THE ECCO PRESS (II, III), 100 W. Broad St., Hopewell NJ 08525, editor-in-chief Daniel Halpern. *Antaeus* is a semiannual that has published poetry by many of our major poets, such as Czeslaw Milosz, Paul Bowles, Robert Hass, Louise Glück, Robert Pinsky, Seamus Heaney, Joyce Carol Oates, W.S. Merwin, James Merrill, Carolyn Forché, Mark Strand and Charles Simic. They say, **"while we do encourage and seek out new writers, we very rarely accept unsolicited manuscripts/poems."** It is 275 pgs., 6×9, offset, flat-spined, with 4-color cover. They have 7,000 subscribers. Subscription: $36. **Sample postpaid: $11.50. Send SASE for guidelines. Reports in 2-3 months. Pays $10/page.** Poetry published in *Antaeus* was selected for inclusion in Best American Poetry 1992. *Antaeus* itself ranked #6 in the "Poets' Pick" category of the June 1993 *Writer's Digest* Poetry 60 list. This category ranks those publications in which poets said they would most like to see their work published.

ANTERIOR POETRY MONTHLY; ANTERIOR BITEWING LTD. (I), (formerly *Recording & Publishing News*), 7735 Brand Ave., St. Louis MO 63135-3212, founded 1988, editor Tom Bergeron, appears 12 times a year using "poems of excellence. Submissions welcome from everyone; however, there is a $1 reading fee per poem submitted unless you are a subscriber. The top three poems in each issue receive awards or $25, $15 and $10 respectively. Other poems may be published with no payment to the author. Entries received after the 15th, extra submissions and poems more suited to later seasons are automatically entered in future month's contest." They have recently published poetry by J. Alvin Speers, Pearl Bloch Segall and Kathleen Lee Mendel. As a sample the editor selected these lines from "The Light" by Barbara N. Paul-Best:

> *Cold are the winds that blow,*
> *Cold as December ice and January snow;*
> *Soothing as a blanket of snow-starred down;*
> *Peaceful as the absence of every sound.*

It is 20 pgs., digest-sized, desktop published and saddle-stapled with colored paper cover. Press run 200-300 for 110 subscribers. Subscription: $12. **Sample postpaid: $1. Please make checks payable to Anterior Bitewing Ltd. "We like cover letters." Send SASE for guidelines. Buys one-time rights.** Anterior Bitewing Ltd. is an imprint for job printing of newsletters and "magazettes." Send SASE for rate sheet. The editor says, "Always resubmit. There's some editor out there somewhere who will love your work. Take advice, make changes accordingly and keep on resubmitting."

ANTHOLOGY OF MAGAZINE VERSE & YEARBOOK OF AMERICAN POETRY (III, IV-Anthology), % Monitor Book Company, P.O. Box 9078, Palm Springs CA 92263, phone (619)323-2270, founded 1950, editor Alan F. Pater. The annual **Anthology** is a selection of the **best poems published in American magazines during the year and is also a basic reference work for poets.** Alan F. Pater says, "We want poetry that is 'readable' and in any poetic form; we also want translations. **All material must first have appeared in magazines.** Any subject matter will be considered; we also would like to see some rhyme and meter, preferably sonnets." They have published poetry by Margaret Atwood, Stanley Kunitz, Robert Penn Warren, Richard Wilbur, Maxine Kumin and John Updike. Indeed, the anthology is a good annual guide to the best poets actively publishing in any given year. For the most part selections are made by the editor from magazines, but some poets are solicited for their work which has been in magazines in a given year. **Cover letters should include name and date or issue number of magazine in which the poem was originally published.**

ANTIETAM REVIEW (IV-Regional), Washington County Arts Council, 7 W. Franklin St., Hagerstown MD 21740, an annual founded 1981, poetry editors Crystal Brown and Ann Knox, looks for **"well-crafted literary quality poems. We discourage inspirational verse, haiku, doggerel." Uses poets only from the states of Maryland, Pennsylvania, Virginia, West Virginia, Delaware and District of Columbia. Needs 18 poems/issue, up to 30 lines each.** Poets they have recently published include Roberta Bevington, Naomi Thiers and Ed Zahniser. The editor chose this sample from "Cold" by David Staudt:

> *Away from her he becomes solid*
> *once again: his ribs rewind around*
> *his lungs, banding tighter and tighter.*
> *He thinks he must feel to her like wood,*
> *or an old stone statue with a crack*
> *inching the length of its thigh.*

AR is 48 pgs., 8½×11, saddle-stapled, glossy paper with glossy card cover and b&w photos throughout. Press run is 1,000. **Sample postpaid: $3.15 back issue, $5.25 current. Do not submit mss from April through September. "We read from October 1 through March 1 annually." Pays $20/poem, depending on funding, plus 2 copies. Buys first North American serial rights.** The editors seem open to all styles of poetry, free and formal, as long as the author is from the designated region. Overall, a good read; but poems have to compete with prose. Ones used, however, are featured in attractive boxes on the page. Work published in *Antietam Review* has been included in the **Pushcart Price** anthology.

THE ANTIGONISH REVIEW (II), St. Francis Xavier University, Antigonish, Nova Scotia B2G 1C0 Canada, phone (902)867-3962, fax (902)867-5153, founded 1970, editor George Sanderson, poetry editor Peter Sanger. This high-quality quarterly "tries to produce the kind of literary and visual mosaic that the modern sensibility requires or would respond to." They want poetry **not over "80 lines, i.e., 2 pgs.; subject matter can be anything, the style is traditional, modern or post-modern limited by typographic resources. Purpose is not an issue."** No "erotica, scatalogical verse, excessive propaganda toward a certain subject." They have published poetry by Milton Acorn, Andy Wainwright, Janice Kulyk-Keefer, M. Travis Lane and Douglas Lochhead. *TAR* is flat-spined, 6×9, 150 pgs. with glossy card cover, offset printing, using "in-house graphics and cover art, no ads." They accept about 10% of some 2,500 submissions/year. Press run is 1,100 for 800 subscriptions. Subscription: $18. **Sample postpaid: $3. No simultaneous submissions or previously published poems.** Editor "sometimes" comments on rejections. **Pays 2 copies.** The poetry editor advises, "The time for free verse form is exhausting itself as a technical possibility. **We are sympathetic to poets working with strong rhythmic patterns.** Poets will have to return to the traditional devices of rhythm, rhyme and manipulation of line length. Many more poets would and could be published if more of them were also readers of the full range of poetry in English, old and new. We are *not* responsible for return of submissions sent with improper postage. **Must include self-addressed stamped envelope (SASE) or International Reply Coupons (IRC) if outside Canada."**

THE ANTIOCH REVIEW (III), Box 148, Yellow Springs OH 45387, phone (513)767-7331, founded 1941, "is an independent quarterly of critical and creative thought . . . **For 45 years, now, creative authors, poets and thinkers have found a friendly reception . . . regardless of formal reputation.**" Poetry editor: David St. John. "We get far more poetry than we can possibly accept, and the competition is keen. Here, where form and content are so inseparable and reaction is so personal, it is difficult to state requirements or limitations. Studying recent issues of *The Review* should be helpful. No 'light' or inspirational verse." They have published poetry by Ralph Angel, Jorie Graham, Mark Strand, Karen Fish, Michael Collier and Andrew Hudgins. Circulation is primarily to their 4,000 subscribers, of which half are libraries. They receive about 3,000 submissions/year, publish 20 pages of poetry in each issue, have about a 6-month backlog. Subscription: $25. **Sample: $5.50. Reads submissions September 1 through May 15 only. General guidelines for contributors available for SASE. Reports in 6-8 weeks. Pays $15/published page plus 2 copies.** Reviews books of poetry in 300 words, single format. This is a beautiful journal featuring some of the best poems being written by new and well-known writers. As David St. John says, "I have a policy of publishing a poet only once during my tenure as poetry editor. It may be a dumb policy, but it's one way to help keep the magazine open to new folks. I'd like to think that there's at least one place where new poets feel they have a shot." Consequently, voices here are varied and exciting.

ANTIPODES (IV-Regional), 8 Big Island, Warwick NY 10990, founded 1987, poetry editor Paul Kane, is a biannual of Australian poetry and fiction and criticism and reviews of Australian writing. They **want work from Australian poets only. No restrictions as to form, length, subject matter or style.** They have published poetry by A.D. Hope, Judith Wright and John Tranter. As a sample the editor selected these lines from "Poetry and Religion" by Les Murray:

> *Religions are poems. They concert*
> *our daylight and dreaming mind, our*
> *emotions, instinct, breath and native gesture*
> *into the only whole thinking: poetry*

The editor says *Antipodes* is 180 pgs., 8½×11, perfect-bound, with graphics, ads and photos. They receive about 500 submissions a year, accept approximately 10%. Press run is 500 for 200 subscribers. Subscription: $20. **Sample postpaid: $17. No previously published poems or simultaneous submissions. Cover letter with bio note required.** The editor says they "prefer submission of photocopies which do not have to be returned." Seldom comments on rejections. **Reports in 2 months. Pays $20/poem plus 1 copy.** Acquires first North American serial rights. Staff reviews books of poetry in 500-1,500 words. Send books for review consideration.

ANYTHING THAT MOVES BEYOND THE MYTHS OF BISEXUALITY (IV-Specialized themes), #24, 2404 California St., San Francisco CA 94115, phone (415)564-2226 (BABN), founded 1991, attention fiction/poetry editor, managing editor Karla Rossi. This quarterly uses **"material only from those who consider themselves bisexual, whether they identify as such or not. Pen names are permissible with written notification,** however author's real name and address must accompany submission (not to be published). Include name(s), address and phone number on each page. Submissions need not address bisexuality specifically, but may be on topics/themes/subjects of interest to bisexuals. Special consideration given to people of color, those differently abled, those living with HIV disease or AIDS, and those whose work has been denied/censored/erased in mainstream literary communities and publications." As a sample here are lines from a poem appearing in *ATM*:

> *No longer coward, traitor to the cause,*
> *I walked Fifth Avenue with them today.*
> *Unpunished by the prejudicial laws,*
> *I wanted, still, to count as proud and gay.*

It is 64 pgs., professionally printed, magazine-sized with glossy paper cover, saddle stapled. Press run is 5,000 for 1,000 subscribers of which 100 are libraries, 3,000 shelf sales. Subscription: $25. **Sample postpaid: $10. Cover letter required.** "Include titles of submission(s) and short (under 30 words) bio." No comments on rejections. "Accepted material cannot be returned. Do not send original copy. Shorter poems are more likely to be accepted. Notification of use will be in the form of 2-copy payment, although notification of acceptance will be given 6-8 weeks upon receipt of submission. *ATM* is published by the Bay Area Bisexual Network (BABN), a nonprofit institution, and is distributed nationally, with a small international distribution." Open to unsolicited reviews. Poets may also send books for review consideration.

‡APALACHEE QUARTERLY; APALACHEE PRESS (II, IV-Themes), P.O. Box 20106, Tallahassee FL 32316, founded 1971, editors Barbara Hamby, Pamela Ball, Claudia Johnson, Bruce Boehrer and Paul McCall, want **"no formal verse."** They have published poetry by David Kirby, Peter Meinke and Jim Hall. *Apalachee Quarterly* is 160 pgs., 6×9, professionally printed and perfect-bound with card cover. There are 55-95 pgs. of poetry in each issue, circulation 700, with 350 subscriptions of which 75 are libraries. "Every year we do an issue on a special topic. Past issues include a Dental, Revenge, Cocktail Party and Noir issues." Subscription: $15. **Sample postpaid: $5. Submit clear copies of up to 5 poems, name and address on each. Simultaneous submissions OK. "We don't read during the summer (June 1 through August 31)." Sometimes comments on rejections. Send SASE for guidelines. Pays 2 copies.** Staff reviews books of poetry. Send books for review consideration.

APPALACHIA (II, IV-Nature), 5 Joy St., Boston MA 02108, phone (617)523-0636, founded 1876, poetry editor Parkman Howe, editor-in-chief Sandy Stott, is a "semiannual journal of mountaineering and conservation which describes activities outdoors and asks questions of an ecological nature." **They want poetry relating to the outdoors and nature—specifically weather, mountains, rivers, lakes, woods and animals. "No conquerors' odes."** They have published poetry by Reg Saner, Macklin Smith, Glenda Cassutt, Mary Oliver and Justin Askins. The editor says it is 160 pgs., 6×9, professionally printed with color cover, using photos, graphics and a few ads. They receive about 200 poems a year, use 10-15. Press run is 10,000. Subscription: $10/year. **Sample postpaid: $5. Submit maximum of 6 poems. "We favor shorter poems—maximum of 36 lines usually." No previously published poems or simultaneous submissions. Cover letter required.** Time between acceptance and publication is 1 year. **Seldom comments on rejections. Send SASE for guidelines. Reports in 4-6 weeks. Pays 1 copy. Acquires first rights.** Staff reviews "some" books of poetry in 200-400 words, usually single format. Offers an annual award, The Appalachia Poetry Prize, given since 1972. The editor says, "Our readership is very well versed in the outdoors—mountains, rivers, lakes, animals. We look for poetry that helps readers see the natural world in fresh ways. No generalized accounts of the great outdoors."

APPALACHIAN HERITAGE; DENNY C. PLATTNER AWARDS (IV-Regional), Hutchins Library, Berea College, Berea KY 40404, phone (606)986-9341, ext. 5260, fax (606)986-9494, founded 1973, editor Sidney Saylor Farr, a literary quarterly with Southern Appalachian emphasis. The journal publishes several poems in each issue, and the editor wants to see **"poems about people, places, the human condition, etc., with Southern Appalachian settings. No style restrictions but poems should have a maximum of 14 lines, prefer 8-10 lines." She does not want "blood and gore, hell-fire and damnation, or biased poetry about race or religion."** She has published poetry by Jim Wayne Miller, Louise McNeill and Bettie Sellers. The flat-spined magazine is 6×9, professionally printed on white stock with b&w line drawings and photos, glossy white card cover with four-color illustration. Issues we have scanned tended toward lyric free verse, emphasizing nature or situations set in nature. **Sample copy: $6. Contributors should type poems one to a page. Simultaneous submissions OK. Requires cover letter giving information about previous publications where poets have appeared. Mss are reported on in 2-4 weeks. Pays 3 copies. Acquires first rights.** Reviews books of poetry. Open to unsolicited reviews. Poets may also send books for review consideration. The Denny C. Plattner Awards go to the authors of the best poetry, article or essay, or short fiction published in the four issues released within the preceding year. The award amount in each category is $200.

APPLEZABA PRESS (III), P.O. Box 4134, Long Beach CA 90804, founded 1977, poetry editor D.H. Lloyd, is "dedicated to publishing modern poetry and distributing to the national market." They publish both chapbooks and flat-spined collections of individual poets and occasional anthologies, about 3 titles/year. **"As a rule we like 'accessible' poetry, some experimental. We do not want to see traditional."** They have published poetry by Leo Mailman, Gerald Locklin, John Yamrus, Toby Lurie and Nichola Manning. These sample lines are from Lyn Lifshin's "Kent State 1970":

> The ROTC building
> still smoking
> the Guard moved in, feet on the
> grass. By
> Monday just
> after noon sirens Blood sinking into warm
> ground. Parents picking up phones
> that burned
> their hands

The books are digest-sized, flat-spined paperbacks with glossy covers, sometimes with cartoon art, attractively printed. **No query. Submit book ms with brief cover letter mentioning other publications and bio. Simultaneous submissions OK. Reports in 3 months. Pays 6-12% royalties and 10 author's copies. Buys all rights, does not return them. Send SASE for catalog to order samples.**

Market categories: (I) Beginning; (II) General; (III) Limited; (IV) Specialized; (V) Closed.

APROPOS (I, IV-Subscribers), RD 4, Ashley Manor, Easton PA 18042, founded 1989, editor Ashley C. Anders, appears 6 times/year, and **publishes all poetry submitted by subscribers (subscription: $25/ year) except that judged by the editor to be pornographic or in poor taste. Maximum length 40 lines — 50 characters/line.** As a sample, the editor selected her own "Simple Poem":

> *If I can write a simple poem*
> *that makes somebody smile,*
> *or wipes away a teardrop,*
> *then my poem will be worthwhile.*
>
> *It need not win a trophy,*
> *for that would not mean as much,*
> *as knowing that my simple poem*
> *and someone's heart will touch.*

It is digest-sized, 80 pgs., plastic ring bound, with heavy stock cover, desktop published. **Sample postpaid: $3. Simultaneous submissions and previously published poems OK. Send SASE for guidelines. Each issue awards prizes of $50, $25 and $10. All poems are judged by subscribers.** Special contests for subscribers are also offered throughout the year at no additional fee. Prizes are $25, $10 and $5.

AQUARIUS (II), Flat 10, Room A, 116 Sutherland Ave., Maida-Vale, London W9 England, poetry editor Eddie Linden, is a literary biannual publishing quality poetry. The latest issue (19/20), guest edited by Hilary Davies, contains poetry, fictional prose, essays, interviews and reviews. Subscription in US $50. **Sample copies: $5. Payment is by arrangement.**

ARARAT (IV-Ethnic), Dept. PM, 585 Saddle River Rd., Saddle Brook NJ 07662, phone (201)797-7600, editor-in-chief Leo Hamalian, is a quarterly magazine **emphasizing Armenian life and culture for Americans of Armenian descent and Armenian immigrants. Any verse that is Armenian in theme.** They do not want to see traditional, sentimental love poetry. Their circulation is 2,400. Sample copy $7 plus 4 first class stamps. Previously published submissions OK. Publishes ms an average of 1 year after acceptance. Submit seasonal/holiday material at least 3 months in advance. Reports in 6 weeks. Buys 6 poems/issue. Pays $10. Buys first North American serial rights and second (reprint) rights to material originally published elsewhere.

ARC; CONFEDERATION POETS PRIZE (II), P.O. Box 7368, Ottawa, Ontario K1L 8E4 Canada, founded 1978, coeditors Nadine McInnis and John Barton, is a biannual of poetry, poetry-related articles, interviews and book reviews. **"Our tastes are eclectic. Our focus is Canadian, but we also publish writers from elsewhere."** They have published poetry by Anne Szumigalski, Heather Spears, Robert Preist and Erin Mouré. The editors say *Arc* is 80-88 pgs., perfect-bound, with laminated 2-color cover, artwork and ads. They receive about 400 submissions a year, accept 40-50 poems. Press run is 580 for 200 subscribers of which 30 are libraries, 100 shelf sales. Single copy: $6 Canadian/US; subscription: $18 Canadian/US. **Cost of sample varies. No previously published poems or simultaneous submissions. Cover letter required. Submit 5-8 poems, single spaced, with name and address on each page. Send SASE for guidelines. Reports in 3-6 months. Pays $25 Canadian/page plus 2 copies. Buys first North American serial rights.** "We do not accept unsolicited book reviews." The Confederation Poets Prize is an annual award of $100 for the best poem published in *Arc.*

ARGONAUT (IV-Science fiction/fantasy), P.O. Box 4201, Austin TX 78765, founded 1972, editor/ publisher Michael Ambrose, is a **"semiannual magazine anthology of science fiction and weird fantasy, illustrated." They want "speculative, weird, fantastic poetry with vivid imagery or theme, up to 30 lines. Prefer traditional forms. Nothing ultramodernistic, non-fantastic."** They have published poetry by John Grey, David Lunde, Robert R. Medcalf, Jr. and Joey Froehlich. The editor describes it as 60 pgs., digest-sized, typeset. They accept 5-8 of 100-200 poems received. Press run is 300 for 50 subscribers of which 3 are libraries. Subscription: $8. **Sample postpaid: $4.95. Submit no more than 5 poems at a time. Editor comments on submissions "occasionally." Send SASE for guidelines. Reports in 1-2 months. Pays 1 copy.** Staff reviews books of poetry. He says, "Too much of what I see is limited in scope or language, and inappropriate for the themes of *Argonaut.* Poets should know what the particular market to which they submit is looking for and not simply shotgun their submissions."

ARIEL, A REVIEW OF INTERNATIONAL ENGLISH LITERATURE (III), English Dept., University of Calgary, Calgary, Alberta T2N 1N4 Canada, phone (403)220-4657, founded 1970, is a "critical, scholarly quarterly with about 5-8 pgs. of poetry in each issue." Though subject matter is open, editors here seem to prefer mostly lyric free verse with attention to form — line, stanza and voice. As a sample here are lines from "Ecstasy!" by Fritz Hamilton:

> *being the*

> Jackson Pollock of
> poetry I
>
> dance over the paper in
> the street with
> my pen poised to
>
> pour my words of
> poetry onto
> the world . . .

Ariel is professionally printed, flat-spined, 100+ pgs., digest-sized, with glossy card cover. Circulation 850, almost all subscriptions of which 650 are libraries. Subscription: $25 institutions; $17 individuals. They receive about 300 freelance submissions of poetry/year, use 20-30. **Sample postpaid: $6. Prefer 4-8 poems. No long poems. No simultaneous submissions. Cover letter required. Reports in 4-6 weeks. Pays 10 offprints plus 1 copy. Editor comments on rejections,** "only occasionally and not by request."

THE ARIZONA UNCONSERVATIVE (II), P.O. Box 23683, Tempe AZ 85285, founded 1991, poetry editor Christopher Ehren Hay, is "a monthly collection of poems, short fiction (less than 500 words), essays and articles relating to contemporary life." They want **"contemporary poetry — try to say something." They do not want "poetry that looks like it was written before this century."** The editor prefers not to include sample lines of poetry because "we'd really rather not limit anyone's idea of the range we are interested in." *AzUn* is 2 double-sided 8½×11 pages of recycled paper, printed from a laser jet and tri-folded. Press run is 250 for 200+ subscribers. Subscription: $1/month. **Sample postpaid: $1. "We would request that out-of-state submitters purchase a sample copy and all are strongly encouraged to subscribe because of untraditional format." Previously published poems and simultaneous submissions OK. Cover letter required.** Time between acceptance and publication is 2 months maximum. **Usually comments on rejections. Send SASE for guidelines. Reports in 1-2 months. Pays 7¢/ line. Buys one-time rights.** The editor says, "Say something that is important to you! Don't just write poetry the way you are told it should be. Write honestly and cut out all the triteness and clichés. In our opinion, rhyming generally limits creative expression because the writer is limiting the range of available words."

ARJUNA LIBRARY PRESS; JOURNAL OF REGIONAL CRITICISM (I, II), 1025 Garner St. D, Space 18, Colorado Springs CO 80905, library founded 1963, press founded 1979, editor Joseph A. Uphoff, Jr. "The Arjuna Library Press is avant garde, designed to endure the transient quarters and marginal funding of the literary phenomenon (as a tradition) while presenting a context for the development of current mathematical ideas in regard to theories of art, literature and performance; photocopy printing allows for very limited editions and irregular format. Quality is maintained as an artistic materialist practice." He wants to see **"surrealist prose poetry, dreamlike, short and long works, not obscene, profane (will criticize but not publish), unpolished work."** He is currently publishing work by Robert Howington and William Passera. As an example the editor has selected these lines from "Little Sister" by Holly Day (first published in *Doppelganger* #13):

> I remember
> waking up
> almost fifteen years ago
> to find a machine hovering
> over our bed
> rapidly transforming my sister
> into a Raggedy-Ann doll

JRC is published on loose photocopied pages of collage, writing and criticism, appearing frequently in a varied format. Press run: 1 copy each. **Pays "notification." Previously published poems and simultaneous submissions OK. Cover letter preferred; include "biography, intent, discourse (theories, ethics, history). I like ingenuity, legibility, convenience, polish. I expect some sympathy for mathematical, logical and philosophical exposition and criticism. These arguments remain our central ambition."** Reviews books of poetry "occasionally." Open to unsolicited reviews. Poets may also send books for review consideration. "Upon request will treat material as submitted for reprint, one-time rights." Arjuna Library Press publishes 6-12 chapbooks/year, averaging 50 pgs. **To submit to the press, send complete ms, cover letter including bio, publications, "any information the author feels is of value." The press pays royalties "by agreement, if we ever make a profit" and copies. Send 50¢ for sample.** The editor says, "English is a representation that conveys its image or preconception by convention. Its idioms and metaphors may be subjunctive (fantasy) or code (governed by the ethics of irony), and we can only have foreknowledge by example. Teaching and learning English can involve ignorance or contempt, but a poverty of the intellect will result from such a philosophical refusal. Though we conceive of a writer's intent we can only agree with facts perceived, by whatever poetic means, as being legitimate."

THE ARK (V), Dept. PM, 35 Highland Ave., Cambridge MA 02139, phone (617)547-0852, founded 1970 (as BLEB), poetry editor Geoffrey Gardner, publishes books of poetry. **"We are unable to take on new projects at this time."** They have published poetry by David Budbill, John Haines, Joseph Bruchac, Elsa Gidlow, W.S. Merwin, Eliot Weinberger, Kathy Acker, George Woodcock, Kathleen Raine, Marge Piercy and Linda Hogan. The editor selected these lines by Kenneth Rexroth (a translation from the Sanskrit) as a sample:

> *You think this is a time of Shiva's waking*
> *You are wrong*
> *You are Shiva*
> *But you dream*

THE UNIVERSITY OF ARKANSAS PRESS; ARKANSAS POETRY AWARD (III), Fayetteville AR 72701, founded 1980, acquisitions editor Scot Danforth, publishes flat-spined paperbacks and hardback collections of individual poets. Miller Williams, director of the press, says, **"We are not interested in poetry that says, 'Guess what I mean' or 'Look what I know.' "** They have published poetry by Frank Stanford, Henri Coulette, Enid Shomer and John Ciardi. As a sample, here is the opening stanza of "The Good Sheriff" by Eric Nelson:

> *Just as we run out*
> *of hope and firewood*
> *spring suddenly shoots*
> *green bullets through.*

That's from his book **The Interpretation of Waking Life**, digest-sized, 81 pgs., flat-spined, elegantly printed on eggshell stock with matte 3-color card cover. **Query with 5-10 sample poems. Replies to queries in 2 weeks, to submissions in 2-4 weeks. No replies without SASE. Ms should be double-spaced with 1½″ margins. Discs compatible with IBM welcome. Pays: 10% royalty** contract plus 10 author's copies. Send SASE for catalog to buy samples. The Arkansas Poetry Award competition is open to any original ms by a living American poet whose work has not been previously published or accepted for publication in book form. Chapbooks, self-published books, and books produced with the author's subsidy are not considered previously published books. No translations. Submit 50-80 pgs., not more than one poem/page, counting title page in page count. An acknowledgments page listing poems previously published should accompany ms. Author's name should appear on the title page only. $10 reading fee. Postmark no later than May 1. Publication the following spring. A $500 cash advance is part of the award.

ARNAZELLA (II), Bellevue Community College, 3000 Landerholm Circle SE, Bellevue WA 98007-6484, phone (206)641-2373, established 1979, advisor Laura Burns-Lewis, is a literary annual, published in spring, using **well-crafted poetry, no "jingles or greeting card" poetry.** They have published poetry by William Stafford, Judith Skillman and Coleen McElroy. The editor describes this student publication (which uses work from off campus) as 75 pgs., 6×8, offset, using photos and drawings. **They are currently accepting submissions only from poets in Washington, Oregon, Idaho, Alaska and British Columbia.** Of 150-200 poems received/year they use about 30. Press run is 500 for 3 subscriptions, one of which is a library. **Sample postpaid: $5. Submit up to 3 poems. Deadline is usually at beginning of February. Send SASE for guidelines. Reports in 1-4 months. Pays 1 copy.**

ARROWOOD BOOKS, INC. (II, IV-Regional), P.O. Box 2100, Corvallis OR 97339, phone (503)753-9539, founded 1985, editor Lex Runciman, is a "small press publisher of quality literary works." He publishes sewn paperbacks and hardcover books, always on acid-free papers, 1-2/year, 60-80 pgs. Poets published include Anne Pitkin, Joseph Powell, Lisa Steinman and Madeline DeFrees. **Query first. Simultaneous submissions and poems previously published in magazines OK. Replies to queries in 3 weeks, to mss in 2 months. Pays royalties and advance.** He offers a 10% writer's discount (limit 1 copy) on samples. He advises, "Write well, and work hard to separate the act of writing from the fear of publishing (or not)."

ART TIMES: CULTURAL AND CREATIVE JOURNAL (II), P.O. Box 730, Mount Marion NY 12456-0730, phone (914)246-6944, editor Raymond J. Steiner, is a monthly tabloid newspaper devoted to the arts that publishes some poetry and fiction. The editor wants to see **"traditional and contemporary poetry no longer than 20 lines but with high literary quality."** He does not want to see **"poorly written, pointless prose in stanza format."** He has published poetry by Helen Wolfert and Anne Mins. *Art Times* focuses on cultural and creative articles and essays. The paper is 16-20 pgs., on newsprint, with reproductions of artwork, some photos, advertisement-supported. Circulation is 15,000, of which 5,000 are by request and subscriptions; most distribution is free through galleries, theatres, etc. They receive 700-1,000 poems/month, use only 40-50 a year. Subscription is $15/year. **Sample: $1 postage cost. Simultaneous submissions OK. Criticism of mss is provided "at times but rarely." They have a 2-year backlog. Guidelines available for SASE. Reports in 6 months. Pays 6 copies plus 1-year subscription.**

ART-CORE! (I); APEX (I, IV-Erotica), P.O. Box 49324, Austin TX 78765, founded 1988, publisher/ editor Patty Puke, is published 3 times/year **using poems of "one page or less, alternative, underground, off-beat, avant-garde, uncensored — typed or visual layout. Occasional theme or special subject issues. No mainstream or lengthy poems."** The editor describes *Art-Core!* as 24 pgs., magazine-sized, offset. Press run is 2,000 for 150 subscribers, 1,000 copies distributed free locally. They accept about 50 of 300 poems submitted/year. Subscription: $7. **Sample postpaid: $3. Cover letter required with submissions. Send SASE for guidelines. Responds within 3 months. Pays 1 copy.** The editor adds, "We are happy to announce *APEX*, a new poetry publication sponsored by Art-Core and Electric Lord Productions. Our premier issue is a book of erotic poetry. Publication is planned annually. We are searching for a select group of poets and artists to participate. Interested parties should submit a short sample of their work and SASE." **Poets should be aware that material submitted for one publication may be included in the other. If you don't want to take the chance that your work may appear in *APEX*, consider another market.**

ARTE PUBLICO PRESS; THE AMERICAS REVIEW (IV-Ethnic), Dept. PM, University of Houston, Houston TX 77204-2090, founded 1972, editor Julian Olivares, publisher Nicolas Kanellos. (Note: *The Americas Review* is also the name of another magazine with a political focus published in Berkeley CA.) Each year the press publishes 20 books of fiction and 2 of poetry by **US Hispanic writers.** They have published books by Gary Soto, Ed Vega and Sandra Cisneros. *The Americas Review* is a triquarterly of fiction and poetry. It is digest-sized, 120-200 pgs., flat-spined. This market features poems in Spanish and English by Latino writers with distinct voices. Much of the verse is freestyle, lyric, and open in terms of length and content. Circulation 3,000; 2,100 subscribers (of which 40% are libraries). Subscription: $15 individual, $20 institution, $20 Mexico and Canada, $25 foreign. **No simultaneous submissions. Reads submissions September 1 through June 30 only. Reports in 4 months. Pays a varying amount plus 5 copies.** Reviews books of poetry in 750-1,000 words, single format; in up to 2,000 words, multi-book. **For book publication, publish first in the magazine. They pay a $500 advance and 25 copies for book publication. Contract stipulates 40% reprint fee to press.**

ARTFUL DODGE (II, IV-Translations), Dept. of English, College of Wooster, Wooster OH 44691, founded 1979, poetry editor Daniel Bourne, is an annual literary magazine that "takes a strong interest in poets who are continually testing what they can get away with successfully in regard to subject, perspective, language, etc., but who also show mastery of current American poetic techniques — its varied textures and its achievement in the illumination of the particular. What all this boils down to is that we require high craftsmanship as well as a vision that goes beyond *one's own* storm windows, grandmothers or sexual fantasies — to paraphrase Hayden Carruth. **Poems can be on any subject, of any length, from any perspective, in any voice, but we don't want anything that does not connect with both the human and the aesthetic. Thus, we don't want cute, rococo surrealism, someone's warmed-up, left-over notion of an avant-garde that existed 10-100 years ago, or any last bastions of rhymed verse in the civilized world.** On the other hand, we are interested in poems that utilize stylistic persuasions both old and new to good effect. We are not afraid of poems which try to deal with large social, political, historical, and even philosophical questions — especially if the poem emerges from one's own life experience and is not the result of armchair pontificating. We often offer encouragement to writers whose work we find promising, but *Artful Dodge* **is more a journal for the already emerging writer than for the beginner looking for an easy place to publish. We also have a sustained commitment to translation, especially from Polish and other East European literatures,** and we feel the interchange between the American and foreign works on our pages is of great interest to our readers. We also feature interviews with such outstanding literary figures as Jorge Luis Borges, W.S. Merwin, Nathalie Sarraute, Stanislaw Baranczak, Omar Pound, Gwendolyn Brooks, John Giorno, William Least Heat-Moon, Cynthia Macdonald, Tim O'Brien, Lee Smith and William Matthews. Recent and forthcoming poets include Naomi Shihab Nye, Walter McDonald, Lola Haskins, Ron Wallace, Alberta Turner, David Ignatow, Jim Daniels, Peter Wild, William Stafford, Karl Krolow (German), Tomasz Jastrun (Polish), Jorge Luis Borges (Spanish), Mahmud Darwish (Palestinian) and Tibor Zalan (Hungarian)." The digest-sized, perfect-bound format is professionally printed, glossy cover, with art, ads. There are about 60-80 pgs. of poetry in each issue. Press run is 1,000 for 100 subscribers of which 30 are libraries. They receive at least 2,000 poems/year, use 60, and the backlog is 1-12 months between acceptance and publication. **Sample: $5 for recent issues, $3 for others. "No simultaneous submissions. Please limit submissions to 6 poems. Long poems may be of any length, but send only one at a time. We**

encourage translations, but we ask as well for original text and statement from translator that he/she has copyright clearance and permission of author." Reports in up to 5 months. Pays 2 copies, plus, currently, $5/page honorarium because of grants from Ohio Arts Council. Open to unsolicited reviews; "query first." Poets may also send books for review consideration; however, "there is no guarantee we can review them!" *Artful Dodge* received an Ohioana Library Association Book Award for Editorial Excellence in 1992.

ARTS END BOOKS; NOSTOC MAGAZINE (II), P.O. Box 162, Newton MA 02168, founded 1978, poetry editor Marshall Brooks. "We publish good contemporary writing. Our interests are broad and so are our tastes. People considering sending work to us should examine a copy of our magazine and/or our catalog; check your library for the former, send us a SASE for the latter." Their publications are distinguished by excellent presswork and art in a variety of formats: postcard series, posters, pamphlets, flat-spined paperbacks and hardbacks. The magazine appears irregularly in print runs of 300-500, about 30 pgs. of poetry in each, 100 subscriptions of which half are libraries. **Sample postpaid: $4.** They receive a few hundred submissions/year, use 25-30. They offer **"modest payment plus contributor's copies. A cover letter is a very good idea for any kind of submission;** we receive *very* few good, intelligent cover letters. What to include? That's up to the writer, whatever he/she feels important in terms of the work, in terms of establishing a meeting." **Tries to report within a few weeks. Discourages simultaneous submissions. Frequently comments on rejected mss.** Reviews books of poetry "on occasion, length varies." Brooks says, "We try to respond warmly to writers interested in making genuine contact with us and our audience."

‡ARUNDEL PRESS; MERCER & AITCHISON (V), 8380 Beverly Blvd., Los Angeles CA 90048, phone (213)852-9852, founded 1984, managing editor Phillip Bevis. Arundel Press "publishes only major texts (as we see them) in limited editions printed letterpress. **We no longer consider unsolicited manuscripts.** Most work is illustrated with original graphics. Mercer & Aitchison publishes definitive editions of major (as we see them) works of poetry, literature and literary criticism." They publish about 3 hardbacks/year. Phillip Bevis recommends to beginning poets the Mercer & Aitchison publication, Clayton Eshleman's **Novices: A Study of Poetic Apprenticeship** (paperback, $12.95). He says, "The only thing worth adding to what is said there is that there are only a handful of poets in America (at the most) making a living *as* poets. The majority of even the most prominent must teach or work in other fields to support their poetic endeavors. Poetry must be something you do because you want to—not for the money."

ASCENT (II), P.O. Box 967, Urbana IL 61801, founded 1975, editor Audrey Curley, appears 3 times/year, using **poetry that is "eclectic, shorter rather than longer."** They have recently published poetry by Stuart Friebert and Nance Van Winckel. As a sample the editor selected these lines from "Driving by the Water's Edge" by Laura Glenn:

> The moon with its dark underside
> hides like a squid in its cloud of ink.
> Silver flashes—a school of trucks with matching light—
> and an old fish lurches toward me
> with rust sequins, outdated fins, and one front light
>
> missing—a nautilus recoiling in its shell,
> I curve slowly around the octopus
> of roads
> heading for home.

The editor describes it as 6 × 9, 64 pgs., professionally printed with matte card cover. They accept about 5% of 750 poems received/year. Print run 900 copies for 250 subscribers of which 90 are libraries. Subscription: $6/year. **Sample postpaid: $2. Pays 3 copies.** This continues as one of the "best buys" in the literary world for its low price, openness to all forms and styles, and relatively quick and encouraging response times. The editor says, "I am usually the sole reader. Poems are rejected or accepted from 2-8 weeks, usually closer to 2 weeks. Acceptances are usually published within the year."

THE ASHLAND POETRY PRESS (V, IV-Anthologies, themes), Ashland University, Ashland OH 44805, founded 1969, editor Robert McGovern, publishes anthologies on specific themes and occasional collections. He has published collections by Harold Witt, Alberta Turner and Richard Snyder. As a sample he selected these lines from "Jacqueline Du Pré" by Leonard Trawick:

> Jacqueline du Pré, when your muscles came untuned,
> wasn't the music still there, all those silent years— —
> just as, after the last note, when players poise their bows
> triumphant for one still moment before the applause,

the whole quartet hangs perfect in the air?

That poem appears in **80 on the 80's: A Decade's History in Verse** edited by Robert McGovern and Joan Baranow. "Watch publications such as *Poets & Writers* for calls for mss, but don't submit otherwise. We do not read unsolicited mss; anthology readings take quite a bit of time." Considers simultaneous submissions. On collections, poet gets 10% royalty; anthologies, poets are paid stipulated price when sufficient copies are sold. Write for book and price list.

ASYLUM (II, IV-Form, translations), P.O. Box 6203, Santa Maria CA 93456, founded 1985, editor Greg Boyd, is "an annual literary anthology with emphasis on short fiction, **the prose poem and poetry.** No restrictions on form, subject matter, style or purpose, though we are especially receptive to prose poems, absurdist writing and contemporary modes of surrealism and dada." They have published poetry by Thomas Wiloch, Russell Edson, Edouard Roditi and Robert Peters. As a sample, the editor selected these lines from "Twenty Shores" by Cynthia Hendershot:

> I dream of a tree with razors
> instead of fruit. Every word
> that falls from your orange tongue
> falls on my palm like a drop of blood.

Asylum is 160-200 pgs., 8½ × 11, perfect-bound, professionally printed with varnished stock cover. They accept about 1% of submissions. Print run is 2,500 for 200 subscriptions of which 20 are libraries. Subscription: $10. **Sample postpaid: $7.95. Put name and address on each page. No simultaneous submissions. Reports in 2 weeks-6 months. Pays 3 copies. Acquires first North American serial rights.** Regarding reviews of books of poetry, "authors should query before submitting material."

ATALANTIK (IV-Ethnic, foreign language), 7630 Deercreek Dr., Worthington OH 43085, phone (614)885-0550, founded 1979, editor Prabhat K. Dutta, is a "literary quarterly **mainly in Bengali** and containing short stories, poems, essays, sketches, book reviews, interviews, cultural information, science articles, cinema/theater news, children's pages, serialized novels, etc., **with occasional English writings (non-religious, non-political.)**" They have published "all major poets of West Bengal, India (Sunil Gangopadhyay, Sakti Chattopadhyay, Manas Roychoudhury, Santi Kumar Ghosh, Bijay K. Dutta, Debi Roy, Manjush Dasgupta, Tanushree Bhattacharya, etc.) as well as of Bangladesh (Shamsur Rahaman, Begum Sufia Kamal, Abu Jafar Obeyadullah, Ashraf Siddique, Al Mahmood, etc.)." As a sample the editor selected these lines from "Voyage" by Anirban Roy Chowdhury:

> I've faced many dangers on my way,
> Storms and tornados, often I've lost my way,
> Many times I've seen death—calling me from a distance away,
> But I've overcome all and I'm a successful sailor today.

"*Atalantik,* the first Bengali literary magazine in USA, was started to keep Bengali language alive to Bengalees in USA. Number of pages averages out to 70. Original printing by electric press in Calcutta, India; USA printing is by offset or photocopy and the number varies according to order; artwork both on the cover and inside the magazine." It is magazine-sized, flat-spined, with b&w matte card cover. Some copies are distributed free. Subscription: $20. **Sample postpaid: $6. Simultaneous submissions and previously published poems OK. Cover letter required; include information about literary career/achievements. Send SASE for guidelines. Reports in 1 month. Pays 1-2 copies.** Reviews books of poetry in 200-2,000 words, single or multi-book format. Open to unsolicited reviews. Poets may also send books for review consideration. "We are actively and seriously considering publishing books under 'Atalantik Publications.'" **For book consideration submit sample poems, cover letter with bio and publications. Simultaneous submissions OK. Pays "15 copies usually, may vary."** Editor sometimes comments on rejections. The operations of a smaller version of *Atalantik* are managed by Keshab Dutta, from 36B, Bakul Bagan Road, Calcutta-700025, India (phone 75-1620) for distribution in India. Prabhat K. Dutta was recognized by Uttarapath, a Swedish literary and cultural organization, for his efforts in publishing *Atalantik*.

‡ATHENA INCOGNITO MAGAZINE (I), 1442 Judah St., San Francisco CA 94122, founded 1980, editor Ronn Rosen, is an annual of experimental writing and other arts. They want **poetry that is** "experimental, surrealist, Dada, etc. 3 pgs. max. No greeting card verse, overly religious poetry or epics." They have recently published poetry by Greg Wallace, Michael McClellan and Steven Saxonberg. As a sample the editor selected these lines (poet unidentified):

> Arrow strikes
> Swims out
> Narrow gap lapped up that vulture
> Heron heron heron
> Of summer brambled.

The editor says the magazine is usually 20-30 photocopied pgs. They receive about 50 poems a year, use approximately 15%. Press run is 200 for 50 subscribers of which 2 are libraries, 50 shelf sales. **"All people submitting poetry *must* buy a sample copy—$5 postpaid." Previously published poems and simultaneous submissions OK. "Name and address required on all pages. SASE also required."** Often comments on rejections. Reports in 1-2 months. Pays 1 copy. The editor says, "Be well read in world poetry, surrealism and Dada, and get inspired."

THE ATLANTEAN PRESS REVIEW; THE ATLANTEAN PRESS (II, IV-Themes, translations), 354 Tramway, Milpitas CA 95035, founded 1990, publisher Patricia LeChevalier. The Atlantean Press was founded to publish Romantic fiction, drama and poetry, beginning with republication of work by Victor Hugo that is out-of-print. *The Atlantean Press Review*, now published quarterly, includes a small amount of poetry as well as fiction, drama and essays. **"We are looking for intelligent, thoughtful, preferably rhyming poems that address human values and aspirations."** As a sample the publisher selected these lines from "No Moments of Sleep, Nature" by Saul Tchernikovski, translated by Michelle Fram-Cohen:

> When my spirit laments, my wounds bemoan,
>   my hopes wear away like the rose in the fall—
> I wander to a place where breakers groan,
>   where a ridge raises its mighty old wall.
> Then I'm ashamed of the waves which, assailing the reefs,
>   the moment they break they return to the cliffs . . .

The Review is 7½ × 7½, perfect-bound. **Sample (232-page edition) postpaid: $14. Reads submissions August 15 through March 1 only. Often comments on rejections. Send SASE for guidelines. Reports in 2 months. Pays up to $2/line plus copies. Buys North American serial rights.** "We'd be very interested in competent translations of Victor Hugo's poetry."

THE ATLANTIC (II), Dept. PM, 745 Boylston St., Boston MA 02116, phone (617)536-9500, founded 1857, poetry editor Peter Davison, assistant poetry editor Steven Cramer, publishes 1-5 poems monthly in the magazine. **Some of the most distinguished poetry in American literature** has been published by this magazine, including work by William Matthews, Mary Oliver, Stanley Kunitz, Rodney Jones, May Swenson, Galway Kinnell, Philip Levine, Red Hawk, Tess Gallagher, Donald Hall and W.S. Merwin. The magazine has a circulation of 500,000, of which 5,800 are libraries. They receive some 75,000 poems/year, of which they use 35-40 and have a backlog of 6-12 months. **Sample postpaid: $3. Submit 3-5 poems with SASE, no simultaneous submissions. Pays about $3/line. Buys first North American serial rights only.** Wants "to see poetry of the highest order; we do *not* want to see workshop rejects. Watch out for workshop uniformity. Beware of the present indicative. Be yourself." Poetry published here has been included in *Best American Poetry 1992*. In addition, *The Atlantic* ranked #9 in the "Poets' Pick" category of the June 1993 *Writer's Digest* Poetry 60 list. This category ranks those publications in which poets said they would most like to see their work published.

ATLANTIS: A WOMEN'S STUDIES JOURNAL (IV-Feminist), Dept. PM, Mount Saint Vincent University, Halifax, Nova Scotia B3M 2J6 Canada, phone (902)443-4450, ext. 319, founded 1975, editor Deborah Poff, managing editor Maurice Michaud or literary editor Margaret Harry, appears twice a year using poetry "certainly no longer than 5 ms pgs.; **should have a feminist perspective, preferably academic. No cutesie greeting card poems about marshmallow women or by men without a hint of feminist consciousness."** They have published poetry by Liliane Welch. The editor describes it as magazine-sized, 150 pgs., flat-spined with card cover. They accept about 5-10% of submissions. Press run is 1,000 with 600 subscribers of which 55% are libraries. Subscription: Canada $25; US $40 (Canadian). **Sample postpaid: $7.50 Canadian. Reports in 6-12 weeks. Pays 1 copy.**

AURA LITERARY/ARTS MAGAZINE (II), Dept. PM, Box 76, University of Alabama at Birmingham, Birmingham AL 35294, phone (205)934-3216, founded 1974, editor Velda Harris, a semiannual magazine that publishes "fiction and art though majority of acceptances are poetry—90-100 per year. Length—open, style open, subject matter open. We are looking for quality poetry. Both first-time and

---

ALWAYS include a self-addressed, stamped envelope (SASE) when sending a ms or query to a publisher within your own country. When sending material to other countries, include a self-addressed envelope and International Reply Coupons (IRCs), available for purchase at most post offices.

often published poets are published here." *Aura* has published work by Lyn Lifshin, Adrian C. Louis and William Miller. The 6×9 magazine is 100-140 pgs., perfect-bound, printed on white matte with b&w photos, lithography and line art. Circulation is 500, of which 40-50 are subscriptions; other sales are to students and Birmingham residents. Subscription: $6. **Sample available for $2.50 postpaid, guidelines for SASE. Writers should submit "3-5 poems, with SASE, no simultaneous submissions, will take even neatly hand written." Reporting time is 2-3 months. Pay is 2 copies.**

AWEDE PRESS (II), Dept. PM, Box 376, Windsor VT 05089, phone (802)484-5169, founded 1975, editor Brita Bergland. Awede is a small press that publishes letterpress books, sewn with drawn-on covers, graphically produced. The editor wants **"contemporary, 'language' poetry with a strong visual interest."** They have published poetry by Charles Bernstein, James Sherry, Rosemarie Waldrop and Hannah Weiner. Awede publishes 2 poetry chapbooks/year, 32 pgs., 6×9, flat-spined. **Freelance submissions are accepted, but author should query first. Queries are answered in 2 weeks, mss reported on in 4-5 months. Simultaneous submissions are acceptable. Pay is in author's copies, 10% of run.** No subsidy publishing, book catalog free on request, with SASE a must. Sample books available at list price of $8-15.

THE BABY CONNECTION NEWS JOURNAL (V), Drawer 13320, San Antonio TX 78213-0320, phone Tues.-Sat. 12:30-5:30 CST (210)493-6278, founded 1986, Ms. Gina G. Morris Boyd, C.I.D.I./editor, is "a monthly news journal to support, educate, move and inspire new and expectant parents in their role of rearing babies and preschoolers up to 5 years of age. Parenting is such a tough job—our publication strives to reward and motivate positive and nurturing parenting skills." They publish **"poetry only on the subjects of mothering, fathering, birthing, pregnancy, child rearing, the power, the love, the passion and momentum, fertility."** They are currently not accepting poetry submissions: "We have received over 6,000 pieces and are overwhelmed." They have published poetry by Alex Grayton, Barbara Kane, E.K. Alasky, Jim McConnell and Laura Rodley. As a sample the editor selected these lines from "Night Music" by Marc Swan:

> *The moon casts a mosaic of light and dark*
> *against her bedroom wall. I lean low to*
> *tuck her in & kiss her goodnight. Dad,*
> *she whispers, look at Peter Pan's shadow. I hug*
> *her tightly, close to my chest. If it gets lost*
> *you can sew it back on. Yes, she says,*
> *   I will.*

The tabloid-sized newsprint publication is 24 pgs. Press run: 30,000 for 1,700 subscriptions of which 10% are libraries. Subscription: $9/year. **Sample postpaid: $3 for 2 different issues. "We also offer a reduced rate subscription of $4.75 for 6 months so we can be assured the poet knows our context and cares enough to follow us for a term." Cover letter with brief personal bio required. Pays 5 copies.** Reviews books of poetry. They also publish 5-8 chapbooks and flat-spined paperbacks/year averaging 16-72 pgs. **Pays 6 copies and honorarium averaging $25.**

‡BABY SUE (I), P.O. Box 1111, Decatur GA 30031-1111, founded 1985, editor Don W. Seven, appears twice a year publishing politically incorrect humor for the extremely open-minded and not easily offended. **"We are open to all styles, but prefer short poems." No restrictions.** They have recently published poetry by Edward Mycue, Susan Andrews, Stephen Fievet and Barry Bishop. The editor says *baby sue* is 20 pgs., offset. "We print prose, poems and cartoons. We usually accept about 5% of what we receive." Single copy: $1.50; subscription: $8 for 4 issues. **Sample postpaid: $2. Previously published poems and simultaneous submissions OK. Deadlines are March 30 and September 30 of each year. Seldom comments on rejections. Reports "immediately, if we are interested." Pays 1 copy.** "We do occasionally review other magazines." The editor adds, "We have received no awards, but we are very popular on the underground press circuit and sell our magazine all over the world."

‡THE BACON PRESS (I), 838 Wittenberg Rd., Mt. Tremper NY 12457, founded 1990, editor T.S. Paul, is a "sporadic" journal of poetry and art, usually appearing 2-3 times/year. They want **"poetry by angels, demons, travelers along the way. New poets welcome."** They have recently published poetry by Mikhail Horowitz and N. Hartigan. As a sample the editor selected these lines from his own poem, "Building The House":

> *Her old lovers stir in their beds*
> *Like iron filings*
> *They will shift and gather in moonlight*
> *To stalk this dream of building*
> *Stalk it with beams and sweat and money*
> *While she sleeps.*

The Bacon Press is 16 pgs., 5½×8½, saddle-stapled with occasional graphics/b&w art. They receive 50-75 poems a year, accept approximately 24. Press run is 100 for shelf sales in local bookstores. **Sample postpaid: $2. Previously published poems and simultaneous submissions OK; "please note if and where previously published. Don't send originals as we do not return manuscripts. Just send SASE for reply."** Time between acceptance and publication is 6 months. **Often comments on rejections. Reports in 1 month. Pays 1 copy. Acquires first or reprint rights.** The editor says, "I find the current 'scene' to be very uplifting for poets. I would encourage beginners to read in public as often as possible, and submit as widely as possible—but send it to *The Bacon Press* first!"

BAD ATTITUDE (I, IV-Lesbian, erotica), P.O. Box 390110, Cambridge MA 02139, founded 1984, contact Jasmine Sterling, is a lesbian sex magazine appearing 4-6 times/year. They want **"lesbian erotic poetry."** Press run is 3,000. Subscription: $24/year. **Sample postpaid: $5. No previously published poems; simultaneous submissions OK. Cover letter required. Seldom comments on rejections. Reports "immediately." Pays 2 copies.** Reviews books of poetry. Open to unsolicited reviews. Poets may also send books for review consideration.

BAD HAIRCUT (II, IV-Social issues), 1055 Adams SE #4, Olympia WA 98501, founded 1987, poetry editors Kimberlea and Ray Goforth, is a "small press magazine with world-wide distribution. Publication schedule varies. **Progressive politics, human rights and environmental themes. Free verse is preferred. Don't want to see anything by bad poets in *love*."** They have recently published poetry by M.C. Alpher and T.L. Toma. As a sample the editors selected these lines by Richard Curtis:

> on a dark road my friend and I
> spoke thoughts and things,
> He felt that life is a balancing. . . .
> That the universal leger balances.
> And I thought of ghettos and death camps
> . . . of plague and cribdeath.
> And I voiced not a word of my views of the world—
> There being disillusion enough, as it is.

Their object is "to inform and inspire others to work for a better world in their own individual ways." *Bad Haircut* is digest-sized, using some art and ads. Of thousands of poems received each year, they say, they use 25. Press run is 1,000 for 300 subscriptions (3 libraries), and it is carried by 4 stores. Subscription: $14. **Sample postpaid: $4. Send SASE for guidelines. No simultaneous submissions. Previously published poetry OK. Cover letter—including "what people do in their lives, why they wrote to us, etc."—required. Rejections in 1 day; acceptances can take up to 6 months. Editors comment on rejections** "always—as poets ourselves, we learned to hate form rejections." **Pays 1 copy. Acquires first North American serial rights.** Open to unsolicited reviews. Poets may also send books for review consideration. They also publish a line of poetry postcards.

THE BAD HENRY REVIEW; 44 Press (II), Box 150045, Van Brunt Station, Brooklyn NY 11215-0001, founded 1981, poetry editors Evelyn Horowitz, Michael Malinowitz and Mary du Passage. They have published poetry by John Ashbery, Gilbert Sorrentino, Stephen Sandy and William Matthews. *The Bad Henry Review* is an annual publishing quality poetry, 64 pgs., digest-sized. Press run is 500-1,000 for 200 subscriptions of which 15 are for libraries; 200-300 for shelf sales. Single copy: $6; subscription: $12/2 issues. **Sample: $4. Submit no more than 5 poems, include SASE. No simultaneous submissions. No previously published poems unless advised. Rarely comments on rejected mss. Pays 1 copy with half price discount for contributors.** The editor comments, "We've done one issue of long poems and we are doing an issue on photography in 1994." 44 Press publishes about 1 book of poetry/year.

‡BAGMAN PRESS (I), P.O. Box 81166, Chicago IL 60681-0166, founded 1989, publisher Bill Falloon, publishes 1 paperback/year—**"emphasis is on 'new' writers who can create powerful first impressions."** They have recently published poetry by J.J. Tindall. **Submit complete ms with SASE. Previously published poems OK; no simultaneous submissions. Cover letter required. Seldom comments on rejections. Replies to queries in 2 weeks, to submitted mss in 6 months or less. Pays 5-10% royalties and 30 author's copies.** "Inland Book Co. is our primary distributor." The editor says this is "an alternative press that would publish a fish, so long as he or she writes well. We try to read everything with an open mind."

‡BAKER STREET PUBLICATIONS; FULL MOON PUBLICATIONS; THE HAUNTED JOURNAL; REALM OF THE VAMPIRE; BAKER STREET GAZETTE; HORIZONS BEYOND; HORIZONS WEST; MIXED BAG; PEN & INK; NIGHTSHADE; REALM OF DARKNESS; THE SALEM JOURNAL; MOVIE MEMORIES; SLEUTH JOURNAL (I, IV-Horror, science fiction, fantasy, mystery, western, themes), P.O. Box 517, Metairie LA 70004-0517, phone (504)733-9138, founded 1983, poetry editors Sharida Rizzuto,

Frances Nordan and Ann Hoyt. All of these magazines, chapbooks, perfect-bound paperbacks, and newsletters use poetry. "**No strict requirements on form, length or style. Must be suitable for horror, mystery, science fiction, fantasy, western or literary.**" They have recently published poetry by Wayne Allen Sallee, John B. Rosenman, Leilah Wendell, John Grey, Lyn Lifshin and Richard David Behrens. As a sample, the editor selected the poem "Starving" by Dwight Humphries, which appeared in *The Haunted Journal*:

> *There is eternal hunger*
> *In my frayed soul;*
> *My heart a fenris wolf*
> *Beneath my ribs that*
> *Starves for all things.*

The editor says, "Most zines are 60-120 pgs., digest-sized; newsletters are magazine-sized and 12-30 pgs., chapbooks and paperbacks vary. All publications include artwork and graphics inside and on covers. All have ads in the back. Most of them contain photos." Their press run is "under 10,000." **Send SASE for guidelines. Sample copies are $3-7.90. Submissions are "preferably typewritten. Author should include a bio sheet." Simultaneous submissions OK, as are previously published poems that are "very good and haven't been published in over 2 years." Reports in 3-6 weeks. Pays "mainly in copies but fees negotiable." For book publications send 3-5 sample poems, bio. Simultaneous submissions OK. Responds to queries in 3-6 weeks, to mss in 1-2 months. Pays 50% royalties after printing and advertising costs are covered. Publishes 6-12 chapbooks/year. Same submission requirements as for other publications.** Sharida Rizzuto advises, "Just be yourself; don't try to imitate anyone else. Respect helpful criticism."

BAKUNIN (II), P.O. Box 1853, Simi Valley CA 93062-1853, founded 1990, editor Jordan Jones, is a semiannual. "**We are looking for poems that challenge accepted pieties and norms. We are also interested in powerful personal poems.**" They want "**avant-garde and mainstream poetry of humor, pathos and social comment. No trite or hackneyed verse; no poem that uses but does not earn the word love.**" They have published poetry by Sandra McPherson, Dennis Schmitz and Benjamin Saltman. As a sample the editor selected the opening lines of "The Aqueduct" by Dorianne Laux:

> *We played there on hot L.A. summers, kids poking through*
> *the slick algae and bloated tires, the delicate rafts*
> *of mosquito eggs. Open boxcars pulled gray squares*
> *of sky overhead as we took apples and crackers*
> *from our pockets and ate, watched the cursing workers*
> *from the can factory gathering at the silver lunch truck*

Bakunin is 96 pgs., digest-sized, offset on acid-free recycled paper, perfect-bound, with laminated cover, b&w artwork and some ads. They receive about 500 submissions a year, publish approximately 5%. The free verse is mostly lyric, and the poems tend to be one-page. Press run is 1,000 for 100 subscribers, 450 shelf sales. Subscription: $8, $10 for institutions. **Sample postpaid: $5. No previously published poems; simultaneous submissions OK, "if the author indicates they are such." Cover letter required.** Time between acceptance and publication is 6-12 months. **Seldom comments on rejections. Send SASE for guidelines. Reports in 2 weeks-3 months. Pays 2 copies. Acquires first North American serial rights.** "We publish 250- to 750-word reviews of single books, magazines or whole presses." The editor says, "*Bakunin* is a magazine for the dead Russian anarchist in all of us."

‡**BALL MAGAZINE; SIDE 'O' FRIES PRESS (I)**, P.O. Box 775, Northampton MA 01061-0775, phone (413)584-3076, founded 1992, first issue May 1993, editor-in-chief Douglas M. Kimball, poetry editor Jennifer Jarrell, is a biannual that "provides a venue for writers/artists whose work may be too risky for other publications. *Ball* considers all styles and formats. We favor diversity and risk taking." As a sample the editors selected these lines from "Radical Feminism Knows No Season" by Jennifer Culp:

> *US nuns in support tended to escape*
> *the grout between the tiles of abortion*
> *and other recent inside storms*
> *as "women par excellence" (that are so attractive to mildew).*
> *Women are different under the eaves;*
> *the divine plan is effective only about two years,*
> *and that radical dignity is 35 feet long and longer.*

The editors describe *Ball* as approximately 75 pgs., 8½ × 11, offset, with color cover, b&w photos, artwork and ads. "*Very* dense layout." They receive about 20 mss/month, accept approximately 5%. Single copy: $6. **No previously published poems; simultaneous submissions OK.** "We run a relaxed ship. We are no more interested in poets' P.R. material than they are in ours. A friendly correspondence is always welcome, however." **Always comments on rejections. Send SASE for**

response. Reports in 2-4 weeks. Pays 2+ copies. Acquires first rights. The editors say "We believe that the (publishing) system is out of whack. Don't let jaded or insensitive editors humiliate you. Write for yourself first. Maybe the world will like your work and maybe only your lover will. Either should taste equally sweet."

THE BANK STREET PRESS; THE PORT AUTHORITY POETRY REVIEW (V), 24 Bank St., New York NY 10014, phone (212)255-0692, founded 1985, poetry editor Mary Bertschmann. A small group of poets meet at the Bank Street home of Mary Bertschmann and publish their poetry annually in a series of flat-spined paperbacks called *The Port Authority Poetry Review*. **Sample $7 including postage and handling.** The Bank Street Press also publishes solo collections of poetry. They have published **Goslings on the Tundra** ($20 including postage and handling) and, more recently, **52 Sonnets** ($12 including postage and handling), both limited, fine print volumes by Mary York Sampson. As a sample the editor selected this sonnet:

> *The progress of this day is worth remark,*
> *The air is full of starch and the blue sky*
> *Is like the rare occurrence of an honest eye*
> *That says in the long hours before dark*
> *There'll be a fair deal, a new life spark;*
> *And well before the sky begins to die,*
> *Before the blood spills in the West nearby,*
> *And the city turns into tombstones stark,*
> *This fine spring day will flaunt its lion heart,*
> *Truth will be allowed, and growth, in this free*
> *Symbiotic mix of justice and light;*
> *Morning, noon, afternoon all counterpart,*
> *A universal purr exclaims as we*
> *Scout this isthmus between the shores of night.*

BANTAM DOUBLEDAY DELL PUBLISHING GROUP (V), 1540 Broadway, New York NY 10036, phone (212)765-6500, **accepts mss only from agents.**

BAPTIST SUNDAY SCHOOL BOARD; LIVING WITH PRESCHOOLERS; LIVING WITH CHILDREN; LIVING WITH TEENAGERS; HOME LIFE (IV-Religious); MATURE LIVING (IV-Religious, senior citizen), Dept. PM, 127 Ninth Ave. N., Nashville TN 37234, the publishing agency for Southern Baptists. "We publish magazines, monthlies, quarterlies, books, filmstrips, films, church supplies, etc., for Southern Baptist churches." **Query with samples.** For most of their publications they want **"inspirational and/or religious poetry. No 'word pictures.' We want poetry with a message to inspire, uplift, motivate, amuse. No longer than 24 lines," typed, double-spaced, no simultaneous submissions. Reports within 2 months, rate of pay figured on number of lines submitted.** The biggest of the monthlies is *Home Life*, which began in 1947. Circulation 750,000; 20,000 subscriptions—a magazine-sized, saddle-stapled, slick magazine, 60+ pgs., illustrated (no ads). Its editor Charlie Warren and assistant editor Mary Paschall Darby say they want **"religious poetry; treating marriage, family life and life in general from a Christian perspective. We rarely publish anything of more than 25 lines." Sample: $1 to authors with SASE! Submit no more than 6 poems at a time. Query unnecessary. Send SASE for guidelines. Reports in 6-8 weeks. Pays $15-24.** *Mature Living: A Christian Magazine for Senior Adults*, founded in 1977, is a monthly mass circulation (330,000) magazine providing "leisure reading for senior adults. All material used is compatible with a Christian life-style." The poetry they use is of Christian content, inspirational, about "nature/God," rhymed, 8-24 lines. Assistant editor Linda Thompson says, **"We dislike free verse or poems where a word is dragged in just to piece out a meter."** Apparently you do not have to be a senior citizen to submit. *Mature Living* is magazine-sized, 52 pgs., saddle-stapled, using large print on pulp stock, glossy paper cover, with color and b&w art. They "receive hundreds" of poems/year, use about 125-150. Most of their distribution is through churches who buy the magazine in bulk for their senior adult members. **For sample, send 9 × 12 self-addressed envelope and 85¢ postage. Reports in 6-8 weeks, but there might be a 3-year delay before publication. Pays $5-25.**

‡E.W. BARHAM PUBLISHING (III), P.O. Box 5, Bowling Green OH 43402, founded 1992, editor Wayne Barham, plans to publish 1-3 paperbacks, 0-1 hardbacks and **1-3 chapbooks/year.** He wants **"poetry that uses evocative imagery, has a sense of the music of words, has a consistent voice and presents the reader with the world renewed. No so-called L-A-N-G-U-A-G-E poetry."** The first book of poetry he published was "the complete works of a completely unknown poet named Mahlon F. Scott" (released in June 1993), though he says it isn't characteristic of what he expects to be publishing in the future. **Query first with list of magazine (and book, if applicable) publications and a sample of 10-12 pages of poetry. Previously published poems and simultaneous submissions OK. Replies to**

queries in 2-3 weeks, to mss in 1-3 months. "All final decisions will be made by the poetry contact person in consultation with other local poets." **Seldom comments on rejections. Pays 12½ to 15% royalties, $150 honorarium and 10 author's copies. Query regarding availability of sample books or chapbooks.** The editor says, "While we're told (mostly by big commercial publishers) that there is no market (i.e. audience) for poetry, we need to be careful that we are not making that claim a self-fulfilling prophesy. There is an audience, but poets have to create it. Give readings at every opportunity. Listen to your listeners; learn from them what still stirs the human soul."

BARNWOOD PRESS; BARNWOOD; BARNWOOD PRESS COOPERATIVE (III), Dept. PM, P.O. Box 146, Selma IN 47383, phone (317)288-0145, founded 1978, editors Tom Koontz, Haven Koontz and Thom Tammaro, publishes *Barnwood* 3 times/year and 1 paperback collection of poetry every 2 or 3 years. **"We have no conscious preconception."** However, they do not want poetry that is "visionless, bigoted, poorly crafted or stereotypical." They have published poetry by Bly, Friman, Goedicke and Stafford. As a sample the editors selected these lines from "Light Casualties" by Robert Francis:

> *Did the guns whisper when they spoke*
> *That day? Did death tiptoe his business?*
> *And afterwards in another world*
> *Did mourners put on light mourning,*
> *Casual as rain, as snow, as leaves?*
> *Did a few tears fall?*

The editors say *Barnwood* is 16 pgs., photo offset and saddle-stitched. They receive about 1,000 poems a year, publish 36. Press run is 500 for 200 subscribers of which 50 are libraries. Subscription: $6/year, "includes membership in Barnwood Press Cooperative which provides discount on Barnwood books." **Sample postpaid: $2. Previously published poems ("please tell us where and when") and simultaneous submissions OK, if noted. Reads submissions September 1 through May 31 only.** Time between acceptance and publication is 1 year. **Seldom comments on rejections. Reports in 1 month. Pays $25/poem plus 5 copies. Buys first North American serial rights only.** Reviews chapbooks of poetry in 500-1,000 words. **Query first for book publication. Replies to queries in 1 month, to mss (if invited) in 1-6 months. Pays 100 author's copies (10% of press run).** The editors add, "While our magazine is chef's choice or taste of the house, we try to recognize a wide variety of effective poems and we look to the poets to show us what can make effective poetry."

‡THE BARRELHOUSE: AN EXCURSION INTO THE UNKNOWN (IV-Science fiction/fantasy/horror), 1600 Oak Creek Dr., Edmond OK 73034, founded 1992, editor-in-chief Doug Coulson, is a quarterly "speculative literature magazine with the general aim of publishing unsurpassable imaginative fiction and poetry for an interested audience." They want **"well-crafted, vivid, literary quality poems. We are interested in poetry exhibiting elements of horror, fantasy, science fiction, dark fantasy, existentialism and those exploring the inner landscapes of the human psyche, both cumulative and individual. We want clear imagery with self-contained ideas that are inspiring in their simple eloquence and thrust. No light, 'airy' inspirational verse or run-of-the-mill love poems or poems without concrete imagery."** They have recently published poetry by Thomas Zimmerman, Lisa Lepovetsky, Keith Allen Daniels and Bruce Boston. As a sample the editor selected these lines from "Stacking the Bones" by Jacie Ragan:

> *eyes aglitter, the rag-tag man sorts the bones,*
> *tosses tibia and femurs like stalks of yarrow,*
> *as if casting our future in the dregs of darkness.*
>
> *the wandering child stacks the bones*
> *like lincoln logs, building a cabin*
> *with stars for shingles, then clambers inside.*

The Barrelhouse is 60-80 pgs., 7×8½, saddle-stapled with coated b&w cover, interior artwork and ads. They receive about 500 poems a year, use approximately 50. Press run is approximately 250 for approximately 100 subscribers. Subscription: $12.50 US/$14.75 Canada/$20.75 overseas. **Sample postpaid: $4.25. Submit a maximum of 10 poems at a time. Previously published poems and simultaneous submissions OK. Cover letter preferred.** Time between acceptance and publication is 4-12 months. **Seldom comments on rejections. Send SASE for guidelines. Reports in 2-3 months. Payment varies—"typically $2-8 plus 2 copies, $2 each for extras." Buys first North American serial or reprint rights.** "We accept materials for review and will at the least respond with short comments on a personal basis—we are very selective on what we review in the magazine." Plans poetry contest in future. Query with SASE for rules.

WILLIAM L. BAUHAN, PUBLISHER (V, IV-Regional), P.O. Box 443, Old County Rd., Dublin NH 03444, phone (603)563-8020, founded 1959, editor William L. Bauhan, publishes poetry and art, especially New England regional books. **Currently accepts no unsolicited poetry.** They have recently published books of poetry by Sarah Singer, Anne Mary, Jane Gillespie and May Sarton.

BAY AREA POETS COALITION (BAPC); POETALK (I), P.O. Box 11435, Berkeley CA 94701-2435, phone (510)814-0683, founded 1974, editor Blaine Hammond. Coalition sends monthly poetry letter, *Poetalk*, to over 400 people. They publish annual anthology (13th—140 pgs., out in February 1992), giving one page to each member of BAPC who has had work published in *Poetalk* during the prior year. *Poetalk* publishes approximately 45 poets in each issue. BAPC has 160 members, 70 subscribers, but *Poetalk* is open to all. **"Predictable rhyme only if clever vocabulary."** Membership: $15 for 12 months' *Poetalk*, copy of anthology and other privileges; extra outside US. Also offers a $50 patronage which includes a membership and anthology for another individual of your choice; a $25 beneficiary/ memorial, which includes membership plus subscription for friend; and subscriptions at $6/year. As a sample the editor selected these lines from "Six Days" by Mary Rudge:

> *Remember*
> *we whirled through flood*
> *coiled and snapped our eel strength*
> *bird bones wheeled wings wide on wind*
> *we felt the rush of shape and distance*

Each poem should be 3×4" maximum, 4 to a page. One poem from each new submitter will usually be printed. Typewritten, single-spaced OK. Simultaneous and previously published work OK. "All subject matter should be in good taste." Poems appear on 3 legal-size pages. Send 4 poems (on 1 page) and a self-addressed, stamped postcard for acknowledgment every 6 months. Response time: 2 weeks-4 months. You'll get copy of *Poetalk* in which your work appears. Write (with SASE) for a free copy. BAPC holds monthly readings, yearly contest, etc.; has mailing list open to local members; a PA system members may use for a small fee. People from many states and countries have contributed to *Poetalk* or entered their annual contests.

BAY WINDOWS (IV-Gay/lesbian), 1523 Washington St., Boston MA 02118, fax (617)266-5973, founded 1983, poetry editors Rudy Kikel and Patricia A. Roth. *Bay Windows* is a weekly gay and lesbian newspaper published for the New England community, regularly using "short poems of interest to lesbians and gay men. Poetry that is 'experiential' seems to have a good chance with us, but we don't want poetry that just 'tells it like it is.' Our readership doesn't read poetry all the time. A primary consideration is giving *pleasure*. We'll overlook the poem's (and the poet's) tendency not to be informed by the latest poetic theory, if it *does* this: pleases. Pleases, in particular, by articulating common gay or lesbian experience, and by doing that with some attention to form. I've found that a lot of our choices were made because of a strong image strand. Humor is *always* welcome—and hard to provide with craft. Obliquity, obscurity? Probably not for us. We won't presume on our audience." They have recently published poetry by Jonathan Bracker, Lesléa Newman, D.S. Lawson, Emma Morgan, Kenneth Pobo and Sheila Rosencrans. As a sample Rudy Kikel selected these lines from James Broughton's "I Look at Every Man":

> *True: he prefers the trivial to the sublime*
> *and cherishes an appetite for ugliness and war.*
> *But watching him move across the world*
> *as if he really knew where he was going*
> *on his solemn missions and foolish quests*
> *I look at every man with affectionate amazement.*

"We try to run four poems (two by lesbians, two by gay men) each month." They receive about 300 submissions/year, use 1 in 6, have a 3-month backlog. Press run is 13,000, 700 subscriptions of which 15 are libraries. Subscription: $40; per issue: 50¢. Sample postpaid: $2. Submit 3-5 poems, "5-25 lines are ideal; include short biographical blurb." Poems by men should be sent care of Rudy Kikel, *Bay Windows*, at the address above; by women, care of Patricia Roth Schwartz, Weeping Willow Farm, 1212 Birdsey Rd., Waterloo NY 13165. Reports in 1 month. Pays copies. Acquires first rights. Editors "often" comment on rejections. They review books of poetry in about 750 words—"Both single and omnibus reviews (the latter are longer)."

BEAR TRIBE PUBLISHING; WILDFIRE MAGAZINE (IV-Nature, themes, ethnic), P.O. Box 9167, Spokane WA 99209, phone (509)258-7275, founded 1965 (the magazine's former name: *Many Smokes Earth Awareness Magazine)*, poetry editor Elisabeth Robinson. The magazine uses short poetry on topics appropriate to the magazine, such as earth awareness, self-sufficiency, sacred places, native people, etc. They want a "positive and constructive viewpoint, no hip or offensive language." They have published poetry by Gary Snyder, W.D. Ehrhart, P.J. Brown and Evelyn Eaton. The quarterly devotes 1-2 pgs. to poetry each issue. Press run is 10,000 for 6,000 subscriptions of which 5% are libraries, 3,500 shelf sales. Subscription: $15. Sample postpaid: $4. Send SASE for guidelines. Reports in "6 months or more." Poets published receive 4-issue subscription. The press publishes books that incorporate Native American poems and songs, but no collections by individuals.

‡BEER & PUB POETRY (I, IV-Themes), %Green Glass Trading Co., Suite 202, 1390 Ocean Dr., Miami Beach FL 33139, phone (305)538-4026, founded 1992, editors Edwin Riley and John Williams, is an annual anthology. "The theme of the poem should relate to beers and pubs of the world. Point-of-view is totally subjective. Judges seek submissions ranging from ridiculous to sublime." Poems should be no longer than 5 double-spaced pages. As a sample the editors selected "Beeriku" by Sheso Sunana:

> Sky's frothy way seams
> the earth to heaven's party
> lift your mug with beer.

The 1992 anthology is 42 pgs., 5¾ × 8¼, professionally printed and saddle-stapled with card cover. It includes 30 poems and a brief introduction by Alan D. Eames, "internationally known beer historian" and author. Sample postpaid: $7.95. Previously published poems and simultaneous submissions OK. Each poem must be accompanied by a $5 reading fee. Submission deadline: October 31 postmark. Reports November 30. Pays 1 copy. Acquires all rights.

‡BEGGAR'S PRESS; THE LAMPLIGHT; RASKOLNIKOV'S CELLAR; BEGGAR'S REVIEW (I), 8110 N. 38th St., Omaha NE 68112, phone (402)453-4634, founded 1977, editor Richard R. Carey. *The Lamplight* is a semiannual (more frequent at times) publication of short stories, poetry, humor and unusual literary writings. "We are eclectic, but we like serious poetry, historically orientated. Positively no religious or sentimental poetry. No incomprehensible poetry." They have recently published poetry by Fredrick Zydek and John J. McKernan. As a sample the editor selected these lines (poet unidentified):

> Lord, why did you curse me with doubt!
> I'm a shot discharged in a wood without trees,
> like a scream that began as a shout.
> Never too far from famine or mire;
> hunger and cold, and all creatures turn bold —
> But, Lord, why did you give me desire!

The Lamplight is 40-60 pgs., 8½ × 11, offset printed and perfect-bound with 65 lb. cover stock. They receive about 300 poems a year, use only 10-15%. Press run is 500 for 300 subscribers of which 25 are libraries. Single copy: $9.50. Sample postpaid: $7 plus 9 × 12 SASE. No previously published poems; simultaneous submissions OK. Cover letter required — "must provide insight into the characteristics of poet. What makes this poet different from the mass of humanity?" Time between acceptance and publication is 4 months to a year. Often comments on rejections. Also offers "complete appraisals and evaluations" for $4/standard sheet, double-spaced. Brochure available for SASE. Reports in 2 to 2½ months. Pays 2 copies plus discount on up to 5. Acquires first North American serial rights. *Raskolnikov's Cellar* is an irregular magazine of the same format, dimensions and terms as *The Lamplight*. However, it deals in "deeper psychologically orientated stories and poetry. It is more selective and discriminating in what it publishes. Guidelines and brochures are an essential to consider this market." Send SASE and $1 for guidelines. Brochures require only SASE. *Beggar's Review* is 20-40 pgs., 8½ × 11, offset printed and saddle-stitched. It lists and reviews books, chapbooks and other magazines. "It also lists and reviews unpublished manuscripts: poetry, short stories, book-length, etc. Our purpose is to offer a vehicle for unpublished work of merit, as well as published material. We like to work with poets and authors who have potential but have not yet been recognized." Lengths of reviews range from a listing or mere caption to 1,000 words, "according to merit." Single copy: $6. Beggar's Press also plans to publish 4-6 paperbacks/year — some on a subsidy basis. "In most cases, we select books which we publish on a royalty basis and promote ourselves. Borderline books only are author-subsidized." Query first with a few sample poems and a cover letter with brief bio and publication credits. "We also like to know how many books the author himself will be able to market to friends, associates, etc." Replies to queries in 1 month, to mss in 2½ months. Pays 10-15% royalties and 3 author's copies. Terms vary for subsidy publishing. "Depending on projected sales, the author pays from 20% to 60%." The editor says, "Our purpose is to form a common bond with distinguished poets whose poetry is marketable and worthy. Poetry is difficult to market, thus we sometimes collaborate with the poet in publishing costs. But essentially, we look for poets with unique qualities of expression and who meet our uncustomary requirements. We prefer a royalty arrangement. Beggar's Press is different from most publishers. We are impressed with concrete poetry, which is without outlandish metaphors. Keep it simple but don't be afraid to use our language to the fullest. Read Poe, Burns and Byron. Then submit to us. There is still a place for lyrical poetry."

‡**BELHUE PRESS (III, IV-Gay)**, Suite A1, 2501 Palisade Ave., Riverdale, Bronx NY 10463, founded 1990, editor Tom Laine, is a small press **specializing in gay male poetry,** publishing 3 paperbacks/ year—no chapbooks. "**We are especially interested in anthologies, in thematic books, in books that get out of the stock poetry market.**" They want "**hard-edged, well-crafted, fun and often sexy poetry. No mushy, self pitying, confessional, boring, indulgent, teary or unrequited love poems—yuch!**" As a sample the editor selected these lines from "Thoth" in the book **Sex Charge** by Perry Brass, which was nominated for a 1991 Lambda Literary Award:

> *How I lie*
> *in your winding sheet, sleeping*
> > *past the wake*
> *of our small end,*
> *a whiter corner in your light,*
> *curled toe to toe*
> *against your parts.*

"**Poets must be willing to promote book through readings, mailers, etc.**" Query first with sample **poems and cover letter. Previously published poems and simultaneous submissions OK.** Time between acceptance and publication is 1 year. **Often comments on rejections. Will request criticism fees "if necessary." Replies to queries and submitted mss "fast." No payment information provided. Write for catalog to order samples.** The editor says, "Poetry, like stand-up comedy, has to do a lot more than just sit on the page and tell us about your hard childhood . . .We're looking for valuable poetry."

BELLFLOWER PRESS (II, IV-Humor, themes, anthology, nature/rural/ecology), Box 87 Dept. WD, Chagrin Falls OH 44022-0087, founded 1974, poetry editor/owner Louise Wazbinski, **publishes poetry books 50% of the time on a subsidized basis.** She wants "**poetry that crystallizes the attitudes held by our society.**" She is also currently looking for poetry on "**being bald—men or women.**" They have published poetry by Judy Kronenfeld. As a sample here are lines from "Lente, Lente" in her book **Shadow of Wings:**

> *Slowly my father wades into his ripe age.*
> *His great barrel chest, split and healed again,*
> *cleaves the pool . . .*
> *I remember when he took the cold air in,*
> *and threw his coat wide.*

Reports in 2-4 weeks on queries, 6-8 weeks on mss. "Contract depends upon subvention by author, usually 50%. Often the author will subsidize a small percentage and receive books as payment. In other cases, there is no subsidy and the author receives a royalty based on the specific arrangements made at the time of agreement."

BELLOWING ARK PRESS; BELLOWING ARK (II), P.O. Box 45637, Seattle WA 98145, phone (206)545-8302, founded 1984, editor Robert R. Ward. *Bellowing Ark* is a bimonthly literary tabloid that "**publishes only poetry which demonstrates in some way the proposition that existence has meaning or, to put it another way, that life is worth living. We have no strictures as to length, form or style; only that the work we publish is to our judgment life-affirming.**" They do not want "academic poetry, in any of its manifold forms." Poets published include Natalie Reciputi, Harold Witt, Katherine Lewis, Susan McCaslin, Muriel Karr and Mark Allan Johnson. As a sample the editor selected these lines from "Ancient Poets" by Paula Milligan:

> *Ancient truth must be the same, then as now.*
> *It endures, for it has no shades*
>
> *Angels in Hesoid's pastures, luminous;*
> *Sight behind Homer's dark eyes*
>
> *Light is bright in any age.*

The paper is tabloid-sized, 28 pgs., printed on electrobright stock with b&w photos and line drawings. This is a lively publication. Almost every poem is accessible, enjoyable and stimulating. All styles seem to be welcome—even long, sequence poems and formal verse. Circulation is 1,000, of which 200+ are subscriptions and 600+ are sold on newsstands. Subscription: $15/ year. Sample postpaid: **$3. The editors say, "absolutely *no* simultaneous submissions." They reply to submissions in 2-6 weeks and publish within the next 1 or 2 issues. Occasionally they**

Market categories: (I) Beginning; (II) General; (III) Limited; (IV) Specialized; (V) Closed.

will criticize a ms if it seems to "display potential to become the kind of work we want." Pay is 2 copies. Reviews books of poetry. Send books for review consideration. Bellowing Ark Press publishes collections of poetry by invitation only. Work published in *Bellowing Ark* appeared in the 1991 **Pushcart Prize** anthology.

BELL'S LETTERS POET (I), P.O. Box 2187, Gulfport MS 39505, founded 1956 as *Writer's Almanac*, 1958 as *Thunderhead for Writers*, 1966 as *Bell's Letters* (a play on words), publisher and editor Jim Bell, is a quarterly **which you must buy ($4/issue, $16 subscription) to be included.** The editor says "many say they stay up with it all night the day it arrives," and judging by the many letters from readers, that seems to be the case. Though there is no payment for poetry accepted, many patrons send awards of $5-20 to the poets whose work they especially like. Subscription "guarantees them a byline each issue." Poems are "4 to 20 lines in good taste." They have recently published poetry by Bonnie Keaton, Helen Courcier, Rudy Zenker and David Collins. As a sample of the spirit of *BL* poetry the editor chose these lines by Linda Noyola:

> You've given me more,
> than I deserve to receive
> with blessings galore
> and sweet peace I've achieved
> simply because . . . I believe.

It is digest-sized, 76 pgs., offset from typescript on plain bond paper (including cover). **Sample with guidelines: $3.** Ms may be typed or even hand-written. No simultaneous submissions. Previously published poems OK "if cleared with prior publisher." Accepted poems by subscribers go immediately into the next issue. "Our publication dates fall quarterly on the spring and autumn equinox and winter and summer solstice. Deadline for poetry submissions is 3 months prior to publication." Reviews books of poetry by subscribers in "one abbreviated paragraph." "The Ratings" is a competition in each issue. Readers are asked to vote on their favorite poems, and the ratings are announced in the next issue, along with awards sent to the poets by patrons.

THE BELOIT POETRY JOURNAL (II), Box 154, RFD 2, Ellsworth ME 04605, phone (207)667-5598, founded 1950, editor Marion K. Stocking, is a well-known, long-standing quarterly of quality poetry and reviews. **"We publish the best poems we receive, without bias as to length, school, subject or form.** It is our hope to discover the growing tip of poetry and to introduce new poets alongside established writers. We publish occasional chapbooks on special themes to diversify our offerings." They want **"fresh, imaginative poetry, with a distinctive voice. We tend to prefer poems that make the reader share an experience rather than just read about it,** and these we keep for up to 3 months, circulating them among our readers, and continuing to winnow out the best. At the quarterly meetings of the Editorial Board we read aloud all the surviving poems and put together an issue of the best we have." They have recently published poetry by Sherman Alexie, Hillel Schwartz, Lola Haskins, Albert Goldbarth and Ursula K. Le Guin. As a sample the editor selected these lines from "Leaving Home" by William Carpenter:

> One evening a teller of tales came to my house.
> He was a blind man and his friend was mute, but they
> knew their fiction and the talking one talked all night.
> He said, "you can't go on this way forever," and he took
> a wing from a roll of wings he had in his pocket and
>   gave me one.
> One. I spent the night flapping around my room.

The journal is 48 pgs., digest-sized, saddle-stapled, and attractively printed with tasteful art on the card covers. All styles of verse—providing they articulate ideas or emotions intelligently and concisely—are featured. The editor is also keen on providing as much space as possible for poems and so does not include contributors' notes. They have a circulation of 1,400 for 575 subscriptions of which 325 are libraries. **Sample copy: $4, including guidelines. SASE for guidelines alone. Submit any time, without query, any legible form.** *"No simultaneous submissions.* Any length of ms, but most poets send what will go in a business envelope for one stamp. Don't send your life's work." No backlog: "We clear the desk at each issue." Pays 3 copies. Acquires first serial rights. Staff reviews books of poetry in an average of 500 words, usually single format. Send books for review consideration. From time to time, poems published in *The Beloit Poetry Journal* have been included in the **Pushcart Prize** anthologies.

BENEATH THE SURFACE (II), % The Dept. of English, Chester New Hall, McMaster University, Hamilton, Ontario L8S 4S8 Canada, founded 1911, editor changes yearly, is a biannual using **"top quality poetry/prose that achieves universality through individual expression."** They want **"quality poetry; any form; no restrictions."** They have published poetry by Dorothy Livesky and John Barlow. As a sample the editor selected these lines from "War Monument" by tristanne j. connolly:

> *a soldier's soul*
> *ascending, but concrete*
> *is heavy to lift*
> *war monument, the cross on top*
> *forgotten til the very last minute*

It is 30-50 pgs., professionally printed, saddle-stapled, with cover art, drawings and b&w photographs. They receive about 250 submissions/year, use approximately 10%. Press run is 150 for 8 subscribers of which 3 are libraries, 92 shelf sales. Subscription: $8/year. **Sample postpaid: $4. No previously published poems or simultaneous submissions. Submit 4-6 poems with cover letter, including short bio and summary of previous publications, if any. Reads submissions September through April only. Often comments on rejections. Reports in 4-6 weeks. Pays nothing—not even copies. Acquires first North American serial rights.** Rarely reviews books of poetry, "though we do include literary essays when submitted." The editor says, "Do not get discouraged. Getting work in respectable literary journals takes much love and even more hard work. Be patient and allow your work to evolve and mature."

BENNETT & KITCHEL (IV-Form), P.O. Box 4422, East Lansing MI 48826, phone (517)355-1707, founded 1989, editor William Whallon, publishes 1-3 hardbacks/year of **"poetry of form and meaning. No free verse, blank verse, off rhyme, sestinas or haiku. Shakespearean sonnets should be as good as those of the Immortal Bard, but lyrics cannot be expected to come close."** As an example of what he likes the editor chose these lines about Gettysburg by L. R. Lind:

> *... there in a cannon's mouth*
> *A bird had built her frail, capricious nest*
> *And filled it with young to fly both north and south.*

Bennett & Kitchel has published **Part Comanche**, 52 poems of rhythm and rhyme, by Troxey Kemper, poet, writer and editor of *Tucumcari Literary Review* (see listing in this section). **Sample postpaid: $6. Simultaneous submissions and previously published poems OK if copyright is clear. Minimum volume for a book "might be 750 lines." If a book is accepted, publication within 9 months. Editor comments on submissions "seldom." Reports in 2 weeks. Terms "variable, negotiable."** He suggests, "Heed the advice of Goethe to Hugo: Work more, write less."

BERKELEY POETRY REVIEW (II), 700 Eshleman Hall, University of California, Berkeley CA 94720, founded 1973, is an annual review "which publishes poems and translations of local as well as national and international interest. **We are open to any form or length which knows how to express itself through that form."** They have published poetry by Ann Kong, Thom Gunn, August Kleinzahler, Robert Hass, Carol Tarlen and Brenda Hillman. As a sample the editors selected these lines from "Second Person Singular" by Dominic Mah:

> *When you are a sleep. You are lying in the backseat,*
> *pretend-sleeping. You are next to the driver, drifting upstairs,*
> *not watching the driver, trying. You watch red lights and*
> *streetlamps and feel a part of privacy. You are learning what*
> *the city looks like at night.*

The editors describe it as a flat-spined paperback, averaging 150 pgs., circulation 500. Subscription: $10/year. **Simultaneous submissions and previously published poems (if not copyrighted) OK. Reads submissions September through June only. Include SASE; allow 2-6 months for reply. Pays 1 copy.**

BERKELEY POETS COOPERATIVE (WORKSHOP & PRESS) (V), Box 459, Berkeley CA 94701, founded 1969, poetry editor Charles Entrekin (plus rotating staff), is "a nonprofit organization which offers writers the opportunity to explore, develop and publish their works. Our primary goals are to maintain a free workshop open to writers and to publish outstanding collections of poetry and fiction by individual writers." The *New York Times* has called it **"the oldest and most successful poetry co-operative in the country."** Chapbooks have been published by Linda Watanabe McFerrin and Chitra Divakaruni. Charles Entrekin says he prefers **"modern imagist—open to all kinds, but we publish very little rhyme."** However, he is currently not accepting unsolicited submissions. They publish two 64-page chapbooks by individuals each year, for which the **poets receive 50% of the profit and 20 copies. You can order a sample book for $3. Criticism sometimes provided on rejected mss.** Poets elsewhere might consider BPWP as a model for forming similar organizations.

‡BIG HEAD PRESS; BIG HEAD PRESS BROADSIDE SERIES (III), P.O. Box 15157, Long Beach CA 90815, founded 1991, editor Scott C. Holstad, associate editor Lisa Lundgren. Big Head Press publishes 1 chapbook/year. The broadside series is bimonthly. **"Social commentary preferred. 40 lines max. No love poetry."** They have recently published poetry by Antler, Arthur Winfield Knight, Lyn

Lifshin, Belinda Subraman and Sal Salasin. As a sample the editor selected these lines from "vegan" by Michael Hathaway:

> when a pig is mauled and crippled
> by rough, impatient men
> in the slaughterhouse
> and dragged off squealing to its death
> it's the same to me
> as if it was my brother

Broadsides are printed on 4½ × 8 cardstock, with author's photo and bio. Of hundreds of submissions, they say they accept 10-15 poems/year. Press run is 250-500, most distributed free. **Sample broadside: $1. Submit 4-10 poems with b&w photo. Previously published poems and simultaneous submissions OK, if noted. Cover letter with brief bio and phone number required.** Time between acceptance and publication is 6-15 months. **Often comments on rejections. Send SASE for guidelines. Reports in 2 weeks to 3 months. Pays 10-15 copies. Acquires one-time rights. "Due to financial constraints, we currently require full subsidation for chapbooks."** Authors then receive 50% of press run. Sample chapbook: $3.

THE BIG NOW; BIG NOW PUBLICATIONS (I, II), 3928 Shenandoah, St. Louis MO 63110, founded 1990, submissions editor Theresa M. Mozelewski, is a semiannual which publishes "good poetry and art, specifically work which displays the artist's consciousness of his/her place in the tradition to which he/she belongs. **We would like to see work by authors who are conscious of form and tradition, though not necessarily formal or traditional. We do not publish poems with predictable, uninspired themes and/or structure."** They have published poetry by Jason Sommer. As a sample the editor selected these lines from "The Dark Family of My First Ever Girlfriend" by Ben Vance:

> You made me dial the phone, a Dallas number, your boyfriend.
> You told him about your grandparents' hiss-whispered shouting
> match over a receipt for a dozen roses your grandmother never received.
> He hung up on you when he realized you were drunk and
> that I was a boy.

It is 30-40 pgs., digest-sized, saddle-stapled, b&w, with possible spot color in the future. They accept approximately 30% of poetry received. Press run is 1,000-1,500. "All are distributed free to various points in St. Louis." **Sample: $1 for postage. Previously published poems and simultaneous submissions OK. "However, please let us know if works are under consideration elsewhere and, if published, where and when."** Time between acceptance and publication is 4-6 months. **Seldom comments on rejections. May charge criticism fees. Reports within 2 weeks. Pays 2 copies. Acquires first or reprint rights.** The editor advises poets to "read; experience; live."

‡BIG RAIN (II), P.O. Box 20764, Sedona AZ 86341, phone (602)284-1763, founded 1990, editor Clint Frakes, is an annual featuring "new voices; new savage tongues." As for poetry, the editor says, **"Make it new." They do not want "topical opportunism."** They have recently published poetry by Anne Waldman, Jack Collom, Jorge Luis Borges and Allen Ginsberg. As a sample the editor selected the opening lines of "Chaos Was an Egg" by Elisabeth Belile:

> Chaos was an egg. A calabash gourd. A river running through all the
> states. Chaos has its strange attractors.

Big Rain is 60 pgs., oversize 11 × 17, professionally printed and saddle-stapled with photography, few ads. They receive 300 poems a year, use 10%. Press run is 2,000 for 100 subscribers, 250 shelf sales. Single copy: $5; subscription: $20. **Sample postpaid: $6. No previously published poems; simultaneous submissions OK. Seldom comments on rejections. Reports in 3 months. Pays 2 copies.** Awards $50 to one poet each issue.

BILINGUAL REVIEW PRESS; BILINGUAL REVIEW/REVISTA BILINGÜE (IV-Ethnic/Hispanic, bilingual/Spanish), Hispanic Research Center, Arizona State University, Tempe AZ 85287, phone (602)965-3867, journal founded 1974, press in 1976. Managing editor Karen Van Hooft says they are "a small press publisher of U.S. Hispanic creative literature and of a journal containing poetry and short fiction in addition to scholarship." The journal contains some poetry in each issue; they also publish flat-spined paperback collections of poetry. **"We publish poetry by and/or about U.S. Hispanics and U.S. Hispanic themes. We do not publish translations in our journal or literature about the experiences of Anglo Americans in Latin America. We have published a couple of poetry volumes in bilingual format (Spanish/English) of important Mexican poets."** They have published poetry by Alberto Ríos, Demetria Martínez, Pablo Medina, Carolina Hospital and Ricardo Pau-Llosa. The editor says the journal, which appears 3 times a year, is 7 × 10, 96 pgs., flat-spined, offset, with 2-color cover. They use less than 10% of hundreds of submissions received each year. Press run is 1,000 for 850+ subscriptions. Subscriptions are $16 for individuals, $28 for institutions. **Sample postpaid: $6**

individuals/$10 institutions. Submit "2 copies, including ribbon original if possible, with loose stamps for return postage." Cover letter required. Pays 2 copies. Acquires all rights. Reviews books of US Hispanic poetry only. Send books, Attn: Editor, for review consideration. **For book submissions, inquire first with 4-5 sample poems, bio, publications. Pays $100 advance, 10% royalties and 10 copies.** Over the years, books by this press have won four American Book Awards and one Western States Book Award.

BIRD WATCHER'S DIGEST (IV-Nature), P.O. Box 110, Marietta OH 45750, founded 1978, editor Mary Beacom Bowers, is a specialized but promising market for **poems of "true literary merit" in which birds figure in some way, at least by allusion.** 2-3 poems are used in each bimonthly issue. Some poets who have appeared here include Susan Rea, Nancy G. Westerfield, Suzanne Freemans and William D. Barney. "Preferred: no more than 20 lines, 40 spaces, no more than 3 poems at a time, no queries." Sample postpaid: $3.50. Reports in 2 months. Pays $10/poem. They have up to a year's backlog and use 12-20 of the approximately 500 poems received each year.

BIRMINGHAM POETRY REVIEW (II, IV-Translations), English Department, University of Alabama at Birmingham, Birmingham AL 35294, phone (205)934-8573, founded 1988, coeditors Robert Collins and Randy Blythe. The review appears twice a year using poetry of **"any style, form, length or subject. We are biased toward exploring the cutting edge of contemporary poetry. Style is secondary to the energy, the *fire* the poem possesses. We don't want poetry with cliché-bound, worn-out language."** They have recently published poetry by Hague, Harrod, Rigsbee, Carpenter, Jaeger, Richards, Schlossman and Miltner. As a sample the editors selected these lines from "A Sickly Child" by Chris Forhan:

> *Often I drowsed,*
> *the dull sound of weeping or whispering*
> *in the hall, or one of my brothers*
> *calling my name from the darkening street.*

They describe their magazine as 50 pgs., 6×9, offset, with b&w cover. Their press run is 600 for Fall Issue, 500 for Spring Issue, 275 subscriptions. Subscription: $3. Sample postpaid: $2. Submit 3-5 poems, "no more. No cover letters. We are impressed by good writing; we are unimpressed by publication credits. It should go without saying, but we receive more and more manuscripts with insufficient return postage. If it costs you fifty-two cents to mail your manuscript, it will cost us that much to return it if it is rejected. Manuscripts with insufficient return postage will be discarded." No simultaneous submissions, and previously published poems only if they are translations. Editor sometimes comments on rejections. Send SASE for guidelines. Reports in 1-4 months. Pays 2 copies and one-year subscription. He says, "Advice to beginners: Read as much good contemporary poetry, national and international, as you can get your hands on. Then be persistent in finding your own voice."

BISHOP PUBLISHING CO. (IV-Themes), 2131 Trimble Way, Sacramento CA 95825, professor Roland Dickison, is a "small press publisher of **folklore in paperbacks, including contemporary** and out-of-print."

BITS PRESS (III, IV-Humor), English Dept., Case Western Reserve University, Cleveland OH 44106, phone (216)795-2810, founded 1974, poetry editor Robert Wallace. **"Bits Press is devoted to poetry. We publish chapbooks (and sometimes limited editions) by young as well as well-known poets. Our main attention at present is given to light verse and funny poems."** The chapbooks are distinguished by elegant but inexpensive format. They have published chapbooks by David R. Slavitt, John Updike and Gerald Costanzo. These sample lines are from Richard Wilbur's **Some Atrocities:**

> *If a sheepdog ate a cantaloupe,*
> *Would it make him frisk like an antelope?*
> *Would he feel all pleased and jolly?*
> *Or would he be a Melon Collie?*

The few chapbooks they publish are mostly solicited. Send $2 for a sample chapbook. Pays poet in copies (10%+ of run). Acquires one-time rights.

BLACK BEAR PUBLICATIONS; BLACK BEAR REVIEW; POETS ELEVEN . . . AUDIBLE (II, IV-Political, social issues), 1916 Lincoln St., Croydon PA 19021-8026, founded 1984, poetry and art editor Ave Jeanne, review and audio editor Ron Zettlemoyer. *Black Bear Review* is a semiannual international literary and fine arts magazine that also publishes chapbooks and holds an annual poetry competition. **"We like well crafted poetry that mirrors real life—void of camouflage, energetic poetry, avant-garde, free verse and haiku which relate to the world today. We seldom publish the beginner, but will assist when time allows. No traditional poetry is used. The underlying theme of *BBR* is social and political, but the review is interested also in environmental, war/peace, ecological and minorities themes."** Recent poets published in *BBR* include Sherman Alexie, Jose Garcia, Alan Akmakjian, Joe Salerno,

CLOSE-UP

Write About the Things You Fear

Toi Derricotte

That brick bungalow
rose out of a storm
of racism like an ark.
We found a way—the post office workers,
the teachers, principals—we found
a nest, a mile of wilderness,
and farmed the bones of our children
out of it. Suburban, up
from the South, our boys
not shot, our girls not pregnant
with belly after belly
of welfare children.
No matter how I hated and feared
the rages, the silences,
we did grow
iron bones.

So reads the first stanza of "The House on Norwood," by Toi Derricotte, from her latest collection of poetry, **Captivity** (University of Pittsburgh Press). And so did Ms. Derricotte develop the iron bones of a poet, a poet who often writes of the rages and silences she has so hated and feared over the years, emotions so closely connected to her experiences of family, race and religion.

"My grandparents owned a funeral home and when I was four or five I would go downstairs and visit the dead bodies," Derricotte says. "I would kneel and say prayers for them. I was in Catholic school from this time on, so I had all kinds of notions and fears about what death meant. Everyone was so proud of me because I was so brave, but actually I was afraid. Sometimes people mask their fears by doing the very thing they're most afraid to do. It was sort of a modus operandi for me in terms of writing; I still write about the things I'm most afraid of."

One of the things she was most frightened of at the age of 12—when she began writing poetry—was her background. While Derricotte is African American, she looks white, and her mother (Creole, from Louisiana) and her father (from Kentucky) are the same light color. She is unsure which country the whiteness comes from. "It didn't get talked about because there was some shame associated with our history," the shame of an African American woman (her grandmother) having been impregnated by a white man. "Society always blames the victims and Black women were blamed for this." Over the years Derricotte has come to understand the link between this specific situation and the overall experience of African Americans.

"My feeling is that our ancestors were exactly right in trying to protect us through silence. The writer of color is often in a double bind. On one hand there is the importance of saving our history and validating it by bringing it out. But there's also the sense of possibly betraying ourselves, our family, our whole race, of corroborating gross stereotypes. I think this is a burden on the writer of color."

Yet what is her burden is also her blessing, for it is this paradox that is at the core of what compels her to write. She was initially drawn to the form of poetry not as a result of reading, "the canon" as she calls it, in school but rather through the poetry of religious ritual and music and her mother's stories. "I feel a great love for the literature I was given in school, but I also feel a great rage," she says. "I mean I didn't read a writer of color all through graduate school."

She quotes James Baldwin as saying, " 'I don't write about race because it's the only thing to write about. I write about it because it's the door I have to go through in order to write about anything else.' " This is why, she says, her poems are about "coming to terms with 'the other,' that part of the self that is the evil, rejected, guilty, isolated part. All of the work I'm doing—the political and spiritual work—is really about loving and accepting the various parts of the self. Matisse said the job of artists is to turn themselves inside out before they die. That's what I'm about—going deeper and deeper and deeper."

A process that hasn't always been easy. While she is now the author of three collections of poetry; has seen her poems appear in countless magazines; has received two fellowships from the National Endowment for the Arts; and has taught in the graduate creative writing programs at University of Pittsburgh, New York University and George Mason University, she remembers well the more difficult times. Her first submission in 1970 ended in rejection. "I thought that meant I was no good. I felt that all editors were smart people—it was like I was submitting my work to God. When I got that rejection I figured it meant I should never write again."

Even now, as she works on an autobiographical work—**The Black Notebooks**—and a book of poetry, she finds herself feeling some of the same pains and uncertainties she had when starting out. "It keeps happening that I think I can't be a poet and then that I can. As recently as my last book, I was thinking I needed to change professions. Writing is a compulsive act for me and sometimes I feel it's really selfish, that I should be doing something better with my time. And then there have been long periods when I think I'm not really that good and it's just not worth it. Then something will happen and I'll say, 'Gee, this is good; I'm glad I'm doing what I'm doing' and then I'm fine."

The keys, she says, are for poets to write or at least "sit down and listen" every day, never throw away first drafts ("that's where the juice is"), do the necessary research to uncover viable markets, constantly submit, enter contests, and strive to become resistant to rejection. "The best poems can get rejected many times; that wonderful poem by William Stafford, 'Traveling Through the Dark'—it was rejected several times before it was published, and now it's considered one of the great poems of American literature."

Derricotte stresses the importance of sending in neat manuscripts with short, business-like cover letters, packages that show careful thought has gone into them. She advises to always resubmit when you get a hand-written note—"that means that they really like your work"—and to cultivate relationships with editors and other writers, "people who will validate what you're doing and deepen your connection to your work." She speaks passionately of the supportive relationships she formed after leaving home in the early 1970s and while attending graduate school at New York University. She also meets monthly with five dear African American women writer friends who are professors in the Washington DC area. "I think that without these connections my poetry might have died."

—Lauri Miller

Andrew Gettler and Walt Phillips. *Poets Eleven . . . Audible* has released poetry on tape by A.D. Winans, Tony Moffeit, Kevin Zepper and Mike Maggio. As a sample from *BBR*, the editor selected these lines from "Photograph" by Leslie L. Fields:

> *I serve the photograph for dinner,*
> *and because there are eight of us,*
> *serve another, of stilt-legged children*
> *pressed against a truck,*
> *arms raised like branches.*
> *We eat slowly, heads down,*
> *knives and forks scraping the plates,*
> *a few drinking water.*

The magazine is perfect-bound, digest-sized, 64 pgs., offset from typed copy on white stock, with line drawings, collages and woodcuts. Circulation of *BBR* is 500, of which 300 are subscriptions; 15 libraries. Price: $5/issue; subscription: $10, $15 overseas. A sample of *BBR*: $5 postpaid; back copies when available are $4 postpaid. Any number of poems may be submitted, one to a page. "Please have name and address on each page of your submissions." Simultaneous submissions are not considered. "Submissions without SASE will be trashed." Guidelines available for SASE. Submissions are reported on in 2 weeks, publication is in 6-12 months. Acquires first North American serial rights. Considers reviews of books of poetry and recent issues of literary magazines, maximum 250 words. Send books for review consideration. The editors explain that *Poets Eleven . . . Audible* was started for accommodation of longer poems for the reader to take part in poetry as a listener; the author may submit up to 10 minutes of original poetry. SASE for return of your tape; sample copies available for $4.50 postpaid. Contributor receives 25% royalties. They also publish two chapbooks/year. Most recently published **A Destiny Going Sour** by Steve Levi. Chapbook series requires a reading fee of $5, complete ms and cover letter. For book publication, they would prefer that "*BBR* has published the poet and is familiar with his/her work, but we will read anyone who thinks they have something to say." Author receives one-half print run. They say, "We appreciate a friendly, brief cover letter. Tell us about the poet; omit degrees or any other pretentious dribble. All submissions are handled with objectivity and quite often rejected material is directed to another market. If you've not been published before—mention it. We are always interested in aiding those who support small press. We frequently suggest poets keep up with **Poet's Market** and read the listings and reviews in issues of *Black Bear*. Most recent issues of *BBR* include reviews on small press markets—current releases of chapbooks and the latest literary magazines. We make an effort to keep our readers informed and on top of the small press scene. Camera-ready ads are printed free of charge as a support to small press publishers. We do suggest reading issues before submitting to absorb the flavor and save on wasted postage. Send your best! Our yearly poetry competition offers cash awards to poets." Annual deadline is November 1. Guidelines are available for a SASE. "Professional black-and-white artwork is used regularly in each issue. Submissions are welcomed."

BLACK BOOKS BULLETIN; BBB: WORDSWORK; THIRD WORLD PRESS (IV-Ethnic), 7822 S. Dobson, P.O. Box 19730, Chicago IL 60619, phone (312)651-0700, fax (312)651-7286. *BBB* is an annual about "Black literature and current issues facing the African-American community using Afrocentric poetry, style open." They have published poetry by Gil Scott Heron, Brian Gilmore, Sonia Sanchez and Keora Petse Kgositsile. Focus is on book reviews. **bbb: wordswork** is a bimonthly journal also focusing on issues facing the African-American community and including Afrocentric poetry. Write, fax or call for further information.

BLACK BOUGH; POETRY & HUMANITIES BOOKSELLER (II, IV-Form), P.O. Box 465, Somerville NJ 08876, founded 1991, editors Kevin Walker and Charles Easter, is a biannual that publishes "haiku and related forms which demonstrate the distinctiveness of haiku as well as its connection to western traditions in poetry." They want "haiku, senryu, tanka, haibun and sequences. No renga, articles, academic essays or long poems." They have published work by Jean Jorgensen, Francine Porad and Penny Harter. As a sample the editor selected this haiku by Jim Kacian:

> *children*
> *running naked*
> *Easter morning*

The editor says *bb* is 30 pgs., digest-sized, professionally printed, saddle-stitched, with cover art, no ads. They receive about 5,200 poems a year, use 5-10%. Press run is 200 for 100 subscribers. Subscription: $7.50. Sample postpaid: $4. No previously published poems or simultaneous submissions. "Submit no more than 20 haiku; prefer several haiku/page." Time between acceptance and publication is 3-6 months. Comments on rejections "if requested." Reports in 3-4 weeks. Pays $1/verse, up to $4 for a long poem or haiku sequence. Acquires first rights. Under Poetry & Humanities (P&H) Bookseller, the editors are also mail-order sellers of poetry on tape. "We distribute Caedmon recordings of famous poets reading their works." Write for free catalog.

BLACK BUZZARD PRESS; BLACK BUZZARD REVIEW; VISIONS—INTERNATIONAL, THE WORLD JOURNAL OF ILLUSTRATED POETRY; THE BLACK BUZZARD ILLUSTRATED POETRY CHAPBOOK SERIES (II), 1110 Seaton Lane, Falls Church VA 22046, founded 1979, poetry editor Bradley R. Strahan, associate editor Shirley G. Sullivan. "We are an independent nonsubsidized press dedicated to publishing fine accessible poetry and translation (particularly from lesser-known languages such as Armenian, Gaelic, Urdu, Vietnamese, etc.) accompanied by original illustrations of high quality in an attractive format. **We want to see work that is carefully crafted and exciting work that transfigures everyday experience or gives us a taste of something totally new; all styles except concrete and typographical 'poems.' Nothing purely sentimental. No self-indulgent breast beating. No sadism, sexism or bigotry. No unemotional pap. No copies of Robert Service or the like. Usually under 100 lines but will consider longer.**" They have published poetry by Ted Hughes, Marilyn Hacker, James Dickey, Allen Ginsberg and Marge Piercy; and Bradley Strahan says that "no 4 lines can possibly do even minimal justice to our taste or interest!" *Visions*, a digest-sized, saddle-stapled magazine finely printed on high-quality paper, appears 3 times a year, uses 56 pages of poetry in each issue. Circulation 750 with 300 subscriptions of which 50 are libraries. **Sample postpaid: $3.50. Current issue: $4.50.** They receive *well* over a thousand submissions each year, use 140, have a 3- to 18-month backlog. "*Visions* is international in both scope and content, publishing poets from all over the world and having readers in 48+ U.S. states, Canada and 24 other foreign countries." *Black Buzzard Review* is a "more or less annual informal journal, dedicated mostly to North American poets and entirely to original English-language poems. We are *letting it all hang out* here, unlike the approach of our prestigious international journal *Visions*, and taking a more wide-open stance on what we accept (including the slightly outrageous)." **Sample postpaid: $3.50. Current issue: $4.50.** It is 36 pgs., magazine-sized, side-stapled, with matte card cover. **"Poems must be readable (not faded or smudged) and *not* handwritten. We resent having to pay postage due, so use adequate postage! No more than 8 pages, please." Reports in 3 days-3 weeks. Pays copies or $5-10 "if we get a grant."** Buys first North American serial rights. Staff reviews books of poetry in "up to 2 paragraphs." Send books for review consideration. To submit for the chapbook series, send samples (5-10 poems) and a *brief* cover letter **"pertinent to artistic accomplishments." Reports in 3 days-3 weeks. Pays in copies. Usually provides criticism.** Send $4 for sample chapbook. Bradley Strahan adds that in *Visions* "We sometimes publish helpful advice about 'getting published' and the art and craft of poetry, and often discuss poets and the world of poetry on our editorial page."

BLACK FLY REVIEW (II), University of Maine, Fort Kent ME 04743, phone (207)834-3162, ext. 118, founded 1980, editors Roland Burns and Wendy Kindred. **"We want poetry with strong, sensory images that evoke a sense of experience, place, person; poetry that generates ideas; no overtly philosophical poetry or bad poetry."** They have published poetry by Walter McDonald, Terry Plunkett, Michael Cadnum and Connie Voisine. The annual is 56 pgs., digest-sized, using woodcuts and prints by Wendy Kindred, professionally printed in small type on tinted, heavy stock with matte card cover with art. They accept 40-50 of 500-600 submissions/year. Press run is 700-1,000 for 50 subscriptions of which 30 are libraries, and 500 shelf sales. **Sample postpaid: $3. No simultaneous submissions or previously published poems. Send SASE for guidelines. Reports in 6 months. Pays 5 copies. Acquires first North American rights.** Roland Burns advises, "The publishing situation for poets is good and getting better. There are more good poets writing in America than at any other time. The essence of poetry is the image that provides sensory focus and that generates a sense of experience, place, persons, emotions, ideas."

BLACK MOUNTAIN REVIEW; LORIEN HOUSE (IV-Themes), P.O. Box 1112, Black Mountain NC 28711-1112, phone (704)669-6211, founded 1969, editor David A. Wilson, is a small press publishing many books under the Lorien House imprint (poetry on a subsidy basis) and the annual *Black Mountain Review*. They want **poetry with "quality form/construction—a full thought, specifically fitting the theme, 16-80 lines. No blatant sex, violence, horror."** As a sample, the editor selected these lines from "Border Crossing" by Judson Jerome in *BMR #7* "On Thomas Wolfe":

> *Many return world-wiser, holy,*
> *tender to busy travelers of here.*
> *Their eyes are objective as glass.*
> *The present cannot betray them.*
> *Their knowledge cannot be uttered or believed.*

BMR is 44 pgs., digest-sized, saddle-stapled, with matte card cover, photocopied from typescript. Press run "about 300" of which they sell about 200. They accept 1-5 poems of about 200 received/year. **Sample postpaid: $6. Previously published poems OK. Send SASE for guidelines. Reports in a few days. Pays 2 copies plus $5 for poems. Buys first or reprint rights.** Staff reviews books of poetry when an issue has room—usually 1-3 books. Send books for review consideration.

Query regarding subsidized book publication. Editor comments on submissions "occasionally," and he offers "full analysis and marketing help" for $1/typed page of poetry. He says, "*Please* send for the current theme. Do *not* send general poetry. Since the current themes are American writers, the poetry must be *on* the writer for the issue. This makes the project more demanding, but some research and original new work will give you a good chance for publication."

BLACK RIVER REVIEW; STONE ROLLER PRESS (II, IV-Translations), Dept. PM, 855 Mildred Ave., Lorain OH 44052-1213, phone (216)244-9654, founded 1985, poetry editor Michael Waldecki, editorial contact Kaye Coller, is a literary annual using **"contemporary poetry, any style, form and subject matter, 50 line maximum (usually), poetry with innovation, craftsmanship and a sense of excitement and/or depth of emotion. Do *not* want Helen Steiner Rice, greeting card verse, poetry that mistakes stilted, false or formulaic diction for intense expression of feeling."** They have published poetry by James Margorian, Adrian Louis, Christopher Franke, Catherine Hammond, Sylvia Foley and Leslie Leyland Fields. As a sample the editor selected these lines from "Drought" by Stephen R. Roberts:

> *The reptilian trunk of a pine crawls up*
> *to needles as loose as an old man's teeth.*
> *There is a fear of frictions.*
> *Poison ivy slumbers in green smiles,*
> *and the crow's harsh voice*
> *could spark the woodpile.*
> *Everything is burned and older.*
> *Children are telling children,*
> *four more weeks and we all die.*

The magazine-sized annual is photocopied from typescript on quality stock, saddle-stapled with matte card cover with art, about 60 pgs., using ads, circulation 400 (sold in college bookstore). **Sample postpaid: $3 (backcopy); $3.50 (current issue); $6 (two copies of any issue). No simultaneous submissions. Will consider previously published poems if acknowledged. Submit between January and May 1, limit of 10. Editor may comment on submissions. Send SASE for guidelines. Pays 1 copy.** Reviews books of poetry. Kaye Coller comments, "We want strong poems that show a depth of vision beyond the commonplace. We don't care if a poet is well-known or not, but we don't publish amateurs. An amateur is not necessarily a new poet, but one who doesn't believe in revision, tends to be preachy, writes sentimental slush, tells the reader what to think and/or concludes the poem with an explanation in case the reader didn't get the point. If we think we can use one or more of a poet's poems, we keep them until the final choices are made in June; otherwise, we send them back as soon as possible. Follow the ms mechanics in **Poet's Market**. **We are also looking for poems written in Spanish. If selected, they will be published with English translation by either the poet or one of our staff."**

THE BLACK SCHOLAR; THE BLACK SCHOLAR PRESS (IV-Ethnic), P.O. Box 2869, Oakland CA 94609, founded 1969, publisher Robert Chrisman, uses poetry **"relating to/from/of the black American and other 'Third World' experience."** The quarterly magazine is basically scholarly and research-oriented. They have published poetry by Ntozake Shange, Jayne Cortez, Andrew Salkey and D.L. Smith. The editor says it is 64 pgs., 7×10, with 10,000 subscribers of which 60% are libraries, 15% shelf sales. "We only publish one issue every year containing poetry." Single copy $5; subscription $30. **Sample back issue: $6 prepaid. Enclose "letter & bio or curriculum vita, SASE, phone number, no originals." Send SASE for guidelines. Pays 10 copies and subscription.** Reviews books of poetry. They also publish 1-2 books a year, average 100 pgs., flat-spined. **Send query letter. For sample books, send 8½×11 SASE for catalog, average cost $10.95 including postage and handling.** "Please be advised—it is against our policy to discuss submissions via telephone. Also, we get a lot of mss, but read *every single one,* thus patience is appreciated."

BLACK SPARROW PRESS (III), 24 Tenth St., Santa Rosa CA 95401, phone (707)579-4011, founded 1966, assistant to the publisher Michele Filshie, publishes poetry, fiction, literary criticism and bibliography in flat-spined paperbacks, hardcovers and deluxe/limited editions (hardback). "We do not publish chapbooks. Our books are 150 pgs. or longer." They have published poetry by Charles Bukowski, Tom Clark, Wanda Coleman, Robert Kelly, Diane Wakoski, John Weiners and Edward Dorn. **Include name and address inside package with ms. Reports in 2 months. Pays 10% minimum royalties plus author's copies.**

BLACK TIE PRESS (III), P.O. Box 440004, Houston TX 77244-0004, phone (713)789-5119, founded 1986, publisher and editor Peter Gravis. "Black Tie Press is committed to publishing innovative, distinctive and engaging writing. We publish books; we are not a magazine or literary journal. We are not like the major Eastern presses, university presses or other small presses in poetic disposition. To get a feel for our publishing attitude, we urge you to buy one or more of our publications before submitting." He is **"only interested in imaginative, provocative, at risk writing. *No rhyme.*"** Published poets include Steve Wilson, Guy Beining, Sekou Karanja, Craig Cotter, Donald Rawley, Dieter Weslowski, Laura Ryder, Toni Ortner and Jenny Kelly. As a sample the editor selected these lines from "Equilibrium," from **Without Feathers**, by Harry Burrus:

> *I sleep suspended on a web of silk*
> *A Zulu warrior crouches*
> *in the tall grass. The tower flashes*
> *its beacon across the landscape*
> *and your spear glistens*
> *in the cold dawn.*

Sample postpaid: $8. "We have work we want to publish, hence, unsolicited material is not encouraged. However, we will read and consider material from committed, serious writers as time permits. Write, do not call about material. *No reply without SASE.*" Cover letter with bio preferred. Reports in 2-6 weeks. Author receives percent of press run. Peter Gravis says, "Too many writers are only interested in getting published and not interested in reading or supporting good writing. Black Tie hesitates to endorse a writer who does not, in turn, promote and patronize (by actual purchases) small press publications. Once Black Tie publishes a writer, we intend to remain with that artist."

THE BLACK WARRIOR REVIEW (II), P.O. Box 2936, Tuscaloosa AL 35486-2936, phone (205)348-4518, founded 1974. They have recently published poetry by David Ignatow, Simon Perchik, Christopher Buckley, Ricardo Pau-Llosa, Sherod Santos and Linda Gregg. As a sample the editor selected these lines from "Coleman Valley Road" by Gerald Stern:

> *The strings are stretched across the sky; one note*
> *is almost endless — pitiless I'd say*
> *except for the slight sagging; one note is*
> *like a voice, it almost has words, it sings*
> *and sighs, it cracks with desire, it sobs with fatigue.*
> *It is the loudest sound of all. A shrieking.*

TBWR is a 6×9 semiannual of 144 pages. Circulation 2,000. **Sample postpaid: $5. Address submissions to Poetry Editor. Submit 3-6 poems, simultaneous (say so) submissions OK. Send SASE for guidelines. Reports in 1-3 months. Awards one $500 prize annually. Pays $5-10/printed page plus two copies. Buys first rights.** Reviews books of poetry in single or multi-book format. Open to unsolicited reviews. Poets may also send books for review consideration to Leigh Ann Sackrider, editor. "We solicit a nationally-known poet for a chapbook section. For the remainder of the issue, we solicit a few poets, but the bulk of the material is chosen from unsolicited submissions. Many of our poets have substantial publication credits, but our decision is based simply on the quality of the work submitted."

‡BLANK GUN SILENCER; BGS PRESS (II), 1240 William St., Racine WI 53402, phone (414)639-2406, founded 1991, editor Dan Nielsen, is "an independent art/lit mag" which appears twice a year "publishing Buk-heads, postDADA freaks and everything in between." They want **poetry that is "tight, concise, startling, funny, honest. Nothing flowery, overly 'poetic,' too academic, rhyming or blatantly pointless."** They have recently published poetry by Charles Bukowski, Gerald Locklin, Fred Voss and Ron Androla. As a sample the editor selected these lines from "Edge" by Mark Weber:

> *where are my John Coltrane records?*
> *o, i sold them when*
> *i was a junkie*
> *they sold good*
> *but now i want to hear them*
> *need to hear the cycle of 5ths played backwards*
> *on "Giant Steps"*
> *one of the purest musicians ever*

The editor says *BGS* is 60-80 pgs., digest-sized, photocopied and saddle-stapled with cardstock cover and b&w art. They accept approximately 200 poems a year. Press run is 300 for 50 subscribers of which 7 are libraries. Single copy: $4; subscription: $8. **Sample postpaid: $3. Previously published poems OK, if notified. No simultaneous submissions. Cover letter required.** Time between acceptance and publication is up to 1 year. **Often comments on rejections. Send SASE for guidelines. Reports within 3 months. Pays up to 3 copies. Acquires first or one-time rights.** Reviews books of poetry in up to 3 pages. Open to unsolicited reviews. Poets may also send books for review consideration. BGS Press publishes 4 chapbooks/year. **Query first with sample poems and cover letter with bio and publication credits. Replies to queries in 1 week, to mss within 1 month. Pays 30 copies. For sample chapbook, send $2.**

BLIND ALLEYS (II); SEVENTH SON PRESS (V), % Michael S. Weaver, Rutgers University, Box 29, Camden NJ 08102, press founded 1981, *Blind Alleys* founded 1982 by Michael S. Weaver, editors Michael S. Weaver and Aissatou Mijiza. They have published poetry by Lucille Clifton, Arthur Winfield Knight, Kimiko Hahn, Peter Harris and Ethelbert Miller. *BA* appears twice a year and is 78 pgs., digest-sized, saddle-stapled, professionally printed on thin stock with matte card cover. Circulation 500. **Sample postpaid: $5. All submissions must be addressed to Michael S. Weaver. Submit about 5 poems in a batch, none longer than 100 lines. Pays 2 copies.** Reviews books of poetry. **The press publishes broadsides but is not presently accepting unsolicited book mss.**

‡BLOCK'S POETRY COLLECTION; ALAN J. BLOCK PUBLICATIONS (I, II), 639 Harrison Ave., Beloit WI 53511, founded 1993, editor Alan J. Block, is a quarterly. **"Poems of shorter length (two pages or less), high quality and unique perspective have a home here." They do not want erotica or religious verse.** The editor says *BPC* is 25 pgs., 5½ × 8½, offset, saddle-stapled, with cover art, no ads. Press run is 100 for 25 subscribers. Subscription: $18. **Sample postpaid: $5. No previously published poems or simultaneous submissions.** Time between acceptance and publication is 6-8 months. **Always comments on rejections. Reports in 1 month. Pays 2 copies.** The editor says, "I am open to most kinds of poetry. I encourage poets to send comments with their poems telling me what they believe are their strong points—and their weak points."

‡BLOODREAMS: A MAGAZINE OF VAMPIRES & WEREWOLVES (IV-Themes), 1312 W. 43rd St., North Little Rock AR 72118, phone (501)771-2047, founded 1991, editor Kelly Gunter Atlas, is a quarterly appearing in January, April, July and October. They primarily publish short fiction, with poetry and artwork used as fillers. **"All styles of poetry are considered, but all poetry *must* relate to vampires or werewolves. We prefer poetry that is 25 lines or less, but will consider longer works if especially well-written. However, we do not accept poems which are longer than one type-written page, single-spaced, unless solicited by the editor."** They have recently published poetry by Dirk Roaché, Lisa S. Laurencot, Roy Martin Nottestad and Joan Aver Kelly. As a sample the editor selected these lines from her own poem, "My Phantom Love":

> *Nostalgia walks in moonlight*
> *and with it, you.*
> *Your shadow dances*
> *along the cold, dark corridors*
> *of my soul,*
> *tempting me to follow.*

Bloodreams is 40-50 pgs., 8½ × 11, computer typeset and photocopied on 20 lb. paper, bound by plastic spiral, with 60 lb. colored paper cover, b&w drawings and 3-5 pgs. of ads. They receive about 60 poems/year, use 4-5/issue. Press run is 100 for 75 subscribers. Subscription: $15/year. **Sample postpaid: $4. Make check or money order payable to Kelly Atlas. Previously published poems and simultaneous submissions OK. Cover letter required. Reads submissions in December, March, June and September.** "Poems are accepted or rejected depending on availability of space in the issue and on the impact the poem has on the editor." **Seldom comments on rejections. Reports in 1-2 weeks. Pays 1 copy. Acquires one-time rights.** "We have a review column, 'Fang and Claw,' where books, comics and vampire/werewolf-related poetry chapbooks are reviewed. It varies from issue to issue." The editor says, "We look for poetry that has mood, atmosphere and description. Make us feel that we are not merely reading it, but experiencing it."

BLUE LIGHT PRESS (V), P.O. Box 642, Fairfield IA 52556, phone (515)472-7882, founded 1988, partner Diane Frank, publishes 3 paperbacks, 3 chapbooks/year. **"We like poems that are emotionally honest and uplifting. Women, Visionary Poets, Iowa Poets, San Francisco Poets. No rhymed poetry or dark poetry." They are currently accepting work by invitation only.** They have published poetry by Rustin Larson, Nancy Berg and Meg Fitz-Randolph. As a sample the editor selected these lines from **The Houses Are Covered in Sound** by Louise Nayer:

> *There was something*
> *moving in a garbage can,*
> *a white light glowing in a spiral.*
> *I thought it was a child,*
> *no the wind, no the part*
> *of myself that glowed.*

That book is 60 pgs., digest-sized, flat-spined, professionally printed, with elegant matte card cover: $10. They have also published two anthologies of Iowa poets. They have an editorial board. "We also work in person with local poets. We have an ongoing poetry workshop, give classes and will edit/critique poems by mail—$30 for 4-5 poems."

BLUE RYDER (II, III), P.O. Box 587, Olean NY 14760, founded 1989, editor Ken Wagner, appears every other month and is subtitled "The Best of the Small Press." It publishes choice reprints from underground, alternative, special interest, small and micropress publications. **They are also now reading original unpublished submissions. "Beat and Modernist do best, though there is no objection to more academic or classical pieces."** They have published poetry by Lyn Lifshin, Thomas Krampf, John Bennett, Patrick McKinnon, Dan Sicoli, Todd Moore and Cheryl Townsend. As a sample the editor selected these lines by Laura Albrecht:

> *You looked into the face of America and saw its stars and stripes teeth*
> *ripping children apart.*

BR is a 11 × 14 tabloid of 16 pgs. or more. Reviews other magazines and reprints excerpts. **Also considers previously published work submitted by writers.** They use up to 18 poets/year. Press run is 3,000 for 600 subscribers of which 4 are libraries, 1,400 shelf sales. Subscription: $8. **Sample postpaid: $3. Submit 2-5 poems. If previously published, send crisp, dark photocopies as they originally appeared, along with name, address and ordering information for the publication — you must still have the rights to the piece. For guidelines, send SASE addressed to** *"The Blue Ryder* **Handbook Pamphlet." Reports in 3 months. Pays 1 copy.** The editor says, "Your very best bet is to send a published chap as I'm always looking for good chaps to excerpt from."

BLUE UNICORN, A TRIQUARTERLY OF POETRY; BLUE UNICORN POETRY CONTEST (II, IV-Translations), 22 Avon Rd., Kensington CA 94707, phone (510)526-8439, founded 1977, poetry editors Ruth G. Iodice, Harold Witt and Daniel J. Langton, wants **"well-crafted poetry of all kinds, in form or free verse, as well as expert translations on any subject matter. We shun the trite or inane, the soft-centered, the contrived poem. Shorter poems have more chance with us because of limited space."** They have published poetry by James Applewhite, Kim Cushman, Charles Edward Eaton, Patrick Worth Gray, Joan LaBombard, James Schevill, John Tagliabue and Gail White. As a sample the editors selected these lines from "The Skater" by R.H. Morrison:

> *Drawn by a silken thread through a maze of air,*
> *she plots its curved geometry*
> *as a white swan*
> *might glide through ice.*
>
> *Her music carves an arabesque of white*
> *in white notation*
> *on a white score.*

The magazine is **"distinguished by its fastidious editing, both with regard to contents and format."** It is 56 pgs., narrow digest-sized, saddle-stapled, finely printed, with some art. It features 40-50 poems in each issue, all styles, with the focus on excellence and accessibility. They receive over 35,000 submissions a year, use about 200, have a year's backlog. **Sample postpaid: $5. Submit 3-5 poems on normal typing paper. No simultaneous submissions or previously published poems. Guidelines available for SASE. Reports in 1-3 months (generally within 6 weeks), often with personal comment. Pays one copy.** They sponsor an annual contest with small entry fee to help support the magazine, with prizes of $100, $75, $50 and sometimes special awards, distinguished poets as judges, publication of 3 top poems and 6 honorable mentions in the magazine. Entry fee: $4 for first poem, $3 for others to a maximum of 5. Write for current guidelines. **Criticism occasionally offered.** "We would advise beginning poets to read and study poetry — both poets of the past and of the present; concentrate on technique; and **discipline yourself by learning forms before trying to do without them.** When your poem is crafted and ready for publication, study your markets and then send whatever of your work seems to be compatible with the magazine you are submitting to."

BLUELINE (IV-Regional), Dept. PM, English Dept., Potsdam College, Potsdam NY 13676, founded 1979, editor-in-chief Allen Steinberg, and an editorial board, "is an annual literary magazine dedicated to prose and **poetry about the Adirondacks and other regions similar in geography and spirit."** They want **"clear, concrete poetry pertinent to the countryside and its people. It must go beyond mere description, however. We prefer a realistic to a romantic view. We do not want to see sentimental or extremely experimental poetry."** Usually 75 lines or fewer, though **"occasionally we publish longer poems"** on **"nature in general, Adirondack Mountains in particular. Form may vary, can be traditional**

Use the General Index to find the page number of a specific publisher. If the publisher you are seeking is not listed, check the " '93-'94 Changes" list at the end of this section.

or contemporary." They have published poetry by Phillip Booth, George Drew, Eric Ormsby, L.M. Rosenberg, John Unterecker, Lloyd Van Brunt, Laurence Josephs, Maurice Kenny and Nancy L. Nielsen. It's a handsomely printed, 112-page, 6×9 magazine with 40-45 pgs. of poetry in each issue, circulation 600. **Sample copies: $4 for back issues.**. They have a 3- to 11-month backlog. **No simultaneous submissions. Submit September 1 through November 30, no more than 5 poems with short bio. Guidelines available for SASE. Reports in 2-10 weeks. Pays copies. Acquires first North American serial rights. Occasionally comments on rejections.** Reviews books of poetry in 500-750 words, single and multi-book format. "We are interested in both beginning and established poets whose poems evoke universal themes in nature and show human interaction with the natural world. We look for **thoughtful craftsmanship rather than stylistic trickery."**

BOA EDITIONS, LTD. (III), 92 Park Ave., Brockport NY 14420, phone (716)637-3844 or (716)473-1896, founded 1976, poetry editor A. Poulin, Jr., **generally does not accept unsolicited mss.** They have published some of the major American poets, such as W.D. Snodgrass, John Logan, Isabella Gardner, Richard Wilbur and Lucille Clifton, and they publish introductions by major poets of those less well-known. For example, Gerald Stern wrote the foreword for Li-Young Lee's **Rose. Query with samples, bio and publication credits. Pays royalties.**

BOGG PUBLICATIONS; BOGG (II), 422 N. Cleveland St., Arlington VA 22201, founded 1968, poetry editors John Elsberg (USA), George Cairncross (UK: 31 Belle Vue St., Filey, N. Yorkshire YO 14 9HU, England), Sheila Martindale (Canada: P.O. Box 23148, 380 Wellington St., London, Ontario NGA 5N9) and Robert Boyce (Australia: 48 Academy Ave., Mulgrave Victoria 3170 Australia). "We publish *Bogg* magazine and occasional free-for-postage pamphlets." The magazine uses a great deal of poetry in each issue (with several featured poets) — **"poetry in all styles, with a healthy leavening of shorts (under 10 lines). Our emphasis on good work per se and Anglo-American cross-fertilization."** This is one of the liveliest small press magazines published today. It started in England and in 1975 began including a supplement of American work; it now is published in the US and mixes US, Canadian, Australian and UK work with reviews of small press publications from all of those areas. It's thick (64 pgs.), typeset, saddle-stitched, in a 6×9 format that leaves enough white space to let each poem stand and breathe alone. They have recently published work by Jon Silkin, John Millett, Tina Fulker, Tim Bowling and Miriam Sagan. As a sample we selected this complete poem, "New Age Rebel," by Paul Dilsaver:

> *she thought Woodstock*
> *was a subdivision*

They accept all styles, all subject matter. "Some have even found the magazine's sense of play offensive. Overt religious and political poems have to have strong poetical merits — statement alone is not sufficient. Prefer typewritten manuscripts, with author's name and address on each sheet. We will reprint previously published material, but with a credit line to a previous publisher." No simultaneous submissions. Prefers to see 6 poems. About 40 pgs. of poetry/issue, print run of 750, 400 subscriptions of which 20 are libraries. Subscription: $12 for 3 issues. **Sample postpaid: $3.50.** They receive over 10,000 American poems/year and use 100-150. "We try to accept only for next 2 issues. SASE required or material discarded (no exceptions)." **Guidelines available for SASE. Reports in 1 week. Pays 2 copies. Acquires one-time rights.** Reviews books and chapbooks of poetry in 250 words, single format. Open to unsolicited reviews. Poets may also send books to relevant editor (by region) for review consideration. Their occasional pamphlets and chapbooks are by invitation only, the author receiving 25% of the print run, and you can get **chapbook samples free for SASE.** Better make it at least 2 ounces worth of postage. John Elsberg advises, "Become familiar with a magazine before submitting to it. Always enclose SASE. Long lists of previous credits irritate me. Short notes about how the writer has heard about *Bogg* or what he finds interesting or annoying in the magazine I read with some interest."

BOMB MAGAZINE (III), Suite 1002 A, 594 Broadway, New York NY 10012, founded 1981, managing editor Lawrence Chua, is a quarterly magazine that "encourages a dialogue among artists of various media. **We encourage poetry by people of color and serious poetry by experienced poets; shorter is better. Experiments with form and language are also encouraged. No limericks, inspirational verse, clever or greeting card styles."** They have published poetry by David Mamet, Harold Pinter and A.C. Purcell. As a sample the editors selected these lines by Agha Shahid Ali:

> *Cries Majnoon:*
> *Those in tatters*
> *May now demand love:*
> *I've declared a fashion*
> *of ripped collars.*
> *The breezes are lost*

> *travellers today,*
> *knocking, asking*
> *for a place to stay.*
> *I tell them*
> *to go away.*

BOMB is 96 pgs., saddle-stitched with 4-color cover. "We receive about 100 manuscripts a month; we accept 2 or 3 every 4 months." Press run is 12,000 for 2,000 subscriptions of which 600 are libraries. Single copy: $4; subscription: $16/year. **Sample postpaid: $5. No previously published poems; simultaneous submissions OK. Cover letter including name, address, telephone number and previous publications required. "Poetry should be legibly typed."** Time between acceptance and publication is 4-6 months. **Reports in 4 months. Pays $50. Buys first North American serial rights.** *Bomb Magazine* ranked #10 in the "Top Pay" category of the June 1993 *Writer's Digest* Poetry 60 list.

BONE & FLESH PUBLICATIONS (II), P.O. Box 349, Concord NH 03302-0349, founded 1988, coeditors Lester Hirsh and Frederick Moe, *Bone & Flesh* literary journal appears annually. "We are looking for quality calibre work from seasoned writers with a literary slant. All forms: prose poems, short fiction, haiku, essays and artwork are welcome. Themes may vary but should focus on the substance of our lives or the link with other lives and times. We do not want to see anything that is overtly fundamentalist, banal, trite or conventional." They have recently published works by Kerry Shawn Keys, Jean Battlo, Michael Heyd, David Chorlton, R. Nikolas Macioci and Michael Wurster. As a sample the editors selected these lines by Lisa Yeager:

> *In wing-tipped shoes*
> *my father danced on the black keys*
> *of the scratched piano*
> *like a drunken exhibitionist,*
> *chasing shadows like crows*
> *picking at his stubbled brain.*

Bone & Flesh is 60-65 pgs., 8×11, saddle-stitched or perfect-bound with occasional supplements. Subscription: $7. **Sample postpaid: $5. Submissions are accepted February through May only.** *Always* **query before submitting. Editors attempt to comment on rejections and provide encouragement "when appropriate." Reports in 1-3 months. Pays copies. Acquires first North American serial rights.** Staff reviews chapbooks of poetry in 100-200 words, single-book format. In addition to the magazine, Bone & Flesh Publications has also published **Next Stop Coney Island** by Bayla Winters and **Old Bones**, a compilation chapbook.

‡**BOOG LITERATURE; MA!; D.A. LEVY POETRY CONTEST (I, II)**, P.O. Box 221, Oceanside NY 11572-0221, founded 1991, editor/publisher David Kirschenbaum. BOOG Literature publishes *MA!*, a quarterly 'zine of poetry, prose and arts reviews, as well as 5-10 chapbooks/year and occasional broadsides. They have recently published poetry by Katie Yates, Allen Ginsberg, Pat McKinnon, Ed Sanders and Carla Harryman. As a sample the editor selected these lines from "Sweet Home Chicago" in **How I Got Here** by Charles Rossiter:

> *The waitress yells "this ain't*
> *the way they do it in LA"*
> *and the band cranks up another notch*
> *and brings it home*
> *to sweet home,*
> *chicago.*

That "chapbook" is 16 pgs., 4¼×5½, saddle-stitched, with card cover. *MA!* is 24 pgs., digest-sized, offset printed and saddle-stitched, with cardstock cover, art, graphics and small press ads. "We accept 10-15 poems per issue, sometimes more, never less." Press run is 200 for 10 subscribers, 100 shelf sales. Single copy: $2.50; subscription: $8. **Sample postpaid: $3. Submit up to 5 poems; 6 short poems can count as 1 poem or page of poetry. Previously published poems and simultaneous submissions OK.** "A friendly cover letter always helps. Most small presses have low circulations, so if your piece was (or may be) published elsewhere, but you think it deserves/needs to be read by more people, send it along (but please tell us when and where it was or will be published)." Time between acceptance and publication is "usually no more than 3 months." **Often comments on rejections. Send SASE for guidelines. Reports in 1-6 weeks. Pays 1 copy. Acquires first North American serial or reprint rights.** "We welcome and will write reviews of either chaps or mags in 250-1,000 words, single or multi-book format." For chapbook or broadside publication, query with sample poems and cover letter including brief bio and publication credits. Reading period for chapbooks is May 1 through July 31 only. Replies to queries within 1 month, to mss within 2 months. Pays 10% of press run; first printing is 100-200 copies. For sample chapbook, "send check or money order for $1.50 to $4.50, and we will select a chap to send in return." Chapbooks are also selected for publication through the d.a. levy poetry contest, named after the late Cleveland poet. Contest entry fee is $5 ($1 of which is earmarked for AIDS charities in Albany, New York). Submissions should include a brief bio, previous publishing credits and credits for all poems included in the chapbook ms. Mss should be 30-40 pgs. in length and have a suggested title. The winner receives $25 and 10 copies of the finished chapbook. All entrants receive 1 copy of the winning chapbook. The press also publishes occasional spoken word cassette compilations. Send tapes of up to 20 minutes of spoken word for consideration. The editor says, "The job of the small press is to get the word out. If it's solid, we will publish it. Also, you need not be published often in the small press to have compiled enough poetry for a chapbook. It's quality, not resume."

‡BOOMTOWN; BOOMTOWN NEWSLETTER; BOOMTOWN HOTLINE; THE IRREGULARS (II), P.O. Box 70428, Pasadena CA 91117, phone (818)796-8472, founded 1992, editor Joseph Buck. *Boomtown* is a semiannual of poetry, fiction and nonfiction. They describe it as an independent journal "that doesn't have (a) a college's name in front of it, (b) poems from the editor, (c) a mutual admiration society, or (d) a lack of love and respect for writers and their work. **Unlike other magazines, we have no length, style or subject restrictions. If it is 75 pages of science fiction haiku erotica, we'll take it if it's great (it better be great)."** They do not offer sample lines of poetry "because the majority of sample lines are by the editor or somebody equally unimportant." The editor says *Boomtown* is 75-100 pgs., 8½×11, professionally printed and saddle-stapled with linen cover, art and ads. They receive about 200 submissions a year, accept approximately 25%. Press run is 500 for 125 subscribers, 375 shelf sales. Subscription: $10, which includes 2 copies of *Boomtown* and at least 4 copies of the *Boomtown Newsletter*, which is "intended to keep people informed of the things we are up to here at *Boomtown* and to provide guidelines for submission. So instead of asking for guidelines via SASE, we will provide a copy of the newsletter gratis." Sample of *Boomtown* postpaid: $6. **No previously published poems or simultaneous submissions. "We require a SASE or a SAE with at least 2 IRCs in order to return acceptances or rejections as well as reviews of submissions. If folks want to tell us about themselves, a cover letter is fine but not required."** Reports in up to 1 month. Pays 1 copy. The Boomtown Hotline (the number in the address line) gives submission information, more information on the most recent issue of *Boomtown* and information on literary events in the area. It also provides information on the Irregulars, "a group of volunteers here in the Pasadena area that does Band-Aid work for pre-existing charities. I encourage people to call the number even if you live in Bahrain. It is in operation 24 hours a day so give it a call when the rates are cheap." The editor adds, "I encourage people to read outside their style. Also subscribe. Any of the other editors in this book could tell you how many people who submit don't actually subscribe. Subscribe. Call. Submit. Get on up and give a damn!"

BOOTS: FOR FOLKS WITH THEIR BOOTS ON! (I, IV-Themes), P.O. Box 766, Challis ID 83226, phone (208)879-4475, founded 1990, editor Ethie Corrigan, is a biannual magazine using **"well-crafted cowboy poetry and historical pieces (Western Americana). No modernistic mumbo-jumbo." They look for poetry with humor as well as nature/rural/ecology, regional (Western) and/or inspirational themes.** They have published poetry by Wallace McRae, Gwen Peterson, Sandy Seaton and Mike Logan. As a sample we selected these lines from "The Quilted History Book" by Marilyn Diamond:

> And see this piece of pale pink
> With flecks of green and rose
> It's from the dress I wore, the night
> Your daddy, he proposed.
> And them squares of creamy ivory
> There must be ten or more,
> They're bits saved from my daddy's shirt
> He died when I was four.

Boots is 56 pgs., web press printed, saddle-stitched, with glossy cover, photos and ads. Press run is 3,000 for 800 subscribers of which 2 are libraries. Single copy: $4.50; subscription: $8. **Sample postpaid: $2.50. Previously published poems OK; no simultaneous submissions. Submit typed poems January through March for fall issue; April through September for spring. Always comments on rejections. Reports "immediately." Pays copies "exact number depends on length."** Reviews related books of poetry "now and then." Open to unsolicited reviews. Poets may send books for review consideration. The editor says poets should be careful when "trying to write about the West if they don't know the background, vocabulary, etc."

‡BORDERLANDS: TEXAS POETRY REVIEW (II, IV-Regional), P.O. Box 49818, Austin TX 78765, founded 1992, appears twice a year publishing "high-quality, outward-looking poetry by new and established poets, as well as brief reviews of poetry books and critical essays. Particularly welcome Texas and Southwest writers." They want **"outward-looking poems that exhibit social, political, geographical, historical or spiritual awareness coupled with concise artistry and some 'lift-off' of the**

imagination. A bit of humor helps. We also want poems in two languages, where the poet has written both versions. Please, no self-regarding, introspective work about the speaker's psyche, childhood or intimate relationships." They have recently published poetry by William Stafford, Donald Finkel, Elton Glaser, Pattiann Rogers and Walter McDonald. As a sample the editors selected these lines from "Before TV Came" by William J. Vernon:

> . . . *Sometimes we sat*

> *on somebody's stoop, watching the sun*
> *descend, the stars appear, the bats*
> *start circling through shadows. A phone*

> *might ring. We might go in for that.*

Borderlands is 80-120 pgs., 5½ × 8½, offset, perfect-bound, with 4-color cover, art by local artists. They receive about 2,000 poems a year, use approximately 120. Press run is 500. Subscription: $14/year. **Sample postpaid: $7.50. No previously published poems; simultaneous submissions OK. Seldom comments on rejections. Send SASE for guidelines. Reports in 4 months. Pays 1 copy. Acquires first rights.** Reviews books of poetry in one page. Also uses 3- to 6-page essays on single poets and longer essays on contemporary critical issues surrounding poetry (query first). They say, "We're pleased to see more American poets turning outward to the world around them, yet writing with artistic subtlety. We believe it's possible—though not easy—for poetry to be both involved and high-quality."

BOREALIS PRESS; TECUMSEH PRESS LTD.; JOURNAL OF CANADIAN POETRY (V), Dept. PM, 9 Ashburn Dr., Ottawa, Ontario K2E 6N4 Canada, founded 1972. Borealis and Tecumseh are imprints for books, including **collections of poetry, by Canadian writers only, and they are presently not considering unsolicited submissions**. Send SASE (or SAE with IRCs) for catalog to buy samples. Poets published include John Ferns and Russell Thornton. These sample lines are by Fred Cogswell:

> *Often in dreams, when powerless to wake*
> *Or move and thereby ease my pounding heart,*
> *I have felt like a mouse that cannot squeal*
> *When the sprung trap pins its broken spine or*
> *Like a rabbit mesmerized by a snake's*
> *Unchanging otherness of lidless eyes.*

The *Journal* is an annual that publishes articles, reviews and criticism, not poetry. **Sample postpaid: $12.95.**

BOSTON LITERARY REVIEW (BLuR) (II), P.O. Box 357, W. Somerville MA 02144, phone (617)625-6087, founded 1984, editor Gloria Mindock, appears twice a year using **"work with a strong voice and individual style; experimental work welcome. Submit 5-10 poems."** They have published poetry by Stuart Friebert, David Ray, Eric Pankey and Richard Kostelanetz. The editor describes it as 24 pgs., approximately 5¼ × 13¼, offset, saddle-stapled, no ads. They publish about 60 of 4,800 poems received/year. Press run is 500 for 55 subscriptions of which 5 are libraries. Subscription: $9/year. **Sample postpaid: $5. Editor comments on submissions "sometimes." Reports in 2-4 weeks. Pays 2 copies. All rights revert to author.**

THE BOSTON PHOENIX: PHOENIX LITERARY SECTION (PLS) (III), 126 Brookline Ave., Boston MA 02215, phone (617)536-5390, founded 1966, poetry editor Lloyd Schwartz, is a monthly book review with one poem in almost every issue. Press run is 150,000. Single copy: $1.50. As **"most poetry is solicited," no submission information was provided. Reports in 1 month. Pays $50.** Open to unsolicited reviews. Poets may also send books for review consideration to Scott Cardell, editor *PLS*. Poems published by this review appear in **Best American Poetry 1992**.

BOSTON REVIEW (II), 33 Harrison Ave., Boston MA 02111, editor Josh Cohen, founded 1975, is a bimonthly arts, culture and politics magazine which uses about **three pages of poetry/issue, or 12 poems a year**, for which they receive about 700 submissions. Poems in select issues seem to echo or somehow complement the prose, which concerns social or literary affairs. The poetry features lyric and narrative verse with an emphasis on voice, often plaintive-sounding or dream-like in tone. Circulation is 20,000 nationally including subscriptions and newsstand sales. **Sample postpaid: $4.** They have a 4- to 6-month backlog. **Submit any time to Kim Cooper, poetry editor, no more than 6 poems, simultaneous submissions discouraged. Cover letter listing recent publications encouraged. Reports in 2 months "if you include SASE." Pay varies. Buys first serial rights.** Reviews books of poetry. Only using *solicited* reviews. Poets may send books for review consideration. Poetry published by this review has been included in **Best American Poetry**. The editor advises, "To save the time of all those involved, poets should be sure to send only *appropriate* poems to particular magazines. This means that a poet should not submit to a magazine that he/she has not read. Poets should also avoid lengthy cover letters and allow the poems to speak for themselves."

BOTTOMFISH (II), Creative Writing Program, De Anza College, 21250 Stevens Creek Blvd., Cupertino CA 95014, editor Robert Scott. This college-produced magazine appears annually. **"Spare us the pat, generic greeting card phrases. We want sharp, sensory images that carry a strong theme."** They have published poetry by Chitra Divakaruni, Janice Dabney and Charles Safford. As a sample here are lines from "Blowout" by Walter Griffin:

> Suddenly you are there, out by the highway, arm
> wrestling the dark with the wheel in your hands
> gauging the distance between odometers and stars
> that shimmer like ghosts in the falling air
> as the wheel comes loose from the column and
> your brakeless car rolls toward the cliff

Bottomfish is 60 pgs., 7 × 8¼, well-printed on heavy stock with b&w graphics, perfect-bound. Circulation is 500, free to libraries, schools, etc., but $4/copy to individual requests. **"Before submitting, writers are strongly urged to purchase a sample copy; subject matter is at the writer's discretion, as long as the poem is skillfully and professionally crafted." Best submission times: September through February 1. Deadline: February 1 each year. Reports in 2-6 months, depend- ing on backlog. Pays 2 copies.** The editor adds, "Nobody likes the stock rejection letter, but no other response is possible. We do make specific requests for changes, however, if we really want to publish something and it has only minor problems."

BOUILLABAISSE (I, IV-Form/style), % Alpha Beat Press, 31 A Waterloo St., New Hope PA 18938, phone (215)862-0299, founded 1991, editors Dave Christy and Ana Pine, is a biannual using **"poetry that reflects life and its ups and downs."** They want **"modern, beat poetry; poetry from the streets of life – no limit. No rhythm, Christian or sweet poetry."** They have recently published poetry by Charles Bukowski, Allen Ginsberg, Merle Tofer and Erling Friis-Baastad. As a sample the editors selected these lines by Janine Pommy Vega:

> Archangel Mary falls into the water
> killing the bridges, the Tappanzee and
> railroad tresks. Her backside against the pier, they promenade
> across her, River Edge to Harlem
> and time runs out

The editors say it is 160 pgs., 8½ × 11, offset, saddle-stitched, with graphics. They receive 200 + submissions a year, accept 30%. Press run is 500 for 350 subscribers of which 5 are libraries. **Subscription: $15. Sample postpaid: $10. Previously published poems and simultaneous submis- sions OK. Cover letter required. Always comments on rejections. Send SASE for guidelines. Reports "immediately." Pays 1 copy.** Reviews books of poetry in 250-500 words. Open to unsolic- ited reviews. Poets may also send books for review consideration. They also publish 2 paperbacks and 2 chapbooks/year. "We work with each individual on their project." **Replies to queries "immediately," to mss within 3 weeks. Pays author's copies.** "We have started a new series of spoken word and music tapes. Send cassette with SASE for consideration for the 'Best of B'baisse' series. Tapes will not be returned. All poets accepted will receive a copy of tapes and additional tapes may be purchased for $5.65 (including postage). Recent cassettes include Ana Christy, Merle Tofer, George Dowden and Haynes/Elliott."

BOULEVARD (II), % editor Richard Burgin, P.O. Box 30386, Philadelphia PA 19103, phone (215)561- 1723, founded 1985, appears 3 times a year. **"We've published everything from John Ashbery to Howard Moss to a wide variety of styles from new or lesser known poets. We're eclectic. Do not want to see poetry that is uninspired, formulaic, self-conscious, unoriginal, insipid."** They have published poetry by Amy Clampitt, Molly Peacock, Jorie Graham and Mark Strand. As a sample, editor Richard Burgin selected these lines from "Three Soundings of January Snow" by Stuart Lishan:

> Snow arias the ground tonight. It quilts
> > the house; it sounds like a samba of whispers,
> Muffled, like a mitten slipped over love, like guilt.

Boulevard is 175 + pgs., digest-sized, flat-spined, professionally printed, with glossy card cover. Poetry herein – mostly free verse but wide-ranging in content, length and tone – is accessible and exciting. Poems have one thing in common: careful attention to craft (particularly line, stanza and voice). Their press run is 2,800 with 700 subscriptions of which 200 are libraries. **Subscription: $12. Sample postpaid: $6. "Prefer name and number on each page with SASE. Encourage cover letters but don't require them. Will consider simultaneous submissions but not previously published poems." Reads submissions September 1 through May 30 only. Editor sometimes comments on rejections. Pays $25-250/poem, depending on length, plus 2 copies. Buys**

first North American serial rights. Open to unsolicited reviews. *Boulevard* ranked #5 in the "Top Pay" category of the June 1993 *Writer's Digest* Poetry 60 list, and poetry published here has also been included in **Best American Poetry 1992.** Richard Burgin says, "We believe the grants we have won from the National Endowment for the Arts etc., as well as the anthologies which continue to recognize us, have rewarded our commitment. My advice to poets: 'Write from your heart as well as your head.' "

BRANCH REDD BOOKS; BRANCH REDD REVIEW; BRANCH REDD POETRY BROADSHEETS; BRANCH REDD POETRY CHAPBOOKS (V), 4805 B St., Philadelphia PA 19120, phone (215)324-1462, editor Bill Sherman, is a "small press publisher of poetry" that **discourages unsolicited mss.** He has published poetry by Allen Fisher, Pierre Joris, Asa Benveniste, Eric Mottram, Kate Ruse-Glason and Shreela Ray. As a sample the editor selected these lines (poet unidentified):

> *Her hair, her blue nightslip, more*
> *Frustration. Earlier*
> *news of Bunting's death.*

The *Branch Redd Review* appears irregularly in varied formats with a press run of 500. **Pays at least 10 copies.** Staff reviews books of poetry. Send books for review consideration.

GEORGE BRAZILLER, INC. (II), 60 Madison Ave., New York NY 10010, phone (212)889-0909, founded 1955, editor Adrienne Baxter, is a major literary publisher. In 1980 they published **Classic Ballroom Dances** by Charles Simic, from which this sample poem, "Bedtime Story, " was selected:

> *When a tree falls in a forest*
> *And there's no one around*
> *To hear the sound, the poor owls*
> *Have to do all the thinking.*
>
> *They think so hard they fall off*
> *Their perch and are eaten by ants,*
> *Who, as you already know, all look like*
> *Little Black Riding Hoods.*

It is 64 pgs., digest-sized, professionally printed, flat-spined, with glossy card cover, $3.95. "**We consider reprints of books of poetry as well as new poems. If submitting a book for reprint,** *all* **reviews of the book should be submitted as well. Submit sample of work, never** *entire* **original pgs.**" Reports in 1 month or less. Payment varies in each case. Buys all rights. The editor says, "We are a small publishing house that publishes few books (in general) each year. Still, we have published many well-known authors and are always open and receptive to new writers of every kind—and from all parts of the world."

THE BRIDGE: A JOURNAL OF FICTION AND POETRY (II), 14050 Vernon St., Oak Park MI 48237, founded 1990, editor Jack Zucker, appears twice a year using "**exciting, largely mainstream poetry.**" They have published poetry by Ruth Whitman and Daniel Hughes. It is digest-sized, 192 pgs., perfect-bound, press run 700. Subscription: $8. **Sample postpaid: $5.** An editorial board of 3 considers mss; decision made by editor and 1 special editor. **Editor comments on submissions "rarely." Pays 2 copies. Acquires first rights.** Reviews books of poetry and prose in 1-10 pgs.

BRILLIANT STAR (IV-Children, religious), % Hill, Baha'i National Center, Wilmette IL 60091, is a Baha'i bimonthly for children, appearing in a magazine-sized format. "**Poems are always illustrated, so think about how your poem will look. Our readers are ages 5-14. Write for** *them* **not for yourself. We do not want to see Christmas themes in any form. If you are not familiar with the Baha'i Faith, research is encouraged.**" As a sample the editor selected these lines from "Hooray for Skin" by Susan Engle:

> *Suppose, when God created skin,*
> *He turned the skinside outside in*
> *So when you talk to Mrs. Jones,*
> *Your eyes meet over fat and bones*
> *And tissues, blue and white and red,*
> *That stretch from toe to hand to head.*
> *It makes me glad to have a skin*
> *To keep the outside boneside in.*

Sample free with 9 × 12 SASE (sufficient postage for 5 oz.); objectives are printed in the masthead. Considers simultaneous submissions. "Contributors receive two copies." The editor urges children who wish to write poetry to avoid "writing about tired subjects like 'dogs as friends' and being 'afraid of the dark.' Write about today's world in fun, exciting language. Write about a realistic fear—guns, drugs, the school dance, my ugly feet, will my parents divorce. Make your poem an engaging short story." This is also good advice for adults who wish to write children's poetry for this publication.

BROKEN STREETS (I, IV-Religious, children), 57 Morningside Dr. E., Bristol CT 06010, founded 1979, poetry editor Ron Grossman, is a **"Christian-centered outreach ministry to poets. Chapbooks are sent free to encourage poets."** The editor wants **"Christian-centered, city poetry, feelings, etc., usually 5-15 lines, haiku, no more than 5 poems at a time, not necessary to query, but helpful."** He has published Bettye K. Wray and Naomi Rhoads. The magazine, which appears 4-5 times a year, is 40-50 pgs., digest-sized, photocopied typescript with card cover. Uses about 150 of the 200 poems submitted/year—by children, old people, etc. Press run is 250. **Sample postpaid: $3.50. Reports in 1 week. No pay but copies.** Reviews books of poetry. Open to unsolicited reviews. Poets may also send books for review consideration. *Broken Streets* ranked #4 in the "Nontraditional Verse" category of the June 1993 *Writer's Digest* Poetry 60 list.

‡BROODING HERON PRESS (III), Bookmonger Rd., Waldron Island WA 98297, founded 1984, co-publishers Sam and Sally Green, **publishes 3 chapbooks/year.** They have **"no restriction other than excellence."** They do not want "prose masquerading as poetry or poems written for form's sake." They have recently published poetry by Denise Levertov, John Haines and Gary Snyder. Submit complete ms of 16-20 poems; no query. Previously published poems OK; no simultaneous submissions. **Cover letter required.** Time between acceptance and publication varies; they have over a 3-year backlog. Always comments on rejections. **Reports within 6 weeks. "We print 300 books per title, bound in paper and cloth. Payment is 10% of the press run. Author retains copyright."** This press has received many awards for fine printing. **Write for catalog to order samples.**

‡BROOKLYN REVIEW (II), 2308 Boylan Hall, Brooklyn College, Brooklyn NY 11210, founded 1974, editors change each year, address correspondence to poetry editor. They have published such poets as Allen Ginsberg, Elaine Equi, Amy Gerstler, Eileen Myles, Alice Notley, Honor Moore, Ron Padgett and David Trinidad. *BR* is an annual, 120 pgs., digest-sized, flat-spined, professionally printed with glossy color cover and art. Circulation 500. **Sample postpaid: $5. "Please send no more than four poems." Cover letter with brief history required. Reads submissions September 1 through December 1 only. Reports in 6 weeks to 6 months. Pays copies.** Poems published in this review have often been selected for inclusion in **Best American Poetry.**

BRUNSWICK PUBLISHING COMPANY (I), Rt. 1, Box 1A1, Lawrenceville VA 23868, founded 1978, poetry editor Walter J. Raymond, is a **partial subsidy publisher. Query with 3-5 samples. Response in 2 weeks with SASE. If invited, submit double-spaced, typed ms. Reports in 3-4 weeks, reading fee only if you request written evaluation. Poet pays 50-80% of cost, gets same percentage of profits for market-tester edition of 500,** advertised by leaflets mailed to reviewers, libraries, book buyers and bookstores. Samples are flat-spined, matte-covered, 54-page paperbacks. **Send SASE for "Statement of Philosophy and Purpose,"** which explains terms, and catalog to order samples. That Statement says: "We publish books because that is what we like to do. Every new book published is like a new baby, an object of joy! We do not attempt to unduly influence the reading public as to the value of our publications, but we simply let the readers decide that themselves. We refrain from the artificial beefing up of values that are not there. . . . We are not competitors in the publishing world, but offer what we believe is a needed service. We strongly believe that in an open society every person who has something of value to say and wants to say it should have the chance and opportunity to do so."

BRUSSELS SPROUT (I, IV-Form), P.O. Box 1551, Mercer Island WA 98040, phone (206)232-3239, Francine Porad, art and poetry editor since 1988. This magazine of **haiku, senryu, tanka and art** appears each January, May and September. **They want "any format (1-5 lines); subject matter open; seeking work that captures the haiku moment in a fresh way."** They have recently published poetry by Elizabeth St. Jacques, Marlene Mountain, Paul O. Williams, George Swede and Elizabeth S. Lamb. As a sample the editor selected these haiku by H.F. Noyes and Matthew Louviere respectively:

spring miracle—   The netmaker
each seed knowing   taking time
what to become   with his shoelace

The magazine is 48 pgs., digest-sized, professionally printed, saddle-stapled with matte b&w card cover featuring an artist each issue. **Sample postpaid: $5.50. Submit only original work, 4-12 poems (can be on one sheet), name and address on each sheet. Do not submit mss from May 25 to June 15. No simultaneous submissions or previously published poems. Send SASE for guidelines. Editor sometimes comments on rejections. Reports in 3 weeks. No payment, other than 3 $10 Editor's Choice Awards each issue.** Reviews books of haiku "sometimes, but list those received with a brief comment or sample of work." Poets may send books for consideration. *Brussels Sprout* sponsors Haiku Northwest, an informal group of writers meeting 5-6 times yearly to share work, and Haiku Northwest Readers, arranging public readings locally. The editor advises, "For the record, no editor enjoys saying 'no.' Keep writing, rewriting and sending out your manuscripts. If you value your work, you will find an editor who feels the same."

BUFFALO SPREE MAGAZINE (II), 4511 Harlem Rd., Buffalo NY 14226, founded 1967, poetry editor Janet Goldenberg, is the quarterly regional magazine of western New York. It has a controlled circulation (21,000) in the Buffalo area, mostly distributed free (with 3,000 subscriptions, of which 25 are libraries). Its glossy pages feature general interest articles about local culture, plus book reviews, fiction and poetry contributed nationally. It receives about 300 poetry submissions/year and uses about 25, which have ranged from work by Robert Hass and Carl Dennis to first publications by younger poets. As a sample the editor selected these lines from "Alien in Spring" by Martha Bosworth:

> *I am a tall pale animal in boots*
> *trampling forget-me-nots and scaring birds*
> *from the lemon tree: with my long-handled claw*
> *I pull down lemons — tear-shaped, dimpled, round,*
> *bouncing they vanish into vines and weeds.*

They use 5-7 poems/issue, **these are selected 3-6 months prior to publication. Sample postpaid: $3.75. Considers simultaneous submissions, "but we must be advised that poems have been or are being submitted elsewhere." Pays $20/poem.**

BYLINE MAGAZINE (IV-Themes), P.O. Box 130596, Edmond OK 73013, founded 1981, editor Marcia Preston, is a **magazine for the encouragement of writers and poets, using 9-12 poems/issue about writers or writing.** As a sample the editor selected these lines from "A Prayer for Words" by John D. Engle, Jr.:

> *I have had enough*
> *of words that sigh*
> *their meekness*
> *on the margins of the mind.*
> *I want the centered word*
> *that holds a high*
> *degree of mystery*
> *no one can find*
> *explained in any*
> *common dictionary.*

Byline is professionally printed, magazine-sized, with illustrations, cartoons and ads. They have about 3,000 subscriptions and receive about 2,500 submissions/year, of which they use 144. **Sample postpaid: $3.50. No more than 4 poems/submission, no reprints. Send SASE for guidelines. Reports within a month. Pays $5-10/poem. Buys first North American serial rights.** Sponsors monthly poetry contests. Send #10 SASE for details. Marcia Preston advises "We are happy to work with new writers, but please read a few samples to get an idea of our style."

C.L.A.S.S. MAGAZINE (IV-Regional), Dept. PM, 900 Broadway, New York NY 10003, phone (212)677-3055, editor Constance M. Weaver, is a monthly magazine, circulation 250,000, covering **Caribbean/American/African Third World** news and views. It has a slick full-sized format with full-color glossy paper cover. Subscription: $15, $20 overseas. **Sample: $2.75. Publishes 10-20 poems a year, 22-30 lines, on appropriate themes. Submit maximum of 10 poems. Pays $10 maximum.**

‡CADMUS EDITIONS (III), P.O. Box 687, Tiburon CA 94920, founded 1979, editor Jeffrey Miller, publishes hardback and paperback editions of poetry: **"only that which is distinguished."** They have published poetry by Federico García Lorca, Tom Clark, Bradford Morrow and Carol Tinker. These sample lines are by Ed Dorn:

> *The common duty of the poet*
> *in this era of massive disfunction*
> *& generalized onslaught upon alertness*
> *is to maintain the plant*
> *to the end that the mumbling horde*
> *bestirs its pruned tongue.*

Query first, no samples, with "an intelligent literate letter accompanied by a SASE." Replies to queries in 1 month, to mss (if invited to submit) in 1-2 months. Contracts are for 5-10% royalties. Comments "occasionally but not often in that most unsolicited submissions do not warrant same."

‡THE CAFÉ REVIEW (II), c/o Yes Books, 20 Danforth St., Portland ME 04101, phone (207)775-3233, founded 1989, editors Steve Luttrell and Mark Souders, is a quarterly which has grown out of open poetry readings held at a Portland cafe. The editors say they aim "to print the best work we can!" They want **"free verse, 'beat' inspired and fresh. Nothing rhyming or clichéd."** They have recently published poetry by Denise Levertov, Gerard Malanga and Anne Waldman. As a sample the editor selected these lines from "Cream Hidden" by Michael McClure, beginning with lines by Rumi:

> *"LIKE CREAM HIDDEN IN THE SOUL OF MILK*
> *no-place keeps coming into place."*
> *No-place is where I am at.*
> *My soil is where no toil*
>   *will upearth it.*

The Review is 50-60 pgs., 5½×8½, professionally printed and perfect-bound with card cover, b&w art, no ads. They receive over 300 submissions a year, accept approximately 25%. Press run is 200 for 50 subscribers of which 8 are libraries, 50-75 shelf sales. Single copy: $3; subscription: $12. Sample postpaid: $4. **No previously published poems or simultaneous submissions. Cover letter with brief bio required. "We usually respond with a form letter indicating acceptance or rejection of work, seldom with additional comments." Reports in 2-4 months. Pays 1 copy.** They also publish 1-2 chapbooks/year. For those interested, poetry readings are still held on second Tuesday evenings, September through May. Write for information.

CALAPOOYA COLLAGE; $1,000 CAROLYN KIZER POETRY AWARDS (II), P.O. Box 309, Monmouth OR 97361, phone (503)838-6292, founded 1981, editor Thomas L. Ferte. *CC* is a literary annual using **"all kinds" of poetry.** They have published poetry by Robert Bly, Joseph Bruchac, Octavio Paz, Marge Piercy, Etheridge Knight, Vassar Miller, William Stafford, Ursula K. LeGuin, Patricia Goedicke, David Wagoner and David Ray. It is 48 pgs., tabloid-sized. Press run is 1,500 for 250 subscribers of which 16 are libraries. They accept about 6% of 6,000 poems received annually. **Sample postpaid: $5. Reads submissions September 1 through June 1 only. Reports in 1-2 months. Pays 2 copies.** Reviews books of poetry in 600-1,000 words. Open to unsolicited reviews. Poets may also send books for review consideration. All poems accepted for publication are eligible for annual $1,000 Carolyn Kizer Poetry Awards.

CALDER PUBLICATIONS LTD.; RIVERRUN PRESS INC; ASSOCIATION CALDER (V), 9-15 Neal St., London WC2H 9TU England, phone (071)497-1741, publisher John Calder, is a literary book publisher. On their list are Samuel Beckett, Breyten Breytenbach, Erich Fried, Paul Eluard, Pier Paolo Passolini and Howard Barker. **"We do not read for the public,"** says John Calder, and he wants **no unsolicited mss.** "Any communication which requires a response should be sent with a SAE."

THE CALIFORNIA QUARTERLY (V), 100 Sproul Hall, University of California, Davis CA 95616, **"Due to state budgetary cuts, *CQ* will not be reading manuscripts through September 1993. Please inquire after this time with a SASE as to the status of the magazine."**

CALLALOO (IV-Ethnic), Dept. PM, Johns Hopkins University Press, 2715 N. Charles St., Baltimore MD 21218, phone (410)516-6987, founded 1976, editor Charles H. Rowell. Devoted to **poetry dealing with North America, Europe, Africa, Latin and Central America, South America and the Caribbean.** They have published poetry by Rita Dove, Jay Wright, Alice Walker, Yusef Komunyakaa, Aimé Césaire, Nicolás Guillén and Michael Harper. Visually beautiful and well-edited with thematic, powerful poems in all forms and styles, this thick quarterly journal features about 15-20 poems in each issue (along with concise and scholarly book reviews). Circulation 1,400, with 1,400 subscriptions of which half are libraries. Subscription: $22, $47 for institutions. **"We have no specifications for submitting poetry except authors should include SASE." Reports in 6 months. Pays copies.** Poetry published in *Callaloo* has been included in **Best American Poetry 1992.**

CALYX, A JOURNAL OF ART & LITERATURE BY WOMEN (IV-Women, lesbian), P.O. Box B, Corvallis OR 97339, phone (503)753-9384, founded 1976, managing editor M. Donnelly, is a journal edited by a collective editorial board, **publishes poetry, prose, art, reviews and interviews by and about women.** They want **"excellently crafted poetry that also has excellent content."** They have published poetry by Diane Glancy, Robin Morgan, Rebecca Seiferle, Lin Max and Carol Ann Russell. As a

---

The Subject Index, located before the General Index, can help you narrow down markets for your work. It lists those publishers whose poetry interests are specialized.

sample the editor selected these lines from "Watching My Mother Dress" by Cornelia Hoogland:

> *She, who loudhosannahed every chore,*
> *cleaned and cared for us while she peeled potatoes,*
> *in one deft spiral paring, who spun rooms*
> *and bottles through her dusting cloth, lingered.*

Each issue is 7×8, handsomely printed on heavy paper, flat-spined, glossy color cover, 125-200 pgs., of which 50-60 are poetry. Poems tend to be lyric free verse that makes strong use of image and symbol melding unobtrusively with voice and theme. **Sample for the single copy price: $8 plus $1.50 postage.** *Calyx* **is open to submissions twice annually: March 1 through April 15 and October 1 through November 15. Mss received when not open to reading will be returned unread. Send up to 6 poems with SASE and short biographical statement. "We accept copies in good condition and clearly readable. We report in 2-6 months." Guidelines available for SASE. Pays copies.** Open to unsolicited reviews. Poets may also send books for review consideration. In past years *Calyx* has received Bumbershoot Small Press Best Literary Journal Awards and the CCLM Literary Magazine Editors Award for Excellence. They say, "Read the publication and be familiar with what we have published."

CAMELLIA; CAMELLIA PRESS INC. (II), P.O. Box 4092, Ithaca NY 14852, editor Tomer Inbar. *Camellia* is a quarterly poetry magazine **"currently available for free in the San Francisco/Oakland Bay area, Madison, Seattle, Ithaca and D.C., or by sending a 52¢ SASE. We publish poetry in the W.C. Williams tradition. The poetry of things, moment and sharpness. We encourage young writers and like to work with the writers who publish with us (i.e., publishing them again to widen the forum or exposure of their work). Our main goal is to get the poetry out. We do not want to see poetry where the poem is subordinate to the poet or poetry where the noise of the poetic overshadows the voice. We look for poetry that is honest and sharp and unburdened."** As a sample the editor selected this poem, "Eyes Gray, " by David Gonsalves:

> *No, it's all*
> *static really . . . you*
> *could measure the length*
> *and width of your*
>
> *street. Or walk*
> *through a cloud*
> *of it, singing*
>
> *there. She was thinking*
> *about you and this.*

Camellia is 20-24 pgs., digest-sized, desktop published. The first thing that catches your eye is the design. The editors make up for this modest-looking, stapled publication with creative typesetting inside, featuring lively avant-garde or imagistic free verse with titles in large points and varied fonts. **"We receive approximately 300-350 poems/issue and publish about 20."** Press run is 500-900. **Subscription: $5/year, $7 overseas. Sample: 52¢ SASE. Simultaneous submissions and previously published poems OK. Reports "ASAP." Pays 2 copies. Editor comments on submissions "if asked for or if I want to see more but am not satisfied with the poems sent.** We currently publish two regular issues per year and are instituting a series of special project issues. The first, a chapbook of poems by Jerry Mirskin entitled **Picture A Gate Hanging Open And Let That Gate Be The Sun,** is now available for $5 from Camellia Press Inc." *Camellia* is supported, in part, by a multi-year grant from the New York State Council on the Arts.

‡CANADIAN AUTHOR; CANADIAN AUTHORS ASSOCIATION (III), Suite 500, 275 Slater St., Ottawa, Ontario K1P 5H9 Canada, poetry editor Sheila Martindale. *Canadian Author*, a quarterly, is magazine-sized, 28 pgs., professionally printed, with paper cover in 2 colors. It contains articles useful to writers at all levels of experience. **Sample postpaid: $4.50. Buys 40 poems a year. "The trend is toward thematic issues and profiles of featured poets, so query letters are recommended." Pays $15 plus one copy.** (See also Canadian Authors Association Literary Awards in Contests and Awards section.)

CANADIAN DIMENSION: A SOCIALIST NEWS MAGAZINE (IV-Political), Dept. PM, 707-228 Notre Dame Ave., Winnipeg, Manitoba R3B 1N7 Canada, phone (204)957-1519, founded 1964, editorial contact Brenda Austin-Smith, appears 6 times/year, using **"short poems on labour, women, native and other issues. Nothing more than one page."** They have published poetry by Tom Wayman and Milton Acorn. It is 48-56 pgs., magazine-sized, slick, professionally printed, with glossy paper cover. Press run is 4,500-5,000 for 3,000 subscriptions of which 800 are libraries, 1,000 shelf sales. **Subscription: $30.50 US ($24.50 Canadian). Sample postpaid: $1.50. Simultaneous submissions OK. Editor comments on**

submissions "rarely." **Reports in 1 month. Pays 5 copies.** Reviews books of poetry in 750-1,200 words, single or multi-book format.

CANADIAN LITERATURE (IV-Regional), 2029 West Mall, University of British Columbia, Vancouver, British Columbia V6T 1Z2 Canada, phone (604)822-2780, founded 1959, poetry editor L.R. Ricou, is a quarterly review which publishes **poetry by Canadian poets. "No limits on form. Less room for long poems."** They have published poetry by Atwood, Ondaatje, Layton and Bringhurst. As a sample the editor selected these lines from "Subtexts" by Susan Ioannou:

> *Imagine words are snow we crawl under*
> *and scratch at matted ice for crocuses.*
>
> *Or, flattened on our backs in white,*
> *that words fan angel wings.*
>
> *And how could we forget*
> *that clouds are words too?*

Each issue is professionally printed, large digest-sized, flat-spined, with 190+ pgs., of which about 10 are poetry. They receive 100-300 submissions/year, of which they use 10-12. Circulation 2,000, two-thirds of which are libraries. **Sample for the cover price: $15 Canadian. No simultaneous submissions or reprints. Reports within the month. Pays $10/poem plus 1 copy. Buys first rights.** Reviews books of poetry in 500-1,000 words, depending on the number of books.

CANADIAN WRITER'S JOURNAL (IV-Themes), Gordon M. Smart Publications, P.O. Box 6618, Depot 1, Victoria, British Columbia V8P 5N7 Canada, is a very **limited market for poetry using only "short poems or portions thereof as part of 'how-to' articles relating to the writing of poetry and occasional short poems with tie-in to the writing theme."** But it is a publication of interest to poets. "Every issue has a variety of how-to and motivational articles for writers, many by accomplished and well-published authors" and "several regular columns with interesting and useful information ranging from writing tips to the viewpoint from behind the editor's desk." It appears quarterly. Subscription: $15. First annual poetry contest held in 1993.

CANAL LINES (I, IV-Regional), 55 Main St. #3, Brockport NY 14420-1903, phone (716)637-0584, founded 1987, editor Joseph Hoffman, appears twice a year. **"Subject matter and style are open, although material connected to New England/Upstate New York is preferred. Length is limited to 100 lines."** They have published poetry by William Heyen, Paul Root, John Sweet and David Michael Nixon. As a sample the editor selected these lines by Skip Harris:

> *I'm just a poor poet workin' hard*
> *on the tenth draft of a sixteen bar blues.*
> *I've been drinkin' all over town.*
> *I always let the barmaids choose*

Canal Lines is digest-sized, 16 pgs., saddle-stapled with matte card cover, photocopied from typescript. The verse inside is varied (free to formal). They accept about 40-50% of 60-70 submissions/year. Press run is 100. **Sample postpaid: $1.50. "A report on any submission takes 6-7 weeks or longer." Pays 3 copies.** Open to unsolicited reviews. The editor says, "Patience and determination are a must. A well-written/thought-out poem may be rejected numerous times before finally finding a 'home.' A rejection slip is *not* a statement of failure, but an ongoing process to bring a poem into the proper light."

CANDLESTONES (I), P.O. Box 10703, St. Petersburg FL 33733, founded 1990, editor Ann Blain, is a quarterly literary arts magazine. "The purpose is to encourage artists and poets who have not been published and share creativity with people who usually do not buy poetry." Uses poetry, b&w art and photos, and short stories. **"I want poetry the poet is proud of. Some long poems are accepted and I always need short poems. No poems containing profanity. No pornographic poetry."** They have recently published poetry by Helen A. Hardy. As a sample the editor selected these lines by Holly Blain:

> *Sun-dappled kisses*
> *Echo off my skin to you*
> *Caught in the web of our love.*
> *We stare*
> *and understand.*

"We accept simultaneous submissions and previously published works. We like cover letters just because they are interesting reading." Seldom comments on rejections. Reports in 3 months. Pays 3 copies. The editor says, "*Candlestones* is an outgrowth of a monthly coffee house held in my home. Most contributors are under 30. Its twofold purpose is to give people a chance to have their creative efforts viewed by others and show the general populace (people who would never buy a book of poetry) the artistic achievement around them. It has been distributed in gas stations, factories, bookstores, record stores and beauty parlors. My advice is to submit. If one place rejects it, submit somewhere else. One poet I know wrote a poem in 1922. When it was submitted in 1990, it was printed. Don't wait so long. But be patient with the small press."

THE CAPE ROCK (II), Department of English, Southeast Missouri State University, Cape Girardeau MO 63701, founded 1964, appears twice yearly and consists of **64 pgs. of poetry and photography, with a $200 prize for the best poem in each issue and $100 for featured photography. "No restrictions on subjects or forms. Our criterion for selection is the quality of the work. We prefer poems under 70 lines; no long poems or books, no sentimental, didactic or cute poems."** They have published poetry by Stephen Dunning, Joyce Odam, Judith Phillips Neeld, Lyn Lifshin, Virginia Brady Young, Gary Pacernik and Laurel Speer. As a sample the editor selected these lines from "At The Rodin Museum, Stanford" by Fred D. White:

> *The lovers unleash their passion on the hot*
> *summer grass of the sculpture garden,*
> *surrounded by metal longing.*
>
> *They drop wild desires into each other's mouths*
> *like mother birds.*

It's a handsomely printed, flat-spined, digest-sized magazine. Their circulation is about 500, with 200 subscribers, of whom half are libraries. **Sample: $3. Guidelines available for SASE.** They have a 2- to 8-month backlog and **report in 1-3 months. Do not submit mss in May, June or July. Pays 2 copies.** This is a solid publication that features a wide selection of forms and styles, leaning in recent years toward free verse that establishes a mood or milieu.

CAPERS AWEIGH MAGAZINE (I, IV-Regional), P.O. Box 96, Sydney, Nova Scotia B1P 6G9 Canada, founded 1992, publisher John MacNeil, is a quarterly of **poetry and short fiction "of, by and for Cape Bretoners at home and away." They want work by Cape Bretoners only. Nothing profane.** The publisher says it is 50-60 pgs., 5×8, desktop published, stapled, including computer graphics and trade ads. Press run is 500. Subscription: $20. **Sample postpaid: $5. No simultaneous submissions. Cover letter required. Seldom comments on rejections. Pays 1 copy.**

CAPPER'S (I, IV-Nature, inspirational, humor), 1503 SW 42nd St., Topeka KS 66609-1265, founded 1879, editor Nancy Peavler, is a biweekly tabloid (newsprint) going to **370,000 mail subscribers, mostly small-town and farm people. Uses 6-8 poems in each issue. They want short poems (4-10 lines preferred, lines of one-column width) "relating to everyday situations, nature, inspirational, humorous."** They have published Helen Harrington, Emma Walker, Sheryl Nelms, Alice Mackenzie Swaim, Ralph W. Seager and Ida Fasel. Send 85¢ for sample. Not available on newsstand. "Most poems used in *Capper's* are upbeat in tone and offer the reader a bit of humor, joy, enthusiasm or encouragement. Short poems of this type fit our format best." **Submit 4-6 poems at a time. No simultaneous submissions. Now returns mss with SASE. Reports within 4-5 months. Pays $3-6/poem. Buys one-time rights.** The editor says "Poems chosen are upbeat, sometimes humorous, always easily understood."

THE CARIBBEAN WRITER (IV-Regional), University of the Virgin Islands, RR 02, P.O. Box 10,000, Kingshill, St. Croix, USVI 00850, phone (809)778-0246, founded 1987, editor Dr. Erika Waters, is an annual literary magazine **with a Caribbean focus. The Caribbean must be central to the literary work or the work must reflect a Caribbean heritage, experience or perspective.** They have recently published poetry by Carolina Hospital, Phillis Gershator and Ian McDonald. As a sample the editor selected the opening lines of "Nineteen Ninety-Two" by Howard Fergus:

> *Dawns 1992 a magic landfall*
> *on a brand new world of gold*
> *in Europe. Columbus makes a second*
> *coming after five hundred years*
> *not to violate virgin peoples*
> *but to carnival God for earlier conquests*

The magazine is handsomely printed on heavy pebbled stock, flat-spined, 160+ pgs., 6×9, with glossy card cover, using advertising and b&w art by Caribbean artists. Press run is 1,000. Single copy: $9 plus $1.50 postage; subscription: $18 for 2 years. **Sample: $5 plus $1.50 postage. Send SASE for guidelines.** (Note: postage to and from the Virgin Islands is the same as within the United States.) **Simultaneous submissions OK. Blind submissions only: name, address, phone number and title of ms should appear in cover letter along with brief bio. Title only on ms. Deadline is September 30 of each year.** The annual appears in the spring. **Pays 2 copies. Acquires first North American serial rights.** Reviews books of poetry and fiction in 500 words. Open to

The Caribbean Writer, the annual literary magazine of the University of the
Virgin Islands, seeks work with a Caribbean focus, says Editor Dr. Erika Waters, and about 50% of the magazine's
content is poetry. "The Caribbean must
be central to the poem or the poem
must reflect a Caribbean heritage, experience or perspective," Waters says.
"It goes without saying, that the African connection is very important in Caribbean literature. We chose this particular cover because it symbolizes that
connection." The cover artist is Marcia
Jameson of St. Croix.

unsolicited reviews. Poets may also send books for review consideration. The magazine annually
awards the Daily News Prize of $250 for the best poem or poems.

CARLETON ARTS REVIEW (II), Box 41, 18th Floor, Davidson Douton Tower, Carleton University,
Ottawa, Ontario K1S 5B6 Canada, phone (613)567-3525, founded 1982, is a 60-page biannual publishing poetry, prose, graphics, reviews and criticism. **"All kinds of poetry accepted and encouraged."** They
have published poetry by Stan Regal, Brian Burke, Calvin White and Alan Packwood. They receive
200-300 poems a year, publish about 10%. Press run is 400 for 50 subscribers most of which are
libraries, 150 shelf sales. Subscription: $7. **Sample postpaid: $3.50. No previously published poems or
simultaneous submissions. "Please include a short biography and list of publications."** Submit in
September or December. Often comments on rejections. Reports in 1-2 months. Pays 2 copies.

CARNEGIE MELLON MAGAZINE (II, IV-Specialized/alumni), Carnegie Mellon University, Pittsburgh PA 15213, phone (412)268-2132, editor Ann Curran, is the **alumni magazine for the university
and limits selections to writers connected with the university.** As a sample here is the opening stanza
of "A Daughter" by Lee Upton:
> Water on the white blossoms,
> warm, almost like the touch of oil.
> To be ridiculous and beautiful was
> one task for a daughter.

Direct submissions to Gerald Costanzo, poetry editor. No payment. Only using staff-written
reviews.

CAROLINA WREN PRESS (II, IV-Women, ethnic, gay/lesbian, social issues), 120 Morris St., Durham NC 27701, phone (919)560-2738, founded 1976, editor-in-chief Elaine Goolsby, poetry editor
Richard Morrison, publishes **"primarily women and minorities, though men and majorities also welcome."** They have published poetry by T.J. Reddy, Jaki Shelton Green, Mary Kratt and Judy Hogan.
As a sample the editor selected these lines from **This Road Since Freedom** by C. Eric Lincoln:
> Come Back
> Martin Luther King
> Play with me
> and hold my hand
> and help me still the turbulence
> the agitation that shakes me
> when I walk the streets of Boston
> where once you drew your strength.

Send book-length mss only. Reports in 2-4 months. Pays 10% of print run in copies. Publishes
1 book/year. Send 9½ × 12 SASE for catalog and guidelines (include postage for 3 ounces).

CAROUSEL MAGAZINE (II), Room 273, University Center, University of Guelph, Guelph, Ontario N1G 2W1 Canada, founded 1983, editor Michael Carbert, is an annual using **"any type of well-written, typed poetry,** as well as short stories, graphics or short plays. **We do not usually publish rhyming poetry. Mss should be well-edited before they are sent. Original, minimalist, off-beat material is encouraged."** They have recently published poetry by Hugh Hood, John Metcalf, Clark Blaise, Terry Griggs and Dionne Brand. It is 89 pgs., flat-spined. Their press run is 500. They accept about 30-40 of 300 pieces received. **Sample postpaid: $5. "We are reluctant to consider simultaneous submissions." Type name and address on each page. Cover letter with short bio and info on past publications required. Send SASE for guidelines. Reports in 3-4 months. Pays 1 copy.**

‡THE CARREFOUR PRESS (V), Box 2629, Cape Town, South Africa 8000, phone (021)477280, founded 1988, managing editors Douglas Reid Skinner and Dee Murch, is a "small press specializing in poetry, fiction, criticism, philosophy," accepting **"manuscripts by invitation only."** They have published poetry by Basil Du Toit, Douglas Livingstone and Israel Ben Yosef. They publish about 6 paperbacks a year averaging 80 pgs. Poets they publish **"should have an established reputation, primarily through magazines." Query with cover letter including previous publication details. Pays 7½-10% royalties and 20 copies.** About a third of their books are subsidized, and the poet "must assist in obtaining sponsorship."

CAT FANCY (IV-Themes, children), P.O. Box 6050, Mission Viejo CA 92690, phone (714)855-8822, founded 1965, editor Debbie Phillips-Donaldson. *Cat Fancy* is a magazine-sized monthly that uses poems on the subject of cats. **"No more than 30 short lines; open on style and form, but a conservative approach is recommended. In our children's department we occasionally use longer, rhyming verse that tells a story about cats. No eulogies for pets that have passed away."** They have published poetry by Lola Sneyd and Edythe G. Tornow. It has a press run of 368,575 for 303,328 subscribers, 37,502 shelf sales. Subscription: $23.97. **Sample postpaid: $4.50. Submit ms with name and address "in upper left-hand corner."** Editor sometimes comments on submissions, **"especially if the ms is appealing but just misses the mark for our audience." Reports in 6-8 weeks. Pays $20/poem plus 2 copies.** She says, "We have an audience that very much appreciates sensitive and touching work about cats. As for advice—get input from knowledgeable sources as to the marketability of your work, and be open to learning how your work might be improved. Then send it out, and hang on. Rejection may not mean your work is bad. We are able to accept very few submissions, and the competition is fierce. Timing and luck have a lot to do with acceptance, so keep trying!"

‡CATALYST: A MAGAZINE OF HEART AND MIND (I, II, IV-Themes), Suite 400, 236 Forsyth St., Atlanta GA 30303, phone (404)730-5785, founded 1986, editor Pearl Cleage, is a biannual designed "to stimulate readers and writers and move people to see the world differently." **They are "open to all types"** of poetry. However, each issue also has a special theme/focus. They have recently published poetry by Sonia Sanchez, Haki Madhubuti, Mari Evans and Amiri Baraka. As a sample we selected these lines from "Log" by Michael Blaine Guista:

> *Three 6-packs down and I'm only 16, practicing*
> *my father's stupor. Words thick as pines*
> *press through the gauzed air*
> *and my walk is familiar, like an old tic.*
> *I'm here and not here and watch myself*
> *like a ghost or the son of a ghost*

The above is from the issue about "The Plague Years" which tries "to tell the truth that emerges during times of great pain and sorrow and even greater confusion." *Catalyst* is 90-120 pgs., 7¾ × 10¾, newsprint, saddle-stapled with glossy cover, limited photographs, no ads. They receive 1,200-1,500 poems a year, accept 125-150. Press run is 5,000 for 1,500 subscribers of which 500 are libraries, 500 shelf sales. Single copy: $2.50; subscription: $10 for 2 years. **Sample: $2.50 and 9 × 12 SAE with 40¢ postage. Previously published poems and simultaneous submissions OK. All submissions must be typed, double-spaced. Include name and address on every page along with a 5-line biographical statement. Send SASE to the above address for theme and guidelines.** Send submissions to: *Catalyst*, Atlanta/Fulton Public Library, 1 Margaret Mitchell Square NW, Atlanta GA 30303. "Immediate acknowledgement will be made of work received but large volume submissions and very small staff mean that final decisions are not made for five to six months after submission." Pays $10-50. "Contributors also receive 2 complimentary copies upon publication of their work."

‡CATAMOUNT PRESS (II, IV-Anthology), 2519 Roland Rd. SW, Huntsville AL 35805, founded 1992, editor Georgette Perry, publishes 1-2 chapbooks and 1 anthology/year. During 1993 she was reading for **Witnessing Earth**, an anthology on nature and the sacred. **For the 1994 anthology, she is looking**

for poems relating to modern scientific ideas. As a sample the editor selected these lines from "The Study" by Virginia Gilbert:

> In Hasanlu, the man with the golden bowl
> is running along a wooden second storey ledge
> as it is being set on fire by foreign armies.
> In Pompeii, a boy cannot believe the incredible heat
> of ashes landing so softly upon him in a place
> to be called, "The House of the Charred Furniture."

That is from the chapbook **The Earth Above**, which is 24 pgs., digest-sized, printed on recycled paper and saddle-stapled. It is available for $3 postpaid. The editor says, **"The best chance for publication is to submit 3-5 poems on appropriate anthology theme."** Shorter poems preferred, **2-page limit. Previously published poems OK. Cover letter with SASE required. Reports in 1 month. Pays copies. Query regarding chapbook publication.**

THE CATHARTIC (II), P.O. Box 1391, Ft. Lauderdale FL 33302, phone (305)967-9378, founded 1974, edited by Patrick M. Ellingham, "is a **small poetry magazine devoted to the unknown poet with the** understanding that most poets are unknown in America." He says, "While there is no specific type of poem I look for, **rhyme for the sake of rhyme is discouraged. Any subject matter except where material is racist or sexist in nature. Overly-long poems, over 80 lines, are not right for a small magazine** normally. **I would like to see some poems that take chances with both form and language.** I would like to see poems that get out of and forget about self ['I'] and look at the larger world and the people in it with an intensity that causes a reader to react or want to react to it. I am gravitating toward work that looks at the darker side of life, is intense and uses words sparingly." **Considers sexually explicit material.** Recently published poets include Terry L. Persun, Keith A. Dodson, Joan Payne Kincaid and Carlos Fuertes. It's a modest, 28-page pamphlet, offset printed from typescript, consisting mostly of poems and appearing twice a year. **Sample postpaid: $3.** He receives over 1,000 submissions/year, uses about 60. No backlog. **Submit 5-10 poems. Simultaneous submissions OK. Guidelines available for SASE. Reports in 1 month. Contributors receive 1 copy.** Uses reviews of small press books as well as some artwork and photography. Send books for review consideration. He advises, "The only way for poets to know whether their work will get published or not is to submit. It is also essential to read as much poetry as possible—both old and new. Spend time with the classics as well as the new poets. Support the presses that support you—the survival of both is essential to the life of poetry."

‡CAT'S EAR (II), P.O. Box 946, Kirksville MO 63501, founded 1992, editor Tim Rolands, appears 3 times/year publishing both poetry and fiction. They want **"poetry that shows an understanding of music and metaphor."** They have recently published poetry by Diane Wakoski, Charles Edward Eaton and X.J. Kennedy. As a sample the editor selected these lines from "Homeland" by Ioanna-Veronika Warwick:

> Yet my deepest bond has not been
> to any country.
> The homeland of the mind
> has no boundaries.
> Books stand open like houses.
> Nobody is foreign.

Cat's Ear is 48-52 pgs., digest-sized, offset and perfect-bound with cover photo. They receive about 500 poems a year, use approximately 20%. Subscription: $10 individuals, $12 institutions.

CATS MAGAZINE (IV-Themes), P.O. Box 290037, Port Orange FL 32129, phone (904)788-2770, fax (904)788-2710, editor Tracey Copeland, is a monthly magazine **about cats, including light verse about cats,** for cat enthusiasts of all types. **Sample copy and writer's guidelines for $2 (postage and handling). All submissions or requests must have SASE. Pays 50¢/line on publication.**

WM CAXTON LTD. (I, IV-Regional), 12037 Hwy. 42, Ellison Bay WI 54210, phone (414)854-2955, founded 1986, publisher K. Luchterhand. **"About 50% of our books involve an author's subvention of production costs with enhanced royalties and/or free copies in return."** Acquires all rights. They want **"any serious poetry, not children's or doggerel."** Poetry must have Northern Midwest author or subject. They have published books of poetry by David Koenig, William Olson and Caroline Sibr. Write or call to purchase sample copies.

CCR PUBLICATIONS; CHRISTIAN POET (II), 2745 Monterey Hwy #76, San Jose CA 95111-3129, founded as Realities Library in 1975, as CCR Publications in 1987, editor and publisher Ric Soos. He has published books of poetry by Ruth Daigon and Ella Blanche Salmi. "Because of economic conditions, we have discontinued our book series. To replace the book series we have started *Christian Poet*. It will be published as often as we have time, poetry and finances. Seven issues appeared in 1992, 15 issues in 1993." *Christian Poet* is one 8½×11 page of colored paper, neatly printed and tri-folded. Subscription: $5 for 12 issues. **Poets may submit up to 15 poems for consideration. Send SASE for guidelines.** The editor says, "Please keep in mind when you contact me that I believe in Jesus Christ, and that anything I publish will be to help further the Gospel if it is for that purpose. **In poetry, I look for items that will not hinder the spread of the Gospel. In other words, the poet need not be Christian, does not need to mention Christ by name, but I will no longer be publishing for Shock Value.**" He publishes those "**who support me in some respect . . . Support is not always financial.**"

THE CENTENNIAL REVIEW (II), 312 Linton Hall, Michigan State University, East Lansing MI 48824-1044, phone (517)355-1905, founded 1957, managing editor Cheryllee Finney, appears 3 times/year. They want "**that sort of poem which, however personal, bears implications for communal experience.**" They have published poetry by David Citino and Dimitris Tsaloumas. As a sample the editor selected these lines from "Those Who Claimed We Hated Them" by Sherri Szeman:

> . . . *We clicked tongues in sympathy*
> *at the blue-black scratchings on their forearms.*
>
> *But we had all suffered during the war.*
> *We suffered, as they did. We had only*
>
> *feigned gaiety at their misfortunes, to*
> *convince our oppressors to spare our homes.*

It is 240 pgs., 6×9, desktop published, perfect-bound, with 3-color cover, art, graphics and ads. They receive about 500 poems a year, accept about 2%. Press run is 1,000 for 800 subscribers. Subscription: $10/year. **Sample postpaid: $5. No previously published poems or simultaneous submissions. Seldom comments on rejections. Send SASE for guidelines. Reports in about 2 months. Pays 2 copies plus 1-year subscription. Acquires all rights. Returns them "when asked by authors for reprinting."**

CENTER PRESS; MASTERS AWARD (III), Box 16452, Encino CA 91416-6452, founded 1980, poetry editor Jana Cain. Center Press (formerly Caravan Press) is "a small press presently publishing approximately 6-7 works per year including poetry, photojournals, calendars, novels, etc. We look for quality, freshness and that touch of genius." In poetry, "**we want to see verve, natural rhythms, discipline, impact,** etc. We are flexible but **verbosity, triteness and saccharine make us cringe.**" They have published books by Bebe Oberon, Walter Calder, Exene Vida, Carlos Castenada, Claire Bloome and G.G. Henke. Their tastes are for poets such as Charles Bukowski, Sylvia Plath, Erica Jong and Bob Dylan. "**We have strong liaisons with the entertainment industry and like to see material that is media-oriented and au courant.**" Sample postpaid: $8. **Query first, with 2-3 poems and brief bio material or curriculum vitae. If invited to submit, send double-spaced, typed ms. "No manuscripts will be read without SASE."** Simultaneous submissions OK. They reply "ASAP." They offer 20% royalty contract, 10-50 copies, advance or honorarium depending on grants or award money. "**Please study what we publish before submitting.**" Criticism offered on rejected mss. (Note: Fee charged if criticism requested.) "We sponsor the Masters Awards, established in 1981, including a poetry award with a $1,500 grand prize annually plus each winner (and the five runners up in poetry) will be published in a clothbound edition and distributed to selected university and public libraries, news mediums, etc. There is a one-time only $10 administration and reading fee per entrant. Further application and details available with a #10 SASE."

UNIVERSITY OF CENTRAL FLORIDA CONTEMPORARY POETRY SERIES (II), % English Department, University of Central Florida, Orlando FL 32816, founded 1970, poetry editors Judith Hemschemeyer and Don Stap, publishes **two 50- to 80-page hardback or paperback collections each year.** They have published poetry by Rebecca McClanahan Devet and William Hathaway. As a sample the editors selected the last lines of the poem "You Ask" by Jean Burden:

> *I walk toward a dark cabin*
> *carrying two flames in my mind,*
> *pressing the weeds down,*
> *What lasts?*
> *The turning day, falling water*
> *over stones, the sweet disorder*
> *of leaves,*
> *moons that come and go,*
> *wings.*

"**Please send a reading fee of $7, a SASE for return of ms and a self-addressed postcard for acknowledgment of receipt of ms.**" Reads submissions September through April. Reports in 2 months.

CHALK TALK (IV-Children), 1550 Mills Rd., RR 2, Sidney, British Columbia V8L 3S1 Canada, phone (604)656-1858, founded 1987, editor Virginia Lee, is a "non-glossy magazine **written by children for children** (with parents' pages), stories, poems, drawings, published 10 months/year. **Any form or subject matter.**" It is magazine-sized, 24 pgs., newsprint. No July or August issues. Approximately 3 pgs. each month are poems. Press run is 3,000 for 1,500 subscribers of which 15% are libraries. Subscription: $16.95 (incl. GST) CDN, $20 US and foreign. **Sample postpaid: $2. Simultaneous submissions OK. Send SASE for guidelines. Pays "as many copies as requested."** Reviews books of poetry.

CHAMINADE LITERARY REVIEW; THE UNTERECKER PRIZES (II, IV-Regional), 3140 Waialae Ave., Honolulu HI 96816, founded 1986, editor Loretta Petrie, appears twice yearly. **"No jingles, pop" poetry.** They have recently published poetry by Robert Parham, Richard Kostelanetz and Norma Gorst. As a sample the editor selected these lines from "Umbra, City of Refuge, Hawaii, 7/11/91" by Maureen Hurley:

> *The*
> *Moon bites*
> *the Sun's lips.*
> *A circle of darkness:*
> *the umbra descends like a*
>
> *tent across the barrier of clouds*
> *as if companion light was trapped*
>
> *deep in the arms of summer, remembering*
> *the past as blue as dreams of fish wanting to*
>
> *be water, becoming water. The birds, just finished*
>
> *with the morning song, begin a hurried evening chorus.*

CLR features the work of many well-known creative writers and thus, at first blush, seems like a mainstream literary magazine. But poems, prose and artwork play off each other for added effect and unify such themes as ecology, love, nature, etc. The handsomely printed magazine averages 175 pgs., flat-spined, 6 × 9 with glossy card cover. They accept about 25% of 500 poems received/year. Press run is 500 for 350 subscribers of which 6 are libraries. Subscription: $10/year, $18/2 years. **Sample postpaid: $4. Previously published poems OK. Pays year's subscription.** Open to unsolicited reviews. The Unterecker Prizes (cash awards) are awarded yearly to Hawaiian poets published in the magazine, and they give **special consideration to Hawaii's writers or Hawaii subject matter.**

CHANGING MEN: ISSUES IN GENDER, SEX AND POLITICS (IV-Feminist), 306 N. Brooks, Madison WI 53715, founded 1979, poetry editor Bob Vance, is described as **"a pro-feminist journal for men — politics, poetry, graphics, news."** He wants work by men and women that "expresses the emotional, intellectual and sensual complexity of living in America in an age enlightened by but not yet freed by feminism, gay liberation, socialism and ethnic beauty. A concern for form and invention is appreciated." They have published poetry by Sidney Miller, Diane Kendig, T. Obatala, Sesshu Foster, Assotto Saint and Denis O'Donovan. Though the poetry is "so varied" the editor felt he could not select 4 representative lines, here are the opening lines of Sholom Aram's "Two Poems on the Theme of Incest" to illustrate the quality, if not variety, of poetry in the magazine:

> *Shameful secrets bind us and hold us apart*
> *like the plastic rings on a six pack of beer.*
> *Who do I protect not to say what they are?*

They use about 6 pgs. of poetry in each magazine-sized issue, circulation 6,000, 2,000 subscriptions of which 10% are libraries. **Sample postpaid: $6. Submit up to 5 poems. Simultaneous submissions OK.** Cover letter not required but appreciated: short, personal, fun, no credit lists, no descriptions of enclosed poems. "Let the poems speak for themselves, but I don't mind short discussion of why one chooses to write (of all things) poetry." Editor sometimes comments on rejections. **Send SASE for guidelines. Reports in 2-8 months. Pays copies.** This publication was nominated for the *Utne Reader* Alternative Press Award in both 1991 and 1992. The editor says, "I am not limited to publishing poems directly related to pro-feminist men's issues, and would prefer to see work that relates to these issues by chance or in an original unexpected way. I am inundated with poems about fathers!"

‡CHANTRY PRESS (III), P.O. Box 144, Midland Park NJ 07432, founded 1981, poetry editor D. Patrick, publishes **perfect-bound paperbacks of "high quality" poetry. No other specifications.** They have published work by Laura Boss, Anne Bailie, Ruth Lisa Schechter and Joanne Riley. These sample lines are from **Winter Light** by Maria Gillan:

> *Remember me, Ladies,*
> *the silent one?*
> *I have found my voice*
> *and my rage will blow*
> *your house down.*

That's from an 80-page book (usually books from this press are 72 pgs.), flat-spined, glossy cover, good printing on heavy paper, author's photo on back, $5.95. **Send SASE for catalog to order sample. Don't send complete ms. Query first, with 5 sample poems, no cover letter necessary. Submission period October through April. Replies to queries in 4 months, to submissions in 4 months. Simultaneous submissions OK. Pays 15% royalties after costs are met and 10 author's copies.** Very short comment "sometimes" on rejected mss. The editor advises: "Do not be rude in inquiring about the status of your manuscript."

CHAPMAN (IV-Ethnic); CHAPMAN PRESS (V), 4 Broughton Place, Edinburgh EH1 3RX Scotland, phone (031)557-2207, founded 1970, editor Joy Hendry, "provides an outlet for new work by **established Scottish writers and for new, up-and-coming writers also,** for the discussion and criticism of this work and for reflection on current trends in Scottish life and literature. But *Chapman* is not content to follow old, well-worn paths; it throws open its pages to new writers, new ideas and new approaches. In the international tradition revived by MacDiarmid, *Chapman* **also features the work of foreign writers and broadens the range of Scottish cultural life.**" They have published poetry and fiction by Alasdair Gray, Liz Lochhead, Sorley MacLean, T.S. Law, Tom Scott and Una Flett. As a sample the editor selected these lines from Judy Steel's poem "For Nicole Boulanger" who, Steel says, "was born in the same year as my daughter and died in the Lockerbie air disaster of 1988":

> *You died amongst these rolling Border hills:*
> *The same our daughters played and rode and walked in -*
> *They make a nursery fit to shape and mould*
> *A spirit swift as water, free as air.*
>
> *But you, west-winging through the Christmas dark*
> *Found them no playground but a mortuary -*
> *Your young life poised for flight to woman's years*
> *Destroyed as wantonly as moorland game.*

Chapman appears 4 times a year in a 6×9, perfect-bound format, 104 pgs., professionally printed in small type on matte stock with glossy card cover, art in 2 colors. Press run is 2,000 for 900 subscribers of which 200 are libraries. They receive "thousands" of freelance submissions of poetry/year, use about 200, **have a 4- to 6-month backlog. Sample: £2.50 (overseas). Cover letter required. No simultaneous submissions. Reports "as soon as possible." Pays £8/page.** Staff reviews books of poetry. Send books for review consideration. **Chapman Press is not interested in unsolicited mss.** The editor says poets should not "try to court approval by writing poems especially to suit what they perceive as the nature of the magazine. They usually get it wrong and write badly."

THE CHARITON REVIEW PRESS; THE CHARITON REVIEW (II), Northeast Missouri State University, Kirksville MO 63501, phone (816)785-4499, founded 1975, editor Jim Barnes. *The Chariton Review* began in 1975 as a twice yearly literary magazine and in 1978 added the activities of the Press, producing "limited editions (not chapbooks!) of **full-length collections . . . for the purpose of introducing solid, contemporary poetry to readers.** The books go free to the regular subscribers of *The Chariton Review*; others are sold to help meet printing costs." The poetry published in both books and the magazine is, according to the editor, **"open and closed forms — traditional, experimental, mainstream.**

Market conditions are constantly changing! If you're still using this book and it is 1995 or later, buy the newest edition of Poet's Market at your favorite bookstore or order directly from Writer's Digest Books.

We do not consider verse, only poetry in its highest sense, whatever that may be. The sentimental and the inspirational are not poetry for us." They have published poets such as Michael Spence, Neil Myers, Sam Maio, Andrea Budy, Charles Edward Eaton, Wayne Dodd and Harold Witt. There are 40-50 pages of poetry in each issue of the *Review*, a 6×9, flat-spined magazine of over a hundred pages, professionally printed, glossy cover with photographs, circulation about 600 with 400 subscribers of which 100 are libraries. They receive 7,000-8,000 submissions/year, of which they use 35-50, with never more than a 6-month backlog. Sample postpaid: $2.50. Submit 5-7 poems, typescript single-spaced. No simultaneous submissions. Do *not* write for guidelines. Pays $5/printed page. Buys first North American serial rights. Contributors are expected to subscribe or buy copies. Open to unsolicited reviews. Poets may also send books for review consideration. *The Chariton Review* continues to be a lively magazine open to all styles and forms with only one criterion: excellence. Moreover, response times here are quick, and accepted poems often appear within a few issues of notification. To be considered for book publication, query first—samples of books $3 and $5. Payment for book publication: $500 with 20 or more copies. Usually no criticism is supplied.

THE CHATTAHOOCHEE REVIEW (II), DeKalb College, 2101 Womack Rd., Dunwoody GA 30338, phone (404)551-3166, founded 1980, editor-in-chief Lamar York, poetry editor (Mr.) Collie Owens, is a quarterly of poetry, short fiction, essays, reviews and interviews, published by DeKalb College. "We publish a number of Southern writers, but *CR* is not by design a regional magazine. In poetry we look for vivid imagery, unique point of view and voice, freshness of figurative language, and attention to craft. All themes, forms and styles are considered as long as they impact the whole person: heart, mind, intuition and imagination." They have recently published poetry by Peter Meinke, David Kirby, Allan Peterson, Bin Ramke, Peter Wild and Cory Brown. As a sample the editors selected these lines from "A Good Date" by David Staudt:

> We walked onto the ice dams after supper,
> cool floors powdered for a two-step.
> Snowfall we couldn't see hissed like sparks
> doused on our wet faces. Under the cliffs,
> reliefers from Packerton drank and howled,
> and domes of visible flakes, thick as glitter
> in souvenirs from the Poconos,
> flickered over cans of sterno or sticks
> where fishermen hunkered in lawnchairs
> over blue slots routered in the ice.

The Review is 6×9, professionally printed on white stock with b&w reproductions of artwork, 90 pgs., flat-spined, with one-color card cover. Its reputation as a premiere literary magazine continues to grow. Recent issues feature a wide range of forms and styles augmenting prose selections. Circulation is 1,000, of which 500 are complimentary copies sent to editors and "miscellaneous VIP's." Subscription: $15/year. Sample postpaid: $4. Writers should send 1 copy of each poem and a cover letter with bio material. No simultaneous submissions. Send SASE for guidelines. Queries will be answered in 1-2 weeks. Reports in 2 months and time to publication is 3-4 months. Pays 2 copies. Acquires first rights. Staff reviews books of poetry and short fiction in 1,500 words, single or multi-book format. Send books for review consideration.

CHICAGO REVIEW (III, IV-Translations), 5801 S. Kenwood, Chicago IL 60637, founded 1946, poetry editor Angela Sorby. "We publish high quality poetry. About 50% of the work we select is unsolicited; the remainder is solicited from poets whose work we admire. Translations are welcome, but please include a statement of permission from the original publisher if work is not in the public domain." They have published poets as diverse as Kathleen Spivack, Billy Collins, Cesare Pavese, Turner Cassity, Michael Donaghy, Meena Alexander and Adrian C. Lewis. "Out of the 1,500 submissions we receive each year, we accept around 50." Editors seem to prefer lyric free verse—some of it leaning toward avant-garde and some quite accessible—with emphasis on voice and content (depicting tense or intriguing topics or situations). Circulation: 2,000. Sample postpaid: $5.50. New submissions read October through June. Response time: 4-6 months, longer in some cases. Payment in copies. Occasionally reviews books of poetry. Open to unsolicited reviews.

CHICKADEE MAGAZINE; THE YOUNG NATURALIST FOUNDATION (IV-Children, nature), Suite 306, 56 The Esplanade, Toronto, Ontario M5E 1A7 Canada, founded 1979, editor Lizann Flatt, is a magazine **for children 3-9 about science and nature** appearing 10 times/year. They want **"evocative poetry; poems that play with words; humorous poetry; no longer than 50 lines. Nothing religious, anthropomorphic; no formal language; no poetry that is difficult to understand."** As a sample they selected these lines from "The Lunch Bunch" by Gwen Molnar:

> The dining room wall to wall
> With birds and beasts and fish,

> *The whole menagerie looked on*
> *As I downed every dish.*

It is 32 pgs., magazine-sized, professionally printed in full-color, with paper cover. They accept 1-2% of every 500 poems received. Circulation: 25,800 within US and 100,000 within Canada. Subscription: $14.95 US. **Sample postpaid: $3.75. Simultaneous submissions considered but not encouraged. Send SASE for writers' guidelines. Pays $10-75/poem plus 2 copies. Buys all rights.** "*Chickadee* is a 'hands-on' science and nature publication designed to entertain and educate 3-9 year olds. Each issue contains photos, illustrations, an easy-to-read animal story, a craft project, puzzles, a science experiment and a pullout poster." The magazine received the 1992 EDPress Golden Lamp Honor Award and Parents' Choice Golden Seal Awards.

CHICORY BLUE PRESS (IV-Women, senior citizens), 795 East St. N., Goshen CT 06756, phone (203)491-2271, founded 1988, publisher Sondra Zeidenstein, **publishes 2-3 chapbooks/year. She is currently open to receiving queries for chapbooks by women poets over age 60. Submit cover letter with only "a line or two of introduction of self and work." Replies to queries and mss (if invited) in 3 months. Seldom comments on rejections. Pays royalties, honorarium or 10 author's copies.** She has published poetry by Honor Moore and Pattiann Rogers. **Samples can be ordered from the press.**

CHILDREN'S BETTER HEALTH INSTITUTE; BENJAMIN FRANKLIN LITERARY AND MEDICAL SOCIETY, INC.; HUMPTY DUMPTY'S MAGAZINE; TURTLE MAGAZINE FOR PRESCHOOL KIDS; CHILDREN'S DIGEST; CHILDREN'S PLAYMATE; JACK AND JILL; CHILD LIFE (IV-Children), 1100 Waterway Blvd., P.O Box 567, Indianapolis IN 46206-0567. This publisher of magazines stressing health for children has a **variety of needs for mostly short, simple poems.** For example, *Humpty Dumpty* is for ages 4-6; *Turtle* is for preschoolers, similar emphasis, uses many stories in rhyme—and action rhymes, etc.; *Children's Digest* is for preteens (10-13); *Jack and Jill* is for ages 7-10. *Child Life* is for ages 9-11. *Children's Playmate* is for ages 6-8. All appear 8 times a year in a 6½×9, 48-page format, slick paper with cartoon art, very colorful. **Sample postpaid: $1.25. Send SASE for guidelines. Reports in 8-10 weeks. Pays $15 minimum.** Staff reviews books of poetry. Send books for review consideration. The editors suggest that writers who wish to appear in their publications study current issues carefully. "We receive too many poetry submissions that are about kids, not for kids. Or, the subject matter is one that adults think children would or should like."

CHIMERA POETRY MAGAZINE FOR CHILDREN; CHIMERA SUMMER POETRY CONTEST (I, IV-Children), P.O. Box 1007, Merchantville NJ 08109, founded 1990, editor Michael Northen, **appears quarterly using "primarily poetry by children (ages 18 and under), poetry written by adults for children and articles on poetry or teaching poetry written by young writers or teachers. For young writers any form or subject is fine (though I am not crazy about love poetry). I use a limited amount of adult poetry for children. It should be under 30 lines and honest (not cute, saccharine or condescending). No adult poetry for adults."** As a sample the editor chose 2 poems, the first, "The Old Tree" by Inez Dawson of Brooklyn, NY, age 11:

> *That lonely old tree*
> *bent all the way down to the ground*
> *sometimes I know how it feels*

And the second, "Artificial Age" by Pandora Rupert of Honolulu, HI, age 17:

> *Materialism is clearly all that counts*
> *As life is destroyed, ounce by ounce,*
> *Gluttony and wealth has robbed all care*
> *Making so many people, so unaware.*

The magazine is "to provide a publication where young writers can have poetry accepted and printed; to give writers for children a forum for writing." It is 52-64 pgs., photocopied from typescript with printed card cover, digest-sized. Press run is 200 for 100 subscribers, including 10 schools and libraries. It is distributed free to contributing teachers and schools. **Subscription: $8/year. Sample: $2.50. Pays adults 1 copy. "Young writers other than Featured Poets do not receive payment. The magazine is kept inexpensive so that young writers, if they wish, can afford copies of issues with their poems in print. I work closely with schools and encourage class submissions by teachers. Schools with several students submitting receive a free copy. Since I encourage beginning poets I have no strict guidelines other than name, address, school and grade should be included on each poem. No SASE is necessary for young writers, though it is appreciated. I like comments from writers about their writing. Acceptance in about one month. I try to comment on serious poetry submitted by individuals. I encourage classroom submissions but cannot respond to each poem."** Reviews books of poetry if written for children or by young writer (under 18). Summer poetry contest runs from June 1 through July 20. Prizes awarded in 2 age groups (5-12, 13-18). No entry fee. Winners printed in summer issue of *Chimera*. He adds, "I also try to assist school districts or towns that are running poetry contests for children. Once a year I publish a chapbook with representative poetry from four talented young writers who have been printed in *Chimera*. This year it was called **Dream Eye**. Basically, I try to do whatever it takes to encourage young poets."

CHIPS OFF THE WRITER'S BLOCK (I, IV-Themes); CATHARSIS (I), P.O. Box 83371, Los Angeles CA 90083, founded 1986, editor Wanda Windham. *Chips* is a bimonthly 16-page, magazine-sized newsletter offering "motivation and preparation for the published and soon-to-be-published writer" and using "occasional poetry related to writing, that is, the writing world of your personal muse, ups and downs of writing life, etc." *Catharsis* is a 40-page, digest-sized quarterly poetry journal using **"poetry of all genres with lengths from 1-40 lines. Poems should be meaningful, expressing your deepest emotions. No forced rhymes. Also no personal journal-type poetry."** As a sample we selected this poem, "Seizing the Moment," by Barbara Grant Richardson:

> You come to me in the darkness
> of the night.
> Seizing the moment of fulfillment
> and reaching the extremity of my soul.
> Where no other has gone
> in the darkness of the night.

Sample postpaid: $3 for *Chips*, $4 for *Catharsis*. Previously published poems and simultaneous submissions OK. Always comments on rejections. Send SASE for guidelines. Reports in 3-6 weeks. Pays 1 copy. Send books for review consideration. *Catharsis* also sponsors ongoing poetry contests. Send SASE for details.

CHIRON REVIEW; CHIRON BOOKS; CHIRON REVIEW POETRY CONTEST (I, II), Rt. 2 Box 111, St. John KS 67576-2212, founded 1982 as *Kindred Spirit*, editor Michael Hathaway, assistant editor Jane Hathaway, contributing editor (poetry) Gerald Locklin, is a tabloid quarterly using photographs of featured writers. **No taboos.** They have recently published poetry by Joan Jobe Smith, Marge Piercy, Antler, Adrian C. Louis and Will Inman. As a sample the editor selected these lines from "The Reservation Cab Driver" by Sherman Alexie:

> 3 a.m., he picks up Crazy Horse hitchhiking.
> "Where are you going?" asks the reservation cab driver,
> "Same place you are." Crazy Horse answers,
> "Somewhere way up the goddamned road."

Each issue is 24-32 pgs. and "contains dozens of poems." Their press run is about 1,000. **Sample postpaid: $3 ($6 overseas or institutions). Send 5 poems "typed or printed legibly." No simultaneous submissions or previously published poems. Send SASE for guidelines. Reports in 2-4 weeks. Pays 1 copy. Buys first-time rights.** Reviews books of poetry in 500-900 words. Open to unsolicited reviews. Poets may also send books for review consideration. **For book publication submit complete ms.** They publish 1-3 books/year, flat-spined, professionally printed, **paying 25% of press run of 100-200 copies.** Their annual poetry contest offers awards of $100 plus 1-page feature in Winter issue, $50, and 5 free subscriptions and a Chiron Press book. Entry fee: $1/poem.

THE CHRISTIAN CENTURY (II, IV-Religious, social issues), Dept. PM, 407 S. Dearborn St., Chicago IL 60605, phone (312)427-5380, founded 1884, named *The Christian Century* 1900, founded again 1908, joined by *New Christian* 1970, poetry editor Dean Peerman. This "ecumenical weekly" is a liberal, sophisticated journal of news, articles of opinion and reviews from a generally Christian point-of-view, **using approximately one poem/issue, not necessarily on religious themes but in keeping with the literate tone of the magazine. "No pietistic or sentimental doggerel, please."** They have published poems by Robert Beum, Joan Rohr Myers, Ida Fasel, Jill Baumgaertner, David Abrams, Catherine Shaw and J. Barrie Shepherd. As a sample the editor selected this poem, "Grain Silos," by James Worley:

> Cathedrals of the oldest preached religion,
> towers erected to the oldest useful god
> (the one now worshiped three times every day
> by those who can, invoked by those who can't)
> these cylinders of homage (oblong praise)
> project a plenty that is its own reward,
> a yearning that has grown its own response:
> the deity whom these raised prayers rise to laud
> resides (when crops are good) in grateful guts.

The journal is magazine-sized, printed on quality newsprint, using b&w art, cartoons and ads, about 30 pgs., saddle-stapled. **Sample postpaid: $2. No simultaneous submissions. Submissions without SASE or SAE and IRCs will not be returned. Pays usually $20/poem plus 1 copy and** discount on additional copies. **Acquires all rights. Inquire about reprint permission.** Reviews books of poetry in 300-400 words, single format; 400-500 words, multi-book.

THE CHRISTIAN SCIENCE MONITOR (II), Dept. PM, 1 Norway St., Boston MA 02115, phone (617)450-2000, founded 1908, an international newspaper. **Poetry used regularly in The Home Forum, editor Alice Hummer. Pays $25 and up.**

THE CHRISTOPHER PUBLISHING HOUSE (II), 24 Rockland St., Commerce Green, Hanover MA 02339, phone (617)826-7474, fax (617)826-5556, managing editor Nancy Lucas, who says **"We will review all forms of poetry." Submit complete ms.**

THE CHRONICLE OF THE HORSE (IV-Themes), P.O. Box 46, Middleburg VA 22117, phone (703)687-6341, founded 1937, assistant editor Cynthia Foley, is a weekly magazine using **short poetry related to horses "the shorter the better. No free verse."** The magazine is devoted to English horse sports, such as horse shows and steeplechasing. It averages 68 pgs., magazine-sized. Subscription: $42. **Sample postpaid: $2. No simultaneous submissions.** Summer **"is not a good time"** to submit. **1-3 editors read poems. Reports in 2-4 weeks. Pays $15/poem. Buys first North American rights.** "We review books submitted to us but do not accept reviews for publication."

‡CHRYSALIS: JOURNAL OF THE SWEDENBORG FOUNDATION (II, IV-Spirituality, themes), Rt. 1 Box 184, Dillwyn VA 23936, founded 1985, editor Carol Lawson, poetry editor Phoebe Loughrey. *Chrysalis*, appearing 3 times/year, is a "journal that draws upon diverse traditions to engage thought on questions that challenge inquiring minds. Each issue addresses a topic from varied perspectives using literate and scholarly fiction, essays and poetry dealing with spiritual aspects of a particular theme." They want **poetry that is "spiritually related and focused on the particular issue's theme. Nothing overly religious or sophomoric."** They have recently published poetry by Julia Randall and Robert Bly. As a sample the editor selected these lines from "Greenspeak" by William Borden:

> *In the dusk the leaves,*
> *arching like a canopy*
> *of fluttering green birds.*
> *spoke to me. They*
>
> *didn't trifle with Syntax*
> *but said everything*
> *at once, instantly, ...*

Chrysalis is 80 pgs., 7½ × 10, professionally printed on archival paper, perfect-bound with coated stock cover, illustrations, photos and ads for other literary publications. They receive about 120 poems a year, use 8-10%. Press run is 3,500 for 3,000 subscribers. Subscription: $20, outside US $25. **Sample postpaid: $6. No previously published poems or simultaneous submissions. Submit no more than 6 poems at one time.** Time between acceptance and publication is 18 months maximum. **Seldom comments on rejections. Send SASE for themes and guidelines. Reports in 2 months. Pays $25 and 5 copies. Buys first-time rights. "We like to be credited for reprints."**

THE CHURCH-WELLESLEY REVIEW; XTRA! (IV-Gay/lesbian), Box 7289, Station A, Toronto, Ontario M5W 1X9 Canada. *The Church-Wellesley Review* is the annual spring supplement for *XTRA! Magazine* (Canada's largest gay/lesbian newspaper.) **"We want short to medium-length poems. Our aim is always quality, not style.** Although **we prefer non-traditional poetry,** we have in the past published a contemporary 30-line 'up-dating' of Chaucer called 'Provincetown Tales.' **Amaze us or amuse us, but just don't bore us."** They have published Patrick Roscoe and Gwen Bartleman. The magazine has a press run of 24,000 and is distributed free. **Mss should include 5-8 poems with name on every page, daytime phone number and 25-word bio. Submissions are accepted January 1 through March 31.** "We do not respond at other times. **We report as soon as possible, definitely by publication in April. We pay an honorarium 1-2 months after publication** but, for heaven's sakes, if you don't hear from us write back!" Staff reviews books of poetry. Send books for review consideration to the attention of Jeff Round. *Xtra*, the review's parent magazine, has received several community awards as well as a journalism award for a column on Living with AIDS.

CIMARRON REVIEW (II), 205 Morrill Hall, Oklahoma State University, Stillwater OK 74078-0135, founded 1967, poetry editors Thomas Reiter, Jeff Kersh and Sally Shigley, is a quarterly literary journal. **"We emphasize quality and style. We like clear, evocative poetry (lyric or narrative) controlled by a strong voice. No obscure poetry. No sing-song verse. No quaint prairie verse. No restrictions as to subject matter,** although we tend to publish more structured poetry (attention to line and stanza). Also, we are conscious of our academic readership (mostly other writers) and attempt to accept poems that everyone will admire." Among poets they have published are Robert Cooperman, James McKean,

David Citino, Tess Gallagher and Albert Goldbarth. This magazine, 6×9, 100-150 pgs., perfect-bound, boasts a handsome design, including a color cover and attractive printing. Poems lean toward free verse, lyric and narrative, although all forms and styles seem welcome. There are 15-25 pages of poetry in each issue, circulation of 500, mostly libraries. **Submit to Deborah Bransford, managing editor, any time, 3-5 poems, name and address on each poem, typed, single- or double-spaced. No simultaneous submissions. Replies within 6-8 weeks. They pay $15 for each poem published. Buys all rights. "Permission for a reprinting is granted upon request."** Reviews books of poetry in 500-900 words, single-book format, occasionally multi-book. All reviews are assigned. Subscription rates: $3/issue, $12/year ($15, Canada), $30 for 3 years ($40, Canada), plus $2.50 for all international subscriptions.

‡**CINCINNATI POETRY REVIEW; CINCINNATI WRITERS' PROJECT (II, IV-Regional)**, Humanities Dept., College of Mount St. Joseph, 5701 Delhi Rd., Cincinnati OH 45233, founded 1975, editor Jeffrey Hillard, "attempts to set local poets in a national context. Each issue includes **a quarter to a third of work by local poets (within about 100 miles of Cincinnati)**, but most are from all over." They use **"all kinds"** of poetry and have published such poets as Enid Shomer, Lynne Hugo deCourcy, Pat Mora, Eve Shelnutt, David Citino, Colleen McElroy, Harry Humes, Keith Wahle and Yusef Komunyakaa. Publishes one issue/year, usually a fall/winter issue. *CPR* is handsomely printed, flat-spined, 80 pgs., digest-sized, all poems, art on the glossy card cover. Circulation is about 1,000, with 92 subscriptions, 20 of which are libraries. They use about 40-60 of 2,000 submissions/year. Subscription: $9 for 4 issues. **Sample: $2. Submit typed mss with address on each poem. Reports in 1-3 months. Pays 2 copies.** Under new editorship, the magazine is expected to continue the tradition of founding editor Dallas Wiebe in publishing the best work it receives, regardless of form, style or content. Each issue offers a poetry contest for poems of all types. The poems judged best and second in each issue receive cash awards of $150 and $50, and they hope to increase it. *CPR* is published by the Cincinnati Writers' Project. Other publications include **The Shadow Family** by Jeffrey Hillard; **The Kansas Poems** by Dallas Wiebe, **Dismal Man** by Jon Christopher Hughes, **River Dwellers — Poems on the Settling of the Ohio River** by Jeffrey Hillard and **Down the River — A Collection of Fiction & Poetry on the Ohio River Valley**.

‡**THE CINCINNATI POETS' COLLECTIVE (II)**, 27 Pleasant Ridge Ave., Ft. Mitchell KY 41017, founded 1988, editor Rebecca Mitchell Sullivan, is an annual poetry magazine. **"I am looking for fresh poetry that takes risks. I would like to see more poetry written about current issues from a conservative or politically incorrect point of view, however no subject is taboo. I do not want overly-didactic or ambiguous poetry; no soapbox material professing to be a poem. I am open to extensively published poets and to those who deserve to be but are not."** Poets recently published include Carol Feiser Laque and MJ Abell. As a sample the editor selected these lines from "Dividends" by Mary Rudbeck Stanko:

> *A rain of light pours like milk*
> *from our lucky star,*
> *filling to its brim the goblet*
> *which we clutch to our chest.*
> *We do not drink it,*
> *yet complain that we do not have*
> *enough;*
> *we are like children wailing*

TCPC is digest-sized, saddle-stapled. Circulation is approximately 150 through bookstore sales and subscriptions. **Submit up to 5 poems at a time. No previously published poems. Simultaneous submissions OK, if noted. Submit mss October 1 through March 1 only. Send SASE for guidelines. Reports in 4-6 months. Pays one copy.**

CITY LIGHTS BOOKS (III), 261 Columbus Ave., San Francisco CA 94133, phone (415)362-1901, founded 1955, edited by Lawrence Ferlinghetti and Nancy J. Peters, achieved prominence with the publication of Allen Ginsberg's **Howl** and other **poetry of the "Beat" school**. They publish **"poetry and advance-guard writing in the libertarian tradition."** Paper and cloth. **Simultaneous submissions OK. Reports in 4-6 weeks. Payment varies.**

CITY SCRIPTUM (I), City College of San Francisco, 50 Phelan Ave., San Francisco CA 94112, phone (415)239-3000, founded 1988, editor-in-chief Brown Miller, appears twice a year using **"any form from closed (traditional) to open (so-called 'free verse') but must be inventive, resonant, memorable, worth reading, nothing trite, wordy, sentimental, or any kind that reveals lack of knowledge about 20th Century verse."** They have published poetry by Lyn Lifshin, A.D. Winans and Seaborn Jones. As a sample the editor selected these lines from "Winter in Auschwitz" by Gayle Leyton:

> *a small boy*
> *has lost his birthday*
> *his mother*

> *keeper of his secrets*
> *wanders under the earth*
> *calling his name*

It is handsomely printed, magazine-sized, 58 pgs. with matte card cover. Press run is 1,000 for 10 subscribers of which 5 are libraries, 20 shelf sales. Subscription: $8. **Sample postpaid: $4 (when available). Do not submit July through August. Send SASE for guidelines. Reports in 2-6 months. Pays 2 copies.** The editor advises, "Read widely. Know the important poetry and poetic theories/criticism of this century. Then strive for a voice and vision of your own. Avoid too much of the discursive. Create surprise/magic that rings true."

THE CLASSICAL OUTLOOK (IV-Themes, translations), Classics Dept., Park Hall, University of Georgia, Athens GA 30602, founded 1924, poetry editors Prof. David Middleton (original English verse) and Prof. Jane Phillips (translations and original Latin verse), "is an internationally circulated quarterly journal (4,000 subscriptions, of which 250 are libraries) for high school and college Latin and Classics teachers, published by the American Classical League." **They invite submissions of "original poems in English on classical themes, verse translations from Greek and Roman authors, and original Latin poems. Submissions should, as a rule, be written in traditional poetic forms and should demonstrate skill in the use of meter, diction and rhyme if rhyme is employed. Original poems should be more than mere exercise pieces or the poetry of nostalgia. Translations should be accompanied by a photocopy of the original Greek or Latin text. Latin originals should be accompanied by a literal English rendering of the text. Submissions should not exceed 50 lines."** They have published work by Francis Fike and Roy Fuller. There are 2-3 magazine-sized pgs. of poetry in each issue, and they use 55% of the approximately 150 submissions they receive each year. They have a 6- to 12-month backlog, 4-month lead time. **Submit 2 copies, double-spaced. Receipt is acknowledged by letter. Poetry is refereed by poetry editors. Reports in 3-6 months. Pays 2 complimentary copies. Sample copies available from the American Classical League, Miami University, Oxford OH 45056 for $7.50. Guidelines available for SASE.** *The Classical Outlook* ranked #7 in the "Traditional Verse" category of the June 1993 *Writer's Digest* Poetry 60 list. Reviews books of poetry "if the poetry is sufficiently classical in nature." *The Classical Outlook* ranked #7 in the "Traditional Verse" category of the June 1993 *Writer's Digest* Poetry 60 list.

CLEANING BUSINESS MAGAZINE; WRITERS PUBLISHING SERVICE CO. (IV-Themes), 1512 Western Ave., P.O. Box 1273, Seattle WA 98111, phone (206)622-4241, fax (206)622-6876, founded 1976, poetry editor William R. Griffin. *CBM* (formerly *Service Business Magazine*) is "a quarterly magazine for cleaning and maintenance professionals" and uses some poetry relating to their interests. "To be considered for publication in *Cleaning Business*, submit poetry that relates to our specific audience—cleaning and self-employment." He has published poetry by Don Wilson, Phoebe Bosche, Trudie Mercer and Joe Keppler. The editor says it is 100 pgs., 8½×11, offset litho, using ads, art and graphics. Of 50 poems received, he uses about 10. Press run is 5,000 for 3,000 subscriptions (100 of them libraries), 500 shelf sales. Single copy: $5; subscription: $20. **Sample postpaid: $3. Send SASE and $3 for guidelines. Simultaneous submissions OK; no previously published poems. Pays $5-10 plus 1 copy.** Writers Publishing Service Co. is an imprint for subsidized publication of poetry (author's expense) and other services to writers. William Griffin suggests that "poets identify a specific market and work to build a readership that can be tapped again and again over a period of years with new books. Also write to a specific audience that has a mutual interest. We buy poetry about cleaning, but seldom receive anything our subscribers would want to read."

CLEVELAND STATE UNIVERSITY POETRY CENTER; CSU POETRY SERIES (II); CLEVELAND POETS SERIES (IV-Regional), Cleveland State University, Cleveland OH 44115, phone (216)687-3986, director Nuala Archer, editors Leonard Trawick and David Evett. The Poetry Center was founded in 1962, first publications in 1971. **The Poetry Center publishes the CSU Poetry Series for poets in general and the Cleveland Poets Series for Ohio poets. "Open to many kinds of form, length, subject matter, style and purpose. Should be well-crafted, clearly of professional quality, ultimately serious (even when humorous). No light verse, devotional verse or verse in which rhyme and meter seem to be of major importance."** They have published poetry by Martha Collins, Eric Trethewey, Phyllis Moss and Jared Carter. As a sample Leonard Trawick selected these lines from **Inland, Thinking of Waves** by Sarah Provost:

> *It seems to be spring, sweetie,*
> *here in the heart of the green*
> *proprieties. The thirsty wind is a rascal,*
> *makes quick work of our splendid*
> *coifs . . . .*

Books are chosen for publication from the entries to the CSU Poetry Center Prize contest. (Write for free catalog and sampler of some 65 Poetry Center books.) Deadline: March 1. Entry fee:

$10. The winner receives $1,000 and publication. They publish some other entrants in the Poetry Series, providing 50 copies (of press run of 1,000) and 10% royalty contract. The Cleveland Poets Series (for Ohio poets) offers 100 copies of a press run of 600. To submit for all series, send ms between December 1 and March 1. Reports on all submissions for the year by the end of July. Mss should be for books of 50-100 pgs., pages numbered, poet's name, address and phone number on cover sheet, clearly typed. Poems may have been previously published (listed on an acknowledgement page). Send SASE for guidelines. The Center also publishes other volumes of poetry, including chapbooks (20-30 pgs.), with a $5 reading fee for each submission (except for Ohio residents).

THE CLIMBING ART (IV-Themes), Fairfield Communications, 5620 S. 49th, Lincoln NE 68516, phone (402)421-2591, founded 1986, editor Scott Titterington, is a quarterly magazine **"read mainly by mountain enthusiasts who appreciate good writing about mountains and mountaineering. We are open to all forms and lengths. The only requirement is that the work be fresh, well-written and in some way of interest to those who love the mountains. If in doubt, submit it."** As a sample we selected "Our Mission" by John Grey:

> *The mountain has size on its side,*
> *the sense that things that big*
> *need not have opinions*
> *or make peace with the world.*
> *We, on the other hand,*
> *are at the bottom,*
> *suburbs, impossible affairs,*
> *promotions missed.*

It is 32 pgs., magazine-sized, professionally printed on heavy stock with glossy card cover. Press run is 3,000 for 1,800 subscribers of which 10 are libraries, 1,200 shelf sales. They use 4-10 poems/issue of 100-200 submissions received/year. Subscription: $18. **Sample postpaid: $4. Simultaneous submissions and previously published poems OK. Reports in 2 months. Pays 3 copies and subscription. Acquires one-time rights.** Reviews books of poetry only if they concern mountains. Open to unsolicited reviews. They also sponsor an annual poetry contest; first prize: $100.

CLOCKWATCH REVIEW (I, II), James Plath, Dept. of English, Illinois Wesleyan University, Bloomington IL 61702, phone (309)556-3352, founded 1983, James Plath is editor, Lynn Devore, James McGowan and Pamela Muirhead are associate editors. "We publish a variety of styles, leaning toward poetry which goes beyond the experience of self in an attempt to SAY something, without sounding pedantic or strained. We like a **strong, natural voice**, and lively, unusual combinations in language. **Something** *fresh, and that includes subject matter as well. It has been our experience that extremely short/long poems are hard to pull off.* Though we'll publish exceptions, we prefer to see poems that can fit on one published page (digest-sized) which runs **about 32 lines or less."** They have published Peter Wild, Martha Vertreace, John Knoepfle, Rita Dove and Peter Meinke. Asked for a sample, the editors say "trying to pick only four lines seems like telling people what detail we'd like to see in a brick, when what we're more interested in is the design of the *house*." The 80-page, semiannual *CR* is printed on glossy paper with colored, glossy cover. They use 7-10 unsolicited poems in each issue, with 1 featured poet. Circulation is 1,400, with 150 subscribers, of which 25 are libraries. They send out 300 complimentary copies and "The balance is wholesale distribution and single-copy sales." **Sample postpaid: $4.** They receive 2,080 submissions/year, use 20-30. No backlog. **Prefer batches of 5-6 poems. "We are not bowled over by large lists of previous publications, but brief letters of introduction or sparse minivitas are read out of curiosity. One poem per page, typed, single-spacing OK, photocopy OK if indicated that it is not a simultaneous submission (which we do NOT accept). Reports in 2 weeks; 2 months if under serious consideration. Payment is 3 copies, and, when possible, small cash awards—currently $5/poem."** They will comment "if asked, and if time permits." Only using staff-written or solicited reviews. Send books for review consideration if not self-published.

CLOUD RIDGE PRESS (V), 815 13th St., Boulder CO 80302, founded 1985, editor Elaine Kohler, a "literary small press for unique works in poetry and prose." They publish letterpress and offset books in both paperback and hardcover editions. In poetry, they want **"strong images of the numinous qualities in authentic experience grounded in a landscape and its people."** The first book, published in 1985, was **Ondina: A Narrative Poem** by John Roberts. The book is 6 × 9¼, handsomely printed on buff stock, cloth bound in black with silver decoration and spine lettering, 131 pages. Eight hundred

Market categories: (I) Beginning; (II) General; (III) Limited; (IV) Specialized; (V) Closed.

copies were bound in Curtis Flannel and 200 copies bound in cloth over boards, numbered and signed by the poet and artist. This letterpress edition, priced at $18/cloth and $12/paper, is not available in bookstores but only by mail from the press. The trade edition was photo-offset from the original, in both cloth and paper bindings, and is sold in bookstores. The press plans to publish 1-2 books/year. **Since they are not accepting unsolicited mss, writers should query first. Queries will be answered in 2 weeks and mss reported on in 1 month. Simultaneous submissions are acceptable. Royalties are 10% plus a negotiable number of author's copies. A brochure is free on request; send #10 SASE.**

CLUBHOUSE; YOUR STORY HOUR (I, IV-Children, teens), Dept. PM, P.O. Box 15, Berrien Springs MI 49103, poetry editor Elaine Trumbo. The publication is printed in conjunction with the **Your Story Hour** radio program, founded 1949, which is designed to teach the Bible and moral life to children. The magazine, *Clubhouse*, started with that title in 1982, but as *Good Deeder*, its original name, it has been published since 1951. Elaine Trumbo says, **"We do like humor or mood pieces. Don't like mushy-sweet 'Christian' poetry. We don't have space for long poems. Best—16 lines or under."** They have published poetry by Lillian M. Fisher, Audrey Osofsky, Sharon K. Motzko, Bruce Bash and Craig Peters. As a sample the editor selected these lines from "Nurses Office" by Eileen Spinelli:

> *And it hurts behind my ear,*
> *And I've got a cut right here,*
> *And a rash between my toes,*
> *And a pimple on my nose.*
> *Ouch, my knee feels sore and tender—*
> *Bumped it on my bike's back fender.*
> *I can't tell you all I've got.*
> *Where's the aspirin?*
> *Bring the cot!*
> *I need T.L.C. and rest.*

Too bad I'll miss that spelling test!
The magazine has a circulation of 10,000, with 10,000 subscriptions of which maybe 5 are libraries. Subscription: $5 for 6 issues/year. **Sample: 3 oz. postage.** Submit mss in March and April. Simultaneous submissions OK. **The "evaluation sheet" for returned mss gives reasons for acceptance or rejection. Writer's guidelines are available for SASE. Pays about $12 for poems under 24 lines plus 2 contributor's copies. Negotiates rights.** The editor advises, "Give us poetry with freshness and imagination. We most often use mood pieces and humorous poems that appeal to children."

‡CLUTCH (II), 109 Liberty St. #1, San Francisco CA 94110, founded 1991, editors Dan Hodge and Lawrence Oberc, is a biannual "alternative/underground literary review." They want **"poetry which explores or reveals an edge, societal edges especially. *Take chances.* Academic, overly studied poems are not considered."** They have recently published poetry by Charles Bukowski, Lorri Jackson, Todd Moore and Robert Peters. As a sample, the editors selected these lines from "1492" by Mitchel Cohen:

> *and the syringe is the size of a lover, O yes!*
> *and the kisses, and the bodies,*
> *and the fleshy zipless hallucinations*
> *that pass for lovers*
> *are no cure, no cure at all . . .*

The editors describe *Clutch* as 60-70 pgs., approximately 5½ × 8½. "Printing, binding and graphics vary with each issue. We receive approximately 120 unsolicited submissions a year, but we accept less than 10% of unsolicited material. The majority of material is solicited." Press run is 300 for 25 subscribers of which 2 are libraries, 50 shelf sales. Single copy: $4; subscription: $10. **Sample postpaid: $5. Make checks payable to Dan Hodge. Previously published poems and simultaneous submissions OK. Cover letter required. Reads submissions February through April and August through October. Seldom comments on rejections. Reports in 1-4 months. Pays 1 copy. Rights revert to authors.** "Open to publishing reviews of books/magazines from underground press." Poets may also send books for review consideration. The editors say, "We advise obtaining a sample copy or otherwise becoming familiar with the kind of poetry we've previously published before considering a submission."

‡COACH HOUSE PRESS (II, IV-Regional), Suite 107, 50 Prince Arthur St., Toronto, Ontario M5R 1B5 Canada, phone (416)979-7374, fax (416)979-7006, founded 1964, poetry editors Michael Ondaatje, Christopher Dewdney and Frank Davey, publishes **"mostly living Canadian writers of poetry and fiction, drama and literary criticism."** They have published finely-printed flat-spined paperback collections by such poets as Phyllis Webb, Michael Ondaatje, Paul Dutton, Diana Hartog, Dionne Brand. They **"lean toward experimental." Query with 10 samples. Cover letter should include bio and**

publication history. **Reports in 3-4 months. Contract is for 10% royalties, 10 copies.** Catalog sent on request. "Also, samples are on display in the Small Press Centre in N.Y.C. **We expect poets to be familiar with the Coach House flavor and to have a few journal publication credits to their name.** You don't have to be famous, but you do have to be good. Make the effort to do a little research on us, and save yourself time and postage. No SASE, no reply . . . and Canada Post does not accept American postage."

COCHRAN'S CORNER (I, IV-Subscribers), 225 Ralston, Converse TX 78109, phone (210)659-5062, founded 1985, poetry editor Billye Keene, is a **"family type" quarterly open to beginners, preferring poems of 20 lines or less. You have to be a subscriber to submit. "Any subject or style (except porn)."** She has published poetry by J. Alvin Speers, Becky Knight and Francesco BiVone. *CC* is 58 pgs. saddle-stapled, desktop published, with matte card cover, press run of 500. Subscription: $20. **Sample: $5 plus SASE. Simultaneous submissions and previously published poems OK. Send SASE for guidelines. Reports in average of 3 months. Pays 2 copies. Acquires first rights.** Reviews books of poetry. Send books for review consideration. Contests in March and July; $3 entry fee for 2 poems. "We provide criticism if requested at the rate of $1 per page. Write from the heart, but don't forget your readers. You must work to find the exact words that mirror your feelings, so the reader can share your feelings."

THE COE REVIEW (II), Coe College, 1220 1st Ave. NE, Cedar Rapids IA 52402, phone (319)399-8660, founded 1972, poetry editor Mae Soule, is "an annual little literary magazine with **emphasis on innovative and unselfconscious** poetry and fiction. We are **open to virtually any and all subject matter."** They have published poetry by James Galvin and Jan Weissmiller. The annual is 100-150 pgs., flat-spined, digest-sized with matte card cover. "Each issue includes 4-8 reproductions of works of art, usually photographs, lithography and etched prints." Circulation is about 500. **Sample postpaid: $4. No simultaneous submissions. Accepted work appears in the next issue, published in Spring. Include** "brief cover letter with biographical information. Submissions between April 1st and September 30th will go unanswered, as we only accept from October 1st through March 31st due to the academic school year." Send SASE for guidelines. **Reports in 6-8 weeks. Pays 1 copy.** The editor says, "We are supportive in the endeavors of poets whose material is original and tasteful. We are eclectic in our publication choices in that variety of subject matter and style make the *Coe Review* exciting."

COFFEE HOUSE PRESS (III), Dept. PM, Suite 400, 27 N. 4th St., Minneapolis MN 55401, phone (612)338-0125, founded 1984, editorial assistant Michael Wiegers, publishes 10 paperbacks/year. They want poetry that is **"challenging and lively; influenced by the Beats, the NY School or Black Mountain. No traditional or formalistic; nothing that relies on conventional assumptions like rhyme and meter."** They have published poetry collections by Victor Hernandez Cruz, Anne Waldman, Andrei Codrescu and Linda Hogan. As a sample the editor selected these lines from "Heading North" by Steve Levine:

> The family that eats together
> eats together and eats together, rides a
> tiny Honda together, two of them, huge
> matching bellies heading north

Previously published poems OK; no simultaneous submissions. Cover letter required. "Please include a SASE if you want your manuscript returned." Seldom comments on rejections. Replies to queries in 1 month, to mss in 6 months. Pays 8% royalties, $500 honorarium and 15 author's copies. Write for catalog to order sample.

COFFEEHOUSE POETS' QUARTERLY (I, II), 3412 Erving, Berthoud CO 80513, founded 1990, editors Ray Foreman and Barbara Shukle. **They want "free verse that is fresh, imaginative and clear, that brings the reader into the poet's experience."** They have published poetry by Albert Huffstickler, David Castleman, T. Kilgore Splake and Terry Everton. As a sample the editors selected the first lines of "The San Francisco Pit Band Blues" by Ray Clark Dickson:

> back when six-a-day vaudeville was alive
> & frisky & the drummer's rim shot tagged
> the dancer's body at the apex of her thrust
> the albino piano player smoked the ivories
> with both hands, keys all nicotined with
> yellow & stained with gin

It is 40 pgs. Press run 300 for 170 subscribers, balance sample copies and shelf sales. They accept about 10% of 2,000 poems submitted/year. "We showcase well-crafted quality poetry from known and unknown poets and promote contact between poets and audience through the Poets' Dialogue Network." Subscription: $8. **Sample, with guidelines, postpaid: $3. Submit up to 5 poems. Reports in about 2 weeks. Pays "with discount on copies."** The editors say, "Good poems convey experience in language, image and psychological clarity. What few poetry readers there are, are intelligent, sophisticated and discerning. Submit only your best work."

COKEFISH; COKEFISH PRESS (I), 31 Waterloo St., New Hope PA 18938, founded 1990, editor Ana Pine, is a monthly journal **with an entry fee of $1/3 poems. "I want to see work that has passion behind it. From the traditional to the avant-garde, provocative to discreet, trivial to the significant. Am interested in social issues, alternative, avant-garde, erotica and humor for people with nothing to hide."** They have recently published poetry by Charles Bukowski, Herschel Silverman, Elliot, Merle Tofer and Dave Christy. As a sample the editor selected these lines from "Contortionist" by Albert Huffstickler:

> *The hardest parts the recovery*
> *Unkinking limbs locked into place*
> *Till distortions become the truer way*
> *There's pain and exposure in realignment . . .*
> *And a blood-deep sorrow you can't account for*

The format is 60 pgs., side-stapled on heavy paper with a cover printed on both sides on colored photocopy paper. Press run is 300 for 150 subscribers. Subscription: $15. **Sample postpaid: $4. Accepts 30% of mss received. Note entry fee: $1/3 poems, additional $1 for additional poems. Simultaneous submissions and previously published poems OK. Cover letter "explaining why the poet chose *Cokefish*" required. Send SASE for guidelines. Reports in 1 week. Pays 1 copy.** Reviews books of poetry in ½ page. Open to unsolicited reviews. Poets may also send books for review consideration. "We publish a motley poetry broadside and will work with poets on publishing their chapbooks and audiotapes through Cokefish Press. Manuscript length up to 40 pages—$5 reading fee." *Cokefish* ranked #1 in the "Nontraditional Verse" category of the June 1993 *Writer's Digest* Poetry 60 list. The editor advises, "Spread the word; don't let your poems sit and vegetate in a drawer. Send me stuff that will make my hair stand up on end."

CO-LABORER MAGAZINE; WOMAN'S NATIONAL AUXILIARY CONVENTION (IV-Religious), P.O. Box 5002, Antioch TN 37011-5002, founded 1935, editor Melissa Riddle, is "a bimonthly publication **that addresses the concerns of today's Christian woman. We're interested in poetry that reflects daily Christian living, personal evangelism and missions-mindedness."** As a sample the editor selected these lines from "Grownups" by Debbie Payne Anderson:

> *"Debbie——ee!"*
> *The cry swells as I climb from the*
> *Car and slam the door behind me.*
> *They press as close as they dare.*
>
> > *Sweet urchins*
> *With their little bloated tummies*
> *And grimy hands extending in welcome.*
> *An inquisitive girl reaches out*
> *To stroke the soft material of my*
> *Dress and pat my pale skin.*

The 32-page magazine uses at least three poems/issue, circulation 15,000. **Sample postpaid: $1. Cover letter including name, address and short bio required. Pays copies.** Staff reviews books of poetry. Send books for review consideration.

COLLAGES & BRICOLAGES, THE JOURNAL OF INTERNATIONAL WRITING (II, IV-Translations, feminist, political, social issues, humor), P.O. Box 86, Clarion PA 16214, founded in 1986, editor Marie-José Fortis. *C&B* is a "small literary magazine with **a strong penchant for literary, feminist, avant-garde work.** Strongly encourages poets and fiction writers, as well as essayists, whether English-speaking or foreign. **(Note: Writers sending their work in a foreign language must have their ms accompanied with an English translation.)** We are presently looking for **poetry that is socially aware—politically engaged. No sexism, racism or glorification of war. We are going towards focus-oriented issues."** As a sample the editor selected these lines by Diane Hamill Metzger:

> *We adapt to the sanction of walls,*
> *Speak brashly the language of impostors*
> *Are shrouded in trappings of brown.*

The annual is magazine-sized, 100+ pgs., flat-spined, with card cover. They accept 5% of 150 poetry submissions/year. Press run is 400. **Sample postpaid: $6, or $3 for back issue. Reads submissions August 15 through November 30 only. Reports in 1-3 months. Pays 2 copies. Acquires first rights.** "It is recommended that potential contributors order a copy, so as to know what kind of work is desirable. **Enclose a personalized letter.** Be considerate to editors, as many of them work on a voluntary basis and sacrifice much time and energy to encourage writers." Marie-José Fortis says, "It is time to stop being too plastic and too polite and too careful. The

Berlin Wall is down. Eastern Europe will bring to us powerful, daring literary voices, with much to tell. The American writer should follow a similar path. With what was revealed as the temptation of war and the neglect of an effort for peace, too many things are left unsaid."

COLLEGE & CAREER PUBLISHING; CALIFORNIA WORK WORLD (I, IV-Children/teen/young adult, students), P.O. Box 900, Ontario CA 91761-8900, founded 1989. *California Work World* is a "monthly newsletter/workbook to help junior high and high school students learn about college and jobs as well as how to be a good citizen in our world and cope with problems encountered along the way." They want **"rhyming poems with messages for teenagers; 5-40 lines. No non-rhyming, free-form verse."** As a sample the editor selected these lines by Beverly Bassler:

> *Success with life's struggles begins with one's self,*
> *Jump in, get your feet wet, get off the shelf!*
>
> *We're all in this world on a stage, in a play;*
> *Each person's unique in his style and his way.*
>
> *Find something of value . . . stay focused . . . begin,*
> *To reach for your goals by the power from within!*

CWW is 16 pgs., glue bound, with puzzles and illustrations. Press run is 6,000. **Sample postpaid: $1. Previously published poems and simultaneous submissions OK.** Time between acceptance and publication is 3-4 months. "Poems are tested with groups of teenagers, and they choose favorites." **Often comments on rejections. "If comments are desired, poet must include SASE." Send SASE for guidelines. Reports in 2-3 months. Pays $20 and 20 copies.**

COLLEGE ENGLISH; NATIONAL COUNCIL OF TEACHERS OF ENGLISH (II), Dept. of English, University of Massachusetts-Boston, 100 Morrissey Blvd., Boston MA 02125-3393, phone (617)287-6733, editor Louise Z. Smith, poetry editors Helene Davis and Thomas Hurley. This journal, which goes 8 times/year to members of the National Council of Teachers of English (membership: $40, includes subscription to *CE*), is a scholarly journal for the English discipline, but includes poetry by such poets as Beth Kalikoff, Peter R. Stillman and E.M. Schorb. It is 100 pgs., perfect-bound, with matte card cover, 7½×9½, circulation 18,000. Poems tend to be wide-ranging in style, form and content. **Sample postpaid: $6. Submit 2 "letter-quality copies" of each poem with cover letter including titles of poems submitted. Reports in 4 months maximum, except for summer submissions. Pays 6 copies.**

COLOR WHEEL; 700 ELVES PRESS (IV-Nature, spiritual), RR 2, Box 806, Warner NH 03278, founded 1990, editor Frederick Moe, associate editor Carol Edson, appears approximately 2 times/year. *"Color Wheel* **uses high quality prose and poetry related to spiritual, ecological and mythological themes. All forms of poetry are welcome, including longer poems (2-4 pages). No rhymed verse."** They have recently published poetry by Walt Franklin, Will Inman, Caryl Porter, Marjorie Power and Gary Lawless. The editor says it is 32-40 pgs., 8×11, saddle-stapled, with heavy cover stock, cover art, graphics and line drawings. They receive about 300 submissions a year, use an average of 5%. Press run is 300 for 30 subscribers of which 4 are libraries, 100+ shelf sales. Single copy: $5; subscription: $10 (2 issues). **Sample back issue postpaid: $4.50. Make checks payable to Frederick Moe. No simultaneous submissions. Cover letter required—include "something that does not keep the writer 'anonymous'!" Reads submissions January 1 through August 15 only. Seldom comments on rejections. Send SASE for guidelines. Reports in up to 1 month. Pays in copies.** Staff reviews books of poetry. Send books for review consideration to Frederick Moe at the above address, or to Carol Edson at 1804 NE 50th, Seattle WA 98105. **700 Elves Press publishes 2 chapbooks/year.** "Some 700 Elves Press chapbooks are thematic anthologies including various writers. I have published chapbooks on elemental poems and plan other thematic chapbooks and occasional individual collections." **Poets should first be published in** *Color Wheel.* **Replies to queries and mss in 1 month. Pays "negotiable" number of author's copies.** For sample chapbooks "send SASE for our small, homespun catalog." Frederick Moe says, *"Color Wheel* is esoteric yet focused in content. Poets should be familiar with the evolution of the magazine and type of material we publish before sending work. I encourage 'new' voices and appreciate creative approaches to the material. I am annoyed by poets who enclose postcards for response rather than a SASE and expect me to recycle their manuscript. I do not respond to such submissions. Inclusion of a SASE allows me to return press information with response and demonstrates concern on the part of the writer for their work. It is worth the extra expense!"

COLORADO NORTH REVIEW (III), Dept. PM, UC 208, University Center, University of Northern Colorado, Greeley CO 80639, phone (303)351-1890, founded 1963 as *Nova*, editor L. Christopher Baxter, appears twice a year (December and May). **"We consider all mss without bias, regardless of style, form, genre or so-called 'schools.' I open all the mail myself and look primarily for poetic integrity, that is a synthesis between original vision and a unique and organic means of expressing it.**

Overly poetic language (i.e. artificial) and clichéd sentiments are frowned upon." They have published poetry by Florence Elon, Anselm Hollo, Robert Long, Phyllis Koestenbaum and Eileen Myles. As a sample the editor selected these lines from "Les L'armes Sanglant DEnfer" by William Hathaway:

> Go ahead! Rename candy tears,
> red as bloody beads we pricked
> on fingertips for holy love
> as kids. The ones stinging spit-
> fire cinnamon we called "red hots."

It is 100-120 pgs., flat-spined (with occasional double issues of up to 220 pgs.), printed on 70 lb. vellum paper. They received over 900 mss for a recent issue, accepted 74 poems from 39 poets (and 12 pieces of fiction). Press run is 2,500 for 65 subscriptions of which 40 are libraries. Subscription: $8. **Sample postpaid: $4.50. No simultaneous submissions. Do not submit mss during June or July. Editor comments "when time allows or in exceptional cases." Send SASE for guidelines. Reports in 1-2 months. Pays 2 copies plus** *CNR* **T-shirts when available.** Reviews books of poetry.

COLORADO REVIEW (II, IV-Translations, themes), Dept. of English, 359 Eddy Bldg., Colorado State University, Ft. Collins CO 80523, phone (303)491-5449, fax (303)491-5601, founded 1955 as *Colorado State Review*, resurrected 1977 under "New Series" rubric, renamed *Colorado Review* 1985, editor David Milofsky, poetry editor Jorie Graham. *Colorado Review* is a journal of contemporary literature which appears twice annually; it combines short fiction, poetry, interviews with or articles about significant contemporary poets and writers, articles on literature, culture and the arts, translations of poetry from around the world and reviews of recent works of the literary imagination. **"We're interested in poetry that explores experience in deeply felt new ways; merely descriptive or observational language doesn't move us. Poetry that enters into and focuses on the full range of experience, weaving sharp imagery, original figures and surprising though apt insight together in compressed precise language and compelling rhythm is what triggers an acceptance here."** They have published poetry by Tess Gallagher, James Galvin and Brendan Galvin. They have a circulation of 1,500, 300 subscriptions of which 100 are libraries. They use about 10% of the 500-1,000 submissions they receive/year. Subscription: $15/year. **Sample postpaid: $5. Submit about 5 poems. Reads submissions September 1 through April 1 only. "When work is a near-miss, we will provide brief comment and encouragement." Reports in 3-6 months. Pays $20/printed page. Buys first North American serial rights.** Reviews books of poetry, both single and multi-book format. Open to unsolicited reviews. Poets may also send books for review consideration. They say, "Our attitude is that we will publish the best work that comes across the editorial desk. We see poetry as a vehicle for exploring states of feeling, but we aren't interested in sentimentality (especially metaphysical)."

COLUMBIA: A MAGAZINE OF POETRY & PROSE; EDITORS' AWARDS (II), Dept. PM, 404 Dodge Hall, Columbia University, New York NY 10027, phone (212)854-4391, founded 1977, is a literary semiannual using "quality short stories, novel excerpts, translations, interviews, nonfiction and **poetry, usually no longer than 2 pgs. Nothing juvenile, sentimental, simply descriptive."** They have published poetry by Henri Cole, Theresa Svoboda, Eamon Grennan and Jimmy Santiago-Baca. It is digest-sized, approximately 180 pgs., with coated cover stock. They publish about 12 poets each issue from 400 submissions. Press run is 1,250 for 1,000 subscriptions of which 100 are libraries, 400 shelf sales. **Sample postpaid: $7. Submit double-spaced mss. "Very brief comments at editor's discretion." Send SASE for guidelines. Reports in 1-3 months. Pays up to 4 copies.** They offer honorarium Editors' Awards for the best poems published annually.

COLUMBIA UNIVERSITY TRANSLATION CENTER; TRANSLATION; TRANSLATION CENTER AWARDS (IV-Translations), 412 Dodge, Columbia University, New York NY 10027, phone (212)854-2305, founded 1972, director Frank MacShane. "Translation Center publishes only foreign contemporary literature in English language translations and also gives annual awards and grants to translators. *Translation* magazine publishes **contemporary foreign poetry/literature in English language translations. (Note: we do no reviews.)"** They have recently published translations of poetry by Silvina Ocampo, Luis Cernuda, Nina Cassian, Eva Toth and Faiz Ahmed Faiz. As a sample we selected these lines from "Body" by Eugénio de Andrade, translated from the Portuguese by Alexis Levitin:

> The sea—whenever I touch
> a body the sea is what I feel
> wave after wave
> against the palm of my hand.

Translation is a biannual, circulation 2,000. Subscription: $18. **Sample postpaid: $9. "All submissions need be preceded by a query. Each issue is specialized to one language and consequently all unsolicited manuscripts have to be limited to that language." Send SASE for guidelines and descriptions of the various award programs they administer.** Columbia University Translation

Center Awards are grants to a translator for an outstanding translation of a substantial part of a book-length literary work. Awards range from $250-2,500 and are designed mainly to recognize excellence. Translations from any language into English are eligible, and specific awards exist for translations from the French Canadian, Dutch, Portuguese and Italian. All applications will automatically be considered for all awards for which they are eligible. The Center generally discourages applicants who are retranslating a work unless a special reason exists.

‡THE COLUMBUS LITERARY GAZETTE; LITERARY FUTURES: A FORUM (I), P.O. Box 141418, Columbus OH 43214, phone (614)262-4425, founded October 1991, editor Bonnie J. Djouadi. *The Gazette* is a monthly "forum for all points of view and walks of life, if pieces are written in a creative form." **They "prefer poems that are easily understandable and that give powerful messages—all walks of life are represented. Rhymed poetry adored. No poems with vulgarity for shock value."** They have recently published poetry by Judith Fannie Rose, Matthew Behling, William Vernon and Nancy J. Fuller. As a sample we selected these lines from "Down by the Pond" by Indigo:

> Woodwind reeds,
> Moored. Paint-drained and creaking
> Loneliness. Cattails, snails,
> And algae film rise.

The Gazette is a 12-page, tabloid-sized newspaper which includes a featured short story, 'Poetry Corner,' 'Young Readers,' 'Young Writers,' essays and other short stories as well as a calendar of literary events, an ongoing novel and advertising. They accept approximately 80% of the poetry received each year and publish 8-10 poems/month. Press run is 1,000 for 135 subscribers, 65 shelf sales. 800 distributed free to front porches, restaurants, hotels, etc. Single copy: $1; subscription: $10. **Sample postpaid: $1.50. No previously published poems; simultaneous submissions OK. "Please type name, address and phone number in top right-hand corner of poem sheet."** Time between acceptance and publication is 1 year. **Poems are reviewed by volunteers who write comments; editor makes final decision. Always comments on rejections. Send SASE for guidelines. Reports in 4 months. Pays 1 copy.** The editor will also select poetry for publication from an author's chapbook. Send chapbooks for consideration. Literary Futures is an open reading forum for poets held at 7:30 p.m. on the third Friday of each month at 245 W. Fifth Ave., Columbus. Write or call for more information. The editor adds, "We attempt to make publishing an enjoyable experience—you will receive a galley proof before printing, a contract to review and, upon publication, may be asked to be a featured reader in Literary Futures: A Forum. We are pleased to accept your poetry *regardless* of your 'literary' credentials."

COMMONWEAL (III, IV-Religious), 15 Dutch St., New York NY 10038, phone (212)732-0800, poetry editor Rosemary Deen, appears every 2 weeks, circulation 20,000, is a general-interest magazine for college-educated readers **by Catholics. Prefers serious, witty, well-written poems of up to 75 lines. Does not publish inspirational poems.** As a sample the editor selected these lines from "One is One," a sonnet by Marie Ponsot:

> Heart, you bully, you punk, I'm wrecked, I'm shocked
> stiff. You? you still try to rule the world—though
> I've got you: identified, starving, locked
> in a cage you will not leave alive . . .

In the issues we reviewed, editors seemed to favor free verse, much of it open with regard to style and content, appealing as much to the intellect as to the emotions. **Sample: $3. Considers simultaneous submissions. Reads submissions September 1 through June 30 only. Pays 50¢ a line. Buys all rights. Returns rights when requested by the author.** Reviews books of poetry in 750-1,000 words, single or multi-book format.

COMMUNICATIONS PUBLISHING GROUP; COLLEGE PREVIEW, A GUIDE FOR COLLEGE-BOUND STUDENTS; DIRECT AIM; A GUIDE TO CAREER ALTERNATIVES; JOURNEY, A SUCCESS GUIDE FOR COLLEGE AND CAREER-BOUND STUDENTS; VISIONS, A SUCCESS GUIDE FOR NATIVE AMERICAN STUDENTS; FIRST OPPORTUNITY, A GUIDE FOR VOCATIONAL TECHNICAL STUDENTS (IV-Youth, themes, ethnic), Dept. PM, #250, 106 W. 11th St., Kansas City MO 64105-1806, phone (816)221-4404, editor Georgia Clark. These five publications are 40% freelance written. All are designed to inform and motivate their readers in regard to college preparation, career planning

The double dagger before a listing indicates that the listing is new in this edition. New markets are often the most receptive to submissions.

and life survival skills. All except *First Opportunity*, which is quarterly, appear in spring and fall. *College Preview* is for Black and Hispanic young adults, ages 16-21. Circ. 600,000. *Direct Aim* is for Black and Hispanic young adults, ages 18-25. Circ. 500,000. *Journey* is for Asian-American high school and college students, ages 16-25. Circ. 200,000. *Visions* is for Native American students and young adults, ages 16-25. Circ. 100,000. *First Opportunity* is for Black and Hispanic young adults, ages 16-21. Circ. 500,000. Sample copy of any for 9×12 SAE with 4 first class stamps. Simultaneous and previously published submissions OK. Submit seasonal/holiday material 6 months in advance. "Include on manuscript your name, address, phone and Social Security numbers." They use free verse. Each magazine buys 5 poems/year. Submit up to 5 poems at one time. Length: 10-25 lines. Writer's guidelines for #10 SASE. Reports in 2 months. Pays $10-50/poem. All these magazines pay on acceptance.

COMMUNITIES: JOURNAL OF COOPERATIVE LIVING (IV-Social issues), Rt. 1, Box 155, Rutledge MO 63563, phone (816)883-5543, founded 1972, managing editor Laird Schaub, is a "quarterly publication on intentional communities, cooperatives, social and global transformation," using poetry relevant to those themes. It is magazine-sized, professionally printed on recycled white stock with 2-color glossy paper cover, 56 pgs., saddle-stapled. Previously published poems and simultaneous submissions OK. No comment on rejections. Pays 3 copies. They also publish a directory of international communities.

A COMPANION IN ZEOR (IV-Science fiction/fantasy), 307 Ashland Ave., McKee City NJ 08232, phone (609)645-6938, founded 1978, editor Karen Litman, is a science fiction, fantasy fanzine appearing *very* irregularly (last published issue December 1990; hopes to publish again this year). "Material used is now limited to creations based solely on works (universes) of Jacqueline Lichtenberg. No other submission types considered. Prefer nothing obscene. Homosexuality not acceptable unless very relevant to the piece. Prefer a 'clean' publication image." As a sample, we selected these lines from "Fire Also Purifies" by Lisa Calhoun:

> *A death is a birth, and the reverse is true,*
> *out of the turmoil emerges something new.*

It is magazine-sized, photocopied from typescript. Press run is 100. Send SASE for guidelines. Cover letter preferred with submissions; note whether to return or dispose of rejected mss. Pays copies. Acquires first rights. "Always willing to work with authors to help in improving their work." Reviews books of poetry. Open to unsolicited reviews. Poets may also send books for review consideration.

‡COMPENIONS; THE WRITER'S CLUB OF STRATFORD (I), P.O. Box 2511, St. Marys, Ontario N4X 1A3 Canada, founded 1983, president Marco Balestrin, is a quarterly publication of The Writer's Club of Stratford. "We print works by the members of the W.C.S. but would like to expand our mandate to include poetry and short fiction by other writers." They want "original, sincerely-written poetry of any form, 30 lines maximum. No cliched or trite poetry. No pornography." They have recently published poetry by Elda Cadogan, Susan Chapman-Bossence and Carol Lease. As a sample Marco Balestrin selected these lines from "5 O'clock Tea" by Helen Charles:

> *"There is no poverty here!"*
> *(pale-blue eyes reflecting emptiness)*
> *tinkle of china against cut glass*

Compenions is 14-20 pgs., 8½×11, photocopied, side-stapled, with computer graphics. They receive about 40 poems a year, use approximately 90%. Press run is 16 ("will increase after further submissions are received"). Sample postpaid: $4. Submit up to 6 poems at a time *with $3.50 reading fee*. Previously published poems and simultaneous submissions OK. Cover letter required. "Please include a SASE (if within Canada) or SAE and 2 IRCs (if outside Canada)." Reads submissions September 1 through June 30 only. "Two to three members read over submissions and choose suitable poems." Often comments on rejections. Reports in 1 month. Pays 2 copies. Balestrin says, "We would like to be a forum providing writers (especially beginners) the opportunity to get published, thereby also exposing ourselves to what is going on 'out there,' in other words, to have a literary relationship beneficial to both parties!"

CONCHO RIVER REVIEW; FORT CONCHO MUSEUM PRESS (IV-Regional), 213 E. Ave. D, San Angelo TX 76903, phone (915)657-4441, founded 1984, poetry editor Gerald M. Lacy. "The Fort Concho Museum Press is entering another year of publishing *Concho River Review*, a literary journal published twice a year. Work by Texas writers, writers with a Texas connection and writers living in the Southwest preferred. Prefer shorter poems, few long poems accepted; particularly looking for poems with distinctive imagery and imaginative forms and rhythms. The first test of a poem will be its imagery." Short reviews of new volumes of poetry are also published. *CRR* is 120-138 pgs., flat-spined, digest-sized, with matte card cover, professionally printed. They use 35-40 of 600-800 poems received/year. Press run is 300 for about 200 subscriptions of which 10 are libraries. Subscription: $12.

Open Nature's Door for Ideas

"A History of Our Land"

*In the old times here the hills moved
like big animals. They ate up
villages and climbed on down
into the sea. And the weather then
was always hungry; it fastened
icy teeth deeper every night and returned
for more. In winter it ate up
everything. The stars didn't care
about anybody. They drilled holes
wherever the clouds opened. Big trees
get together now and whisper their stories
about when bears were the only people.*

Photo by Kit Stafford

William Stafford

William Stafford is one of the most widely published and popular poets writing today. Since the early 1950s, he has sold individual poems to such magazines as *The Atlantic*, *Poetry* and *The New Yorker*. He has placed so many collections of verse that to list them would fill an entire page of print. In fact, in his biographical sketch, Stafford no longer notes the total number of poetry books he has published over the years.

Here's why: In four years (1988-92), Stafford published 13 poetry collections, including **Writing the World** (Alembic); **A Scripture of Leaves** (Brethren); **Fin, Feather, Fur** (Honeybrook); **Kansas Poems** (Woodley Memorial); **Passwords** (HarperCollins); **The Long Sign the Wind Makes** (Adrienne Lee); **The Animal That Drank Up Sound**, a children's book (Harcourt Brace Jovanovich); and **My Name Is William Tell** (Confluence).

By the time you will have read this close-up, he undoubtedly will have published several more collections.

He describes his method of composition in his 1978 classic, **Writing the Australian Crawl: Views on the Writer's Vocation**, published by the University of Michigan Press. Simply, Stafford shows up to compose each day, pen and paper in hand, and lets the poem happen, word by word, image by image. "We can't keep from thinking," he writes.

In 1983, I had the opportunity to witness Stafford at work. At the time, I was director of the Southwest Cultural Heritage Festival at Oklahoma State University and awarded our Medal of Arts to him. Afterward, at a Native American art show on campus, I saw him take a reporter's notebook from his back pocket. He would look at the paintings and weavings and scribble in his pad. I had assumed he was taking notes. Later I learned that he had composed the first draft of a poem.

Before he left campus, Stafford gave an interview to *Cimarron Review*—I was poetry editor at the time—and discussed the writing process in more depth:

"Despite my appearance and my age and alertness, I feel the predatory impulse all the time in language. It's not just sound; it's not just image," says Stafford. "It might be hesitations in speech. It could be anything. . . . Even a lot of mistakes or weaknesses in language are exciting."

There are few mistakes or weaknesses in the poem included here, "A History of Our Land," reprinted from **My Name Is William Tell**, winner of the 1992 Western States Book Award for Lifetime Achievement in Poetry.

Stafford says that he wanted the poem to elicit two responses from readers: "Impossible!" and "Of course!

"Hills, fixed as they are," he notes, "did move. And ate villages, while the weather gobbled up things. And the stars—you know how indifferent they are, even now. And the trees. . . ." In discussing the poem, Stafford—always on the lookout for the muse—seems inspired to create again. "Now I am sorry that I didn't keep going, sorry I was so limited. Wait—a new move occurs to me: the rocks then, didn't they hold and then hide their memories? Here comes a new section—'What Big Rocks Remember.' I'll write that tomorrow."

Perhaps Stafford writes so readily about nature and geography because of his varied experiences. Over the years he has tended sugar beet fields, worked at oil refinery and construction sites, joined the Forest Service and taught at schools across the country. In 1994 he plans to write poems, assemble collections, celebrate his 80th birthday and find time to hike and bike in the outdoors.

Stafford advises poets to "open the door to nature. Learn to listen to the surroundings trying for our attention. It is easy to forget how solicitous the world is for us. We get to bending over the page and trying to remember how Keats did it, or maybe Frost poking around among the snowy woods."

Although every poet should know tradition, Stafford notes, a more direct approach often leads to the best nature poetry. "We can get the flood of reminders by sniffing, looking, listening, even lying down and letting the sky invite us outward. Be ready for whatever suggests itself to you at the moment," he says.

"You never know till afterwards what each little tap at the door might mean."
—*Michael J. Bugeja*

Stafford shows up to compose each day, pen and paper in hand, and lets the poem happen, word by word, image by image.

Sample postpaid: $4. "Please submit 3-5 poems at a time. Use regular legal-sized envelopes—no big brown envelopes; no replies without SASE. Type must be letter-perfect, sharp enough to be computer scanned." Reports in 1-2 months. Pays 1 copy. Acquires first rights. The editor says, "We're always looking for good, strong work—from both well-known poets and those who have never been published before."

CONFLUENCE PRESS (II, IV-Regional), Lewis-Clark State College, Lewiston ID 83501, phone (208)799-2336, founded 1975, poetry editor James R. Hepworth, is an "independent publisher of fiction, poetry, creative nonfiction and literary scholarship. We are open to formal poetry as well as free verse. No rhymed doggerel, 'light verse,' 'performance poetry,' 'street poetry,' etc. We prefer to publish work by poets who live and work in the northwestern United States." They have published poetry by John Daniel, Greg Keeler, Nancy Mairs and Wendell Berry. They print about 2 books a year. "Please query *before* submitting manuscript." Query with 6 sample poems, bio, list of publications. Replies to queries in 3 weeks. Pays $500 advance and 10% royalties plus copies. Buys all rights. Returns rights if book goes out of print. Send SASE for catalog to order samples.

CONFRONTATION MAGAZINE (II), English Dept., C.W. Post Campus of Long Island University, Greenvale NY 11548-0570, founded 1968, editor-in-chief Martin Tucker, is "a semiannual literary journal with interest in all forms. Our only criterion is high literary merit. We think of our audience as an educated, lay group of intelligent readers. We prefer lyric poems. Length generally should be kept to 2 pages. No sentimental verse." They have published poetry by Karl Shapiro, T. Alan Broughton, David Ignatow, Philip Appleman, Jane Mayhall and Joseph Brodsky. Basically a magazine, they do on occasion publish "book" issues or "anthologies." It's 190+ pgs., digest-sized, professionally printed, flat-spined, with a circulation of about 2,000. A visually beautiful journal, and well-edited, each issue features about 15-20 poems of varying lengths. The magazine is recommended not only for its "showcase" appeal, but also for the wide range of formal and free styles, displaying craft and insight. They receive about 1,200 submissions/year, publish 150, have a 6- to 12-month backlog. Sample postpaid: $3. Submit no more than 10 pgs., clear copy. Do not submit mss June through August. "Prefer single submissions." Reports in 6-8 weeks. Pays $5-50 and copy of magazine. Staff reviews books of poetry. Send books for review consideration.

CONJUNCTIONS (III), Dept. PM, Bard College, Annandale-on-Hudson NY 12504, founded 1981, managing editor Bradford Morrow, is an elegant journal appearing twice/year. "Potential contributor should be familiar with the poetry published in the journal." They have published poetry by John Ashbery, Robert Kelly, Charles Stein and Michael Palmer. As a sample here are lines from "Paulownia" by Barbara Guest:

> *ravenous the still dark a fishnet—*
> *robber walk near formidable plaits*
> *a glaze—the domino overcast—*
> *violet. shoulder.*

Like *The Quarterly*, this publication is distributed by Random House. It is 400+ pgs., 6×9, flat-spined, professionally printed. Issues reviewed feature mostly lyric free verse with occasional sequences and stanza patterns (some leaning toward the avant-garde). Poems compete with prose, with more pages devoted to the latter. Press run is 5,500 for 600 subscribers of which 200 are libraries. Subscription: $18. Sample postpaid: $10. Pays copies.

THE CONNECTICUT POETRY REVIEW (II), P.O. Box 3783, New Haven CT 06525, founded 1981, poetry editors J. Claire White and James William Chichetto, is a "small press that puts out an annual magazine. We look for poetry of quality which is both genuine and original in content. No specifications except length: 10-40 lines." The magazine has won high praise from the literary world; they have published such poets as Gary Metras, Robert Peters, Peter Wild and Linda Pastan. Each issue seems to feature a poet. As a sample the editors selected these lines by Odysseus Elytis (translated by Jeffrey Carson):

> *Maybe I'm still in the state of a medicinal*
> *herb or of a cold Friday's snake*
> *Or perhaps of one of those sacred beasts*
> *with its big ear full of heavy sounds*
> *and metallic noise from censers.*

The flat-spined, large digest-sized journal is "printed letterpress by hand on a Hacker Hand Press from Monotype Bembo." Most of the 45-60 pgs. are poetry, but they also have reviews. Editors seem to favor free verse with strong emphasis on voice (and judicious use of image and symbol). They receive over 900 submissions a year, use about 20, have a 3-month backlog. Press run is 400 for 80 subscribers of which 35 are libraries. Sample postpaid: $3.50. Reports in 3 months. Pays $5/poem plus 1 copy. The editors advise, "Study traditional and modern styles.

Study poets of the past. Attend poetry readings. And write. Practice on your own."

CONNECTICUT RIVER REVIEW; NATIONAL FALL POETRY CONTEST; BRODINE CONTEST; CON-NECTICUT POETRY SOCIETY (II), Dept. PM, P.O. Box 2171, Bridgeport CT 06608, founded 1978, appears twice yearly. Editor Robert Isaacs. They want poetry that has **"depth of emotion, the truly seen (imaginary or actual), in which sound and sense are one. All forms are welcome, except haiku. We look for high quality, well-crafted poems."** They have published poetry by Joseph Bruchac, Donald Jenkins, Simon Perchik, Viola Shipley and Paul Zimmer. Each of the plain but attractively printed, digest-sized issues contains about 40 pgs. of poetry, has a circulation of about 500, with 175 subscriptions of which 5% are libraries. They receive about 2,000 submissions/year, use about 70. Subscription: $10. **Sample postpaid: $5. Submit no more than 3-5 poems. No simultaneous submissions. Poems over 40 lines have little chance of acceptance, unless exceptional. Deadlines: February 15 and August 15. Guidelines available with SASE. Rejections within 2 weeks, acceptances could take 2 months. Pays 1 copy.** The National Fall Poetry Contest, deadline August 1, has a $2 entry fee/poem and prizes of $100, $50 and $25. Send SASE for rules. The Brodine Contest, Box 112, Stratford CT 06497. Guidelines available in February; send SASE. Deadline is July 15, $2 fee/poem. Three cash awards plus publication in the *Connecticut River Review*.

CONTEXT SOUTH (II), 2100 Memorial Blvd. #4504, Kerrville TX 78028, founded 1988, editor/publisher David Breeden, appears twice a year using **"any form, length, subject matter. Looking for strong rhythms, clear vision. Nothing sentimental."** They have recently published poetry by Andrea Hollander Budy, Simon Perchik and Peter Drizhal. As a sample the editor selected these lines by Dean Taciuch:

> *The myth remains with us even after the land*
> *has emptied itself into shallow basins our faces*
> *stare back through waves and fields where*
> *the water ran and covered our heads in song.*

It is 65 pgs., digest-sized, saddle-stapled, using fiction, criticism and book reviews as well as poetry. They accept less than 1% of poems received. Press run is 500 for 60 subscribers of which 6 are libraries. **Sample: $5. Simultaneous submissions OK. Reads submissions January 1 through March 31 only. Pays 1 copy. Acquires first serial rights.** Reviews books of poetry in 500 words maximum. Open to unsolicited reviews. Poets may also send books for review consideration. The editor advises, "Read every poem you can find from the beginning of time. Every poem encapsulates the tradition."

THE COOL TRAVELER (I, IV-Themes), Dept. PM, P.O. Box 11975, Philadelphia PA 19145, phone (215)440-0592, founded 1988, editor Bob Moore, appears 4 times/year, using **"poetry that contains references about places, especially different countries, but I'll look at it all."** They have published poetry by Brandel France, John J. Koller and Anne Louise Huffman. Its format is long and slender, about 64 pages, saddle-stapled. Press run is 1,000 copies. "We are in over 100 bookstores nationally and some in Canada and England. Our publication continues to grow in popularity. We only accept about 15 poems/year now. This is an important change." Subscription: $10. **Sample: $3. Submitting poets should, in a cover letter, "say something about themselves—a short one or two lines to be printed with their work." Editor comments on submissions "often." Reports in 1 month, sometimes asks for rewrites. Pays in copies.** Reviews books of poetry in 1,000 words or so, single or multi-book format. The editor says, "There are many local papers and publications that want poetry."

COPPER BEECH PRESS (III), P.O. Box 1852, English Dept., Brown University, Providence RI 02912, phone (401)863-2393, founded 1973, poetry editor Randy Blasing, publishes **books of all kinds of poetry**, about three 64-page, flat-spined paperbacks a year. They have recently published Christopher Buckley, Margaret Holley, Jordan Smith and Steven Cramer. **Query with 5 poems, biographical information and publications. Considers simultaneous submissions. Do not submit queries from Memorial Day to Labor Day. Replies to queries in 1 month, to mss in 3 months. Pays 10% of press run. For sample books, call or write for free catalog.**

CORNERSTONE (IV-Religious), Jesus People USA, 939 W. Wilson, Chicago IL 60640, phone (312)989-2080, editor Dawn Herrin, is a mass-circulation (50,000), low-cost ($2/copy) bimonthly directed at youth, covering **"contemporary issues in the light of Evangelical Christianity."** They use avant-garde, free verse, haiku, light verse, traditional—"no limits except for epic poetry. (We've not got the room.)" Buys 10-50 poems/year, uses 1-2 pgs./issue, has a 2- to 3-month backlog. Sample: $2. **Submit maximum of 5 poems. Cover letter required. Send SASE for guidelines. Pays $10 for poems having 1-15 lines, $25 for poems having 16 lines or more. Buys first or one-time rights.** Open to unsolicited reviews. Poets may also send books for review consideration. In past years, *Cornerstone* has received numerous awards from the Evangelical Press Association (including second place for poetry) as well as a Medal of Distinctive Merit from the Society of Publication Designers and a regional Award of Design Excellence from *Print* magazine.

CORNFIELD REVIEW (II), Dept. PM, Ohio State University, 1465 Mt. Vernon Ave., Marion OH 43302-5695, phone (614)389-2361, fax (614)389-6786, founded 1974, is an annual of poetry, artwork, short fiction and personal narrative. **"We are open to all forms of high quality poetry, and we are interested in new talent."** It is 6×9, flat-spined, printed on heavy slick stock with b&w graphics, glossy cover with art, approximately 40-48 pgs. Their press run is about 500. **Sample postpaid: $5. No simultaneous submissions or previously published poems. Send no more than 5 poems with brief cover letter. Submissions should be typed. Reports within 2-3 months. Pays 3 copies. Copyright reverts to contributor.**

CORONA (II), Dept. of History and Philosophy, Montana State University, Bozeman MT 59717, phone (406)994-5200, founded 1979, poetry editors Lynda and Michael Sexson, "is an interdisciplinary annual bringing together reflections from those who stand on the edges of their disciplines; those who sense that insight is located not in things but in relationships; those who have deep sense of playfulness; and those who believe that the imagination is involved in what we know." In regard to poetry they want **"no sentimental greeting cards; no slap-dash."** They have published poems by Wendy Battin, William Irwin Thompson, Frederick Turner and James Dickey. Asked for a sample, they said, "See journal for examples. We are not interested in cloned poems or homogenized poets." Journal is perfect-bound, 125-140 pgs., professionally printed. They use about 20-25 pgs. of poetry/issue. Press run is 2,000. **Sample postpaid: $7. Submit any number of pages. No simultaneous submissions. Reports in 1 week to 9 months. Payment is "nominal" plus 2 contributor's copies.** The editors advise, "Today's poet survives only by the generous spirits of small press publishers. Read and support the publishers of contemporary artists by subscribing to the journals and magazines you admire."

COSMIC TREND; PARA*phrase (I, IV-Themes, love/romance/erotica), Sheridan Mall Box 47014, Mississauga, Ontario L5K 2R2 Canada, founded 1984, Cosmic Trend poetry editor George Le Grand, *PARA*phrase* editor Tedy Asponsen. Cosmic Trend publishes 2 chapbook anthologies and narrated music cassettes a year of **"New Age mind-expanding material of any style, short or medium length; also: humorous, unusual or zany entries (incl. graphics) with deeper meaning. We ignore epics, run-of-a-mill romantic and political material."** They have recently published poetry by Jay Bradford Fowler, Jr., Joanna Nealon, Thea Vanderplaats and Susan P. Humphreys. As a sample the editor selected these lines by Jiri Jirasek:

> *I will seal some happiness*
> *in a pebble of my hope*
> *and throw it in the universe*
> *like a message in a bottle*
> *for your God to read.*

PARA*phrase — Newsletter of Cosmic Trend (irregular: 2-3 times a year) — publishes "condensed life-stories and/or visions with insight, beyond the normal and related poetry." **Submit poems with name and address on each sheet. They will consider simultaneous submissions and previously published poems "with accompanied disclosure and references." Pays 1 copy/published project. Rights revert to authors upon publication. Send $1 for guidelines or $5 for sample publication and guidelines.** Brief guidelines: $1 for each two poems submitted, plus $1 for postage. Minimum fee $2 plus postage ("No US postal stamps, please.") **Response time is usually less than 3 weeks. Editor "often" comments on submissions.** Reviews books of poetry. Open to unsolicited reviews. Poets may also send books for review consideration, attn. Tedy Asponsen. Cosmic Trend publishes electronic music cassette tapes in addition to their poetry/music anthology accompaniments. They say, "Share your adventure of poetry beyond the usual presentation! Cosmic Trend can choose your poems for narration with music and inclusion into our cassette accompaniments to our illustrated anthologies."

COSMOPOLITAN (IV-Women), 224 W. 57th St., New York NY 10019, founded 1886, is a monthly magazine "aimed at a female audience 18-34," part of the Hearst conglomerate, though it functions independently editorially. They want **"freshly-written free verse, not more than 25 lines, either light or serious, which addresses the concerns of young women. Prefer shorter poems, use 1-4 poems each issue. Poems shouldn't be too abstract. The poem should convey an image, feeling or emotion that our reader could perhaps identify with. We do publish mostly free verse, although we're also open to well-crafted rhyme poems. We cannot return submissions without SASE."** They have a circulation of 2,987,970. **Buy sample at newsstand. Reports in 3-5 weeks. Pays $25.** "Please do not phone; query by letter if at all, though queries are unnecessary before submitting."

COTEAU BOOKS; THUNDER CREEK PUBLISHING CO-OP; WOOD MOUNTAIN SERIES (III, IV-Regional, children), 401-2206 Dewdney Ave., Regina, Saskatchewan S4R 1H3 Canada, phone (306)777-0170, founded 1975, managing editor Shelley Sopher, is a "small literary press that publishes poetry, fiction, drama, anthologies, criticism, children's books—only by Canadian writers." They have published poetry by Nancy Mattson, Kim Morrissey, Anne Szumigalski, Patrick Lane and Dennis Cooley and 2 anthologies of Saskatchewan poetry. **Writers should submit 30-50 poems "and indication of whole ms," typed; simultaneous and American submissions not accepted. Cover letter required; include publishing credits and bio and SASE or SAE with IRC if necessary. Queries will be answered in 2-3 weeks and mss reported on in 2-4 months. Authors receive 10% royalty; 10 copies.** Their attractive catalog is free for 9×12 SASE, or SAE with IRC, and sample copies can be ordered from it. The editor says: "Membership has changed through the years in the Thunder Creek Publishing Co-op, but now stands at ten. Each member has a strong interest in Canadian writing and culture. Generally, poets would have published a number of poems and series of poems in literary magazines and anthologies before submitting a manuscript." However, the imprint Wood Mountain Series is for first collections, reflecting their commitment to publishing new writers. The press has had two books nominated for The Lampbert Memorial Award and one nominated for The Governor-General's Award for Poetry.

COTTONWOOD; COTTONWOOD PRESS (II, IV-Regional), Box J, 400 Kansas Union, University of Kansas, Lawrence KS 66045, founded 1965, poetry editor Philip Wedge. **The press "is auxiliary to *Cottonwood Magazine* and publishes material by authors in the region. Material is usually solicited." For the magazine they are looking for "strong narrative or sensory impact, non-derivative, not 'literary,' not 'academic.' Emphasis on Midwest, but publishes the best poetry received regardless of region. Poems should be 60 lines or less, on daily experience, *perception.*"** They have published poetry by Rita Dove, Allen Ginsberg, Walter McDonald, Patricia Traxler and Ron Schreiber. The magazine, published 3 times/year, is 112+ pgs., 6×9, flat-spined, printed from computer offset, with photos, using 15-20 pages of poetry in each issue. They have a circulation of 500-600, with 150 subscriptions of which 75 are libraries. They receive about 2,000 submissions/year, use about 30, have a maximum of 1-year backlog. Single copy: $5. **Sample postpaid: $3. Submit up to 5 pgs. No simultaneous submissions. They sometimes provide criticism on rejected mss. Reports in 2-5 months. Pays 1 copy.** The editors advise, "Read the little magazines and send to ones you like."

COUNCIL FOR INDIAN EDUCATION (IV-Ethnic, themes), 517 Rimrock Rd., Billings MT 59102, phone (406)252-7451, founded 1963, poetry editor Sally Old Coyote, is a nonprofit corporation publishing material (small paper-bound books) to use in schools with Indian students. "We publish one poetry book per year. All content is approved by an intertribal editorial board." They want **"poetry on Native American themes or cowboy poetry. No vulgarity, sex, prejudice or complaining."** They have published poetry by Jess Schwiddi. As a sample the editor selected these lines:

> Eyes on the sunrise: nature's way
> Rhythm of the Indian's great new day
> Dance to the rhythm
> Chant and hum
> Never loose the rhythm of the rawhide drum.

Previously published poems and simultaneous submissions OK. Often comments on rejections. Replies to mss in 2-6 months. Pays author's copies. Write for catalog.

COUNTRY JOURNAL (II), P.O. Box 8200, Harrisburg PA 17105, phone (717)657-9555, poetry editor Donald Hall, editor Peter V. Fossel, is a bimonthly magazine featuring country living **for people who live in rural areas or who are thinking about moving there. They use free verse and traditional.** Average issue includes 6-8 feature articles and 10 departments. They have published poetry by Mary Oliver and Wendell Berry. As a sample the editors selected these lines from "The Springs Under the Lake" by Kate Barnes:

> The rest of the way
> I didn't talk. I could almost hear the words
> combining in her mind, the lines gathering
> inside her head like butter when it suddenly
> starts to come, when it clumps up thick in the churn.

Of 4,000-5,000 poems received each year they accept 10-12. Circulation 200,000. Subscription: $24. **Sample postpaid: $4. Submit seasonal material 1 year in advance. Reports in 1-2 months. Editor comments on submissions "seldom." Pays $50/poem on acceptance. Buys first North American serial rights.**

COUNTRY WOMAN; REIMAN PUBLICATIONS (IV-Women, humor), P.O. Box 643, Milwaukee WI 53201, founded 1970, managing editor Kathy Pohl. *Country Woman* "is a bimonthly magazine dedicated to the lives and interests of country women. Those who are both involved in farming and ranching and those who love country life. In some ways, it is very similar to many women's general interest magazines, and yet its subject matter is closely tied in with rural living and the very unique lives of country women. We like short (4-5 stanzas, 16-20 lines) traditional rhyming poems that reflect on a season or comment humorously or seriously on a particular rural experience. Also limericks and humorous 4- to 8-line filler rhymes. No experimental poetry or free verse. Poetry will not be considered unless it rhymes. Always looking for poems that focus on the seasons. We don't want rural putdowns, poems that stereotype country women, etc. All poetry must be positive and upbeat. Our poems are fairly simple, yet elegant. They often accompany a high-quality photograph." *CW* has published poems by Hilda Sanderson, Edith E. Cutting and Ericka Northrop. *CW,* appearing 6 times a year, is magazine-sized, 68 pgs., glossy paper with much color photography. Subscription: $16.98/year, $2/copy. They receive about 1,200 submissions of poetry/year, use 40-50 (unless they publish an anthology). Their backlog is 1 month to 3 years. "We're always welcoming submissions." Sample postpaid: $2. Submit maximum of 6 poems. Photocopy OK if stated not a simultaneous submission. Reports in 2-3 months. Pays $10-25/poem plus copy. Buys first rights (generally) or reprint rights (sometimes). They hold various contests for subscribers only. One of their anthologies, **Cattails and Meadowlarks: Poems from the Country,** is 90+ pgs., saddle-stapled with high-quality color photography on the glossy card cover, poems in large, professional type with many b&w photo illustrations. The editor says, "Any poem that does not have traditional rhythm and rhyme is automatically passed over."

THE COUNTRYMAN (IV-Rural), Sheep St., Burford, Oxon OX18 4LH England, phone 0993 (Burford) 822258, founded 1927, editor Christopher Hall, is a bimonthly magazine "on rural matters." The editor wants **poetry on rural themes, "accessible to general readership but not jingles."** As a sample the editor selected this complete poem, "January omen," by Jane A. Mares:

> At the cold birth of the year
> I saw what was better unseen:
> The Raven or Grimcrag, the grief-bringer,
> With his tone of ill-tidings,
> A-top the tall stone,
> Wiping his bill clean.

It is a handsome, flat-spined, digest-sized magazine, 200+ pgs., using popular articles and ads. Submissions should be short. Reporting time is "within a week usually," longer if from outside the country. Time to publication is "3 months-3 years." Pays a maximum of £20/poem. Buys all rights "but we stipulate never to refuse permission to reprint at author's wish." Staff reviews books of poetry in "25 words upwards." Send books for review consideration. The editor says, "Not all our poems are *about* birds or flowers or animals. Personal reaction to rural experience is valued if it comes in a form to which our readers (high-income, quiet not violently green British for the most part) can relate. We get quite a few American submissions which I always read with much interest, not least because of my own love of the few American landscapes I know. Too often these submissions are too obviously American (because of tell-tale species or phrases) and I generally rule these out because 95% of my readers expect a British mag."

COVER MAGAZINE (I), P.O. Box 1215, Cooper Station, New York NY 10276, founded 1986, contact editor/publisher Jeffrey C. Wright, is a "broad-based arts monthly covering all the arts in every issue, a 40-page tabloid sold on newsstands and in select bookstores nationwide." They want **"shorter poems—2-24 lines generally, favoring new romantic work. Nothing stodgy or simplistic."** They have published poetry by Robert Creeley and Molly Peacock. As a sample the editor chose one line:

> Let all but love be now our foe.

Cover tries "to reach a cutting edge/front-line audience in touch with the creative fields." Entirely supported by subscriptions, sales and ads. Press run is 9,000 for 900 subscribers (11 of them libraries), 1,200 shelf sales. Out of 250 submissions of poetry they accept 25. Single copy: $2; 1-year subscription: $15. **Sample postpaid: $3.50. Submit 4-5 poems with cover letter. Editor often comments on submissions. Reports in 2 months. Pays nothing, not even a copy.** Open to unsolicited reviews. Poets may also send books for review consideration. Offers annual poetry contest, for subscribers only.

‡COWBOY MAGAZINE (IV-Themes), P.O. Box 126, La Veta CO 81055, founded 1990, editor Darrell Arnold, is a quarterly "for people who value the cowboy lifestyle." They want **"authentic poetry about the life of cowboys/ranchers. Don't even try if you don't know about cowboys."** They have recently published poetry by Red Steagall, Baxter Black and Mike Logan. The editor says *Cowboy Magazine* is 48 pgs., 9 × 11, stapled. They receive about 100 poems a year, "can use about 5%." Press run is 12,000 for 8,000 subscribers of which 10 are libraries, 4,000 shelf sales. Single copy: $4; subscription: $16. **Sample postpaid: $4.50. Previously published poems OK; no simultaneous submissions. Cover letter required.** Time between acceptance and publication is 1 year. **Seldom comments on rejections. Reports on submissions "as soon as I can get to them." Pays $20. Buys one-time rights.** Staff reviews related books of poetry. Send books for review consideration. The editor says, "The best cowboy poetry is written by people who have worked on ranches as cowboys. If you have no such experience, you shouldn't try to write for us. We prefer *highly polished work* that is perfectly rhymed and metered."

‡COYOTE CHRONICLES: NOTES FROM THE SOUTHWEST (I, II, IV-Themes, regional), #196, 600 S. Dobson, Mesa AZ 85202, founded 1993, editor Jody Namio, is a "small press publisher of fiction, poetry, nonfiction and scholarly publications, publishing a biannual literary journal. Limited subsidy publishing services offered to selected authors." She wants "poetry with emphasis on progressive political themes and ideas, ecology etc. No religious, fantasy or 'scenery' poetry." They have published poetry by Norman German, John Grey, Mark Maire and Richard Davignon. As a sample she selected these lines (poet unidentified):

> Last night I went to bed intoxicated again. You watched
> "Ghandi," repressing violence.
> Today, I am drinking too much coffee,
> smoking too many cigarettes.
> You say you'll be late . . .

CC is 48-80 pgs., 8½ × 11, professionally printed, saddle-stitched. They accept 10-15% of 1,000 + poems received a year. Subscription: $12. Sample postpaid: $4. Guidelines available for SASE. Submit with cover letter and bio. They consider simultaneous submissions and previously published poems. "Backlog of submissions at this time." Editor sometimes comments on rejections, "more substantial critiques on request." Reports in 6-8 weeks. Pays 5 copies. "Contributors encouraged to buy additional copies." Publishes several chapbooks a year averaging 64 pgs. For chapbook consideration either query or send ms with cover letter and bio. Reports in 12-14 weeks. "Large backlog at this time, but we welcome all submissions." Payment "varies with author." Send SASE for catalog to buy samples.

CRAB CREEK REVIEW (II), 4462 Whitman Ave. N., Seattle WA 98103, phone (206)633-1090, founded 1983, editor Linda J. Clifton, appears 2 times/year, 32 pgs., attractively printed on newsprint. They publish poetry which is "free or formal, with clear imagery, wit, voice that is interesting and energetic, accessible to the general reader rather than full of very private imagery and obscure literary allusion; also translations." They have published poetry by Elizabeth Murawski, Maxine Kumin, William Stafford and Eastern European, Japanese, Chinese and Latin American writers. They have about 20 pgs. of poetry in each issue, circulation 350, 200 subscriptions of which 20 are libraries. They receive 400-500 submissions/year from which they choose 50-60 poems. Subscription: $8/volume of 3 issues. Sample postpaid: $3. No simultaneous submissions. Type name and address on each page. Acquires first North American serial rights. Rights revert to author upon publication.

CRAZYHORSE (II), Dept. PM, Dept. of English, University of Arkansas, Little Rock AR 72204, phone (501)569-3160, founded 1960, managing editor Zabelle Stodola, poetry editor Ralph Burns, fiction editor Judy Troy, is a highly respected literary magazine appearing twice a year. They have published poetry by Alberto Rios, Mark Jarman, Bill Matthews and Yusef Komunyakaa. As a sample, here are the closing lines from "For Victor Jara: Mutilated and Murdered, the Soccer Stadium, Santiago, Chile" by Miller Williams (see listing for University of Arkansas Press):

> Would we have stayed to an end or would we have folded our faces?
> Awful and awful. Good friend. You have embarrassed our hearts.

It is 145 pgs., 6×9 offset. Press run is 900. Subscription: $10. Sample postpaid: $5. No submissions May through August. Reports in 1-2 months. Pays $10/printed page plus 2 copies. Offers two $500 awards for best poem and best story. Reviews books of poetry. To get a sense of the quality of the magazine, see the anthology, **The Best of Crazyhorse** (University of Arkansas Press, 1990).

CRAZYQUILT QUARTERLY (II), P.O. Box 632729, San Diego CA 92163-2729, founded 1986, editor Jackie Ball, is a literary quarterly which has recently published poetry by B.Z. Niditch, Judson Jerome, Charles B. Dickson and Alan Seaburg. As a sample the editor selected these lines from "Road with Cypress and Star" by Charles Fishman:

> Earlier, the trees are earth,
> then water and flame — but here
> they are smoke, dark green smoke
> . . . turrets of blue wind.

The magazine is 90+ pgs., digest-sized, saddle-stapled, professionally printed on good stock with matte card cover. Circulation 200. Subscription: $14.95. Sample: $4.50 plus $1 postage; back issue: $2.50. Submit one poem to a page. Previously published poems and simultaneous submissions OK. Reports in 10-12 weeks, time to publication 12-15 months. Pays 2 copies. Acquires first rights.

CREAM CITY REVIEW (II), P.O. Box 413, Dept. of English, University of Wisconsin at Milwaukee, Milwaukee WI 53201, phone (414)229-4708, editor-in-chief Sandra Nelson, poetry editors Aedan Hanley, Paul August and Cynthia Belmont, is a nationally distributed literary magazine published twice a year by the Creative Writing Program. The editors will consider **any poem that is well-crafted and especially those poems that "have a voice, have place or play with the conventions of what poetry is. We get very little humor or parody, and would enjoy getting more."** They have published poetry by May Sarton, Philip Dacey, Amiri Baraka, Tess Gallagher, Cathy Song, Mary Oliver and Philip Levine. They do not include sample lines of poetry; "We prefer not to bias our contributors. We strive for variety—vitality!" *CCR* is 5½×8½, perfect-bound, with full-color cover on 70 lb. paper. This journal is fast becoming a leader in the literary world. It's lovely to look at—one of the most attractive designs around—with generous space devoted to poems, all styles (but favoring free verse). Press run is 2,000, 300+ subscriptions of which 15 are libraries. **Sample postpaid: $5. "Include SASE when submitting and please submit no more than 5 poems at a time."** Simultaneous submissions OK. **Editors sometimes comment on rejections. Send SASE for guidelines. Reports in 2 months, longer in summer. Payment varies with funding and includes 2 copies. Buys first rights.** Reviews books of poetry in 1-2 pgs. Open to unsolicited reviews. Poets may also send books to Aedan Hanley, senior poetry editor, for review consideration. **"We give an award of $100 to the best poem published in *Cream City Review* each year."** They add, "We are always looking for strong poems on any subject." *Cream City Review* ranked #6 in the "Nontraditional Verse" category of the June 1993 *Writer's Digest* Poetry 60 list.

CREATIVE WITH WORDS PUBLICATIONS (C.W.W.); SPOOFING (IV-Themes); WE ARE WRITERS, TOO (I, IV-Children, seniors), Box 223226, Carmel CA 93922, founded 1975, poetry editor Brigitta Geltrich, **offers criticism for a fee.** It focuses "on furthering **folkloristic tall tales** and such; creative writing abilities in **children** (poetry, prose, language-art); creative writing in **senior citizens** (poetry and prose)." The editors publish on a wide range of themes relating to human studies and the environment that influence human behaviors. **$5 reading fee/poem, includes a critical analysis.** The publications are anthologies of children's poetry, prose and language art; anthologies of special-interest groups such as senior citizen poetry and prose; and *Spoofing: An Anthology of Folkloristic Yarns and Such*, which has an announced theme for each issue. **"Want to see: folkloristic themes, poetry for and by children; poetry by senior citizens; topic (inquire). Do not want to see: too mushy; too religious; too didactic; expressing dislike for fellowmen; political; pornographic; death and murder poetry."** Latest themes are "A CWW Christmas"; "It's a Matter of Love"; "A CWW Easter"; "A Time for Seasons and Holidays" and "Tall Tales and Fairy Tales from a Different Perspective." Guidelines available for SASE. *Spoofing!* and *We are Writers, Too!*, an anthology of poems by children, are low-budget publications, photocopied from typescript, saddle-stapled, card covers with cartoon-like art. **Submit 20-line, 40 spaces wide maximum, poems geared to specific audience and subject matter.** They have published poetry by Melissa Rifkin, Dyran Peak and Lisa Preston. As a sample the editor selected these lines by Bethany Miller:

> . . . Soon I'll grow weary and my footsteps will tire;
> The air will be bursting with light.
> Then I'll lay me down on the bare, frozen ground.
> And I'll sleep with God tonight.

"Query with sample poems, short personal biography, other publications, poetic goals, where you read about us, for what publication and/or event you are submitting." They have "no conditions for publication, but **CWW** is dependent on author/poet support by purchase of a copy or copies of publication." They offer a 20% reduction on any copy purchased. The editor advises, "Trend is proficiency. Poets should research topic; know audience for whom they write; check topic for appeal to specific audience; should not write for the sake of rhyme, rather for the sake of imagery and being creative with the language. Feeling should be expressed (but no mushiness). Topic and words should be chosen carefully; brevity should be employed."

THE CREATIVE WOMAN (IV-Women, feminist, themes), #288, 126 E. Wing, Arlington Hts. IL 60004, phone (708)255-1232, founded 1977, editor Margaret Choudhury, "is published four times a year. **We focus on a special topic in each issue, presented from a feminist perspective."** They want poetry **"recognizing, validating, celebrating women's experience, especially fresh and original style."** They have published poetry by Marge Piercy and Larissa Vasilyeva. As a sample here are lines from "The Fishwife's Declaration of Independence" by Olivia Diamond:

> This fishwife cries to ply her cutter
> in deeper more crystal schools of marlin
> and never peddle her fry in any market;
> her coach is kinetic, her compass private,
> her steerage personal, her passage free,
> and no husband stands at the helm.

The Creative Woman is magazine-sized, 40 pgs., professionally printed with b&w graphics, ads.

They use about 5% of several hundred unsolicited poems received each year. Press run is 2,000 for 600 subscriptions (65 libraries). Subscription: $16, $20 institutions. **Sample postpaid: $5. Mss should be double-spaced, name and address on each page. No simultaneous submissions or previously published poetry. Cover letter required. Reports within up to 1 year. Pays 4 copies and opportunity to purchase more at half price.** Staff reviews related books of poetry. Send books for review consideration.

CREATIVITY UNLIMITED PRESS; ANNUAL CREATIVITY UNLIMITED PRESS POETRY COMPETITION (I), 30819 Casilina, Rancho Palos Verdes CA 90274, phone (213)541-4844, founded 1989, editor Shelley Stockwell, publishes annually a collection of poetry submitted to their **contest, $4 fee for 1-5 poems;** prizes of $300, $150 and $75 in addition to publication. Deadline: December 31. "Clever spontaneous **overflows of rich emotion, humor and delightful language encouraged. No inaccessible, verbose, esoteric, obscure poetry. Limit 3 pgs. per poem double-spaced, one side of page.**" As a sample the editor selected her own "Freeway Dilemma":

> *Of all enduring questions*
> *A big one I can't answer;*
> *How come, whenever I change lanes,*
> *The other lane goes faster?*

They also accept freelance submissions for book publication. Query first. "Poems previously published will be accepted provided writer has maintained copyright and notifies us." Editor comments on submissions "always. Keep it simple and accessible." Sample copies of their anthologies available for 40% off list.

CREEPING BENT (III), Dept. PM, 433 W. Market St., Bethlehem PA 18018, phone (215)866-5613, founded 1984, editor Joseph Lucia, a literary magazine that focuses on serious poetry, fiction, book reviews and essays, with very occasional chapbooks published under the same imprint. **"Please note that during much of 1994 we will be accepting very little (possibly no) unsolicited material. We publish only work that evidences a clear awareness of the current situation of poetry. We take a special interest in poems that articulate a vision of the continuities and discontinuities in the human relationship to the natural world."** The editor does not want "any attempt at verse that clearly indicates the writer hasn't taken a serious look at a recent collection of poetry during his or her adult life." They have published work by Turner Cassity, Charles Edward Eaton, Renée Ashley, Brigit Kelly, Walter McDonald, Donald Revell, Harry Humes and Patricia Wilcox. As a sample, the editor selected these lines from Mark Stevick's "Idiom":

> *The language of objects is not*
> *unknown to us. What they mean*
> *they articulate to our eyes and*
> *our hands; we listen and learn*
> *from them as we can, make them*
> *our ambassadors. You, listening*
> *in your room, will recognize*
> *your debt to their reliable idiom,*
> *though they are not yours, nor you.*

Creeping Bent is digest-sized, nicely printed on heavy stock with some b&w artwork, 48-64 pgs., saddle-stapled with glossy white card cover printed in black and one other color. It appears at least once a year, sometimes more often. Circulation is 250, of which 175 are subscriptions, 25 go to libraries, and 25 are sold on newsstands. Subscription: $6/year. **Sample postpaid: $3. "Absolutely no simultaneous submissions!" Guidelines for SASE. Reporting time is usually 2-3 weeks and time to publication is 6 months at most. Pay is 2 copies plus a 1-year subscription.** The editor says, "Before submitting to any magazine published by anyone with a serious interest in contemporary writing, make certain you understand something about the kind of work the magazine publishes. Be familiar with current styles and approaches to poetry, even if you eschew them."

CRESCENT MOON (II, IV-Anthology, love/romance/erotica, occult, religious, spirituality, women/feminism), 18 Chaddesley Rd., Kidderminster, England DY10 3AD, founded 1988, editor Jeremy Robinson, publishes about 10 books and chapbooks/year on **arrangements subsidized by the poet.** He wants "**poetry that is passionate and authentic. Any form or length.**" Not "**the trivial, insincere or derivative. We are putting together some anthologies of new American poetry, particularly love poetry and women's poetry. We would like to hear from interested poets. If the response is good enough, we will publish a regular twice-yearly anthology of new American poetry.**" Anthologies now available ($20 each): *Pagan America: An Anthology of New American Poetry, Love in America: An Anthology of Women's Love Poetry* and *Mythic America: An Anthology of New American Poetry.* They have also recently published studies of Arthur Rimbaud, Rainer Maria Rilke and Shakespeare. As a sample the editor selected the first of five stanzas from his "Aphrodite's Mirror":

> *Shaving one day in Aphrodite's mirror,*
> *Using her sea-foam as ointment and the shell*
> *For a basin, I caught sight of myself*
> *In that speckled glass and wondered if*
> *This love of ours was going to last beyond*
> *A mere Rising-From-The-Sea-Attended-By-Nymphs.*

The above is from the chapbook **Black Angel** which is 45 pgs., flat-spined, photocopied from typescript, digest-sized, with matte card cover. **Sample, postpaid, in response to "written requests." Inquiries welcome. Cover letter with brief bio and publishing credits required with submissions. Replies to queries in 1 month, to mss in 2 months.**

CRICKET, THE MAGAZINE FOR CHILDREN; LADYBUG, THE MAGAZINE FOR YOUNG CHILDREN (IV-Children), P.O. Box 300, Peru IL 61354, *Cricket* founded 1973, *Ladybug* founded 1990, editor-in-chief Marianne Carus. *Cricket* is a monthly, circulation 120,000, using **"serious, humorous, nonsense rhymes, limericks" for children. They do not want "forced or trite rhyming or imagery that doesn't hang together to create a unified whole." They sometimes use previously published work.** The attractive 7×9 magazine, 64 pgs., saddle-stapled, color cover and b&w illustrations inside, receives over 1,000 submissions/month, uses 10-12, and has up to a 2-year backlog. *Ladybug*, also monthly, circulation 120,000, is similar in format and requirements but is aimed at younger children (ages 2-7). **No query. Submit no more than 5 poems—up to 100 lines (2 pgs. max.) for *Cricket*; up to 20 lines for *Ladybug*, no restrictions on form. Sample of either: $2. Guidelines available for SASE. Reports in 3-4 months. Payment for both is up to $3/line and 2 copies. "All submissions are automatically considered for both magazines."** *Cricket* holds poetry contests for children ages 5-9 and 10-14. Current contest themes and rules appear in each issue. *Cricket* has received Parents' Choice Awards every year since 1986. The magazine also ranked #2 in the "Top Pay" category of the June 1993 *Writer's Digest* Poetry 60 list. *Ladybug*, launched in 1990, received Parents' Choice Awards in 1991 and 1992.

‡**THE CRITIC (II)**, 6th Floor, 205 W. Monroe St., Chicago IL 60606, founded 1940, is a Catholic literary and cultural quarterly. **"Poetry is a minor aspect of the publication. No word games, doggerel, light verse or haiku."** They have recently published poetry by Samuel Hazo and Martha Vertreace. The editor says *The Critic* is 128 pgs., 7×10, perfect-bound, no ads. Press run is 2,500 for 2,000 subscribers of which about 200 are libraries. Subscription: $20. **Sample postpaid: $6. No previously published poems or simultaneous submissions. Cover letter required. Seldom comments on rejections. Reports in 1-3 months. Pays $25-50. Buys first serial rights.**

‡**CROSS ROADS: A JOURNAL OF SOUTHERN CULTURE (IV-Regional)**, P.O. Box 726, University MS 38677, founded 1992, founding editor Ted Olson, is biannual. "*Cross Roads* serves as a forum for a wide range of responses to the South from creative, academic, popular and folk perspectives; one fourth to one half of each issue is creative writing (poetry, fiction, drama and nonfiction essays)." They want **"poetry by Southerners and poetry (by anyone) about the South. We would like to see high-quality poetry about any aspect of southern culture (southern history, southern folkways, southern identity, southern art/music, etc.—in short, any aspect of the southern experience). Nothing overly sentimental, stereotyping or awkwardly rhyming. Also no 'local color' poetry."** They have recently published poetry by A.R. Ammons, Arthur Winfield Knight, Alice Cabaniss Bass and Jeff Daniel Marion. As a sample the editor selected these lines from "The Crater, Vicksburg" by Franz K. Baskett:

> *Standing on the lip of The Crater*
> *I think about what it feels like*
> *To hold a gun and shoot.*
> *The heft of two and a half pounds*
> *Of blue steel. To shoot. To feel*
> *The kick. To aim and squeeze off.*
> *But not like it was done here.*
> *No Sir.*

ALWAYS include a self-addressed, stamped envelope (SASE) when sending a ms or query to a publisher within your own country. When sending material to other countries, include a self-addressed envelope and International Reply Coupons (IRCs), available for purchase at most post offices.

Cross Roads is 72-80 pgs., digest-sized, perfect-bound, with b&w photographs, music notation and several ads. They receive 100 poems a year, use 10 to 15. Press run is 800 for 50 subscribers of which 10 are libraries. Subscription: $9 for individuals, $12 for institutions. Sample postpaid: $4.50. No previously published poems or simultaneous submissions. Cover letter required. Include "a short biographical statement explaining background and connection with the South or interest in the study of Southern culture. One paragraph is enough." Committee reads submissions August 1 through May 1 only. Seldom comments on rejections. Reports within 3 months. Pays 1 copy. Acquires first North American serial rights. The editor says, "We would consider reviewing extraordinary books by Southerners and/or about the South, though reviewing is not one of our primary goals."

CROSS-CULTURAL COMMUNICATIONS; CROSS-CULTURAL REVIEW OF WORLD LITERATURE AND ART IN SOUND, PRINT, AND MOTION; CROSS-CULTURAL MONTHLY; CROSS-CULTURAL REVIEW CHAPBOOK ANTHOLOGY; INTERNATIONAL WRITERS SERIES (II, IV-Translations, bilingual), Dept. PM, 239 Wynsum Ave., Merrick NY 11566-4725, phone (516)868-5635, fax (516)379-1901, founded 1971, Stanley H. and Bebe Barkan. Stanley Barkan began CCC as an educational venture, a program in 27 languages at Long Island University, but soon began publishing collections of poetry translated into English from various languages—some of them (such as Estonian) quite "neglected"—in bilingual editions. During the 70s he became aware of Antigruppo (a group against groups), a movement with similar international focus in Sicily, and the two joined forces. **CCR** began as a series of chapbooks (6-12 a year) of collections of poetry translated from various languages and continues as the **Holocaust, Women Writers, Latin American Writers, Asian-American Writers, International Artists, Art & Poetry, Jewish, Israeli, Dutch, Turkish,** and **Long Island** and **Brooklyn Writers Chapbook Series** (with a number of other permutations in the offing)—issued simultaneously in palm-sized and regular paperback and cloth-binding editions and boxed and canned, as well as audiocassette and videocassette. **All submissions should be preceded by a query letter with SASE. The Holocaust series is for survivors. Send SASE for guidelines. Pays 10% of print run.** In addition to publications in these series, CCC has published anthologies, translations and collections by dozens of poets from many countries. As a sample the editor selected the beginning of a poem by Pablo Neruda, as translated by Maria Jacketti:

> *Quartz opens its eyes in the snow*
> *and covers itself with thorns,*
> *slides into whiteness,*
> *becomes its own whiteness:*

That's from the bilingual collection **Heaven Stones,** the second in the **Cross-Cultural Review International Writers Series** published in 1992. It is 80 pgs., digest-sized, smythe-sewn paper and cloth, professionally printed with photo of the Chilean poet on the back—$15 (paperback), $25 (cloth). **Sample chapbook postpaid: $7.** *Cross-Cultural Monthly* focuses on bilingual poetry and prose. Subscription: $36. **Sample postpaid: $3. Pays 1 copy.** CCC continues to produce the International Festival of Poetry, Writing and Translation with the International Poets and Writers Literary Arts Week in New York and currently directs a multicultural poetry series at the Barnes & Noble Superstore in Manhattan.

CRUCIBLE; SAM RAGAN PRIZE (II), Barton College, College Station, Wilson NC 27893, phone (919)399-6456, founded 1964, editor Terrence L. Grimes, is an annual using **"poetry that demonstrates originality and integrity of craftsmanship as well as thought. Traditional metrical and rhyming poems are difficult to bring off in modern poetry. The best poetry is written out of deeply felt experience which has been crafted into pleasing form. No very long narratives."** They have published poetry by Robert Grey, R.T. Smith and Anthony S. Abbott. As a sample the editor selected these lines from "Toward Short Off Mountain" by Mary C. Snotherly:

> *So dense the fog, each man trudged alone,*
> *accompanied only by a stumble of boots,*
> *slap of laurel, by his own separate breathing,*
> *and like thunder roll, the barks resounding.*

It is 100 pgs., 6×9, professionally printed on high-quality paper with matte card cover. Good type selection and point sizes highlight bylines and titles of poems. Press run is 500 for 300 subscribers of which 100 are libraries, 200 shelf sales. **Sample postpaid: $5. Send SASE for guidelines for contests (prizes of $150 and $100), and the Sam Ragan Prize ($150) in honor of the Poet Laureate of North Carolina. Submit between Christmas and mid-March. Reports in 3 months or less.** "We require 3 unsigned copies of the manuscript and a short biography including a list of publications, in case we decide to publish the work." No comments on rejections. Editor leans toward free verse with attention paid particularly to image, line, stanza and voice. However, he does not want to see poetry that is "forced."

CUMBERLAND POETRY REVIEW; THE ROBERT PENN WARREN POETRY PRIZE (II, IV-Translations), Dept. PM, P.O. Box 120128, Acklen Station, Nashville TN 37212, phone (615)373-8948, founded 1981, is a biannual, 75-100+ pgs., 6×9, flat-spined. *CPR* presents poets of diverse origins to a widespread audience. "Our aim is to support the poet's effort to keep up the language. We accept special responsibility for reminding American readers that not all excellent poems in English are being written by U.S. citizens. We have published such poets as Laurence Lerner, Donald Davie, Emily Grosholz and Rachel Hadas." Circulation: 500. As a sample the editorial board selected these lines by Seamus Heaney:

> When Dante snapped a twig in the bleeding wood
> a voice sighed out of blood that bubbled up
> like sap at the end of green sticks on a fire.

Sample postpaid: $7. Submit poetry, translations or poetry criticism with SASE or SAE with IRC. Reports in 3 months. Acquires first rights. Returns rights "on request of author providing he acknowledges original publication in our magazine." They award The Robert Penn Warren Poetry Prize annually. Winners receive $500, $300 and $200. For contest guidelines, send SASE.

CUTBANK; THE RICHARD HUGO MEMORIAL POETRY AWARD (II), English Dept., University of Montana, Missoula MT 59812, phone (406)243-5231, founded 1973, coeditors Judy Blunt and Bob Hackett, an annual publishing "the best poetry, fiction, reviews, interviews and artwork available to us." Offers 2 annual awards for best poem and piece of fiction, The Richard Hugo Memorial Poetry Award and The A.B. Guthrie, Jr. Short Fiction Award. Winners announced in spring issue. They have recently published poetry by Gary Gildner, James Galvin and Greg Pape. As a sample the editor selected these lines from "The One True God" by Pattiann Rogers:

> He runs his hand through the ground
> and up the inner trunk of the laurel cherry
> in spring, pushing before his fingers
> earth-light like white blossoms forced outward
> through a thousand pores.

There are about 80 pgs. of poetry in each issue, which has a circulation of about 500, 250+ subscriptions of which 10-20% are libraries. Single copy: $6.95; subscription: $12/two issues. **Sample postpaid: $4. Submission guidelines for SASE. Submit 3-5 poems, single-spaced. Simultaneous submissions OK if informed. Reads submissions August 15 through February 1 only. Reports in 2 months. Pays in copies. "All rights return to author upon publication."** Staff reviews books of poetry in 500 words, single or multi-book format. Bob Hackett says, "The narrative poem should not be simply a journalistic first-person experience. The full imaginative, linguistic onus bears on the simple narrative poem, if it is to succeed."

CWM (II, IV-Themes), % Geof Huth, 317 Princetown Rd., Schenectady NY 12306, (or % David Kopaska-Merkel, 1300 Kicker Rd., Tuscaloosa AL 35414, phone (205)553-2284), founded 1990, co-geologians Ge(of Huth) and David Kopaska-Merkel. (These "geologians" also edit dbqp and *Dreams and Nightmares*, but *CWM* has no relation to their other imprints.) This magazine, published annually on **set themes, is "not tied down by ideas of proper style, form or substance, and presents work for the person of divergent tastes. The only considerations will be length and quality (as we see it). Extremely long poems will be at a disadvantage. Poems must be on the theme of the issue. The theme for the 1994 issue is 'Archaeology of the Soul.'** Unusual pieces of any kind are welcome, and should be submitted in whatever form the author deems most suitable." As a sample the geologians chose these lines from "The Drowned" by Jonathan Brannen:

> Once boatloads of pilgrims
> arrived to worship
> the drowned children
> whose bodies miraculously whole
> and uncorrupted were on display

Press run is 100. **Send SASE for guidelines. Reports within 6 weeks. Pays "at least one copy."** Staff reviews books of poetry and poetry journals. Send books for review consideration.

CYANOSIS (IV-Themes), Suite 30, 318 Mendocino Ave., Santa Rosa CA 95404, founded 1989, editor Darin DeStefano, is a biannual forum for artists and writers of various disciplines to present controversial, experimental or provocative work. They want **"experimental art, poetry dealing with themes of science or sociology, poetry with thematic experimentation, a sense of craft and unusual form or language use. 1-10 pages. Lean toward disturbing or provocative topics. No 'poor me' poems. Autojournalistic poetry that is poorly executed is often embarasing to read."** They have published poetry by Daniel Davidson, George Albon, David Bromige and Gwendolyn Albert. As a sample the editor selected these lines from "Malleable" by John McNally:

> Skin riddle comic modesty. Clifftop guillotine hands. Beneath his lid a razor, a

lurking wreck, the stunned soldier dry as the prow of a cactus flower.
The editor says it is 150 pgs., perfect-bound, offset, with coated cover. They receive about 500 poems a year, accept approximately 12%. Press run is 1,000 for 300 subscribers of which 25 are libraries, 500 shelf sales. Single copy: $6.95; subscription: $14 (2 issues). **Sample postpaid: $7. No simultaneous submissions. Informative cover letter requested. "Would like to know as much as possible about the writer." Often comments on rejections. Send SASE for guidelines — "prefer you send work with request." Reports in 2-6 weeks. Pays 1-3 copies. Offers $25 honorarium "for outstanding submission" to 1 contributor/issue.** Reviews books of poetry. Open to unsolicited reviews. Poets may also send books for review consideration. The editor says, "Forget the market, forget selling and fame. Allow the words in your blood to make the paper. Allow the marrow of your dreams to speak. If money is involved, sew the lips shut and be done with it."

DAGGER OF THE MIND; K'YI-LIH PRODUCTIONS; BREACH ENTERPRISES (IV-Science fiction/ fantasy/horror), 1317 Hookridge Dr., El Paso TX 79925, phone (915)591-0541, founded 1989, executive editor Arthur William Lloyd Breach, assistant editor Sam Lopez, wants **"poetry that stirs the senses and emotions. Make the words dance and sing, bring out the fire in the human soul. Show flair and fashion. No four-letter words, nothing pornographic, vulgar, blasphemous, obscene and nothing generally in bad taste."** They have published poetry by Jessica Amanda Salmonson. The quarterly *DOTM* is magazine-sized, saddle-stapled, with high glossy covers. They use about 50 of 100-150 poems received/year. Press run 4,000-5,000 with 100 subscribers. Subscription: $8/half year, $16/year. **Sample postpaid: $3.50. "Send in batches of 10. I will consider simultaneous submissions only if told in advance that they are such. Include cover letter with published credits, a very brief bio and kinds of styles written. Length is open as is style. Be creative and try to reflect something about the human condition. Show me something that reflects what is going on in the world. Be sensitive but not mushy. Be intelligent not sophomoric. Don't try to carbon copy any famous poet. You lead the way — don't follow. I don't like the trend toward blood and gore and obscenity. Report back in 1 month tops." Pays $1-5/poem plus 1 copy. Buys first North American serial rights and reprint rights.** *"DOTM* is devoted to *quality* horror. The key word is quality. *DOTM* is a publication under the division of K'yi-Lih Productions whose main heading is Breach Enterprises. All publications to appear in the market will come under K'yi-Lih Productions." The editor will evaluate work and review books of poetry for a fee, depending on length and quantity. Send books for review consideration. He says, "I'm planning an anthology of Lovecraftian related material. The paperback will be predominantly Cthulhu Mythos fiction, but I do intend to publish some poetry."

DAILY MEDITATION (V), Box 2710, San Antonio TX 78299, editor Ruth S. Paterson, is a **nonsectarian** religious quarterly that publishes **inspirational poems up to 14 lines, but is currently not accepting poetry submissions. Sample postpaid: $1.**

THE DALHOUSIE REVIEW (II), Suite 314, Sir James Dunn Bldg., Halifax, Nova Scotia B3H 3J5 Canada, founded 1921, phone (902)494-2541, is **a prestige literary quarterly preferring poems of 40 lines or less.** As a sample the editor selected these lines from "Weather" by Alan R. Wilson:

The rain that plummets
to the roofs of houses,

the wind that pitches
like a heavy object
into trees,

the sleet that drops
the faces of the men
and women hurrying by —

the freefall of turbulence.

The review is 136 pgs., 6 × 9 professionally printed on heavy stock with matte card cover. Relatively few poems are featured in each issue, but ones that are tend to be free verse with emphasis on image and voice. Individual copies range in cost from $6.50-25. Subscription: $19/year within Canada, $28/year outside Canada (both in Canadian dollars). **Contributors receive $3 for a first poem. For each poem after (in the same issue) he or she will receive $2/poem, 2 complimentary copies of issue and 15 offprints.**

DAM (DISABILITY ARTS MAGAZINE) (IV-Theme), 10 Woad Lane, Great Coates, Grimsby DN37 9NH Great Britain, phone/fax 0472-280031, founded 1991, editor Roland Humphrey, is a quarterly that "has two primary concerns: access to the arts and the promotion of disability arts — disability as subject for art rather than merely metaphor." They want **any poetry where disability is the theme.**

"Nothing thoughtless." As a sample the editor selected these lines by Pete Kalu:

> We are the flurry of heads
> tracking conversation.
> the talking hands
> like underwater communicators
> without movement, the beached whales

DAM is 64 pgs., 6⅞ × 9¹³⁄₁₆, perfect-bound, with full-color laminated card cover and photos, "designed to be kept." Press run is 1,500 for 1,000 subscribers of which 100 are libraries. Single copy: £2 (£6 international); subscription: £12 (£18 outside E.E.C.). No previously published poems or simultaneous submissions. Seldom comments on rejections. Reports in 3 months maximum. Pays disabled people only—£5 a poem (variable)—£15 a page.

DANCE CONNECTION (IV-Themes), #603, 815 1st St. SW, Calgary, Alberta T2P 1N3 Canada, phone (403)237-7327, founded 1983, editor Heather Elton, appears 5 times a year and uses **poems about dance—"any length, format, subject except bad poetry talking about the extended graceful lines of ballet."** It is magazine-sized, 60 pgs., desktop published, saddle-stapled. Press run 3,000 for 1,200 subscribers of which 35 are libraries, 400 newsstand sales. Subscription: $19 individuals, $29 institutions. **Sample postpaid: $4. Deadline for their literary issue is May 1. Reports in 3 months. Pays 3 copies and "occasional honorarium." Acquires all rights. Returns rights.** The editor says they "very occasionally publish poetry. When we get larger we will publish more, but now space is a precious commodity for review/calendars/news/columns and feature departments."

DANDELION (II); BLUE BUFFALO (IV-Regional), The Alexandra Centre, 922-9th Ave. SE, Calgary, Alberta T2G 0S4 Canada, phone (403)265-0524, founded 1975, poetry editors Deborah Miller and Allan Serafin, managing editor Barbara Kermade-Scott, appears twice a year. They want **"quality— We are open to any form, style, length. No greeting card verse."** They have published poetry by Claire Harris, Susan Ioannou and Robert Hilles. As a sample the editor selected these lines by Roger Nash:

> On Sabbath evenings, a slow hand
> tuned the guitar. A fast hand
> moved the shifting stars. And, somewhere,
> while we were growing up, there was a street still
> made of gold of tin of slush

Dandelion is 102 pgs., 6 × 9, with full-color cover, professionally printed and bound. They accept about 10% of 600 mss received. Press run 750. **Sample postpaid: $6. Submit in January through March and July through September for issues in June and December. Cover letter with bio required. Send SASE for a short statement of their needs. Reports in 4-6 weeks. Pays honorarium plus 1 copy. Acquires one-time rights.** Reviews books of poetry in 500-1,200 words; preference is for books by Alberta writers. Open to unsolicited reviews. Poets may also send books for review consideration to Reviews Editor. *blue buffalo* is a magazine which falls under the Dandelion Magazine Society umbrella. *blue buffalo* is also published twice yearly, but **submissions are accepted *only* from Alberta writers.**

JOHN DANIEL AND COMPANY, PUBLISHER; FITHIAN PRESS (II), a division of Daniel & Daniel, Publishers, Inc., P.O. Box 21922, Santa Barbara CA 93121, phone (805)962-1780, founded 1980, reestablished 1985. John Daniel, a general small press publisher, specializes in literature, both prose and poetry. Fithian Press is a subsidy imprint open to all subjects. **"Book-length mss of any form or subject matter will be considered, but we do not want to see pornographic, libelous, illegal or sloppily written poetry."** He has recently published books by Max Brand, Daniel Green and Hugo Walter. As a sample John Daniel selected "Go Little Book" from the book **Mind and Blood** by John Finlay:

> Go little book to the party,
> But hide your moral crumb.
> Be cunning. Act as if to say,
> I'm hungry, Sir, and dumb.

He publishes 10 flat-spined paperbacks, averaging 64 pgs., each year. **For free catalog of either imprint, send 10 sample poems and bio. Reports on queries in 2 weeks, on mss in 2 months. Simultaneous submissions and disks compatible with Macintosh OK. Pays 10-75% of net receipts royalties. Buys English-language book rights. Returns them upon termination of contract.** Fithian Press books (50% of his publishing) are subsidized, the author paying production costs and receiving royalties of 50-75% of net receipts. Books and rights are the property of the author, but publisher agrees to warehouse and distribute for one year if desired. John Daniel advises, "Poetry does not make money, alas. It is a labor of love for both publisher and writer. But if the love is there, the rewards are great."

DAUGHTERS OF SARAH (IV-Feminist, religious, social issues, themes), 3801 N. Keeler, Box 411179, Chicago IL 60618, phone (312)736-3399, founded 1974, editor Reta Finger, a quarterly magazine "integrating feminist philosophy with biblical-Christian theology and making connections with social issues." The magazine includes only "occasional" poetry. The editor says, **"Do not prefer rhyming poetry; must be short enough for one 5½ × 8½ page, but prefer less than 20 lines. Topics must relate to Christian feminist issues, but prefer specifics to abstract terminology."** She does not want **"greeting card type verse or modern poetry so obscure one can't figure out what it means."** As a sample she chose the following lines by Ann Bailey:

> *Who would lay her head on stone,*
> *Would crush the dark to dust?*
> *What dreamstruck one will hurl herself toward holiness*
> *and fight for her own blessings?*
> *Who here would risk her life to wrestle with the Lord?*

The magazine is digest-sized, 64 pgs., with photos and graphics, web offset. Its circulation is 4,500, of which 4,400 are subscriptions, including about 250 libraries; bookstore sales are 50. Single copy: $4.50; subscription: $18/year. Back issues available for $3.50. **Considers simultaneous submissions. Guidelines are available for SASE. Poets should submit two copies of each poem (prefers shorter poems) to the editor, who reports in 1-2 months; time to publication is 3-18 months.** *Daughters of Sarah* **pays $15-30/poem plus 2-3 copies. Buys one-time rights. "Write first for list of upcoming themes, since we mostly choose our poetry to fit with a particular theme."**

DBQP; ALABAMA DOGSHOE MOUSTACHE; A VOICE WITHOUT SIDES; &; HIT BROADSIDES; THE SUBTLE JOURNAL OF RAW COINAGE; DBQPRESCARDS (IV-Form), 317 Princetown Rd., Schenectady NY 12306, founded 1987, poetry editor Ge(of Huth). "dbqp is the name of the overall press. *Alabama Dogshoe Moustache* publishes **language poetry (usually very short) & visual poetry.** *A Voice Without Sides* is an occasional magazine in very small runs (about 24 copies) and in strange formats (in jars, as earrings, etc.); it uses the same type of poetry as *ADM*. *&* is a series of leaflets each featuring a single poem. *Hit Broadsides* is a broadside series. *The Subtle Journal of Raw Coinage* is a monthly that publishes coined words but occasionally will publish an issue of *pwoermds* (one-word poems such as Aram Saroyan's 'eyeye') or poems written *completely* with neologisms. *dbqprescards* is a postcard series publishing mostly poetry. These publications are generally handmade magazines, leaflets, broadsides and objects of very small size. **I am interested only in short language poetry and visual poetry. No traditional verse or mainstream poetry."** They have published poetry by John M. Bennett, Bob Grumman and Jonathan Brannen. As a sample the editor selected this complete poem by damian lopes:

> *the small boy walks*
> *like turning pages*
> *& runs like an alphabet*
> *without vowels*

Their major poetry magazine is *Alabama Dogshoe Moustache*, which appears in various formats up to 15 pgs., magazine-sized, held together with thread, staples, fasteners, or packaged inside containers. Its press run is 100-125 with 10 subscriptions. Price per issue 40¢-$2.50. **Sample: $1 or $2 postpaid. Catalog available for SASE. Reports within 2 weeks. Pays "at least 2 copies."** Staff occasionally reviews books of poetry. Send books for review consideration. The editor says, "Most of the poetry I reject is from people who know little about the kind of poetry I publish. I don't mind reading these submissions, but it's usually a waste of time for the submitters. If you are familiar with the work of the poets I publish, you'll have a much better idea about whether or not I'll be interested in your work."

‡DE YOUNG PRESS; THE NEW CRUCIBLE (I), Rt. 1 Box 76, Stark KS 66775, founded 1964, publisher Mary De Young. *The New Crucible* is an environmental magazine appearing 8 times/year. They publish environmental, political, free-thought, health, rural farm/garden and general interest articles. **They are open to all forms and styles of poetry but nothing epic-length. Also, no religious poetry, explicit sex or obscene language.** They have recently published poetry by Alan Rickard and Branley Branson. As a sample the editor selected these lines from Branson's "Ruminations on Raking Leaves":

> *What color windrows itself in the lurch*
> *Of cycles on the sleepy grass I've wooed*
> *All summer to grow. The leaves cannot lie*
> *Where they fall for their inner stuff will taint*
> *The soil and next year's hairy rootlets will die*
> *(All this comes by way of word of mouth)* ...

The editor says *The New Crucible* is approximately 30 pgs., 8½ × 11, perfect-bound, with b&w cover. Subscription: $50/12 issues. **Sample postpaid: $5. No previously published poems; simultaneous submissions OK. Cover letter required.** Time between acceptance and publication is 6 months. **Reports within 2 weeks if SASE included. Pays 2 copies. Rights remain with author.** De Young Press is a subsidy publisher. **"Authors should write for particulars. Can be flexible with arrangements."**

‡THE DEAD REBEL NEWS; CONTEMPORARY AESTHETICS (II), (formerly *Axe*), 421 Park St., Oxford PA 19363, founded 1990, "non-editor" Robert Nagler. Both *TDRN* and *CA* are irregularly published literary newsletters using **very short ("flash" and minimal) fiction and experimental literature of all types.** *TDRN* has published R. Kostelanetz, J.M. Bennett, S. Murphy, G. Huth, Malok and Musicmaster R. Howington. As a sample the editor chose these lines from his own work, "She Turns the Ceramic Dogs in, Toward the Living Room, Meaning: My Husband is Here":

> *The energy of the stroke derives from the quick pivoting*
> *of the waist, the motion of the backdownward, and the full*
> *force of the arm, elbow bent.*

TDRN and *CA* are single-sheet, double-sided photocopied leaflets with few graphics. **Subscription and samples are available for one business-size SASE.** The editor adds, "The answer to a frequent query: our title, 'The Dead Rebel', is taken from the name of a tattoo parlor in Germany."

DENVER QUARTERLY (II), Dept. of English, University of Denver, Denver CO 80208, phone (303)871-2892, founded 1965, editor Donald Revell, is a quarterly literary journal that publishes fiction, poems, book reviews and essays. **There are no restrictions on the type of poetry wanted.** Poems here (mostly free verse) focus on careful use of language—poetic diction—emphasizing image and symbol and leaning occasionally toward the avant-garde. Length is open, with some long poems and sequences also featured. They have published poetry by James Merrill, Linda Pastan and William Matthews. *Denver Quarterly* is 6×9, handsomely printed on buff stock, average 160 pgs., flat-spined with two-color matte card cover. Press run is 1,000 for 600 subscribers (300 to libraries) and approximately 300 shelf sales. Subscription: $15/year to individuals and $18 to institutions. **Samples of all issues after Spring 1985 are available for $5 postpaid. No submissions read between May 15 and September 15 each year. Send SASE for guidelines. Reports in 2-3 months. Pays 2 copies and $5/page.** Reviews books of poetry. Poetry published in *Denver Quarterly* has been included in **Best American Poetry 1992.**

DESCANT (III, IV-Regional), Box 314, Station P, Toronto, Ontario M5S 2S8 Canada, founded 1970, editor-in-chief Karen Mulhallen, is "a quarterly journal of the arts committed to being the finest in Canada. **While our focus is primarily on Canadian writing we have published writers from around the world."** Some of the poets they have published are Lorna Crozier, Stephen Pender and Libby Scheier. As a sample the editor selected these lines from "Isla Grande" by Lake Sagaris:

> *I had caught children in my womb like clams*
> *watched them pried open and consumed and tossed away*
> *and still I was young.*

It is an elegantly printed and illustrated flat-spined publication with colored, glossy cover, over-sized digest format, 140+ pgs., heavy paper, with a circulation of 1,200 (800 subscriptions, of which 20% are libraries). They receive 1,200 freelance submissions/year, of which they use less than 10, with a 2-year backlog. **Sample postpaid: $8. Guidelines available for SASE. Submit typed ms, unpublished work not in submission elsewhere, name and address on first page and last name on each subsequent page. Include SASE with Canadian stamps or SAE and IRCs. Reports within 4 months. Pays "approximately $100." Buys first-time rights.** Karen Mulhallen says, "Best advice is to know the magazine you are submitting to. Choose your markets carefully."

DESCANT: TEXAS CHRISTIAN UNIVERSITY LITERARY JOURNAL (II), English Dept., Box 32892, Texas Christian University, Fort Worth TX 76129, phone (817)921-7240, founded 1956, editors Betsy Colquitt, Stan Trachtenberg and Harry Opperman, appears twice a year. They want **"well-crafted poems of interest. No restrictions as to subject matter or forms. We usually accept poems 40 lines or fewer but sometimes longer poems."** They have published poems by Walter McDonald and Lyn Lifshin. It is 6×9, 92 pgs., saddle-stapled, professionally printed, with matte card cover. Poems in issues we read tended to be lyric free verse under 50 lines with short line lengths (for added tension). "We publish 30-40 pgs. of poetry per year. We receive probably 4,000-5,000 poems annually." Their press run is 500 for 350 subscribers. Single copy: $6; volume: $12, $18 foreign. **Sample postpaid: $4. No simultaneous submissions. Reports in 6-8 weeks, usually no more than 8 months until publication. Pays 2 copies.**

THE DEVIL'S MILLHOPPER PRESS; THE DEVIL'S MILLHOPPER; KUDZU POETRY CONTEST; SAND RIVER POETRY CONTEST (II), College of Humanities, University of South Carolina at Aiken, 171 University Parkway, Aiken SC 29801, founded 1976, editor Stephen Gardner, assistant editor JoAnn Biga, publishes one magazine issue of *The Devil's Millhopper* each year and one chapbook, winner of an annual competition. **They want to see any kind of poetry, except pornography or political propaganda, up to 100 lines.** Some of the poets they have published are Susan Ludvigson, Ann Darr, Lynne H. deCourcy, Ricardo Pau-Llosa, Katherine Soniat, Walt McDonald, R.T. Smith, Dorothy Barresi and Richard Frost. The magazine is 32-40 pgs., digest-sized, saddle-stapled, printed on good stock with card cover and using beautiful b&w original drawings inside and on the cover. The print run of *Devil's Millhopper* is 500. The annual chapbook has a print run of 600, going to 375 subscribers of which 20 are libraries. **Sample postpaid: $2.50. Send regular, non-contest submissions September and October only. They want name and address on every page of submissions; simultaneous submissions acceptable. Sometimes the editor comments on rejected mss. Reports usually in 2 months. Pays copies.** Acquires first North American serial and reprint rights. Rights automatically revert to author upon publication. Send SASE for their annual Kudzu Poetry Contest rules (prizes of $50, $100 and $150, $3/poem entry fee), annual Sand River Contest for poetry in traditional fixed forms (prizes of $300, $150 and $50, $3/poem entry fee), chapbook competition rules and guidelines for magazine submissions. Send Kudzu contest submissions September 1-October 15; Sand River Contest submissions June 1-July 1; chapbook contest submissions January 1-February 1. Chapbook competition requires either $5 reading fee or $9 subscription for 2 years. Pays $50 plus 50 copies. The editor advises, "There is no substitute for reading a lot and writing a lot or for seeking out tough criticism from others who are doing the same."

DIALOGUE: A JOURNAL OF MORMON THOUGHT; MARGARET RAMPTON MUNK POETRY AWARD (IV-Religious), P.O. Box 658, Salt Lake City UT 84110, founded 1966, poetry editor Susan Elizabeth Howe, "is an independent quarterly established to express Mormon culture and to examine the relevance of religion to secular life. It is edited by Latter-Day Saints who wish to bring their faith into dialogue with the larger stream of Judeo-Christian thought and with human experience as a whole and to foster artistic and scholarly achievement based on their cultural heritage. The views expressed are those of the individual authors and are not necessarily those of the Mormon Church or of the editors." **They publish 6-8 poems in each issue, "humorous and serious treatments of Mormon topics or universal themes from a Mormon perspective. Under 40 lines preferred. Must communicate with a well-educated audience but not necessarily sophisticated in poetic criticism. Free verse OK but only if carefully crafted."** They have published poetry by Michael Collins, R.A. Christmas, May Swenson and Linda Sillitoe. The editor selected these sample lines from "You Heal" by Emma Lou Thayne:

> After things happen, under the scarring
> you heal. It takes its jagged course
> upward and then . . .

They have a circulation of 4,000-4,500 subscriptions of which 150 are libraries. The journal has an elegant 6×9 format, 170+ pgs., with color, artistically decorated cover and tasteful b&w drawings within. They receive about 200 submissions/year, use 35-40. **Sample postpaid: $7. Submit typed ms in triplicate, 1 poem/page with name, address and telephone number on each sheet. Acknowledges in 10 days, reports in 3 months. Payment is 10 offprints plus one contributor's copy.** Acquires first publication rights. Reviews "books by Mormon poets or about Mormon themes and/or culture." Open to unsolicited reviews. Poets may also send books to Book Review Editor for review consideration. They sponsor the Margaret Rampton Munk Poetry Award annually; three prizes: first, $100; second, $75; third, $50.

JAMES DICKEY NEWSLETTER (III), DeKalb College, 2101 Womack Rd., Dunwoody GA 30338, founded 1984, editor Joyce M. Pair, a biannual newsletter devoted to critical articles/studies of James Dickey's works/biography and bibliography. They **"publish a few poems of** *high* **quality. No poems lacking form or meter."** As a sample here are the opening lines from "Haft Blossom" by R.T. Smith:

> Long-sleeping, I rose in the morning
> and opened the door to sunlight.
> Trough water woke me with sunlight,
> dark and the other stars having
> yielded their power . . .

It is 30+ pgs. of ordinary paper, neatly offset (back and front), with a card back-cover, stapled top left corner. The newsletter is published in the fall and spring. Single copy: $3.50; subscription to individuals $5/year, $10 to institutions. **Sample available for $3.50 postage. Contributors should follow MLA style and standard ms form, sending 1 copy, double-spaced. Cover letter required. Pays 5 copies.** Acquires first rights. Reviews "only works on Dickey or that include Dickey." Open to unsolicited reviews. The editor's advice is: "Acquire more knowledge of literary history, metaphor, symbolism and grammar, and, to be safe, the poet should read a couple of our issues."

DICKINSON STUDIES; HIGGINSON JOURNAL; DICKINSON-HIGGINSON PRESS (I), 1330 Massachusetts Ave. NW, Apt. 503, Washington DC 20005-4150, phone (202)638-1671, founded 1968, poetry editor F.L. Morey. *Dickinson Studies* and *Higginson Journal* are publications of Dickinson-Higginson Press (membership $50 individuals, $100 for libraries for 3 years). They are semiannuals, sometimes with bonus issues, all distributed free to about 250 subscribers of which 125 are libraries.

● Just as this edition of **Poet's Market** went to press, we were notified of the death of F.L. Morey and the suspension of his publications and press.

Dickinson Studies is principally for scholarship on Emily Dickinson, but uses poems about her. *Higginson Journal* has a special poetry issue about every two years and uses a few poems in each issue. As a sample we selected these lines from "At the Shore" by Christine J. Eder:

> Birds scatter at other's movements
> leap into air, circle,
> scream, land again. Waves
> dance—pumped with energy . . .

The journals are both digest-sized, about 30 pgs., saddle-stapled, typeset with card covers and b&w art. **Sample postpaid: $4. "A $5 reading fee must be included for each poem submitted. This does not guarantee publication, but will bring critique within 2 weeks usually."** Open to unsolicited reviews. Poets may also send books for review consideration.

DIE YOUNG (V), 420 Orangewood Dr., Lafayette LA 70503, founded 1990, editors Jesse Glass, Jr., and Skip Fox, is a journal appearing irregularly, **generally accepting no unsolicited poetry.** They have published poetry by Robert Creeley, Karl Shapiro, Richard Eberhart, Kathleen Raine, Burton Raffel and Tom Clark. **Sample postpaid: $3. Those who wish to submit may query with SASE. Address query to Skip Fox.** Despite their requested "closed" market coding, *Die Young* ranked #6 in the "New Poets" category of the June 1993 *Writer's Digest* Poetry 60 list. This category ranks those markets who often publish poets whose work is new to their publication. Thus, chances of acceptance here may be greater than indicated.

‡DIEHARD (III), 3 Spittal St., Edinburgh, Scotland EH3 9DY, phone (031)229-7252, founded 1990, editors Ian King and Sally Evans, publishes 6 hardbacks and 1-2 chapbooks/year. **They want "the heavyweight stuff, no fractured prose, politics and pious piffle."** As examples of poets published the editor lists Keats, Oscar Wilde and John Skelton. "A book is a book. Write me a book rather than ply me with a heap of scraps from magazines. **No reply unless interested, do not send SAE. Use your own name, keep it accurate, keep it legible." Reporting is "slow." They pay 5% royalties plus 6 copies.** The editor says, "Anyone attempting subsidy will be booted out the door that fast and it might cause an international incident. We are actually quite a major antiquarian bookshop (Grindles of Edinburgh) with a bindery and letterpress printing facilities (for shop use only). As most of our staff are writers or former publishers of some description, we like to keep Diehard going as a sideline where quality of production really matters."

‡A DIFFERENT DRUMMER (II, IV-Ethnic, translations); SONGS OF THE CITY ANNUAL POETRY CONTEST (II, IV-Themes); CHEAP JAKE ANNUAL CHAPBOOK CONTEST (II), 84 Bay 28th St., Brooklyn NY 11214, founded 1989, editor/publisher Nicholas Stix. *ADD*, a magazine of literature, art and ideas, appears 6 times a year. **"I am promiscuous in my likes (style and theme-wise) and don't want to discourage someone from submitting an excellent poem written in a generally undistinguished genre. I do not expect poetry to toe a political line. Spare me impostors, masquerading as poems: incoherent fragments, uninspiring prose set in short 'poetry-like' lines and literal statements of the writer's moral superiority or love of another person, place or thing. Also: no poems that explain themselves through a preface or epilogue, or poems on the difficulties of writing poetry, unless extremely witty." They lean toward work that is "urban, ethnic (Jewish and black)."** They have recently published poetry by Stewart David Ikeda, Paul J. Hamill, Damienne Real and Barbara M. Simon. As a sample the editor selected these lines from "Style" by William Russell:

> "I told the nigger,
> I told the nigger,"
> And he stiff-fingers the air
> to defy God—
>   out loud,
>   in the open;
> his words clearly spoken for the bronze beauty at his side,
>   Because the pay phone he pretends to talk in
>   is broken.

ADD is 52 pgs., 8 × 11, flat-spined, professionally printed, with glossy cover. Press run 20,000 for about 2,000 subscriptions, about 2,500 shelf sales. Subscription: $15. **Sample postpaid: $5.** Do not submit mss in October, November or December, except for contests. Send SASE for guidelines. Pays a minimum of 5 copies. "Allow 4-6 months for a response. I read all submissions, screening out approximately 98% and discussing the rest with my editors. There are no requirements, but potential contributors are expected to read *ADD* before submitting work." They use translations with original works (author must secure rights of work not in public domain.) Open to unsolicited reviews. Poets may also send books for review consideration. Their annual Songs of the City Contest (Prizes of $100, $75, $50, plus publication in *ADD* and copies; entry fee: $5/poem; deadline February 1) is for **poems on urban themes.** The Cheap Jake Chapbook contest (Prize of $150, plus publication and copies; entry fee: $10/ms; 24-page limit; deadline February 1; each entrant receives a copy) **has no thematic or stylistic restrictions. Send SASE for rules of either contest.** The editor says, "Don't be a slave to the muse, forcing all of your thoughts and feelings into a 'poetic' form. Work in as many forms of prose and poetry as possible. That way you are more likely to find the style appropriate to your expression. Be your own toughest critic. Proofread and analyze your work carefully. Never rush out a poem before its time. Avoid the company of poets. Above all, do as I say, not as I do."

DIONYSOS: THE LITERATURE AND ADDICTION TRIQUARTERLY (IV-Theme), University of Wisconsin, 1800 Grand Ave., Superior WI 54880, phone (715)394-8465, founded 1989, editor Roger Forseth. *Dionysos* publishes "work and information on any aspect of the relation between addiction and the cultural/aesthetic scene, including articles, book and article reviews, film and theater commentary, occasional poems and short stories, interviews, research and critical notes." They want **"short poems, primarily, on alcohol/drugs/addiction only. No sentimental or *purely* confessional poetry."** They have published poetry by Hayden Carruth and William Wyatt. As a sample the editor selected the last lines of "Alcoholic" by Judson Jerome:
> *The sonofabitch (God bless him) drank and died*
> *because we understood away his pride.*

They receive about 10 poems a year, use 2. Press run is 350 for 200 subscribers of which 30 are libraries, 10 shelf sales. Single copy: $3 ($4 overseas); subscription: $8. **Previously published poems and simultaneous submissions OK. Submit 2 copies with SASE. Cover letter with vita required. Deadlines: 1st of September, January and May for issues appearing October, February and June.** Time between acceptance and publication is 3-6 months. **Always comments on rejections. Reports by "return mail." Pays 5 copies.** Staff reviews related books of poetry. Send books for review consideration.

‡DISABILITY RAG (IV-Specialized), P.O. Box 145, Louisville KY 40201, founded 1981, fiction/poetry editor Anne Finger, appears 6 times a year. *"Disability Rag* is the nation's leading disability rights magazine." **The editors have no restrictions as to form, length or style of poetry. "We are interested in material by disabled writers or about the disability experience. Nothing sappy, sentimental, stereotyped or cliched."** They have recently published poetry by Kenny Fries and Cheryl Marie Wade. The editor says *DR* is approximately 32 pgs., 8½×11, b&w graphics on newsprint, some advertising. They receive about 100 poems a year, accept approximately 10%. Press run is 5,000 for 4,500 subscribers of which approximately 10% are libraries, 350 shelf sales. Single copy: $3.95; subscription: $17.50 individuals, $35 institutions, $42 international. Sample postpaid: $4.50. Previously published poems OK, **"provided they have not appeared in a publication that circulates to the disabled community." No simultaneous submissions. Cover letter required.** Time between acceptance and publication is 6-12 months. **Often comments on rejections. Send SASE for guidelines. Reports within 2 weeks. Pays $25/ poem plus 2 copies. Buys first North American serial rights.** "We do publish reviews of disability-related poetry collections; our reviews run approximately 250-500 words."

DOC(K)S; EDITIONS NEPE; ZERROSCOPIZ; ANTHOLOGIES DE L 'AN 2.000; LES ANARTISTES (II, IV-Bilingual/foreign language), Le Moulin de Ventabren, 13122 Ventabren, France 13122, uses **"concrete, visual, sound poetry; performance; mail-art; metaphysical poetry,"** not "poesie à la queue-leu-leu" . . . whatever that means. They have published work by J.F. Bory, Nani Balestrini, Bernard Heidsieck, James Koller, Julien Blaine and Franco Beltrametti. The magazine *Doc(k)s* is published 4 times a year and has a circulation of 1,100, of which 150 are subscriptions. **Pay for poetry is 5 copies. There are no specifications for submissions.** *Doc(k)s* is an elegantly produced volume, 7×10, over 300 pgs., flat-spined, using heavy paper and glossy full-color card covers. Most of it is in French. "We cannot quote a sample, because concrete poetry, a cross between poetry and graphic art, requires the visual image to be reproduced." Nepe Editions publishes collections of poetry, mostly in French.

Market categories: (I) Beginning; (II) General; (III) Limited; (IV) Specialized; (V) Closed.

DOLPHIN LOG (IV-Children, themes), Suite 402, 870 Greenbrier Circle., Chesapeake VA 23320, phone (804)523-9335, founded 1981, editor Elizabeth Foley, is a bimonthly educational publication for children offered by The Cousteau Society. "Encompasses all areas of science, ecology and the environment as they relate to our global water system. Philosophy of magazine is to delight, instruct and instill an environmental ethic and understanding of the interconnectedness of living organisms, including people." They want to see "poetry related to the marine environment, marine ecology or any water-related subject matter to suit the readership of 7- to 15-year-olds and which will fit the concept of our magazine. Short, witty poems, thought-provoking poems encouraged. No dark or lengthy ones (more than 20 lines). No talking animals." The editor excerpted these sample lines from "Garbage Pirates" by Marianne Dyson:

Their treasure bags ready
The garbage pirates three,
Set sail in a wagon boat
Upon the Sidewalk Sea.

They steer around bottle fish
With broken, jagged teeth,
And pinch their noses at the smell
Of trash on Driveway Beach.

It is magazine-sized, 20 pgs., saddle-stapled, offset, using full-color photographs widely throughout, sometimes art, no advertising. It circulates to 100,000 members, approximately 860 library subscriptions. Membership: $28/year for a Cousteau Society family membership, $10/year for *Dolphin Log* only. **Sample: $2 plus 9×12 SAE with 75¢ postage. Double-spaced submissions. Reports within 2 months. Pays $25 on publication and 3 copies. Rights include one-time use in** *Dolphin Log*, **the right to grant reprints for use in other publications, and worldwide translation rights for use in other Cousteau Society publications.** The editor advises, "Become familiar with our magazine by requesting a sample copy and our guidelines. We are committed to a particular style and concept to which we strictly adhere and review submissions consistently. We publish only a very limited amount of poetry each year."

DOLPHIN-MOON PRESS; SIGNATURES (II, IV-Regional), P.O. Box 22262, Baltimore MD 21203, founded 1973, president James Taylor, is **"a limited edition (500-1,000 copies) press which emphasizes quality work (regardless of style), often published in unusual/'radical' format."** The writer is usually allowed a strong voice in the look/feel of the final piece. "We've published magazines, anthologies, chapbooks, pamphlets, perfect-bound paperbacks, records, audio cassettes and comic books. **All styles are read and considered, but the work should show a strong spirit and voice. Although we like the feel of 'well-crafted' work, craft for its own sake won't meet our standards either."** They have recently published work by Michael Weaver, John Strausbaugh, Josephine Jacobsen and William Burroughs. They have also previously published a collection by the late Judson Jerome, **The Village: New and Selected Poems,** $10.95 paperback, $15.95 hardcover. **Send SASE for catalog and purchase samples or send $10 for their 'sampler' (which they guarantee to be up to $20 worth of their publications). To submit, first send sample of 6-10 pgs. of poetry and a brief cover letter. Replies to query in 2-4 weeks, to submission of whole work (if invited) in 2-4 weeks. Payment in author's copies. Acquires first edition rights.** Three of the books published by this press have been nominated for the Pulitzer Prize. "Our future plans are to continue as we have since 1973, publishing the best work we can by local, up-and-coming and nationally recognized writers—in a quality package."

THE DOMINION REVIEW (II), Old Dominion University, Bal 220, English Dept., Norfolk VA 23529-0078, phone (804)683-3991, founded 1982, faculty advisor Wayne Ude, Creative Writing, says, **"There are no specifications as to subject matter or style, but we are dedicated to the free verse tradition and will continue to support it."** They have published poetry by Bob Perlongo, Paul Genega and Grace P. Simpson. *TDR* is flat-spined, 80 pgs., digest-sized, professionally printed, and appears each spring. They have 300 subscriptions. **Sample: $3. They will not consider previously published poems. Cover letter and brief bio requested. Submissions read from September 1 through December 7; allow to March 15 for replies. Guidelines available for SASE. No pay. Acquires first North American serial rights.**

‡DRAGONGATE PRESS (V), 508 Lincoln St., Port Townsend WA 98368, publishes poetry but **accepts no unsolicited mss.** Catalog available.

DRAGON'S TEETH PRESS; LIVING POETS SERIES (III), El Dorado National Forest, 7700 Wentworth Springs Rd., Georgetown CA 95634, founded 1970, poetry editor Cornel Lengyel. Published poets include Francis Weaver, Marcia Lee Masters and Stanley Mason. As a sample, the editor selected the beginning lines of "Not Just By Word of Mouth Alone" from **The Thirteenth Labor** by Ronald Belluomini:

> *My sole being elliptic*
> *I have now and anciently dreamt in*
> *the treasuries of hope about*
> *a scheme to elude delusion's wrath,*
> *but I have broken*
> *my egg-shaped dream with collusion's fact.*

Dragon's Teeth Press "**subsidy publishes 25% of books** if book has high literary merit, but very limited market"—which no doubt applies to books of poetry. They publish other books on 10% royalty contract. **Simultaneous submissions OK. Reports in 2 weeks on queries, 1 month on mss.**

DREAM INTERNATIONAL QUARTERLY (I, IV-Themes), % Tim Scott, Apt. 2B, 4147 N. Kedvale Ave., Chicago IL 60641, phone (312)794-0751, founded 1981, senior poetry editor Tim Scott. **"Poetry must be dream-inspired and/or dream-related. This can be interpreted loosely, even to the extent of dealing with the transitory as a theme. Nothing written expressly or primarily to advance a political or religious ideology."** They have recently published poetry by Tina Marie Spell, Kathleen Youmans and Marie A. Vega. As a sample the editor selected these lines from "Dis Here Place" by Barbara Ann Elmore:

> *I'm gonna win me the lottery*
> *Lie at the welfare line*
> *Fix da dice so I get snake eyes*
> *all de night*

DIQ is 64-84 pgs., 8½×11, with vellum cover and drawings. "Also offer a deluxe edition with protective plastic overlay and toothcomb binding." They receive about 150 poems a year, accept about 20. Press run is 300 for 200 subscribers of which 4 are libraries. Single copy: $6.50; subscription: $25 for 2 years. **Previously published poems and simultaneous submissions OK. Cover letter including publication history, if any, and philosophy of creation required. "As poetry submissions go through the hands of two readers, poets should enclose one additional first class stamp, along with the standard SASE."** Do not submit mss between Thanksgiving and New Year's. Time between acceptance and publication is 1 year. **Comments on rejections if requested. Send $1 for guidelines. Reports in 1-4 weeks. Pays 1 copy, "less postage." Acquires first North American serial or reprint rights.** Staff considers reviewing books of poetry "if the poet is a former contributor to *DIQ*. Such reviews usually run to about five hundred words." Tim Scott says, "Don't get discouraged. Discouragement is the beginning writer's biggest enemy. If you are good at your craft, you will eventually find an outlet for it. Know your literary predecessors and the tradition in which you are working. Read everything from Shakespeare and Donne to Baudelaire and Rimbaud, from Crane and Hopkins to Plath and Sexton."

THE DREAM SHOP; VERSE WRITERS GUILD OF OHIO; OHIO HIGH SCHOOL POETRY CONTESTS (IV-Membership, students), interim coordinator Amy Jo Zook, 3520 St. Rte. 56, Mechanicsburg OH 43044, founded 1928. The Verse Writers Guild of Ohio is a state poetry society open to members from outside the state, an affiliate of the National Federation of State Poetry Societies. *The Dream Shop* is their poetry magazine, appearing three times a year. Only members of VWG may submit poems. They do not want to see poetry which is highly sentimental, overly morbid or porn—and nothing over 40 lines. **"We use beginners' poetry, but would like it to be good, tight, revised. In short, not first drafts. Too much is sentimental or prosy when it could be passionate or lyric. We'd like poems to make us think as well as feel something."** They have published poetry by Yvonne Hardenbrook, Frankie Paino, Bonnie Jacobson and J.A. Totts. The editor selected these sample lines from "Portrait of Daruma (Hakuin Ekaku, 1685-1768)" by Jim Brooks:

> *How is it the word "tango"*
> *follows me into this corner*
> *of shaped light, follows me*
> *among sacred statues—wooden,*
> *bronze and sandstone eyes*
> *closed or half-closed on faces*
> *full of quiet, full of almost*
> *too remote tranquility? . . .*

"Ours is a forum for our members, and we do use reprints, so new members can get a look at what is going well in more general magazines." Annual dues including *The Dream Shop*: $15. Senior (over 65): $12. Single copies: $2. The magazine is computer typeset, digest-sized, 52 pgs., with matte card cover. **"All rights revert to poet after publication."** The Verse Writer's Guild sponsors an annual contest for unpublished poems written by high school students in Ohio with categories of traditional, modern, and several other categories. March deadline, with 3 money awards in each category. For contest information write Verse Writer's Guild of Ohio, 1798 Sawgrass Dr., Reynoldsburg OH 43068.

DREAMS AND NIGHTMARES (IV-Science fiction/fantasy), 1300 Kicker Rd., Tuscaloosa AL 35404, phone (205)553-2284, founded 1986, editor David C. Kopaska-Merkel, is published quarterly. The editor says, **"I want to see intriguing poems in any form or style under about 60 lines (but will consider longer poems). All submissions must be either science fiction, fantasy or horror (I prefer supernatural horror to gory horror). Nothing trite or sappy, very long poems, poems without fantastic content, excessive violence or pointless erotica. Sex and/or violence is OK if there is a good reason."** He has published poetry by Lisa Kucharski, Robert Frazier, Donna Zelzer, Ed Mycue, D.F. Lewis, Wendy Rathbone and Thomas Wiloch. As a sample he selected these lines from "Bad Vintage" by Jonathan Yungkans:

> Drank so much she nearly drowned,
>   spun
> in a whirlpool of furniture, walls, men
> with pasty faces, hands on glass,
>   watching her
> ready to join, them, floating like she was.

It has 24 pgs., digest-sized, photocopied from typescript, saddle-stapled, with a colored card stock cover and b&w illustrations. They accept about 80 of 1,000-1,500 poems received. Press run is 200 for 70 subscriptions. Subscription: $5/4 issues. Lifetime subscription: $50 (includes available back issues). **Samples $1.25 in stamps. Send SASE for guidelines. No simultaneous submissions. "Rarely" uses previously published poems. Reports in 2-10 weeks. Pays $3/poem plus 2 copies. Buys first North American serial rights.** The editor reviews books of poetry "for other magazines; I do not publish reviews in *DN*." Send books for review consideration. He says "There are more magazines publishing fantastic poetry than ever before, and more good fantastic poetry is being written, sold for good money and published. The field is doing very well."

DRUID PRESS (II), Dept. PM, 2724 Shades Crest Rd., Birmingham AL 35216, phone (205)967-6580, founded 1981, president Anne George. **"We do individual chapbooks. We want to see concrete images, free verse, any subject matter. No June-moon rhymes."** They have published poetry by R.T. Smith, Sue Walker, Sue Scalf, John Brugaletta and many others. **Sample books postpaid: $4. For chapbook or book consideration query with 5 samples, bio, publications. Simultaneous submissions OK, but no previously published material. Reports in 3 weeks. Pays "negotiable"** number of author's copies.

DRY CRIK REVIEW (IV-Nature/rural/ecology, themes), P.O. Box 44320, Lemon Cove CA 93244, founded 1991, editor John C. Dofflemyer, is a quarterly **of** cowboy poetry. "The function of *Dry Crik Review* is to inspire and communicate not only within the range livestock culture but to enhance an understanding of the people and dilemmas facing this livelihood with the urban majority, honestly. **Well-crafted expression must demonstrate insight gained from experience within this rural culture. Topics range from pastoral to political, humorous to serious. No slapstick doggerel or barnyard-pet poetry, please! Prefer shorter unpublished works."** They have recently published poetry by Paul Zarzyski, Kell Robertson, Charles Potts, Rod McQueary, Greg Keeler and Linda Hasselstrom. As a sample the editor selected these lines from "Stolen Moments" by Laurie Wagner Buyer:

> Unfolding, face raised to night sky,
> so little to remind me, still I recall
> the flicker of a squaw-brush fire outside
> the womb of the lodge, steam swirled with cedar scent,
> sweat rivulets between my breasts, your voice
> chanting low, plaintive, ancient sounds,
> out of the night, out of the earth, out of a time forgotten.

It is 70 pgs., digest-sized, photocopied from typescript on quality textured paper with matte card cover. It features free and formal verse with a distinct Western flavor. This magazine is lively and engaging with a sense of humor and social commitment to the land and environment—a rare combination. Press run is 800 for 400 subscribers of which 25 are libraries, 20% shelf sales. Subscription: $20. **Sample postpaid: $7, some back issues more. No simultaneous submissions. Submission quantity 1-5. Cover letter preferred with first submission. Send SASE for guidelines. Reports within 3 months. Pays 2 copies. Acquires one-time rights.** Staff reviews books of poetry in 350-400 words, single format. Send books for review consideration.

‡**DUCKABUSH JOURNAL (II)**, P.O. Box 390, Hansville WA 98340-0390, founded 1988, editors Gary Parks and Tom Snyder, appears twice a year. **"We consider all types of writing as long as it's correctly edited and spell-checked. No greeting card verse."** They have published poetry by James Bertolino, Alice Derry and Tim McNulty. As a sample the editors selected these lines by Gloria Boyer:

> *Everything was a sensation she could never place:*
> *night dragging its thin fingers across the glass,*
> *a leaf bug clicking the beads of its abacus.*
> *Already winter was coming and her body curled*

It is 70+ pgs., digest-sized, flat-spined, with matte card cover. Press run is 350 for 25 subscribers of which 3 are libraries, 250 shelf sales. They accept about 10% of poetry received. Subscription: $10. **Sample postpaid: $3. Reports within 6 weeks. Pays 2 copies.** Staff reviews books of poetry. Tom Snyder says, "We read everything. The two editors have very different styles and ranges of taste. Anything is possible."

DUENDE PRESS (IV-Form/style), P.O. Box 571, Placitas NM 87043, founded 1964, editor Larry Goodell, is interested in **avant-garde Earth poetry.** In a "serious and sincere attempt to start up an exchange for poet-publishers," he says, **"I will publish your work only if you publish mine. Inquiries welcome."**

DUST (FROM THE EGO TRIP); CAMEL PRESS (IV-Themes), HC 80, Box 160, Big Cove Tannery PA 17212, phone (717)573-4526, founded 1981, poetry consultant Katharyn Howd Machan, publisher James Hedges, who describes himself as "editor/printer of scholarly and scientific journals, does occasional poetry chapbooks for fun." *Dust (From the Ego Trip)* is "an intermittent journal of personal reminiscences." For it he wants **"autobiographical material (can address any subject, but written from the viewpoint of an active participant in the events described). Mss should average about 2,500 words and can be one long poem or a collection of related shorter poems. Any style OK, and any language using the roman alphabet. No religious (evangelizing) material or other material written primarily to advance a point of view. Any topic is OK, and coarse language is OK, but only if used artistically."** As a sample James Hedges selected these lines by recent author Richard Watson:

> *Take a bow*
> *for your fans*
> *you old men*
> *collecting cans*
> *A modern miracle*
> *God's design*
> *changing aluminum*
> *into wine*

He publishes 1-2 chapbooks a year under the Camel Press imprint, average 20 pgs. **Query with "a few sample poems." Cover letter not required,** "but I like the personal contact and the show of sincere interest." No bio or publications necessary because, "we judge on material only, status of poet is irrelevant." **Simultaneous submissions and previously published material OK. Reports in 10 days. Pays 50 copies plus half of net after production costs are recovered.** He is open to subsidy publishing poetry of "artistic merit," though he has never done any. To buy samples, request catalog. He says, "I always write a cover letter, but I'm not a poetry critic, just a considerate publisher. I do a bit of poetry because I want to encourage the art and broaden my catalog. Everything I publish is handset in metal type and letterpress printed on fine paper. The authors are expected to do most of the promotion. Press run normally 500, and I give away about 400 copies to friends, plus 50 for the author. The author can order more copies in advance if he expects to sell a large number. Financial arrangements are negotiable."

THE EAGLE (IV-Ethnic), Eagle Wing Press, Inc., P.O. Box 579MO, Naugatuck CT 06770, phone (203)729-0035, founded 1981, poetry editor James D. Audlin, is an **American Indian newspaper** appearing every other month. **Poems must be on American Indian themes or written by American Indians. "Try to avoid 'typical' pieces that try to sound 'Indian.' We are looking for clear, concise, strong poetry."** They have published poetry by Marcella Taylor and John Fox. As a sample the editor selected lines from the poem "We the Criminals" by Sean Lawrence:

> *selling white lies*
> *in a blind man's trade*
> *sorting through beads*
> *in a timeless charade*
> *of meaningless treaties*
> *and the money we made.*

The newspaper is tabloid-sized, about 28 pgs., unstapled, with graphics and ads, circulation 4,000 with 1,500 subscriptions of which 120 are libraries, about 600 shelf sales. Subscription: $10/year 3rd class, $15/year 1st class. **Sample postpaid: $2.50. Requires cover letter with biographical information, including tribal affiliation(s) if any. Pays 5 copies, up to 5 more on request. "Rights revert to author after publication, with *Eagle* reserving right to reprint."** Reviews books of poetry by Native Americans. Send books for review consideration.

‡**EAGLE'S FLIGHT; EAGLE'S FLIGHT BOOKS (I, IV-Translations)**, #822, 2501 Hunter's Hill, Enid OK 73703, phone (405)233-1118, founded 1989, editor and publisher Shyamkant Kulkarni, is a quarterly "platform for poets and short story writers—new and struggling to come forward." **They want "well-crafted literary quality poetry, any subject, any form, including translations. Translations should have permission of original poets."** They have recently published poetry by Mike Cluff and Kent Clair Chamberlain. As a sample the editor selected these lines from "The Last Straw" by Lisa Eastwood:

> . . . *We hope*
> *This last straw, this last flake of*
> *cotton wool, this last grain of wheat*
> *and golden dust meant to do the last*
> *job comes handy to someone needy like*
> *these ants crawling over my body*
> *getting cold.*

Eagle's Flight is 8-12 pgs., 7 × 8½, printed on colored paper and saddle-stapled, including simple art, few ads. They receive about 50 poems/year, accept 10%. Press run is 200 for 100 subscribers. Subscription: $5. **Sample postpaid: $1. No previously published poems or simultaneous submissions. Cover letter required. Reads submissions January 1 to June 30. Time between acceptance** and publication is 1 year. **Seldom comments on rejections. Send SASE for guidelines. Reports in 2-3 months. Pays 2 copies or 1-year subscription. Acquires first publication rights.** Reviews books of poetry in 250-750 words, single format. Under Eagle's Flight Books, they publish 1 paperback/year. "Up to now we have been publishing our own books, but **if somebody wants to share publishing cost, we can help or undertake publishing a book/anthology. We don't have selling organizations. Anybody interested in this may enquire."** Replies to queries in 1 month. "We also plan to organize a contest and publish anthologies of poetry. Award "depends on our enthusiasm at that time and availability of funds." The editor says, "We expect poets to be familiar with our publication and our expectations and our limitations. To be a subscriber is one way of doing this. Everybody wants to write poems and, in his heart, is a poet. Success lies in getting ahead of commonplace poetry. To do this one has to read, to be honest, unashamed and cherish decent values of life in his heart. Then success is just on the corner of the next block."

EARTH'S DAUGHTERS: A FEMINIST ARTS PERIODICAL (IV-Women/feminism, themes), Box 622, Station C, Buffalo NY 14209, phone (716)837-7778, founded 1971. The "literary periodical **with strong feminist emphasis**" appears 3 times a year, irregularly spaced. Its "format varies. Most issues are flat-spined, digest-sized issues of approximately 60 pgs. We also publish chapbooks, magazine-sized and tabloid-sized issues. Past issues have included broadsheets, calendars, scrolls and one which could be assembled into a box." **Poetry can be "up to 40 lines (rare exceptions for exceptional work), free form, experimental—we like unusual work. All must be strong, supportive of women in all their diversity. We like work by new writers, but expect it to be well-crafted. We want to see work of technical skill and artistic intensity. We rarely publish work in classical form, and we never publish rhyme or greeting card verse."** They have published poetry by Christine Cassidy, Rose Romano, Lyn Lifshin, Helen Ruggieri, Joan Murray, Susan Fantl Spivack, "and many fine 'unknown' poets, writers and artists." They publish poetry by men if it is supportive of women. As a sample the editor selected *#36 Over the Transom* "A Shape Soft Enough to Wear" by Lynn Martin:

> . . . *Two women can talk the night*
> *into a shape soft enough to wear*
> *one more time. It's almost as if*
> *The same onion planted over & over,*
> *never decays, grows like a prayer . . .*

"Our purpose is to publish primarily work that otherwise might never be printed, either because it is unusual, or because the writer is not well known." Subscription: $14/3 issues for individuals; $22 for institutions. **Sample postpaid: $4. Simultaneous submissions OK. "Per each issue, authors are limited to a total of 150 lines of poetry, prose or a combination of the two. Submissions in excess of these limits will be returned unread. Business-size envelope is preferred, and use sufficient postage—we do not accept mail with postage due." Send SASE for guidelines.** Some issues have themes, which are available for SASE after April of each year. Length of reporting time is atrociously long if ms is being seriously considered for publication, otherwise within 3 weeks. **Pays 2 copies and reduced prices on further copies.** Editor comments "whenever we have time to do so—we want to encourage new writers." The collective says: "Once you have submitted work, please be patient. We only hold work we are seriously considering for publications, and it can be up to a year between acceptance and publication. If you must contact us (change of address, notification that a simultaneous submission has been accepted elsewhere), be sure to state the issue theme, the title(s) of your work and enclose SASE."

EASTERN CARIBBEAN INSTITUTE (I, IV-Regional), P.O. Box 1338, Frederiksted, U.S. Virgin Islands 00841, phone (809)772-1011, founded 1982, editor S.B. Jones-Hendrickson, editorial contact Cora Christian, is a "small press publisher with plans to expand," **especially interested in poetry of the Caribbean and Eastern Caribbean.** As a sample here are lines from "The Proxies" in S.B. Jones-Hendrickson's A Virgin Islands Sojourn?:

> *When the land is up for the giving*
> *And votes are to get*
> *Some people pull their ranking*
> *And shaft your big bet*

Their books are softcover, averaging 60 pgs. Sample copies available for purchase. **Submit 5 sample poems, cover letter with bio and previous publications. Simultaneous submissions and previously published poems OK. Reads submissions January to May only. Reports in 1 month. Pays 50 copies.** The editor says, "In our part of the world, poetry is moving on a new level. People who are interested in regional poetry should keep an eye on the Caribbean region. There is a new focus in the Virgin Islands."

EDICIONES UNIVERSAL (IV-Ethnic, foreign language, regional), 3090 SW 8th St., Miami FL 33135, phone (305)642-3234, founded 1964, general manager Marta Salvat-Golik, is a small press subsidy publisher of **Spanish language books. "We specialize in Cuban authors and themes."** They have published books of poetry by Olga Rosalo and Amelia del Castillo. **Poets "must be able to purchase in advance 75% of the copies, due to the fact that poetry does not sell well." Poets receive the copies they paid for. Submit sample, bio, publications. Reports in 1 month.**

EIDOS MAGAZINE: SEXUAL FREEDOM AND EROTIC ENTERTAINMENT FOR WOMEN, MEN & COUPLES (IV-Erotica/Women), P.O. Box 96, Boston MA 02137, founded 1982, poetry editor Brenda Loew Tatelbaum. "Our press publishes erotic literature, photography and artwork. Our purpose is to provide an alternative to women's images and male images and sexuality depicted in mainstream publications like *Playboy, Penthouse, Playgirl*, etc. We provide a forum for the discussion and examination of two highly personalized dimensions of **human sexuality: desire and satisfaction.** We do not want to see angry poetry or poetry that is demeaning to either men or women. We like experimental, avant-garde material that makes a personal, political, cultural statement about sensu-sexuality." They have recently published poetry by David C. Ward, Susan Hussey, Vicky Feeley, Richard Hay Jr., Anne Richey and Mark Spitzer. As a sample the editor selected "Infatuations" by Cheryl Townsend:

> *Every thing I see is a phallus symbol*
> *every crotch ahead looks like home*
> *I am a magnet they're north & I'm*
> *south looking wanting and needing*
> *thinking of Pavlov feeling like*
> *Eve wanting the first one again*
> *and forever*

Eidos is professionally printed, tabloid-format, with fine photography and art, **number of poems/ issue varies,** print run 10,000, over 7,000 subscriptions. **Sample postpaid: $10.** They receive hundreds of poems/year, use about 50. No backlog right now. **1 page limit on length, format flexible, simultaneous submissions OK. Comment or criticism provided as often as possible. Guidelines available for SASE. Only accepts sexually explicit material. Reports in 1-2 months. Pays 1 copy. Acquires first North American serial rights.** Open to unsolicited reviews. Poets may also send books for review consideration. Brenda Loew Tatelbaum advises, "There is so much poetry submitted for consideration that a rejection can sometimes mean a poet's timing was poor. We let poets know if the submission was appropriate for our publication and suggest they resubmit at a later date. Keep writing, keep submitting, keep a positive attitude."

THE EIGHTH MOUNTAIN PRESS; EIGHTH MOUNTAIN POETRY PRIZE (IV-Women, feminist), 624 SE 29th Ave., Portland OR 97214, founded 1985, editor Ruth Gundle, is a "small press publisher of **feminist literary works by women."** They have published poetry by Karen Mitchell, Irena Klepfisz, Maureen Seaton and Lori Anderson. They publish 1 book of poetry every other year, averaging 128 pgs. **"We now publish poetry *only* through the Eighth Mountain Poetry Prize." Pays 8-10% royalties. Buys all rights. Returns rights if book goes out of print.** The Eighth Mountain Poetry Prize is a biennial award of a $1,000 advance and publication for a ms of 50-120 pgs. written by a woman, no restrictions as to subject matter. Send SASE for rules. **Submit during January in even numbered years; postmark deadline: February 1. Entry fee: $15.** "The selection will be made anonymously. Therefore, the ms must have a cover sheet giving all pertinent information (title, name, address, phone number). No identifying information except the title should appear on any other ms page. The contest will be judged by a different feminist poet each year, whose name will be announced after the winning ms has been chosen." Previous judges have included Andre Lorde, Linda Hogan, Marilyn Hacker and Judy Grahn.

EL BARRIO; CASA DE UNIDAD (V, IV-Ethnic, regional), Dept. PM, 1920 Scotten, Detroit MI 48209, phone (313)843-9598, founded 1981, poetry editor Marta Lagos. They publish **poetry from Latino residents of the SW Detroit area concerning life, family, politics, repression, etc., but do not normally accept unsolicited material. Query first.** They have published poetry by Lolita Hernandez, Gloria House and Jose Garza. As a sample the editor selected these lines from "Let Us Stop This Madness" by Trinidad Sanchez, Jr.:

> Let us destroy the factories
> that make the guns
> that shoot the bullets
> that kill our children.
> Let us take a stand
> to share life,
> to break bread
> with each other.

El Barrio is published "to keep the Latino people of the SW Detroit area informed, to give them an opportunity to speak to the community." It appears 3-4 times a year, is magazine-sized, about 28 pgs., professionally printed with commissioned art on the matte card cover, using up to 3 poems/issue. Their press run is 5,000, $3/issue, $12 for a subscription. **"Please call for a sample copy." They sometimes use previously published poems.** The press has published 2 anthologies: **Detroit: La Onda Latina en Poesía—Latin Sounds in Poetry,** Vols. I and II ($6 each).

EL TECOLOTE (IV-Ethnic), P.O. Box 40037, San Francisco CA 94140, phone (415)252-5957, founded 1970, is a monthly "community newspaper with **subject matter primarily about the Latino/Chicano community in America.** Much cultural coverage in general, but not a lot of poetry." They want **"short (1 page or less) poems inspired by life in U.S. Latino communities or in Latin America. Would like to see poetry that acknowledges the struggle of Latino/Latinas who must live in a culture different from their own.** The struggle both uncovers our history and creates a positive role model for the future. Open to poetry by either sex, sexual preference, and all ages." They have published poetry by Manilio Argueta from El Salvador. *El Tecolote* (The Owl) is a tabloid, 16 pgs., using art, graphics and ads. Press run 10,000. They accept about 1 out of 10 pages of poetry submitted. **Submit double-spaced, with name and address on each sheet. Simultaneous submissions and previously published poems OK.** Open to unsolicited reviews. Poets may also send books for review consideration, attn. L. Gutierrez.

‡ELDRITCH TALES MAGAZINE OF WEIRD FANTASY; YITH PRESS (IV-Horror), 1051 Wellington Rd., Lawrence KS 66049, editor Crispin Burnham, is "a semiannual magazine of **supernatural horror,"** circulation 500. **Buys 5-10 poems on horror themes each year. Submit maximum of 3 poems, 5-20 lines. Pays 10-25¢/line.** Open to unsolicited reviews. Poets may also send books for review consideration. The editor says, "Poems should have a steady meter—should be able to read them aloud."

11TH ST. RUSE; BIG FISH (I), 322 E. 11th St. #23, New York NY 10003, phone (212)475-5312, founded 1987, editor Lucid. *11th St. Ruse* appears every 3 months, 4 pgs. mimeo, wants **poems "short, without subterfuge, preferably written very quickly."** They have published poetry by Teres d' Compagnie and Richard Kostelanetz. As a sample the editor selected these lines from "Why I Hate Violins" by Antimony:

> I hate violins because you
> Need to take a stick and
> Teach them to behave.

Press run is 250. Single copy: 33¢. **Sample postpaid: 50¢. Make checks payable to Ellen Carter. Reports in 1 day-3 months. Pays 1 copy.** Open to unsolicited reviews. Poets may also send books for review consideration. "I have another magazine, *Big Fish*, and I am currently seeking poems in foreign languages without translations."

ELF: ECLECTIC LITERARY FORUM (Elf Magazine) (II), P.O. Box 392, Tonawanda NY 14150, founded 1990, editor C.K. Erbes, is a quarterly. **"Subject matter and form are open, but we are looking for well-crafted poetry. We prefer poems of 30 lines or less, but will consider longer poems. No trite, hackneyed, ill-crafted effluvia."** They have published poetry by Gwendolyn Brooks, Joyce Carol Oates, John Dickson, Martha Vertreace, David Romtvedt and John Tagliabue. As a sample the editor selected these lines from "Blues Sonata in Spring Flat" by Gerald Wild:

> You have wrapped yourself in the black silence
> Egyptian queens know in their jeweled repose.
> You plagued me through an empty, haunted winter.
> Days groaned into months. Wired to baffling dreams,
> long nights bore no peace.

Elf is 52-56 pgs., magazine-sized, with semi-gloss cover, professionally printed, saddle-stapled.

They use approximately 140 poems/year. Circulation 5,000. Subscription: $12. **Sample postpaid: $4.50. Send SASE for guidelines. "Accepted writers are asked to submit a bio of 25 words or less." Poems are circulated to an editorial board of professional poets and writers. Editor comments when possible. Reports in 4-6 weeks. Pays 2 copies. Acquires first North American serial rights.** Staff reviews books of poetry. Publishers only may send books for review consideration.

ELK RIVER REVIEW (I, II), 606 Coleman Ave., Athens AL 35611-3216, founded 1991, editor John Chambers, associate editors Steve Bailey, Amy Champlin, Katharyn Graham and Tom McDougle, is a semiannual review of poetry and short fiction. **"Open to all types of poetry, no line limit. We want poems that are well-crafted, musical, provocative."** They have recently published poetry by Charles Ghigna, Andrew Hudgins, Sue Scalf, Sue Walker, William Miller, Tom Drinkard and Anne George. As a sample we selected these lines from "Snowflakes and Satellites" by Bettye Cannizzo:

> One delights the eye like a baby's smile,
> tickles the tongue like a Margarita.
> The other jolts the imagination like poetry,
> stimulates the mind like philosophy.

ERR is 62-84 pgs., 7×9, offset, saddle-stitched, with 80 lb. glossy cover with b&w photo and b&w line drawings inside. Press run is 600 of which 25 go to libraries. Subscription: $12. **Sample postpaid: $6.50. Submit 3-5 poems at a time; name, address and phone number on each page. No previously published poems. Cover letter required. Include "succinct biographical facts and publishing credits (if any)." Often comments on rejections. Send SASE for guidelines. Reports in 2-4 months. Pays 3 copies. Acquires first rights.** Reviews novels and poetry collections (including chapbooks) of regional interest. Open to unsolicited reviews; query first. Poets may also send books for review consideration.

ELLIPSE (V, IV-Translations, bilingual), C.P. 10, FLSH Université de Sherbrooke, Sherbrooke, Quebec J1K 2R1 Canada, phone (819)821-7000, founded 1969, editors M. Grandmangin/C. Bouchara, **publishes Canadian poetry in translation.** That is, on facing pages appear either poems in English and a French translation or poems in French and an English translation. **Currently they are not accepting unsolicited mss.** They have recently published poetry by E. Birney, G. Godin and A. Piché. As a sample, these are lines from "Letters & Other Worlds" by Michael Ondaatje:

> My father's body was a town of fear
> He was the only witness to its fear dance
> He hid where he had been that we might lose him
> His letters were a room his body scared

translated as "Lettres et autres mondes" by Charly Bouchara:

> Le corps de mon père était une ville d'effroi
> seul témoin de sa danse de la peur
> il cachait ses destinations afin que nous le perdions
> Ses lettres une chambre terrifiée par son corps

The magazine appears twice yearly in an elegant flat-spined, 6×9 format, professionally printed, 120+ pgs. Subscription: $12. **Sample postpaid: $5.**

ELLIPSIS MAGAZINE (II), Westminster College of Salt Lake City, 1840 S. 1300 East, Salt Lake City UT 84105, phone (801)484-7651, founded 1967, appears twice a year using **"all kinds of good poetry. Limited on space."** They have published work by William Stafford, William Kloefkorn, Lyn Lifshin and Ron Carlson. The editor describes it as 80-112 pgs., digest-sized, flat-spined. Subscription: $12/year. **Sample postpaid: $8. Responds within 3 months. Pays $15/page plus 1 copy.**

EMBERS (II), P.O. Box 404, Guilford CT 06437, phone (203)453-2328, founded 1979, poetry editors Katrina Van Tassel, Charlotte Garrett and Mark Johnson, a "poetry journal of talented new and occasional well-known poets." The editors say, **"no specifications as to length, form or content. Interested in new poets with talent; not interested in lighter way-out verse, porn or poetry that is noncomprehensible."** They have recently published poetry by Terry Wolverton and Brendan Galvin. As a sample, the editors selected these lines from "The Time Change: April" by Lynn deCourcy:

> Soon the time will change
> and change ahead, advancing
> into summer's wild and heady growth,
> but tonight this cold rain is ringing
> through my skull, the tension
> of straining rivers rising in me. . .

Embers is digest-sized, nicely printed on white stock with an occasional b&w photograph or drawing, 52 pgs., flat-spined with one-color matte card cover handsomely printed in black; it appears twice a year—spring/summer and fall/winter. Single copy: $6; subscription: $11/year.

Sample postpaid: $3. Submissions must be typed, previously unpublished, with name, address and brief bio of poet. Deadlines: "basically March 15 and October 15, but we read continuously." Cover letter preferred. Pay for acceptance is 2 copies. Rights revert to author after publication. They sponsor a chapbook contest, deadline January 15. Winner is reported by March 1. Write for details. Editors' advice is "Send for sample copies of any publication you are interested in. Be patient. Most editors read as quickly as they can and report likewise. If a poet sends in work at the beginning of a reading time, or long before a deadline, he/she will have to wait longer for answers. *Embers* editors are interested in the poet's voice and would like to read up to five submissions showing variety of subject, form, etc."

EMERALD COAST REVIEW; WEST FLORIDA LITERARY FEDERATION; FRANCIS P. CASSIDY LITERARY CENTER; THE LEGEND; BACK DOOR POETS; WISE (WRITERS IN SERVICE TO EDUCATION) (IV-Regional), P.O. Box 1644, Pensacola FL 32597, located at WFLF/Cassidy Literary Center, Pensacola Cultural Center, 402 S. Jefferson St., Pensacola FL 32501. The WFLF was founded in 1987 and began the Cassidy Literary Center, a regional writers' resource and special collection library. One of their programs is WISE, which provides over 50 area writers who volunteer their time to share their writing and writing experiences with local students. They sponsor a Student Writers Network for students in grades 9-12 and scholarships for area college student writers. They publish *The Legend*, a newsletter bringing literary arts news to 800-1,000 area writers and their supporters. Back Door Poets, one of their subgroups, conducts open microphone poetry readings the third Saturday of each month and sponsors "Poetry & Patriotism," a non-stop, 24-hour vigil reading of American poetry in Seville Square to commemorate American Independence Day. Membership in WFLF ranges from $5/year for students to $350 and up for life-time memberships. The *Emerald Coast Review* is an annual limited to Gulf Coast regional writers. Sample postpaid: $12. Send SASE for guidelines. Submit with required form (included in guidelines) May 1 to July 31. Pays copies.

EMRYS JOURNAL (II), P.O. Box 8813, Greenville SC 29604, founded 1982, managing editor Robin Visel, an annual, wants "all kinds of poetry, though we don't publish poems of more than 2-3 pgs." They have published poetry by Linda Pasten, Maxine Kumin, R.T. Smith, Neal Bowers, Jim Peterson and Carl Dennis. As a sample, here are lines from "Gargoyles" by Gail Regier:

> *Gray nights they vomit rain*
> *Out into the wind's skirl.*
> *They curse us*
> *And their curses come to pass.*

It is handsomely printed, 6×9, flat-spined, up to 120 pgs. "For our last issue we received about 650 poems from 40 states. We printed 10." Press run 350 for 250 subscribers of which 10 are libraries. Sample postpaid: $10. Editor never comments on rejections. Send SASE for guidelines. Pays 5 copies. They say, "We try to report within 6 weeks of the end of our reading period," but don't indicate when the reading period is.

THE EMSHOCK LETTER (IV-Subscribers), P.O. Box 411, Troy ID 83871-0411, phone (208)835-4902, founded 1977, editor Steve Erickson, appears 3-12 times a year, occasionally with **poetry and other writings by subscribers**. It is **"a philosophical, metaphysical, sometimes poetic expression of ideas and events. It covers a wide range of subjects and represents a free-style form of expressive relation. It is a newsletter quite unlike any other."** The editor describes it as magazine-sized, 5-7 pgs., photocopied from typescript on colored paper. Subscription: $25. Pays 2 copies following publication. "Poets (who are subscribers) should submit poetry which contains some meaning, preferably centering on a philosophic theme and preferably 50 lines or less. Any good poetry (submitted by a subscriber) will be considered for inclusion and will receive a personal reply by the editor, whether or not submitted material is published in *The Emshock Letter*." Editor will promptly discard any and all material submitted by nonsubscribers. Poets must become subscribers prior to submitting any material! Reviews books of poetry only if written by subscribers.

‡ENCODINGS: A FEMINIST LITERARY JOURNAL (IV-Women/feminism), P.O. Box 6793, Houston TX 77265, founded 1989, editor Jacsun Shah. *Encodings* appears "randomly, twice a year," using **"high quality poetry with a feminist perspective; especially interested in women's ways of knowing, women's invention and use of language."** They aim "to give women who have little chance of being published elsewhere (because of radical content) a chance to be heard." As a sample the editor selected these lines from "Puffer and Whale" by Jacquelyn Shawh:

> *With you, I'm a little fish,*
> *puffer used to being belly-up*
> *BB eyes bulging.*
>
> *You're a beached whale, with me,*

> *bleaching in our winter glare,*
> *fat sides going all dry.*

Encodings is 40-60 pgs., 7 × 8½, photocopied from typescript and saddle-stapled with glossy card cover. Press run is 300 for 60 subscribers of which 1 is a library. Subscription: $9. **Sample post-paid: $4.50. Submit up to 5 poems at a time. Cover letter with brief bio preferred. Send SASE for guidelines. Editor "occasionally" comments on rejections. Reports in 2-3 months. Pays 2 copies.**

ENITHARMON PRESS (V), 36 St. George's Ave., London N7 0HD England, phone (071)607-7194, fax (071)607-8694, founded 1969, poetry editor Stephen Stuart-Smith, is a publisher of fine editions of poetry and literary criticism in paperback and some hardback editions, about 12 volumes/year averaging 80 pages. **"Substantial backlog of titles to produce, so no submissions possible before 1995."** They have published books of poetry by John Heath-Stubbs, Phoebe Hesketh, David Gascoyne, Jeremy Hooker, Frances Horovitz, Ruth Pitter, Edwin Brock and Jeremy Reed.

‡ENVOI (II), 44 Rudyard Rd., Biddulph Moor, Stoke-on-Trent, Staffs ST8 7JN United Kingdom, founded 1957, editor Roger Elkin, appears 3 times/year using poetry, articles about poetry and poets, and reviews. "1) *Envoi* does not subscribe to any one particular stable, school or style of contemporary poetry writing and has catholic tastes; 2) To be selected, **poetry must be sincere in its emotional and intellectual content; strongly integrated in form and contemporary in its subject matter** — while a poem may be set in classical times or depend heavily on mythic archetypes, its overall 'texture' must have contemporary relevance; 3) *Envoi* requires writing that is daring in its subject matter and challenging in its expressive techniques — in short, work that takes risks with the form, the language and the reader; 4) *Envoi* is however still interested in traditional verse structures (the villanelle, pantoum, sonnet) but these must subscribe to the points listed in 2); and 5) *Envoi* is looking for writing that sustains its creative strengths over a body of poems, or sequence. These criteria are prescriptive, rather than proscriptive; gates rather than hurdles. The over-riding concern is the creation of access for writers and readers to as wide a variety of contemporary poetry as space will allow." *Envoi* is digest-sized, 120+ pgs. perfect-bound, professionally printed with matte card cover. "The emphasis is on giving space to writers so that the reader can begin to assess the cumulative strengths of any one author over a body of work. This means that competition for space is very keen. I handle between 250 and 300 poems per week and can only feature the equivalent of 100 poems three times a year!" Press run is 1,000 including 20+ library subscriptions. Subscription: £10 or $25 ("preferably in bills rather than checks because of the high cost of conversion rates") or equivalent number of IRCs. Single copy: £3 ($7). **Sample: £2 ($5 bills). Submit no more than 6 poems, or a long poem of up to 6 sides; each poem on a separate page, bearing name and address; an accompanying SAE with 3 IRCs for return. Reports in 1-2 months. Pays 2 copies.** Roger Elkin says *"Envoi* presents the work of any one poet by a group of poems, up to six. Space is given to long(er) poems and short sequences, or extracts from longer sequences. We have a First Publication Feature for writers who have not appeared in national publications previously, and each issue contains a 'reading' of a modern poem or an article on poetic style, as well as an Editors' Backlist which draws attention to poetry collections that readers may have overlooked in the past. The Review section has been expanded in length to feature more comprehensive articles. Each issue also features a competition with prizes totalling £200; prize-winning poems are published along with a full adjudicator's report. We also feature poems in collaboration, as well as translations."

EPIPHANY: A JOURNAL OF LITERATURE (II), P.O. Box 2699, University of Arkansas, Fayetteville AR 72701, founded 1990, editors Gordon Grice and Bob Zordani, associate editor Graham Lewis, is a quarterly of poetry (to 600 lines), fiction, creative nonfiction, translations and interviews. **"Excellence is our only criterion. We like both free verse and formal verse."** They have recently published poetry by Alicia Ostriker, R.S. Gwynn, Lucia Cordell Getsi, Martha Vertreace, Bruce Guernsey, Simon Perchik and Trent Busch. As a sample the editor selected these lines by Jonathan Harrington:

> *Old man,*
> *your eyes*
> *the color of spoiled milk,*
> *every evening I saw you*
> *on the corner*

Use the General Index to find the page number of a specific publisher. If the publisher you are seeking is not listed, check the " '93-'94 Changes" list at the end of this section.

> *under the streetlight,*
> *your hand outstretched,*
> *a few coins*
> *sparkling in your upturned palm.*

Epiphany is digest-sized, saddle-stapled, with card cover. They receive 3,000 poems a year, use less than 4%. Press run is 300. Subscription: $12. Sample postpaid: $4. Include name and address on poems. Simultaneous submissions OK if you notify them of acceptance elsewhere. Reports in 1-2 months. Pays 1 copy. Send books for review consideration. The editor adds, "We'll be doing some chapbook contests. Watch for ads in *Poets & Writers*."

EPOCH; BAXTER HATHAWAY PRIZE (III), 251 Goldwin Smith, Cornell University, Ithaca NY 14853, phone (607)255-3385, founded 1947, has a distinguished and long record of publishing exceptionally fine poetry and fiction. They have published work by such poets as Ashbery, Ammons, Eshleman, Wanda Coleman, Molly Peacock, Robert Vander Molen and Alvin Aubert. The magazine appears 3 times a year in a professionally printed, 6×9, flat-spined format with glossy color cover, 100+ pgs., which goes to 1,000 subscribers. They use less than 1% of the many submissions they receive each year, have a 2- to 12-month backlog. Mostly lyric free verse, with emphasis on voice and varying content and length, appears here (and, occasionally, avant-garde or "open" styles) — some of it quite powerful. Sample postpaid: $5. "We *don't read* unsolicited mss between May 15 and September 15." Reports in 2 months. Occasionally provides criticism on mss. Pays 50¢/line. Buys first serial rights. The annual Baxter Hathaway prize of $1,000 is awarded for a long poem or, in alternate years, a novella. Write for details. Poetry published in *Epoch* was also selected for inclusion in Best American Poetry 1992. The editor advises, "I think it's extremely important for poets to read other poets. I think it's also very important for poets to read the magazines that they want to publish in. Directories are not enough."

EQUINOX PRESS (V); BRITISH HAIKU SOCIETY; BLITHE SPIRIT (IV-Form/style, translations), Sinodun, Shalford, Braintree Essex CM7 5HN England, phone 0371-851097, founded 1990, c/o Mr. David Cobb. Equinox publishes poetry (mainly haiku and senryu), 1-2 volumes/year. They have a waiting list at present and are unable to consider submissions. BHS publishes a quarterly journal, *Blithe Spirit*, a quarterly newsletter and other occasional publications (pamphlets, folios). *Blithe Spirit* publishes mainly haiku, senryu and tanka sent in by society members, but one section, "The Pathway," accepts originals in any language plus a translation in one of English, French or German, and is open to nonmembers. As a sample the Equinox editor selected this haiku (poet unidentified):

> *a cloudless sky*
> *painters stretch ladders*
> *to their farthest rungs*

Staff reviews books of poetry. Send books for review consideration. The Museum of Haiku Literature, Tokyo, gives a quarterly best-of-issue award (£50). In addition, BHS administers the annual James W. Hackett Haiku Award (currently £60). Rules of entry are available annually in the spring. Send SASE (or SAE and IRC from outside England).

‡ESSENCE (V, IV-Women, ethnic), 1500 Broadway, New York NY 10036, phone (212)642-0649, founded 1970, poetry editor Angela Kinamore. "*Essence* caters to the needs of today's Black women." They publish poetry with humor or poetry dealing with love/romance, politics, religion, social issues or spirituality. However they are currently not accepting poetry submissions. They have recently published poetry by Margaret Walker Alexander and Pinkie Gordon Lane. As a sample the editor selected these lines from "Ode to My Sons" by Mari Evans:

> *I am the vessel from whence you came*
> *the lode filled with imaginings*
> *aside from dreams my longing cannot*
> *touch your reaching nor can I direct*
> *your quest . . .*

Essence is a mass-circulation consumer magazine with an upscale tone. It is 140+ pgs., slick stock with full-color art, photos and ads.

EUROPEAN JUDAISM (IV-Religious, ethnic), Kent House, Rutland Gardens, London, England SW7 1BX, phone (071)584-2754, founded 1966, poetry editor Ruth Fainlight, is a "twice-yearly magazine with emphasis on European Jewish theology/philosophy/literature/history, with some poetry in every issue. It should preferably be short, as it is often used as filler, and should have Jewish content or reference. We do not want hackneyed, overblown rubbish." They have published poetry by Alan Sillitoe, Erich Fried and Dannie Abse. As a sample the editor selected these lines by Moris Farhi:

> *why does a man have to die*
> *leaving remains*

> *if die he must*
> *why not*
> *incorporeal*
> *like memory*

It is a glossy, elegant, 7×10, flat-spined magazine, rarely art or graphics, 68 pgs. They have a print run of 950, about 50% of which goes to subscribers (few libraries). Single copy: $9; subscription: $18. **Sample can be obtained gratis from Pergamon Press, Headington Hill Hall, Oxford, England 0X3 OBW. Pays 1 copy.**

EVANGEL (IV-Religious), P.O. Box 535002, Indianapolis IN 46253-5002, weekly since 1897, poetry editor Vera Bethel, **publishes an 8-page paper for adults. Nature and devotional poetry, 8-16 lines, "free verse or with rhyme scheme."** The circulation is 35,000; it is sold in bulk to Sunday schools. **Sample for 6×9 SASE. SASE required with submissions. Simultaneous submissions OK. Reports in 1 month. Pays $10.** The editor advises, "Do not write abstractions. Use concrete words to picture concept for reader."

EVENT (II, IV-Themes), Douglas College, P.O. Box 2503, New Westminster, British Columba V3L 5B2 Canada, founded 1971, editor Dale Zieroth, is "a literary magazine publishing **high-quality contemporary poetry,** short stories and reviews. **All good-quality work is considered."** They have published poetry by Tom Wayman, Elisabeth Harvor and Richard Lemm. These sample lines are from "Poetry" by Don Domanski:

> *is it a side street or a cat's jaw?*
> *cerecloth or the body's flesh?*
> *I've named it the heart's pillow*
> *wind in a mirror   cloud-rope*
> *lighthouse on the edge of a wound*
> *beadwork   the mote's halo   wolf-ladder*

Event appears three times a year. It is 128+ pgs., 6×9, flat-spined, glossy-covered and finely printed with a circulation of 1,000 for 700 subscriptions, of which 50 are libraries. **Sample postpaid: $5. They comment on some rejections. Reports in 2-3 months. Pays honorarium. Sometimes they have special thematic issues, such as: work, feminism, peace and war, coming of age.**

THE EVERGREEN CHRONICLES (IV-Gay/lesbian), P.O. Box 8939, Minneapolis MN 55408, is "a semiannual literary journal dedicated to presenting the best of lesbian and gay literary and visual artists. **The artistry presented is not limited to 'gay' or 'lesbian' themes, but extends to life, in all its dimensions."** Subscription: $15. Sample: $7.95 plus $1 postage. **"Send 4 copies of your work, up to 10 pgs. of poetry. Please include cover letter with short biographical paragraph describing yourself and your work. Deadlines: July 1 and January 1." Pays 1 copy. Acquires first-time rights.** Staff reviews books of poetry in 500 words, single format. Send books for review consideration.

EXIT 13 (II), % Tom Plante, 22 Oakwood Ct., Fanwood NJ 07023, phone (908)889-5298, founded 1987, poetry editor Tom Plante, is a "contemporary poetry annual" using **poetry that is "short, to the point, with a sense of geography."** They have recently published poetry by Randy Fingland, Penny Harter, Joel Lewis, Errol Miller and Marjorie Power. As a sample the editor selected these lines by Carol Gordon:

> *These are the flowers I almost*
> *gave you, once,*
> *then stopped,*
> *thinking them ordinary.*

Exit 13, #5, was 56 pgs. Press run is 300. **Sample postpaid: $6,** *payable to Tom Plante.* **They accept simultaneous submissions and previously published poems. Reads submissions March 1 through November 30 only. Send SASE for guidelines. Reports in 3 months. Pays 1 copy. Acquires first-time and possible anthology rights.** Staff reviews books of poetry and magazines in a "Publications Received" column, using 25-30 words/listing. Send books for review consideration. The editor advises, "Write about what you know. Study geography. *Exit 13* looks for adventure. Every state and region is welcome. Send a snapshot of an 'Exit 13' road sign and receive a free copy of the issue in which it appears."

EXPEDITION PRESS (II, IV-Love, religious), #2306, 105 E. Walnut St., Kalamazoo MI 49007-5253, publisher Bruce W. White, publishes chapbooks of love poems and religious poems. "I dislike violence." He likes to see **"fresh new approaches, interesting spatial relationships, as well as quality artwork. We dislike political diatribes."** He has published poetry by J. Kline Hobbs, Jim DeWitt, Martin Cohen and C. VanAllsburg. **Submit ms of 20-30 pgs. and brief bio. Simultaneous submissions**

OK. Ms on cassette OK. Reports in 1 month. Pays 100 copies. Bruce White provides "much" criticism on rejected mss.

EXPERIMENT IN WORDS; HOMEMADE ICE CREAM PRESS WRITER, POET AND ARTIST OF THE YEAR AWARDS (II), P.O. Box 470186, Ft. Worth TX 76147, founded 1990, editor/publisher Robert W. Howington. *EIW* appears irregularly. The editor says, "I'll look at anything sent, but prefer very short stories, 500 words or less, and one-page poems. I also am doing two other litmags—*Bukowski and Serial Killers* and *Flaming Envelopes*—so any submission to *EIW* will also be considered for those two publications." They have recently published poetry by Charles Bukowski, Todd Moore, Justice Howard, Lyn Lifshin, terry everton, Mark Weber and Cheryl A. Townsend. As a sample the editor selected these lines from "no wonder they're nearly extinct" by Gerald Locklin:

> the bar-snack display
> features
>
> EAGLE
> NUTS

EIW is magazine-sized, side-stapled, photocopied from typescript on mimeo paper, 60-70 pgs. Press run is 150. Subscription: $5. **Sample: $5 check, cash or stamps. Make check payable to Robert W. Howington. Cover letter with brief bio required with submissions. Reports in 1-3 months. Pays 1 copy. Acquires one-time rights.**

EXPERIMENTAL BASEMENT PRESS (IV-Form/style), #A-191, 3740 N. Romero Rd., Tucson AZ 85705, phone (602)293-3287, founded 1990, editor C.L. Champion, publishes *Experimental Basement* 3 times/year and 2-4 chapbooks/year as well as "poems written on mediums such as toilet paper, golf balls, matchbook covers—everything really, as long as it's readable." He wants "**the oddest and most bizarre stuff possible, visual, conceptual or language poetry** that breaks an egg and expands the beauty of language/poetry. **No mainstream poetry; no rhyme, unless experimenting with it.**" He has published poetry by John Bennett and Paul Weinman. As a sample here is the first stanza of "Meet Jack" by Pauline Brick, C.L. Champion and Tim O. Pratt:

> bAlD mArK anD
> waIt Lin
> e. acRosS buiLdinG to LefT mEeT mY NeIghBoR.
> JacK.

He says every issue of *Experimental Basement* is printed differently. Press run is 250 for 25 subscribers. Subscription: $8 for 3 issues. **Sample, including guidelines, postpaid: $3. No previously published poems. Always comments on rejections. Reports "same day." Pays 1 copy. For chapbook consideration, query with 5-10 poems.** "If the poet is shy as an umbrella, then there is no need for a bio or letter; however, I enjoy reading the things." **Replies to queries and mss "same day." Pays 10 author's copies.** The editor says, "Write what comes from the gut, what pleases your own self. I like anything experimental. I often enjoy inserting 'insertabus experimentus' into the magazines—poetry printed on weird objects. I also love to review books and chapbooks."

EXPLORATIONS (II), 11120 Glacier Highway, Juneau AK 99801, editor Professor Art Petersen, phone (907)789-4418, founded 1980. The annual literary magazine of the University of Alaska, Southeast. "**The editors respond favorably to 'language really spoken by men and women.'** Standard form and innovation are encouraged as well as appropriate and fresh aspects of imagery (allusion, metaphor, simile, symbol . . .)." The editor selected this sample from "Seven come eleven" by Charles Bukowski:

> I've never ever quite met
> anybody
> like myself—
> living with deadly calm
> inside this hurricane of hell.

It is digest-sized, nicely printed, with front and back cover illustration in one color, saddle-stapled. The editors tend to go for smaller-length poems (with small line breaks for tension) and often print two on a page—mostly lyric free verse with a focus on voice. They offer first prizes of $100 and second prizes of $50 for poetry and prose and publish the best of the submissions received. A prominent poet or writer serves as judge (1992: Charles Bukowski: 1993: James B. Hall). **An entry/reading fee is required: $2/poem (up to 5, 60 lines maximum) $4/story (up to 2, 3,500 words maximum); those paying reader/contest entry fees of $4 or more will receive a copy of the publication. Submit entries with 3- or 4-line biography January through March. Submissions are reported on in May, publication is annual, out in May or June. Mss must be typed with name and address on the back. Simultaneous submissions OK.** "Replies for unselected manuscripts made only to SASE." **Pays 2 contributor copies. Acquires one-time rights.**

EXPLORER MAGAZINE; EXPLORER PUBLISHING CO. (I, IV-Inspirational, nature, love), P.O. Box 210, Notre Dame IN 46556, phone (219)277-3465, founded 1960, editor and publisher Raymond Flory, a semiannual magazine that contains **short inspirational, nature and love poetry** as well as prose. The editor wants **"poetry of all styles and types; should have an inspirational slant but not necessary. Short poems preferred—up to 16 lines. Good 'family' type poetry always needed. No real long poetry or long lines; no sexually explicit poetry or porno."** He has published poems by Alecia Elswick Price, Gerald Walsh, Jesus E. Rodriques, Mary Lee Richardson and Sean Mclain Brown. As a sample the editor selected these lines from "Wrestling With Angels" by Linda Suddarth Greer:

> *But when I ride with*
> *and accept this angel*
> *gladness breaks like the morning*
> *and the gift that broke the heart*
> *is also the most precious*

Explorer is digest-sized, photocopied from typed copy (some of it not too clear) on thin paper, 31 pgs., cover of the same paper with title superimposed on a water-color painting, folded and saddle-stapled. Circulation is 200. Subscription: $6/year. **Sample available for $3, guidelines for SASE. Pay is 1 copy. Subscribers vote for the poems or stories they like best and prizes are awarded; four prizes each issue: $25, $20, $15 and $10; first-prize winner in each issue receives a plaque along with the cash prize. In addition to the regular cash prizes, there is also an editor's choice award, the Joseph Flory Memorial Award, named after the editor's late father. Award is $10 and a plaque. Recent winner: Gary R. Goude's "The Green Chameleon." Writers should submit 3-4 poems, typed. Material must be previously unpublished; no simultaneous submissions. Reporting time is 1 week and time to publication 1-2 years.** Explorer Publishing Company does not presently publish books except for an anthology about every 4 years; it is a paperback, digest-sized book with an average page count of 20. The editor says, "Over 90% of the poets submitting poetry to *Explorer* have not seen a copy of the magazine. Order a copy first—then submit. This will save poets stamps, frustration, etc. This should hold true for whatever market a writer is aiming for!"

EXPRESSIONS FORUM REVIEW (I), 2837 Blue Spruce Lane, Wheaton MD 20906, founded 1991, is a quarterly of poetry, **"any kind, any form, 20 lines maximum. No sex-related matters, no obscenity."** Single copy: $3; subscription: $12. **Previously published poems and simultaneous submissions OK. Submit 1-4 poems with $3 reading fee. Typewritten poems preferred; do not send original copies. Seldom comments on rejections. Send SASE for guidelines. Reports in 1 month. Pays 1 copy.** Open to unsolicited reviews. Poets may also send books for review consideration. Reading fee includes entry into spring and fall poetry contests. 1st prize: $100; 2nd: $50; 3rd: $25 (and 25 honorable mentions). The editor says, "Speak from the heart and soul."

EXQUISITE CORPSE (II), P.O. Box 25051, Baton Rouge LA 70894, founded 1983, editor Andrei Codrescu (whom you can often hear in commentary segments of "All Things Considered," The National Public Radio news program). This curious and delightful monthly ($20/year), when you unfold it, is 6" wide and 16" long, 20 pgs., saddle-stapled, professionally printed in 2 columns on quality stock. The flavor of Codrescu's comments (and some clues about your prospects in submitting here) may be judged by this note: "A while ago, alarmed by the number of poems aimed at the office—a number only the currency inflation and Big Macs can hold candles to—we issued an edict against them. Still they came, and some even came live. They came in the mail and under the door. We have no poetry insurance. If we are found one day smothered under photocopy paper, who will pay for the burial? The *Corpse* wants a jazz funeral. Rejections make poets happy. Having, in many cases, made their poems out of original, primal, momentary rejections, the rejection of these rejections affirms the beings forced to such deviousness." He has published poetry by Carol Bergé, Charles Plymell, Lawrence Ferlinghetti, Alice Notley and many others. You'll find all styles and forms here, even short light verse. Most examples are freestyle, leaning toward expressionism (effective use of symbol), and accessible, too. Translations also seem welcome. **Payment: "Zilch/Nada." You take your chances inserting work into this wit machine. As of 1990 this is their policy: ". . . we are abolishing the SASE-based privacy system . . . Your submissions will be answered directly in the pages of our publication. Look for your name and for our response to your work in the next *Corpse*. We will continue returning your submissions by SASE if you wish, but as to what we think of your *écriture*, please check 'Body Bag,' our new editorial column. Please rest assured that your work will receive the same malevolently passionate attention as before. Only now we are going to do it in public."** Here's an example: "We were excited by 'The Wind Got Excited' until the puppy-hero got too excited and leapt off the 13th floor. That was cruel . . . " Comments you want, comments you get! Poetry that did make it into this magazine, however, can also be found in **Best American Poetry 1992.**

FABER AND FABER, INC. (V), 50 Cross St., Winchester MA 01890, phone (617)721-1427, editor Betsy Uhrig, has a distinguished list of poetry publications but is accepting **no unsolicited mss.**

FAMILY EARTH (I, IV-Ecology), 129 W. Lincoln Ave., Gettysburg PA 17325, managing editor Denise Weldon-Siviy, founded 1990, is a family-oriented annual focusing on the environment, using poetry that **"must deal in some way with the environment. Shorter poems, 10-30 lines, are preferred. Cannot consider material over 40 lines due to page layout. All forms and styles are acceptable. No laments abusive to working mothers. I am still receiving a high percentage of negative—world is awful will end any minute—poetry. Anything with a positive attitude has a good chance."** As a sample here are lines from "Swan Song—USA" by Charlotte Partin:

> *Redwood, cypress, maples,*
> *cotton fields—celebrate me*
> *from freeway to Main Street.*

FE is 28 pgs., digest-sized, photocopied, with colored paper cover. Press run is 300 for 150 subscriptions, 150 shelf sales. They accept about 25% of 100 submissions received/year. Subscription: $3/year. **Sample postpaid: $2. Editor always comments on rejections. Send SASE for guidelines. Reports in 2 weeks. Pays $1-3/poem on acceptance plus 1 copy. Buys one-time rights.** Reviews books of poetry if they deal with the environment, conservation, etc. Open to unsolicited reviews. Poets may also send related books for review consideration.

FARMER'S MARKET; MIDWEST FARMER'S MARKET, INC. (II), P.O. Box 1272, Galesburg IL 61402, founded 1981, editors Jean C. Lee, John Hughes, Lisa Ress, Tracey Rose and Romayne Rubinas, is a biannual seeking **"to provide a forum for the best of regional poetry and fiction."** They want poems that are **"tightly structured, with concrete imagery, reflective of the clarity, depth and strength of Midwestern life. Not interested in highly abstract work or light verse."** They have recently published poetry by John Knoepfle, Jeffrey Hillard, Margo Maxwell, Martha Vertreace, Mary Catherine McDaniel and R.T. Smith. As a sample, they offer these lines from "The Art of Skipping Stones" by James Scruton:

> *One throw like that can keep*
> *you on the shore all night,*
> *stone after frantic stone*
> *flying against dark water,*
> *so many that for days*
> *your empty palm will hold*
> *their cold, accumulated weight*

FM is digest-sized, 100-140 pgs., perfect-bound with card cover, handsomely printed with graphics and photos. The poems are almost always accessible . . . clear, crafted lyric free verse. All in all, this is an enjoyable read. Circulation 700 for 150 subscriptions, of which 20 are libraries. They receive about 1,500 submissions/year, of which they use 50-60, have a 6-month backlog. **Sample: $4.50 plus $1 postage and handling. Submit up to 10 pages, typed. Would rather not have simultaneous submissions. Reports in 6-8 weeks (summer replies take longer). Pays 1 copy.** Acquires one-time rights. They comment on rejections, **"only if we think the work is good."** This publication has received numerous Illinois Arts Council Literary Awards, and work published here was selected for the 1991 **O. Henry Prize** anthology.

‡FARRAR, STRAUS & GIROUX/BOOKS FOR YOUNG READERS (II, IV-Children), 19 Union Square W., New York NY 10003, phone (212)741-6900, founded 1946, contact Editorial Dept./Books for Young Readers. They publish one book of children's poetry "every once in awhile," in both hardcover and paperback editions. **They are open to book-length submissions of children's poetry only.** They have recently published collections of poetry by Valerie Worth and Deborah Chandra. As a sample the editor selected "Suspense" from Chandra's book **Balloons:**

> *Wide-eyed*
> *the sunflowers*
> *stare and catch their summer*
> *breath, while I pause, holding basket*
> *and shears.*

Query first with sample poems and cover letter with brief bio and publication credits. Poems previously published in magazines and simultaneous submissions OK. Seldom comments on rejections. Replies to queries in 1-2 months, to mss in 1-3 months. "We pay an advance against royalties; the amount depends on whether or not the poems are illustrated, etc." Also pays 10 author's copies.

FAT TUESDAY (II), RD2 Box 4220, Manada Gap Rd., Grantville PA 17028, founded 1981, poetry editors F.M. Cotolo, Kristen von Oehrke, B. Lyle Tabor and Lionel Stevroid, is an annual which calls itself "**a Mardi Gras of literary and visual treats featuring many voices, singing, shouting, sighing and shining, expressing the relevant to irreverent.** On Fat Tuesday (the Tuesday before Ash Wednesday, when Lent begins) the editors hold The Fat Tuesday Symposium. In ten years no one has shown up." They want "**prose poems, poems of irreverence, gems from the gut. Usually shorter, hit-the-mark, personal stuff inseparable from the voice of the artist. Form doesn't matter.**" They have published poetry by Mark Cramer, Mary Lee Gowland, Chuck Taylor, Patrick Kelly, Charles Bukowski, Gerald Locklin and Randy Klutts. As a sample they offer these lines by John Quinnett:

> It is enough to be alive,
> To be here drinking this cheap red wine
> While the chili simmers on the stove
> & the refrigerator hums deep into the night.

The digest-sized magazine is typeset (large type, heavy paper), 36-50 pgs., saddle-stapled, card covers, (sometimes magazine-sized, unbound) with cartoons, art and ads. Circulation 200 with 20-25 pgs. of poetry in each issue. They receive hundreds of submissions each year, use 3-5%, have a 3- to 5- month backlog. **Sample postpaid: $5. No previously published material. "Handwritten OK; we'll read anything." Reads submissions August 1 through November 22. Reports in 1-2 weeks. Pays 1 copy. Rights revert to author after publication.** The editors say, "Our tip for authors is simply to be themselves. Poets should use their own voice to be heard. Publishing poetry is as lonely as writing it. We have no idea about current trends, and care less. We encourage all to buy a sample issue to see what they have which best fits our style and format, and also to help support the continuation of our publication. We rely on no other means but sales to subsidize our magazine, and writers should be sensitive to this hard fact which burdens many small presses."

FEELINGS: AMERICA'S BEAUTIFUL POETRY MAGAZINE; ANDERIE POETRY PRESS; QUARTERLY EDITOR'S CHOICE AWARDS (I, II), P.O. Box 85, Easton PA 18044-0085, phone (215)559-9287, founded 1989, editors Carl and Carole Heffley, a quarterly magazine, uses "**high-quality (free, blank or rhymed), understandable poems on any aspect of life, no more than 20 lines, no pornography. Likes traditional as well as hard-biting prose and poetry.**" They have recently published poetry by Salvatore Galioto, Patricia Lawrence and Marian Ford Park. As a sample here are the opening lines from "Winter Walk" by Diana Baker:

> I walk home on winter days
> no longer than my thumb.
> the wind arches its back
> and blows the moon into
> a curved icicle.
> the stars glisten like ice
> chips on the shades of night
> all pulled by five

Feelings is magazine-sized, saddle-stapled with heavy paper cover, professionally printed on lightweight paper, using "photography appropriate to the season or subject." Subscription: $20. **Sample postpaid: $5.50. Cover letter with background, credits ("something about the writer") required with submissions. Send SASE for guidelines. Reports in 6 weeks. Pays $10 for 3 Editor's Choice Awards in each issue. Acquires first rights.** Also runs several contests throughout the year with prizes ranging from $10 to $50. "**We publish chapbooks, info/price list upon request with SASE.**" Mss on "how-to" write, publish poetry welcome. Payment for articles varies.

FEH! A JOURNAL OF ODIOUS POETRY (IV-Themes, humor), #603, 147 Second Ave., New York NY 10003-5701, founded 1986, editors Simeon Stylites and Morgana Malatesta, appears twice a year, using "**silliness and nonsense, but** *good* **silliness and nonsense; nasty stuff, but** *good* **nasty stuff; insanity; truth.**" They have recently published poetry by Jerm Boor and Vassar W. Smith. As a sample the editors selected these lines by Ferdinand "Skeet" Giaclepousse:

> I believe in God and Bigfoot
> and the right to worship as I please.
> I've seen angels, demons and the Virgin Mama
> in the midst of my D.T.'s

It is 24 pgs., 8½ × 11 with photocopied paper cover. Their press run is 200 with about 35 subscriptions, and sales through bookstores. **Sample postpaid: $2. Considers simultaneous submissions and previously published poems. Editors sometime comment on rejections, if asked. Send SASE for guidelines. Reports within 6 weeks. Pays 1 copy. Acquires one-time rights.** Simeon Stylites says, "The purpose and function of *Feh!* is, simply, to pour out clouds of righteous fire onto the reason-fleeing writers of poems that no one can understand. We see the high places that are given to fools, eunuchs and 'academic' poets, and the chalice-cup of Sense overflows with tears! We listen to the lamentations of the ten thousand cacographer-martyrs, and we hear their cry that a grand Rectification is due! And we're just doing our bit to help bring it about."

FELLOWSHIP IN PRAYER (IV-Religious), 291 Witherspoon St., Princeton NJ 08542, phone (609)924-6863, founded 1950, editor M. Ford-Grabowsky, is an interfaith bimonthly **"concerned with prayer, meditation and spiritual life"** using poetry **"pertaining to spirituality; brief."** It is digest-sized, professionally printed, 48 pgs., saddle-stapled with glossy card cover. Press run is 10,000. They accept about 2% of submissions received. Subscription: $16. **Sample free. Double-space submissions. Simultaneous submissions and "sometimes" previously published poems OK. Reports in 1 month. Pays 5 copies.** Staff reviews books of poetry in 75 words, single format. Send books for review consideration.

FEMINIST STUDIES (IV-Women), %Women's Studies Program, University of Maryland, College Park MD 20742, founded 1969, poetry editor Alicia Ostriker, **"welcomes a variety of work that focuses on women's experience, on gender as a category of analysis, and that furthers feminist theory and consciousness."** They have published poetry by Janice Mirikitani, Paula Gunn Allen, Cherrie Moraga, Audre Lorde, Judith Small, Milana Marsenich, Lynda Schraufnagel, Valerie Fox and Diane Glancy. The elegantly-printed, flat-spined, 250-page paperback appears 3 times a year in an edition of 8,000, goes to 7,000 subscribers, of which 1,500 are libraries. There are **4-10 pgs. of poetry in each issue. Sample postpaid: $10. Manuscripts are reviewed twice a year, in May and December. Deadlines are May 1 and December 1. Authors will receive notice of the board's decision by June 30 and January 30. No pay.** Commissions reviews of books of poetry. Poets may send books to Claire G. Moses for review consideration.

"The Fiddlehead *philosophy is to encourage and promote mainly writing and some art," says Sabine Campbell, associate editor of the Canadian literary magazine. "Approximately half of what we publish is poetry." The magazine, published by the University of New Brunswick, always chooses the work of New Brunswick artists for its covers. Though not directly related to the publication's contents, "this painting promotes any theme we have by its excellence," Campbell says. The cover artist is Brigid Toole Grant of Fredericton, New Brunswick.*

THE FIDDLEHEAD (II, IV-Regional, students), Campus House, University of New Brunswick, P.O. Box 4400, Fredericton, New Brunswick E3B 5A3 Canada, founded 1945, poetry editors Robert Gibbs, Robert Hawkes and Don MacKay. From its beginning in 1945 as a local little magazine **devoted mainly to student writers, the magazine retains an interest in poets of the Atlantic region and in young poets** but prints poetry from everywhere. It is **open to good work of every kind, looking always for vitality, freshness and surprise.** Among the poets whose work they have published are Joe Blades, Cory Brown, rienzi crusz and Daniel Sundahl. As a sample, the editor chose a stanza by Karen Connelly:

> We are not in the forest
> and there are no guns under the bed now,
> no wolf-threats, no axe-bladed animal nights.
> This is the gleaming city
> where the gravel is thing and false
> and salty over ice.

The Fiddlehead is a handsomely printed, 6×9, flat-spined paperback (140+ pgs.) with b&w graphics, colored cover, usually paintings by New Brunswick artists. Circulation is 1,000. Subscription: $18/year (US). **Sample: $6 (US). They use less than 10% of submissions. Reporting time 2-6 months, backlog 6-18 months. Pay is $10-12/printed page.** Reviews books by Canadian authors only.

FIELD; FIELD TRANSLATION SERIES; CONTEMPORARY AMERICAN POETRY SERIES; O.C. PRESS (II, IV-Translations), Rice Hall, Oberlin College, Oberlin OH 44074, phone (216)775-8408, founded 1969, editors Stuart Friebert and David Young, is a literary journal appearing twice a year with "emphasis on poetry, translations and essays by poets." They want the **"best possible"** poetry. They have published poetry by Thylias Moss, Seamus Heaney, Charles Simic and Sharon Olds. The handsomely printed digest-sized journal is flat-spined, has 100 pgs., rag stock with glossy card color cover. Although most poems fall under the lyrical free verse category, you'll find narratives and formal work here on occasion, much of it sensual, visually appealing and resonant. Circulation 2,500, with 800 library subscriptions. Subscription: $12 a year, $20 for 2 years. **Sample postpaid: $6. Reports in 2 weeks, has a 3-6 month backlog. Pays $20-30/page plus 2 copies.** They publish books of translations in the Field Translation Series, averaging 150 pgs., flat-spined and hardcover editions. **Query regarding translations. Pays 7½-10% royalties with some advance and 10 author's copies.** They also recently inaugurated a Contemporary American Poetry Series with the publication of a collection of new and selected poems by Dennis Schmitz. This new series is by invitation only. Write for catalog to buy samples. Work published in *Field* appears in **Best American Poetry 1992.**

FIGHTING WOMAN NEWS (IV-Women, themes), 6741 Tung Ave. W., Theodore AL 36582, founded 1975, poetry editor Debra Pettis, provides "a communications medium for **women in martial arts, self-defense, combative sports.**" They want **poetry "relevant to our subject matter and nothing else."** They have published poetry by Dana Ridgeway. As a sample the editor selected these lines from "Practice" by Cathy Drinkwater Better:

> become
> the moment
> concentrate
> be one
> with the impact
> timing
> is all

Fighting Woman News appears quarterly in a magazine-sized, saddle-stapled format, 24 pgs. or more, finely printed, with graphics and b&w photos, circulation 3,500. **Sample postpaid: $3.50,** "and if you say you're a poet, we'll be sure to send a sample with poetry in it." Uses only 1 or 2 poems in each issue. "If your poem *really* requires an audience of martial artists to be appreciated, then send it." **Simultaneous submissions OK. Cover letter required.** Poets should include "who they are and possibly why submitting to *FWN*." **Replies "ASAP." Pays copies. Acquires one-time rights.** Open to unsolicited reviews. Poets may also send books for review consideration. "Because our field is so specialized, most interested women subscribe. It is not a requirement for publication, but **we seldom publish a nonsubscriber.**" The editor advises, "Read first; write later. To guarantee publication of your poem(s), submit a hard-core martial arts nonfiction article. Those are what we really need! Fighters who are also writers can have **priority access to our very limited poetry space by doing articles.** Please do not send any poems if you have not read any issues of *FWN*."

FIGMENT: TALES FROM THE IMAGINATION (IV-Science fiction/fantasy), P.O. Box 3128, Moscow ID 83843-0477, founded 1989, editors Barb and J.C. Hendee, is a quarterly using **science fiction and fantasy poems.** They have recently published poetry by Bruce Boston, Steve Sneyd and W. Gregory Stewart. As a sample, here are lines from "Advice from an Old Hand, to a Young Man Shipping Out" by Lori Ann White:

> Poor boy. I hear you weep for Mother Earth.
> Tell me, does your mother love you well?
> Does she cradle you on acid clouds? Swaddle you in muck?
> You should mourn a woman, not a heartless shell.
> Why praise a hunk of rock for giving birth?

Figment is 60 pgs., digest-sized, saddle-stapled, printed in Bookman 9.0, with glossy bond cover. Press run is 500 for 200+ subscribers, 50-100 shelf sales. Subscription: $14.50. **Sample postpaid: $4. Send SASE for guidelines. Reports in 2 months. Pays $2-10 plus 1 copy. Buys first North American serial rights. Rights revert on publication.** The editors say, "We expect our genre poetry to be written for 'readers,' not other poets."

THE FIGURES (V), 5 Castle Hill Ave., Great Barrington MA 01230-1552, phone (413)528-2552, founded 1975, publisher/editor Geoffrey Young, is a small press publishing poetry and fiction. They have published poetry by Lyn Hejinian, Clark Coolidge, Ron Padgett and Christopher Dewdney. **They pay 10% of press run. However, they currently do not accept unsolicited poetry.**

FINE MADNESS (II), P.O. Box 31138, Seattle WA 98103-1138, founded 1982, president Louis Bergsagel. *Fine Madness* is a twice-yearly magazine. **They want "contemporary poetry of any form and subject. We look for highest quality of thought, language and imagery. We look for the mark of the individual: unique ideas and presentation; careful, humorous, sympathetic. No careless poetry, greeting card poetry, poetry that 10,000 other people could have written."** They have published poetry by Tess Gallagher, David Young and Caroline Knox. As a sample the editor selected these lines from "Natural History of an Idea" by Melinda Mueller:

> *Ice is over with quickly, while a knife, say, keeps happening,*
> *long after skin has healed. And the mind that thinks this—*
> *this is strangely consoling—is another event among the rest.*
>
> *Not that that's the end of it. There's the phone*
> *that rings, the avalanche of lights on that suburban hill*
> *across the lake, the incessant evening . . .*

Fine Madness is digest-sized, 64 pgs., perfect-bound, offset printing, 2-3 color card cover. Their press run is 800 for 100 subscriptions of which 10 are libraries. They accept about 40 of 1,000 poems received. Subscription: $9. Sample postpaid: $4. **Guidelines available for SASE. Submit 3-5 poems, preferably originals, not photocopy, 1 poem/page. No previously published poems or simultaneous submissions. Reports in 2-3 months. Pays 1 copy plus subscription.** Open to unsolicited reviews. Poets may also send books for review consideration to John Malek. They give 2 annual awards to editors' choice of $50 each. *Fine Madness* has had poetry selected for inclusion in Macmillan's **The Best American Poetry** in 1990, 1991, 1992 and 1993. Coeditor Sean Bentley says, "If you don't read poetry, don't send us any."

FIREBRAND BOOKS (IV-Feminist, lesbian, ethnic), 141 The Commons, Ithaca NY 14850, phone (607)272-0000, founded 1984, editor and publisher Nancy K. Bereano, "is a **feminist and lesbian** publishing company committed to producing quality work in multiple genres by ethnically diverse women." They publish both quality trade paperbacks and hardbacks. As a sample, here is a stanza of a sestina, "great expectations," from the book **Living As A Lesbian** by Cheryl Clarke:

> *dreaming the encounter intense as engines*
> *first me then you oh what a night*
> *of rapture and risk and dolphin*
> *acrobatics after years of intend-*
> *ing to find my lesbian sources in the window*
> *of longing wide open in me*

The book is 94 pgs., flat-spined, elegantly printed on heavy stock with a glossy color card cover, a photo of the author on the back, $7.95. **Simultaneous submissions acceptable with notification. Replies to queries within 2 weeks, to mss within one month. Pays royalties.** Send for catalog to buy samples.

FIREWEED: A FEMINIST QUARTERLY (IV-Women), P.O. Box 279, Station B, Toronto, Ontario M5T 2W2 Canada, phone (416)323-9512, founded 1978, edited by the Fireweed Collective, is a feminist journal of writing, politics, art and culture that **"especially welcomes contributions by women of color, working-class women, native women, lesbians and women with disabilities."** As a sample we selected the opening lines of "These Military Men" by Joy Hewitt Mann:

> *My husband was*
> *a military man.*
> *Dinner*
> *5:30*
> *sharp.*
> *No give.   No take.*

It is 88 pgs., 6¾ × 9¾, flat-spined, with 3- or 4-color cover. Poems tend to be freestyle lyrics leaning toward avant-garde, with some room for rhymed verse and stanza patterns. Press run is 2,000. Subscription: $18 individuals, $27 institutions in Canada, $24 individuals, $36 institutions in US. **Sample postpaid: $4 in Canada, $6 in US. Simultaneous submissions OK.** Editor comments on submissions "occasionally." **Pays $20/contributor/issue plus 2 copies.**

FIREWEED: POETRY OF WESTERN OREGON (IV-Regional), 1330 E. 25th Ave., Eugene OR 97403, founded 1989, is a quarterly publishing the work of **poets living in Western Oregon or having close connections to the region. However, poems need not be regional in subject; any theme, subject, length or form is acceptable.** They have published poetry by Vern Rutsala, Barbara Drake, Lisa Steinmann and Lex Runciman. As a sample they selected these lines from "Fault" by Barbara La Morticella:

> *Quick hold me;*
> *for once, let me hold you.*
>
> *Our children's suitcases are packed,*
> *and even the hills move in waves.*

Fireweed is 44 pgs., digest-sized, laser printed and saddle-stapled with card cover. "We receive several hundred poems and publish about ¼ or ⅓ of them." Press run is 200 for 125 subscribers of which 10 are libraries, 25 shelf sales. Subscription: $10. **Sample postpaid: $2.50. No previously published poems; simultaneous submissions OK. Cover letter with brief bio required. Often comments on rejections. They do not publish guidelines for poets but will answer inquiries with SASE. Reports in 2-4 months. Pays 1 copy. Acquires first North American serial rights.** Reviews books of poetry by Oregon poets in 500-750 words, single format. Open to unsolicited reviews. Oregon poets may also send books for review consideration. *Fireweed* received a 1992 publisher's grant from the Oregon Institute of Literary Awards. They add, "We occasionally have special issues organized by theme, compiled by a guest editor or focused on newcomers to *Fireweed*. Support your local magazines by sending work and buying subscriptions! Submit to the smaller little publications *first!*"

FIRST HAND (IV-Gay, subscribers), Box 1314, Teaneck NJ 07666, phone (201)836-9177, founded 1980, poetry editor Bob Harris, is a **"gay erotic publication written mostly by its readers."** The digest-sized monthly has a circulation of 70,000 with 3,000 subscribers of which 3 are libraries and uses 1-2 pgs. of poetry in each issue. They have published poetry by Michael Swift and Robert Patrick. As a sample the editor selected these lines from "To a Model" by Karl Tierney:

> *I assure you, I mean no*
> *disrespect when I discover,*
> *beyond sex and half asleep,*
> *you deflate to only half the monster*
> *and will be that much easier*
> *to battle out the door at dawn.*

Submit poems no longer than 1 typed page. No queries. Editor Bob Harris sometimes comments on rejected mss. Reports in 6 weeks. Pays $25/poem. They have an 18-month backlog. Reviews books of poetry. The editor advises, "Make sure what you're writing about is obvious to future readers. **Poems need not be explicitly sexual, but must deal overtly with gay situations and subject matter."**

FIRST TIME; NATIONAL HASTINGS POETRY COMPETITION (I, II), Burdett Cottage, 4 Burdett Place, George St., Hastings, East Sussex TN34 3ED England, phone 0424-428855, founded 1981, editor Josephine Austin, who says the biannual magazine is **open to "all kinds of poetry—our magazine goes right across the board—which is why it is one of the most popular in Great Britain."** The following lines are from "Why a Poet?" by R.M. Griffiths:

> *Of all types of people*
> *and all their differences in depth,*
> *the poet is the deepest,*
> *Or is it just the most vacuous?*

The digest-sized magazine, 24 pgs., saddle-stapled, contains several poems on each page, in a variety of small type styles, on lightweight stock, b&w photographs of editor and 1 author, glossy one-color card cover. Sample: £1 plus postage. "Please send dollars." **Poets should send 10 poems. Poems submitted must not exceed 30 lines, must not have been published elsewhere, and must have name and address of poet on each. Cover letter required. Maximum time to publication is 2 months. Pay is 1 copy. The annual National Hastings Poetry Competition for poets 18 and older offers awards of £150, £75, and £50, £1/poem entry fee.** Editor Josephine Austin has received The Dorothy Tutin Award "for services to poetry." She advises, "Keep on 'pushing your poetry.' If one editor rejects you then study the market and decide which is the correct one for you. Try to type your own manuscripts as longhand is difficult to read and doesn't give a professional impression. Always date your poetry — ©1994 and sign it. Follow your way of writing, don't be a pale imitation of someone else—sooner or later styles change and you will either catch up or be ahead."

FISHDRUM (II, IV-Regional, religious), 626 Kathryn Ave., Santa Fe NM 87501, founded 1988, editor Robert Winson, Brooklyn editor Suzi Winson, 40 Prospect Park W. #2D, Brooklyn NY 11215, is a literary magazine appearing 2-4 times a year. "I love West Coast poetry, the exuberant, talky, often elliptical and abstract 'continuous nerve movie' that follows the working of the mind and has a relationship to the world and the reader. Philip Whalen's work, for example, and much of Calafia, The California Poetry, edited by Ishmael Reed. Also magical-tribal-incantatory poems, exemplified by the future/primitive Technicians of the Sacred, ed. Rothenberg. *FishDrum* has a soft spot for schmoozy, emotional, imagistic stuff. Literate, personal material that sings and surprises, OK?" They have published poetry by Philip Whalen, Joy Harjo, Arthur Sze, Nathaniel Tarn, Alice Notley, John Brandi, Steve Richmond, Jessica Hagedorn, Leo Romero and Leslie Scalapino. As a sample the editor selected these lines from "Glossolalia" by Kate Bremer:

> *Everywhere I look I see amino acids on the ground.*
> *When I close my eyes, I see molecules and pieces of Sanskrit:*
> *I hear syllables and alphabets.*

FD is 80 pgs., perfect-bound, professionally printed. "Of 300 or so unsolicited submissions last year, accepted fewer than twenty." Press run 500 for 100 subscriptions of which 10 are libraries, 400 shelf sales. Subscription: $20 for 4 issues. **Sample postpaid: $5. Reports quickly. Pays 2 copies. In addition, contributors may purchase advance copies at $3 each. Acquires first serial rights.** Reviews books or chapbooks of poetry in long essays and/or capsule reviews. Open to unsolicited reviews. Poets may also send books for review consideration. Robert Winson adds, "**We're looking for New Mexico authors,** also prose: fiction, essays, what-have-you, and artwork, scores, cartoons, etc.—just send it along. **We are also interested in poetry, prose and translations concerning the practice of Zen. We publish chapbooks, but solicit these from our authors.** '*Fish-Drum Magazine* On The Air' is a monthly radio show that plays reasonably high audio quality cassettes, live and studio, submitted to us, and provides playlists. We will interview some authors as they come through town—drop us a note."

‡5 AM (III), 1109 Milton Ave., Pittsburgh PA 15218, founded 1987, editors Patricia Dobler, Lynn Emanuel, Ed Ochester and Judith Vollmer, is a poetry publication that appears twice a year. They are **open in regard to form, length, subject matter and style. However, they do not want poetry that is** "**religious or naive rhymes.**" They have recently published poetry by Rita Dove, Elton Glaser, Alicia Ostriker and Alberto Rios. The editors describe *5 AM* as a 24-page, offset tabloid. They receive about 3,000 poems a year, use approximately 5%. Press run is 1,000 for 550 subscribers of which 22 are libraries, about 300 shelf sales. Single copy: $3; subscription: $10 for 4 issues. **Sample postpaid: $2. No previously published poems or simultaneous submissions. Each editor chooses 25% of the magazine. Seldom comments on rejections. Reports within 3 months. Pays 2 copies. Acquires first rights.**

‡FIVE FINGERS REVIEW; FIVE FINGERS PRESS (III, IV-Themes, translations), P.O. Box 15426, San Francisco CA 94115, founded 1984, editors John High and Thoreau Lovell, is a literary biannual publishing "diverse, innovative and challenging writing by writers of various aesthetics. Some of the better-known poets they have published are Kathleen Fraser, John Yau, Rosmarie Waldrop and Leslie Scalapino. As a sample the editors selected these lines from "When She Was Dying" by Fanny Howe:

> *On the green seat heading everyone*
> *Home, time was credible but rupture now*
> *The problem to figure out.*

Five Fingers Review is 150 pgs., 6×9, nicely printed on buff stock, flat-spined with one-color glossy card cover. Circulation is 1,000 copies, 25% of which go to libraries. Single copy: $9; subscription: $15/year. **Sample postpaid: $7. Simultaneous submissions OK. Reporting time is 3-6 months and time to publication is 4 months. Pay is 2 copies.** Open to unsolicited reviews. Poets may also send books for review consideration. Five Fingers Press also publishes a perfect-bound book series. The advice of the editors is: "Pick up a copy of the magazine. Be committed to craft and to looking at the world in fresh, surprising ways."

FLIPSIDE (II), Dixon Hall, California University of Pennsylvania, California PA 15419, founded 1987, poetry editor L.A. Smith, is a literary tabloid appearing twice a year **using poetry. "Sentimentality is forbidden."** They have published poetry by Charles Bukowski and Arthur Winfield Knight. As a sample the editor selected the poem "Mother Lover" by Michael Bagamery:

The Subject Index, located before the General Index, can help you narrow down markets for your work. It lists those publishers whose poetry interests are specialized.

> *Make-up on that face*
> *Like rubble.*
> *Ivy won't run up a building*
> *Unless it stands.*

The tabloid is 64 pgs., professionally printed. Press run 5,000, distributed free to the public, libraries, writing schools, colleges, advertisers, poets, etc. They accept less than 5% of hundreds of poems submitted. **Sample postpaid: $2. Send SASE for guidelines. Reports in 2 months. Pays as many copies as you want.**

THE FLORIDA REVIEW (II), Dept. of English, University of Central Florida, Orlando FL 32816, phone (407)823-2038, founded 1972, editor Russ Kesler, is a "literary biannual with emphasis on short fiction and poetry." They want **"poems filled with real things, real people and emotions, poems that might conceivably advance our knowledge of the human heart."** They have published poetry by Knute Skinner, Elton Glaser and Walter McDonald. It is 128 pgs., flat-spined, professionally printed, with glossy card cover. Press run is 1,000 for 400 subscribers of which 50 are libraries. Shelf sales: 50. **Sample postpaid: $4.50. Submit no more than 6 poems. Simultaneous submissions OK. Editor comments on submissions "occasionally." Send SASE for guidelines. Reports in 1-3 months. Pays 3 copies, small honorarium occasionally available. Acquires all rights. Returns rights "upon publication, when requested."** Reviews books of poetry in 1,500 words, single format; 2,500-3,000 words, multi-book. Send books for review consideration.

FLUME PRESS (II), 773 Sierra View, Chico CA 95926, phone (916)342-1583, founded 1984, poetry editors Casey Huff and Elizabeth Renfro, publishes poetry chapbooks. **"We have few biases about form, although we appreciate control and crafting, and we tend to favor a concise, understated style, with emphasis on metaphor rather than editorial commentary."** They have published chapbooks by Tina Barr, Randall Freisinger, Leonard Kress, Carol Gordon, Gayle Kaune, Luis Omar Salinas and Judy Lindberg. As a sample, the editors selected these lines from "Touch Pool" by Pamela Uschuk:

> *Around and around*
> *the holding pool, rays soar*
> *like squadrons of angels, now and then lifting*
> *a wing to test the edge*
> *as if they would swim through the glass to the sea*

Chapbooks are chosen from an annual competition, March 1 through June 30. $6 entry fee. Submit 20-28 pgs., including title, contents and acknowledgments. Name and address on a separate sheet. Considers simultaneous submissions. "Flume Press editors read and respond to every entry." Winner receives $100 and 25 copies. Sample: $5 plus $1.50 postage and handling.

FOLIO: A LITERARY JOURNAL (II), Dept. of Literature, Gray Hall, The American University, Washington DC 20016, phone (202)885-2973, founded 1984, editors change annually, is a biannual. They have published poetry by Jean Valentine, Henry Taylor and William Stafford. There are 12-20 poems published in each 64- to 72-page issue. It is 6×9, perfect-bound, neatly printed from typeset. **Sample postpaid: $5. Submit up to 6 pgs. with brief bio/contributor's note from August to November 1 or January to March 1. Considers simultaneous submissions. Reads submissions September 1 through March 1 only. Comments on rejections "when possible." Pays 2 copies. Acquires first rights.** They also sponsor a contest open to all contributors with a $75 prize for the best poem of the fall and spring issue. A poem published by this journal was selected for inclusion in **Editor's Choice III.**

FOOLSCAP (I, II), 78 Friars Road, East Ham, London E6 1LL England, phone 081-470-7680, founded 1987, editor Judi Benson, appears twice yearly (summer and winter). **"We are looking for poetry which surprises as well as informs. We look for confidence and a sense of humor, though veer away from flippancy and trite over-used rhyme. We like our poetry to reflect today's world and the issues that concern us all without laborious political banner waving. In other words, we are looking for craft as much as statement."** They have recently published poetry by Ian Duhig, Frances Wilson and Sal Salasin. As a sample the editor selected, "Filmclip: Leningrad, October, 1935," by Ken Smith:

> *Dark comes early, and wet snow.*
> *The citizens hurry from work,*
> *scarfed, buttoned, thinking of supper,*
> *the tram clanking and squealing*
> *in whose glass an arm has wiped*
> *a V of lit space wherein smoke,*
> *old and young wrapped for winter,*
> *eyes focussed somewhere ahead,*
> *dreaming perhaps of a sausage,*
> *of bread, coffee, a warm bed,*

> *a bullet in the back of the brain.*
> *Then they're gone. Next comes*
> *the future. It looks like the past.*

The editor describes *Foolscap* as approximately 52 pgs., A4, camera-ready photocopying, with b&w illustrations. "No ads, no reviews, no frills, though we do include short prose pieces and welcome good translations." They accept about 120 of 1,200 poems received/year. Press run is between 160-200 for 100+ subscribers. "Copies also sold at poetry readings, bookshops, libraries and to universities." Subscription: $16/£6. Submit **"no more than 6 poems at a time. Cover letter indicating whether or not to return ms required. Best if overseas not to have to return. Allow ample IRCs and 1-2 months for response. Publication could take as long as a year due to backlog of accepted material." Pays 1 copy.** The editor says,"We accept a wide range of styles from both unpublished poets as well as well-known poets from all geographical locations. We advise people to get a copy of *Foolscap* before submitting and suggest 'new' poets share their work with others before submitting."

FOOTWORK: THE PATERSON LITERARY REVIEW; HORIZONTES; ALLEN GINSBERG POETRY AWARDS; THE PATERSON POETRY PRIZE; PASSAIC COUNTY COMMUNITY COLLEGE POETRY CENTER LIBRARY (II, IV-Regional, bilingual/foreign language), Poetry Center, Passaic County Community College, Cultural Affairs Dept., College Blvd., Paterson NJ 07505-1179. A wide range of activities pertaining to poetry are conducted by the Passaic County Community College Poetry Center, including the annual literary magazine *Footwork*, founded 1979, editor and director Maria Mazziotti Gillan, using **poetry of "high quality" under 100 lines.** They have published poetry by David Ray, Diane Wakoski, William Stafford, Sonia Sanchez, Laura Boss and Marge Piercy. *Footwork: The Paterson Literary Review* is magazine-sized, 160 pgs., saddle-stapled, professionally printed with glossy card 2-color cover, using b&w art and photos, circulation 1,000 with 100 subscriptions of which 50 are libraries. **Sample postpaid: $5. Simultaneous submissions OK. Send no more than 5 poems/submission. Reads submissions September through January only. Reports in 1 year. Pays 1 copy. Acquires first rights.** *Horizontes*, founded in 1983, editor José Villalongo, is an annual Spanish language literary magazine using **poetry of high quality no longer than 20 lines. Will accept English translations, but Spanish version must be included.** They have published poetry by Nelson Calderon, Jose Kozer and Julio Cesar Mosches. *Horizontes* is magazine-sized, 120 pgs., saddle-stapled, professionally printed with full color matte cover, using b&w graphics and photos, circulation 800 with 100 subscriptions of which 20 are libraries. **Sample postpaid: $4. Accepts simultaneous submissions. "On occasion we do consider published works but prefer unpublished works." Reads submissions September through January only. Reports in 3-4 months. Pays 2 copies. Acquires first rights.** Staff reviews books of poetry. Send books for review consideration. The Poetry Center of the college conducts The Allen Ginsberg Poetry Awards Competition each year. Entry fee $5. Prizes of $150, $25 and $10, deadline March 1. Send SASE for rules. They also publish a **New Jersey Poetry Resources** book, the **PCC Poetry Contest Anthology** and the **New Jersey Poetry Calendar**. The Paterson Poetry Prize of $1,000 is awarded each year (split between poet and publisher) to a book of poems published in the previous year. Publishers should write with SASE for application form to be submitted by February 1. Passaic County Community College Poetry Center Library has an extensive collection of contemporary poetry and seeks small press contributions to help keep it abreast. The Distinguished Poetry Series offers readings by poets of international, national and regional reputation. Poetryworks/USA is a series of programs produced for UA Columbia-Cablevision.

FOR POETS ONLY (I), P.O. Box 4855, Schenectady NY 12304, founded 1985, poetry editor L.M. Walsh, **requires a $3 entry fee for each poem submitted, which may win a $10 prize (at least five promised for each issue). Others accepted are paid for with one copy of the magazine. Acquires one-time rights.** In an issue of 35 pgs. of poems—some with more than one to a page—16 were awarded prizes. They have published poetry by J. Bernier, C. Weirich and Alice Mackenzie Swaim. *FPO* is 36 pgs., digest-sized, saddle-stapled, photocopied from typescript with glossy card cover. It appears quarterly. The editor rejects about 10% of poetry received. Press run is 200. Single copy: $3. **Sample postpaid: $3.50. Any subject. No pornography. No comments on rejections.** The editor advises, "For beginning poets: a quote from Horst Bienek in his **The Cell:** 'We are distressed but *not in despair*, distressed but *not destroyed*, persecuted but *not forsaken*, cast down but *not destroyed.*'"

FOREST BOOKS (III, IV-Translations), 20 Forest View, Chingford, London E4 7AY United Kingdom, phone 081-529-8470, founded 1984, director Brenda Walker, publishes 15-20 paperbacks/year. They have published **Enchanting Beasts: An Anthology of Modern Women Poets in Finland**, a handsomely printed flat-spined book of 126 pgs. **Pays 10% royalties plus 20 copies.** Samples may be purchased through Dufour Editions, P.O. Box 449, Chester Springs PA 19425.

THE FORMALIST; THE FORMALIST POETRY AWARD (II, IV-Form, translations), 320 Hunter Dr., Evansville IN 47711, founded 1990, editor William Baer, appears twice a year, "dedicated to *metrical poetry written in the great tradition of English-language verse.*" This is one of a handful of magazines that publish formal (rhymed, metered) poetry *exclusively*. The poems here are among the best in the genre—a joy to read—tastefully edited so that each verse plays off the other. They have published poetry by Donald Justice, Mona Van Duyn, John Updike, Maxine Kumin, Karl Shapiro, X.J. Kennedy, May Swenson, John Frederick Nims, W.D. Snodgrass and Louis Simpson. As a sample the editor chose the opening stanza from "The Amateurs of Heaven" by Howard Nemerov:

> *Two lovers to a midnight meadow came*
> *High in the hills, to lie there hand in hand*
> *Like effigies and look up at the stars,*
> *The never-setting ones set in the North*
> *To circle the Pole in idiot majesty,*
> *And wonder what was given them to wonder.*

"We are interested in metrical poetry written in the traditional forms, including ballads, sonnets, couplets, the Greek forms, the French forms, etc. We will also consider metrical translations of major formalist non-English poets—from the Ancient Greeks to the present. We are not, however, interested in haiku (or syllabic verse of any kind) or sestinas. Although we do publish poetry which skillfully employs enjambment, we have a marked prejudice against excessive enjambment. Only rarely do we accept a poem over 2 pages, and we have no interest in any type of erotica, blasphemy, vulgarity or racism. Finally, like all editors, we suggest that those wishing to submit to *The Formalist* become thoroughly familiar with the journal beforehand." Subscription: $12. Sample postpaid: $6.50. *The Formalist* considers submissions throughout the year, 3-5 poems at one time. No simultaneous submissions, previously published work, or disk submissions. A brief cover letter is recommended and a SASE is necessary for the return of the mss. Reports within 2 months. Pays 2 copies. Acquires first North American serial rights. The Formalist Poetry Award offers $1,000 and publication in *The Formalist* for the best unpublished *sonnet*. The final judge is a poet of national reputation. Entry fee: $2/sonnet. Postmark deadline: May 30. See also the contest listing for the World Order of Narrative and Formalist Poets. Contestants must subscribe to *The Formalist* to enter. *The Formalist* ranked #5 in the "Traditional Verse" category of the June 1993 *Writer's Digest* Poetry 60 list, and work published in *The Formalist* appears in *Best American Poetry 1992.*

‡**THE FOUR DIRECTIONS; SNOWBIRD PUBLISHING COMPANY (IV-Ethnic)**, P.O. Box 729, Tellico Plains TN 37385, phone (615)982-7261, founded 1991, publisher William Meyer. *The Four Directions* is an American Indian literary quarterly designed to further American Indian literature. All authors must be of American Indian heritage, and they want poetry that reflects or touches commom/uncommon American Indian concerns. They have recently published poetry by Joe Bruchac and Victoria Lena Manyarrows. The editor says it is 60-68 pgs. with approximately 54 pgs. of poetry, short stories, articles and reviews. They receive about 80 poems a year, use approximately 30. Press run is 400 for 120 subscribers of which 60 are libraries, 150 shelf sales. Subscription: $20, $24 institutions. Sample postpaid: $6. Previously published poems and simultaneous submissions OK. Cover letter required. Often comments on rejections. Reports in 3-6 weeks. Pays $10 for full-page of poetry. Buys one-time rights. Accepts reviews of all media, including books of poetry. Reviews range from 200 to 2,000 words. Snowbird Publishing Company publishes books but "so far we have not published any books of poetry." Query first with sample poems and cover letter with brief bio and publication credits. "Poetry may be previously published or not, but must be of professional quality." Replies to queries and mss in 4-6 weeks. Pays 10-18% royalties and 10 author's copies. The editor says, "The field of American Indian literature is the fastest growing literary effort in North America. We tend to seek writing that furthers the growth of the Indian spirit."

‡**FOUR QUARTERS (II, III)**, La Salle University, 20th and Olney Aves., Philadelphia PA 19141, phone (215)951-1700, founded 1951, editor John J. Keenan, is a semiannual cultural magazine which targets the college educated. It includes poetry, fiction, articles and essays. They have recently published poetry by X.J. Kennedy, David Ignatow, Joyce Carol Oates and William Stafford. As a sample the editor selected the opening lines from "Losing the Farm" by Barbara Daniels:

> *What we had is gone, the stone porch, bright fall*
> *loading trees with light, the sheep that blundered*
> *through the open door. Beyond the thin wall*
> *the old woman thumped her stick and made me wonder . . .*

FQ is 64 pgs., 7×10, professionally printed and designed, flat-spined with card cover. Poems generally appear one to a page. They receive approximately 100 submissions a year, accept 15. Press run is 1,000. Single copy: $4; subscription: $8 for 1 year, $13 for 2 years, $20 for 3 years. Sample postpaid: $5. Previously published poems ("occasionally") and simultaneous submissions OK. Reads submissions September 1 through May 1 only. Poems are circulated to an editorial board. Seldom comments on rejections. Send SASE for guidelines. Reports in approximately 3-6 months. Pays $2/line. Buys all rights. Returns them. Open to unsolicited reviews.

FOX CRY (II), University of Wisconsin Fox Valley, 1478 Midway Road, P.O. Box 8002, Menasha WI 54952-8002, phone (414)832-2600, founded 1973, editor Professor Don Hrubesky, is a literary annual using poems up to 50 lines long, deadline February 15. They have published poetry by Shirley Anders, David Graham, Clifford Wood and Laurel Mills. As a sample, the editor selected these lines (poet unidentified):

> She was out there with the leaves
> the old woman bent but broad of back
> In long even pulls, she collected
> the detritus of the sun's decline.

Their press run is 400. Sample postpaid: $5. Submit maximum of 3 poems from September 1 through February 15 only. Simultaneous submissions considered. Send SASE for guidelines. Pays 1 copy.

FRANK: AN INTERNATIONAL JOURNAL OF CONTEMPORARY WRITING AND ART (II, IV-Form, translations), Frank Brooks, B.P. 29, 94301 Vincennes Cedex France, founded 1983, editor David Applefield. *Frank* is a literary semiannual that "encourages work of seriousness and high quality which falls often between existing genres. Looks favorably at true internationalism and stands firm against ethnocentric values. Likes translations. Publishes foreign dossier in each issue. Very eclectic." There are no subject specifications, but the magazine "discourages sentimentalism and easy, false surrealism. Although we're in Paris, most Paris-poems are too thin for us. Length is open." They have published poetry by Rita Dove, Derek Walcott, Duo Duo, Raymond Carver, Tomas Tranströmer, James Laughlin, Breytenbach, Michaux, Gennadi Aigi, W.S. Merwin, Edmond Jabes, John Berger, and many lesser known poets. The journal is 224 pgs., digest-sized, flat-spined, offset in b&w with color cover and photos, drawings and ads. Circulation is 4,000, of which 2,000 are bookstore sales and subscriptions. Subscription: $30 (individuals), $60 (institutions) for 4 issues. Sample postpaid: $9 airmail from Paris. Guidelines available for SASE. Poems must be previously unpublished. The editor often provides some criticism on rejected mss. Submissions are reported on in 3 months, publication is in 3-6 months. Pay is $5/printed page and 2 copies. Editor organizes readings in US and Europe for *Frank* contributors. He says, "Send only what you feel is fresh, original, and provocative in either theme or form. Work of craft that also has political and social impact is encouraged."

FREDRICKSON-KLOEPFEL PUBLISHING CO. (F-K BOOKS) (I, IV-Themes), 7748 17th SW, Seattle WA 98106, phone (206)767-4915, "established 1983 as an outlet for J. Fred Blair's poetry and pamphlets, went public 1990," editor John F. Blair, publishes anthologies on specific themes. He "tries to publish at least one selection from each contributor; 1,000 words max, likes strong viewpoint, vibrant poetics, earthy style. A collection of poems and short prose on one subject from a myriad of sources establishes a panoramic discourse or Antho-logue. Wants mss from male and female poets on maleness for 'Hold the Macho.' Also wants positive items about the work-a-day life for 'Our Daily Bread.' Have a glut of negative things (are poets afraid of work?) already and nothing for counterpoint. Ergo: No dialogue." He has published poetry by Ralph La Charity, Judith Skillman, John Grey and Jeffrey Zable. As a sample the editor selected these lines from "Beyond Games" by Joanne Seltzer:

> You tell me to be grateful
> for the things I do have.
> Two eyes. Twenty eight teeth.
> What about my losses?
> Hope. Unanswered Valentines.
> Snowflakes that melt in my hand.

Reports in 3 months. "After book is completed, contributors may purchase copies at print cost for promotion in their locales. They should make a small profit wholesaling them and get full mark-up on the ones they retail. Any profit I make will be shared across the board with contributors."

FREE FOCUS (I, IV-Women/feminist); OSTENTATIOUS MIND (I, IV-Form/style), P.O. Box 7415, New York NY 10116-7415, *Free Focus* founded 1985, *Ostentatious Mind* founded 1987, poetry editor Patricia D. Coscia. *Free Focus* "is a literary magazine only for creative women, who reflect their ideas of love, nature, beauty and men and also express the pain, sorrow, joy and enchantment that their lives generate. *Free Focus* needs poems of all types on the subject matters above. Nothing x-rated, please. The poems can be as short as 2 lines or as long as 2 pages. The objective of this magazine is to give women poets a chance to be fullfilled in the art of poetry, for freedom of expression for women is seldom described in society." They have published poetry by Helen Tzagoloff, Elizabeth Hahn

Ph.D., Patricia A. Pierkowski, D.R. Middleton, Crystal Beckner, Elaine F. Powell, Kris Anderson, Carol L. Clark and Mary Anderson. As a sample the editor selected these lines from "A Woman I Once Knew" by Maura Schroeder:

> She sleeps in the desert alone,
> Carving ancestral bone,
> from waking mountains.
> She sleeps in the desert alone,
> Wading in salt-soaked rivers,
> with wounds unfolded.

Ostentatious Mind "is a co-ed literary magazine for material of stream of consciousness and experimental poems. The poets deal with the political, social and psychological." They have published poetry by Paul Weinman, Rod Farmer, L. Mason, Dr. John J. Soldo, Carl A. Winderl, James W. Penha, and Joe Lackey. As a sample the editor selected this poem, "Poetic Wax," by Sheryl L. Nelms:

> comes in 1.5 liter
>
> bottles
>
> at Majestic
> Liquors

Both magazines are printed on 8 × 14 paper, folded in the middle and stapled to make a 10-page (including cover) format, with simple b&w drawings on the cover and inside. The two magazines appear every 6-8 months. Sample of either is $3.50 postpaid. Poems should be typed neatly and clearly on white typing paper. Submit only 3 poems at one time. Simultaneous submissions and previously published poems OK. Send SASE for guidelines. Reports "as soon as possible." Pays 1-2 copies. The editor says, "I think that anyone can write a poem who can freely express intense feelings about their experiences. A dominant thought should be ruled and expressed in writing, not by the spoken word, but the written word."

FREE LUNCH (II), P.O. Box 7647, Laguna Niguel CA 92607-7647, founded 1988, editor Ron Offen, is a "poetry journal interested in publishing whole spectrum of what is currently being produced by American poets. Also features a 'Mentor Series,' in which an established poet introduces a new, unpublished poet. Mentors have included Maxine Kumin, James Dickey, Lucille Clifton and Kenneth Koch. Especially interested in experimental work and work by unestablished poets. Hope to provide all serious American poets with free subscription. For details on free subscription send SASE. No restriction on form, length, subject matter, style, purpose. Don't want cutsie, syrupy, sentimental, preachy religious or aggressively 'uplifting' verse. No aversion to form, rhyme." Poets recently published include David Citino, Billy Collins, David Ray, Paul Violi and Leila Zeiger. As a sample the editor selected these lines from "Gristle in The Cellar" by R.T. Smith:

> Beetroot, rutabaga,
> turnip, parsnip —
> I celebrate what
> hides from the light
> what drills deep
> in sweet soil . . .

FL is published 3 times a year. It is 32-40 pgs., saddle-stapled, digest-sized, attractively printed and designed, featuring free verse that shows attention to craft with well-knowns and newcomers alongside each other. Press run is 1,200 with 150 subscriptions of which 10 are libraries. Subscription: $12 ($15 foreign). Sample postpaid: $5 ($6 foreign). "Submissions must be limited to 3 poems and are considered only between September 1 and May 31. Submissions sent at other times will be returned unread. Although a cover letter is not mandatory, we like them. We especially want to know if a poet is previously unpublished, as we like to work with new poets." They will consider simultaneous submissions. Editor usually comments on rejections and tries to return submissions in 2 months. Send SASE for guidelines. Pays 1 copy plus subscription. He quotes Archibald MacLeish, " 'A poem should not mean/ But be.' Poetry is concerned primarily with language, rhythm and sound; fashions and trends are transitory and to be eschewed; perfecting one's work is often more important than publishing it."

FRENCH BROAD PRESS (III), Dept. PM, The Asheville School, Asheville NC 28806, phone (704)255-7909, founded 1989, publishers Jessica Bayer and J.W. Bonner, publishes 20- to 40-page chapbooks. "Any style or form welcome. Considers sexually explicit material." They have published poetry by Thomas Meyer, Jeffrey Beam and Jonathan Williams. "We're slow. May take 6 months to respond to a ms and up to 2 years before publication. Many of our poets have paid 'in kind': typesetting mss and covers on disks or pasting up the book for printing." Pays 10% of press run. Write to buy samples or order from The Captain's Bookshelf, 31 Page Ave., Asheville NC 28801.

FRIENDS JOURNAL (II, IV-Themes), Dept. PM, 1501 Cherry St., Philadelphia PA 19102, phone (215)241-7277, founded 1827 as *The Friend* and 1844 as *Friends Intelligencer,* 1955 as *Friends Journal,* appears monthly, magazine-sized, circulation 9,500+. Subscription: $21/year. "The *Journal* seeks poetry that resonates with Quakerism and Quaker concerns, such as peace and nonviolence, spiritual seeking, the sanctuary movement, the nuclear freeze." No multiple or simultaneous submissions. Pays 2 copies/poem.

‡**FRITZ (I)**, P.O. Box 170694, San Francisco CA 94117, founded 1991, editor Lisa McElroy, is a biannual publication open to new writers/artists "that is accessible and soulful. I'm open to all kinds of poetry." They have recently published poetry by Rane Arroyo and Nancy Bonnell-Kangas. As a sample the editor selected these lines from Arroyo's "Thinking of AIDS, That Treblinka Just Blinks Away":

> *"I will be buried*
> *wearing the red shoes*
>
> *of the sun on my death*
> *day." The test results:*
> *I'm negative. Love,*
> *I won't be smoke up*
>
> *your criminal chimney.*

Fritz is 24 pgs., 8½ × 11, offset, saddle-stitched, with line drawings and b&w photos. They receive under 50 poems a year, use approximately 5%. Press run is 300 for 100 shelf sales. Single copy: $2. **Sample postpaid: $3. Previously published poems and simultaneous submissions OK. Cover letter with short bio required.** "I only publish twice a year if possible and there's no set publishing time. I mull over my choices for a month or so and when I have a reasonable amount of material, I decide if things fit together well. Since *Fritz* is only 24 pages long, I try to make its content 'gel.' " Send SASE for guidelines. **Reports in 1-2 months. Pays 3 copies. Acquires one-time rights.** The editor says, "I encourage purchasing a sample issue so the writer will have some idea of what he/she is submitting to. I mostly publish fiction, but I always reserve 3 to 4 pages in the back for poetry. I feel it's important to keep those pages open to poets because there's so few outlets in the U.S. for new authors to publish. Although the magazine is small, it's been well-received in the U.S. and overseas. Distribution ranges from the Western U.S. to New York City to Australia and I'm hoping to expand with our next issue."

"Most of our magazine is devoted to new poetry," says Jeremy Page, editor of The Frogmore Papers, a literary quarterly published in Kent, England. "We chose this cover because it is so different from what you normally see on the covers of small press publications, at least in England," he says. "Our policy is to choose covers that differ radically in style from each other in order to reflect the catholicity of the contents of the magazine." This cover was designed by Allan Hardcastle.

FROGMORE PAPERS; FROGMORE POETRY PRIZE (III), 42 Morehall Ave., Folkestone, Kent CT19 4EF England, founded 1983, poetry editor Jeremy Page, is a literary quarterly with emphasis on new poetry and short stories. "Quality is generally the only criterion, although pressure of space means very long work (over 100 lines) is unlikely to be published." They have published poetry by B.C.

Leale, Geoffrey Holloway, Myra Schneider, Frances Wilson, Linda France, Pauline Stainer and John Latham. As a sample the editor selected these lines by Elizabeth Garrett:

> *I rock on my heels and test*
> *My breath's spillage on the air.*
> *I shall fold it with the weather*
> *For safe keeping, in a camphor chest.*

The magazine is 26 pgs., saddle-stapled with matte card cover, photocopied in photoreduced typescript. Their press run is 250 with 80 subscriptions. They accept 5% of poetry received. Subscription: £7 ($12). **Sample postpaid: £2.50 ($4). Considers simultaneous submissions. Editor sometimes comments on rejections. Reports in 3-6 months. Pays 1 copy.** Staff reviews books of poetry in 2-3 sentences, single format. Send books for review consideration to Sophie Hannah, reviews editor, 127 Horton Rd., Manchester M14 7QD England. Write for information about the annual Frogmore Poetry Prize. The editor says, "My advice to people starting to write poetry would be: Read as many recognized modern poets as you can and don't be afraid to experiment."

FROGPOND: BIANNUAL HAIKU JOURNAL; HAIKU SOCIETY OF AMERICA; HAIKU SOCIETY OF AMERICA AWARDS/CONTESTS (IV-Form, translation), % Japan Society, 333 E. 47th St., New York NY 10017, has been publishing *Frogpond* since 1978, now edited by Sylvia Forges-Ryan, and **submissions should go directly to her** at 87 Bayard Ave., North Haven CT 06473. *Frogpond* is a perfect-bound biannual of 80 pgs., 5½ × 8½, of haiku, senryu, haiku sequences, renga, more rarely tanka, and translations of haiku. It also contains essays and articles, book reviews, some news of the Society, contests, awards, publications and other editorial matter — a dignified, handsome little magazine. Poets should be familiar with modern developments in English-language haiku as well as the tradition. **Haiku should be brief, fresh, using clear images and non-poetic language. Focus should be on a moment keenly perceived. Ms. Forges-Ryan hopes contributors will be familiar with contemporary haiku and senryu as presented in** The Haiku Handbook (Wm. J. Higginson) and The Haiku Anthology (Cor van den Heuvel, Ed.). Recent contributors include John J. Dunphy, Peter Duppenthaler, Ebba Story, Wally Swist, Tom Clausen and Pamela Connor. Considerable variety is possible, as these two examples from the magazine illustrate:

> *An old woman with bread*
> *waves the geese down*
> *from the sky.*
> — Alexis Rotella

> *over the earth's edge*
> *they all go — the white clouds*
> *and the one sailboat*
> — George Swede

Each issue has between 38 and 44 pages of poetry. The magazine goes to 600 subscribers, of which 15 are libraries, as well as to over a dozen foreign countries. **Sample postpaid: $10. Make check payable to Haiku Society of America.** They receive about 8,000 submissions/year and use about 400-450. **Accepted poems usually published within 6-12 months, reporting within 6 weeks. They are flexible on submission format: haiku on 3 × 5 cards or several to a page or one to a page or half-page. Ms. Forges-Ryan prefers 5-20 at one submission. No simultaneous submissions.** They hope contributors will become HSA members, but it is not necessary, and all contributors receive a copy of the magazine in payment. Send SASE for Information Sheet on the HSA and submission guidelines. Poetry reviews usually 1,000 words or less. Open to unsolicited reviews. Poets may also send books for review consideration. Four "best-of-issue" prizes are given "through a gift from the Museum of Haiku Literature, Tokyo." The Society also sponsors the Harold G. Henderson Haiku Award Contest, The Gerald Brady Senryu Award Contest, The Haiku Society of America Renku Contest, The Nicholas A. Virgilio Memorial Haiku Competition for High School Students and gives Merit Book Awards for books in the haiku field.

FRONTIERS: A JOURNAL OF WOMEN STUDIES (IV-Feminist), Mesa Vista Hall, Room 2142, University of New Mexico, Albuquerque NM 87131-1586, founded 1975, is published 3 times a year and **uses poetry on feminist themes.** They have published work by Audré Lorde, Janice Mirikitani, Carol Wolfe Konek and Opal Palmer Adisa. The journal is 200-208 pgs., 6 × 9, flat-spined. Circulation 1,000. **Sample: $8. No simultaneous submissions. Reports in 3-5 months. Pays 2 copies.** "We are not currently publishing reviews of books, poetry or otherwise. However, we consider review essays, if from a clear theoretical perspective."

‡FUGUE (I), Room 200, Brink Hall, University of Idaho, Moscow ID 83843, founded 1991, is a biannual literary digest of the University of Idaho, created to give exposure to beginning writers and poets. **They have "no limits" on type of poetry. "We're not interested in trite or quaint verse. Nothing self-indulgent or overly metaphoric to the point of being obscure."** They have recently published poetry by Ricardo Sanchez and Maria Theresa Maggi. As a sample the editor selected these lines from Maggi's "The Appointment":

> *. . . the conceptual warble of arms and legs*
> *caught me in cold waves*

> at the isinglass window, slicing
> its heavy and not quite
> willing prisoners, my parents
> and all parents, in a tide
> of dulled longing and shadows.

The editor says *Fugue* is 48-52 pgs., digest-sized, saddle-stapled. They receive 50 to 100 poems/semester, use 15-20 poems/issue. Press run is 200+ for 30-50 subscribers of which 2 are libraries. Sample postpaid: $3. No previously published poems or simultaneous submissions. Reads submissions September 15 through April 15 only. Seldom comments on rejections. Send SASE for guidelines. Reports in 1-3 months. Pays roughly $5-10 plus one copy. Buys first North American serial rights. The editor says, "Proper manuscript format and submission etiquette is expected; submissions without proper SASE will not be read or held on file."

FUTURIFIC MAGAZINE (IV-Themes), Foundation for Optimism, Terrace 3, 150 Haven Ave., New York NY 10032, phone (212)297-0502, founded 1976, publisher Balint Szent-Miklosy, is a monthly newsmagazine dealing with **current affairs and their probable outcomes**. "We pride ourselves on the accuracy of our forecasting. No other limits than that the poet try to be accurate in predicting the future." They want to see "positive upbeat poetry glorifying humanity and human achievements." *Futurific* is magazine-sized, 32 pgs., saddle-stapled, on glossy stock, with b&w photos, art and ads, circulation 10,000. Subscription: $120; for students and individuals: $60. Sample postpaid: $10. Pays 5 copies. The editor says, "*Futurific* is made up of the words Future-Terrific. Poets should seek out and enjoy the future if they want to see their work in *Futurific*."

G.W. REVIEW (II, IV-Translations), Marvin Center Box 20, George Washington University, Washington DC 20052, phone (202)994-7288, founded 1980, editor Sarah E. Kenny, appears 2 times a year. "The magazine is published for distribution to the university community, the Washington, D.C. metropolitan area and an increasing number of national subscribers." They have published poetry by William Stafford, Jean Valentine, Carol Muske, Jeffrey Harrison and Richard Peabody. It is 64 pgs., perfectbound with cover photograph. They receive about 3,300 poems a year and accept 50-60. Their annual press run averages 4,000 copies. Subscription: $5/year, $8/2 years. Sample postpaid: $3. They consider simultaneous submissions but not previously published poems. Cover letter, including present career and recent publications, required. The staff does not read manuscripts from May 15 through August 15. Editor sometimes comments on rejections when the staff likes the work but thinks it needs to be revised. Reports in 1-3 months. Pays 5 copies.

‡GAIA: A JOURNAL OF LITERARY & ENVIRONMENTAL ARTS; WHISTLE PRESS, INC. (II, IV-Political, social issues), P.O. Box 709, Winterville GA 30683, phone (706)549-1810, founded 1992, editor-in-chief Robert S. King, is a quarterly. "Poetry may explore any subject; other work should center on environmental, social or political themes. We seek a riveting blend of intellect, emotion and beautiful language. No poetasters please." They have recently published poetry by Ann Fox Chandonnet, Stuart Friebert, Paul Grant and Ann Struthers. As a sample the editor selected these lines from "If" by Gale Warner:

> Stumble back to the meadow, swim
> in the stream, grasp at brambles,
> burrow in the earth, begging
> forgiveness, tearing our flesh, worshipping
> the astonishingly harmless lives
> of the beasts.

The editor says *Gaia* is 40 pgs., 8½ × 11, offset, saddle-stapled, with b&w art and photos, no ads. Press run is 500 for 102 subscribers of which 7 are libraries, 250 shelf sales. Subscription: $9. Sample postpaid: $4. Submit up to 10 poems. Previously published poems OK; no simultaneous submissions. Often comments on rejections. Send SASE for guidelines. Reports within 3 months maximum. Pays 2 copies and 4-issue subscription. Acquires all rights. Returns rights upon written request of the author. Whistle Press, Inc. publishes 2 chapbooks/year. "Currently chapbooks are published as single-author issues of our magazine. We plan to begin a separate book series in late 1994." Pays 25 author's copies. They are also planning to sponsor several poetry contests beginning this year. Entries will require a small fee. Query for details.

GAIN PUBLICATIONS (V), P.O. Box 2204, Van Nuys CA 91404, phone (818)786-1981, founded 1982. Currently accepts no unsolicited poetry.

GAIRM; GAIRM PUBLICATIONS (IV-Ethnic, foreign language), 29 Waterloo St., Glasgow G2 6BZ Scotland, editor Derick Thomson, founded 1952. *Gairm* is a quarterly, circulation 2,000, which uses poetry in Scottish Gaelic only. It has published the work of all significant Scottish Gaelic poets, and much poetry translated from European languages. An anthology of such translations, **European Poetry in Gaelic**, is available for £7.50 or $15. *Gairm* is 96 pgs., digest-sized, flat-spined with coated card cover. **Sample: $3.50. Reads submissions October 1 through July 31 only.** Staff reviews books of poetry in 500-700 words, single format; 100 words, multi-book format. Send books for review consideration. **All of the publications of the press are in Scottish Gaelic.** One of them, *Uirsgeul Myth*, poems in Gaelic with English translations, by Christopher Whyte, received a Saltire Literary Award for a First Book.

GÁVEA-BROWN PUBLICATIONS; GÁVEA-BROWN: A BI-LINGUAL JOURNAL OF PORTUGUESE-AMERICAN LETTERS AND STUDIES (IV-Ethnic, bilingual), Box O, Brown University, Providence RI 02912, phone (401)863-3042, founded 1980, editors Onésimo T. Almeida and George Monteiro, is a small press publisher of books and a journal **relating to the Portuguese-American experience.** They publish flat-spined collections of poetry in their journal. They have published poetry by Jorge de Sena, João Teixeira de Medeiros and Thomas Braga. *Gávea-Brown* is handsomely printed, 100+ pgs., digest-sized, flat-spined, with a glossy colored card cover. Its "purpose is to provide a vehicle for the **creative expression of the Portuguese immigrant experience.**" It has a circulation of 450. Subscription: $15 (double issue). **Sample postpaid: $15 for a double issue, $7.50 for a pre-1982 single issue. Reports in 3 months. Pays 3 copies.** Has a 1-year backlog. Reviews books of poetry "related to the area covered by our journal." **Submit sample poems and query regarding book publication. Pays copies.** The books resemble the journal in format.

GAZELLE PUBLICATIONS (V), 5580 Stanley Dr., Auburn CA 95602, founded 1976, editor Ted Wade, is a publisher for home schools and compatible markets including **books of verse for children but is not currently considering unsolicited manuscripts.**

GENERATOR; GENERATOR PRESS (V), 8139 Midland Rd., Mentor OH 44060, founded 1987, poetry editor John Byrum, is an annual magazine "devoted to the presentation of **language poetry and 'concrete' or visual poetic modes.**" They have published poetry by Susan Bee, Charles Bernstein, Bruce Andrews, Sheila E. Murphy, Stephen Ratcliffe and Ron Silliman. As a sample the editor selected these lines by Tom Beckett:

> *Sex and thought are identical — only reversed*
> *Insulated between witness and wetness*
> *one never knows what one needs*
> *Things get done in a major miniseries*
> *The world is all that takes the place*
> *of allegorical invasions*

Generator is magazine-sized, side-stapled, using b&w graphics, photocopied, with matte card cover. Press run is 200 copies for 25 subscriptions of which 10 are libraries. **Sample postpaid: $5.** Generator Press also publishes the **Generator Press chapbook series. Approximately 4 new titles/year. They are not currently accepting unsolicited manuscripts for either the magazine or chapbook publication.** The editor adds, "Worthwhile writers do not need advice and should not heed any but their own."

‡**GEORGETOWN REVIEW (II)**, Box 227, 400 E. College St., Georgetown KY 40324, founded 1992 (first issue Spring 1993), is a biannual literary journal publishing fiction and poetry — no criticism or reviews. They want **"honest, quality work; not interested in tricks."** The editor says it is 100-120 pgs., 6×9, perfect-bound, with heavy stock cover, graphics and ads. They receive about 1,000 submissions a year, "take maybe 10%." Press run is 1,000. Subscription: $10/year. **Sample postpaid: $5. No previously published poems; simultaneous submissions OK. Submit no more than 5 poems at a time. Reads submissions September 1 through May 1 only.** Poems are read by at least 3 readers. Sometimes comments on rejections. **Reports in 2-4 months. Pays 2 copies. Acquires all rights. Returns rights provided "our name is mentioned in any reprint."**

GEORGIA JOURNAL (IV-Regional), P.O. Box 27, Athens GA 30603-0027, phone (404)354-0463, poetry editor Janice Moore. *Georgia Journal* is a quarterly magazine, circulation 15,000, covering the state of Georgia. **They use poetry "mostly from Southern writers but not entirely. It should be suitable for the general reader."** They have recently published poetry by former President Jimmy Carter, Stephen Corey, Blanche Farley, Michael Chitwood and June Owens. As a sample Janice Moore selected these lines from "Next Door" by John Stone:

> *of a sudden*
> *with no fanfare*
> *but much finesse*
>
> *the gingko that*

CLOSE-UP

Keep Your Senses Alive in Writing

"Sometimes a Son"

Sometimes a son
will surprise you   come to sit
on the side of your bed
where you lie with a broken leg
everyone else seems to have forgotten
He will balance three pieces
of grape smeared toast
on a too small plate   drink orange juice
from your best crystal   You don't mind
this particular morning   the first sun
flashing off the leaves outside your window
He will tell you his funniest stories
fragments of toast   crumbling
onto the sheets   You will not brush them away
Your son will tell you these things
you've heard before
They will seem new now   as beside you he
shakes your whole bed with his laughter

Janice Townley Moore

Janice Townley Moore aspires to write lean, direct poems as is "Sometimes a Son," which originally appeared in the anthology **The Tie That Binds** (Papier-Mache Press, 1988).

"Poems should be rendered through the senses," Moore says. "Early in my days of submitting poetry to journals, an editor rejected my poems but added a postscript: 'Senses alive! Keep writing!'

"I think that keeping one's senses alive is imperative in writing the successful poem."

In addition to sensory images, Moore tries to use what she calls "resonant language," endowing her lines with another layer of meaning and depth. To accomplish this, she says, "I try to be very cautious with the use of adjectives. I go through my poems and make myself defend every adjective. Finally, I revise with attention to how the poem *sounds*."

Moore has published poems in such magazines as *Southern Poetry Review*, *Southern Humanities Review* and *Kansas Quarterly* and in several respected anthologies. She is a native of Atlanta and lives in Hayesville, North Carolina, (close to the North Georgia mountains) where she teaches in the English department of Young Harris College.

She has edited poetry for *Georgia Journal* since 1985. Moore says its subscribers are interested in state history and local points of interest. What sets *Georgia Journal* apart from other regional magazines that focus almost exclusively on nonfiction is its two pages of poetry in each issue.

"In the early 1980s," Moore says, "the magazine used poems mostly as fillers, and now I hope we have some readers who open the magazine to read the poems *first*. And I believe we are acquiring such an audience."

Most, but not all, of the poetry published in *Georgia Journal* is by Southern writers. Moore is particularly proud that her magazine was among the first to accept verse by former President Jimmy Carter. (Two of Carter's poems — "Miss Lillian Sees Leprosy for the First Time" and "Priorities of Some Mexican Children" — appeared in the Fall 1992 issue.)

Moore says poets planning to submit work should realize that *Georgia Journal* is not a literary magazine. "The subject matter should be general, not academic, and grounded in an experience with which the general reader can identify."

That doesn't mean poems must relate to Georgia, she says. However, since the magazine is included in the libraries of public schools, topics should be in good taste and suitable for a general audience.

Moore also emphasizes that although topics and themes should be universal, they also should be accessible, upbeat and "rendered with words and images that make the experience *new*."

She leans toward free verse — "if rhyme is used, I like it to be subtle" — and appreciates material to suit the quarterly issues of the magazine.

To increase your chances with seasonal material, Moore says poems should be sent six to nine months in advance. (Autumn poems, for example, can be submitted as early as late January for the Fall issue.)

As for topics, seasonal poems should relate to times of the year rather than specific holidays. "I've got one right here whose first line is about making sweet potato souffle in September. In this case, the month helped. However, I don't want poems about months but ones that grow out of, or seem appropriate to, the seasons. For instance, I don't often take Christmas poems, but would take a good poem about angels if its theme tied in with the season."

Finally, Moore warns against these common weaknesses: "wordiness along with clichéd language and what I call graphic acrobatics — weird patterns of word spacing and placement that one would be afraid to trust even the best printer with!"

As poet and editor, Moore says, "I think the characteristics of what I consider a good poem remain about the same whether I am trying to write poetry or select poems for *Georgia Journal*."

—*Michael J. Bugeja*

❝I try to be very cautious with the use of adjectives. I revise with attention to how the poem *sounds*.❞

—Janice Townley Moore

> *has blazed all month*
> *has acquiesced*

Georgia Journal is 80 pgs., 8½ × 11, saddle-stapled and professionally printed on glossy paper with color cover. Recent issues featured accessible narrative and lyric free verse. Content was genuinely open and varied, from nature and personal poems to war and meditative verse. About 8-10 poems appear in each issue. **Sample: $3. Submit maximum of 3-4 poems, maximum length 30 lines. "A brief cover letter with previous publications is fine, but keep it brief." Send SASE for guidelines. Reports in 2-3 months. Pays copies. Acquires first rights.** Staff selects books by Georgia authors to review.

UNIVERSITY OF GEORGIA PRESS; CONTEMPORARY POETRY SERIES (II), Terrell Hall, University of Georgia, Athens GA 30602, phone (706)542-2830, press founded 1938, series founded 1980. Series editor Bin Ramke, publishes four collections of poetry/year, **two of which are by poets who have not had a book published,** in simultaneous hardcover and paperback editions. They have recently published poetry by Jacqueline Osherow, Arthur Vogelsang, Susan Stewart and C.D. Wright. As a sample the editor selected these lines from "The Sciences Sing a Lullabye" by Albert Goldbarth:

> *Physics says: go to sleep. Of course*
> *you're tired. Every atom in you*
> *has been dancing the shimmy in silver shoes*
> *nonstop from mitosis to now.*
> *Quit tapping your feet. They'll dance*
> *inside themselves without you. Go to sleep.*

That is from the book **Heaven and Earth: A Cosmology** for which Goldbarth won the 1992 National Book Critics Circle Award. **"Writers should query first for guidelines and submission periods. Please enclose SASE." There are no restrictions on the type of poetry submitted,** but "familiarity with our previously published books in the series may be helpful." **$10 submission fee.** Manuscripts are *not* returned after the judging is completed.

THE GEORGIA REVIEW (III), The University of Georgia, Athens GA 30602-9009, phone (706)542-3481, founded 1947, editor Stanley W. Lindberg, associate editor Stephen Corey. They have published poetry by Galway Kinnell, Yusef Komunyakaa, Pattiann Rogers, Gerald Stern, Lisel Mueller, Seamus Heaney, Linda Pastan, Albert Goldbarth, Rita Dove and Charles Simic. "Also have featured first-ever publications by many new voices over the years, but encourage all potential contributors to become familiar with past offerings before submitting." As a sample, Stephen Corey selected these lines from "Black" by Andrea Hollander Budy:

> *. . . Passion*
> *travels in the dark—the animal*
> *we do not truly know, the one*
> *we never pet, the one so foreign*
> *to our lives we do not have a sense*
> *of what it eats or where it sleeps, and only know*
> *its death.*

This is a distinguished, professionally printed, flat-spined quarterly, 200+ pgs., 7 × 10, glossy card cover. They use 60-70 poems a year, less than one-half of one percent of those received. Circulation: 6,500. Subscription: $18/year. **Sample postpaid: $6. No submissions accepted during June, July and August. Rarely uses translations. Submit 3-5 poems. No simultaneous submissions. Reports in 1-3 months. Pays $2/line. Buys first North American serial rights.** Reviews books of poetry. "Our poetry reviews range from 500-word 'Book Briefs' on single volumes to 5,000-word essay reviews on multiple volumes." *The Georgia Review* is one of the best literary journals around. It respects its audience, edits intelligently and has won or been nominated for awards in competition with such slicks as *The Atlantic, The New Yorker* and *Esquire*. Work appearing here has also been included in **Best American Poetry 1992**. In addition, *The Georgia Review* ranked #3 in the "Poets' Pick" category of the June 1993 *Writer's Digest* Poetry 60 list. This category ranks those publications in which poets said they would most like to see their work published. Needless to say, competition here is extremely tough. All styles and forms are welcome, but response times can be slow during peak periods in the fall and late spring.

GEPPO HAIKU WORKSHEET; HAIKU JOURNAL MEMBERS' ANTHOLOGY; YUKI TEIKEI HAIKU SOCIETY (I, IV-Form, membership), P.O. Box 1250, Gualala CA 95445, phone (707)882-2226, *Geppo* founded 1977 and first published by the Yuki Teikei Haiku Society, editor Jane Reichhold. *Geppo* is devoted to haiku and haiku criticism; contest winners and **"members' haiku only are published here."** It is a bimonthly mimeographed newsletter for members using **haiku, especially traditional haiku: 17 syllables with a KIGO."** Press run is 200. *HJ* appears every 2 years and "contains the winning haiku voted on in *Geppo*." The editor describes *HJ* as "around 60 pgs., 5½ × 8½, nicely printed on heavy paper, card stock cover." Press run is 300 for 100 subscriptions of which 10 are libraries. Membership in the Yuki Teikei Haiku Society is $15/year and includes 6 issues of *Geppo*. **Sample of *Geppo* available for SASE. Sample of *HJ* postpaid: $4.50. Send SASE for guidelines. Simultaneous submissions and previously published poems OK.** They have an annual contest in the spring. Send SASE for rules.

THE GETTYSBURG REVIEW (II), Gettysburg College, Gettysburg PA 17325, phone (717)337-6770, founded 1988, editor Peter Stitt, is a multidisciplinary literary quarterly using **any poetry except that which is "badly written."** They accept 1-2% of submissions received. As a sample the editor selected these lines by Dick Allen:

> *Placards lifted, the marchers of the Sixties*
> *Stood in green meadows. Then folk songs began*
> *Rising from their lips like blue leaves in summer*
> *And time was a slipstream where a Phantom jet*
> *Rolled in the sun. The lovers ran their hands*
> *Over the rice fields and the panting oxen.*

Press run is 4,500 for 2,000 subscriptions. **Sample postpaid: $7. Pays $2/line.** Essay-reviews are featured in each issue. They are open to unsolicited reviews. Poets may also send books for review consideration. In six years, Editor Peter Stitt, a leading literary critic and reviewer, has created a well-edited and -respected journal that features a tantalizing lineup of poems in all styles and forms. Competition is keen, and response times can be slow during heavy submission periods, especially in the late fall. Work appearing in *The Gettysburg Review* has been included in **Best American Poetry** and **Pushcart Prize** anthologies. The review itself ranked #4 in the "Top Pay" category of the June 1993 *Writer's Digest* Poetry 60 list.

GIANTS PLAY WELL IN THE DRIZZLE (V), 326-A 4th St., Brooklyn NY 11215, founded 1983, editor Martha King, is a poetry newsletter appearing 2-6 times/year. The editor wants **"energy in breath, sound, intellect, passion in wit, in irreverence, in high seriousness, and oh those dirty dogs."** They have published poetry by Robert Creeley, Sheila Murphy, Laurie Price and Tom Clark. As a sample the editor selected these lines from "Found in a Finch Egg" by Brent MacKay:

> *All the misspent loose change of youth*
> *hard raining down the skull's softest rut*
> *seems but a blue folded fin*
> *tucked in a pocket*
> *lost in the wash.*

It is 10 pgs., stapled at the corner. Press run 800 for 650 on a free mailing list. **Sample free for a first class stamp. Currently not accepting poetry submissions, query if interested.** "This is a free publication. Friends send stamps and money to keep it going. Please ask for a sample when querying! The very small format imposes some limits as to length." Open to unsolicited reviews.

GINGER HILL (II), c/o English Dept., Room 314, Spotts World Cultures Building, Slippery Rock University, Slippery Rock PA 16057, phone (412)738-2043, founded 1963, is an annual literary magazine using **"academic poetry, with preference for excellent free verse, but all forms considered. 27-line limit. No greeting card verse, no sentimentality, no self-serving or didactic verse."** They have recently published poetry by Elizabeth R. Curry, B.Z. Niditch and Robert Cooperman. It is digest-sized, "varies in format and layout every year," perfect-bound, with 2,000 distributed free. **Submissions must be postmarked on or before December 1 of each year. Send SASE for guidelines. Pays 2 copies.** They say, "We choose about 5-10% of all submissions. Excellence is stressed."

GIORNO POETRY SYSTEMS RECORDS; DIAL-A-POEM POETS (V), 222 Bowery, New York NY 10012, phone (212)925-6372, fax (212)966-7574, founded 1965, poetry editor John Giorno, "star of Andy Warhol's movie, *Sleep* (1963)," who publishes a poetry magazine in three formats: LP record, Compact Disc and cassette; and a videopak series. He originated Dial-A-Poem in 1968, installing it in many cities in the United States and Europe. He says he has published poetry on the surface of ordinary objects: Matchbook Poems, T-Shirt Poems, Cigarette Package Poems, Window Curtain Poems, Flag Poems, Chocolate Bar Poems, and Silk-Screen and Lithograph Poem Prints. He started the AIDS Treatment Project in 1984. **No submission information provided.**

‡GLB PUBLISHERS (III, IV-Gay/lesbian), P.O. Box 78212, San Francisco CA 94107, phone (415)243-0229, founded 1990, associate editor John Hanley. "We are **cooperative publishers. Founded for gay, lesbian and bisexual writers. Authors share cost of printing and promotion but have much control over cover design, typefaces, general appearance."** They publish 1-2 paperbacks and 1-2 hardbacks/year. They want **"book-length collections from gay, lesbian or bisexual writers. Nothing antagonistic to gay, lesbian or bisexual life-styles."** They have recently published poetry by Robert Peters, Paul Genega and Thomas Cashet. **Previously published poems OK; no simultaneous submissions.** Cover letter required. "Author should explain intention for poems and expectations for sales of books." Often comments on rejections. Replies to queries in 10 days, to mss in 1 month. Pays 15-25% royalties and 20 author's copies. However, author shares cost of printing and promotion. Check bookstores for samples.

GLOBAL TAPESTRY JOURNAL; BB BOOKS (II), Spring Bank, Longsight Rd., Copster Green, Black-burn, Lancs. BB1 9EU United Kingdom, founded 1963, poetry editor Dave Cunliffe. "Experimental, avant-garde—specializing in exciting high-energy new writing. Mainly for a bohemian and counter-culture audience. Poetry in the Beat tradition. Don't want contrived, traditional, pompous and aca-demic or pretentious mainstream." Also considers sexually explicit material. In addition to the maga-zine, *Global Tapestry Journal*, BB Books publishes chapbooks. "We want honest, uncontrived writing, strong in form and content. We don't want 'weekend hobby verse' and poetry without energy." They have recently published poetry by David Tipton, Joy Walsh, Belinda Subraman, Ellen Zaks and Jim Burns. As a sample the editor selected these lines by Lisa Kucharski:

> the system doesn't fit where our
> body's going to
> we make square corners
> and walk around them in curves

GTJ is 9×6, 72 pgs., saddle-stapled, typeset in a variety of mostly small sizes of type, rather crowded format, casual pasteup, with b&w drawings, photos, collages, display and classified ads, with a 2-color matte card cover, circulation 1,150 with 450 subscriptions of which 50 are libraries. Subscription (4 issues): $20. **Sample postpaid: $3. Send SASE for guidelines. Considers pre-viously published poems. Cover letter, with clear address, telephone number and short publish-ing history, required. Responds "soon," has an 18-month backlog. Pays 1 copy. Open to unsolic-ited reviews.** Poets may also send books for review consideration. **BB Books publishes about 4 chapbooks of poetry/year. To submit for chapbook publication send 6 samples, cover letter giving publication credits. Pays 10% of press run in copies. Send SASE (SAE with IRCs if foreign) for catalog to buy samples.** David Cunliffe comments, "The United Kingdom has a limited number of magazines and small press ventures publishing poetry from unknowns. Many little mags are self-publishing cliques or small-time vanity operations. Simultaneous submissions and simultane-ous publication are often resented. There is much readership crossover among the non-poet subscribers and they resent seeing the same work in many magazines over a short period. We typeset for a few United Kingdom mags and publishers and we see this in the setting jobs we do every week. Many of the editors circulate poet blacklists to help prevent this tendency from spreading."

DAVID R. GODINE, PUBLISHER, Horticultural Hall, 300 Massachusetts Ave., Boston MA 02115. Prefers not to share information. "One result of being listed in reference guides like **Poet's Market** is the submission of massive amounts of unsolicited manuscripts. Godine is a small company, and we simply do not have the staff to handle all of the unsolicited writing we receive. We have never accepted any work from the piles of unsolicited material we receive, so we have decided that it is not worth our while to be listed in directories."

‡**GOING DOWN SWINGING (II)**, P.O. Box 64, Coburg, Melbourne, Victoria 3058 Australia, founded 1980, editors Kevin Brophy and Myron Lysenko, is an annual using **"poetry that's tackling contempo-rary literary, social, political issues. Poetry that's alive now. No racist or sexist poetry."** They have recently published poetry by Eric Beach, Gail Schilke, Steven Herrick and Dorothy Porter. As a sample the editors selected these lines from "Einstein, Buddhism and My Stiff Neck" by Grant Caldwell:

> Einstein didn't discover relativity
> he just had a relatively good understanding of it.
> Did/does this make him a Buddhist?
> Some people I know
> and Tina Turner
> claim to be Buddhists.

It is flat-spined, digest-sized. Press run 1,000 for 200 subscribers of which 30 are libraries, 700 shelf sales. **Sample postpaid: $6 (A). Editors often comment on rejections. Report in 2-4 months.**

Market conditions are constantly changing! If you're still using this book and it is 1995 or later, buy the newest edition of Poet's Market at your favorite bookstore or order directly from Writer's Digest Books.

Pay 1 copy and a "small fee." They say, "We are primarily an Australian magazine, but we are open to new and outstanding writing from overseas. Our aim is to publish the work of new, young and generally unknown writers whose work excites and interests us. We review small press books." Open to unsolicited reviews. Poets may also send books for review consideration.

GOLDEN ISIS MAGAZINE; AGE OF AQUARIUS; GOLDEN ISIS PRESS; POEM OF THE YEAR CONTEST (I, IV-Mystical/Occult), P.O. Box 4862, Chatsworth CA 91313, founded 1980, editor Gerina Dunwich. "*Golden Isis* is a mystical literary magazine of poetry, magick, pagan/Egyptian artwork, Wiccan news, occult fiction, letters, book reviews and classified ads. Occult, Egyptian, cosmic, euphonic and Goddess-inspired poems, mystical haiku and magickal chants are published. We are also interested in New Age spiritual poetry, astrological verses and poems dealing with peace, love and ecology. All styles considered; under 60 lines preferred. We do not want to see pornographic, Satanic, sexist or racist material." They have recently published poetry by H.L. Prosser, Eileen Kernaghan and Timothy Kevin Perry. As a sample the editor selected these lines from "Full Circle" by Mary Shifman:

> *The Goddess steps inside my heart*
> *To share me with Her dance*
> *The Horned God plies his minstrel art*
> *And all the world enchants*

The magazine is digest-sized, 15-20 pgs., desktop published, saddle-stapled with paper cover. International circulation is 5,000. Single copy: $3; subscription: $10/year. "No postal money orders, please." Submit 1 poem/page, typed single-spaced, name and address on upper left corner and the number of lines on upper right corner. Previously published poems and simultaneous submissions OK. Occasionally comments on rejected material. Reports within 2-3 weeks. Pays 1 copy. All rights revert back to author upon publication. Reviews books of poetry, "length varies." Open to unsolicited reviews. Poets may also send books for review consideration. *Age of Aquarius* is a digest-sized "psychedelic journal of 60s counter-culture in the 90s." Sample: $3. Circulation: 3,600. Pays 1 copy. Golden Isis Press is now accepting mss for chapbook publication. Send complete ms and $5 reading fee. "Please make checks payable to Golden Isis. We offer a small advance, 10 free copies of the published work, and 10% royalty on every copy sold for as long as the book remains in print." Sample chapbook (Circle of Shadows by Gerina Dunwich): $3.95. The magazine sponsors an annual "Poem of the Year" contest that offers cash prizes. Entry fee: $1/poem. Deadline: December 1. No limit on number of poems entered. Poems should be up to 60 lines, any form, with author's name and address on upper left corner of each page. Free guidelines and contest rules for SASE. *Golden Isis* is a member of W.P.P.A. (Wiccan/Pagan Press Alliance).

GOLDEN QUILL PRESS (I), RFD #1, Avery Rd., Francestown NH 03043, publishes a great deal of poetry on a subsidy basis. Submit complete ms. Reports in 2 weeks on queries, 1 month on submissions. Pays maximum 10% royalties.

GOOD HOUSEKEEPING (II, IV-Humor, women), Hearst Corp., 959 8th Ave., New York NY 10019, poetry editor Andrea Krantz, circulation 5,000,000, women's magazine, uses up to 3 poems/issue for which they pay $10/line. Light verse and traditional. Submit up to 10 poems; maximum length: 25 lines. They no longer return or critique manuscripts. "We look for poems of emotional interest to American women. Must be wholesome, clever, upbeat or poignant. Poets whose work interests us will hear from us within 4-5 weeks of receipt of a manuscript. We ask that poets send inexpensive copies of their work, and do *not* enclose SASEs or postage. We do accept multiple submissions." Cover letter with name, address and credits required. Send seasonal material 6-12 months before publication date. Submit short humorous verses, anecdotes and 'daffinition' to "Light Housekeeping" editor, Rosemary Leonard. Enclose SASE because they do return these mss. Pays $25 for 2-4 lines; $50, 5-8 lines. Buys first North American serial rights. Usually overstocked. *Good Housekeeping* ranked #1 in the "Top Pay" category of the June 1993 *Writer's Digest* Poetry 60 list.

GOOSE LANE EDITIONS (III, IV-Regional), 469 King St., Fredericton, New Brunswick E3B 1E5 Canada, phone (506)450-4251, fax (506)459-4991, managing editor S. Alexander, founded 1956, a small press publishing Canadian fiction, poetry and literary history. Writers should be advised that Goose Lane considers mss by Canadian poets only. They receive approximately 400 mss/year, publish 10-15 books yearly, 3 of these being poetry collections. Writers published include M. Travis Lane, John B. Lee and Claire Harris. As a sample the editor selected these lines from "Elegy: In Memory of David Anderson, 1970-1987" published in **Clarity Between Clouds** (1991) by Susan Ioannou:

> *This wilderness under a road,*
> *moment by moment changing,*
> *constantly gathers into itself and absorbs*

> *time, shape, a thousand minuscule deaths,*
> *and sings back a fluid permanence*
>
> *where nothing, ever, is lost*
> *but, passing at dawn, remembered.*

Unsolicited Canadian mss considered if individual poems have been previously published in literary journals. Cover letter required; include name and address and where work was previously published. SASE essential (IRCs or Canadian postage stamps only). Reports in 3-4 months. Authors may receive royalty of up to 10% of retail sale price on all copies sold. Copies available to author at 40% discount.

GOSPEL PUBLISHING HOUSE; PENTECOSTAL EVANGEL; LIVE; HICALL; JUNIOR TRAILS (IV-Religious, children/teens), The General Council of the Assemblies of God, 1445 Boonville, Springfield MO 65802, phone (417)862-2781, fax (417)862-0416, editor Richard G. Champion. *Pentecostal Evangel* is a weekly magazine containing **inspirational articles and news of the Assemblies of God for members of the Assemblies and other Pentecostal and charismatic Christians,** circulation 280,000. **Religious and inspirational poetry.** "All poems submitted to us should be related to religious life. We are Protestant, evangelical, Pentecostal, and any doctrines or practices portrayed should be in harmony with the official position of our denomination (Assemblies of God)." **Free sample copy and writer's guidelines. Submit maximum 3 poems. Submit seasonal/holiday material 6 months in advance. Reports in 3 months. Pays 50-75¢/line on acceptance. Buys first and/or second rights.** *Live* is a weekly for adults in Assemblies of God Sunday schools, circulation 200,000. **Traditional free and blank verse, 12-20 lines.** "Please do not send large numbers of poems at one time." Submit seasonal material 1 year in advance; do not mention Santa Claus, Halloween or Easter bunnies. **Free sample copy and writer's guidelines for 7×10 SAE and 40¢ postage.** Letters without SASE will not be answered. **Pays 25¢/line on acceptance. Buys first and/or second rights.** *HiCall* is a weekly magazine of **Christian fiction and articles for teenagers, 12-17,** circulation 78,000. **Free verse, light verse and traditional, 10-40 lines. Buys 50 poems/year. Submit seasonal/holiday material 18 months in advance. Simultaneous and previously published submissions OK if typed, double-spaced, on 8×11 paper. Reports in 6 weeks. Sample copy for 8×11 SAE and 2 first class stamps; writer's guidelines for SAE. Pays 25¢/line for first rights, 15¢/line for second rights; minimum of $2.50.** *Junior Trails* is a weekly tabloid covering religious fiction and biographical, historical and scientific articles with a spiritual emphasis for boys and girls ages 10-11, circulation 75,000. **Free verse and light verse. Buys 10-15 poems/year. Submit seasonal/holiday material 15 months in advance. Simultaneous and previously published submissions OK. Reports in 2-4 weeks. Sample copy and writer's guidelines for 9×12 SAE and 2 first class stamps. Pays 20¢/line on acceptance. Buys first and/or second rights.** "We like poems showing contemporary children positively facing today's world."

GOTTA WRITE NETWORK LITMAG; MAREN PUBLICATIONS (I, IV-Science fiction/fantasy, subscription), 612 Cobblestone Circle, Glenview IL 60025, fax (708)296-7631, founded 1988, editor/publisher Denise Fleischer, is a desktop published semiannual, saddle-stapled, 36-page magazine featuring "general poetry, articles, short stories and market listings. *GWN* now spans 40 states, Canada and England. Half of the magazine is devoted to science fiction and fantasy in a section called 'Sci-Fi Galleria.' **I'm open to well-crafted, clear poetry that doesn't have to be dissected to understand its message. Poetry that leaves the reader with a special feeling. Can be of any genre. No sexually graphic material, obscenities or lengthy poetry.**" She has published poetry by H.R. Felgenhauer, John Grey, C.R. Riehle, Anne Simon and C. David Hay. As a sample, the editor selected these lines from "i saw isolde once" by Charles Rampp:

> *hidden more fully than warblers*
> *in forest's morning woods, quiet*
> *as mushroom fairy dance ring*
> *in the churchyard, this love of ours.*

"*Gotta Write Network* subscribers receive more than a magazine. In subscribing, they become part of a support group of both beginners and established poets. I offer critiques at request, will even retype a poem to point out spelling errors and suggest other appropriate markets. Members are from all walks of life: housewives, religious persons, seniors, nursing home residents. Five reside in prisons." Press run: 200 for 70 subscribers. "I'm striving to give beginners a positive starting point and to encourage them to venture beyond rejection slips and writer's block. Publication can be a reality if you have determination and talent. There are over a thousand U.S. litmags waiting for submissions. So what are you waiting for?" Subscription: $12.75. **Sample postpaid: $5. Include a cover letter and SASE with submissions. Reports in 1-2 months. Pays 1 copy. Acquires first North American serial rights.** Pays $5 for assigned by-mail interviews with established paperback authors and small press editors. Maren Publications has published 1 chapbook, **Poetry Cafe,** and a short story anthology, **Life In General.** She adds, "Write the way you feel the words. Don't let others mold you into an established poet's style. Poetry is about personal imagery that needs to be shared with others."

GRAFFITI OFF THE ASYLUM WALLS (IV-Humor, erotica, fetishes), P.O. Box 515, Fayetteville AR 72702-0515, founded 1991, "curator" BrYan Westbrook, is an "illiterary journal published whenever I receive enough suitable material." He wants **"stuff you would be afraid to show your mother, priest and/or shrink; also anything that can make me laugh. No formal poetry; no pro-religious or animal rights poetry; nothing boring."** They have published poetry by Cheryl Townsend, Belinda Subraman, harland ristau and Scott C. Holstad. As a sample the editor selected these lines from "Cheap Date" by Richard Cody:

> *His hands played over her fine young body,*
> *seeking to unleash forbidden pleasures.*
> *"You better enjoy this . . ." he whispered.*
> *"You're going back to the graveyard tomorrow."*

GOTAW is 8½ × 11, laser printed, stapled with colored paper cover, drawings and cartoons. Press run is 200. "Due to the irregular publishing schedule, I do not offer subscriptions; but, if requested, will notify interested parties whenever an issue is due." **Sample postpaid: "$2.50 (checks made out to BrYan Westbrook) or will trade copies with other editors." Previously published poems and simultaneous submissions OK. Cover letter required.** "I do not want to just see a list of previous publications. I want to know who you are more than where you've been." **Often comments on rejections. Send SASE for guidelines. Reports "usually next day, never more than 2 weeks." Pays 1 copy. Acquires one-time rights.** Staff will review *"anything* someone wants to send me. Length varies with how much I think needs to be said." Sponsors annual chapbook contest. There is a $3 reading fee and 24-page limit. Deadline: September 17. Winner receives 27 copies; all others receive a copy of winning chapbook. BrYan Westbrook says, "Throughout history the preserved literature of any period has mainly been what the people of that time actually enjoyed. Scholars have placed these works upon lofty pedestals and declared them the only true art. It's time we stop trying to imitate what others have considered entertainment and get on with creating the art we really want for ourselves. *GOTAW* is my contribution to this endeavor."

GRAHAM HOUSE REVIEW (II, IV-Translations), Box 5000, Colgate University, Hamilton NY 13346, phone (315)824-1000, ext. 262, founded 1976, poetry editors Peter Balakian and Bruce Smith, appears yearly. **"We publish contemporary poetry, poetry in translation, essays and interviews. No preferences for styles or schools, just good poetry."** They have published poems by Seamus Heaney, Marilyn Hacker, Maxine Kumin, Michael Harper and Carolyn Forché. *GHR* is digest-sized, flat-spined, 120 pgs., professionally printed on heavy stock, matte color card cover with logo, using 100 pgs. of poetry in each issue. They receive about 2,000 freelance submissions of poetry/year, use 20-50. One of the best "reads" in the literary world, this publication features well-crafted free verse depicting emotionally tense or intellectually stimulating ideas and themes. It welcomes translations and has an "international" flavor. Circulation 500, with 300 subscriptions of which 50 are libraries. **Sample postpaid: $7.50. Reports in 2 months or less. Pays 2 copies.**

GRAIN; SHORT GRAIN CONTEST (II), Box 1154, Regina, Saskatchewan S4P 3B4 Canada, phone (306)757-6310, is a literary quarterly. **"Grain strives for artistic excellence, seeks material that is accessible as well as challenging to our readers. Ideally, a *Grain* poem should be well-crafted, imaginatively stimulating, distinctly original."** They have recently published poetry by Evelyn Lau and Jay Meek. The editor selected as a sample the opening of "The Children" by Patrick Lane:

> *The children are singing.*
> *Hear them as they rise out of the deep hollows,*
> *the tangles of wildwood and wandering vines.*
> *They are lifting from the shadows*
> *where the black creek water flows*
> *over mud and stones. They have left behind*
> *the green whip of a snake*
> *thrown like a thin necklace into the trees . . .*

It is digest-sized, professionally printed with chrome-coated cover, 144 pgs., circulation 1,800+, with 1,300 subscriptions of which 100 are libraries. Subscription: $19.95 (Canadian), $23.95 for US, $25.95 for other foreign destinations. They receive about 700 freelance submissions of poetry/year, use 80-140 poems. **Sample: $5 plus IRC (or 80¢ Canadian postage). They want "no poetry that has no substance." Submit maximum of 8 poems. Cover letter required. Include "The number of poems submitted, address (with postal or zip code) and phone number." Send SASE for guidelines. Reports in 3-4 months. Pays $30+/poem. Buys first North American serial rights.** The editor comments, "Only work of the highest literary quality is accepted. Read several back issues." *Grain* holds an annual Short Grain Contest. Entries are either prose poems (a lyric poem written as a prose paragraph or paragraphs in 500 words or less) or postcard stories (also 500 words or less). Prizes in each category, $250 first, $150 second, $100 third and honorable mentions. All winners and honorable mentions receive regular payment for publication in *Grain*. Entry fee of $20 (Canadian) allows up to two entries in the same category, and includes a one-year subscription. Additional entries are $5 each. Entries are normally accepted between January 1 and April 30.

GRAND STREET, Room 906, 131 Varick St., New York NY 10013. Prefers not to share information. "We already receive enough poetry submissions to keep us very busy."

GRASSLANDS REVIEW (I, II), NT Box 13706, Denton TX 76203, phone (817)565-2127, founded 1989, editor Laura B. Kennelly, is a magazine **"to encourage beginning writers and to give creative writing class experience in editing essays, fiction, poetry; using any type of poetry; shorter poems stand best chance."** They have recently published poetry by Jay R. Prefontaine, Paul Foreman, Jill C. Miller, Ray Mizer, Linda O'Brien, Taylor Graham and David Alpaugh. As a sample the editor selected these lines by Therese Arceneaux:

> And now, years later, to recall the wind,
> the wet sand, the wide wavering light
> that flowed, that gathered between sea and sky—
> Mornings new-made, fresh rising from the shore,
> each seeming the first of new Edens lost and found—
> To remember, to taste the salt of blood, of tears
> in the soft air.

GR is 88 pgs., professionally printed, digest-sized, photocopied, saddle-stapled with card cover. They accept 20-40 of 400 submissions received. Press run 300. Subscription (2 issues): $4 for individuals, $10 institutions. **Sample postpaid: $2. Submit only during October and March, no more than 5 poems at a time. Editor comments on submissions "sometimes." Reports in 10-12 weeks. Pays 2 copies.**

GRAVEN IMAGES (I), P.O. Box 2412, Bellingham WA 98227, founded 1991, editor Clayton Walter, is a quarterly of **"free verse poetry—up to 30 lines; subject: life, imagination, fact, fiction, feelings."** They do not want **"rhyming poetry."** They have recently published poetry by Robyn Stevens, Jeff Flugel and Larry L. Randall. As a sample the editor selected these lines by Brian Kaufman:

> I long for a genuine syndrome
> that will leave me unable to work
> Let me be minimally crippled
> Before it is too late

GI is 32 pgs., digest-sized, photocopied, stapled with card stock cover. Press run is 250 for 78 subscribers. Single copy: $2.50; subscription: $10 plus $2.40 postage. **Sample postpaid: $3.10. No simultaneous submissions. Cover letter with brief background info required. Often comments on rejections. Reports within 2 months. Pays 1 copy.** Reviews chapbooks. The editor says, "Please *do not* send love poems, nature poems or first person introspections relating the miserable nature of life. Please *do* send expressions of surprise, anger, joy, terror, passion, lust. Try to make me feel, feel, feel!"

GRAYWOLF PRESS (V), Suite 203, 2402 University Ave., Saint Paul MN 55114, phone (612)641-0077, founded 1975, poetry editor Scott Walker, **does not read unsolicited mss.** They have published poetry by Tess Gallagher, Linda Gregg, Jack Gilbert, Chris Gilbert and William Stafford. **Pays 7½-10% royalties, 10 author's copies, advance negotiated.**

GREAT LAKES POETRY PRESS (V, IV-Anthology), Box 56703, Harwood Heights IL 60656, phone (312)792-0375, founded 1987, poetry editor Chuck Kramer. Great Lakes publishes **books that are organized around specific themes or topics.** For instance, in 1992 they published Step into the Light: Poems from Recovery. As a sample the editor selected these lines from "Steps" by Will Casey:

> Where it took me
> was why I took the trip
> commuting again and again
> to soft edges and warm glows

"Manuscripts for these books are solicited through newspaper advertising and personal contact. We do not read unsolicited material." They also publish single author collections of poetry on both a commercial and subsidy basis. "For more information, let us know what you have in mind (include a SASE) and we'll get back to you."

‡**GREAT RIVER REVIEW (II)**, 211 W. 7th, Winona MN 55987, founded 1977, poetry editor Orval Lund, is published "three times every two years." They want **"high quality contemporary poetry that uses image as the basis for expression. Suggested submission: 4-6 poems."** They have published poetry by Jack Myers, Thom Tammaro, Margaret Hasse, Michael Dennis Browne, Pam Harrison and Tom Hennen. *GRR* is 6×8, elaborately printed, with a featured poet in each issue. They use about 50 poems/issue, receive about 500, use 5-10%. Press run is 750 for 300-400 subscribers of which 30-50 are libraries, and 200-300 newsstand or bookstore sales. Subscription: $9 for two issues. **Sample postpaid: $4.50. Simultaneous submissions discouraged.** Editor "sometimes" comments on rejections. Reports in 4-10 weeks, 4-12 months between acceptance and publication. Pays 2 copies. Reviews books of poetry.

"We publish poetry that is concerned with issues of ecological sanity, social justice, war and peace and consider our work a poetical alternative to a toxic and militaristic culture," says Green Fuse *Editor Brian Boldt. The cover is a sheep petroglyph, a Native American rock writing from the Colorado River Basin, circa 800-1,000 A.D. "The petroglyph was selected because it represents graphically what to a large degree we seek poetically: an artistic, vivid and accessible evocation of the natural world."*

Number Seventeen
Fall & Winter 1992-93

GREEN FUSE (III, IV-Political, ecology, social issues), 3365 Holland Dr., Santa Rosa CA 95404, phone (707)544-8303, founded 1984, editor Brian Boldt, is published in April and October. **"We are looking for accessible free verse—with strong concrete details and images—that celebrates earth's beauty, the harmony in diversity, and poetic sanity and truth in an age of prosaic lies and madness. We no longer accept simultaneous submissions and previously published work (unless, of course, you've written the perfect *Green Fuse* poem). Sentimental and religious work, poems submitted without SASE and work stinking of nicotine will be folded into origami."** They have recently published poetry by Antler, John Brandi, David Chorlton, Denise Levertov and Elliot Richman. As a sample the editor selected these lines from "The Good News" by Gary Lawless:

> *Roads disappear, and the caribou wander through.*
> *The beaver just gets tired of it, reaches*
> *through the ice, grabs*
> *the trapper's feet,*
> *pulls him down.*
> *Wolves come back on their own,*
> *circle the statehouse, howl at the sportswriters,*
> *piss on the ATVs.*
> *Trees grow everywhere.*
> *The machines stop,*
> *and the air is full of birdsong.*

Green Fuse is 52 pgs., digest-sized, offset, perfect-bound, with b&w illustrations on the cover and throughout. They receive 1,800 poems a year and accept about 70. Press run is 500 for subscriptions, shelf and reading sales. Subscriptions: $14 for 3 issues, $17 for 4. Sample postpaid: $4. **"Please submit no more than three poems—or 60 lines or less."** Do not submit mss February through March and August through September. Editor "sometimes" comments on rejections.

Send SASE for guidelines. Reports within 3 months. Pays 1 copy, more to featured poets. Acquires first rights.

GREEN MOUNTAINS REVIEW (II), Johnson State College, Johnson VT 05656, phone (802)635-2356, founded 1975, poetry editor Neil Shepard, appears twice a year and includes poetry (and other writing) by well-known authors and promising newcomers. They have published poetry by Denise Levertov, William Stafford, Hayden Carruth, Theodore Weiss, Roger Weingarten and Amy Clampitt. *GMR* is digest-sized, flat-spined, 90-120 pgs. Of 300 submissions they publish 30 authors. Press run is 1,000 for 200 subscriptions of which 20 are libraries. Subscription is $8.50/year. **Sample postpaid: $4.75. Submit no more than 5 poems. No simultaneous submissions. Cover letter with greetings and personal information required. Reads submissions September 1 through May 15 only. Editor sometimes comments on rejection slip. Send SASE for guidelines. Reports in 2-3 months. Pays 1 copy. Acquires first North American serial rights.** Send books for review consideration.

GREEN WORLD PRESS (V, IV-Animals, nature), P.O. Box 9024, Bethlehem PA 18018, phone (215)867-6447, founded 1987, editor/publisher Jean Pearson, is a "small press publisher of poemcards and poetry notecards, **began publishing poetry chapbooks in 1992, by invitation only.**" She publishes "poems reflecting a a pantheistic or heavy ecological world view. No cynical, sentimental, human-centered poems." She has published poetry by Sarah Kirsch and Tommy Olofsson. As a sample the editor selected these lines by Paulus Utsi:

> The fire doesn't burn
> if you lack love
> The reindeer cannot live
> if you lose faith in him.

"At present I produce poetry postcards and notecards for non-profit organizations such as The Wildlife Information Center (Allentown, PA) and PAWS (Philadelphia). I also published **The Reindeer's Land**, a chapbook of poems, by Paulus Utsi in 1993. Poets should understand the nature and behavior of live animals and plants before writing about them." **Sample poemcards postpaid: 50¢.**

GREENHOUSE REVIEW PRESS (V), 3965 Bonny Doon Rd., Santa Cruz CA 95060, founded 1975, publishes a series of poetry chapbooks and broadsides. **"Unsolicited mss are not accepted."** Send SASE for catalog to buy samples.

GREEN'S MAGAZINE (I, II); CLOVER PRESS (V), P.O. Box 3236, Regina, Saskatchewan S4P 3H1 Canada, founded 1972, editor David Green. *Green's Magazine* is a literary quarterly with a balanced diet of short fiction and poetry; Clover Press publishes chapbooks. They publish **"free/blank verse examining emotions or situations." They do not want greeting card jingles or pale imitations of the masters.** They have published poetry by Sheila Murphy, Mary Balazs, Robert L. Tener, B.Z. Niditch, Joyce Carbone and Arthur Winfield Knight. As a sample the following lines are from "First Church of Christ Itinerant" by Joan Ritty:

> Weekdays he figures
> our income tax returns,
> but Sundays in March
> he preaches as if wrong
> is the only way
> this congregation does things.
> His sermons are palettes
> of muddy blue and grey,
> temptation is bright red
> sin
> alizarin crimson.

The magazine is digest-sized, 100 pgs., with line drawings. A sample chapbook is also digest-sized, 60 pgs., typeset on buff stock with line drawings, matte card cover, saddle-stapled. Circulation is 400. Subscription: $12. **Sample postpaid: $4. Guidelines available for SASE. (International Reply Coupons for U.S. queries and/or mss.) The editor prefers typescript, complete originals. Submissions are reported on in 2 months, publication is usually in 3 months. Pays 2 copies. Acquires first North American serial rights.** Occasionally reviews books of poetry in "up to 150-200 words." Send books for review consideration. Freelance submissions are accepted for the magazine but not for books; query first on latter. Comments are usually provided on rejected mss. "Would-be contributors are urged to study the magazine first."

THE GREENSBORO REVIEW; GREENSBORO REVIEW LITERARY AWARDS; AMON LINER POETRY AWARD (II), English Dept., University of North Carolina, Greensboro NC 27412, phone (919)334-5459, founded 1966, editor Jim Clark. *TGR* appears twice yearly and showcases well-made verse in all styles and forms, though shorter poems (under 50 lines) seem preferred. They have published poetry by Donald Junkins, Naomi Clark, Stuart Friebert and Elizabeth Kirschner. As a sample the editor selected these lines from "She Tries to Narrow Down His Doubts" by Leigh Palmer:

> . . .*We contend*
> *our lives are more than leaves*
> *or lentils. That sweet dunce,*
>
> *the body, understanding none of this,*
> *still aches to blossom with the blossoming*
> *of everything that dies.*

The digest-sized, flat-spined magazine, 120+ pgs., colored matte cover, professional printing, uses about 25 pgs. of poetry in each issue. Circulation 500 for 300 subscriptions of which 100 are libraries. Uses about 2.5% of the 2,000 submissions received each year. Sample postpaid: $4. "Submissions (of no more than 5 poems) must arrive by September 15 to be considered for the Winter issue (acceptances in December) and February 15 to be considered for the Summer issue (acceptances in May). Manuscripts arriving after those dates will be held for consideration with the next issue." No simultaneous submissions. Cover letter not required but helpful. Include number of poems submitted. Reports in 2-4 months. Pays 3 copies. Acquires first North American serial rights. They offer the Amon Liner Poetry Award for the best poem appearing in the magazine. They also sponsor an open competition for the Greensboro Review Literary Awards, $250 for both poetry and fiction each year. Send SASE for guidelines.

GROVE ATLANTIC (V), 849 Broadway, New York NY 10003. Grove Press and Atlantic Monthly Press merged in February 1993. **They currently accept no unsolicited mss.**

GRUE MAGAZINE (IV-Horror), Box 370, New York NY 10108, founded 1985, editor Peggy Nadramia, a horror fiction magazine "with emphasis on the experimental, offbeat, rude." The editor wants **"poems of any length including prose-poems, with macabre imagery and themes. Not interested in Poe rip-offs, (although we'll look at rhyming poems if subject is weird enough), 'straight' vampire, ghost or werewolf poems."** She has published poetry by t. Winter-Damon, W. Gregory Stewart, Steve Sneyd, Robert Frazier, G. Sutton Breiding and Bruce Boston. As a sample she selected these lines from "Angels of Anarchy" by Andrew Darlington:

> *in the red light from the dashboard*
> *my mistress hands me the knife,*
> *she wears a carnelian in her fly,*
> *her needle extracts the moth from my tongue,*
> *where its eggs are laid beneath my skin.*
> *The moon sheds blood over the Headrow*
> *where I dissolve in double shadows.*

The magazine is digest-sized, 96 pgs., offset, with a glossy b&w cover, "sharp" graphics, and "a centerfold that is unique." It appears 3 times a year and has a press run of 3,000, of which 500 are subscriptions and 1,000 are newsstand sales. Subscription: $13/year. **Sample postpaid: $4.50. Submit up to 5 poems at a time. The editor usually provides criticism of rejected mss. Guidelines are available for SASE. Submissions are reported on in 3 to 6 months and time to publication is 12 to 18 months. Poets receive 2 copies plus $5/poem upon publication to a maximum of $5/ issue.** Her advice is: "We like poems that go for the throat, with strong, visceral controlling images. We're also interested in poems that comment upon, or challenge the conventions of, the horror genre itself."

GUERNICA EDITIONS INC.; ESSENTIAL POET SERIES, PROSE SERIES, DRAMA SERIES; INTERNATIONAL WRITERS (IV-Regional, translations, ethnic/nationality), Box 633 Station NDG, Montreal, Quebec H4A 3R1 Canada, founded 1978, poetry editor Antonio D'Alfonso. "We wish to bring together the **different and often divergent voices that exist in Canada and the U.S. We are interested in translations. We are mostly interested right now in prose poetry and essays.**" They have recently published work by Gérald Godin, Anne Dandurand and Clément Marchand (Quebec); Mario Luzi, Antonio Porta and Giorgio Caproni (Italy); Marco Fraticelli and Antonino Mazza (Canada); and Diane Raptosh, Giose Rimanelli and Anthony J. Tamburri (USA). **Query with 1-2 pgs. of samples. Send SASE (Canadian stamps only) or SAE and IRCs for catalog.** The editor comments, "We are interested in promoting a polycultural view of literature by bridging languages and cultures. Besides our specialization in international translation, we also focus on the work of Italian, Italian/Canadian and Italian/American writers."

GUILD PRESS; FULL CIRCLE SERIES (I, IV-Ethnic), Dept. PM, P.O. Box 22583, Robbinsdale MN 55422, founded 1978, senior editor Leon Knight, **"the leading publisher of minority authors in Minnesota," wants poems to 40 lines max., nothing sexually graphic.** They have published poetry by Gary

Smith, Bernard U. Finney, Jr. and Nancy Ellen Williams (Big Mama). As a sample the editor selected these lines (poet unidentified):

> *I thought poetry*
> > *made a difference*
> > *. . .*
> *But photography*
> > *doesn't alter sunsets:*
> *poetry does not*
> > *restrain the wind*

The Full Circle Series are **annual anthologies of 35-50 poets. Individual collections are published "by invitation only" to poets who have appeared in the "open-invitation" anthologies. Send SASE for guidelines. Pays copies.**

‡**GULF COAST: A JOURNAL OF LITERATURE AND FINE ART (II)**, Creative Writing Program, Dept. of English, University of Houston, Houston TX 77204-3012, founded 1986, is a semiannual journal using visual art, interviews, poetry, fiction and critical essays on film and art. They are **"completely open to all styles, forms and subjects of poetry."** They have recently published poetry by John Ashbery, Thomas Lux, X.J. Kennedy, Mary Adams and Patricia Goedicke. The editor says *Gulf Coast* is 100-190 pgs., 6×9, offset, perfect-bound, with full color cover and full color art and b&w reproductions inside. They receive 300-700 poetry submissions/year, use 10-30%. Press run is 900 for 150 subscribers of which 10 are libraries, 500 shelf sales. Single copy: $7; subscription: $20 for 2 years. **Inquire about sample copy. No previously published poems. Reads submissions September 1 through May 15 only. Send SASE for guidelines. Reports in 1-3 months. Pays 2 copies. Acquires all rights. Returns rights upon publication.** Reviews books of poetry in 500-1,000 words. Open to unsolicited reviews. Poets may also send books for review consideration to Lance Larsen above address.

GULF STREAM MAGAZINE (II), English Dept., Florida International University, North Miami Campus, North Miami FL 33181, phone (305)940-5599, founded 1989, editor Lynne Barrett, associate editors Chris Gleason and Hamish Ziegler, is the biannual literary magazine associated with the creative writing program at FIU. They want **"poetry of any style and subject matter as long as it is of high literary quality."** They have published poetry by Gerald Costanzo, Judith Berke and Naomi Shihab Nye. The handsome magazine is 90+ pgs., digest-sized, flat-spined, printed on quality stock with glossy card cover. They accept less than 10% of poetry received. Press run: 750. Subscription: $7.50. **Sample postpaid: $4. Submit no more than 5 poems. No simultaneous submissions. Reads submissions September 15 through April 30 only. Editor comments on submissions "if we feel we can be helpful." Send SASE for guidelines. Reports in 6-8 weeks. Pays 2 free subscriptions. Acquires first North American serial rights.**

GUT PUNCH PRESS (III), P.O. Box 105, Cabin John MD 20818, founded 1987, editor Derrick Hsu, publishes 1-2 paperbacks/year. They want **"free verse with an innovative edge and possibly a sense of humor. No language school or formal narrative style."** They have published poetry collections by Richard Peabody and Sunil Freeman and an anthology of African-American poetry edited by Alan Spears. **Query first with sample poems and cover letter with brief bio and publication credits. No poems previously published in book form or simultaneous submissions.** Time between acceptance and publication is 1 year. **Often comments on rejections. Replies to queries in 1 month, to mss (if invited) in 3 months. Pays royalties ("determined on an individual basis") and 50 author's copies. For sample books, send SASE for list and order form.** Most books are $7.95 postpaid. Fingering the Keys by Reuben Jackson won the 1992 Columbia Book Award, awarded by the Poetry Committee of the Greater Washington DC Area.

GUYASUTA PUBLISHER (I), The Sterling Building, 440 Friday Rd., Pittsburgh PA 15209, phone (412)821-6211, fax (412)821-6099, founded 1988, owner Cynthia Shore-Sterling. "Guyasuta offers both straight and co-op publishing. We publish approximately 25 collections of poetry each year. Our line has recently been expanded to trade paperback, self-help and quality short fiction." As a sample the owner selected these lines from Sheila Fiscus' poem "Thoughts From The Throne" from her book **Just A Housewife:**

> *As I sit naked on the porcelain throne,*

The double dagger before a listing indicates that the listing is new in this edition. New markets are often the most receptive to submissions.

My life files by, a procession of household care products.
But what of my heart, my soul, my joy of living?
Are they to be flushed into the sewer
By consummate daily tasks?

They will consider simultaneous submissions and unsolicited manuscripts of 25-60 poems throughout the year. For further information send SASE for catalog and guidelines. Sample: $5.95 (includes shipping). They also own a 67-acre farm in New York which is presently being developed into Guyasuta Writers and Artists Colony.

GYPSY (II); VERGIN' PRESS (V), % Belinda Subraman and S. Ramnath, 10708 Gay Brewer, El Paso TX 79935, founded 1984 (in Germany), general editor Belinda Subraman, publishes poetry, fiction, interviews, articles, artwork and reviews. She wants **poetry that is "striking, moving, but not sentimental, any style, any subject matter."** They have published poetry by Peter Wild, Jay Griswold, Antler and Katharyn Howd Machan. As a sample she selected these lines by Lou Hertz:

Oh yes I look.
I know better, but I can't resist.
I know she's having fun at my expense
And yet I'm flattered.
She could be teasing someone else.
Not me.

Gypsy appears twice a year, with subscribers and contributors from the U.S., Canada, England, Europe and other countries. It is 56-90 pgs., magazine-sized, offset, usually with a hard spine. Circulation is 1,000 for 300 subscriptions of which 40 are libraries, about 20 shelf sales. Single copy: $8; subscription: $14/year. **Sample postpaid: $7. Editor sometimes comments on rejections. Reports in 1-3 months. Pays 1-3 copies or $5-15.** Open to unsolicited reviews. Poets may also send books for review consideration. She publishes **2-3 books/year under the Vergin' Press imprint but at present is not accepting unsolicited submissions for these.** New writers establish themselves with her by acceptance in *Gypsy*. Belinda Subraman says, "This is not a place for beginners. I'm looking for the best in all genres. Although I don't have anything against work of total self-absorption (guess I write some of that myself), I am just about fed up with it. I'd like to see work with a more universal appeal, a searching to connect, an understanding or a trying to understand other peoples in the universe. Please do not submit blindly. **We are planning a series of paperback anthologies on important issues. Send SASE for details.** Also please be advised that poetry is only about ⅓ (or less) of our focus these days. We value other forms of expression equally (if not more)."

HAIGHT ASHBURY LITERARY JOURNAL (II, IV-Social issues), 558 Joost Ave., San Francisco CA 94127, phone (415)221-2017, founded 1979-1980, editors Joanne Hotchkiss, Alice Rogoff and Will Walker, is a newsprint tabloid that appears 1-3 times a year. They use **"all forms and lengths, including haiku. Subject matter sometimes political, but open to all subjects. Poems of background—prison, minority experience—often published, as well as poems of protest and of Central America. Few rhymes."** They have recently published poetry by Leslie Simon, Jack Micheline, Edgar Silex, Leticia Escamilla and Bill Shields. The tabloid has photos of featured poets on the cover, uses graphics, ads, 16 pgs., circulation 2,000-3,000. $35 for a lifetime subscription, which includes 3 back issues. $12 for 4-issue subscription. **Sample postpaid: $3. Make checks payable to Alice Rogoff. Send SASE for guidelines. Submit up to 6 poems or 8 pgs. "Please put name and address on every page and include SASE."** Each issue changes its theme and emphasis. Reports in 2-3 months. Pays 3 copies.

HAIKU HEADLINES: A MONTHLY NEWSLETTER OF HAIKU AND SENRYU (IV-Form), 1347 W. 71st, Los Angeles CA 90044, founded 1988, editor/publisher David Priebe, uses **haiku and senryu only. The editor prefers the 5/7/5 syllabic discipline, but accepts minimalist haiku which display pivotal contrast and appropriate imagery.** They have published haiku by Matthew Louviere, Dorothy McLaughlin, Mark Arvid White and Yvonne Hardenbrook. As a sample the editor selected these haiku by Rengé:

whatever language
random objects speak: the rain
speaks it fluently

carnival balloon
rising up . . . and up . . . fading
into the darkness

The newsletter is 8 pgs., 8½×11, stapled and punched for a three-ring notebook, desktop published. They accept about 10% of submissions. Their press run is 300 with 160 subscriptions of which 3 are libraries. Subscription: $18. **Sample postpaid: $1.50. Haiku may be submitted with up to 10/single page. Submissions are "answered with proof sheets of acceptances, suggested revisions sheets, with occasional notes on originals—within 4-6 weeks." Pays 1 copy with SASE,** or free extra copy to subscribers. Monthly contest Readers' Choice Awards: The Awards Kitty (average $20—contributions of postage stamps by the voters) is divided half for the 1st place winner; two runners-up share the other half. *HH* sponsored a Rhyming Haiku Contest (prizes

$100, $50, $25) and published **Ecopoems**, an anthology of the 100 winners in 1991. In 1992, *HH* sponsored a contest (prizes $100, $75, $50) and published the calendar book **Timepieces: Haiku Week-at-a Glance 1993**, which is forecast as an annual project. Write for details.

HALF TONES TO JUBILEE (II), English Department, Pensacola Junior College, 1000 College Blvd., Pensacola FL 32504, phone (904)484-1400, founded 1986, faculty editors Walter Spara and Allan Peterson, is an annual literary journal featuring poetry and short fiction. They have published poetry by R.T. Smith, Sue Walker, Larry Rubin and Simon Perchik. As a sample we selected these lines from "Penpal Who Has Not Written" by Andrea Hollander Budy:

> *You are the one I've never met who*
> *wrote so splendidly when I needed you*
> *and I am the one who, after awhile, let*
> *years grow like a row of taverns*
> *between receiving and giving*
> *back. . .*

HTTJ is digest-sized, 100+ pgs., perfect-bound with matte card cover, professionally printed. Press run is 500. They receive 1,000 submissions/year, use 50-60. Subscription: $4. **Sample: $4. No previously published work, no simultaneous submissions, SASE mandatory. Cover letter with bio and/or publication history preferred. Reads submissions August 1 through May 15 only. Reports in 2-3 months, faster when possible. Pays 2 copies. Acquires first rights.** *HTTJ* sponsors an annual poetry competition, $300 first prize, $200 second, $100 third. Entry fee: $2/poem. Send SASE for rules, deadlines. In addition to numerous awards from the Florida Press Association, *Half Tones to Jubilee* has received two national awards, a first place with merit from the American Scholastic Press Association, and first place, Southern division, literary magazine competition, Community College Humanities Association.

HANGING LOOSE PRESS (V); HANGING LOOSE (I, II, IV-Teens/students), 231 Wyckoff St., Brooklyn NY 11217, founded 1966, poetry editors Robert Hershon, Dick Lourie, Mark Pawlak and Ron Schreiber. **The press accepts no unsolicited book mss, but welcomes work for the magazine.** The magazine has published poetry by Paul Violi, Donna Brook, Kimiko Hahn, Ron Overton, Jack Anderson and Frances Phillips. *Hanging Loose* is 96 pgs., flat-spined, offset on heavy stock with a 2-color glossy card cover. One section contains **poems by high-school-age poets. The editor says it "concentrates on the work of new writers."** It appears 3 times a year. **Sample postpaid: $6.50. Submit 4-6 "excellent, energetic" poems. No simultaneous submissions. "Would-be contributors should read the magazine first." Reports in 1-12 weeks. Pays small fee and 3 copies.**

HANGMAN BOOKS (IV-Regional), 2 May Rd., Rochester, Kent ME1 2HY England, founded 1982, editor Jack Ketch, publishes selected books of poetry on a cooperative basis. Jack Ketch says, "We receive no grant, **therefore we expect the writers to put their money where their mouth is. We don't advertise this fact as we are not a vanity press, we only approach a writer with this proposal if we are sufficiently impressed with their work and want to help them (this is very rare)."** They want "personal" poetry, **"none rhyming, none political, bla bla bla."** They have published poetry by Criss Broderick, N. Sparkes and B. Childish. As a sample the editor selected these lines from **May My Piss Be Gentle** by Mark Lowe:

> *all those tears*
> *all that madness and grief*
> *in that big old house of ours*
> *and i think back*
> *and it's like i'm drowning*
> *in a whole fucking river*
> *of unnecessary sadness*

That is from a handsomely printed flat-spined book, 110 pgs. **60% of press run belongs to poet.**

HANSON'S SYMPOSIUM (II), 113 Merryman Court, Annapolis MD 21401, phone (410)626-0744, founded 1988, is an annual using **"all forms, styles, subjects and points of view reflective of intelligence and a sense of beauty."** As a sample the editor selected these lines from "Strains of Melody in the Dark" by Shannon Rogowski:

> *With cold and ruthless pen did I extract*
> *Each drop, transcendental and abstract*
> *Beliefs, pains, exultations and desires,*
> *And each ideal to which a mind aspires.*
> *So when I have withered and lost my gloss,*
> *I will not fear death. I cannot be lost.*

It is magazine-sized, 75-100 pgs., saddle-stapled with matte card cover. Press run is 3,000 for

1,500 subscriptions including 2 library systems. "We receive thousands of poems per year, publish about 30-40 per year." Sample postpaid: $6. Now reads submissions year-round. Editor seldom comments on submissions. Reports in 2 months. Pays $25-50 plus 1 copy. Buys first North American serial rights. "Previous publication is not a prerequisite. We'd rather see honest, careful art, than a resume." The editor adds, "Due to the limited space in our publication, and due to its unique nature, we require that all writers interested in being published in *Hanson's Symposium* review a sample copy before submitting work."

HARCOURT BRACE & COMPANY; HB CHILDREN'S BOOKS; GULLIVER BOOKS; JANE YOLEN BOOKS (IV-Children), 1250 Sixth Ave., San Diego CA 92101, phone (619)699-6810, HB Children's Books, Gulliver Books and Jane Yolen Books publish hardback and trade paperback books for children. They have published books of children's poetry by Jane Yolen, Arnold Adoff, James Dickey, e.e. cummings, Lee Bennett Hopkins and Carl Sandburg. **Submit complete ms. Pays favorable advance, royalty contract and copies. Send SASE for guidelines and book catalog.**

HARD ROW TO HOE; MISTY HILL PRESS (I, IV-Nature/rural/ecology), P.O. Box 541-I, Healdsburg CA 95448, phone (707)433-9786. *Hard Row to Hoe,* taken over from Seven Buffaloes Press in 1987, editor Joe E. Armstrong, is a "book review newsletter of literature from rural America with a section reserved for short stories (about 2,000 words) and **poetry featuring unpublished authors. The subject matter must apply to rural America including nature and environmental subjects. Poems of 30 lines or less given preference, but no arbitrary limit. No style limits. Do not want any subject matter not related to rural subjects.**" As a sample the editor selected "Cheers" by Donna Kalchik:

> No one told them
> When they set out
> To be farmers
> That some years
> They would lean
> Over glasses of whiskey
> Celebrating harvest
> Like a wake.

HRTH is magazine-sized, 12 pgs., side-stapled, appearing 3 times a year, 3 pgs. reserved for short stories and poetry. Press run 300. **Subscription: $7/year. Sample postpaid: $2. Send SASE for guidelines. Editor comments on rejections "if I think the quality warrants." Pays 3 copies. Acquires one-time rights.** Reviews books of poetry in 600-700 words. Open to unsolicited reviews. Poets may also send books for review consideration. *Hard Row to Hoe* was selected by *Small Press Review* as one of the 10 best newsletters in the U.S.

HARP-STRINGS; EDNA ST. VINCENT MILLAY AWARD; ELIZABETH B. BROWNING SONNETS AWARD; DYLAN THOMAS VILLANELLE AWARD (II), P.O. Box 640387, Beverly Hills FL 34464, founded 1989, editor Madelyn Eastlund, appears 3 times/year. **They want poems of "14-70 lines, narratives, lyrics, ballads, sestinas, rondeau, redouble, blank verse. Nothing 'dashed off,' trite, broken prose masquerading as poetry."** They have recently published poetry by Barbara Nightingale, Robert Cooperman, Robin Shectman and Anne Marx. As a sample the editor selected a stanza from "Witness in the Pines" by Glenna Holloway:

> She was a water witch, my great grandmother,
> quenching generations of need, dousing
> scoffers, dowsing through collective faith,
> herself the ranking believer.

It is 36 pgs., digest-sized, saddle-stapled, professionally printed in colored ink on quality colored matte stock with matte card cover. She accepts 5-10% of poems received. Press run 100 for 75 subscribers. **Subscription: $20. Sample postpaid: $5.50 for previous year, $6.50 for current year. Pays 1 copy. Acquires one-time rights.** "I am interested in seeing poems that have won awards but have not been published." Sponsors 3 contests each year: Elizabeth B. Browning Sonnets Award (Shakespearean or Petrarchan Sonnet, deadline March 15); Edna St. Vincent Millay Award (narrative from 32 to 75 lines, deadline July 15); Dylan Thomas Villanelle Award (deadline November 15). Entry fee: $2/poem, $5/3 poems. Cash awards of $10-40 and publication. "Stanley Kunitz once said, 'Poetry today has become easier to write but harder to remember.' *Harp-Strings* wants poetry to remember, poetry that haunts, poetry the reader wants to read again and again."

THE HARTLAND POETRY QUARTERLY; HARTLAND PRESS (I, II, IV-Children, themes), Dept. PM, 168 Fremont, Romeo MI 48065, phone (313)752-5507, founded 1989, contact David Bock. **"Prefer 24 lines or less; no style restrictions; no pornography—none—nada—nil! Looking for serious poems by Viet Nam veterans and I mean serious—don't send the one-and-only angry poem—I got that stuff**

coming out of my ears. Very, very open to good children's poems written only by children under 15 for a special 'coming out' part of the magazine." They have published poetry by Loriann Zimmer, T. Kilgore Splake and Laurence W. Thomas. Their quarterly is digest-sized, spine-stapled, 25-30 pgs. They accept about 15% of 300-500 poems received/year. Press run 500, with 70 subscribers of which 15 are libraries, 300 shelf sales. Subscription: $8. **Sample postpaid: $1. Include bio with submission. Reports in 8-10 weeks. Pays 2 copies.** Reviews books of poetry. **They publish 2 chapbooks/year of poets already published in the quarterly. Pays 20 copies.** The editor says, "Write about what you have lived. Read, read, write, write—repeat cycle 'till death. Support as many small publications as you can afford."

THE HARVARD ADVOCATE (IV-Specialized/university affiliation), Dept. PM, 21 South St., Cambridge MA 02138, phone (617)495-0737, founded 1866, is a quarterly literary magazine, circulation 4,000, publishes **poetry, fiction and art only by those affiliated with Harvard University. Sample: $5. In submitting state your exact relationship to Harvard. Does not pay.** Reviews books of poetry in 1,000 words, single or multi-book format.

‡HAUNTS (IV-Science fiction/fantasy/horror), Nightshade Publications, P.O. Box 3342, Providence RI 02906, phone (401)781-9438, is a "literary quarterly geared to those fans of the 'pulp' magazines of the 30s, 40s and 50s, with tales of **horror, the supernatural and the bizarre. We are trying to reach those in the 18-35 age group.**" Circulation: 1,000. **Sample: $3.95 plus $1 postage. Uses free verse, light verse and traditional, about 12-16 poems a year. Send a maximum of 3 poems. Cover letter including "brief introduction of the writer and the work submitted" required. Send SASE for guidelines. Pays $3/poem.**

HAWAII PACIFIC REVIEW (II), 1060 Bishop St., Honolulu HI 96813, founded 1986, editor Elizabeth Fischel, is a semiannual literary journal "publishing quality poetry, short fiction and personal essays from writers worldwide. **Our journal seeks to promote a world view that celebrates a variety of cultural themes, beliefs, values and viewpoints. Although we do publish beginning poets on occasion, we do not publish amateurish poetry. We wish to further the growth of artistic vision and talent by encouraging sophisticated and innovative poetic and narrative techniques.**" They have recently published poetry by Robert Cooperman and D.A. Feinfeld. As a sample the editor selected the second stanza of Feinfeld's "Grande Baigneuse" (Picasso):

> An olive mist slips into the scene
> With only the barest pulse,
> Draws back from her massive stillness.
> Shadows beckon through the grey light,
> Expecting that at last she will rise
> And gather the evening about her.

HPR is 80-120 pgs., 6×9, professionally printed on quality paper, perfect-bound, with coated card cover; each issue features original artwork. Mostly free verse, poems here tend to be insightful, informative and well-made with an emphasis on cultural diversity. They receive 800-1,000 poems, accept 30-40. Press run is approximately 1,000 for 200 shelf sales. Single copy: $5-6. **Sample postpaid: $3. No previously published poems; simultaneous submissions OK. Cover letter with 5-line professional bio including prior publications required. Seldom comments on rejections. Send SASE for guidelines. Reports within 3 months. Pays 2 copies. Acquires first North American serial rights.** The editor says, "Many of the poems we receive are more personal therapy than true art. Good poetry is eye-opening; it investigates the unfamiliar or reveals the unfamiliar or unexpected in the familiar. Good poetry does more than simply express the poet's feelings; it provides both insight and unexpected beauty."

HAWAI'I REVIEW (I, II), % Department of English, University of Hawai'i, 1733 Donaghho Rd., Honolulu HI 96822, phone (808)956-8548, poetry editors Alan Aoki and Annie Fanning. "We are interested in all sorts of poetry, from free verse to formal lyricism, rhyme and meter; heroic narrative, haiku, light verse, satire and experimentation; we're also interested in poems translated from other languages; and while *Hawai'i Review* has published poets with established reputations like Eric Chock and W.S. Merwin, the beginner is also welcome." They have published poetry by Lyn Lifshin, Lois-Ann Yamanaka and Tony Quagliano, and translations by Carolyn Tipton and Alexis Levitin. As a sample the editors selected the poem "The Pearl" by Cai Qi-Jiao, translated by Edward Morin and Dennis Ding:

> The wound inside
> The oyster's tender body
> Expands into a hard, rough obstruction.
> Month by month, year after year,
> Wrapped in layer upon adhesive layer,
> It becomes mellow and smooth.

> *Here you see crystaline grief and sea tears,*
> *Yet all humankind treasures it!*
> *I sense that it still wears the salt smell of the ocean,*
> *That its glistening teardrops bear*
> *The laments of sun, moon, stars, and clouds.*

HR appears 3 times yearly and is 160 pgs., 6½ × 9½, flat-spined, professionally printed on heavy stock with b&w or color cover, 150 subscriptions of which 40 are libraries. Up to 1,800 are used by University of Hawai'i students. Subscription: $15/one year; $25/two years. **Sample: $5. Send SASE for guidelines. "Artwork to accompany poetry is welcomed." Editors rarely comment on rejections. Reporting time: 3-4 months.** Publication 9-12 months thereafter. **Pays $10-60 plus 2 copies. Buys first North American serial rights.** Does not normally review books, but "authors can query" or send books for review consideration to Tamara Moan, chief editor. The editorial staff rotates each year, so content varies. Sometimes one staff rejects work that has "come close" and suggests sending the same manuscript in the next year to see what the new editors think. *Hawai'i Review* ranked #8 in the "New Poets" category of the June 1993 *Writer's Digest* Poetry 60 list. This category ranks those markets who often publish poets whose work is new to their publication. The editors say, "Good poetry shows more than pseudo-literary erudition; it will, as Anthony Wallace says, *sing* and *mean*."

HAYDEN'S FERRY REVIEW (II), Matthews Center, Arizona State University, Tempe AZ 85287-1502, phone (602)965-1243, founded 1986, managing editor Salima Keegan, is a handsome literary magazine appearing twice a year. They have published poetry by Dennis Schmitz, Maura Stanton, Ai, and David St. John. *HFR* is 6 × 9, 120+ pgs., flat-spined with glossy card cover. Press run is 1,000 for 100 subscribers of which 30 are libraries, 500 shelf sales. They accept about 3% of 2,800 submissions annually. Subscription: $10. **Sample postpaid: $6. "No specifications other than limit in number (6) and no simultaneous submissions. We would like a brief bio for contributor's note included." Submissions circulated to two poetry editors. Editor comments on submissions "often." Send SASE for guidelines. Reports in 8-10 weeks of deadlines. Deadlines: February 28 for Spring/Summer issue; September 30 for Fall/Winter. Contributors receive galley proofs. Pays 2 copies.**

‡HEART ATTACK MAGAZINE; CORONARY PRESS (I, IV-Horror), 518 Lowell St., Methuen MA 01844, founded 1991, executive editor/publisher David Gordon, associate editor Michael Dillon, appears 4-6 times a year using horror fiction, nonfiction, a little poetry, art, photos, humor, comics, etc.; "general magazine interests in horror genre." **They want any horror poetry, metered, rhymed, free verse, etc. "May include eroticism and profanity (if necessary). No haiku."** They have recently published poetry by Wayne Edwards, Richard L. Levesque and S.L. Shrewsbury. As a sample the editors selected these lines from "Battlefield" by John Grey:

> *Body hooked on a spike,*
> *a flag of flesh*
> *refusing to wave*
> *no matter how*
> *strong the breeze.*

Heart Attack is approximately 80 pgs., 8½ × 11, professionally printed, saddle-stitched, glossy 80 lb. text cover with color, photos, art and ads. They receive about 500 poems a year, use approximately 10-15%. Press run is 1,000 for over 500 subscribers, beginning shelf sales. Subscription: $11 for one-half year (3 issues). **Sample postpaid: $4. Submit no more than 6 poems at a time; no more than 2 pages/poem. No previously published poems; simultaneous submissions OK. Cover letter required.** Time between acceptance and publication is 3-9 months. **Always comments on rejections. Send SASE for guidelines. Reports in 2-6 weeks. Pays 1 copy. Acquires first North American serial rights.** "We review books and magazines but a review copy doesn't guarantee a review for we are flooded in that department." In 1991, *Heart Attack* was nominated by the Small Press Writers & Artists Organization (SPWAO) as "Best New Magazine/Editor." David Gordon says, "Poetry should have a feel to it, not tell a story. Don't write a story and omit the punctuation and call it poetry. It should give the reader an emotional attack on the emotion you are trying to elicit (i.e., fear or disgust, repulsion or darkness in our case)."

HEAVEN BONE PRESS; HEAVEN BONE MAGAZINE (II, IV-Spiritual, nature/ecology), P.O. Box 486, Chester NY 10918, phone (914)469-9018, founded 1986, poetry editor Steve Hirsch, publishes poetry, fiction, essays and reviews with **"an emphasis on spiritual, metaphysical, esoteric and ecologi-**

Market categories: (I) Beginning; (II) General; (III) Limited; (IV) Specialized; (V) Closed.

cal concerns." They have published poetry and fiction by Charles Bukowski, Marge Piercy, Kirpal Gordon and Hart Sprager. As a sample the editor chose "Five-Petaled Regular Corolla Rose" by Edward Mycue:

> has surrounding fingers that play
> with your nose from the inner en-
> velope. This is not the Rose of
> Sharon. That spindling hollyhock
> is as near to a rose as a hemlock.
> The rosary has five sacred mysteries
> and five decades of Ave Marias, &
> each begins with a paternoster, ends
> with a Gloria, repeated in formula
> like a prayer or/and magic-mystic
> charm: more of a path than pastime.
> Rose, you single step, pilgrimage,
> you Rose, of colored hope, chafe.
> You are window, compass, pleasantly
> rote: I know you now, know you not.

Heaven Bone is 64 pgs., magazine-sized, saddle-stapled, using b&w art, photos and ads, on recycled bond stock with glossy 4-color recycled card cover. They have a press run of 2,500. Of 250-350 poems received they accept 18-30. Subscription: $14.95. **Sample postpaid: $5. Submit 3-10 poems. Simultaneous submissions and previously published poems OK "if notified." Reports in 2 weeks to 6 months, up to 6 months until publication. Pays 2 copies. Acquires first North American serial rights.** Reviews books of poetry. Open to unsolicited reviews. Poets may also send books for review consideration. The press offers an annual chapbook contest. 1992 winner: **The Old Way,** by Janine Pommy-Vega. Send SASE for guidelines. Editor advises, "Please be familiar with the magazine before sending mss. Break free of common 'poetic' limitations and speak freely with no contrivances. No forced end-line rhyming please. Channel the muse and music without being an obstacle to the poem."

HELICON NINE EDITIONS; MARIANNE MOORE POETRY PRIZE (III), P.O. Box 22412, Kansas City MO 64113, phone (913)722-2999, founded 1977, editor Gloria Vando Hickok. Helicon Nine, formerly a literary magazine, now is a publisher of books of poetry as well as fiction, creative nonfiction and anthologies. **"Our one requirement is excellence; nothing pedestrian."** They have published poetry by Joyce Carol Oates, Grace Paley, Ellen Gilchrist and James Dickey. As a sample the editor selected these lines from "A Physics of Postwar Music" by Biff Russ from her first book, **Black Method,** winner of the 1991 Marianne Moore Poetry Prize:

> The first lesson was science:
> you held your violin towards the light,
> cupping your hand behind its waist,
> showing me that (except for a small piece of wood
> propped between front and back) I would see
> nothing inside.
>
> Afterwards you started to play: the sound came out
> of its emptiness, shaped like the human body.

They are not encouraging submissions at this time. Please query with cover letter including names of prior publishers. "Payment varies, but we're in the publishing business to *help* poets and authors, not to hinder them or take advantage. We publish *beautiful* books and try to get them into the hands of readers. We have national distributors making sure our books are made available throughout the States. We also aggressively pursue new markets and book reviews and advertise in many trade publications as well as exhibit at the ABA, etc." The Marianne Moore Poetry Prize is given annually, $1,000 for an unpublished poetry ms of at least 50 pgs. The award includes publication by Helicon Nine Editions. Write for guidelines. Helicon Nine received the Kansas Governor's Arts Award in 1991 for making "a significant contribution" to the arts in that state.

‡HELIKON PRESS (V), 120 W. 71st St., New York NY 10023, founded 1972, poetry editors Robin Prising and William Leo Coakley, "tries to publish the best contemporary poetry in the tradition of English verse. We read (and listen to) poetry and ask poets to build a collection around particular poems. We print fine editions illustrated by good artists. Unfortunately we cannot encourage submissions."

HELLAS: A JOURNAL OF POETRY AND THE HUMANITIES; THE HELLAS AWARD (II, IV-Form), 304 S. Tyson Ave., Glenside PA 19038, phone (215)884-1086, founded 1988, editor Gerald Harnett. *Hellas* is a semiannual that wants poetry of **"any kind but especially poems in meter. We prize elegance and formality in verse, but specifically encourage poetry of the utmost boldness and innovation, so long as it is not willfully obscurantist; no ignorant, illiterate, meaningless free verse or political poems."** They have published poetry by Hadas, Steele, Moore, Butler, Kessler and many others. As a sample we selected these lines from "Seed" by Charley Custer:

> *Within the hard damp dark, marooned*
> *in rot between dead root and weed*
> *through every bitter winter wound*
> *and solstice, is the seed.*

It is 172 pgs., 6×9, flat-spined, offset, using b&w art. Press run is 750. Subscription: $14. **Sample postpaid: $8.75. Send SASE for guidelines. They will not consider simultaneous submissions or previously published poems. Reports in 3-4 months. Editor comments on rejections "happily if requested. If I don't understand it, I don't print it. On the other hand, we don't want obvious, easy, clichéd or sentimental verse." Pays 1 copy. Acquires first North American serial rights.** The *Hellas* Award ($200) is open to *Hellas* subscribers only and is awarded annually to the finest poem entered in the contest. Poems may be submitted to both *Hellas* and the contest simultaneously at any time throughout the year, but the annual deadline is August 31. Winner is published in fall issue of *Hellas*. Enclose SASE if submission is to be returned. They also sponsor the *Hellas* readings, held at various locations in Philadelphia. Send SASE for guidelines. In its first years, *Hellas* was voted the "Best New Journal of 1991" by the Conference of Editors of Learned Journals. Their flyer says, *"Hellas is a lively and provocative assault on a century of modernist barbarism in the arts. A unique, Miltonic wedding of paideia and poesis, engaging scholarship and original poetry, Hellas has become the forum of a remarkable new generation of poets, critics and theorists committed to the renovation of the art of our time . . .* **Meter is especially welcome, as well as rhymed and stanzaic verse. We judge a poem by its verbal artifice, its formal harmony and its truth. Lines should not end arbitrarily, diction should be precise: we suggest that such principles can appear 'limiting' only to an impoverished imagination. To the contrary: we encourage any conceivable boldness and innovation, so long as it is executed with discipline and is not a masquerade for self-indulgent obscurantism. . . . We do not print poems about Nicaragua, whales or an author's body parts. We do specifically welcome submissions from newer authors."**

HEN'S TEETH (V), P.O. Box 689, Brookings SD 57006, founded 1988, editor Janice H. Mikesell. She expects to publish a book every 2 years but **will not be open for submissions. "I publish material that I have either written or co-edited only. Unsolicited material, unless accompanied by a SASE, will not be returned."** She has published **Women Houses & Homes: an anthology of prose, poetry and photography**, $8 postage paid, a 52-page, saddle-stapled book, cut with a roof-line top, professionally printed with a cover photograph of a "painted lady" Victorian house. Most recent publication is **A Survivor's Manual: a book of poems**, $8 postage paid, a 52-page, perfect-bound quality paperback with an arresting cover photo.

HERESIES (IV-Women/feminism, lesbian, themes), P.O. Box 1306, Canal St. Station, New York NY 10013, founded 1977, editorial collective, is a "feminist publication on art and politics." **Poetry "must be by women and fit into the specific issue theme."** Mostly free verse lyrics are featured here, though all of it accessible. They have published poetry by Adrienne Rich, Alice Walker and Margaret Randall. *Heresies*, one of the oldest and best-known feminist publications, appears 1-2 times a year in a 96-page, flat-spined, magazine-sized format, offset with half-tones, 2-color glossy card cover, using nonprofit, book related exchange ads. They accept about 5 out of 100 submissions. Press run is 5,000 for 1,500 subscriptions of which a fourth are libraries, 1,500 shelf sales. Single copy: $8; subscription: $27/4 issues. **Sample back issue postpaid: $6. Simultaneous submissions OK. Manuscripts should be submitted in duplicate. Send SASE for guidelines. Reports in 8-12 months. Pays small honorarium plus 3 copies.**

HERSPECTIVES (I, IV-Women, feminism), Box 2047, Squamish, British Columbia V0N 3G0 Canada, phone (604)892-5723, founded 1989, editor Mary Billy, uses **"poetry that expresses women's lives in a positive experiential way—open to almost anything by, for or about women. Nothing obscure, intellectual, wheel-spinners."** As a sample the editor selected these lines by Gert Beadle:

> *When they have closed*
> *The windows where I fled*
> *And gave the empty house*
> *to fire*
> *Will they remember how*

> *I loved a mystery*

It appears quarterly in a 40- to 50-page stapled format. Uses 4-6 poems/issue. Press run is 250 for 85 subscribers of which 1 is a library. Subscription: $22-35 ($35-45 US); $40-50 for businesses and organizations. **Sample postpaid: $6. Simultaneous submissions and previously published poetry OK. Cover letter required. Editor often comments on rejections. Pays 1 copy.** Reviews books of poetry in 500-750 words. Open to unsolicited reviews. Poets may also send books for review consideration. They also use fiction and other writing. "We are mainly interested in giving new writers exposure. I don't like poetry that is so obscure only the mentally defective can understand it. We are about openness and ideas, about women's creative expression, wherever that may lead them. The name says it all: HER-spectives. We don't print material by men although they are welcome as subscribers."

HIGH PLAINS LITERARY REVIEW (III), Suite 250, 180 Adams St., Denver CO 80206, phone (303)320-6828, founded 1986, editor Robert O. Greer, associate poetry editor Ray Gonzalez, appears 3 times/year using "**high quality poetry, fiction, essays, book reviews and interviews.**" The format is 135 pgs., 70 lb. paper, heavy cover stock. Subscription: $20. **Sample postpaid: $7. Pays $10/published page for poetry.**

HIGH PLAINS PRESS (IV-Regional), P.O. Box 123, Glendo WY 82213, phone (307)735-4370, founded 1985, poetry editor Nancy Curtis, considers poetry "**specifically relating to Wyoming and the West, particularly those poems based on historical people/events. We're mainly a publisher of historical nonfiction, but do publish a book of poetry about every other year.**" They have published poetry by Peggy Simson Curry, Robert Roripaugh and Mary Alice Gunderson. As a sample she quoted these lines from the book **No Roof But Sky** by Jane Candia Coleman. The poem is "Geronimo photographed at Ft. Sill (1905)":

> *Bring me the elusive images*
> *of my life, and I will smile for you—*
> *over and over—an exchange of illusions*
> *like the dying change into light.*

Reports in 2 months, publication in 18-24 months. Pays 10% of sales. Buys first rights. Catalog available on request; sample chapbooks: $5. No Roof But Sky won the Wrangler Award for "accuracy and literary merit in portraying the West" in the poetry category from the National Cowboy Hall of Fame.

HIGH/COO PRESS; MAYFLY (IV-Form), 4634 Hale Dr., Decatur IL 62526, phone (217)877-2966, founded 1976, editors Randy and Shirley Brooks. High/Coo is a small press publishing nothing but **haiku in English.** "We publish haiku poemcards, minichapbooks, anthologies and a bibliography of haiku publications in addition to paperbacks and cloth editions and the magazine *Mayfly*, evoking emotions from contemporary experience. We are not interested in orientalism nor Japanese imitations." They recently published the **Midwest Haiku Anthology** which included the work of 54 haiku poets. **They publish no poetry except haiku.** They have published haiku by Virgil Hutton, Lee Gurga and Wally Swist. As a sample the editors selected this haiku by Bill Pauly:

> *country field—*
> *home run rolling*
> *past the headstones*

Mayfly is 16 pgs., saddle-stapled, 3 × 5, professionally printed on high-quality stock, one haiku/page. It appears in January and August. They publish 32 of an estimated 1,800 submissions. Subscription: $8. **Sample postpaid: $4. A Macintosh computer disk of haiku-related stacks is available for $10 postpaid. Guidelines available for SASE. Submit no more than 5 haiku/issue. No simultaneous submissions or previously published poems. Pays $5/poem and no copies.** High/Coo Press considers mss "**by invitation only.**" Randy Brooks says, "Publishing poetry is a joyous work of love. We publish to share those moments of insight contained in evocative haiku. We aren't in it for fame, gain or name. We publish to serve an enthusiastic readership. **Please note that we have changed our policy of requiring contributors to be subscribers, so submissions are open from all writers.**"

HIGHLIGHTS FOR CHILDREN (IV-Children), 803 Church St., Honesdale PA 18431, phone (717)253-1080, founded 1946, appears every month except July-August is a combined issue. Using **poetry for children aged 2-12.** "**Meaningful and/or fun poems accessible to children of all ages. Rarely publish a poem longer than 16 lines, most are shorter. No poetry that is unintelligible to children, poems containing sex, violence or unmitigated pessimism.**" They have published poetry by Nikki Giovanni, Aileen Fisher, John Ciardi, A.A. Milne, Myra Cohn Livingston, Langston Hughes and William Jay Smith. It is generally 44 pgs., magazine-sized, full-color throughout. They purchase 6-10 of 300 submissions/year. Press run 3.3 million for approximately 3 million subscribers. Subscription: $21.95 (one year; reduced rates for multiple years). **Submit ms typed with very brief cover letter. Please indicate if simultaneous submission. Editor comments on submissions "occasionally, if ms has merit or author seems to have potential for our market." Reports "generally within 1 month." Payment: "money varies" plus 2 copies. Buys all rights.** The editor says, "We are always open to submissions of poetry not previously published. However, we purchase a very limited amount of such material. We may use the verse as 'filler,' or illustrate the verse with a full-page piece of art. Please note that we do not buy material from anyone under 16 years old."

‡**HILLTOP PRESS (V, IV-Science fiction)**, 4 Nowell Place, Almondbury, Huddersfield, West Yorkshire HD5 8PB England, founded 1966, editor Steve Sneyd, publishes books of **"mainly science fiction poetry nowadays," but does not accept unsolicited mss. Query with proposals for relevant projects.** Recent publications include **War of the Words**, an anthology of humorous science fiction verse from the 30s to the 70s, including John Brunner, A. Vincent Clarke and C.S. Yond (John Christopher); and **The Fantastic Muse**, reprinting a 1938 article and 1939 poem by science fiction giant Arthur C. Clarke. From that poem, "The Twilight of A Sun," come these representative lines:

> The Intellect, pure, unalloyed, on courage eternally
> buoyed,
> Will span the vast gulfs of the void and win a new planet's
> fair face.
> For one day our vessels will ply to the uttermost depths
> of the sky,
> And in them at the last we shall fly, ere the darkness
> sweeps over our race.

They pay **"ample" author's copies.** "I have limited quantities of a number of earlier chapbooks. These can be had as samples, 5 all different, for £1.50 UK or $3 US, postage paid. (Checks payable to S. Sneyd. US orders: will also accept $ bills or small denomination, unused US stamps). My advice for beginning poets is (a) persist—don't let any one editor discourage you. 'In poetry's house are many mansions,' what one publication hates another may love; (b) be prepared for the possibility of long delays between acceptance and appearance of work—the small press is mostly self-financed and part time, so don't expect it to be more efficient than commercial publishers; (c) *always* keep a copy of everything you send out, and put your name and address on *everything* you send."

HIPPOPOTAMUS PRESS; OUTPOSTS POETRY QUARTERLY; OUTPOSTS ANNUAL POETRY COMPE-TITION (II, IV-Form), 22 Whitewell Rd., Frome, Somerset BA11 4EL England, *Outposts* founded 1943, Hippopotamus Press founded 1974, poetry editor Roland John, who explains, "*Outposts* is a general poetry magazine that welcomes all work either from the recognized or the unknown poet. **The Hippopotamus Press is specialized, with an affinity with Modernism. No Typewriter, Concrete, Surrealism.** The press publishes 6 full collections per year." They have published in *OPQ* poetry by John Heath-Stubbs, Peter Dale and Elizabeth Jennings. *Outposts* is digest-sized, 70-100 pgs., flat-spined, litho, in professionally set small type, using ads. Of 120,000 poems received he uses about 300. Press run is 3,000 for 2,800 subscriptions of which 10% are libraries, 2% of circulation through shelf sales. Subscription: $24. **Sample postpaid: $8. Simultaneous submissions, previously published poems OK. Cover letter required. Reports in 2 weeks plus post time. Pays $8/poem plus 1 copy.** Copyright remains with author. Staff reviews books of poetry in 200 words for "Books Received" page. Also uses full essays up to 4,000 words. Send books for review consideration, attn. M. Pargitter. The magazine also holds an annual poetry competition. Hippopotamus Press publishes 6 books a year, averaging 80 pgs. **For book publication query with sample poems. Simultaneous submissions, previously published poems OK. Reports in 6 weeks. Pays 10% royalties plus 20 paper copies, 6 cloth. Send for book catalog to buy samples.**

HIRAM POETRY REVIEW (II), P.O. Box 162, Hiram OH 44234, founded 1967, poetry editors Hale Chatfield and Carol Donley, is a semiannual with occasional special supplements. **"We favor new talent—and except for one issue in two years, read *only* unsolicited mss."** They are interested in "all kinds of high quality poetry" and have published poetry by Grace Butcher, David Citino, Michael Finley, Jim Daniels, Peter Klappert and Harold Witt. As a sample they offer these lines from "Three Musics" by William Johnson:

> Grief has a sound
> the way snow ticks
> and falls away
> from the metal light pole.

There are 30 + pgs. of poetry in the professionally printed, digest-sized, saddle-stapled magazine (glossy cover with b&w photo). It has a circulation of 400, 250 subscriptions of which 150 are libraries. They receive about 7,500 submissions/year, use 50, have up to a 6-month backlog.

Although most poems appearing here tend to be lyric and narrative free verse under 50 lines, exceptions occur (a few longer, sequence or formal works can be found in each issue). Single copy: $4; subscription: $8. **Sample: free! No simultaneous submissions. "Send 4-5 fresh, neat copies of your best poems." Reports in 2-5 months. Pays 2 copies plus year's subscription. Acquires first North American serial rights.** Reviews books of poetry in single or multi-book format, no set length. Send books for review consideration.

‡HIS GARDEN MAGAZINE (I, IV-Inspirational), 216 N. Vine St., Kewanee IL 61443, founded 1992, editor/publisher Margi L. Washburn, is an inspirational magazine appearing 3 times/year. "I like to print a good variety of uplifting poetry. Free style, traditional—all forms. I like longer poetry with deep meaning. Anything goes as long as it's inspirational and clean." They have recently published poetry by Dann R. Ward, Betty Mowery and Sidney Jeanne Seward. As a sample the editor selected the opening lines from "Are You Home, Lord?" by Naidine D'Angelo:

> *I stopped by Your house today*
> *a radiant forest of yellow and red*
> *to see if You were home*
> *but there was no answer*

HG is 32-40 pgs., 8½×11, side-stapled with colored paper cover, original artwork, copyright-free clip art and barter ads. They receive about 250 poems a year, accept approximately 50-75. Press run is 150 for 25 subscribers, 25 shelf sales. Subscription: $10. **Sample postpaid: $3.50. Submit 5 poems maximum. Previously published poems and simultaneous submissions OK. "Even though I don't require a cover letter, I love to get them." Always comments on rejections. Send SASE for guidelines. Reports in 2 months. Pays $5/submission plus 1 copy. Buys one-time rights.** Reviews books of poetry in 200-2,500 words. Open to unsolicited reviews, query first. The editor says, "I love poetry that pulls at the soul or shows God's majesty in the world around us. I also like to see those in need and hurting reflected in a poem."

‡HOB-NOB (V), 994 Nissley Rd., Lancaster PA 17601, phone (717)898-7807, founded 1969, poetry editor Mildred K. Henderson, is a small literary semiannual with certain 'family' emphasis. About ¼ poetry, ¾ prose. They are "filled up with poetry from first-time submitters through 1994." They publish "poetry preferably up to 16-line limit, light or humorous verse, serious poetry on vital current themes, people, nature, animals, etc. Religious poetry is also acceptable. No erotica, horror, suicide, excess violence, murder, overly depressing themes, especially utter hopelessness." They have recently published poetry by Effie Mihopoulos, C. David Hay and Patrick J. Cauchi. As a sample Mildred Henderson selected these lines from "The Fence Post" by Cathryn Hoellworth:

> *Wrinkled and leaning,*
> *rails gone,*
> *still it stands*
> *Proud settler*
> *staking a claim*
> *to fertile dreams.*

Hob-Nob is 80 pgs., magazine-sized, saddle-stapled, offset, on 20 lb. bond and heavier cover, printed from photoreduced typescript. It offers free ads to subscribers and exchange publications. About 20 new poets are featured in each issue. Print run is 500. Subscription: $6. **Sample postpaid: $3.50. Send SASE for guidelines. Pays 1 copy for first appearance only. After that you have to subscribe to be accepted. When open, she accepts submissions only in January and February of each year, 2-year wait for first-time contributors. Material received at other times will be returned unread. She prefers not to have simultaneous submissions.** The editor comments on rejections "especially if I can think of a way a rejected item can be salvaged or made suitable to submit elsewhere." **Reports in 2 months. Acquires first rights only.** The Readers Choice contest, every issue, pays $10 for first prize, lesser amount for other place (unless special prizes are offered by readers). Awards are on the basis of votes sent in by readers. The editor advises, "Poets and would-be poets should read contemporary poetry to see what others are doing. Most of what I receive does not seem to be rhymed and metered anymore, and unless a poet is extremely skilled with rhyme and meter (few are), he will find free verse much easier to deal with. I told one poet recently that the content is vital. Say something new, or if it's not new, say it in a new way. Nobody wants to see the same old 'June-moon-spoon' stuff. Patterns can be interesting, even without formal rhyme and meter. Take an unusual viewpoint. Notice the imagery in the poem quoted above, for an example. Let your imagination soar!"

‡HOBO STEW REVIEW (I), #2, 71 Marion St., Somerville MA 02143-3913, founded 1984, is a quarterly seeking poetry that is "honest, evoking emotions—from multi-stanzas to single lines. No hateful or self-centered poetry. No limericks." They have recently published poetry by Lyn Lifshin, T.S. Dean and Edward Mycue. *HSR* is 14 pgs., 8½ × 11, computer typeset and photocopied, side-stapled with 60 lb. card stock cover. They receive 100-200 poems/year, accept 30-40. Press run is 45, most distributed free to coffee shops, universities and clubs. Subscription: $5/year. **Sample postpaid: $2. No previously published poems or simultaneous submissions. Always comments on rejections. Send SASE for guidelines. Reports in 2-4 weeks or more. Pays 1 copy.** Reviews books of poetry in up to 1,000 words. Open to unsolicited reviews. Poets may also send books for review consideration. The editor says, "Keep it all honest, provoking and fun! Try reading out loud—alone and at public readings—to find your voice."

‡HOLD THE PICKLE; EXTRA CHEESE (I), 7942 Convoy Court, San Diego CA 92111-1212, founded 1991, editor Richard A. Seffron. *Extra Cheese* appears yearly using poetry, prose, art, reviews and commentary. They **"like shorter, serious poetry; prefer nonrhyming; lean toward new talent, honesty in the voice/words of the poem. Nothing racist or demeaning."** They have recently published poetry by Rane Arroyo, Glenn Sheldon, Leonard Cirino and Lyn Lifshin. The editor says *Extra Cheese* is 8½ × 11, photocopied, saddle-stapled. Press run is 1,000. Single copy: $5. **Previously published poems and simultaneous submissions OK. Cover letter required. "No cover letter—gets stuffed back in—no reply." Seldom comments on rejections. Send SASE for guidelines. Reports in 1-6 weeks "worst case." Pays 1 copy "unless otherwise arranged."** Reviews books of poetry in 50-500 words. Open to unsolicited reviews. Poets may also send books for review consideration. Hold the Pickle also publishes 1-2 paperbacks and about 6 chapbooks/year. **Query first with sample poems and cover letter with brief bio and publication credits. "Recycled poetry is fine. Sample poems a must. Nothing fancy in packaging. I'm interested in the words only." Replies to queries and mss in 2-6 weeks.** Splits press runs for books and chapbooks. Usual press run for chapbooks is 400 copies. Write for current catalog. The editor says, "I'm a very small press with limited resources. I look for writers passionate about—in love with—poetry. Nothing turns me off more than a nice cover letter over a pile of weak poetry. The press is moving away from the magazine toward chapbooks and paperbacks."

HOLIDAY HOUSE, INC. (IV-Children), Dept. PM, 425 Madison Ave., New York NY 10017, phone (212)688-0085, founded 1936, editor-in-chief Margery Cuyler, is a trade children's book house. They have published hardcover books for children by Myra Cohn Livingston. They publish 3 books a year averaging 32 pages but are interested in publishing more poetry books for ages 8-12. **Submit 5 sample poems. No simultaneous submissions or previously published poems. Cover letter listing any publishing experience required. Editor rarely comments on rejections. Offers an advance and royalties.**

THE HOLLINS CRITIC (II), P.O. Box 9538, Hollins College VA 24020, phone (703)362-6317, founded 1964, editor John Rees Moore, appears 5 times yearly, publishing critical essays, poetry and book reviews. **They use a few short poems in each issue, interesting in form, content or both.** They have recently published poetry by Agnes N. Johnston, Jeff Mock, Eric Thretheway and Ann Folwell Stanford. As a sample the editor selected these lines from "In Memoriam" (for Roger Hecht 1926-1990) by Wade Newman:

> Because you disdained a graveside poem,
> Preferring to spare your friends a funeral,
> You determined that your bones
> And skin be burned away until nothing remained
> But a small pile of ashes
> And the hope that the soul survives the flesh.
> Forgive us, then, today's trespasses
> As we gather in one body to touch your death.

The Hollins Critic is 20 pgs., magazine-sized. Circulation 500. **Sample: $1.50. Submit up to 5 poems, none over 35 lines, must be typewritten. Cover letter preferred. Reports in 6 weeks (slower in the summer). Pays $25/poem plus 5 copies.** Open to unsolicited reviews. Poets may also send books for review consideration. Traditionally, verse here has been open as to form and style with poems that please the mind, eye and senses. As the magazine is occasionally overstocked, your best bet is to send for a sample copy and inquire as to whether editors are reading unsolicited submissions.

HOLMGANGERS PRESS; KESTREL CHAPBOOK SERIES (V), 95 Carson Ct., Shelter Cove, Whitethorn CA 95589, phone (707)986-7700, founded 1974, editor Gary Elder, was "founded primarily to bring out **young or unjustly ignored 'older' poets.** We have since published collections of fiction, novels, history, graphic art and experimental works as well." **Holmgangers Press is currently not accepting unsolicited mss. Replies to queries in 3-4 days, to mss (if invited) in 1 month.**

HENRY HOLT & COMPANY (V), 115 W. 18th St., New York NY 10011, **accepts no unsolicited poetry.**

HOME PLANET NEWS (II), Dept. PM, P.O. Box 415, Stuyvesant Station, New York NY 10009, phone (718)769-2854, founded 1979, editors Enid Dame and Donald Lev, is a tabloid (newsprint) journal, appearing 3-4 times a year presenting a "lively, eclectic and comprehensive view of contemporary literature." They want **"honest, well-crafted poems, open or closed form, on any subject, but we will not publish any work which seems to us to be racist, sexist, ageist, anti-semitic or has undue emphasis on violence. Poems under 30 lines stand a better chance. We lean somewhat toward poetry with urban sensibility but are not rigid about this."** They have recently published poetry by Alicia Ostriker, Tuli Kupferberg, Denise Duhamel, Will Inman, Andrew Glaze, Robert Peters, Carl Solomon and Rose Romano. As a sample the editors selected these lines from "Clotheslines" by Robbie Casey:

> Clothes on a rope
> gallop in the wind
> freer than the bodies they cover
> will ever be

They use approximately 13 full 11×16 pgs. of poetry in each 24-page issue. Circulation 1,000 with 400 subscriptions of which 8 are libraries. Of 1,200 submissions/year, they use about 50-60. Publication could take one year from acceptance. Subscription: $8/year. **Sample postpaid: $3. Submit 3-6 poems typed double-spaced, with SASE. Reports within 3 months. Pays 4 copies and year's subscription.** Reviews books of poetry. Open to unsolicited reviews. Poets may also send books for review consideration. "We cosponsor 'Day of the Poet,' a poetry festival and contest which takes place each October in Ulster County, New York." Poetry by Daniel Berrigan published in *Home Planet News* appeared in the **Pushcart Prize** anthology.

HONEST ULSTERMAN (II, IV-Regional), 31 West Park Rd., Kew, Surrey TW9 4DA United Kingdom, founded 1968, editors Robert Johnstone and Tom Clyde, is a literary magazine appearing 3-4 times a year using **"technically competent poetry and prose and book reviews. Special reference to Northern Irish and Irish literature. Lively, humorous, adventurous, outspoken."** They have published poetry by Seamus Heaney, Paul Muldoon, Gavin Ewart, Craig Raine, Fleur Adcock and Medbh McGuckian. The editor describes it as "75-100 pgs., A5 (digest-sized), photolithographic, phototypeset, with photographs and line drawings. Occasionally color covers." Press run: 1,000 for 300+ subscriptions. Subscription: $28. **Sample postpaid: $7. "Potential contributors are strongly advised to read the magazine before submitting two copies of their work." Editor comments on submissions "occasionally." Pays "a nominal fee"** plus 2 copies. Reviews books of poetry in 500-1,000 words, single or multi-book format. Open to unsolicited reviews. Poets may also send books for review consideration. They also publish occasional poetry pamphlets.

HOPEWELL REVIEW; POETRY IN MOTION (IV-Regional), Suite 701, 47 S. Pennsylvania St., Indianapolis IN 46204-3622. *Hopewell Review* (formerly *Arts Indiana Literary Supplement*) is an annual publication using poems and short stories by residents of Indiana. **"Writers should send no more than three poems and/or one short story with a manuscript-sized SASE and a brief biography. Poems of 40 lines or less will stand best chance of publication." Simultaneous submissions OK if so noted. Deadline March 1. Send SASE for guidelines. Pays $35 for each accepted poem.** One poem will be selected by Reginald Gibbons, editor-in-chief of *TriQuarterly*, for a $500 cash award of excellence. *Poetry in Motion* selects 12 poems to be printed on advertising placards and displayed inside Indianapolis METRO buses and other public spaces, a new poem each month. Open to poets 18 or older living within Marion and contiguous counties of Indiana. **Submit 4 copies of no more than 3 poems no longer than 17 lines, 81 spaces/line; include SASE for notification. Deadline mid-June. Send SASE for entry information.**

HOPSCOTCH: THE MAGAZINE FOR GIRLS (IV-Children), P.O. Box 164, Bluffton OH 45817-0164, phone (419)358-4610, founded 1989, editor Marilyn B. Edwards, is a bimonthly magazine for **girls 6-12. "No length restrictions. In need of short poems for various holidays. Nothing abstract, experimental."** They have published poetry by Bette Killion, Sue Carloni and Cathy Drinkwater Better. As a sample we selected the last lines of "Grandma Was A Dancer?" by Barbara Early-Fezzey:

> Grandma was really a dancer?
> It should come to me as no surprise.
> When she holds me and kisses me sweetly
> I see her love dance in her eyes.

The editor describes *Hopscotch* as "full-color cover, 50 pgs. of 2-color inside, 7×9, saddle-stapled." They use about 30-35 of some 2,000 poems received/year. Press run 9,000 for 8,200 subscribers of which 7,000 are libraries, 200 to inquiring schools and libraries. Subscription: $15. **Sample postpaid: $3. Submit no more than 6 poems/submission. Cover letter preferred; include experience and where published. Reports in 2-4 weeks. Pays $10-40. Buys first American serial rights.** The few poems in this children's magazine address the audience, challenging young girls to pursue their dreams. To see how, order a sample copy (or check one out at the library) because it is too easy for poets who write children's verse to forget that each magazine targets a specific audience . . . in a specific way. *Hopscotch* received the Parents Choice Gold Medal Award for 1992.

HOUGHTON MIFFLIN CO. (V), 2 Park St., Boston MA 02108, founded 1850, poetry editor Peter Davison. Houghton Mifflin is a high-prestige trade publisher that puts out both hardcover and paperback books, but **poetry submission is by invitation only and they are not seeking new poets at present.** They have issued poetry books by Donald Hall, May Swenson, Ai, William Matthews, Margaret Atwood and Andrew Hudgins. **Authors are paid 10% royalties on hardcover books, 6% royalties on paperbacks (minimum), $1,000 advance and 12 author's copies.**

HOUSE OF MOONLIGHT (I), 15 Oakwood Rd., Bracknell, Berkshire RG12 2SP United Kingdom, founded 1981, editor John Howard, publishes 4-page leaflets of poems by individual poets at irregular intervals. **"Poems on love, death and the universe—common themes expressed in an uncommon way. Long poems up to 100 lines preferred."** They have published poetry by Steve Sneyd and John Francis Haines. **Pays 5 copies. Acquires all rights. Returns rights if "acknowledgment that I published first."** The editor says, "I am happy to receive submissions/inquiries from the United States—but only ones enclosing International Reply Coupons can be responded to. Checks payable to 'House of Moonlight' and/or in US currency are not acceptable. Also if poetry is to be regarded as a 'disposable ms' then it should be marked as such."

HOUSEWIFE-WRITER'S FORUM (IV-Women, humor), P.O. Box 780, Lyman WY 82937, phone (307)786-4513, founded 1988, editor/publisher Diane Wolverton, is a magazine of "prose, poetry, information and open forum communication for and by housewives or any woman or man who writes while juggling a busy schedule. **We have no specifications as to form, subject, style or purpose. Length maximum 30 lines. We publish both serious poetry and humorous. Nothing pornographic, but erudite expression is fine."** As a sample she selected these lines from "Off Limits" by Katherine H. Brooks:

> *I used to save a lot of stuff.*
> *Till Mother hollered "That's enough!"*
> *And made me have, all day, a fear*
> *That something nice would disappear.*
> *I hurried home from school, to see*
> *What damage had been done to me,*
> *And when I went to find the rocks*
> *I'd hidden underneath my socks,*
> *I saw it—almost in a flash—*
> *That all my things were in the trash.*

Diane Wolverton describes the magazine as "a small market for women who aspire to write for larger women's markets or support each other in the quest for finding time and energy to write." It is 48 pgs., desktop published, using some art, graphics and ads, appearing bimonthly. Press run is 1,500. **Sample postpaid: $4. "Simultaneous submissions are OK." Send SASE for guidelines. Reports in 2 months. Pays 1 copy plus $1-2/poem. Buys first-time rights.** She holds contests in several categories, humorous and serious, with $2/poem fee, May 31 deadline. *Housewife-Writer's Forum* received a 1st place award for magazine editing from Wyoming Media Professionals. The editor adds, "I like to see poems that have a strong central purpose and use the language to express it beautifully, powerfully."

HOWLING DOG (II), 8419 Rhode, Utica MI 48317, founded 1985, editor Mark Donovan, is a literary journal of "letters, words and lines." The editor likes **"found poetry, graphically interesting pieces, humorous work, avant-garde, experimental, fun and crazy. All forms. All subjects, but we tend to have a light satirical attitude towards sex and politics."** He has published poems by Arthur Winfield Knight, Keith Wilson, John Sinclair, Carlos Cumpian and M.L. Liebler. As a sample the editor selected these lines by Kurt Olsson:

> *The children made such a fuss about seeing*
> *the Indian graveyard that, of course, the stand*
> *of silver birch disappointed them—so we didn't stop,*
> *continued on instead up the remains of a logger's road*

Create a Distinctive Voice

"Possession"

Inside me lives someone who writes poems,
Someone who has no words but from time to time
Borrows my words, whirls them through the dance
Of his purposes, then returns them.

My only evidence for his existence
Comes when I find poems on my desk
Ready for me to revise.
            When did this happen?

Though I have never known who scribbled them
In secret, still I know my job.
I find them ready and waiting, I take over.
Possession they say is nine points in the poem.

Copyright 1984 by Peter Davison

Peter Davison

Photo by Paula Deimling

Peter Davison knows well that moment of finding poems on a desk. On his desk at home in Gloucester, Massachusetts, the poems are his own, but they also share space with a book he's writing about poets.

In Boston, he's the editor every poet wants a response from. An editor with a seven-day-a-week schedule and thousands of poems waiting to be read.

You can't accuse Davison, though, of not knowing how poets feel. An accomplished poet, he has published nine volumes of his own poetry. He has also edited some of America's best poets, including May Swenson, Mary Oliver, Stanley Kunitz and Donald Hall, as well as prose authors such as William Least Heat-Moon.

Today at Houghton Mifflin Company, Davison heads his own imprint, Peter Davison Books, publishing books on nature, history, biography and other topics. He also oversees the publication of HM's poetry books. And for the past 21 years, he has been the poetry editor for *The Atlantic*.

Much of Davison's time as an editor is spent reading, and looking for potential authors for his prose imprint and for poets whose work stimulates the imagination and the ear.

"I don't know why it takes people six months [to decide whether to publish a book]," says Davison, who has edited around 500 books in his 43-year career. "It is just as easy to read a book the week it comes in rather than to wait three months."

At *The Atlantic*, it is the sound of a poem that first gets Davison's attention. "It's wonderful when you come across a poet like W.S. Merwin who's exploring the sound of the language and the interrelation of meaning."

Davison looks for poetry that "jumps off the page—I can hear it. I can hear a voice. I can hear a distinctive voice. It's not flat, present tense, insulting, not self-descriptive. I'm looking for something that really has an original ring to it. I want it to sound different from the rest of the magazine."

He enjoys discovering new poets and poetry, and publishing work by established writers. "Poetry is language on the verge of breaking into meaning," Davison says, quoting Kunitz, one of his favorite poets. "It's that moment of being on the verge that's so exciting."

Some of the poets in *The Atlantic*'s upcoming inventory are familiar names in the magazine: Philip Levine, Merwin and Oliver. Others are newcomers.

Good poets can write on almost any subject for the monthly magazine, not necessarily on New England themes as some poets incorrectly assume. "Since the 19th century, *The Atlantic* has had more subscribers in California than it has in all of New England put together," he says.

Davison acknowledges there is "very little that you can state in formulaic terms" when describing the ideal *Atlantic* poem. He enjoys receiving poems written in strict forms, such as ballades and pantoums, but says many poets today aren't adept at handling these forms.

He urges writers to read extensively—to understand poetry forms and the kinds of poetry that earn bylines and invitations to submit books. "Read the magazine," he says, emphasizing the word *read* as if it's part of a recited poem. "People find it much harder to read than to write."

Davison's poetry knowledge and sense of the sound of words are especially evident at poetry readings. Davison's poems sound like Davison *talking* about what he values—writing, father, mother, familiar terrain, the family dog—the rhythm and sound of the lines enhancing what he says.

Whether Davison is thinking about the marketplace depends on whether he is writing or acquiring titles for his imprint. "The poet really shouldn't think about the market too much," he observes. "Poets who have no difficulty in the marketplace are those who stand out as individuals, poets who establish an identity."

As an editor at Houghton Mifflin, Davison's focus on the marketplace enables writers he publishes to concentrate on their writing. He becomes a publicist for their books. "The job of the business people is to keep the warehouse empty, and the job of the editors is to keep the warehouse full," he says. "The poetry editor guides the plan . . . and has to keep an eye on the backlist."

Houghton Mifflin will publish five books of poetry in 1994 in addition to Peter Davison Books' five nonfiction titles. However, Davison is not interested in unsolicited manuscripts. Instead he invites writers to submit material, based on his reading of books and review copies and recommendations from colleagues. "If you really have a sense of the identity of the poet's language," says Davison, "that is one of the things that makes that language break into meaning"—and one way that the poet can eventually break into print.

Davison usually works with poets in the early stages of a book. "I make suggestions about small things, rhymes, scansion, images that don't work," he says.

If the book is a collection of poems, Davison will sometimes make suggestions about the order of the poems. He also provides encouragement, when needed. "The editor is there to get the author's and publisher's spirits up."

Davison acknowledges that a break in the summer reading schedule would be nice, but for now, as writer, editor, publisher and lecturer, he works year-round in "one of the dangerous trades"—the title of his 1991 nonfiction book about poetry.

"You have to be possessed by it," he says, referring to poetry. Isn't that also true at the editor's desk?

—*Paula Deimling*

Howling Dog appears 2 times a year. It is 64 pgs., digest-sized, flat-spined, offset. Press run 500 for 100 subscriptions of which 3 are libraries. They receive some 4,000 submissions/year, use maybe 150. Subscription: $20/4 issues. **Sample postpaid: $4. Send SASE for guidelines. Submit 3-4 poems with name and address on each page. "We don't use much rhyme or poems under 10 lines." Simultaneous submissions OK. Previously published poems OK "but let us know." Reporting time 2-3 months, "longer if we like it." Pays with copies and discount. Acquires first-time rights.** Reviews books of poetry in 200 words, single format. Open to unsolicited reviews. Poets may also send books for review consideration. **They are not presently considering book mss.** Mark Donovan says, "We produce an effect similar to the howl of a dog with its foot caught in the fence. Something that may not be pleasant or permanent, yet still heard by everyone in the neighborhood. We only accept the highest quality contemporary artistic expressions."

HRAFNHOH (IV-Form, religious), 32 Stryd Ebeneser, Pontypridd, Wales via GB, phone 0443 492243, founded 1987, editor Joseph Biddulph, is a small press magazine seeking **"metrical verse."** They use **"poetry in traditional verse forms with a Christian inspiration and purpose, with an active concern for metrical technique and conveying a serious message in an evocative and entertaining style."** They have published poetry by John Waddington-Feather, M.A.B. Jones, Joe Keysor and many others. The editor describes *Hrafnhoh* as digest-sized, 24 pgs., typeset, illustrated with carefully-researched heraldic illustrations and other sketches. He accepts about 1 of 6-10 poems received, but is not always able to published even if accepted. Press run is 100-500. **Sample postpaid: £3 outside Europe. Simultaneous submissions and previously published poems OK. Reports as soon as possible. Pays "in free copies as required."** The editor says, "Almost all unsolicited manuscripts are in one form—free verse—and without substance, i.e., without a definite purpose, message or conclusion. I am anxious to obtain verse with a strong technique, particularly on Pro-life and Christian subjects."

‡HUBBUB (II), 5344 SE 38th Ave., Portland OR 97202, founded 1983, editors L. Steinman and J. Shugrue, appears twice a year (except on rare occasions is a single "double issue"). *Hubbub* is designed "to feature a multitude of voices from interesting contemporary American poets. **We look for poems that are well-crafted, with something to say. We have no single style, subject or length requirement and, in particular, will consider long poems. No light verse."** They have recently published poetry by Madeline DeFrees, William Matthews, Carolyn Kizer, Agha Shahid Ali and Alice Fulton. The editors describe *Hubbub* as 35-45 pgs., 5½ × 8½, offset, saddle-stitched, cover art only, usually no ads. They receive about 800 submissions/year, use approximately 10%. Press run is 350 for 100 subscribers of which 12 are libraries, about 150 shelf sales. Single copy: $2.50; subscription: $5/year. **Sample postpaid: $2.65 (volumes 1-8), $3.15 (volumes 9, 11 and following), $6.25 (volume 10 only). Submit 3-6 typed poems (no more than 6). No previously published poems or simultaneous submissions. Send SASE for guidelines. Reports in 1-2 months. Pays 2 copies. Acquires first North American serial rights.** "We review one to two poetry books a year in short (3-page) reviews; all reviews are solicited. We do, however, list books received/recommended." Send books for consideration. Outside judges choose poems from each volume for three awards: Vi Gale Award ($100), Adrienne Lee Award ($50) and Walter Hall Award ($25). There are no special submission procedures or entry fees involved.

THE HUDSON REVIEW; THE BENNETT AWARD (III), 684 Park Ave., New York NY 10021. *The Hudson Review* is a high-quality, flat-spined quarterly, considered one of the most prestigious and influential journals in the nation. Editors welcome all styles and forms. However, competition is extraordinarily keen, especially since poems compete with prose. **Non-subscribers may submit poems only between April 1 and September 30. Reports in 6-8 weeks. Pays 50¢ a line for poetry.** They also sponsor the Bennett Award, established in memory of Joseph Bennett, a founding editor of *HR*. Every other year $15,000 is given to honor a writer "of significant achievement, in any literary genre or genres, whose work has not received the full recognition it deserves, or who is at a critical stage in his or her career—a stage at which a substantial grant might be particularly beneficial in furthering creative development. There are no restrictions as to language or nationality. **The Bennett Award is not open to nominations, and *The Hudson Review* will not accept nominations or applications in any form."**

HUDSON VALLEY ECHOES (II), P.O. Box 7, La Grangeville NY 12540, founded 1985, editor Marcia W. Grant, poetry editor Ann Bragdon, "is a national literary quarterly that features quality prose and poetry from well-established as well as emerging writers. *Hudson Valley Echoes* has no rigid specifications as to form, length, subject matter or style. **Excellence is the determining factor. Usual length of accepted poems is 25-45 lines, longer if exceptional. Editors want to see poems whose ideas and imagery are clearly focused, well-crafted and unusual. No sing-song rhyme, erotica or effusive amateur efforts."** They have published poetry by Robert Cooperman, Johy Grey, Ruth Daigon and John M. Davis. As a sample the editor selected these lines from "Roadside Mortal" by R. Nikolas Macioci:

> *I grow orange, oxidized by four o'clock*
> *windshield reflections. Cows drip sun, flick the*

> *excess from their tails. Plump milkweed ash scatters*
> *before it is touched. Tribal leaves gather,*
> *war painted, dance a zigzag step, a zigzag step,*
> *charge the wind like perfect warriors.*

HVE is 5½ × 8½, 44 pgs., saddle-stapled, offset with matte cover and interior pages printed on recycled paper. It is a lively little magazine. First, the poems are top-rate (mostly free verse). Second, the magazine is well-edited and attractively produced. Third, it contains small features that indicate editorial love: a letters section, quotes from poets like Frost and Jong, illustrations and contributor's notes! Press run averages 300 for about 100 subscriptions, of which 12 are libraries. Distributors provide some shelf sales. Subscription: $15 (libraries, $12). **Sample postpaid: $4.50 current issue; $3 back issue. "Five poems should be the maximum submitted at one time. Include name and address on every submission. Contributor's notes requested." Previously published submissions considered if poet owns rights. Editor "rarely" comments on submissions. Send SASE for guidelines. Reports in generally 6-12 weeks. Pays 1 copy. Acquires onetime rights.** The editor advises poets to read good poetry in order to know good poetry. "Familiarize yourself with our magazine before you submit."

THE HUMAN QUEST (IV-Political), 1074 23rd Ave. N., St. Petersburg FL 33704, editor Edna Ruth Johnson, is a "humanistic monthly dealing with society's problems, especially peace. We use practically no poetry." It is magazine-sized, appears 9 times a year, circulation 10,000, of which 1,000 go for library subscriptions. **Send for free sample. Pays copies.**

‡THE HUNTED NEWS; THE SUBOURBON PRESS (I), P.O. Box 9101, Warwick RI 02889, founded 1990, editor Mike Wood. *The Hunted News* is a biannual "designed to find good writers and give them one more outlet to get their voices heard." As for poetry, the editor says, **"The poems that need to be written are those that need to be read."** They do not want to see **"the poetry that does not need to be written or which is written only to get a reaction or congratulate the poet."** As a sample the editor selected these lines (poet unidentified):

> *Birds who strike window panes with*
> *a heavy thud*
> *are misinformed.*
> *They've been sabotaged by outmoded*
> *weather charts*
> *In miniscule and mugging ways*
> *they resemble our finest actors*
> *Bury them in sand . . .*
> *and wait.*

The editor says *THN* is 25-30 pgs., 8½ × 11, photocopied, unstapled. "I receive over 200 poems per month and accept perhaps 10%." Press run is 150-200. **Sample free with SASE. Previously published poems OK; no simultaneous submissions. Always comments on rejections. Send SASE for guidelines. Reports in 1 month. Pays 1 copy, more on request.** "I review current chapbooks and other magazines and do other random reviews of books, music, etc. Word count varies." The Suboubon Press publishes 2 chapbooks/year. **Query first with a few sample poems and cover letter with brief bio and publication credits. Replies to both queries and mss in 1 month. Pays 15-20 author's copies. "No subsidies unless given voluntarily." Send SASE for information about samples.** The editor says, "Please write because it keeps you alive, not to impress anyone or to justify the lies you tell about yourself. People are starving for great writing; don't settle for just an act. The small press can be as inbred and self-lauding as the academic world; write and be alone, and readers will find you."

‡HURRICANE ALICE (IV-Feminist), Lind Hall, 207 Church St. SE, Minneapolis MN 55455, founded 1983, acquisitions editor Toni McNaron, is a quarterly feminist review that publishes a maximum of 1-2 poems/issue. Poems should be **infused by a feminist sensibility (whether the poet is female or male) and "should have what we think of as a certain analytic snap to them."** They have published poetry by Alice Walker, Ellen Bass, Patricia Hampl and Nellie Wong. The magazine is a "12-page folio, table of contests on cover, plenty of graphics." Circulation is 500-1,000, of which 350 are subscriptions and about 50 go to libraries. Single copy: $1.95; subscription: $10 (or $8 low-income). **Sample postpaid: $2.50. Considers simultaneous submissions. Reports in 3-4 months and time to publication is 3-6 months. Pays 5-10 copies.** Reviews books of poetry. The editor says, "Read what good poets have already written. If someone has already written your poem(s), listen to the message. Spare the trees."

HYACINTH HOUSE PUBLICATIONS; BROWNBAG PRESS; PSYCHOTRAIN (II, IV-Translations), P.O. Box 120, Fayetteville AR 72702-0120, founded 1989, contact Shannon Frach. *Brownbag Press* and *PsychoTrain* are both semiannual magazines. *Brownbag Press* seeks "forceful writing full of spark and vigor for a widely diverse, intelligent, fairly left-of-center audience." *PsychoTrain* uses "bizarre, avant-garde material with a delightfully psychotic edge. Heady and chaotic." The editors want **poetry that is "avant-garde, confessional, contemporary, erotic, experimental, gay/lesbian, pagan/occult or punk. Also dada, surrealism and decadent writing at its best. Be bold. Morbid humor is always a plus here. No religious poetry, inept rhyming, overly-academic poetics or saccharine writing of any description. We prefer two-fisted, dynamic, very intense poetry. We are always interested in good translations—especially translations of lively (if not outright brazen) material from countries which tend to favor tame, non-confrontational, bland poetry for the bulk of their literary exports. Don't be afraid to show us street language from any culture."** They have recently published poetry by Tom Caufield, Marianne Moro, Cheryl Townsend, Arthur Winfield Knight, Serena Fusek and Belinda Subraman. As a sample the editors selected these lines from "Jesus on a pogo stick" by Randal Seyler:

> *Wrapped in the stars and stripes*
> *sleeping behind a McDonald's—*
> *bloody palms and a pawn ticket*
> *won't buy a McDLT when*
> *the rapture comes.*

Brownbag is 24 pgs., digest-sized; *PsychoTrain* is 20 pgs., magazine-sized. Both are photocopied and stapled with card covers. Press run for each is 300 for 100+ subscribers, 125+ shelf sales. **Sample postpaid: $3 for *Brownbag*, $3 for *PsychoTrain*. Previously published poems and simultaneous submissions OK.** Time between acceptance and publication is 1 year. **Often comments on rejections. Send SASE for guidelines. Reports in "2 weeks to 6 months—depends on the backlog." Pays 1 copy. Acquires one-time rights.** Open to unsolicited reviews "if pertaining to the type of material we would normally review." Poets may also send appropriate books to Randal Seyler for review consideration. "We would also consider doing a special issue featuring alternative writers from Arkansas, should we get enough submissions to warrant the project. We'd like to see more submissions from our home state—there are some very fine writers of a national calibre working here, and we like to encourage them." Hyacinth House has also just started **a chapbook series. "Presently we're using solicited material only**—please don't send us unsolicited chapbook mss at this time. We will be doing approximately seven chapbooks this year, all from authors who have first appeared in our magazines. We don't take chapbook submissions 'out of the blue'—we like to know who we're working with." The editors say, "Hyacinth House is a very friendly place to send submissions. We may end up having to reject your submissions, but we'll still respect you in the morning. We encourage both new and established 'name' writers to submit here. Anyone sending us material should be aware that we don't like pretentious, windy, overly-serious poetry; we also dislike smarmy, trite rhymes about God and family. Send those to your hometown newspaper, not us. Don't send us poems that only took you five minutes to write. Also, please be aware that when you submit to one Hyacinth House publication, you're submitting to them all. If you submit to *Brownbag*, but the piece would work better in *PsychoTrain*, that's where it's going."

‡ICE COLD WATERMELON (IV-Ethnic, erotica, gay/lesbian), 2394B Adina Dr., Atlanta GA 30324, founded 1990 as *Mots Et Images: Press-Work Project*, editors M.C. Young and Simoné, appears annually (usually around October/November). **"Want to see brave poetry, with an edge, that gives us a look into any facet of being African-American in America. Want to see poetry with voice and character using fresh imagery. Erotica/gay/lesbian writings especially encouraged. Prejudiced toward the more economical poem but will consider longer poems if they show promise. Do not want to see anything that tries too hard. No academic or 'selfish' personal poetry. Nothing trite or mundane."** As a sample the editors selected these lines from "Act of Freedom Right On" by M.C. Young:

> *personally*
> *i find my*
> *slightly*
> *nappy*
> *tresses*
> *to be*
> *exquisite*
> *however unarresting*

The editors describe it as 30-50 pgs., digest-sized, professionally printed, saddle-stapled, with card cover. They accept about 45 of 400 submissions received annually. Press run 200 with 5 library subscriptions. "Most copies distributed free to other editors, publishers and writing institutions." **Subscription: $10 for 2 years. Submit 5 poems, typed. Send SASE for guidelines. Reports in 2-4 weeks, up to 18-month backlog. Pays 3 copies. Editors often comment on rejections.** They say, "What we want is the unusual and extraordinary. We want fresh new slants on life in the U.S.A. for the African-American. In your writing, we want you to have no qualms about telling the truth as you know it and allowing us to explore the dimensions with you."

ICON; HART CRANE AWARD (II), English Dept., Kent State University, Trumbull Campus, 4314 Mahoning Ave. NW, Warren OH 44483, phone (216)847-0571, founded 1966, faculty advisor Dr. Robert Brown, appears twice a year. **"We prefer experimental poetry, poetry that takes risks in terms of form and subject matter, but will consider anything well-written. No religious, sentimental, formulaic or prosaic poetry."** They have published poetry by Gay Brewer and William Greenway. As a sample the editor selected these lines from "To an Abused Wife" by Mark Fitzpatrick:

> The gods will grow plankton
> Around their faces, green-
> spotted, like a tombstone . . .

It is digest-sized, 40-80 pgs., saddle-stapled, with matte card cover. Poems and a few illustrations/photos grace the pages of this professionally printed and designed magazine. Artwork is especially attractive, not so much illustrating poems as lending a mood to the entire issue. They accept 5% of 1,000 poems submitted. Press run 1,000 for 50 subscribers of which 10 are libraries. Distributed free to students and faculty. Subscription: $5. **Sample postpaid: $2. Submit September 1 through March 1 only. Reports in 1-3 months. Pays 2 copies.** The Hart Crane Award of $100 for poetry is given annually.

‡**THE ICONOCLAST (I)**, 1675 Amazon Rd., Mohegan Lake NY 10547, founded 1992, editor/publisher Phil Wagner, is a general interest literary publication appearing 8 times/year **"for those who find life absurd and profound."** They want **"poems that have something to say—the more levels the better. Nothing sentimental, religious, obscure or self-absorbed."** The Iconoclast is 16 pgs., 8½ × 11, cornerstapled, typeset and photocopied on 20 lb. white paper, with b&w art, graphics and ads. They receive about 100 poems a year, use between 5-10%. Press run is 225 for 150 subscribers. Subscription: $12 for 10 issues. **Sample postpaid: $1.25. Previously published poems and simultaneous submissions OK,** though they say **"previously published and simultaneous submissions must be demonstrably better than others."** Time between acceptance and publication is 2-4 months. **"Poems are subject to the extremely fallible judgements of the editor-in-chief." Often comments on rejections. Reports in 2-4 weeks. Pays 1 copy, 40% discount on extras. Acquires one-time rights.** Reviews books of poetry in 250 words, single format.

IHCUT (I), P.O. Box 612, Napavine WA 98565, founded 1989, contact Larry L. Randall, is an inexpensively produced newsletter appearing every other month. **"I am open to anything so long as it is exciting and original. I am more open to shorter poetry, and the purpose should be to birth a new type of animal or way of thinking. I would rather not see rhyming poetry."** They have recently published poetry by Julie Brinson Yopp, John Sweet, Lyn Lifshin and Tracy Lyn Rottkamp. As a sample the editor selected these lines from an untitled poem by Dawn Zapletal:

> Ooooohhhh!
> Aaaahhh!
> Hhhhmmmmm!
> Yeah!

It is 15-20 pgs., photocopied, side-stapled on ordinary paper. Press run 20. **Sample postpaid: $2. Previously published poems and simultaneous submissions OK. Cover letter including "likes and dislikes, personal stuff" required. "It annoys me when a poet does not include a cover letter,** which to me is a poem in itself." **Send SASE for guidelines. Reports in 1 week. Pays 1 copy.**

UNIVERSITY OF ILLINOIS PRESS (III), 54 E. Gregory Dr., Champaign IL 61820, phone (217)333-0950, founded 1918, poetry editor Laurence Lieberman, publishes **collections of individual poets, 65-105 pgs. Submissions by invitation only.** Poets they have published include Brendan Galvin, Sandra McPherson, Michael Harper, Robert Wrigley and Lynn Emanuel. **Also publishes thematic collections, "for which letters of inquiry should be addressed to Richard L. Wentworth, editor-in-chief." Offers royalty contract and 10 copies.**

‡**THE ILLINOIS REVIEW; ILLINOIS WRITERS, INC. (II)**, English Department/4240, Illinois State University, Normal IL 61761-6901, phone (309)438-7705, founded 1992, first issue fall 1993, editor Jim Elledge. The Illinois Review appears twice a year and supersedes Illonis Writers Review. **"We're open to any 'school'—experimental to traditional, alternative to mainstream—by recognized, unknown and marginalized poets. Translations and prose poems are acceptable. Selection for publication is based on excellence of poems not reputation of poets. We look for poetry that reveals control of language and form, that engages the intellect and emotions simultaneously and that is honest. No specifications as to length, etc. We do not want to see poetry that is sentimental, religious, filled with abstractions or 'self-therapy.'"** Among the poets appearing in their premiere issue are Gary Soto, Lisa Ress, Rochelle Ratner, David Trinidad, Kelly Cherry, Albert Goldbarth, Alison Stone and William Matthews. As a sample the editor selected these lines from "Nightfall" by Yusef Komunyakaa:

> Every Saturday night someone new

> *Is on his arm, her low-cut gown*
> *A school of angelfish.*

The editor says the review is 64 pgs., 5½×8½, perfect-bound, offset, with b&w cover art. Press run is 500 for 300 subscribers of which 5 are libraries. Subscription: $10. **Sample postpaid: $6. No previously published poems or simultaneous submissions. Reads submissions August 1 through May 1 only. Seldom comments on rejections. Reports in 1-2 months. Pays 2 copies and year's subscription. Acquires all rights. Returns rights upon publication.** "However, we ask contributors to notify us if they reprint their work from the *Review* and to acknowledge the *Review* when reprinting." Reviews books of poetry "but only those of Illionis authors or presses." Query first. They will be inaugurating The Heartland Award in 1994. Send SASE for guidelines. Individuals or institutions interested in becoming members of Illinois Writers, Inc., which includes a one-year subscription to both *The Illinois Review* and the *I.W.I. Newsletter*, may also send SASE for membership rates. The editor says, "While *The Illinois Review* is published by Illinois Writers, Inc., an organization dedicated to supporting in-state writers, it is not a regional journal but publishes work by poets throughout the U.S. and elsewhere, as well as by Illinois residents. It is truly eclectic. Potential contributors are advised to buy a sample before submitting, but this is not a requirement."

ILLUMINATIONS (II), Ryde School, Queens Rd., Ryde, Isle of Wight PO33 3BE England, founded 1982, editor Simon Lewis, is an annual "international magazine of contemporary writing, mainly poetry, some prose, some in translation." They want **"poetry with something to say and a sense of nerve as well as style." They do not want to see "anything twee or bland."** They have published poetry by Glyn Maxwell, Jack Mapanje and Diane Wakoski. As a sample we selected the first stanza of "When Your Time Has Gone" by Thomas Kretz:

> *Thin grey hair*
> *a skirt around a bald dome*
> *which can no longer hula*
> *to the drum of exotic ideas . . .*

Illuminations is 40 pgs., approximately 5⅞×8¼, professionally printed, saddle-stitched, with heavy paper cover. They accept 5-10% of the poetry received. Press run is 500 for 300 subscribers of which 10 are libraries, 50 shelf sales. Single copy: £3 ($5); subscription: £10 ($20) for 3 issues. **Sample postpaid: "variable (£3 upwards)." Previously published poems OK; no simultaneous submissions. Cover letter including "very brief biographical details" required. Seldom comments on rejections. Reports within 2 months. Pays 3 copies, "2 of same issue, 1 of next."** The editor says, "I look for good *poems* rather than at poets' resumes. My judgment is unashamedly subjective."

IMAGO: NEW WRITING; CITY OF BRISBANE POETRY AWARD (II, IV-Regional), (formerly *Imago Literary Magazine*), School of Communication and Organisational Studies, Q.U.T., GPO Box 2434, Brisbane 4001 Queensland, Australia, phone (07)864-2976, founded 1988, appears three times a year, publishing "the best Australian writing, placing particular emphasis on Queensland writing and culture, but also welcoming submissions from overseas. Poems preferably short—up to about 50 lines, most from 12-25 lines. Our main criterion is good writing." They have published poetry by Tom Shapcott, Bruce Dawe, Graeme Wilson and Nancy Cato. As a sample we selected these lines from "Falling Away" by Rosemary Allan-Coleman:

> *How discomfited we are by beauty*
> *that has had its day*
> *rose gone blowsy*
> *fungus leaking fluids*
> *flesh falling in folds.*

It is 90 pgs., digest-sized, with glossy card cover. They accept about 10% of 500 poems from about 150 writers. Press run 800 for 350 subscribers of which 36 are libraries. Subscription: $A21 in Australia. **Sample postpaid: $A9.50. Comments if requested. Reports in 1-6 months. Pays $A30-40 plus 1 copy. Buys first Australian serial rights.** They publish the winning poems of the City of Brisbane Poetry Award (annual). Reviews books of poetry in 600 words—"usually commissioned. Unsolicited reviews would have to be of books relevant to *Imago* (Queensland or writing)." Send books for consideration.

IMPLOSION PRESS; IMPETUS (I, II, IV-Erotica, women), 4975 Comanche Trail, Stow OH 44224, phone (216)688-5210, founded 1984, poetry editor Cheryl Townsend, publishes *Impetus*, a quarterly literary magazine, chapbooks, special issues. The editor would like to see **"strong social protest with raw emotion. No topic is taboo. Material should be straight from the gut, uncensored and real. Absolutely no nature poetry or rhyme for the sake of rhyme, oriental, or 'Kissy, kissy I love you' poems. Any length as long as it works. All subjects okay, providing it isn't too rank.** *Impetus* is now publishing an annual erotica and all female issue. Material should reflect that theme." They have published poetry by Ron Androla, Kurt Nimmo and Lonnie Sherman. As a sample the editor selected these lines from "Gun-shy" by B. Arcus Shoenborn:

>*Instead,*
>*I hid in my bedroom.*
>*Soaked between blooded sheets,*
>*I explored immaculate concepts.*
>*Then my white heart severed;*
>*It gushed rivers of angry rapists.*
>*One flagged a revolver;*
>*he held it to my head and said,*
>*I'd live, but couldn't tell.*

The 7½×9 magazine is photocopied from typescript, saddle-stapled. Press run is about 500, with 300 subscriptions. Generally a 3-month backlog. Sample postpaid: $4; make check payable to Cheryl Townsend. The editor says, "I prefer shorter, to-the-point work." Include name and address on each page. Previously published work OK if it is noted when and where. Send SASE for guidelines. Usually reports within 2 months. Pays 1 copy. Acquires first rights. In her comments on rejections, the editor usually refers poets to other magazines she feels would appreciate the work more. Reviews books of poetry. Open to unsolicited reviews. Poets may also send books for review consideration. She says, "Bear with the small press. We're working as best as we can and usually harder. We can only do so much at a time. Support the small presses!"

‡IMPROVIJAZZATION NATION (I), HQ, 19th Supcom, Unit 15015, P.O. Box 2879, APO AP 96218-0171, founded 1991, editor Dick Metcalf, who is currently stationed in Korea. *Improvijazzation Nation* is a quarterly "devoted to networking; prime focus is tape/music reviews, includes quite a bit of poetry." They want "experimental, visual impact and non-establishment poetry, no more than 15 lines. No hearts and flowers, shallow, epic." They have recently published poetry by John M. Bennett, Joan Payne Kincaid and Anthony Lucero. The editor says *IN* is 20 pgs., 8½×11, photocopied, no binding. They receive 50-100 poems a year, use approximately 50%. Press run is 100. Single copy: $1.50 or 5 first class stamps. Sample postpaid: $2. Previously published poems and simultaneous submissions OK. Often comments on rejections. Reports within a week or two. "No payment, no contributor's copies, no tearsheets; poets must buy the issue their work appears in." Reviews books of poetry. Also accepts short essays/commentary on the use of networking to void commercial music markets, as well as material of interest to musical/artist improvisors.

INDIA CURRENTS (IV-Ethnic, regional), P.O. Box 21285, San Jose CA 95151, phone (408)274-6966, founded 1987, editor Arvind Kumar, is a monthly magazine about Indian culture in the U.S. They want "poetry that offers an insight into India, Indians, Indian Americans; very brief works stand a better chance of acceptance." They do not want "poetry that exploits mystery or exoticism about India or long poems (over 300 words). Readership is 70% Indian, 30% non-Indian." They have published poetry by Chitra Divakaruni. It is 72 pgs, 8½×11, offset, newsprint, saddle-stitched. They receive 50-75 submissions a year, "accept fewer than 12." Press run is 27,000 for 9,000 subscribers. Rest distributed free at stores, restaurants and libraries. Single copy: $1.95; subscription: $19.95. Sample postpaid: $3. Previously published poems and simultaneous submissions OK. Cover letter with brief bio and background required. Time between acceptance and publication is 6-12 months. Send SASE for guidelines. Reports in 3 months. Reviews books of poetry in 300 words maximum. Open to unsolicited reviews. Poets may also send books for review consideration. The magazine received a Cultural Awareness through Journalism Award from the Federation of Indo-American Associations in 1991. The editor says, "*India Currents* has a heavy tilt in favor of arts. We feel that arts can contribute to global understanding and peace by bringing it about at a personal level. America needs to learn about India just as India needs to learn about America."

INDIANA REVIEW (II), 316 N. Jordan Ave., Indiana University, Bloomington IN 47405, founded 1982, is a biannual of new fiction and poetry. "In general the *Review* looks for fresh, original poems of insight, poems that are challenging without being obtuse. We'll consider all types of poems—free verse, traditional, experimental. Reading a sample issue is the best way to determine if *IR* is a potential home for your work. Any subject matter is acceptable if it is written well." They have recently published poetry by David Mura, Charles Flowers, David Jauss, Larissa Szporluk and Pattiann Rogers. The magazine uses about 40-60 pgs. of poetry in each issue (6×9, flat-spined, 200 pages, color matte cover,

---

Market categories: (I) Beginning; (II) General; (III) Limited; (IV) Specialized; (V) Closed.

professional printing). The magazine has 1,000 subscriptions of which 120 are libraries. They receive about 8,000 submissions/year of which they use about 60. **Sample postpaid: $7. Submit no more than 4-5 pgs. of poetry. "Please indicate stanza breaks on poems over 1 page. Simultaneous submissions very strongly discouraged."** Pays $5/page when available ($10 minimum/poem), plus 2 copies and remainder of year's subscription. Buys first North American serial rights only. **"We try to respond to manuscripts in two to three months. Reading time is often slower during summer months."** This magazine's reputation continues to grow in literary circles. It is generally accepted now as one of the best publications, featuring all styles, forms and lengths of poetry (much of it exciting or tense). Brief book reviews are also featured in some issues. Send books for review consideration.

INDIGO MAGAZINE: THE SPANISH-CANADIAN PRESENCE IN THE ARTS (IV-Foreign languages, translations, themes), Room 252, Atkinson College, York University, North York, Ontario M3T 1P3 Canada, phone (416)736-2100, ext. 6632, founded 1989, editor-in-chief Prof. Margarita Feliciano, appears twice a year using **"poetry to be thematically of Hispanic contents if written in French or English (not the case if written in Spanish)."** They have published poetry by Rafael Barreto-Rivera and Rosemary Sullivan. As a sample the editor selected these lines (poet unidentified):

> *I was born on this lip of stone*
> *Jutting out over the jungle*
> *I've never wanted to go down.*
> *As a child I would run to the edge to catch the birds*
> *or follow the lizards with my hand along the ledges.*

It is 150+ pgs., professionally printed, flat-spined, with glossy card cover. "I accept 50% of submissions (about 40)." Press run 300 for 50 subscribers. Subscription: $25. **Cover letter, including background on the poet, required with submissions. Price of sample, payment, reporting time not given. The editor says she always comments on rejections.** Open to unsolicited reviews.

INFINITY LIMITED: A JOURNAL FOR THE SOMEWHAT ECCENTRIC (II), P.O. Box 2713, Castro Valley CA 94546, phone (510)581-8172, founded 1988, editor-in-chief Genie Lester, is a "literary quarterly dedicated to presenting emerging talent attractively illustrated. Staff artists illustrate most work, but we encourage writer-artists to submit their own illustrations." They want poetry that **"deals in an original way with concerns common to all of us."** They have recently published poetry by William Nesbit, Norman Kraeft, Norman Kirk and Kenneth Johnson. As a sample the editor selected the first lines of "The Buddhas of Borobudur" by I.B. Nelson:

> *The Buddhas of Borobudur*
> *stare in ageless silence*
> > *the patience of stone.*
> *The carved maidens and young men*
> *a reverie in frozen dance*
> *broken only by crackling grit echoes*
> > *of curious slow foot steps*

It is magazine-sized, "printed on 60 lb. bond with parchment cover (2-3 color)" and appears "more or less quarterly, 4 times a year. We receive about 40 submissions per week, use about 25 poems per issue." Press run 1,000 for 250+ subscriptions. Subscription: $10. **Sample postpaid: $3.95. Send SASE for guidelines. Simultaneous submissions and occasionally previously published poems OK. "Bio info is helpful if work accepted." Reads submissions January 1 through June 1 and September 1 through November 15. Reports within 6 months, "but we read everything." Editor comments on submissions "if writing or art shows promise." Pays 2 copies.** Acquires one-time or first reprint rights. Open to unsolicited reviews. Poets may also send books for review consideration. The editor says, "We are small but growing rapidly, probably because we are willing to work with our writers and artists and we make an effort to present material attractively."

INKSHED—POETRY AND FICTION (II); INKSHED PRESS (V), 387 Beverley Rd., Hull, N. Humberside HU5 1LS England, founded 1985, editorial director Anthony Smith, poetry editor Lesli Markham, is a biannual using **"any good quality poetry, traditional or contemporary, not sexist or racist."** They have published poetry by Gerald Locklin, Richard Paul Schmonsees and Roshan Kagda. As a sample the editors selected this poem, "Glass Vase," by Mary Maher:

> *A blower's alter-lung*
> *it swung against the hour from the fire.*
>
> *The roundness swells*
> *and thins with each restraining breath.*
>
> *The song is silent but seen:*

only the membrane sings phrased in steam.

timed in old alder spoons
worn smooth by wind's sublimated tongue.

Air, glazed and cool
keys the eye.

Inkshed is digest-sized, perfect-bound, 80 pgs., printed on gloss paper from typeset. Their press run is 500 with 200 subscriptions. Subscription: $12 for 2 issues. **Sample postpaid: $5. "Please send cash only & U.S. dollars or Sterling—dollar cheques are too expensive to exchange." They consider simultaneous submissions and previously published poems. Cover letter required. Reports in 1 month. Pays 1 copy.** Reviews books of poetry in 150-200 words/book. Open to unsolicited reviews. Poets may also send books for review consideration to Reviews Editor, *Inkshed*, 21 Sycamore Court, Park Grove, Hull HU5 2UL England. **Inkshed Press publishes 1 chapbook/year averaging 30 pgs., but only by invitation.** Anthony Smith advises, "Please study what is being written today—note trends but don't copy—be an individual, that's what poetry is about."

INKSTONE: A MAGAZINE OF HAIKU (IV-Form), P.O. Box 75009, Hudson Bay P.O., Toronto, Ontario M4W 3T3 Canada, founded 1982, poetry editors Keith Southward, Marshall Hryciuk and J. Louise Fletcher, "is a publication dedicated to the development of a distinctive English language haiku and to the craft of writing as it relates to haiku. Submissions reflecting these concerns are welcomed. We publish haiku and related forms, plus reviews, articles related to haiku. **Poems must be haiku or related but we use a very liberal definition of haiku."** They have published haiku by Carol Montgomery, Alexis Rotella, Akira Kowano and Guy Beining. There are roughly 20 pgs. of poetry and reviews/articles in the digest-sized format, 40 pgs., offset from typescript, matte card cover. Circulation 100. They accept "perhaps 10%" of the poems submitted each year. Poems appear as space permits, usually in the next issue after acceptance. **Sample postpaid: $5.50. Submit any number of poems, preferably 1 per 5½ × 8½ sheet, typewritten.** Editor "occasionally" comments on rejections. **Reports within 6 weeks. Pays 1 copy. Acquires first serial rights.** Reviews books of poetry in 1 to 3 pgs., single or multi-book format. Open to unsolicited reviews. Poets may also send books for review consideration "with an indication that it is a review copy."

INKY BLUE (I), 3200 North Rd., Greenport NY 11944, founded 1989 by Cat Spydell, editor as of December 1992 is Yvonne Lieblein, appears biannually or thereabouts. In 1993, Yvonne Lieblein moved production from San Francisco to the East coast where she continues her predecessor's quest for **"thought-provoking poetry, with a tendency to avoid the mundane. No sexist, red-necked-beer-bellied-middle-American-women-are-only-good-if-they-have-flat-heads poetry."** She has recently published poetry by John Platt, Jon Davies, Richard Davignon and Marcia Cohee. As a sample the editor selected these lines from "zoned" by Scott C. Holstad:

he be wearin
deep
dish
shirt
say
java cool
dig
wit stone cold
tune of
fountain jetting
into liquid
air . . . . .

The magazine averages 45 pgs. and is digest-sized with matte card cover. Press run is 85-300 depending on funding. The editor accepts 40% of submissions. Subscription: $10/year. **Sample: $5 plus $1 postage and handling. Previously published poems and simultaneous submissions OK. Poems without a SASE or without the poet's name and address on each page will not be considered. Pays 1 copy.** Rights revert to poet after publication. *Inky Blue* ranked #10 in the "New Poets" category of the June 1993 *Writer's Digest* Poetry 60 list. This category ranks those markets who often publish poets whose work is new to their publication. The editor says, "Between changing hands, stacks of new submissions and our move, things have been hectic. I write each submitting poet a personal letter and take the time to critique the work if that's requested or if I had more than two cups of coffee that morning. Be patient, I'm wading out of the pile of poetry in my office. My advice: Get your work out there! We're not setting any boundaries except for length. Poems over two pages long have to set the world on fire to be considered."

INNISFREE MAGAZINE (II), P.O. Box 277, Manhattan Beach CA 90266, phone (310)545-2607, fax (310)546-5862, founded 1981, editor Rex Winn, appears every other month with many short stories and poetry. "Items of merit: Entertainment value—humor, fright, emotional experience; Something for the reader to take away—inspiration, enlightenment, interesting information; Writing craft—structure, style and technique." They have published poetry by William Doreski, Barry Sheinkopf and Josephine C. Radai. As a sample, the editor selected these lines by Arlene Joffee Pollack:

> My impulses ride herd on me
> And I, astonished,
> Powerless, stare
> At the world around me
> Through a beggar's eyes,
> Rattling the empty beggar cup
> And yet ashamed to own the cup
> At all.

It is 56 pgs., magazine-sized, saddle-stapled, professionally printed with matte card cover. Verse seems to play second fiddle to fiction here, but the editor tries to make space for all types, haiku to formal (including verse by children). They accept about 15% of poetry received. Press run 350-500 for 200 subscribers of which 3 are libraries. Subscription: $25. **Sample postpaid: $5. Previously published poems and simultaneous submissions OK. Reads submissions January 1 through September 30. Send SASE for guidelines. Pays "splattered awards" but no copies. Acquires first rights. "If a person asks, I will comment. Sometimes I can't resist anyway!"** Reviews books of poetry. Send books for review consideration.

INSECTS ARE PEOPLE TOO; PUFF 'N' STUFF PRODUCTIONS (I, IV-Theme), P.O. Box 146486, Chicago IL 60614, phone (312)772-8686, founded 1989, publisher H.R. Felgenhauer, an infrequent publication focusing solely on "poems about insects doing people things and people doing insect things." The first issue was a collection of the publisher's own poems. As a sample he selected these lines from "Resist and You Will be Destroyed":

> Geometrical abstraction of space-vehicle-ness sprouts conquest.
> Inferior species succumb to superior weapons, transport and
> communication systems blistering through onion skinned civilizations.
> They were bigger and better and all around us; we expanded right
> into their hoary mouths, razor sharp venom spouting ruin . . .

Insects is 8½ × 11, stapled down the side, with card cover, b&w art and graphics. Press run is 400. Single copy: $3. **Sample postpaid: $4. Previously published poems and simultaneous submissions OK. Often comments on rejections. Reports "immediately." Pay varies.** Open to unsolicited reviews. Poets may also send books for review consideration. Puff 'N' Stuff Productions publishes 1 chapbook/year. **Replies to queries and mss in 10 days. Pay is negotiable.** H.R. Felgenhauer says, "Hit me with your best shot. Never give up—editors have tunnel-vision. The *BEST* mags you almost *NEVER* even hear about. Don't believe reviews. Write for yourself. Prepare for failure, not success."

‡INSOMNIA & POETRY (I), P.O. Box 4453, Stamford CT 06907-0453, founded 1991, publishes irregularly, "but at least four times a year. This publication was started to give poets more opportunity to express themselves without the pressures of editorial intimidation (cover letters, guidelines, etc.). Please send us your most poignant poetry—as the publication's title suggests. We try not to discriminate." They have recently published poetry by Sal Morgera, Bill Holler and Patrick Stephen Prince. As a sample the editor selected these lines from "My Place" by Frederick J. Verhoeven Jr.:

> Imaginations explode
> into a million decadent
> wonderful ideas
> We laugh in my den
> at those bound by the second hand
> going in circles

Insomnia & Poetry is 8 pgs., 8½ × 11, photocopied with occasional photographs accompanying poems. Press run is 250, all distributed free—left in libraries, bookstores and at colleges. **Sample postpaid: $1. Previously published poems and simultaneous submissions OK. Reports ASAP. Usually pays 2 copies and subscription at poet's request.** The editor says, "We don't think poetic expression is some privilege to be 'crafted' by only a select bunch. We think of it as human expression that can be shown by anyone—a cathartic endeavor for all."

INTERIM (II), Department of English, University of Nevada, Las Vegas, Las Vegas NV 89154, phone (702)739-3172, magazine, founded in Seattle, 1944-55, revived 1986. Editor A. Wilber Stevens, associate editors James Hazen and Joseph B. McCullough, English editor John Heath-Stubbs. Member

CLMP, New York. Indexed in **Index of American Periodical Verse.** Appears twice a year, **publishing the best poetry and short fiction it can find, no specific demands in form, new and established writers.** They have published poems by John Heath-Stubbs, William Stafford, Richard Eberhart, Diane Wakoski, Stephen Stepanchev, Jim Barnes and Anca Vlasopolos. As a sample we selected these lines from "Winter's Tale" by Charlotte F. Otten:

> *Her voice is silent now,*
> *sunk deep into the tap root of her brain.*
> *A stroke that struck her throat*
> *blizzarded all sound.*
> *Words swirl around her like an early snow*
> *clinging to unfallen leaves.*

Interim is 48 pgs., 6×9, professionally printed and saddle-stapled with coated card cover. Press run is 600. Individual subscription: $8 one year, $13 two years, $16 three years; libraries: $14/year. **Sample copy: $5. Submit 4-6 poems, SASE and brief biographical note. No simultaneous submissions. Decision in 2 months. Pays two contributor's copies and a two-year subscription.** *Interim* acquires copyright. Poems may be reprinted elsewhere with a permission line noting publication in *Interim.* Starting short poetry review. Send books for review consideration.

INTERNATIONAL BLACK WRITERS; BLACK WRITER MAGAZINE (I, IV-Ethnic), P.O. Box 1030, Chicago IL 60690, founded 1970, contact Mable Terrell, executive director. *BWM* is a "quarterly literary magazine to showcase new writers and poets and provide educational information for writers. **Open to all types of poetry."** The editor describes it as 30 pgs., magazine-sized, offset printing, with glossy cover, circulation 1,000 for 200 subscriptions. Subscription: $19/year. **Sample postpaid: $1.50. Reports in 10 days, has 1 quarter backlog. Pays 10 copies. For chapbook publication (40 pgs.), submit 2 sample poems and cover letter with short bio. Simultaneous submissions OK. Pays copies. For sample chapbook send SASE with bookrate postage.** They offer awards of $100, $50 and $25 for the best poems published in the magazine and present them to winners at annual awards banquet. *IBW* is open to all writers.

‡**INTERNATIONAL POETRY REVIEW (II, IV-Translation),** Dept. of Romance Languages, UNC-Greensboro, Greensboro NC 27412, phone (909)334-5655, fax (909)334-5404, founded 1975, editor Mark Smith-Soto, is a biannual primarily publishing **translations of contemporary poetry with corresponding originals (published on facing pages) as well as original poetry in English.** They have recently published poetry by Fred Chappell, Lyn Lifshin, Pureza Canelo, Jaime Sabines and Olga Orozco. As a sample the editor selected these lines from "Poema de Invierno" by Chilean poet Jorge Teillier:

> *En la casa ha empezado la fiesta.*
> *Pero el niño sabe que la fiesta está en otra parte,*
> *y mira por la ventana buscando a los desconocidos*
> *que pasará toda la vida tratando de encontrar.*

translated as "Winter Poem" by Mary Crow:

> *In the house the party has begun.*
> *But the child knows the party is somewhere else,*
> *and he looks out the window searching for the strangers*
> *he will spend his whole life trying to find.*

IPR is 84 pgs., 5½×8½, professionally printed and perfect-bound with 2-3 color cover. "We accept 10% of original poetry in English and about 80% of translations submitted." Press run is 500 for 200 subscribers of which 100 are libraries. Subscription: $10 individuals, $15 institutions. **Sample postpaid: $5. Submit no more than 10 pages of poetry. No previously published poems; simultaneous submissions OK. Seldom comments on rejections. Send SASE for guidelines. Reports in 1 month. Pays 1 copy. All rights revert to authors and translators.** Occasionally reviews book of poetry. Open to unsolicited reviews. Poets may also send books for review consideration. The editor says, "We strongly encourage contributors to subscribe. We get too much original poetry and not enough translation. We prefer poetry in English to have an international or cross-cultural theme."

‡**INTERNATIONAL POETS ACADEMY; INTERNATIONAL POETS (I, IV-Membership),** 5, Mohamed Hussain Khan Lane, Royapettah, Madras 600-014, India, founded 1981, poetry editor Prof. Syed Ameeruddin. The Academy publishes books by members (for a price) and brings out special numbers of *International Poets,* their quarterly journal publishing poetry by members, "highlighting the poems of selected poets with detailed bio-data and with a scholarly critical article focusing the main features of the selected poet's poetry to the world audience, with a photograph of the poet published on the front cover." **Membership is $40 a year. Life fellow membership is $100.** They have recently published poetry by Naomi F. Faust (USA), Eda Howink (USA), David Moe (USA) and Rhee Han Ho (South Korea). The editor describes the quarterly as 5¼×8½, perfect-bound; printed in Madras. Reviews

books of poetry. They also publish 3 chapbooks/year subsidized by the poets. For details contact the Academy.

INTERNATIONAL POETS OF THE HEART; THE LAY POET (I), P.O. Box 463, Midvale UT 84047-0463, founded 1988, poetry editor Bob Curtis. International Poets of the Heart is an organization "for the mutual interaction of the ideas and ideals as concepts from the heart. Our purpose is the meaningful communication of these concepts, 'heart to heart.' " They publish *The Lay Poet* annually. It contains "up to 100 of the best submissions we receive throughout the year (deadline: October 1). We consider almost all types of poetry up to 36 lines in length. We favor poetry of a romantic or humorous nature." Send SASE for guidelines before submitting. There is no submission or reading fee required, however "notification of publication will be the current edition" which poets may purchase for $5 postpaid.

INTERSTATE RELIGIOUS WRITERS ASSOCIATION (IRWA) NEWSLETTER AND WORKSHOPS (V, IV-Membership, religious), 104 Meadow Lane, Tipton IA 52772, founded 1981, coeditors Marvin Ceynar and Barbara Ceynar, publishes a newsletter that "gives information mostly about religious writing but also information about secular publications that religious people feel comfortable publishing in." It uses **poetry by members suitable for an ecumenical Christian readership, but is not currently accepting mss.** *IRWA Newsletter* appears 6 times a year, magazine-sized, 11 pgs., 200 subscribers. Subscription: $12. **Sample postpaid: $2.15.**

INTERTEXT (V, IV-Translations), 2633 E. 17th Ave., Anchorage AK 99508-3207, founded 1982, poetry editor Sharon Ann Jaeger, is "devoted to producing lasting works in every sense. We specialize in poetry, translations and short works in the fine arts and literary criticism. **We publish work that is truly excellent—no restrictions on form, length or style. Cannot use religious verse.** Like both surrealist and realist poetry, poetry with intensity, striking insight, vivid imagery, fresh metaphor, musical use of language in both word sounds and rhythm. Must make the world—in all its dimensions—come alive." To give a sense of her taste she says, "I admire the work of Louise Glück, William Stafford, Jim Wayne Miller, Eleanor Wilner, Antonio Ramos Rosa and Rainer Maria Rilke." As a sample the editor chose these lines by Louis Hammer from **The Mirror Dances:**

> *From this room with its coarse bed*
> *we see the path of fire,*
> *Suddenly the vertebra cracks,*
> *it pushes toward us*
> *the wheel of human matter.*
> *All the gods are men*
> *with a fissure of darkness.*

She says, **"Given the projects we have in train, Intertext will not be looking at any unsolicited mss until 1995."** Query first with 3 samples only and SASE. "Cover letter optional—the sample poems are always read first—but no form letters, please. If sample poems are promising, then the complete ms will be requested." Simultaneous queries OK. Payment: 10% royalty after costs of production, promotion and distribution have been recovered. No longer publishes chapbooks but only "full-length collections by poets of demonstrated achievement."

INTRO (IV-Students), AWP, Old Dominion University, Norfolk VA 23529-0079, phone (804)683-3839, founded 1970, publications manager D.W. Fenza. See Associated Writing Programs in the Organizations Useful to Poets section of this book. **Students in college writing programs belonging to AWP may submit to this consortium of magazines publishing student poetry, fiction and plays.** They are open as to the type of poetry submitted except they do not want "non-literary, haiku, etc." As to poets they have published, they say, "In our history, we've introduced Dara Wier, Carolyn Forché, Greg Pope, Norman Dubie and others." Circulation 9,500. **Programs nominate *Intro* works in the fall. Ask the director of your writing program for more information.**

‡INVERTED-A, INC.; INVERTED-A HORN (I), 401 Forrest Hill, Grand Prairie TX 75051, phone (214)264-0066, founded 1977, editors Amnon Katz and Aya Katz, a very small press that evolved from publishing technical manuals for other products. "Our interests center on justice, freedom, individual rights and free enterprise." *Inverted-A Horn* is a periodical, magazine-sized, offset, usually 9 pages, which appears irregularly; circulation is 300. **Freelance submissions of poetry for *Horn* and chapbooks are accepted. They publish 1 chapbook/year.** The editors do not want to see anything "modern, formless, existentialist." As a sample, they quote the following lines by F.L. Light:

> *He played the scourger, not perforce disgraced,*
> *And gratified New York, not stricken down.*
> *On provocation giving fight he faced*
> *Latrociny to vanquish it alone.*

Queries are reported on in 2 weeks, mss in 2 months. Simultaneous submissions are OK. Pay

is one free copy and a 40% discount on further copies. Samples: "A recent issue of the *Horn* can be had by merely sending a SASE (subject to availability)." The editor says "I strongly recommend that would-be contributors avail themselves of this opportunity to explore what we are looking for. Most of the submissions we receive do not come close."

IOTA (II), 67 Hady Crescent, Chesterfield, Derbyshire S41 0EB Great Britain, phone +44246-276532 (UK: 0246-276532), founded 1988, editor David Holliday, is a quarterly wanting "any style and subject; no specific limitations as to length, though, obviously, the shorter a poem is, the easier it is to get it in, which means that poems over 40 lines can still get in if they seem good enough. No concrete poetry (no facilities), or self-indulgent logorrhea." They have recently published poetry by Michael Hatwell, Paul Greene, Sophie Hannah, James Kirkup, Alun Rees and Thomas Kretz. As a sample the editor selected these lines by Nuriel Gibson:

> The boy soprano
> interceded for me
> at the altar
> divining my silence
> in perfect pitch.

Iota is printed from typescript, saddle-stapled, 36 pgs., with colored paper cover. Their press run is 400 with 200 subscriptions of which 6 are libraries. They publish about 200 of 4,000 poems received. Subscription: $8 (£4). Sample postpaid: $2 (£1) "but sometimes sent free." The editor prefers name and address on each poem, typed, "but provided it's legible, am happy to accept anything." He considers simultaneous submissions, but previously published poems "only if outstanding." First report in 1-3 weeks (unless production of the next issue takes precedence) but final acceptance/rejection may take up to a year. Pays 2 copies. Acquires first British serial rights only. Editor usually comments on rejections, "but detailed comment only when time allows and the poem warrants it." Reviews books of poetry in about 200 words, single or multi-book format. Open to unsolicited reviews. Poets may also send books for review consideration. He says, "I am after crafted verse that says something; self-indulgent word-spinning is out. All editors have their blind spots; the only advice I can offer a beginning poet is to find a sympathetic editor (and you will only do that by seeing their magazines) and not to be discouraged by initial lack of success. Keep plugging!"

THE IOWA REVIEW (II), Dept. PM, 308 EPB, University of Iowa, Iowa City IA 52242, phone (319)335-0462, founded 1970, editor David Hamilton (first readers for poetry and occasional guest editors vary), appears 3 times a year in a flat-spined, 200-page professionally printed format. The editor says, "We simply look for poems that at the time we read and choose, we admire. No specifications as to form, length, style, subject matter or purpose. There are around 30-40 pgs. of poetry in each issue and currently we like to give several pages to a single poet." They receive about 5,000 submissions/year, use about 100. Editors of this influential journal do seem open to all styles and lengths, with most poems falling into the lyric free verse category. Diction, for the most part, is accessible although some examples show degrees of experimentation with form. In all, poems evoke intriguing situations or ideas. Circulation 1,200-1,300 with 1,000 subscriptions of which about half are libraries. Subscription: $18. Sample postpaid: $6. Reads submissions September 1 through May 1 only. Their backlog is "around a year. Sometimes people hit at the right time and come out in a few months." Occasional comments on rejections or suggestions on accepted poems. They report in 1-4 months. Pays $1 a line, 2-3 copies and a year's subscription. Buys first North American serial rights. Poetry published in *The Iowa Review* has also been included in Best American Poetry 1992. The editor advises, "That old advice of putting poems in a drawer for 9 years was rather nice; I'd at least like to believe the poems had endured with their author for 9 months."

IOWA WOMAN (IV-Women), Dept. PM, P.O. Box 680, Iowa City IA 52244, phone (319)277-8077, founded 1976, poetry editor Sandra Adelmund. "We are a literary quarterly with interest in women's issues. It is a literary magazine that has received national recognition for editorial excellence. We are publishing work by women, about women, and for women. Prefer contemporary poetry that is clear and concise. Prefer narrative and lyric. No greeting card verse." They have published poetry by Lyn Lifshin, Alice Friman, Rochelle Nameroff and Jeane Emmons. As a sample the editor selected these lines by Maria S. Wickwire:

> She forgot and forgot, releasing
> small things with infinite patience and love
> gently pulling threads from the tapestry she had kept so long in place.
>
> As she forgot the foxes, they came out from the trees
> and leaned their soft noses into her palms.
> All the forgotten birds came down in a flock, returning their wordless songs.

Iowa Woman is elegantly printed, 48 pgs., magazine-sized, 4-color cover with "original cover art and illustrations." Of 2,000 poems received "I accept about 30." Press run is 4,000 for 2,000 subscriptions. **Sample postpaid: $4. No simultaneious submissions. Guidelines available for SASE. Pays subscription and extra copies. Acquires first-time rights.** Reviews books of poetry in 500-1,000 words. Open to unsolicited reviews. Poets may also send books to Book Editor for review consideration. "No guarantee that books sent will be reviewed; this is at the discretion of our reviewers." They hold an annual poetry contest with first place prize of $150. $6 entry fee, 3 poems, for non-subscribers. Last year's judge was Ellen Bryant Voigt. All entrants receive a copy of the issue with the winners. Deadline December 15.

IRON PRESS; IRON (II), 5 Marden Terrace, Cullercoats, North Shields, Tyne & Wear, NE30 4PD England, phone (091)2531901, founded 1973, poetry editors Peter Mortimer and David Stephenson, "publishes contemporary writing both in magazine form (*Iron*) and in individual books. Magazine concentrates on poetry, the books on prose and drama." They are **"open to many influences, but no 19th century derivatives please, or work from people who seem unaware anything has happened poetically since Wordsworth."** Peter Mortimer says, "Writing is accepted and published because when I read it I feel the world should see it—if I don't feel that, it's no good. What's the point of poetry nobody understands except the poet?" The poets they have recently published include John Whitworth, Richard Kostelanetz and Sharon Olds. *Iron* is 8¼ × 7¾, flat-spined, professionally printed in small type, 1-3 columns, using b&w photos and graphics, three-color glossy card cover, about 50 pgs. of poetry in each issue, circulation 1,000; 600 subscriptions of which 50 are libraries. **Sample: $10 (bills only, no checks) postpaid, or £3. Submit a maximum of 5 poems. "Just the poems—no need for long-winded backgrounds. The poems must stand by themselves." He reports in "2 weeks maximum." Pays £10/page. He always comments on rejections "provided poets keep to our maximum of 5 poems per submission."** Staff reviews books of poetry. Send books for review consideration % Val Laws, Reviews Editor. They do not invite poetry submissions for books, which they commission themselves. The editor advises, "Don't start submitting work too soon. It will only waste your own and editors' time. Many writers turn out a few dozen poems, then rush them off before they've learnt much of the craft, never mind the art." And about his occupation as editor, this journalist, poet, playwright and humorist says, "Small magazines and presses contain some awful writing, which is inevitable. They also contain a kind of truth which the large commercial organizations (over-burdened with marketing men, accountants and financial advisors) have long forgotten. And the good writing in small presses more than compensates for the awful."

ISRAEL HORIZONS (IV-Ethnic), #403, 224 W. 35th St., New York NY 10001, founded 1952, editor Ralph Seliger, poetry consultants Rochelle Ratner and Jon Shevin. A quarterly Socialist-Zionist periodical which **uses poetry reflecting Israeli and Jewish culture and concerns.** *Israel Horizons* reflects the Israeli left and the Zionist peace camp in Israel, including but not exclusively *Mapam* and the National Kibbutz (*Artzi*) Federation; it deals with current challenges to Israeli Society and the world Jewish community from a Socialist-Zionist perspective and examines questions confronting democratic socialism in our day. It includes editorial comments, regular columns on various topics and book and film reviews. It has an international readership with readers in the U.S., Israel, Canada and 22 other countries. The publication is 8½ × 11, 32-40 pgs. Press run is 5,000. Subscription: $15/year. **Sample: $3 and SASE.**

ISSUES (IV-Religious), P.O. Box 424885, San Francisco CA 94142, founded 1973, is an 8- to 12-page newsletter offering a Messianic Jewish viewpoint on Christian beliefs and using some **poetry relevant to that cause.** Circulation 50,000, all distributed free. **Send SASE for free sample. Considers simultaneous submissions. Pays.**

ITALIAN AMERICANA (IV-Ethnic), URI/CCE, 199 Promenade St., Providence RI 02908-5090, founded 1974, editor Carol Bonomo Albright, appears twice a year using **2-4 poems "on Italian-American subjects, no more than 3 pgs. No trite nostalgia; no poems about grandparents."** As a sample the editor selected these lines from "Inside the Inside of the Moon" by Brian McCormick:

> *Armstrong's hop from module videos*
> *To earth: Mom Vecchio lays down a heart.*
> *She asks, "When is he going to go in?"*
> *This puts a stop to the conversation.*

It is 150-200 pgs., 6 × 9, professionally printed, flat-spined. Press run is 2,000 for 1,500 subscribers of which 260 are libraries, the rest individual adult subscribers. Subscription: $25. **Sample postpaid: $12.50. Cover letter not required "but helpful." Name on first page of ms only. Do not submit mss in December or January.** They have 2 readers, anonymous peer review of mss. **Occasionally comments on rejections. Reports in 4-6 weeks. Pays year's subscription. Acquires first rights.** Reviews books of poetry in 1,000 words, multi-book format. Open to unsolicited reviews. Poets may also send books for review consideration to Prof. John Paul Russo, English Dept., University of Miami, Coral Gables FL 33124.

ITALICA PRESS (IV-Translations), #605, 595 Main St., New York NY 10044-0047, phone (212)935-4230, founded 1985, publishers Eileen Gardiner and Ronald G. Musto, is a small press publisher of **English translations of Italian works** in Smyth-sewn paperbacks, averaging 175 pgs. They have recently published **Guido Cavalcanti, The Complete Poems**, a dual language (English/Italian) book with English translation and introduction by Marc Cirigliano. **Query with 10 sample translations of important 20th Century or medieval and Renaissance Italian poets. Include cover letter, bio and list of publications. Simultaneous submissions OK, but translation should not be "totally" previously published. Reports on queries in 3 weeks, on mss in 3 months. Pays 7-15% royalties plus 10 author's copies. Buys English language rights. Editor sometimes comments on rejections.**

JACKSON'S ARM (III), % Sunk Island Publishing, Box 74, Lincoln LN1 1QG England, founded 1985, editor Michael Blackburn, is a small press publisher of poetry chapbooks and translations. "No specifications as to subject or style. **The poetry I want to publish should be vigorous and imaginative, with a firm grasp of everyday realities. Nothing bland, safe or pretentious.**" The press publishes occasional chapbooks, books, cards and cassettes. However, the editor says **he does not usually accept freelance submissions. Pays in copies: 10% of print run.** Mr. Blackburn advises, "Read everything you can, in particular *contemporary* poets and writers. Get hold of all the 'small' poetry magazines you can, as well as the more commercial and prestigious."

JAPANOPHILE (IV-Ethnic), P.O. Box 223, Okemos MI 48864, phone (517)349-1795, founded 1974, poetry editor Earl R. Snodgrass, is a literary quarterly about Japanese culture (not just in Japan). Issues include articles, art, a short story and **poetry. They want haiku or other Japanese forms or any form if it deals with Japan, Japanese culture or American-Japanese relations. (Note: karate and ikebana in the US are examples of Japanese culture.)** They have published poetry by Linda McFerrin, Dan Weinrich, Alexis Rotella, David Swirnoff, Lenard D. Moore, Mimi Hinman and reprints of Basho. There are 10-15 pgs. of poetry in each issue (digest-sized, about 56 pgs., saddle-stapled). They have a circulation of 400 with 100 subscriptions of which 30 are libraries. They receive about 500 submissions a year, use 70, have a 1-month backlog. **Sample postpaid: $4. Summer is the best time to submit. Cover letter required; include brief bio and credits if any. Send SASE for guidelines. Reports in 2 months. Pays $1 for haiku and up to $15 for longer poems.** Open to unsolicited reviews. Poets may also send books for review consideration, attn. Vada L. Davis. They sponsor a haiku contest. Deadline: September 30. Send SASE for details. They also publish books under the Japanophile imprint, but so far none have been of poetry. Query with samples and cover letter (about 1 pg.) giving publishing credits, bio.

JEOPARDY (II), College Hall 132, Western Washington University, Bellingham WA 98225, phone (206)650-3118, founded 1964, is an annual with an editorial staff of usually 3-5 people. "**We are willing to look at anything, but space limitations make publishing overlong stories, poems, essays difficult. Prefer poetry of no more than 3 single-spaced pages in length.**" They have published poetry by William Stafford, James Bertolino, Chris Jacox-Kyle, David Lee, Sam Hamill and Naomi Clark. The editor describes it as 108 pgs., size varies, offset. They occasionally review poetry. They use about 50 of 500 submissions received. Press run 4,000. **Sample postpaid: $4. Send SASE for guidelines. Reads submissions September 1 through January 15. Reports in February. Pays 2 copies.** When funds are available they offer competition for cash prizes. Past judges have included Madeline DeFrees, Ingrid Hill and Irene McKinney.

JEWISH CURRENTS (V), Suite 601, 22 E. 17th St., New York NY 10003, phone (212)924-5740, founded 1946, editor Morris U. Schappes, is a magazine appearing 11 times a year that publishes **poetry on Jewish themes. "We have been forced to declare a temporary moratorium on all poetry acceptances owing to the size of our backlog of material already accepted and awaiting publication in this category."** The editor says it is 48 pgs., 5×8, offset, saddle-stapled. Press run is 2,700 for 2,600 subscribers of which about 10% are libraries. Subscription: $20/year. **Sample postpaid: $2. Pays 6 copies.** Reviews books of poetry. Open to unsolicited reviews. Poets may also send books for review consideration.

JEWISH SPECTATOR (IV-Religious), 4391 Park Milano, Calabasas CA 91302, phone (818)591-7481, founded 1935, editor Robert Bleiweiss. *Jewish Spectator* is a 64-page Judaic scholarly quarterly that welcomes **poetry on Jewish themes. Subscribers: 1,200. No simultaneous submissions or previously published poems. Cover letter with brief bio (2-3 lines) required. Reports in 6 weeks. Pays 2 copies.**

Open to unsolicited reviews. Poets may also send books for review consideration.

JOE SOAP'S CANOE (II), 30 Quilter Rd., Felixstowe, Suffolk IP11 7JJ England, phone 0394-275569, founded 1978, poetry editor Martin Stannard, is engaged in "magazine and occasional booklet/chapbook publication; for a new poetry of optimism and despair, **caters especially to poets who are awake. I really only ever want to see good poetry, but life isn't like that. I'll promise to read whatever I'm sent. No limits, as long as it's in English."** They have published work by Tom Raworth, Lydia Tomkiw, Kenneth Koch, Paul Violi and Geoff Hattersley. As a sample the editor selected these lines from "The Paris Essays" by Lori Cummin-Meadows:

> There are so many wounded people. The indelible ink will never
> come out of that shirt, said the lank blonde. For a moment I
> thought I had spoken for the first time. I'm waiting to go home,
> have an itch between my legs, feel like all my sex-bits are losing
> contact with Control Central. D'you have any sort of schedule?
> Time's an abstract, and that's all there is to it. Do you feel okay?
> You look awful.

Joe Soap's Canoe appears annually, 100 pgs., perfect-bound format—"it's really a paperback book." The editor describes the magazine as "quite brilliant—in fact, of all the poetry magazines published in the U.K. it's one of the 2 or 3 always worth reading. It's certainly never boring. Some people hate it. I can relate to that . . ." They receive "thousands" of submissions each year, use 60-70. Press run is 400-500, for 200 subscribers of which 32 are libraries. Single copy: £4 or $8; subscription: £6 or $12 overseas. **Sample: $2 or £1.25. No simultaneous submissions. Cover letter required. Reads submissions April through September only. The editor comments on rejections "only when I'm provoked." Reports within 2 months. Pays in copies.** Send 9×5 envelope with return postage for catalog to buy samples. Any advice for poets? "No—the world is too large and poetry too various. I'm no advice agency and no tipster. Beginners should simply begin. And know when to stop. Reading the magazine before submitting may save them and me time, as well as doing some small thing for the world of trees."

THE JOHNS HOPKINS UNIVERSITY PRESS (V), 2715 N. Charles St., Baltimore MD 21218, founded 1878, editor-in-chief Eric Halpern. "One of the largest American university presses, Johns Hopkins is a publisher mainly of scholarly books and journals. We do, however, publish short fiction and poetry in the series Johns Hopkins: Poetry and Fiction, edited by John Irwin on 10% royalty contracts. **Unsolicited submissions are not considered."**

THE JOURNAL (III), Department of English, Ohio State University, 164 W. 17th Ave., Columbus OH 43210, founded 1972, coeditors Kathy Fagan and Michelle Herman, appears twice yearly with reviews, essays, quality fiction and poetry. **"We're open to all forms; we tend to favor work that gives evidence of a mature and sophisticated sense of the language."** They have published poetry by David Baker, T.R. Hummer, Cynthia Ozick and Carol Frost. The following sample is from the poem "The Helmet of Mambrino" by Linda Bierds:

> I would know that tumble often, that
> explorer's slide, belief to belief, conviction
> to its memory, to conviction. Once I placed
> my marker-coin on Mt. Whitney's double, lost in a mist,
> convinced I had climbed to the highest land. Once
> I charted a lake from opal air.

The Journal is 6×9, professionally printed on heavy stock, 80-100 pgs., of which about 40 in each issue are devoted to poetry. They receive about 4,000 submissions/year, use 200, and have a 3- to 6-month backlog. Press run is 1,500. Subscription: $8. Sample: $5. **On occasion editor comments on rejections. Pays copies and an honorarium of $25-50 when funds are available. Acquires all rights. Returns rights on publication.** Reviews books of poetry. Contributing editor David Citino advises, "However else poets train or educate themselves, they must do what they can to know our language. Too much of the writing that we see indicates that poets do not in many cases develop a feel for the possibilities of language, and do not pay attention to craft. Poets should not be in a rush to publish—until they are ready." (Also see Ohio State University Press/*The Journal* Award in Poetry.)

Use the General Index to find the page number of a specific publisher. If the publisher you are seeking is not listed, check the " '93-'94 Changes" list at the end of this section.

‡JOURNAL OF ASIAN MARTIAL ARTS (IV-Themes), 821 W. 24th St., Erie PA 16502, phone (814)455-9517, fax (814)838-7811, founded 1991, editor-in-chief Michael A. DeMarco, is a quarterly "comprehensive journal on Asian martial arts with high standards and academic approach." They want poetry about Asian martial arts and Asian martial art history/culture. They have no restrictions provided the poet has a feel for, and good understanding of, the subject. They don't want poetry showing a narrow view. "We look for a variety of styles from an interdisciplinary approach." The editor says the journal is 128 pgs., 8½×11, perfect-bound, with soft cover, b&w illustrations, computer and hand art and ads. Press run is 5,000 for 500 subscribers of which 50 are libraries, the rest mainly shelf sales. Single copy: $9.75; subscription: $32 for 1 year, $55 for 2 years. Sample postpaid: $10. Previously published poems OK; no simultaneous submissions. Cover letter required. Often comments on rejections. Send SASE for guidelines. Reports in 1-2 months. Pays $1-100 and/or 1-5 copies. Buys first and reprint rights. Reviews books of poetry "if they have some connection to Asian martial arts; length is open." Open to unsolicited reviews. Poets may also send books for review consideration. The editor adds, "We offer a unique medium for serious poetry dealing with Asian martial arts. Any style is welcome if there is quality in thought and writing."

JOURNAL OF NEW JERSEY POETS (II, IV-Regional), English Dept., County College of Morris, Randolph NJ 07869, phone (201)328-5471, founded 1976, editor Sander Zulauf. This biannual periodical uses poetry from current or former residents of New Jersey. They want "serious work that is regional in origin but universal in scope." They do not want "sentimental, greeting card verse." Poets published include Lesley Choyce, Alfred Starr Hamilton, Simon Perchik, Carole Stone and Mordecai Marcus. As a sample, the editor selected the following excerpt from "Poem Arrived At While Eating Cauliflower" by Joe Weil:

> Each cauliflower
> is a miniature brain
> gathered on my plate.
>
> My fork is tentative.
> I've already eaten too many
> "Intellects":
> Plato's overactive logos . . .
> Berlioz's theories on orchestration.
> I sit Plato and Berlioz down
> in this winter park of my brain.

Published February (spring) and July (autumn), digest-sized, offset, with an average of 64 pgs. Press run is 500. Subscription: $7/year. Sample: $4. There are "no limitations" on submissions; SASE required, reporting time is 3-6 months and time to publication within 1 year. Pays 2 copies/published poem. Acquires first North American serial rights. Only using solicited reviews. Send books for review consideration. "We plan to offer brief reviews of 100-150 words. An annual 'Books Received' list is slated for Spring."

JOURNAL OF POETRY THERAPY (IV-Themes), Dept. PM, Human Sciences Press, 233 Spring St., New York NY 10013-1578, phone (212)620-8471, founded 1987. Poetry mss should be sent to journal editor, Dr. Nicholas Mazza, School of Social Work, Florida State University, Tallahassee FL 32306-2024. They use "poems that could be useful in therapeutic settings, prefer relatively short poems; no sentimental, long poems." They have published poetry by Ingrid Wendt and Virginia Bagliore. As a sample the editor selected these lines from "all too often, love" by Elaine Preston:

> like our hunger
>   in the house where we warmed our fingers
>   and laughed against cracks in walls
>   long since plastered shut against the cold

"The *Journal* is devoted to the use of the poetic in health, mental health education and other human service settings." The quarterly is 64 pgs., flat-spined, digest-sized, using 3-6 pgs. for poetry. They accept approximately 10% of 100 poems received. There are 500 subscriptions. Subscription: $38 (US), $46 (international) for individuals; $125 (US), $145 (international) for institutions. Write publisher for free sample. Submit maximum of 3 poems, 4 copies of each with name on only 1 of them. Editor "occasionally" comments on rejections. Include a SASE. Pays 1 copy.

JOURNAL OF THE AMERICAN MEDICAL ASSOCIATION (JAMA) (II, IV-Themes), 515 N. State, Chicago IL 60610, phone (312)464-2417, founded 1883, associate editor Charlene Breedlove, has a "Poetry and Medicine" column and publishes poetry "in some way related to a medical experience, whether from the point-of-view of a healthcare worker or patient or simply an observer. No unskilled poetry." They have published poetry by Diane Ackerman and Daisy Aldan. As a sample the editor selected these lines from "The Virus" by Floyd Skloot:

> *I know this is not personal.*
> *Like a windowpane latticed*
> *with crystals of snow. I am*
> *simply a host the virus uses*
> *to enact its sole pattern*
> *of growth. I could be rock,*
> *a broth of monkey kidneys*
> *and Medium 199.*
> *I could be you.*

JAMA, magazine-sized, flat-spined, with glossy paper cover, has 360,000 subscribers of which 369 are libraries. They accept about 7% of 550 poems received/year. Subscription: $66. **Sample postpaid: free. Pays up to 3 copies. "We ask for a signed copyright release, but publication elsewhere is always granted free of charge."**

‡JOURNEYMEN (II, IV-Specialized), 513 Chester Turnpike, Candia NH 03034, founded 1991, editor Paul S. Boynton, is a quarterly described as "one of the men's movement's leading magazines, featuring interviews with prominent movement leaders and feature stories and columns on modern men and the issues they face in a changing world. Our purpose is to serve as a means for opinions and perspectives among men to be communicated, pooled and used to shed light upon a long silent topic: being male. **Unless you are familiar with current men's movement trends and/or 'men's issues,' don't submit to us. Themes must be applicable to men in modern world. No rhyming poetry unless excellent. 10-45 lines or thereabouts. No haiku. Our audience is men, so we want poetry that will speak to men.** Suggested themes: fatherhood, sons, substance abuse, power/powerlessness, mythopoetic/gay/legal issues, leisure, or anything else men experience." The editor says *Journeymen* is 32+ pgs., 8½×11, printed and stapled with color photo cover. "We're in our 3rd year and growing better and bigger with every issue. We get over 1,000 poems a year, use only 4-10." Press run is 4,000 for 3,000 subscribers, 500+ shelf sales. Single copy: $4.95; subscription: $18/year. **Sample postpaid: $5.50. Send no more than 6 poems. No previously published poetry; simultaneous submissions OK. Cover letter required.** Time between acceptance and publication is up to a year. **Seldom comments on rejections. Reports in 2 months. Pays 1 copy. Rights revert to poet.** The editor says, "You should be familiar with the flavor of our magazine before submitting. If you're not, it'll probably show. Send for a sample. We prefer male poets because *Journeymen* is a forum for men."

‡JOURNEYS (I), 636 Lachman Lane, Pacific Palisades CA 90272, founded 1990, editor George Kalmar, is biannual. **"We are looking for poetry that gives thought to man's relationship to nature and the current human condition in general. However, we are not interested in 'nature poetry' or poetry which is a simple description of nature. We will consider any poetry from writers who have been writing for some time."** Each issue includes a poem from Theodore Roethke to whose memory the magazine is dedicated, and the editor quoted one of these to indicate his taste:

> *I would with the fish, the blackening salmon,*
>   *and the mad lemmings,*
> *The children dancing, the flowers widening.*
> *Who sighs from far away?*
> *I would unlearn the lingo of exasperation,*
>   *all the distortions of malice and hatred*

The editor describes *Journeys* as being 30-40 pgs., digest-sized, saddle-stapled. Press run is 1,000. Subscription: $12. **Sample postpaid: $4. No previously published poems or simultaneous submissions. Poems are circulated to an editorial board. Reports in 3 weeks. Pays 2 copies.** The editor adds, "We strongly suggest that those submitting their work be familiar with Roethke's work and the work of his contemporaries. As editor, I am interested in poetry in the voice of the modern post-war American poets (Williams, Stevens, etc.). We will review all submissions in English from any part of the world."

JUDI-ISMS; K'TUVIM: WRITINGS—A JEWISH JOURNAL OF CREATIVITY (IV-Ethnic, religious, themes, anthology), 27 W. Penn St., Long Beach NY 11561, phone (516)889-7163, founded 1986, poetry editor Judith Shulamith Langer Caplan. Judi-isms is the overall name of the press. Judi-isms recently published its second chapbook, **From Adam to Zipporah: Poems about Jewish Personalities**, which featured poems by Enid Dame, Judah Goldin, Rodger Kamenetz, Helen Papell, Lucy Cohen Schmeidler, Michael Sabin and Shulamith Surnamer. As a sample the editor selected these lines from "Anne and Margot Frank" by Robert Stern:

> *imagine the light Rembrandt*
> *would have used to paint*

Anne and Margot
a splash of gold in shadows
their faces would have been
Jewish Madonnas or Ruth
and Esther reading together

From Adam to Zipporah is magazine-sized, 36 pgs., saddle-stapled; sample copy: $6. **Judi-isms** is currently interested in submissions dealing with the following themes for future collections: a) **Something Shakespearean This Way Comes,** poems and short stories inspired by Shakespeare that tie in with the Bard and/or his individual works; b) **It's All Relative,** poems about grandparents, aunts, uncles and cousins; c) **The Nuclear Family,** poems about mothers and fathers, sons and daughters, spouses and siblings; d) **Containers of Judaism,** poems about objects, ceremonies or foods symbolizing Judaism such as a mezuzzah, a mikvah, a torah, a bat mitzvah or cholent; e) **Anne Frank.** "I am open to all styles of poetry, including free verse, but I also enjoy seeing carefully crafted verse forms such as sestinas, pantoums, villanelles, sonnets and alphabet poems." Simultaneous submissions and reprints acceptable. Name and address should be on each page. Editor sometimes comments on rejections. Reports within 3-6 months. Pays copies. All rights revert to author upon publication.

JUGGLER'S WORLD (IV-Themes), % Ken Letko, College of the Redwoods, 883 W. Washington Blvd., Crescent City CA 95531-8361, phone (707)464-7457, founded 1982, literary editor Ken Letko, is a quarterly magazine, **using poems about juggling. "Only restriction is that all content is focused on juggling."** They have published poetry by Robert Hill Long, Barbara Goldberg and Margo Wilding. As a sample the editor selected these lines from "Street Mime" by Ann B. Knox:

. . . a girl
smiles, the man bows to her, then
spreads his hands wide and silver
balls lift in an arc high
over his head. Faces pivot

JW is 40 pgs., magazine-sized, saddle-stapled, professionally printed on glossy stock with 2-color glossy paper cover. Press run is 3,500, circulated to more than 3,000 jugglers in more than 20 countries. They receive 50-100 poetry submissions/year, use 4-8 poems. Subscription: $18. **Sample: "$2 or $3 depending on issue." They will consider previously published poems. Editor** sometimes comments on rejections, suggesting some revision. Reports in 1-4 months. Pays 1 copy. **Acquires first or one-time rights.** The editor urges poets to "provide insights."

JULIAN ASSOCIATES; NIGHT OWL'S NEWSLETTER; OUR WRITE MIND (I, IV-Themes), P.O. Box 488, La Porte TX 77572-0488, phone (713)470-8748, editor Robin Parker. Julian Associates publishes *NON,* a newsletter, and *OWM,* a magazine, both of which use **poetry relevant to their themes only: living by night or writing.** "Anything with a clear message. Humor is a plus! Poems that are all image and no clear meaning waste our time." They have published poetry by Lynn Bradley. **Previously published poems and simultaneous submissions OK, but tell the editor about them.** *OWM* appears annually, *NON* is quarterly. *NON* is magazine-sized, corner-stapled, press run 100-200; *OWN* press run 250. Sample (of *NON*) postpaid: $3.50. Send SASE for guidelines. Reports in 1-2 months. Both publications pay at least $1 plus at least one copy. Buys one-time rights.

KAIMANA: LITERARY ARTS HAWAII; HAWAII LITERARY ARTS COUNCIL (III, IV-Regional), P.O. Box 11213, Honolulu HI 96828, founded 1974, editor Tony Quagliano. *Kaimana,* a semiannual, is the magazine of the Hawaii Literary Arts Council. **Poems with "some Pacific reference are preferred--Asia, Polynesia, Hawaii--but not exclusively."** They have published poetry by Howard Nemerov, John Yau, Reuben Tam, Robert Bly, Joe Balaz, Anne Waldman and Joe Stanton. As a sample the editor selected "Next Time" by Naomi Shihab Nye:

Gingko trees live 1,000 years.
Eating the leaves will clear your brain.
When I heard about them, I thought of my mother,
how much I would like to sit under one with her
in the ancient shade, nibbling
the flesh, the stem, the central vein.

It is 64-76 pgs., 7½ × 10, stapled, with high-quality printing. Press run 1,000 for 600 subscribers of which 200 are libraries. Subscription: $12. **Sample postpaid: $5. Cover letter with submissions preferred.** Sometimes comments on rejections. Reports with "reasonable dispatch." Pays 2 copies. The editor says, "Hawaii gets a lot of 'travelling regionalists,' visiting writers with inevitably superficial observations. We also get superb visiting observers who are careful craftsmen anywhere. *Kaimana* is interested in the latter, to complement our own best Hawaii writers."

KALEIDOSCOPE: INTERNATIONAL MAGAZINE OF LITERATURE, FINE ARTS, AND DISABILITY (IV-Themes), 326 Locust St., Akron OH 44302, phone (216)762-9755, founded 1979, editor-in-chief Dr. Darshan C. Perusek, consulting poetry editor Christopher Hewitt. *Kaleidoscope* is based at United Disability Services, a nonprofit agency. **Poetry should deal with the experience of disabilty but not limited to that when writer has a disability. "*Kaleidoscope* is interested in high-quality poetry with strong imagery and evocative language. Works should not use stereotyping, patronizing or offending language about disability."** They have recently published poetry by Sheryl Nelms, Jack Coulehan and Margaret Robison. As a sample, they offer these lines from "Grating Parmesan" by Barbara Crooker:

> Together, we hold the rind of the cheese,
> Scrape our knuckles on the metal teeth.
> You put your fingers in the fallen crumbs:
> "Snow," you proudly exclaim, and look at me.
> Three years old, nearly mute,
> But master of metaphor.

Circulation 1,500, including libraries, social service agencies, health-care professionals, universities and individual subscribers. Single copy: $5; subscription: $9 individual, $14 agency. **Sample: $4. Submit photocopies with SASE for return of work. Limit 5 poems/submission. All submissions must be accompanied by an autobiographical sketch. Deadlines: March and August 1. Reports back in 3 weeks, acceptance or rejection may take 6 months. Pays $10-125. Rights return to author upon publication.** Staff reviews books of poetry. Send books for review consideration to Gail Willmott, senior editor.

KALLIOPE, a journal of women's art (IV-Women, translations, themes), 3939 Roosevelt Blvd., Jacksonville FL 32205, phone (904)381-3511, founded 1978, editor Mary Sue Koeppel, a literary/visual arts journal published by Florida Community College at Jacksonville; the emphasis is on women writers and artists. The editors say, **"We like the idea of poetry as a sort of artesian well—there's one meaning that's clear on the surface and another deeper meaning that comes welling up from underneath. We'd like to see more poetry from Black, Hispanic, Native American women, and more translations. Nothing sexist, racist, conventionally sentimental. We will have one special theme issue each year. Write for specific guidelines."** Poets published include Elaine Terranova, Marge Piercy, Kathryn Machan Aal, Dixie Partridge and Sue Saniel Elkind. As a sample, the editor selected the following lines by Ruth Moon Kempher:

> But I sail hot, sail cold, depending
> not on externals, but on that queer greed
> driving, from sea to street
>   on to dark hedgerows
> shadowed alleys, like a creature
> chased, like Cinderella
> shoes in hand.

Kalliope calls itself "a journal of women's art" and publishes fiction, interviews, drama and visual art in addition to poetry. The magazine, which appears 3 times a year, is 7¼ × 8¼, flat-spined, handsomely printed on white stock, glossy card cover and b&w photographs of works of art. Average number of pages is 80. Poems here are lively, celebratory and varied in form, style and length. The circulation is 1,250, of which 400-500 are subscriptions, including 80 library subscriptions, and 600 copies are sold on newsstands and in bookstores. Subscription: $10.50/year or $20/2 years. **Sample: $7. Guidelines can be obtained for SASE. Poems should be submitted in batches of 3-7 with brief bio note, phone number and address. Because all submissions are read by several members of the editing staff, response time is usually 3-4 months. Publication will be within 6 months.** Criticism is provided "when time permits and the author has requested it." Contributors receive 3 copies. Acquires first publication rights. Reviews books of poetry, "but we prefer groups of books in one review." Open to unsolicited reviews. Poets may also send books for review consideration. The editor says, "*Kalliope* is a carefully stitched patchwork of how women feel, what they experience, and what they have come to know and understand about their lives . . . a collection of visions from or about women all over the world. Send for a sample copy, to see what appeals to us, or better yet, subscribe!"

KANGAROOS AND BEANS (I), P.O. Box 40231, Redford MI 48240, phone (313)537-9425, founded 1989, editor Gregg Nannini, appears a year. **They want "poetry that excites or strikes a philosophical chord. No actual restrictions. Write from the heart and don't hold back, but use good taste. No pornography or private angst."** They have published poetry by Jeanette Picardi and Kathleen Meade. As a sample the editor selected these lines from Meade's "Attempts to Enter a Pastoral Painting":

> Her fingers press the oil,
>   extract lanolin from sheep.
> Her tongue searches the Italian Vale.

It is 20 pgs., 8½×11, photocopied from typescript and corner-stapled. Press run 500. Subscription: $4. **Sample postpaid: $2. Make check payable to Gregg Nannini. Simultaneous submissions OK. Reports in 6 months. Pays 2 copies. All rights revert to author upon publication.** Staff reviews books of poetry. Send books for review consideration.

KANSAS QUARTERLY; KANSAS ART COMMISSION AWARDS; SEATON AWARDS (II, IV-Regional, themes), The English Dept., Kansas State University, Manhattan KS 66506, phone (913)532-6716, founded 1968 as an outgrowth of *Kansas Magazine,* editors Ben Nyberg, John Rees and G.W. Clift, is "a magazine devoted to the culture, history, art and writing of mid-Americans, but not restricted to this area." It publishes poetry in all issues. They say, **"We are interested in all kinds of modern poetry except limericks, extremely light verse or book-length mss."** They have published poetry by David Ray, Tom Hansen, Eugene Hollahan, Elizabeth Rees, Kathleen Spivack, David Citino, Robert McNamara, Roger Finch, Ronald Wallace, Mark Nepo, Peter Cooley and David Kirby. There are an average of 80 pgs. of poetry in each creative issue, circulation 1,150-1,350 with 721 subscriptions of which 50% are libraries. They receive 10,000 submissions/year, use 300-400. There is at least a 12- to 18-month backlog unless a poem fits into a special number—then it may go in rapidly. **Sample postpaid: $6 ($8 for double number). Submit "enough poems to show variety (or a single poem if author wishes), but no books. Typed, double-spaced, OK. No queries. We consider, reluctantly, simultaneous submissions." Reports in 1-3 months. Pays 2 copies and yearly awards of up to $200/poet for 6-10 poets.** The *Kansas Quarterly*/Kansas Art Commission Awards are $200 (1st prize), $150 (2nd), $100 (3rd), $75 (4th) and up to 5 honorable mentions ($50). There are also similar prizes in the Seaton Awards (to native-born or resident Kansas poets). The editors **often comment on rejections, even at times suggesting revision and return.** An excellent market, this magazine has been known on occasion to pack the work of more than 60 poets in its 200 pages/issue. All styles are welcome, but response times can be slow. Editors say, "Our only advice is for the poet to *know* the magazine he is sending to: consult in library or send for sample copy. Magazines need the support and their published copies should provide the best example of what the editors are looking for. We believe that we annually publish as much generally good poetry as nearly any other U.S. literary magazine—between 250 and 400 poems a year. Others will have to say how good it really is."

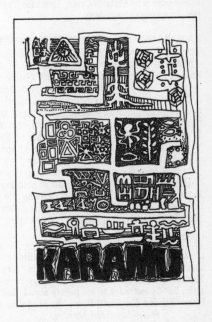

"This cover, designed especially for Karamu, is in harmony with our emphasis on artistic expression," says Editor Peggy L. Brayfield. "Also it suggests something of the overtones of the word karamu—a Swahili word for 'gathering place'—in its motifs." Poetry and fiction are the two major genres of writing represented in the publication. "We publish 35-45 poems in each annual issue," Brayfield says. The cover was designed by Gaye Harrison of Charleston, Illinois.

KARAMU (II), Dept. of English, Eastern Illinois University, Charleston IL 61920, phone (217)581-5614, founded 1966, editor Peggy Brayfield, is an annual whose "goal is to provide a forum for the best contemporary poetry and fiction that comes our way. We especially like to print the works of new writers. We like to see poetry that shows a good sense of what's being done with poetry currently. We like poetry that builds around real experiences, real images and real characters and that avoids abstraction, overt philosophizing and fuzzy pontifications. In terms of form, we prefer well-structured free verse, poetry with an inner, sub-surface structure as opposed to, let's say, the surface structure of rhymed quatrains. We have definite preferences in terms of style and form, but no such preferences in terms of length or subject matter. Purpose, however, is another thing. We don't have much interest in the openly didactic poem. If the poet wants to preach against or for some political or religious viewpoint, the preaching shouldn't be so strident that it overwhelms the poem. The poem should first be a poem." They have recently published poetry by David Bond, Mary McDaniel, Pamela Donald and Karen Subach. As a sample the editor chose these lines from "We Begin Here" by Steven Blaski:

> Your death broke into you as if it were a door
> of glass that you smashed your body through.
> Still, each night I followed you to the rooms
> of my ravaged childhood, where you wore
> the hellish body that performed in the freak show
> of intensive care . . .

The format is 120 pgs., 5 × 8, matte cover, handsomely printed (narrow margins), attractive b&w art. The most recent issue carries 60 pgs. of poetry. They have also recently published a special oversized issue of *Karamu* on the theme "Looking Back at the Sixties" available for $7.25 postpaid. They have a circulation of 350 with 300 subscriptions of which 15 are libraries. They receive submissions from about 300 poets each year, use 40-50 poems. Never more than a year—usually 6-7 months—between acceptance and publication. **Sample: $3; 2 recent issues: $4. Poems—in batches of no more than 5-6—may be submitted to Peggy Brayfield. "We don't much care for simultaneous submissions. We read September 1 through June 30 only, for fastest decision submit February through May. Poets should not bother to query. We critique a few of the better poems. We want the poet to consider our comments and then submit new work."** Payment is one contributor's copy. **Acquires first serial rights.** The editor says, "Follow the standard advice: know your market. Read contemporary poetry and the magazines you want to be published in. Be patient."

KATYDID BOOKS (V), 1 Balsa Rd., Santa Fe NM 87505, founded 1973, editors/publishers Karen and Thomas Fitzsimmons, publishes 3 paperbacks and 1 hardback/year. "We publish three series of poetry: Asian Poetry in Translation, European Writing in Translation and American Poets." They have published poetry by Makoto Ooka, Shuntaro Tanikawa and Ryuichi Tamura. **However, they are currently not accepting submissions.**

KAWABATA PRESS; SEPIA POETRY MAGAZINE (I, II, IV-Anthology), Knill Cross House, Millbrook, Torpoint, Cornwall, United Kingdom, founded 1977, poetry editor Colin David Webb, publishes **"nontraditional poetry, prose and artwork (line only), open to all original and well thought-out work. I hate rhymes, traditional poems and dislike 'genre' stories. I want original and thought-provoking material."** They have published poetry by Jacques de Lumiére and Steve Walker. *Sepia* is published 3 times a year in an inexpensively produced, digest-sized, 32-page, saddle-stapled format, photoreduced from typescript, with narrow margins and bizarre drawings. They receive 250 submissions/year, use 50-60. Press run is 150 for 75 subscribers of which 5-6 are libraries. Single copy: 50p.; subscription: £1 ($3) a year. **Sample: 50p. ($1). Submit 6-10 pgs., typed. Simultaneous submissions OK. Reports in 10 days. Pays free copy.** Reviews books of poetry in 50-100 words. Open to unsolicited reviews. Poets may also send books for review consideration. Under the imprint of Kawabata Press Colin Webb also publishes anthologies and collections. **Query with 6-10 poems and "maybe a brief outline of intent." Poet gets 50% of profits (after cost of printing is covered) and 4 copies.** A book catalog of Kawabata Press publications is on the back of *Sepia*, for ordering copies. The editor always comments on rejections and advises, "Strike out everything that sounds like a cliché. Don't try any tricks. Work at it, have a feeling for what you write, don't send 'exercise' pieces. Believe in what you send."

KELSEY REVIEW (IV-Regional), Mercer County Community College, P.O. Box B, Trenton NJ 08690, phone (609)586-4800, founded 1988, editor-in-chief Robin Schore, is an annual published by Mercer County Community College. It serves as "an outlet for literary talent of people living and working in Mercer County, New Jersey only." They have no specifications as to form, length, subject matter or style, but do not want to see poetry about "kittens and puppies." As a sample here are opening lines from "Fifteen Thousand Pesos" by Madeline Hoffer:

> It is a lop-sided beehive,
> This Cancun—all queens and workers.
> The touristas are pampered prettily,
> Waited on, hand and foot, by those
> Who come from towns hours away
> To live and work and worry
> For fifteen thousand pesos.
> Five dollars a day.

Kelsey Review is 64 glossy pgs., 7 × 11, with paper cover and line drawings; no ads. They receive about 50 submissions a year, accept 6-10. Press run is 1,500. All distributed free to contributors, area libraries and schools. **No previously published poems or simultaneous submissions. Submit no more than 6 poems, typed, under 2,000 words. Deadline: May 1. Always comments on rejections. Reports in May of each year. All rights revert to authors.**

KENNESAW REVIEW (II), English Dept., Kennesaw State College, P.O. Box 444, Marietta GA 30061, phone (404)423-6297, founded 1987, poetry editor Don Russ, editor Robert W. Hill, appears twice a year. **"Open to any form, style or subject; we are looking for high-quality, finely crafted contemporary poetry of all kinds."** They have published poetry by David Bottoms, Malcolm Glass, Larry Rubin, Eve Shelnutt, R.T. Smith and Lewis Turco. As a sample the editor selected these lines from "Raising the Dead" by Ron Rash:

> *The quick left weeks ago, most voluntarily.*
> *Those who remain are brought up, row by row,*
> *into the fading light*
> *of this November afternoon.*

It is 100+ pgs., 6×9, flat-spined, professionally printed, with embossed matte card cover. They accept about 20 of 2,000 poems received. Press run is 1,000. Subscription: $5. **Sample postpaid: $1. Submit no more than 5 poems. Reports within 3 months. Pays 5 copies.**

THE KENYON REVIEW (III), Dept. PM, Kenyon College, Gambier OH 43022, phone (614)427-3339, founded 1939, editor Marilyn Hacker, associate editor for poetry Eleanor Bender, is a quarterly review containing poetry, fiction, criticism, reviews and memoirs. It is **one of the country's leading literary publications.** Under Marilyn Hacker's editorship, this magazine continues to blossom, featuring all styles and forms, lengths and subject matters—a real openness. But this market is more closed than others because of the volume of submissions typically received during each reading cycle. Issues contain work by such poets as Cyrus Cassells, Judith Ortiz Cofer, Joy Harjo, Richard Howard, Josephine Jacobsen, Alicia Ostriker, Sherod Santos and Quincy Troupe. The elegantly printed, flat-spined, 7×10, 180+ pg. format has a circulation of 4,000 with 3,200 subscriptions of which 1,100 are libraries. They receive about 3,000-4,000 freelance submissions a year, use 50-60 (about 50 pgs. of poetry in each issue), have a 1-year backlog. The editor urges poets to read a few copies before submitting to find out what they are publishing. Sample postpaid: $7. **Unsolicited submissions are read from September 1 through March 31** *only.* **Reports in 3 months. Pays $15/page for poetry, $10/page for prose. Buys first North American serial rights.** Reviews books of poetry in 2,500-7,000 words, single or multi-book format. "Reviews are primarily solicited—potential reviewers should inquire first." Poetry published in *The Kenyon Review* was also selected for inclusion in *Best American Poetry 1992.* In addition, *The Kenyon Review* ranked #8 in the "Poets' Pick" category of the June 1993 *Writer's Digest* Poetry 60 list. This category ranks those publications in which poets said they would most like to see their work published.

KEYSTROKES; COMPUWRITE ANNUAL POETRY CONTEST; WRITERS ALLIANCE (IV-Themes), P.O. Box 2014, Setauket NY 11733, founded 1981, executive director of Writers Alliance, Kiel Stuart. Writers Alliance sponsors, in addition to its quarterly newsletter *Keystrokes*, workshops and other activities devoted to building a "dedicated arts community." Membership: $15. You needn't be a member to enter its annual poetry contest (poems about writing with a computer, prize of computer software with a retail value of at least $100, subscription to and publication in the newsletter, January 15 deadline) or to submit poetry to the newsletter **"up to 10 lines on the subject of writing or using a computer or word processing system. 4-6 lines works best. We don't want anything that strays from the subject matter of writers, writing and using computers for that task."** They have published poetry by Karen Elizabeth Rigley and Margaret Park Bridges. As a sample the editor selected this poem, "Dilemma," by Beatrice G. Davis:

> *Free-lancer—hyphenated*
> *Freelancer—compounded*
> *Free lancer—separated*
>
> *Which am I?*
> *That's a typesetter's decision*
> *It would seem.*

Keystrokes is 12 pgs., desktop published (on folded sheets of 8½×11 paper). "Receive about a dozen poems a year; room for 8-10 but less than 50% accepted." Subscription: $15 (with membership). **Sample postpaid: $3.50. "All checks are payable to Kiel Stuart. This is essential." Previously published poems OK** if they did not appear in a competing magazine or more recently than 6 months. Editor frequently comments on rejections. Send SASE for guidelines. **Reports in 6-8 weeks. Pays 2 copies. Acquires one-time rights.** Reviews books of poetry in 250 words, single format. The editor advises, "Treat your craft with respect. Learn the business aspects of being a poet and adhere to those rules. Sloppiness or failure to stick to standard ms format or (worst of all) failure to enclose SASE with ANY communication does NOT indicate an artistic soul."

KIOSK (II), 306 Clemens Hall, SUNY, Buffalo NY 14260, founded 1985, editor Nick Gillespie, is an annual literary magazine using **poetry of "any length, any style, especially experimental." Submit in batches of five.** They have recently published Raymond Federman, Sheila Murphy and Charles Bernstein. As a sample the editor selected these lines by Seth Frechie:

> The intent
> to say it without awkwardness,
> "I ——————"
> A grave uttering,
> the gravity—

The editor describes *Kiosk* as flat-spined, digest-sized. Of 400 poems they accept 10-15. **Free sample (if available) with SAE and 4 first-class stamps. Reads submissions September 1 through April 30 only.** Cover letter not required, "but we suggest one be included." **Reports within 2 months. Pays 1 copy.**

KITCHEN TABLE: WOMEN OF COLOR PRESS (IV-Women, ethnic), P.O. Box 908, Latham NY 12110, phone (518)434-2057, founded 1981, is "the only publisher in North America committed to producing and distributing the work of Third World women of all racial/cultural heritages, sexualities and classes." They publish flat-spined paperback collections and anthologies. **"We want high quality poetry by women of color which encompasses a degree of consciousness of the particular issues of identity and struggle which women of color face."** They publish an average of one book of poetry every other year and have published three anthologies, two of which contain poetry. All books are published simultaneously in hardback for library sales. **Simultaneous submissions OK if they are informed. Ms should be typed, double-spaced.** General comments usually given upon rejection. **Send SASE for guidelines.** They reply to queries in 2 months, to full ms submissions (if invited) in 6 months. **Payment is 7% royalties for first 10,000 copies, 8% thereafter, and 10 copies.** Write for catalog to purchase samples. The editors say, "We are particularly interested in publishing work by women of color which would generally be overlooked by other publishers, especially work by American Indian, Latina, Asian American and African American women who may be working class, lesbian, disabled or older writers."

ALFRED A. KNOPF (V), 201 E. 50th St., New York NY 10022, poetry editor Harry Ford. Over the years Knopf has been one of the most important and distinguished publishers of poetry in the United States. **"The list is closed to new submissions at this time."**

KRAX; RUMP BOOKLETS (II, IV-Humor), 63 Dixon Lane, Leeds, Yorkshire LS12 4RR England, founded 1971, poetry editors Andy Robson et al. *Krax* appears twice yearly, and they want poetry which is **"light-hearted and witty; original ideas. Undesired: haiku, religious or topical politics, $1,000 bills." 2,000 words maximum.** All forms and styles considered. As a sample the editor chose these lines from "He Devoted His Life to Art & Bus Timetables" by Patric Cunnane:

> . . . jobs to settle into
> children to raise
> Weird concepts
> With consequences lasting a lifetime . . .

Krax is 6×8, 48 pgs. of which 30 are poetry, saddle-stapled, offset with b&w cartoons and graphics. Single copy: £1.50 ($3); subscription: £6 ($12). They receive up to 1,000 submissions/year of which they use 6%, have a 2-3 year backlog. **Sample: $1 (75p). "Submit maximum of 6 pieces. Writer's name on same sheet as poem. SASE or SAE with IRC encouraged but not vital." Reports within 2 months. Pays 1 copy.** Reviews books of poetry (brief, individual comments; no outside reviews). Send books for review consideration. *Rump Booklets* are miniature format, 3×4, 16-page collections. **Query with "detailed notes of projected work." Send SASE for catalog.** The editor says, "Sadly banks will not accept checks made payable to the magazine but for convenience we can take IRCs, dollar bills and postage stamps."

The Subject Index, located before the General Index, can help you narrow down markets for your work. It lists those publishers whose poetry interests are specialized.

KUMQUAT MERINGUE; PENUMBRA PRESS (I, II), P.O. Box 5144, Rockford IL 61125, phone (815) 968-0713, founded 1990, editor Christian Nelson, appears approximately 3 times/year using **"mostly shorter poetry about the small details of life, especially the quirky side of love and sex. Not interested in rhyming, meaning of life or high-flown poetry."** They have recently published works by Gina Bergamino, Terry J. Fox, Shawn M. Tomlinson, T. Kilgore Splake, Doreen Cristo and Ianthe Brautigan. As a sample the editor selected these lines from "Leaping Lizards" by Emile Luria:

> *After we made love . . . Kate said,*
> *"You're so weird, really,*
> *Even weirder that I thought."*
> *And I thought, could she taste the salt,*
> *Feel the sea lapping on my back?*
> *I went to sleep wondering*
> *About dinosaurs and lungfish*
> *And the deepest reaches of the sea*

It is digest-sized, 32-36 pgs., "professionally designed with professional typography and nicely printed." Press run 500 for 250 subscribers. Subscription: $8 (3 issues). **Sample postpaid: $4. "We like cover letters but prefer to read things about who you are, rather than your long list of publishing credits. Previously published and simultaneous submissions are OK, but please let us know."** Send SASE for guidelines. Usually reports in 50 days, often comments on submissions. **Pays 1 copy. Poets retain all rights.** The magazine is "dedicated to the memory of Richard Brautigan." The editor advises, "Read *Kumquat Meringue* and anything by Richard Brautigan to get a feel for what we want, but don't copy Richard Brautigan, and don't copy those who have copied him. We just want that same feel. We also have a definite weakness for poems written 'to' or 'for' Richard Brautigan. When you get discouraged, write some more. Don't give up. Eventually your poems will find a home. We're very open to unpublished writers, and a high percentage of our writers had never been published anywhere before they submitted here."

KWIBIDI PUBLISHER; KID'S PLAYYARD; THE JOURNAL OF THE NATIONAL SOCIETY OF MINORITY WRITERS AND ARTISTS; THE WRITERS' AND ARTISTS' AID (I, IV-Ethnic, children, membership), P.O. Box 3424, Greensboro NC 27402-3424. Kwibidi founded 1979, *JNSMWA* 1981, *KP* 1986. Editor Dr. Doris B. Kwasikpui. Kwibidi Publisher **"needs poems, one-act plays, short stories, articles, art, jokes, book reports, research papers and how-to-do and make, for books,** *Kid's Playyard* (a biannual magazine for kids of all ages) and *JNSMWA*." Publication limited to minorities. As a sample the editor selected this poem (poet unidentified):

> *Poems are desperate screams of drowning thoughts*
> > *sinking faster with every word,*
> *Bellowing verses of pain and despair*
> > *to surface buoyantly and to be heard.*

Reads submissions January 1 through August 30 only. Publishes much of the material received and often responds with suggestions. Send SASE for guidelines. Reports in about 3 weeks. Upon acceptance, requires membership in the National Society of Minority Writers and Artists ($15/year). Pays in copies.

LA BELLA FIGURA (I, II, IV-Ethnic), P.O. Box 411223, San Francisco CA 94141-1223, founded 1988, editor Rose Romano, is a quarterly using poetry "any form, any length, about Italian-American culture and heritage or anything of special significance to Italian-Americans. Nothing insulting to I-As: no negative stereotypes, no complaining about I-A ways without affection, no spelling accents (such as tacking an *a* to the end of every other word) and no apologies for being I-A." They have published poetry by Rina Ferrarelli, Maria Mazziotti Gillan, Dan Sicoli and Gigi Marino. *La Bella Figura* is 10 pgs., magazine-sized, quality offset. Their press run is 200 with 200 subscriptions of which 5 are libraries. Subscription: $8. **Sample postpaid: $2.** Send SASE for guidelines. Pays 3 copies. Acquires one-time rights. "All potential contributors are asked to fill out a very short form to describe their Italian background and experience as an Italian-American. Part of the reason for *LBF* is to create family. Therefore, I welcome friendly, informative cover letters. I will gladly consider previously published poems. No simultaneous submissions." Reviews related books of poetry in 200-250 words. Open to unsolicited reviews. Poets may also send books for review consideration. The editor adds, "Few people understand our culture and, therefore, cannot appreciate poetry based on its symbols and secrets. Many I-As are simply 'writing American' or not being published. Write what you are—not what you saw in a movie by an American. I'd like to include work by all I-As—lesbians, gays, heterosexuals and those who are half-Italian but who feel Italian very strongly, first through fourth or fifth generations."

LA CARTA DE OLIVER (II, IV-Bilingual/foreign language, translations), Luis M. Campos 157, Boulogne, C.P. 1609, Prov. de Buenos Aires, Argentina, editors Matias Serra Bradford and Santiago Espel, is a bilingual poetry journal appearing twice a year. **They want poetry up to 20 lines maximum.** They have published poetry by J.E. Pacheco (Mexico), E. Roditi (France), R. Humphreys (Wales), P. Green (England), N. Parra (Chile), B. Aleksic (Yugoslavia) and I. Cohen (USA). As a sample the editors selected "Callimachus (2)" by Alfredo Veiravé:

> As in the epigrams of Callimachus I leave this brief sentence
> between the teeth of antiquity: search for me in the garden
>   of the shadows
> and for comfort think I passed through the end of the tunnel
> and knew it all while I arrived at the light on the other end.

La Carta de Oliver is 28 pgs., 5¾×8¼, saddle-stapled, professionally printed, with card cover. Poems appear in both English and Spanish. A recent issue also included a section of poems in Welsh, Portuguese and French. They receive 500-1,000 poems, accept approximately 50. Press run is 500 for 150 subscribers, 50 shelf sales and hand distribution. Subscription: $10/year. **Sample postpaid: $4. Previously published poems and simultaneous submissions OK. Cover letter required. Seldom comments on rejections. Reports in 2-3 months. Pays 2 copies.** The editors say, "We place *La Carta de Oliver* outside the world's literary cabaret and outside each country's literary ivory stage but, in Dylan Thomas' words, 'For the common wages/Of their most secret heart.' "

LACTUCA (II, IV-Translations), P.O. Box 621, Suffern NY 10901, founded 1986, editor/publisher Mike Selender, appears 3 times a year. **"Our bias is toward work with a strong sense of place, a strong sense of experience, a quiet dignity and an honest emotional depth. Dark and disturbing writings are preferred over safer material. No haiku, poems about writing poems, poems using the poem as an image, light poems or self-indulgent poems. Readability is crucial. We want poetry that readily transposes between the spoken word and printed page. First English language translations are welcome provided that the translator has obtained the approval of the author."** They have published poetry by Charles Bukowski, James Purdy, Juliette Graff, Gail Schilke, Julia Nunnally Duncan, Judson Crews and Michael Pingarron. As a sample the editor selected these lines from "Brook" by Joe Cardillo:

> Out in the fields,
> chainsaws elbow-greasing it
> all day
> tire and click off one at a time
> as if to say in relief
> this day is finally over

Lactuca is digest-sized, 72 pgs., saddle-stapled, laser printed or offset on 24 lb. bond with matte card cover, no ads. They receive "a few thousand poems a year of which less than 5% are accepted." Circulation 500 for 150 subscriptions. Subscription: $10/3 issues, $17/6 issues. **Sample postpaid: $4. "We do not print previously published material. We comment on rejections when we can. However the volume of mail we receive limits this." Reports within 3 months, "usually within one." Pays 2-5 copies "depending on length." Acquires first rights.** Reviews books of poetry. Open to unsolicited reviews. Poets may also send books for review consideration. He says, "The purpose of *Lactuca* is to be a small literary magazine publishing high-quality poetry, fiction and b&w drawings. Much of our circulation goes to contributors' copies and exchange copies with other literary magazines. *Lactuca* is not for poets expecting large circulation. Poets appearing here will find themselves in the company of other good writers."

LAKE SHORE PUBLISHING; SOUNDINGS (I, IV-Anthology), 373 Ramsay Rd., Deerfield IL 60015, phone (708)945-4324, founded 1983, poetry editor Carol Spelius, is an effort "to put out decent, economical volumes of poetry." **Reading fee: $1/page. They want poetry which is "understandable and *moving*, imaginative with a unique view, in any form. Make me laugh or cry or think. I'm not so keen on gutter language or political dogma—but I try to keep an open mind. No limitations in length."** They have published poetry by Richard Calisch, Margo LaGattuta, Gertrude Rubin, Anne Brashler and Thea Hain. The editor selected these sample lines from "Slow Miracle" by Christine Swanberg:

> There were times when walking here
> would not have been enough, times
> my restless spirit needed an ocean,
>   not this river, serene and simple.

The first 253-page anthology, including over 100 poets, is a paperback, at $7.95 (add $1 mailing cost), which was published (in 1985) in an edition of 2,000. It is flat-spined, photocopied from typescript, with glossy, colored card cover with art. **Soundings II is scheduled for early 1994. Submit any number of poems, with $1/page reading fee, and a cover letter telling about your other publications, biographical background, personal or aesthetic philosophy, poetic goals and** principles. Simultaneous submissions OK. Any form or length. "Reads submissions anytime, but best in fall." Reports within 8 months. Pays 1 copy and half-price for additional copies. "All rights return to poet after first printing." The editor will read chapbooks, or full-length collections, with the possibility of sharing costs if Lake Shore Publishing likes the book ($1/page reading fee). "I split the cost if I like the book." She advises, "I'm gathering poems for a small anthology, Love Gone Away, and a collection of poems for children." Sample copy of anthology or random choice of full-length collections to interested poets: $5.

LANDFALL (IV-Regional), Oxford University Press, P.O. Box 11-149, Ellerslie, Auckland 5 New Zealand, founded 1947, originally published by Caxton Press, now published by Oxford University Press and appearing twice a year (in May and November). They say, "We plan for *Landfall* to continue to be the flagship journal for New Zealand writing and literature both locally and internationally. It will continue to commission writing about aspects of New Zealand literature and the arts, to publish the best new fiction and poetry, and to review books." **They do not want to see poetry except by New Zealanders.** As not all of their new policies were established at the time **Poet's Market** went to press, interested New Zealand poets should write for further information.

PETER LANG PUBLISHING, INC. (IV-Translations), 62 W. 45th St., New York NY 10036, phone (212)302-6740, fax (212)302-7574, publishes primarily scholarly monographs in the humanities and social sciences. List includes **critical editions of great poets of the past. Submit descriptive cover letter** and *curriculum vita.*

LANGUAGE BRIDGES QUARTERLY (I, IV-Ethnic, foreign language), P.O. Box 850792, Richardson TX 75085, founded 1988, editor Eva Ziem, "is a **Polish-English bilingual forum for Polish matters. One of its purposes is to introduce the English-speaking reader to Polish culture. The subject is Poland and the Polish spirit**: a picture of life in Poland, mainly after World War II, with emphasis on the new and ponderous Polish emigration problems." For more information send SASE.

L'APACHE: AN INTERNATIONAL JOURNAL OF LITERATURE & ART (I, IV-Ethnic), P.O. Box 71, Wheeler OR 97147, founded 1986, editor Kathryn Vilips, appears twice a year. "We prefer short fiction, articles and poetry on the Indians, or any ethnic group. One way to get an immediate rejection is to include sex, drugs or violence. You can allude to love without descriptive scenes or four-letter words. Although we prefer typewritten double-spaced submissions on 8 × 11 paper, *L'Apache* will not reject a poem simply because a writer does not have access to a typewriter. All we ask is that you print or write legibly." They have published poetry by Barbara Jennings and Elizabeth Brooks Preddy. As a sample the editor selected these lines from "I Wonder and Wait" by Noel De Luca :

> The tides roll in . . .
> and I have waited, along lonely shores . . .
> but that which you love so dearly
> never returns . . .

The editor describes *L'Apache* as 6 × 9, "full-color cover. Drawings suitable for framing, high gloss, varnished heavy covers, 144 pgs., each journal a collector's edition." Their press run is 5,000 with most subscribers being libraries. Subscription: $18. Sample: $5 plus SAE and 94¢ postage. No simultaneous submissions or previously published poems. Editor sometimes comments on rejections. Guidelines available for SASE. Pays $5-10/poem.

LATEST JOKES NEWSLETTER (IV-Humor), P.O. Box 023304, Brooklyn NY 11202-0066, phone (718)855-5057, editor Robert Makinson. *LJN* is a monthly newsletter of humor for TV and radio personalities, comedians and professional speakers. They use light (humorous) verse from 2-8 lines. Circulation 250. Sample: $3 and 1 first class stamp. Submit maximum 3 poems at one time. Submit seasonal/holiday material 3 months in advance. Reports in 3 weeks. Pays 25¢/line.

‡**THE LAUREATE LETTER (I)**, 899 Williamson Trail, Eclectic AL 36024-9275, founded 1993, editor Brenda Williamson, is a monthly newsletter open to submissions of poetry, short-short-short stories, articles on writing, artwork and other short miscellaneous writings or creative works. It will also periodically contain markets, contests, reviews and other items of interest to writers. As for poetry, they want "any form, but prefer titled, 36 lines maximum. Any subject or style. However, no jibberish or extremely mushy garbage." They receive about 500 poems a year, accept 30%. Press run is 500 for 300 subscribers of which 17 are libraries. Subscription: $10. Sample postpaid: $1. Previously published poems and simultaneous submissions OK. Send SASE for guidelines. Reports in 1-4 weeks "most of the time." No pay in cash or copies, but no fee required for publication. Acquires one-time rights. The editor says, "This is a new publication, but space is limited. Much material will be passed up because of length, so length needs to be a top priority."

LAUREL REVIEW (III); GREENTOWER PRESS (V), Dept. of English, Northwest Missouri State University, Maryville MO 64468, phone (816)562-1265, founded 1960, coeditors Craig Goad, David Slater and William Trowbridge. *LR* is a literary journal appearing twice a year using **"poetry of highest literary quality, nothing sentimental, greeting card, workshop, spit and whistle."** They have published poetry by George Starbuck, Marcia Southwick, Albert Goldbarth, David Citino and Pattiann Rogers. This handsome journal (128 pgs., 6×9) features excellent poems—usually more than 20 each issue—in all styles and forms. Press run is 750 for 400 subscriptions of which 53 are libraries, 100 shelf sales. Subscription: $8/year. **Sample postpaid: $5. Submit 4-6 poems/batch.** Reads submissions September 1 through May 31 only. Reports in 1 week-4 months. Editor "does not usually" comment on submissions. Pays 2 copies plus 1-year subscription. Rights revert to author upon publication. Greentower Press accepts no unsolicited mss.

THE LEADING EDGE (I, IV-Science fiction/fantasy), 3163 JKHB, Provo UT 84602, phone (801)378-2456, executive editor Michael Carr. *The Leading Edge* is a magazine appearing 3 times a year. They want **"high quality poetry related to science fiction and fantasy, not to exceed 3-4 typewritten, double-spaced pages. No graphic sex, violence or profanity."** They have published poetry by Michael Collings and Thomas Easton. As a sample the editors picked these lines from "An Astronaut Discusses a Black Hole Binary System" by Russell W. Asplund:

> It looks like a sink
> A cosmic drainhole slightly clogged in
> Some cosmic downpour
> The star a carelessly dropped
> Bar of soap slowly dissolving
> In God's shower

The editors describe the magazine as 6×9, 140 pgs., using art. They accept about 15 out of 150 poems received/year. Press run is 500, going to 100 subscriptions (10 of them libraries) and 300 shelf sales. Single copy: $2.95; subscription: $8. **Sample postpaid: $3.50. Submit with no name on the poem, but with a cover sheet with name, address, phone number, length of poem, title and type of poem. Simultaneous submissions OK, but no previously published poems. Send SASE for guidelines.** Reports in 3-4 months. Pays $5/typeset page plus 2 copies. Buys first North American serial rights. Open to unsolicited reviews. Poets may also send books for review consideration. They say, "We accept traditional science fiction and fantasy poetry, but we like innovative stuff. If a poet has a good idea, go with it."

THE LEDGE POETRY AND FICTION MAGAZINE (II), 64-65 Cooper Ave., Glendale NY 11385, founded 1988, editor-in-chief Timothy Monaghan, appears twice a year and "searches for **high-quality poetry that is gritty, arresting and/or provocative in nature, though we will publish a great poem even if it doesn't meet these criteria. We suggest poems not exceed 60 lines in length, though again, we will publish the long poem if it so impresses us."** Recent contributors include Robert Cooperman, George Held, Joyce Stewart and Evan Zimroth. *The Ledge* is 80 pgs., digest-sized, typeset and perfect-bound with glossy cover. They accept 2% of poetry submissions. Circulation is 500, including 100+ subscribers. Subscription: $15 for 2 years, $9 for 1 year. **Sample postpaid: $5. Send up to 5 poems at a time. "We do not consider previously published work, though we will consider simultaneous submissions, if so informed."** Reports in 2 months, longer if under serious consideration. Pays 1 copy. Acquires one-time rights. The editor says, "Poets should take as much consideration in the presentation of their work as they expect the editor to take in the reading of the work."

LEFT CURVE (II, IV-Social issues), P.O. Box 472, Oakland CA 94604, phone (510)763-7193, founded 1974, editor Csaba Polony, appears "irregularly, about every 10 months." They want **poetry that is "critical culture, social, political, 'post-modern,' not purely formal, too self-centered, poetry that doesn't address in sufficient depth today's problems."** They have published poetry by Jack Hirschman, Sarah Menefee and Etel Adan. As a sample the editor selected these lines by HM:

> my unfriend the machine awakens me
> to a world one step removed
> from the dark, from the grave

The editor describes it as "about 100 pgs., offset, flat-spined, Durosheen cover." Press run is 1,200 for 150 subscribers of which 50 are libraries, 800 shelf sales. Subscription: $20/3 issues (individuals). **Sample postpaid: $7. Cover letter stating "why you are submitting" required.** Reports in 3-6 months. Pays 3 copies. Open to unsolicited reviews. Poets may also send books for review consideration.

LEGEND: AN INTERNATIONAL "ROBIN OF SHERWOOD" FANZINE (I, IV-Fantasy), Dept. PM 1036 Hampshire Rd., Victoria, British Columbia V8S 4S9 Canada, phone (604)598-2197, founded 1989, editor Janet P. Reedman, appears approximately once a year. She wants **"fantasy poetry dealing with/**

based on episodes of the British TV series 'Robin of Sherwood.' Length is open. No porn or dull poetry about mundane matters." She has published poetry by Julianne Toomey, Frances Quinn and Steve Sneyd. The magazine is 170+ pgs., spiral-bound, photocopied from typescript, uses much b&w art. Press run is 130+. Accepts 80-90% material from 2 dozen or so. "Will help with rewrites; prefer to outright rejection." Sample: $17 US, $18 Canadian. No previously published poems. Typed or hand-written mss acceptable. Reports in 1-10 weeks, usually sooner. Nearly always comments on rejections. For US submissions/inquiries: "Rather than IRCs please send 2 loose US stamps." Pays: "a substantial discount." Acquires first North American serial rights.

L'EPERVIER PRESS (V), 1326 NE 62nd, Seattle WA 98115, founded 1977, editor Robert McNamara, is a "small press publisher of contemporary American poetry in perfect-bound and casebound books." **Currently not accepting submissions.** He has published books by Bruce Renner, Linda Bierds, Frederic Will and Paul Hoover. The press publishes 2 poetry books each year, 6×9 with an average page count of 64, some flat-spined paperbacks and some hardcovers. **Second Sun** by Bill Tremblay, is handsomely printed on heavy buff stock, 81 pgs., with glossy card cover in grey, yellow and white; there is a b&w landscape photo on the front cover and a photo of the author on the back; the book is priced at $6.95.

‡LIBIDO: THE JOURNAL OF SEX AND SEXUALITY (I, IV-Erotica, humor), P.O. Box 146721, Chicago IL 60614, founded 1988, editors Marianna Beck and Jack Hafferkamp, is a quarterly. **"Form, length and style are open. We want poetry of any and all styles as long as it is erotic and/or erotically humorous. We make a distinction between erotica and pornography. We want wit not dirty words."** They have recently published poetry by Gordon Lester-Massman and William Borden. As a sample the editors selected these lines by Ralph Tyler:

> 'Twas brillig in that cheap hotel
> The looking glass had cataracts
> All mimsey were the bureau drawrs
> The paper was a glimpse of hell
> "Come to my arms, my beamish boy"
> Her scarlet mouth invited him.

It is 72 pgs., digest-sized, professionally printed, flat-spined, with 2-color varnished card cover. Press run: 9,500 for 3,500 subscribers, 3,500 shelf sales ("it's growing quickly") and 1,500 single issues by mail. They accept about 5% of poetry received. Subscription: $26 in US, $36 outside. **Sample postpaid: $7. Cover letter including "a one-sentence bio for contributors' page" required with submission. Reports in 4-6 months. Pays $0-25 plus 2 copies.** Send books for review consideration "only if the primary focus is love/eroticism."

LIBRA PUBLISHERS, INC. (I), Suite 383, 3089C Clairemont Dr., San Diego CA 92117, phone (619)571-1414, poetry editor William Kroll, publishes two professional journals, *Adolescence* and *Family Therapy*, plus books, primarily in the behaviorial sciences but also some general nonfiction, fiction and poetry. "At first we published books of poetry on a standard royalty basis, paying 10% of the retail price to the authors. Although at times we were successful in selling enough copies to at least break even, we found that we could no longer afford to publish poetry on this basis. Now, unless we fall madly in love with a particular collection, **we require a subsidy.**" They have published books of poetry by Martin Rosner, William Blackwell, John Travers Moore and C. Margaret Hall. **Prefers complete ms but accepts query with 6 sample poems, publishing credits and bio. Replies to query in 2 days, to submissions (if invited) in 2-3 weeks. Ms should be double-spaced. Send 9×12 SASE for catalog.** Sample books may be purchased on a returnable basis.

LIFTOUTS MAGAZINE; PRELUDIUM PUBLISHERS (V), Dept. PM, 1503 Washington Ave. S., Minneapolis MN 55454, phone (612)333-0031, founded 1971, poetry editor Barry Casselman, is a "publisher of experimental literary work and work of new writers in translation from other languages." Currently accepting no unsolicited material. *Liftouts* appears irregularly. It is 5½×8, offset, 50-150 pgs. Press run is 1,000. Reviews books of poetry.

Market categories: (I) Beginning; (II) General; (III) Limited; (IV) Specialized; (V) Closed.

LIGHT (II), Box 7500, Chicago IL 60680, founded 1992, editor John Mella, is a quarterly of **"light and occasional verse, satire, wordplay, puzzles, cartoons and line art."** They do not want "greeting card verse, cloying or sentimental verse." As a sample the editor selected "The Cow's Revenge" by X.J. Kennedy:

> *Obligingly, the mild cow lets us quaff*
> *The milk that she'd intended for her calf,*
> *But takes revenge: In every pint she packs*
> *A heavy cream to trigger heart attacks.*

The editor says *Light* is 40 pgs., stapled or sewn, including art and graphics. Single copy: $4; subscription: $12. **No previously published poems or simultaneous submissions. Submit one poem on a page with name, address, poem title and page number on each page.** Seldom comments on rejections. **Send SASE for guidelines. Reports in 3 months or less. Pays 2 copies.** Open to unsolicited reviews. Poets may also send books for review consideration.

LIGHT AND LIFE MAGAZINE (IV-Religious), Dept. PM, Free Methodist Church of North America, P.O. Box 535002, Indianapolis IN 46253-5002, phone (317)244-3660. *Light and Life* is a religious monthly magazine. Guidelines available. **"Poems are used only as they relate to an article in the magazine. No 'fillers' or descriptive poems are used."** They also conduct annual writing contests with varying rules and prizes (send SASE for rules December through March). **"We are looking for short, well-written devotional or inspirational pieces and poetry . . . offering unique insights into the great themes of the Bible. Poems should rhyme and flow with a recognizable rhythm pattern. Avoid obscure allusions and unfamiliar language. Maximum length: 20 lines. Each submission should be typed on plain white paper, double-spaced, at least 1" margin on all sides, no erasable bond, name, address and telephone number on each ms, each submission on a separate sheet of paper, even if they are short pieces."** Response time 4-6 weeks. Pays $7.50-10. Buys first rights.

LIGHTHOUSE (I, IV-Children), P.O. Box 1377, Auburn WA 98071-1377, founded 1986, is a magazine "with a delightful variety of fiction and poetry that maintains time-honored values," appearing every other month. It has a children's section. **They want poems up to 50 lines, "G-rated, ranging from light-hearted to inspirational."** They have recently published poetry by Sharon Lee Roberts, C. David Hay and David L. Roper. As a light-hearted sample the editor selected "No Navigator, Me" by Kathleen Y. Bergeron:

> *I think that there will never be*
> *A map that makes good sense to me.*
> *Each squiggly line and tiny word*
> *To me just borders on absurd.*
> *If you'd your destination see,*
> *I should not navigator be!*

The editor describes *Lighthouse* as 56 pgs., digest-sized, some simple activities and illustrations in children's section. Press run is 300 for 100 subscribers. Subscription: $7.95. **Sample postpaid: $3 (includes guidelines). "Prefer typed, double-spaced, each poem on a separate sheet for evaluating purposes." Send SAE with first class stamp for guidelines. Reports in 2 months, publication within a year. Pays up to $5/poem.** Buys first North American serial rights.

LILITH MAGAZINE (IV-Women, ethnic), Suite 2432, 250 W. 57th St., New York NY 10107, phone (212)757-0818, founded in 1975, editor-in-chief Susan Weidman Schneider, poetry editor Alicia Ostriker, "is an independent magazine with a Jewish feminist perspective" which uses **poetry by Jewish women "about the Jewish woman's experience. Generally we use short rather than long poems. Run 4 poems/year. Do not want to see poetry on other subjects."** They have published poetry by Irena Klepfisz, Lyn Lifshin, Yael Messinai, Sharon Neemani, Marcia Falk and Adrienne Rich. It is glossy, magazine-sized. "We use colors. Page count varies. Covers are very attractive and professional-looking (one has won an award). Generous amount of art. It appears 4 times a year, circulation about 10,000, about 5,000 subscriptions." Subscription: $16 for 4 issues. Sample postpaid: $5. **Send no more than 3 poems at a time; advise if simultaneous submission.** Editor "sometimes" comments on rejections. **Send SASE for guidelines. Reports in 2-3 months.** She advises: "(1) Read a copy of the publication before you submit your work. (2) Be realistic if you are a beginner. The competition is *severe*, so don't start to send out your work until you've written for a few years. (3) Short cover letters only. Copy should be neatly typed and proofread for typos and spelling errors."

LILLIPUT REVIEW (II, IV-Form), 207 S. Millvale Ave. #3, Pittsburgh PA 15224, founded 1989, editor Don Wentworth, is a tiny (4½ × 3.6 or 3½ × 4¼) 12- to 16-page magazine, appearing irregularly and **using poems in any style or form no longer than 10 lines.** They have recently published poetry by Albert Huffstickler, Lonnie Sherman, Lyn Lifshin, Cynthia Hendershot and Carl Jablonski. As a sample the editor selected "Postcard" by Bart Solarczyk:

> *A light wet snow*
> *waters the back yard.*
> *I watch from the sofa.*
> *I miss your small hands.*

LR is printed from typescript on colored paper and stapled. Press run is 225. **Sample: $1 or SASE. Submit no more than 3 poems. Currently, every other issue is a broadside featuring the work of one particular poet. Send SASE for guidelines. Reports usually within 2 months. Pays 2 copies/poem. Acquires first rights.** Editor comments on submissions "occasionally—always at least try to establish human contact."

LIMBERLOST PRESS; THE LIMBERLOST REVIEW (II), HC 33, Box 1113, Boise ID 83706, phone (208)344-2120, founded 1976, coeditors Richard and Rosemary Ardinger. Limberlost Press publishes poetry, fiction and memoirs in letterpressed chapbooks, flat-spined paperbacks and other formats. *Limberlost Review* appears "fairly regularly. **We want the best work by serious writers. No restrictions on style or form.**" They have published poetry by William Stafford, Lawrence Ferlinghetti, Charles Bukowski, Allen Ginsberg, John Clellon Holmes, Nancy Stringfellow, Robert Creeley and Gino Sky. The editor describes *LR* as digest-sized ("varies. One issue has been devoted to a series of 20 letterpressed poem postcards."). **Issues through 1995 will be devoted to letterpressed chapbooks.** It has a press run of 500-1,000. **Sample postpaid: $10. No simultaneous submissions. For chapbook submission, submit samples, bio and prior publications.** Editor sometimes comments on rejections. **Reports on queries in 1 week, on submissions in 1-2 months. Pays a varied number of author's copies.** "We like interested poets to be familiar with our press work."

LIMESTONE: A LITERARY JOURNAL (II), Dept. of English, 1215 Patterson Office Tower, University of Kentucky, Lexington KY 40506-0027, phone (606)257-6976, founded as *Fabbro* in 1979, as *Limestone* in 1986, editor Tim Dunn, is an annual seeking "**poetry that matters, poetry that shows attention to content and form. We're interested in all poetics, but we do watch for quality of thought and a use of language that will wake up the reader and resonate in his/her mind.**" They have published poetry by Wendell Berry, Guy Davenport, Michael Cadnum, Noel M. Valis and James Baker Hall. It is 6×9, perfect-bound, offset. They accept 5-10 of 100-150 poems submitted annually. Press run is 500 for 30 subscriptions (20 of them libraries). **Sample postpaid: $3. Simultaneous submissions and previously published poems OK. Submit 1-10 pgs. Reports in 3-6 months. Pays 3 copies.** "If you're considering publication," the editor advises, "read as much poetry as possible. Listen carefully. Work over your poems till you're sick of them. The lack of such care shows up in many of the mss we receive."

LIMITED EDITIONS PRESS; ART: MAG (III), P.O. Box 70896, Las Vegas NV 89170, phone (702)734-8121, founded 1982, editor Peter Magliocco, "have become, due to economic and other factors, more limited to a select audience of poets as well as readers. We seek to expel the superficiality of our factitious culture, in all its drive-thru, junk-food-brain, commercial-ridden extravagance—and stylize a magazine of hard-line aesthetics, where truth and beauty meet on a vector not shallowly drawn. Conforming to this outlook is an operational policy of **seeking poetry from solicited poets primarily, though unsolicited submissions will be read, considered and perhaps used infrequently.** Sought from the chosen is a creative use of poetic styles, systems and emotional morphologies other than banally constricting." They have published poetry by Belinda Subraman, Cheryl Townsend and Bill Chown. As a sample the editor selected these lines from "Twelawney and The Romantics" by Alan Catlin:

> *I've buried all the great ones from my generation*
> *Writers talk about how great they were*
> *Still none of those living have seen a heart*
> *on fire*

ART: MAG, appearing in 1-2 large issues of 400+ copies/year, is limited to a few poets and chapbooks are compiled within the magazine itself. "This consolidation means no distinct chapbooks are planned outside the magazine." **Sample issues are the cover price of the particular latest issue, $4-7, postpaid. Submit up to 5 poems. No previously published poems; simultaneous submissions OK.** Sometimes comments on rejections. **Send SASE for guidelines. Reports within 3 months. Pays 1 copy. Acquires first rights.** Staff reviews books of poetry. Send books for review consideration.

‡LINCOLN SPRINGS PRESS (II), P.O. Box 269, Franklin Lakes NJ 07417, founded 1987, editor M. Gabrielle, publishes 1 paperback and 1 hardback book of poetry each year. They have recently published poetry by Maria Mazziotti Gillan, Justin Vitiello and Abigail Stone. **Query first with sample poems and cover letter with brief bio and publication credits. No previously published poems; simultaneous submissions OK.** Seldom comments on rejections. **Replies to queries in 2-4 weeks, to mss in 2-3 months. Pays 15% royalties.**

LINES N' RHYMES (I), 5604 Harmeson Dr., Anderson IN 46013, phone (317)642-1239, founded 1989, editor Pearl Clark, appears every other month using **"some poetry to 40 lines—use some 4 lines, most between 12-20 lines. I like poems concerning life, belief in God's guidance. Nothing pornographic or occult."** They have published poetry by Ainsley Jo Phillips, Ruth E. Cunliffe and Rosina Clifford. As a sample the editor selected these lines from "Ben Franklin's Bird" by Dr. Harry Snider:

> For had the Congress stood with Ben,
> The turkey would be national;
> Protected in its coop or pen
> By federal law, irrational.
> And then upon Thanksgiving Day,
> With turkey kills illegal;
> Around our tables folks would pray,
> "Lord, help us eat this eagle."

It is photocopied on 6 legal-sized colored sheets, sometimes 5. Press run is 50. 3-5 shelf sales. Subscription: $5/6 issues. **Sample: $1. "I receive 170 poems/year—accept 70%. I pay nothing for poetry used. I award 'Editor's Choice' to 2 poets/issue at $1. I give preference to subscribers. However, I also use poetry from non-subscribers."** Previously published poems OK. Reviews books of poetry and comments in current issue. Open to unsolicited reviews. Poets may also send books for review consideration. She holds a limerick contest each September with 3 prizes of $5 each, open only to subscribers.

LINES REVIEW (III), Edgefield Rd., Loanhead, Edinburgh EH20 9SY Scotland, phone (031)440-0246, founded 1952 ("the oldest continuing Scottish literary magazine"), editor Tessa Ransford. *LR* is a quarterly. **"I like to accept from 4-6 poems in traditional page format, though with energy and intelligence in use of language, form and content. No unusual typography, concrete, sensation-seeking, nostalgic, dully descriptive or fanatically political poetry."** They have published poetry by Norman MacCaig, Gozo Yoshimasu, George Szirtes and Amy Clampitt. Press run 750 for 500 subscribers of which 100 are libraries, 100 shelf sales. **Sample postpaid: £2.32. Cover letter required with submissions;** include information relevant to the poems. **"Double spacing helps, and clear indication whether a page break is or is not also a stanza break, and careful attention to punctuation—that it is as it will be printed."** Reports in 2-3 weeks. Pays £10/page plus 1 copy. Staff reviews books of poetry. Tessa Ransford is also director of Scottish Poetry Library (see listing under Organizations) and offers a School of Poets and Critical Service through the library. *LR* often has special issues devoted, for example, to poetry from Glasgow, Japan, America, Canada. They also publish translations. Their spring, 1992, issue celebrated the magazine's 40th anniversary.

‡**LINQ (II, IV-Regional)**, c/o English Dept., James Cook University, Townsville, Queensland 4811 Australia, phone (077)814336, founded 1971, secretary Ms. M. Miles. *LiNQ* (Literature in North Queensland) is a 180-page biannual which "aims to publish works of a high literary standard, encompassing a wide and varied range of interest." They have recently published poetry by Justin Macdonnell and David Reiter. They receive about 250 poems a year, use approximately 10%. Press run is 350 for 160 subscribers of which 30 are libraries, 180 shelf sales. Single copy: $8; subscription: $20, $30 overseas (Australian). **Sample back issue postpaid: $3 (Australian). No previously published poems or simultaneous submissions. "LiNQ rotates its editors. Each volume is the responsibility of an individual editor, with occasional co-editorial advice." Often comments on rejections.** Reports "ASAP." Payment is subject to grant funding. Author retains copyright. Reviews books of poetry in 1,000 words. Open to unsolicited reviews. Poets may also send books for review consideration. The editors say, *"LiNQ* aims for a broadly based sympathetic approach to creative work, particularly from new and young Australian writers." The secretary adds, "Attention to presentation is a very important criteria taken into consideration by editors. Intending contributors should take note of this."

LINTEL (II), P.O. Box 8609, Roanoke VA 24014, phone (703)982-2265 or 345-2886, founded 1977, poetry editor Walter James Miller, who says, **"We publish poetry and innovative fiction of types ignored by commercial presses. We consider any poetry except conventional, traditional, cliché, greeting card types, i.e., we consider any artistic poetry."** They have published poetry by Sue Saniel Elkind, Samuel Exler, Adrienne Wolfert and Edmund Pennant. As a sample the editor selected these lines by Nathan Teitel:

> loneliness
> is a Mexican earring
> and fear
> a crushed cigarette

The book from which this was taken, **In Time of Tide**, is 64 pgs., flat-spined, digest-sized, professionally printed in bold type, hard cover stamped in gold, jacket with art and author's photo on back. Walter James Miller asks that you **query with 5 sample poems. Reads submissions January** and August only. He replies to the query within a month, to the ms (if invited) in 2 months. "We consider simultaneous submissions if so marked and if the writer agrees to notify us of acceptance elsewhere." Ms should be typed. Pays royalties after all costs are met and 100 copies. Buys all rights. Offers usual subsidiary rights: 75%/25%. To see samples, send SASE for catalog and ask for "trial rate" (50%). "We like our poets to have a good publishing record in literary magazines, before they begin to think of a book."

LINWOOD PUBLISHERS (II), P.O. Box 371819, Decatur GA 30037-1819, phone (404)408-6082, founded 1982, poetry editor Bernard Chase, was "organized as an independent small press, primarily to publish the poetry of known, unknown and little known poets." They have published in both paper and hardback editions. The editor says he is interested in **"quality poetry of any form."** They have published poetry by Simon Perchik, Carl Lindner, Barbara Unger, T.S. Wallace, George Gott, Isabella Pupurai Matsikidze and Barbara Crooker. As a sample the editor selected these lines from **Touch The Concrete** by Anthony Grenek, Jr.:

> *When dark clouds appear*
> *And again we doubt our goal,*
> *We search for ways to salvage*
> *Our heart, our mind, and soul.*
>
> *We realize in trying*
> *There has to be some pain,*
> *But once we see the rainbow,*
> *We've made it through the rain*

They will consider freelance submissions of book mss. It is your option whether to query first, send samples or complete mss. Your cover letter should give publication history and bio. They try to reply to queries within 1 month, to mss within a year. They prefer typed ms. Simultaneous submissions OK. Contracts are for 5-10% royalties and author's copies (negotiated). Send 7 × 10 SASE with 3 oz. postage for catalog. "Sample copies of our publications can be purchased directly from the publisher." Bernard Chase advises, "Feel no intimidation by the breadth, the depth of this craft of which you have chosen to become a part. Although we are very open to beginners, we do not as a rule respond with comments, suggestions or criticisms."

‡LITE MAGAZINE: THE JOURNAL OF SATIRE AND CREATIVITY; THE LITE CIRCLE, INC.; LITE CIR-CLE BOOKS (I), P.O. Box 26162, Baltimore MD 21210, phone (410)719-7792, founded 1989, editor/publisher David W. Kriebel. *Lite Magazine* is a biannual "general literary publication including humorous columns, reviews and perspective pieces and one interview in each issue." They want "creative, thoughtful, beautiful poetry, generally 1 page or less in length. No overly-erotic, exploitative or dogmatic poetry. Also, no political or preachy religious poems." They have recently published poetry by Bill Jones. The editor says *Lite* is generally 40 pgs., 8 × 10, newsprint with b&w photos, original art and ads. They receive about 150 poems a year, accept 20-25%. Press run is 10,000 for 100 subscribers, the rest distributed free to colleges, writing groups and art galleries. Single copy: free; subscription: $13 (includes membership in Lite Circle, Inc.) Sample postpaid: $2.25. Previously published poems and simultaneous submissions OK. Cover letter required. Seldom comments on rejections—"Only when authors ask for it." Send SASE for guidelines. Reports in 3-6 months. Pays 5 copies. Acquires one-time rights. Reviews books of poetry. Lite Circle Books publishes 2 paperbacks/year. "We are just getting into book publishing. **Right now we operate as a subsidy press. Terms are settled on a contract-by-contract basis.**" Their first two books, **The Laughing Ladies** and **Stations In a Dream**, are each available as a sample for $6.95 plus postage. The Lite Circle, Inc. sponsors poetry readings and offers an annual contest with $75 first prize, $45 second. Send SASE for information. The editor says, "Be persistent. The market is tight, but if you are willing to work with the small presses, they will work with you. *Lite* is very kind to new writers."

LITERARY FOCUS POETRY PUBLICATIONS; ANTHOLOGY OF CONTEMPORARY POETRY; INTER-NATIONAL POETRY CONTESTS: FALL CONCOURS, SPRING CONCOURS, SUMMER CONCOURS (I, IV-Anthology), P.O. Box 36242, Houston TX 77236-0242, phone (713)541-4626, founded 1988, editor-in-chief Adrian A. Davieson. **Purchase of anthology may be required of poets accepted for publication.** Literary Focus publishes anthologies compiled in contests, 3 times/year, with prizes of $500, $300 and $100, plus "Distinguished Mention" and "Honorable Mention." **"Contemporary poetry with no restriction on themes. 20-line limit. Maximum submission 15 poems, minimum 3 poems. No abusive, anti-social poetry."** As a sample the editor selected these lines from his own poem, "Delayed Journey":

> *I saw the footsteps retracing to*
> *A lost moment, then there was a*
> *Whisper of ancient sorrows long*

> Left in the trail of endless
> Struggles.

The digest-sized anthologies are either flat-spined or saddle-stapled, 70 pgs., typeset. **Previously published poems and simultaneous submissions OK. "In order to evaluate serious entries, a $5 entry fee is now required for the first three poems. Poems are evaluated on an individual basis by a panel of five editors chaired by editor-in-chief. Poets are notified of acceptance two weeks after deadlines." Send SASE for guidelines.** Reviews books of poetry.

LITERARY OLYMPICS, INC. (IV-Anthology, translations), P.O. Box 178407, San Diego CA 92177, phone (619)276-6199, founded 1984, president and editor Elizabeth Bartlett, is an international organization "to encourage and promote public interest in poetry by honoring leading contemporary poets from all over the world on the occasion of the Olympics every four years. The newest anthology, **Literary Olympians 1992**, contains poems by 132 poets from 65 countries in 55 languages, including English translations." They have published poetry by Maxine Kumin, Josephine Jacobsen, Octavio Paz and Odysseus Elytis. As a sample the editor selected these lines from "Horse Play" by Ayyappa Panikar:

> Four gallant horses
> galloped forth.
> One was white, one was black,
> one was red, one was brown.
> One had four legs,
> one had three,
> one had two,
> the fourth had one leg. . . .

Poets may submit unpublished English poems up to 30 lines, with cover letter, in 1994 and 1995 for Literary Olympians 1996. Each poet and translator receives a copy of the anthology. "Besides appearing in the anthology, poets are candidates for gold, silver and bronze medals awarded by a jury of literary scholars. We also hope to raise enough funds to clear expenses and then pay each contributor an additional honorarium." **Literary Olympians 1992** was published by Ford Brown & Co. ($22.95 paperback, $29.95 hardcover plus postage and handling). The editor says, "We rely heavily on qualified translators to obtain poems and permissions to translate and publish. Poets familiar with **Literary Olympians** can best judge the quality of our selection."

THE LITERARY REVIEW: An International Journal of Contemporary Writing (III), Fairleigh Dickinson University, 285 Madison Ave., Madison NJ 07940, phone (201)593-8564, founded 1957, editor-in-chief Walter Cummins, a quarterly, seeks **"work by new and established poets which reflects a sensitivity to literary standards and the poetic form." No specifications as to form, length, style, subject matter or purpose.** They have published poetry by Robert Cooperman, Gary Fincke, José Bergamin, Tomasz Jastrun and R.S. Thomas. The magazine is 6×9, flat-spined, 128+ pgs., professionally printed with glossy color cover, using 20-50 pgs. of poetry in each issue, circulation 2,500, 900 subscriptions of which one-third are overseas. They receive about 1,200 submissions/year, use 100-150, have 6-12 months backlog. Poems appearing here show careful attention to line, image and form—largely lyric free verse. Editors of recent issues also seem particularly open to translations. **Sample postpaid: $5, request a "general issue." Submit no more than 5 poems at a time, clear typing, simultaneous submissions OK, no queries. At times the editor comments on rejections. Reports in 2-3 months. Pays copies. Acquires first rights.** Reviews books of poetry in 500 words, single format. Open to unsolicited reviews. Poets may also send books for review consideration. *The Literary Review* ranked #10 in the "Nontraditional Verse" category of the June 1993 *Writer's Digest* Poetry 60 list, and one of the poems published in this review was selected for inclusion in **Editor's Choice III**. They advise, "Read a general issue of the magazine carefully before submitting."

LITERATURE AND BELIEF (II, IV-Religious), 3076-E Jesse Knight Humanities Building, Brigham Young University, Provo UT 84602, phone (801)378-2304, founded 1981, editor Jay Fox, is the "annual journal of the Center for the Study of Christian Values in Literature." It uses "affirmation poetry in the Judeo-Christian tradition." They have published poetry by Ted Huges, Donnel Hunter, Leslie

---

Market conditions are constantly changing! If you're still using this book and it is 1995 or later, buy the newest edition of Poet's Market *at your favorite bookstore or order directly from* Writer's Digest Books.

Norris and William Stafford. It is handsomely printed, flat-spined. Single copy: $5 US, $7 outside US. They conduct an annual contest with $100 first prize for poetry.

LITTLE RIVER PRESS (V), 10 Lowell Ave., Westfield MA 01085, phone (413)568-5598, founded 1976, editor Ronald Edwards, publishes **"limited editions of poetry collections, chapbooks and postcards of New England Poets."** They have published poetry by Steven Sossaman, Wanda Cook and Frank Mello. However, they currently do not accept unsolicited poetry. **Pays 60% of run.**

LIVING POETS SOCIETY (I, IV-Ethnic), P.O. Box 8555, New York NY 10116-4654, founded 1991, editor-in-chief Gabrellar Jordan, is a bimonthly newsletter of "inspirational writing and poetry and community news and development." The editor wants **poetry with "style, creativity and substance"** from African-Americans but will also accept poems from other groups. No **"poems that most people will not understand."** As a sample the editor selected these lines (poet unidentified):

> *The day we heard that Martin died,*
> *Our hope, and all who came so far*
> *Died too with him, our brightest star,*
> *The symbol, and the movement's pride.*
> *He'd never reach the other side*

The newsletter is 6-8 double-sided pgs., side-stapled, with some drawings. Press run is 35-60. Both 4- and 6-issue subscriptions are offered, $4 and $6 respectively. **Previously published poems and simultaneous submissions OK. Bio requested.** Time between acceptance and publication is 3 months. **No pay at the present time. "Poets have all rights to their work."** The editor says, "You don't have to buy the newsletter to contribute."

LMNO PRESS (I, II), P.O. Box 862, Westminster MD 21158, founded 1991, editor Laurie Precht. *LMNO Press* publishes yearly in July. It accepts **concrete, narrative poetry under 100 lines and short stories. *"Whatever gets published must make sense!* And please, no poetry about cats, death, religion or about writing poetry. Also, no chapbooks."** As a sample she selected these lines from "Los Angeles is Beirut, 1992" by Wendy Deal:

> *Violence spreads*
> *through the senses*
> *an angry whispering rush.*
> *Accept the wildfire of the mind.*
> *Fall into it like loving*
> *in a black hole.*

LMNO Press is digest-sized, 40 pgs. Press run is 200. It is distributed through subscription and at poetry readings, local bookshops and literary fairs. Subscription or **sample copy postpaid: $3. "Don't send cash; please send check or money order made out to Laurie Precht."** Submit 3-6 poems. **Simultaneous submissions OK; no previously published work. Mss should be typed with name on everything. Editor comments if the poem needs work before it is published. Reports in 3-6 months. Pays 1 copy.** She advises, "Go deeply into your writing. Draw on your experiences; let the reader live what you know. And don't dawdle on the same worn topics—pick something new and go!"

THE LOCKHART PRESS (II), Box 1207, Port Townsend WA 98368, phone (800)659-4364, founded 1982, poetry editor Russell A. Lockhart, Ph.D, began as a publisher of fine handmade hardbound books, now expanding to chapbooks and paperbacks, is interested in, but not limited to, "poetry having its origin in or strongly influenced by dreams." No specifications as to form, length or style. All handmade editions include special readings by the poets on tape. Limited deluxe editions cost $75 or more. As a sample the editor selected these lines from Marc Hudson's **Journal for an Injured Son:**

> *My boy also is a swimmer, for whom desire*
> *annihilates distance. He is my dolphin, my little Odysseus.*
> *Death could not steal from his eyes*
> *the dawn of his homecoming.*

Query with 5 samples, usual bio, credits information. Replies to query in 2 weeks, reports on submission (if invited) in 3 months. Ms should be clear in any form—simultaneous submissions or discs compatible with Macintosh OK. Sometimes comments on rejections. Contract is for 15% royalties (after cost recovery) plus 10 copies (handmade), 100 copies (trade). Buys all rights. Return negotiable. To see a sample, you may ask for one on approval.

LODESTAR BOOKS (IV-Children/teen, anthology), 375 Hudson St., New York NY 10014, phone (212)366-2627, affiliate of Dutton's Children's Books, a division of Penguin USA, founded 1980, editorial director Virginia Buckley, is a trade publisher of **juvenile and young-adult nonfiction, fiction and picture books. "A good anthology would be OK, or poetry for the very young child. No adult poetry.**

Although we have not published any poetry or anthologies, we are open to submissions; writers should be familiar with the juvenile market. Best place to start is in the bookstore rather than the library."

LONDON MAGAZINE (II), 30 Thurloe Place, London SW7 England, founded 1954, poetry editor Alan Ross, is a literary and art monthly using **poetry "the best of its kind."** Editors seem open to all styles and forms, including well-made formal works. Some of the best poems in England appear here. It is a 6×8½, perfect-bound, elegant-looking magazine, with card cover, averaging about 150 pages six months a year. They accept about 150 of 2,000 poems received each year. Press run is 5,000 for 2,000 subscribers. Subscription: £28.50 or $67. **Sample postpaid: £4.75. Cover letter required with submissions. Reports "very soon." Pays £20/page. Buys first British serial rights.** Reviews books of poetry in up to 1,200 words. Open to unsolicited reviews. Poets may also send books for review consideration. Alan Ross says, "Quality is our only criterion."

LONG ISLAND QUARTERLY (IV-Regional), P.O. Box 114, Northport NY 11768, founded 1990, editor and publisher George Wallace, is a quarterly using **poetry by people on or from Long Island. "Surprise us with fresh language. No conventional imagery, self-indulgent confessionalism, compulsive article-droppers."** They have published poetry by David Ignatow and William Heyen. As a sample here are lines from "Watermill" by Claire Nicholas White:

> *This pioneer's house, lonely as a shroud*
> *once housed the trapped soul of a sad wife.*
> *I knew her there chained to her loom*
> *in a land not her own, bending her head*
> *to peer through small panes over land eastward*
> *   from where she came*

LIQ is a handsome publication whose clean design (28 pgs., digest-sized, saddle-stapled, professionally printed on quality stock with matte card cover) enhances the image-based, mostly lyric free verse inside. Most contributions show attention to craft and structure. Press run is 250 for 150 subscribers of which 15 are libraries, 50-75 shelf sales. Subscription: $12. **Sample postpaid: $3. Cover letter including connection to Long Island region required. Name and address on each page. Submissions without SASE not returned. Responds in 3 months. Pays 1 copy.** The editor advises "(1) Go beyond yourself; (2) Don't be afraid to fictionalize; (3) Don't write your autobiography—if you are worth it, maybe someone else will."

LONG ISLANDER; WALT'S CORNER (II), 313 Main St., Huntington NY 11743, phone (516)427-7000, fax (516)427-5820, founded 1838 by Walt Whitman, poetry editor George Wallace, is a weekly newspaper, 25,000 circulation, using **unrhymed poetry up to 40 lines "grounded in personal/social matrix, no haiku, inspirational."** They have published poetry by David Ignatow, David Axelrod and R.B. Weber. As a sample the editor selected these lines from "The Gleaners" by L. Dellarocca:

> *They bend, clutch earth by its*
> *straw season and sing*
> *while we loosen our belts.*

It is "48 pgs., newsprint." They use 52 of about 1,000 poems submitted each year. Subscription: $18. **Sample postpaid: $2.50. Simultaneous submissions OK. Editor "normally" comments on rejections. Pays 1 copy.** Staff reviews books of poetry. Send books for review consideration.

LONG SHOT (II), P.O. Box 6238, Hoboken NJ 07030, founded 1982, published by Danny Shot, edited by Jack Wiler, Jessica Chosid and Tom Polhamus, is, they say, "writing from the real world." They have published poetry by Charles Bukowski, Sean Penn, Allen Ginsberg, Marianne Faithfull, Amiri Baraka and June Jordan. It is 144+ pgs., flat-spined, professionally printed with glossy card cover using b&w photos, drawings and cartoons. It comes out twice a year. Press run is 1,500. Subscription: $20 for 2 years (4 issues). **Sample: $6. Simultaneous submissions OK. Reports in 2 months. Pays 2 copies.** Unlike other publishers, Danny Shot says they receive "too many requests for writer's guidelines. This is a waste of our time. Just send the poems."

LONGHOUSE (II); SCOUT (V); ORIGIN PRESS (V), Green River R.F.D., Brattleboro VT 05301, founded 1973, editor Bob Arnold. *Longhouse* is a literary annual using **poems "from the serious working poet" from any region in any style.** They have published poetry by Hayden Carruth, Janine Pommy-Vega, Bobby Byrd, Sharon Doubiago, George Evans, Lorine Niedecker, Tim McNulty and Alan Lau. Its format is unusual: a thick packet of looseleaf 8½×14 sheets, photocopied from typescript, in a handsomely printed matte cover. Press run 200. **Sample postpaid: $10. Pays 2 copies.** Reviews books of poetry. **They publish chapbooks and books (manuscripts solicited only) under the imprints of Longhouse and Scout.** "We are also a bookshop and mail-order business for modern first editions and modern poetry and small presses. We encourage poets and readers looking for collectible modern first editions and scarce—and not so scarce—books of poetry and small press magazines to send a donation for our catalog; whatever one can afford." Bob Arnold says, "Origin Press is best known as Cid Corman's press. One of the quiet giants in American poetry/plus the wide scope of international work. Established in the early 1950s in Boston, it has moved around as Cid went with his life: France, Italy, Boston, for many years now in Kyoto, Japan. Cid has merged with Longhouse in that we now edit and publish a few items together. He continues to edit, translate and publish from Kyoto. His own books are heavily based in our bookshop and mail order catalog."

LOOM PRESS (II), P.O. Box 1394, Lowell MA 01853, founded 1978, editor Paul Marion, a small press publisher of books, chapbooks and broadsides. Poets recently published include William O'Connell, Ann Fox Chandonnet and Jane Brox. As a sample the editor selected the following lines from "By the Merrimack" by Helena Minton:

> It's like the place one falls
> in and out of love: now sharp,
> now sweet, the wrists
> plunged in, the same
> steady pressure of longing or regret.

Books are perfect-bound, 6×9, with an average page count of 64. The chapbooks are saddle-stitched, 6×9, with an average page count of 20. Writers should query first for book and chapbook publication, sending credits, 5 sample poems and bio. Queries will be answered in 1 month, mss reported on in 6 weeks. Simultaneous submissions will be considered. Time to publication is 6-12 months. Royalties of 10% are paid on books and chapbooks, plus 5% of print run. Samples are available at $5 each. The editor comments on mss "when time allows." He says, "Please support the small publishers who make poetry available."

LOONFEATHER (I, IV-Regional), Bemidji Community Arts Center, 426 Bemidji Ave., Bemidji MN 56601, phone (218)751-4869, founded 1979, poetry editors Betty Rossi and Marshall Muirhead, is a small press publisher of the literary magazine *Loonfeather* appearing 2 times a year, "primarily but not exclusively for Minnesota writers. Prefer short poems of not over 42 lines, rhymed verse only if well done, no generalizations on worn-out topics." They have published poetry by Nancy Paddock, William Borden and Mark Vinz. As a sample the editors selected these lines from "Tornado Salad" by Joan Wolf Prefontaine:

> Not to worry then, there will always be storms and hunger
> and if we are lucky, a tornado salad made by someone we love
> after we've stepped up from the darkness to measure out our worth,
> after we've endured together whatever danger will pass.

Loonfeather is 6×9, 48 pgs., saddle-stapled, professionally printed in small type with matte card cover, using b&w art and ads. Subscription: $7.50/year; single copy current issue: $5 (Fall '88 through current year); back issues: $2.50. Submission deadlines January 31 and July 31 for May and November publications. Pays 2 copies.

LOS HOMBRES PRESS (IV-Form), P.O. Box 632729, San Diego CA 92163-2729, phone (619)688-1023, founded 1989, publisher Jim Kitchen, publishes haiku only. As a sample the editor selected these lines from **Desert Storm: A Brief History** by Lenard Moore:

> September sunrise
> Marine leaving for the Persian Gulf
> looks back at his wife

He says that book is a digest-sized, flat-spined, professionally printed paperback (glossy card cover), $6.95. "We publish only one book per year." Submit with cover letter including publication record and biographical information. Pays 10% royalties plus 10 copies. Buys North American rights.

LOTHROP, LEE & SHEPARD BOOKS (V), 1350 Avenue of the Americas, New York NY 10019, founded 1859, editor-in-chief Susan Pearson. "We do not accept unsolicited mss."

LOTUS PRESS, INC. (V); NAOMI LONG MADGETT POETRY AWARD (IV-Ethnic) P.O. Box 21607, Detroit MI 48221, phone (313)861-1280, fax (313)342-9174, founded 1972, editor Naomi Long Madgett. "With one exception of a textbook, we publish books of poetry by individual authors, although we have three anthologies and two sets of broadsides, one with a teachers' guide for use in secondary schools. We occasionally sponsor readings. Most, but not all, of our authors are black." Their most recent anthology is **Adam of Ifé: Black Women in Praise of Black Men.** Currently, they are not accepting unsolicited mss. They have published poetry by Oliver LaGrone, May Miller, James A. Emanuel and Selene de Medeiros. As a sample the editor selected these lines by Monifa Atungaye:

> my last swim
> and final push into this whiteness

> *your bright roundness*
> *peering through narrow wooden bars . . .*
> *marks the beginning of me.*

Query. Response is usually within 6 weeks. Pays 25 author's copies; others may be ordered at a discount. Poets are not expected to contribute to the cost of publication. "Copies may be ordered from our catalog, which is free upon request. We do not give samples." The editor adds, "The newly established Hilton-Long Foundation announced its first annual Naomi Long Madgett Poetry Award in 1993. The award goes to a manuscript by an African-American poet who is 60 years of age or older. Interested persons may write for details."

LOUISIANA LITERATURE; LOUISIANA LITERATURE PRIZE FOR POETRY (II, IV-Regional), P.O. Box 792, Southeastern Louisiana University, Hammond LA 70402, editor David Hanson, appears twice a year. They say they **"receive mss year round although we work through submissions more slowly in summer. We consider creative work from anyone though we strive to showcase our state's talent. We like poetry with original language use and strong images which go beyond themselves."** They have published poetry by Sue Owen, Catharine Savage Brosman, Diane Wakowski, Claire Bateman and Kate Daniels. The editor chose these sample lines by Rodger Kamenetz:

> *Gobs of meat knobbed with fat sink below my spoon.*
> *The waiter sweeps a fifth of sherry past my nose.*
> *The surface doused, "And more?" he asks, one eye on the next*
> *table, crumpled bills, dead crabs sprawled on plates.*
> *I want more and more, the sherry clears a window*
> *on the grease like ice on a filthy pond.*
> *I was so hungry when I read the words, "Turtle Soup."*

The magazine is a large (6¾ × 9¾) format, 100 pgs., flat-spined, handsomely printed on heavy matte stock with matte card cover (using engravings). Subscription: $10 for individuals, $12.50 for institutions. Open to unsolicited reviews. Poets may also send books for review consideration; include cover letter. The Louisiana Literature Prize for Poetry offers a $400 award. **Guidelines for SASE.**

LOUISIANA STATE UNIVERSITY PRESS (II), Baton Rouge LA 70893, phone (504)388-6294, founded 1935, poetry editor L.E. Phillabaum, is a highly respected publisher of collections by poets such as Lisel Mueller, Julia Randall, Fred Chappell and Henry Taylor. **Query with 6-8 sample poems, publication credits. Simultaneous submissions OK. Replies to queries in 1 month, to submissions (if invited) in 3-4 months.** Pays royalties plus 10 author's copies.

THE LOUISVILLE REVIEW (II, IV-Children/teen), Dept. PM, 315 Bingham Humanities, University of Louisville, Louisville KY 40292, phone (502)588-6801, founded 1976, faculty editor Sena Jeter Naslund, appears twice a year. **They use any kind of poetry except translations, and they have a section of children's poetry (grades K-12).** They have published poetry by Richard Jackson, Jeffrey Skinner, Maura Stanton, Richard Cecil, Roger Weingarten and Greg Pape. *TLR* is 200 pgs., flat-spined, 6 × 8¾. They accept about 10% of some 700 pieces received a year. **Sample postpaid: $4. "Poetry by children must include permission of parent to publish if accepted. In all of our poetry we look for the striking metaphor, unusual imagery and fresh language. We do not read in summer. Poems are read by 3 readers; report time is 1-2 months and time to publication is 2-3 months."** Pays 1 copy.

LOW-TECH PRESS (V), 30-73 47th St., Long Island City NY 11103, founded 1981, editor Ron Kolm, has published work by Hal Sirowitz, John Yau and Jennifer Nostrand. As a sample the editor selected these lines (poet unidentified):

> *They firebombed*
> *the dinner table*
> *taking us completely*
> *by surprise.*

"I am only interested in short poems with clear images. Since almost nobody gets paid for their work, I believe in multiple submissions and multiple publishings. Even though we publish only solicited mss, I respond right away to any mail the press receives."

LUCIDITY; BEAR HOUSE PUBLISHING (I), Route 2, Box 94, Eureka Springs AR 72632-9505, founded 1985, editor Ted O. Badger. *Lucidity* is a quarterly of poetry. **Submission fee required—$1/poem for "juried" selection by a panel of judges or $2/poem to compete for cash awards of $15, $10 and $5. Other winners paid in both cash and in copies. In addition, the editor invites a few guest contributors to submit to each issue. Contributors are encouraged to subscribe or buy a copy of the magazine.** The magazine is called *Lucidity* because, the editor says, "I have felt that too many publications of verse lean to the abstract in content and to the obscure in style." They are **"open as to form. 40-line limit due to format. No restriction on subject matter except that something definitive be given to the reader." Purpose: "to give a platform to poets who can impart their ideas with clarity."** He does not want **"religious, nature or vulgar poems."** Recently published poets include Diane Krueger, Dalian Moore, Edna Gammill and E.A. Henderson. As a sample of the type of verse sought, the editor offers these lines (poet unidentified):

> *Time . . . a river turning wheels,*
> *Grinding finely the grist,*
> *ever flowing . . . unstinted.*

The magazine is photocopied from typescript, digest-sized, saddle-stapled, 72 pgs. with matte card cover. It's a surprisingly lively small press magazine featuring accessible narrative and lyric poetry, with almost equal space given to free and formal verse. Press run 270, 165 subscribers. Subscription: $10. **Sample postpaid: $2.50. Simultaneous submissions OK. Send SASE for guidelines. Reports in 2-3 months, a 3-month delay before publication. Buys one-time rights.** Bear House Press is a self-publishing arrangement by which poets can pay to have booklets published in the same format as *Lucidity*, prices beginning at 50 copies of 32 pgs. for $140. Publishes 10 chapbooks/year. The editor says, "We welcome new unpublished poets with something to say."

LULLWATER REVIEW (II), Box 22036, Emory University, Atlanta GA 30322, phone (404)727-6184, founded 1989, editor revolves, appears 3 times/year. They want **"original, imaginative treatment of emotional and intellectual topics. No mere wordplay. Ideas and concepts should be emphasized. Nothing overtly sentimental or with little craftsmanship."** They have published poetry by Turner Cassity, Kelly Cherry, Daniel Corrie, Charles Edward Eaton and R.T. Smith. As a sample the editor selected these lines from "Kicking Back in Timbuktu" by Robert Parham:

> *This swamp is not foreign,*
> *the Deep South, asleep much longer than we,*
> *yet we nap fitfully, fired by half-dreamed*
> *visions of happenings so antiseptic,*
> *our conscious nap for novelty invades the final spot*
> *a dream can live, can dance with meaning, sober, and mad.*

Lullwater Review is a handsome, 6×9, flat-spined magazine, 96 pgs. Press run is 2,000. Subscription: $12. **Sample postpaid: $5. Will consider simultaneous submissions. Reads submissions August 1 through May 31 only. Send SASE for guidelines. Reports in 2 months or less. Pays 3 copies. All rights revert to author upon publication.** "*Lullwater* places no limits on theme or style; the sole criterion for judging submitted work is its excellence. While much of the poetry we publish is free verse, we hold in high regard well-crafted formal poems. We expect our contributors to be acquainted with the broad field of contemporary poetry and able to find within that field a voice uniquely their own."

LUNA BISONTE PRODS; LOST AND FOUND TIMES (IV-Style), 137 Leland Ave., Columbus OH 43214, founded 1967, poetry editor John M. Bennett, may be the zaniest phenomenon in central Ohio. John Bennett is a publisher (and practicioner) of **experimental and avant-garde writing**, sometimes sexually explicit, and art in a bewildering array of formats including the magazine, *Lost and Found Times*, postcard series, posters, chapbooks, pamphlets, labels and audiocassette tapes. You can get a **sampling of Luna Bisonte Prods for $5.** Numerous reviewers have commented on the bizarre *Lost and Found Times*, "reminiscent of several West Coast dada magazines"; "This exciting magazine is recommended only for the most daring souls"; "truly demented"; "Insults . . . the past 3,000 years of literature," etc. Bennett wants to see **"unusual poetry, naive poetry, surrealism, experimental, visual poetry, collaborations—*no* poetry workshop or academic pablum."** He has published poetry by I. Argüelles, G. Beining, B. Heman, R. Olson, J. Lipman, B. Porter, C.H. Ford, P. Weinman, E.N. Brookings, F.A. Nettelbeck, D. Raphael, R. Crozier, S. Sollfrey, M. Andre and N. Vassilakis. As a sample the editor selected part of a poem by Sheila E. Murphy:

> *lakeside quasi (anything imaginative plings wursted renditions*
> *of wavy (fragrant light is sure tiempo*
> *manifest corrosive blond spots glyph and*
> *genus wood light ornery or kind mid-length corrosive excerpts*
> *in the neck of spring we walk (these metal feeling chairs*
> *(economy slow as dished collapse we woodwind extra*

The digest-sized, 52-page magazine, photoreduced typescript and wild graphics, matte card cover with graphics, has a circulation of 350 with 75 subscriptions of which 30 are libraries. **Sample postpaid: $4. Submit any time—preferably camera-ready (but this is not required). Reports in 1-2 days. Pays copies. All rights revert to authors upon publication.** Staff reviews books of poetry. Send books for review consideration. **Luna Bisonte also will consider book submissions: query with samples and cover letter (but "keep it brief").** Chapbook publishing

Concentrate on the Small

"Indian Summer's End"

The charmed and timeless trees of yesterday
With unseen dancers writhe and moan;
This wind will pare our golden world away
Down to the dark and whistling bone.

(from **We Thought at Least the Roof Would Fall**)

With the life span of some poetry publications never
exceeding 10 issues, *The Lyric* stands as a testament to
tenacity. Founded in 1921 by John Richard Moreland
under the sponsorship of the Norfolk, Virginia Poet's
Club, it is the oldest magazine in North America in
continuous publication devoted to traditional poetry.

Having survived the efforts of a half-dozen editors
over several decades, *The Lyric* passed into the hands
of Leslie Mellichamp and his wife, Elizabeth, in 1976.
A poet himself, Mellichamp published a collection of

Leslie Mellichamp

his own verse, **We Thought at Least the Roof Would Fall** (Pocahontas Press), in 1987.

As editor (having also served as an electrical engineer, a university English
teacher and a professor of European Intellectual History), he reads all of the 3,000-
4,000 poems submitted annually, from which he chooses approximately 250 for publication. "When I can't make up my mind," he says, "I turn to my wife, the managing
editor, whose comments do the trick."

One of the rewards of finding work to publish, says Mellichamp, is coming across
the work of a talented new poet. "Joy comes when a freshly minted 19- or 20-year-
old poet joins our many established writers, some in their seventh, eighth and ninth
decades," he says. He encourages beginning poets to familiarize themselves with
"good poetry that has stood the test of time," and advises them to avoid tackling
"cosmic themes" in their work.

"The meaning of life, the problem of evil, the frustrations of the human condition,
philosophical and social, etc.—the great themes are tough even for seasoned poets,"
he says. "Concentrate on the small. I published two delightful poems in *The Lyric*
not long ago: one about a paper cup, the other about an empty picture hook on the
wall. If a phrase or image comes too readily to the pen or keyboard, distrust it—it's
probably badly overworked. But don't struggle so hard for originality that your language becomes bizarre or unintelligible."

Mellichamp says that, while workshops can be helpful to poets learning their
craft, he is ambivalent about their value for more established poets. "I'm possibly
wrong, but I think routine workshopping may be counterproductive for the mature
poet," he says. "I'm reminded of Frost's saying, 'A poem cannot be worried into
being.' Perhaps workshops imply too much talk about a poem, sapping creative energy that could go into writing one. However, I know there are good poets who swear
by them."

Participation in readings can also be a "mixed bag" for both poet and audience, says Mellichamp. "Readings can be stimulating, even thrilling, for both the poet and listener. But they are often frustrating for both: The poet often has to struggle so hard to be understood that the poem loses its lilt, its life. The listener often needs a copy of the poem to really follow it."

Regarding networking, Mellichamp says, "I'm not sure I know what this means. If it means collaboration in the creation of poetry, I distrust it. If it means critically reading each other's work, it's almost a necessity. If it means exchanging market advice, it's worthwhile. But when all is said and done, writing poetry is a solitary affair."

The Lyric isn't a good market for poems expressing social and political outrage or foul language. "I don't want to see poems lamenting social or political ills—not that there aren't any, but because they seldom make good lyric poetry," says Mellichamp. "Milton could bring it off; Shelley, perhaps. I don't want to see erotica, obscenity or vulgarity. Poets that need them to express themselves will find plenty of outlets; indeed, gutter language is indispensable for some of them."

Similarly, as a traditional poetry magazine, *The Lyric* has little concern for trends. Mellichamp concedes that, while there is an increased interest in formal poetry, he doesn't anticipate it becoming a major movement. "In our finger-painting, doing-one's-own-thing, multicultural milieu, a disciplined return to the Western tradition in poetry seems unlikely to become an irresistible ground swell," he says.

Ground swell or no, *The Lyric* has clearly stood the test of time, and we can count on its continued presence and contribution to the field of poetry. "It is no small comfort," says Mellichamp, "to know *The Lyric* has survived for 73 years and has offered a refuge for civilized, musical, accessible poetry and a showcase for some of the best lyric poetry written in this century."

—*Roseann Biederman*

66 **If a phrase or image comes too readily to the pen or keyboard, distrust it. 99**

—Leslie Mellichamp

usually depends on grants or other subsidies and is usually by solicitation. He will also consider subsidy arrangements on negotiable terms.

LUNA VENTURES; POLY; SCIFANT; UNKNOWN; SWASHBUCKLER; BACKWOODS; OWLHOOTERS (IV-Themes, science fiction), P.O. Box 398, Suisun CA 94585-0398, founded in the 1930s, editor Paul Doerr. This publisher puts out a number of monthly newsletters, all of which use poetry on appropriate subjects. *Poly* is about alternate life-styles such as polygamy and group marriage. *SCIFANT* focuses on science fiction, fantasy and horror and is published in microfiche only. *Unknown* is about "anomalies, the mysterious, the unusual, such as witchcraft, appearances and disappearances, Bigfoot, UFOs." *Swashbuckler* is about Renaissance Faires, fencing, swashbuckling and related topics. *Back-woods* deals with subsistence farming, animals and survival. *Owlhooters* is about treasure, prospecting, bounty hunting, collecting, etc. All use **poetry relevant to their themes**. All are 12 pgs. condensed type except *SCIFANT*, which is 98 pgs. **Sample postpaid: $2.50, except *SCIFANT* is $3 (add 50¢ if outside the US). Submit poems typed, single-spaced, with name and address on each page. Pays at least 1 copy, others at discount.** Acquires first or one-time rights.

THE LUTHERAN JOURNAL (IV-Religious), Dept. PM, 7317 Cahill Rd., Edina MN 55439, phone (612)941-6830, editor The Rev. Armin U. Deye, is a family quarterly, 32 pgs., circulation 136,000, for Lutheran Church members, middle age and older. They use **poetry "related to subject matter,"** traditional, free verse, blank verse. **Sample free for SASE. Simultaneous submissions OK. Pays.**

THE LYRIC; LYRIC ANNUAL COLLEGE POETRY CONTEST (II, IV-Form, students), 307 Dunton Dr. SW, Blacksburg VA 24060, founded 1921 ("the oldest magazine in North America in continuous publication devoted to the publication of **traditional poetry**"), poetry editor Leslie Mellichamp, uses about 50 poems each quarterly issue. "We use rhymed verse in traditional forms, for the most part, with an occasional piece of blank or free verse. 35 lines or so is usually our limit. Our themes are varied, ranging from religious ecstasy to humor to raw grief, but we feel no compulsion to shock, embitter or confound our readers. We also avoid poems about contemporary political or social prob-lems—grief but not grievances, as Frost put it. Frost is helpful in other ways: if yours is more than a lover's quarrel with life, we're not your best market. And most of our poems are accessible on first or second reading. Frost again: don't hide too far away. Poems must be original, unpublished and not under consideration elsewhere." They have published poetry by Anne Barlow, John J. Brugaletta, R.H. Morrison, Rhina P. Espaillat, Barbara Loots, Amy Jo Schoonover, Alfred Dorn, Eunice de Chazeau, Gail White, Neill Megaw and Alice Mackenzie Swaim. The editor selected these sample lines by R.L. Cook:

> Forever young, unwary, beautiful,
> Yet in their folly wiser than the world;
> Under a cloud of years the bright girls go
> And in their flesh the future rests unfurled.

It is digest-sized, 32 pgs., professionally printed with varied typography, matte card cover, has a circulation of 850 with 800 subscriptions of which 290 are libraries. They receive about 5,000 submissions/year, use 200, have an average 3-month backlog. Subscription: $10 US, $12 Canada and other foreign countries. **Sample postpaid: $3. Submit up to 5 poems. Send SASE for guide-lines. Reports in 1 month (average). Pays 1 copy,** and all contributors are eligible for quarterly and annual prizes totaling over $900. *The Lyric* also offers a poetry contest in traditional forms for fulltime undergraduate students enrolled in any American or Canadian college or university, prizes totaling $500. Send SASE for rules. *The Lyric* ranked #1 in the "Traditional Verse" category of the June 1993 *Writer's Digest* Poetry 60 list. Leslie Mellichamp comments, "Our *raison d'être* has been the encouragement of form, music, rhyme and accessibility in poetry. We detect a growing dissatisfaction with the modernist movement that ignores these things and a growing interest in the traditional wellsprings of the craft. Naturally, we are proud to have provided an alternative for over 70 years that helped keep the true roots of poetry alive."

M.A.F. PRESS; THIRTEEN POETRY MAGAZINE (I, IV-Form), Box 392, Portlandville NY 13834-0392, phone (607)286-7500, founded 1982, poetry editor Ken Stone. *Thirteen Poetry Magazine* "publishes only 13-line poetry; any theme or subject as long as in 'good' taste. We seek to publish work that touches the beauty of this life." They have published poetry by Pamela Portwood, Ida Fasel, Will Inman, Stan Proper, Janet Carncross Chandler and Marion Cohen. As a sample the editor selected "Leaving" by John Craig:

> And still the memory
> of you standing, waving good-bye.
> I should have turned around then
> for the sadness of your eye.

Thirteen appears quarterly in a magazine-sized, 40 page, saddle-stapled format, photocopied from typescript, matte card cover with b&w cartoon. Circulation is 350 for 130 subscriptions of which 20 are libraries. Ken Stone accepts about 100 of the 300 submissions he receives each year. **Sample postpaid: $2.50. Submit 4-6 poems. No reprint material. "We have even taken hand-written poems. As to queries, only if 13 lines gives the poet problems." Comments on rejections "especially if requested." Send SASE for guidelines. Reports "immediately to 2 weeks." Pays 1 copy.** The editor advises, "Send more poetry, less letters and self-promotion. Read the 'want lists' and description listings of magazines for guidelines. When in doubt request information. Read other poets in the magazines and journals to see what trends are. Also, this is a good way to find out what various publications like in the way of submissions."

M.I.P. COMPANY (IV-Foreign language, erotica), P.O. Box 27484, Minneapolis MN 55427, founded in 1984, contact Michael Peltsman, publishes 3 paperbacks/year. **They only publish Russian erotic poetry written in Russian.** They have published poetry collections by Mikhail Armalinsky and Aleksey Shelvakh. **Previously published poems and simultaneous submissions OK. Replies to queries in 1 month. Seldom comments on rejections.**

MACFADDEN WOMEN'S GROUP; TRUE CONFESSIONS; TRUE ROMANCES; TRUE LOVE; TRUE STORY; SECRETS; MODERN ROMANCES (I), Dept. PM, 233 Park Ave. S., New York NY 10003, phone (212)979-4800. **Address each magazine individually; do not submit to Macfadden Women's Group.** Each of these romance magazines uses poetry—usually no more than 1 poem/issue. **Their requirements vary; readers should study them individually and write for guidelines.** These mass-circulation magazines (available on newsstands) are obviously a very limited market, yet a possible one for beginners—especially those who like the prose contents and are tuned in to their editorial tastes.

THE MACGUFFIN (II), Schoolcraft College, 18600 Haggerty Rd., Livonia MI 48152, phone (313)462-4400, ext. 5292, founded 1983, editor Arthur Lindenberg, who says, *"The MacGuffin* is a literary magazine which appears three times each year, in April, June and November. We publish the best poetry, fiction, nonfiction and artwork we find. We have no thematic or stylistic biases. **We look for well-crafted poetry. Long poems should not exceed 300 lines. Avoid pornography, trite and sloppy poetry."** *The MacGuffin* has recently published poetry by Kathleen Ripley Leo, Stephen Dunning and Daniel James Sundahl. As a sample the editor selected lines from "Neruda" by Peter Brett:

> *The women pass like calendar days*
> *leaving in mind the aftertaste of*
> *mango, papaya days with high fore-*
> *heads and astonished eyes . . .*

The MacGuffin is 144 pgs., digest-sized, professionally printed on heavy buff stock, with matte card cover, flat-spined, with b&w illustrations and photos. Circulation is 500, of which 120 are subscriptions and the rest are local newsstand sales, contributor copies and distribution to college offices. Single copy: $3.75; subscription: $10. **Sample postpaid: $3. The editorial staff is grateful to consider unsolicited manuscripts and graphics." Writers should submit no more than 6 poems of no more than 300 lines; poems should be typewritten. Mss are reported on in 8-10 weeks and the publication backlog is 6+ months. Pays 2 copies,** "occasional money or prizes." The magazine also sponsors an annual contest with a $100 first prize for Michigan poets only; they hope to be able to sponsor a national competition soon. *The MacGuffin* ranked #8 in the "Traditional Verse" category of the June 1993 *Writer's Digest* Poetry 60 list. The editor says, "We will always comment on 'near misses.' Writing is a search, and it is a journey. Don't become sidetracked. Don't become discouraged. Keep looking. Keep traveling. Keep writing."

MACMILLAN PUBLISHING CO.; CHARLES SCRIBNER'S SONS; ATHENEUM; COLLIER, 866 Third Ave., New York NY 10022. Prefers not to share information.

MAD RIVER PRESS (V), Dept. PM, State Road, Richmond MA 01254, phone (413)698-3184, founded 1986, editor Barry Sternlieb, publishes 3 broadsides and 1 chapbook/year, **"all types of poetry, no bias,"** but none unsolicited. They have recently published poetry by Gary Snyder, Hayden Carruth, W.S. Merwin, Louise Gluck and Ann Fox Chandonnet. Call or write for information.

THE MADISON REVIEW; FELIX POLLAK PRIZE IN POETRY (II), Dept. of English, Helen C. White Hall, 600 N. Park St., Madison WI 53706, founded 1978, poetry editors Allison Cummings and John Merchant, want **poems that are "smart and tight, that fulfill their own propositions. Spare us: love poems, religious or patriotic dogma, light verse. We'd like to see poetry in ethnic/nationality, form/ style, gay/lesbian, humor (not light verse, though), political, social issues and women/feminism categories."** They have published work by Lise Goett, Lisa Steinman and Richard Tillinghast. As a sample the editors selected these lines from "Gulls" by Jerry Mirskin:

Now it's the sharp and damp smell of gasoline
and now the sun, the full theater of the sun
torching the town, so the windows
of the houses along the shore burn like glasses of tea.

The Madison Review is published in May and December, with 15-20 poems selected from a pool of 750. Sample back issue postpaid: $2.50. Submit maximum of 6 poems. No simultaneous submissions. Usually reports in 4 months, may be longer in summer. Pays 2 copies. "We do appreciate a concise cover letter with short bio information." The Felix Pollak Prize in Poetry is for $500 and publication in *TMR*, for "the best group of three unpublished poems submitted by a single author." Send SASE for rules before submitting for prize or see announcement for guidelines in *AWP* or *Poets & Writers* magazines. Submissions must arrive during September—winner announced December 15. *The Madison Review* ranked #10 in the "Traditional Verse" category of the June 1993 *Writer's Digest* Poetry 60 list. The editors say, "Contributors: Know your market! Read before, during and after writing. Treat your poems *better* than job applications!"

THE MAGAZINE OF SPECULATIVE POETRY (IV-Science fiction), Box 564, Beloit WI 53512, founded 1984, editors Roger Dutcher and Mark Rich, a quarterly magazine that publishes "the best new speculative poetry. We are especially interested in narrative form, but interested in variety of styles, open to any form, length (within reason), purpose. We're looking for the best of the new poetry utilizing the ideas, imagery and approaches developed by speculative fiction and will welcome experimental techniques as well as the fresh employment of traditional forms." They have published poetry by Brian Aldiss, Jane Yolen, William Stafford, Ron Ellis and S.R. Compton. As a sample Roger Dutcher chose these lines from "Time Machines" by Steve Rasnic Tem:

The Big Bang tide sends us chasing
each of our moments through space
trying to escape the collapse
and our own heat-death
when all time runs backward
and we leap from our graves

The digest-sized magazine, 20-24 pgs., is offset from professional typesetting, saddle-stapled with matte card cover. They accept less than 10% of some 500 poems received/year. Press run is 100-200, going to nearly 100 subscribers of which 4 are libraries. Subscription: $11. Sample postpaid: $3.50. No previously published poems or simultaneous submissions. Prefer double-spaced. Editor comments on rejections "on occasion." Send SASE for guidelines. Reports in 1-2 months. Pays 3¢/word, minimum $3 plus copy. Buys first North American serial rights. Reviews books of speculative poetry. Query on unsolicited reviews. Send speculative poetry books for review consideration.

MAGIC CHANGES (IV-Themes), P.O. Box 658, Warrenville IL 60555-0658, phone (708)416-3111, founded 1978, poetry editor John Sennett, is published every 18 months, in an unusual format. Photocopied from typescript on many different weights and colors of paper, magazine-sized, stapled along the long side (you read it both vertically and horizontally), taped flat spine, full of fantasy drawings, pages packed with poems of all varieties, fiction, photos, drawings, odds and ends—including reviews of little magazines and other small press publications. It is intended to make poetry (and literature) fun—and unpredictable. Each issue is on an announced theme. "*Magic Changes* is divided into sections such as 'The Order of the Celestial Otter,' 'State of the Arts,' 'Time,' 'Music' and 'Skyscraper Rats.' A magical musical theme pervades." They have recently published poetry by Sue Standing, Caleb Bullen, Hugh Ogden, Brian Shaw, Chris Robbins, Joan Eades, Patricia A. Davey and Walt Curtis. As a sample the editor selected these lines from "Satchmo" by Roberta Gould:

Satchmo's teeth gleam
like the diamond "LA"
on his ring
and his cheeks shine
like the sun he
lifts in his horn

There are about 100 pgs. of poetry/issue, circulation 500, 28 subscriptions of which 10 are libraries. Sample postpaid: $5. Submit 3-5 poems anytime. He says "no query," but poets might want to know about upcoming themes. The editor sometimes comments on rejections and offers criticism for $5/page of poetry. Reports in 2-4 months. Pays 1 or 2 copies. Acquires first North American serial rights. Reviews books of poetry in "usually about 500 words." Open to unsolicited reviews. Poets may also send books for review consideration.

‡**THE MAGIC MOUNTAIN (I)**, P.O. Box 7161, Syracuse NY 13261, founded 1993, editors Greg Carter and Susan Harris, is a quarterly forum for individual thought, subtitled "The Syracuse Quarterly of Growth and Expression." They want to see **"the work of individuals. My only criteria are strength and uniqueness of vision. No politically correct mush."** They have recently published poetry by M. Kettner and Cheryl Townsend. The editor says it is approximately 40 pgs., 5½ × 8½. Press run is 500. Subscription: $10/year. **Sample postpaid: $2.50 and 6 × 9 SAE. No previously published poems; simultaneous submissions OK. Often comments on rejections. Reports within 2-3 weeks. Pays 2 copies. Acquires one-time rights.** Staff reviews books of poetry. Send books for review consideration. The editor says, "Potential contributors may wish to read an issue prior to submitting their work. Politically correct mush may be returned with some rather negative comments."

MAGIC REALISM (II, IV-Fantasy); A THEATER OF BLOOD (II, IV-Horror), Pyx Press, P.O. Box 620, Orem UT 84059-0620, founded 1990, editors C. Darren Butler and Julie Thomas. *Magic Realism* appears 2-3 times/year using poetry **"of depth and imagination.** *Magic Realism* **subverts reality by shaping it into a human mold, bringing it closer to the imagination and to the subconscious. Inner reality becomes empirical reality. We always need good short poems of 3-12 lines."** It is typeset, offset printed, digest-sized, 60 pgs. with card cover using b&w art. They use 5-15 poems/issue. Press run is 500. **Sample postpaid: $4.95. Send #10 SASE for guidelines. Reports in 2-6 months. Pays 1 copy. Acquires first North American serial or one-time rights** *and* **non-exclusive reprint rights. Editor often comments.** He says, "I am looking for literary work based in exaggerated realism. Fantasy should permeate the reality, give it luster. My needs are somewhat flexible. For example, I occasionally publish genre work, or glib fantasy of the sort found in folktales and fables." *A Theater of Blood* is an irregular publication appearing every 6-10 months. "We try to publish material in any form or category that promotes a sense of wonder or terror or awe." They want **"intense literary horror; bizarre, surprising, surreal, absurd, fantastic and horrific work of all sorts. No obscene, gory, gratuitous, pornographic or trite material. No clichés or tropes of category horror."** They have recently published poetry by Denise Dumars, Ann K. Schwader and William John Watkins. It is 32 pgs., digest-sized, photocopied, saddle-stapled, with b&w cover art. Press run is 200. Subscription: $7/3 issues. **Sample postpaid: $2.50. Previously published poems and simultaneous submissions OK, "if labeled clearly as such."** Time between acceptance and publication is 6-18 months. **Often comments on rejections. Send SASE for guidelines. Reports in 2-6 months, "often much faster." Pays 1 copy. Acquires first or one-time rights.** "We review unsolicited books, chapbooks and magazines as space permits; reviews generally run one half to two pages."

THE MALAHAT REVIEW (II); LONG POEM PRIZES (II, IV-Form), P.O. Box 1700, University of Victoria, Victoria, British Columbia V8W 2Y2 Canada, phone (604)721-8524, founded 1967, editor Derk Wynand, is "a high quality, visually appealing literary quarterly which has earned the praise of notable literary figures throughout North America. Its purpose is to publish and promote poetry and fiction of a very high standard, both Canadian and international. **We are interested in various styles, lengths and themes. The criterion is excellence."** They have recently published poetry by Angela Ball, Dieter Weslowski and Marjorie Stelmach. As a sample the editor selected these lines from "Sleep Movements of Leaves" by Toni Sammons:

> imagination is like being slightly deaf
> — what you almost hear
> keeps you balanced on precipices of air
> your head woven from cobwebs
> like a white-eye's nest

They use 50 pgs. of poetry in each issue, have 1,800 subscriptions of which 300 are libraries. They use about 100 of 2,000 submissions received/year, have no backlog. Topics and length in this handsome publication are particularly open, though editors show a distinct taste for free verse exhibiting craft and focus. Subscription: $20. **Sample postpaid: $7. Submit 5-10 poems, addressed to Editor Derk Wynand. The editors comment if they "feel the ms warrants some attention even though it is not accepted." Send SASE for guidelines. Reports within 3 months. Pays $20 per poem/page plus 2 copies** and reduced rates on others. Reviews books of poetry. The Long Poem Prizes of $400, plus publication and payment at their usual rates, entry fee $20 (which includes a year's subscription), is for a long poem or cycle 5-15 pgs., (flexible minimum and maximum), deadline March 1.

The double dagger before a listing indicates that the listing is new in this edition. New markets are often the most receptive to submissions.

THE MANDEVILLE PRESS (III), Old Hall, Norwich Rd., South Burlingham, Norfolk NR13 4EY England, phone 0493-750-804, founded 1972, editors Peter Scupham and John Mole, publishes hand-set pamphlets of the work of individual poets. They want **"formal poetry, intelligence guiding emotion. No formless poetry, emotion eliminating intelligence."** They have published poetry by Anthony Hecht, Patric Dickinson, Edward Lowbury and Bernard O'Donoghue. **Interested poets may query. Replies to queries in 1 week, to mss (if invited) in 1 month. Pays 10 author's copies. Send SASE for catalog to buy samples.**

THE MANHATTAN REVIEW (II, IV-Translations), Apt. 45, 440 Riverside Dr., New York NY 10027, phone (212)932-1854, founded 1980, poetry editor Philip Fried, tries **"to publish American and foreign writers, and we choose foreign writers with something valuable to offer the American scene. We like to think of poetry as a powerful discipline engaged with many other fields. We want to see ambitious work. Interested in both lyric and narrative. Not interested in mawkish, sentimental poetry.** We select high-quality work from a number of different countries, including the U.S." They have published poetry by A.R. Ammons, Bei Dao, Ana Blandiana, Baron Wormser, Judson Jerome and Penelope Shuttle. As a sample the editor selected these lines by Adam Zagajewski:

> The shoes of Auschwitz, in pyramids
> high as the sky, groan faintly:
> Alas, we outlived mankind, now
> let us sleep, sleep:
> We have nowhere to go.

The *MR* is now "an annual with ambitions to be annual." The magazine has 60+ pgs., digest-sized, professionally printed with glossy card cover, photos and graphics. Press run is 500 for 85 subscribers of which 35 are libraries. It is also distributed by Bernhard DeBoer, Inc. They receive about 300 submissions/year, use few ("but I do read everything submitted carefully and with an open mind"). "I return submissions as promptly as possible." Single copy: $5; subscription: $10. **Sample: $6.25 with 6×9 envelope. Submit 3-5 pgs. No simultaneous submissions. Cover letter with short bio and publications required. Editor sometimes comments "but don't count on it." Reports in 10-12 weeks. Pays copies.** Staff reviews books of poetry. Send books for review consideration. Philip Fried advises, "Don't be swayed by fads. Search for your own voice. Support other poets whose work you respect and enjoy. Be persistent. Keep aware of poetry being written in other countries."

MANKATO POETRY REVIEW (II), Box 53, English Dept., Mankato State, Mankato MN 56001, phone (507)389-5511, founded 1984, editor Roger Sheffer, is a semiannual magazine that is **"open to all forms of poetry. We will look at poems up to 60 lines, any subject matter."** They have published poetry by Edward Micus, Judith Skillman and Walter Griffin. As a sample the editor chose the following lines from a poem by Richard Robbins:

> Sage connects to lava rock mile by mile.
> West of Atomic City, blue flowers
> in the craters of the moon.

The magazine is 5×8, typeset on 60 lb. paper, 30 pgs., saddle-stapled with buff matte card cover printed in one color. It appears usually in May and December and has a circulation of 200. Subscription: $5/year. **Sample postpaid: $2.50. Do not submit mss in summer (May through August). "Please indicate if simultaneous submission, and notify." Send SASE for guidelines. Reports in about 2 months; "We accept only what we can publish in next issue." Pays 2 copies.** The editor says, "We're interested in looking at longer poems—up to 60 lines, with great depth of detail relating to place (landscape, townscape)."

‡MANNA; MANNA FORTY, INC. (I, IV-Nature/ecology, religion, psychology), P.O. Box 766, Bolivar MO 65613-0766, phone (405)995-4906, founded 1986, literary format 1991, editor Richard D. Kahoe. As their "Mission Statement" says: "*manna*, a quarterly literary-professional journal, advances and publishes interests of manna forty, inc., a Missouri not-for-profit corporation. *manna* promotes ideals of a holistic view of truth and beauty, expressed in poetry, appropriate prose and pen sketches. It focuses on nature (natural living, ecology, environmental issues), religion (Christian and ecumenical) and psychology (and related sciences), and especially the interfaces of these areas." **They are open to all styles of poetry up to 50 lines. They want poetry related to religion, nature and psychology. "Prefer content integrating two or three of these areas. No mushy sentimentality, highly obscure verse or doggerel (except possibly in short humorous context)."** They have recently published poetry by Tom Padgett, Eldonna DeWeese and Betty Gipson. As a sample the editor selected these lines from "Baptism at Walden" by Anne Ierardi:

> I am choosing, I am chosen.
> Birth again, wholly Me, wholly Other,
> standing on solid ground yet ready for

> *the waters to receive me.*
> *The hour has come.*

manna is 8 pgs., 8½ × 11, desktop-published and professionally printed on 70 lb. recycled stock, with line drawings. Press run is 400 for 50 subscribers of which 5 are libraries, 250 distributed free to community groups. Subscription: free ("donation encouraged"). Sample available for one first class stamp. "Contributors who can are asked (but not required) to make donation toward costs, generally $5-10, depending on length of poem." Previously published poems and simultaneous submissions OK. Cover letter required. "Prefer to receive 2-6 poems on separate pages, but we're not picky." Deadlines: February 15, May 15, August 15 and November 15. Publication appears one month later. Often comments on rejections. Send SASE for guidelines. Reports in 1-4 months. Pays "5 copies direct to poet, 10 we mail to addresses provided by poet. If contributor does not make donation, we reserve rights to 50% of subsequent cash income from the writing." The editor says, "If the poem seems to fit our subject guidelines, send it to us and we'll give it full consideration. Beginners encouraged, but we prefer poems not to *sound* like beginners."

MANNA (I, II), 2966 W. Westcove Dr., West Valley City UT 84119-5940, founded 1978 by Nina Wicker, poetry editors Roger A. Ball, Brad Cutler and Rebecca Bradley, is "a small poetry magazine for the middle-of-the-road poet. We like humor, short poems with feeling, farm poems, inspirational poetry; we mostly use free verse, some rhyme. We do not want long poems. Prefer short quality poems with feelings. Images, tone and thoughtful use of language important." They have recently published poetry by Sheryl L. Nelms, Errol Miller, Robert R. Hentz, Michael Estabrook and Patricia Higginbotham. As a sample the editor selected these lines from "November waits quietly" by Susan Noe Rothman:

> *While waiting for the bread to rise, I wandered*
> *past the barn, coffee mug in hand*
> *I gazed at the mountainside—saw—*
> *empty hairbrushes, rakes, arms thin—bent—shaking*
> *little old men waiting for winter—*

The magazine is 35-40 pgs., 7 × 8½, photocopied from laser printed type and saddle-stapled with card cover, comes out twice a year, using nothing but poetry; circulation 200+, with 100 subscriptions. They receive 600 submissions/year, use about 200, and generally have less than a 6-month backlog. Subscription: $6. Sample postpaid: $3.50. Submit 3-5 poems any time ("please do not submit a lone poem"). "No simultaneous submissions please. Send SASE for additional guidelines." Reports in 3 weeks or less. "Publication is payment," but they give 3 small prizes ($7, $5 and $3) for the best in each issue. Acquires first North American serial rights. *Trilobite Broadsides*, included with each issue of *Manna*, use 3-10 published or unpublished poems, printed on a folded 8½ × 11 sheet. Sample for a quarter and SASE. "Please provide acknowledgement for previously published works." Reports in less than 6 months. Author receives 25 copies. They also sponsor an annual chapbook contest between January 1 and April 1. Submit 24 published or unpublished poems. Entry fee: $7. Prize: 50 "high-quality, *handbound* copies" and $50. Sample postpaid: $6. Send SASE for details before submitting. The editor advises, "Trust instinct and *write*. Submit poems that give your audience a unique vision. Use language and images worthy of that vision. Don't send sentimental love poetry."

‡MANOA: A PACIFIC JOURNAL OF INTERNATIONAL WRITING (II), 1733 Donaghho Rd., Honolulu HI 96822, founded 1989, poetry editor Frank Stewart, appears twice a year. "We are a general interest literary magazine, open to all forms and styles. We are not for the beginning writer, no matter what style. We are not interested in Pacific exotica." They have published poetry by John Updike, Norman Dubie, Walter Pavlich and Eugene Ruggles. It is 200+ pgs., 7 × 10, offset, flat-spined using art and graphics. They accept about 2% of 3,000 submissions received/year. Press run 1,800 for 700+ subscribers of which 30+ are libraries, 300+ shelf sales. Subscription: $18/year. Sample postpaid: $10. Send SASE for guidelines. Reports in 6 weeks. Pay "competitive" plus 2 copies. Seldom comments on rejections. They review current books and chapbooks of poetry. Open to unsolicited reviews. Poets may also send books for review consideration, attn. reviews editor. This magazine, one of the most exciting new journals in recent years, has become well known for the quality and diversity of its verse. It has also received a Design Excellence Award from the American Association of University Presses and Best Journal of the Year Award from the Council of Editors of Learned Journals. The editor says, "We welcome the opportunity to read poetry submissions from throughout the country. We are not a regional journal, but we do feature work from the Pacific Rim, national and international, especially in our reviews and essays. We are not interested in genre or formalist writing for its own sake, or picturesque impressions of the region."

‡MANUSHI (II), C/202, Lajpat Nagar 1, New Delhi 110024 India, phone 6839158 or 6833022, founded 1979, editor Madhu Kishwar, is a bimonthly "journal about women and society." **They look for "good poetry with social relevance." They do not want poetry "which makes no point."** They have recently published poetry by Archana Verma, Indu Jain and Amrita Pritam. As a sample the editor selected these lines (poet unidentified):

> Today, once again
>> She crumpled a poem,
>>> Lit the fire with it,
>>>> And put up the water for tea

Manushi is 44 pgs., approximately 8 × 10½, offset, saddle-stapled with glossy full-color cover. "We receive a considerable number of poems, accept about 10%." **No previously published poems or simultaneous submissions. Cover letter required. Often comments on rejections. Reports "fairly soon." Pays "as many copies as author requires."**

‡MAROVERLAG (III, IV-Foreign language), Riedingerstr. 24, 8900 Augsburg Germany, phone 0821/416033, founded 1970, editor Lothar Reiserer. **Maroverlag publishes paperbacks and some hardcover books of poetry, one a year, averaging 80 pages.** The books are in German, but they have published a number of English and American poets (for example, Charles Bukowski, La Loca and Raymond Carver). **Submit sample of 4-5 poems and bio. Pays 5-10% royalties.**

MARYLAND POETRY REVIEW; MARYLAND POETRY AND LITERARY SOCIETY (II), Drawer H, Catonsville MD 21228, founded 1985, edited by Rosemary Klein, "is interested in promoting the literary arts in Maryland as well as nationally and internationally. **We are interested in strong, thoughtful poetry with a slight bias to free verse. All submissions are read carefully.** *MPR* is open to good poets who have not published extensively as well as to those who have." They have published poetry by Celia Brown, Elisabeth Stevens, Enid Shomer and Joseph Somoza. As a sample the editor selected these lines from "The Fool's Dark Lantern" by Michael Fallon:

> Like a fly that spins
> in wounded circles on the sill
> his thoughts revolve around a single thought:
> there is only so much time
> in which to know

MPR is professionally printed in small type on quality eggshell stock, 7 × 11, 75 pgs., saddle-stapled with a glossy b&w card cover. It appears twice a year in double issues (Spring/Summer and Fall/Winter). In the past they have done special issues on confessional, Irish, Hispanic and Australian poetry. Query about possible future special issues. **Sample postpaid: $7. Submit no more than 5 poems at a time with brief bio. No simultaneous submissions. "We read submissions only in January, April and September but accept all year." Reports in 3-6 months. Pays 1 copy.** Subscription and Maryland Poetry and Literary Society membership is $17 ($12 for students and senior citizens; $20 for member and spouse; $25 for institutions). Book reviews are generally solicited. Send books for review consideration, attn. Robert Cooperman. "We run a yearly poetry/fiction contest (January through June) and sponsor manuscripts for Baltimore's Artscape Literary Festival."

‡THE UNIVERSITY OF MASSACHUSETTS PRESS; THE JUNIPER PRIZE (II), P.O. Box 429, Amherst MA 01004, phone (413)545-2217, founded 1964. The press offers an annual competition for the Juniper Prize, in alternate years to first and subsequent books. In 1994, for instance, the prize is for a subsequent book. In 1995 only "first books" will be considered: mss by writers whose poems have appeared in literary journals and/or anthologies but have not been published, or been accepted for publication, in book form. **Submissions should be approximately 60 pgs. in typescript (generally 50-60 poems). Include paginated contents page.** A list of poems published in literary journals and/or anthologies must also accompany the ms. Such poems may be included in the ms and must be identified. **Entry fee: $10. Entries must be postmarked not later than September 30.** The award is announced in April/May and publication is scheduled for winter. The amount of the prize is $1,000 and is in lieu of royalties on the first print run. **Send SASE for guidelines and/or further information.**

THE MASSACHUSETTS REVIEW (II), Memorial Hall, University of Massachusetts, Amherst MA 01003, founded 1959, editors Paul Jenkins and Anne Halley. Mostly free verse, all lengths and topics, appears here, with emphasis in recent issues on narrative work. An interesting feature: Editors run poems with long-line lengths in smaller type, to fit on the page without typographical interruption (as in other journals). They have published poetry by Marge Piercy, Michael Benedikt and Eavan Boland. The editors describe this quarterly as offset (some color used in art sections), 6 × 9. They receive about 2,500 poems a year, use about 50. Press run is 1,600 for 1,100-1,200 subscriptions of which 1,000 are libraries, the rest for shelf sales. Subscription: $15 (US), $20 outside US, $17 for libraries. **Sample** postpaid: $5.75. No simultaneous submissions or previously published poems. Read submissions October 1 through June 1 only. Send SASE for guidelines. Reports in 6 weeks. Pays minimum of $10, or 35¢/line, plus 2 copies.

‡MATRIX (IV-Regional), Box 100, Ste. Anne de Bellevue, Quebec H9X 3L4 Canada, founded 1975, is a literary publication appearing 3 times a year using **quality poetry by Canadians without restriction as to form, length, style, subject matter or purpose.** They have published poetry by George Elliott Clarke, Joy Kogawa, David McFadden, Carolyn Smart and Douglas Barbour. There are 5-8 pgs. of poetry in each issue. The magazine is 8½ × 11, 80 pgs., stapled, professionally printed, glossy cover with full-color art and graphics, circulation 2,000. They receive about 500 submissions/year, use 20-30, have a 6-month backlog. Subscription: $15 Canadian, $20 international. **Sample postpaid: $10 (Canadian funds). Submit 6-10 poems. No simultaneous submissions. Reports in 3 months. Pays $10-40/ poem.** Editor sometimes comments on rejections. Reviews books of poetry. Send books for review consideration, marked "Review copy."

MATURE YEARS (IV-Senior citizen), P.O. Box 801, 201 8th Ave. South, Nashville TN 37202, phone (615)749-6292, founded 1954, editor Marvin W. Cropsey, is a quarterly, circulation 80,000. "The magazine's purpose is to help persons understand and use the resources of Christian faith in dealing with specific opportunities and problems related to aging. **Poems are usually limited to fifteen lines and may, or may not, be overtly religious. Poems should not poke fun at older adults, but may take a humorous look at them. Avoid sentimentality and saccarine. If using rhymes and meter, make sure they are accurate.**" As a sample the editor selected these lines by Carole Johnston:

> What is winter
> but a large and cold
> secret that somehow
> keeps me warm . . . for
> I know where sweet
> daffodils lie sleeping.
> I know the graves of
> six brave crocuses
> and the tulip colors
> of next spring.

It is 100 + pgs., magazine-sized, saddle-stapled, with full-color glossy paper cover. **Submit season and nature poems for spring during December through February; for summer, March through May; for fall, June through August; and for winter, September through November. Send SASE for guidelines. Reports in 2 months, a year's delay before publication. Pays 50¢-$1/line.**

‡THE MAVERICK PRESS, (II, IV-Regional), Rt. 2 Box 4915, Eagle Pass TX 78852, phone (210)773-1836, founded 1991, editor Carol Cullar, publishes a biannual of "outstanding Texas writers and other mavericks whose works represent the contemporary scene. Each issue is individually named (i.e., the April 1993 issue was titled *Culebra*)." They are **looking for "strong, uncluttered figurative language to 100 lines. No diatribes on current events or political posturings, no smut."** They have recently published poetry by Lyn Lifshin, Errol Miller, Richard Kostelanetz and Kenneth Pobo. As a sample the editor selected these lines from "White Pickets, for a painting by Judi Betts" by Ava Leavell Haymon:

> a moment's wobble of planet against star
> fence slats
> absolute paper of a frontal assault
> by a skidding tricky sun
> this way, only this way, only once

The editor says it is 74 pgs., 5½ × 8½, saddle-stapled. Cover is an original block print by the editor, inside illustrations include b&w line drawings or block prints by contributors. They receive 1,000-2,000 poems a year, accept 4-8%. Press run is 250 for 100 subscribers of which 12 are libraries, 120 shelf sales. Subscription: $13.50. **Sample postpaid: $7.50. No previously published poems or simultaneous submissions. Cover letter with brief bio preferred. Submit up to 5 poems. "Author's name and address must appear on every page submitted. Prefer standard size paper and envelopes 6 × 9 or larger."** Time between acceptance and publication is a year and a half maximum. "All entries are sorted into Texans/Non-Texans, then read impartially. Outstanding pieces are reread and resorted later with slight consideration made to Texas writers. Final selections are made after consultation with Rio Bravo Literary Arts Council." Often comments on rejections. Criticism provided, if requested. Fee negotiated on a job-by-job basis, minimum $25. **Send SASE for guidelines. Reports in 6-8 weeks. Pays 2 copies. "All rights retained by authors."** The editor says, "We are looking for strong, uncluttered, figurative language and prefer free verse, although the exception is considered. Main criterion is excellence. Beginners: presentation is important, but content is paramount."

MAYAPPLE PRESS (V, IV-Regional, women), P.O. Box 5473, Saginaw MI 48603-0473, phone (517)793-2801, founded 1978, publisher/editor Judith Kerman, publishes **"women's poetry, Great Lakes regional poetry"** in chapbooks. They want **"quality contemporary poetry rooted in real experience and strongly crafted. No greeting card verse, sentimental or conventional poetry."** They have published chapbooks by Judith Minty, Evelyn Wexler and Toni Ortner-Zimmerman. They **"rarely"** accept freelance submissions. **Query with 5-6 samples. Check** *Poets & Writers* **for open times.** "We are not likely to publish unless poet accepts a *primary* role in distribution. Reality is only poets themselves can sell unknown work." **Pays 10% of run. Publishes on "cooperative" basis.** "Generally poet agrees to purchase most of the run at 50% of cover price." Editor **"sometimes comments (very briefly)"** on rejections. She says, "Poets must create the audience for their work. No small press 'white knight' can make an unknown famous (or even sell more than a few books!)."

THE EDWIN MELLEN PRESS (II), P.O. Box 450, Lewiston NY 14092, phone (416)658-5726, founded 1973, poetry editor Mr. Paul Challen, is a scholarly press. "We do not have access to large chain bookstores for distribution, but depend on direct sales and independent bookstores." **They pay 2 copies, no royalties.** "We require no author subsidies. However, we encourage our authors to seek grants from Councils for the Arts and other foundations because these add to the reputation of the volume." They want **"original integrated work—living unity of poems, preferably unpublished poetry, encompassable in one reading."** They have recently published poetry by W.R. Elton and Albert Cook. Their books are 64 pgs., 6×9, softcover binding, no graphics. Price $9.95. **Submit 40+ sample poems with cover letter including bio, publications. "We do not print until we receive at least 100 prepaid orders. Successful marketing of poetry books depends on the author's active involvement.** We send out up to 15 free review copies to journals or newspapers, the names of which may be suggested by the author. Authors may purchase more copies of their book (above the 2 free copies provided) at the same 20% discount (for quantities of 10 or more) which we allow to bookstores. An author may (but is not required to) purchase books to make up the needed 100 prepublication sales." Paul Challen says, "We seek to publish volumes unified in mood, tone, theme—most poets try to include too much within one volume."

MEMES (II), % 38 Molesworth Rd., Plympton, Plymouth, Devon PL7 4NT United Kingdom, founded 1989, editor Norman Jope, appears approximately twice a year, **"is particularly responsive to work that exhibits awareness of the *wider* dimensions of human experience and which is conscious both of contemporary realities and their possible denouements.** The title of the magazine refers to the linguistic equivalent of genes (legacies passed on from present to futurity) and the aim of the magazine is to drop as many potent memes as possible into the human timestream. Preference is for more 'modernist' material (especially with 'occult' or generally 'speculative' themes). Work from an anti-authoritarian perspective or from authors seeing themselves as 'surrealists' is also liable to please." They have published poetry by Dan Raphael, Thomas Wiloch, Sheila E. Murphy, Misha, Peter Redgrove and Belinda Subraman. As a sample here are the opening lines of "Dream (Undated)" by Hilary Hayes:

> *Fast fading it flies—this memory on night-dark wings*
> *This memory of dreams I dreamed last night.*
> *A tent of night-dark hair, the sudden shock*
> *Of recognition bent over me.*

Average size is 36-44 pgs., digest-sized, saddle-stapled, desktop published in small type on light paper with light card cover. Press run 200+ ("rising"), for 25 subscriptions by libraries, about 50 shelf sales. Subscription and samples for **cash only: $10/2 issues, $6/copy. "Contributors should read at least one issue before submitting material." Reports in 6 weeks. Pays 1 copy.** They review books, including poetry, in 50-500 words. Send books for review consideration. Like most U.K. journals, this one favors free verse that is not exclusively concerned with personal experience (as is most U.S. poetry) but attempts to make a larger statement about the poet's environment.

MENNONITE PUBLISHING HOUSE; PURPOSE; STORY FRIENDS; ON THE LINE; WITH (IV-Religious, children), 616 Walnut Ave., Scottdale PA 15683-1999, phone (412)887-8500. Send submissions or queries directly to the editor of the specific magazine at address indicated. The official publisher for the Mennonite Church in North America seeks also to serve a broad Christian audience. **Each of the magazines listed has different specifications, and the editor of each should be queried for more exact information.** *Purpose*, editor James E. Horsch, a "monthly in weekly parts," circulation 17,500, is for adults of all ages, its focus: **"action oriented, discipleship living."** It is 5⅜×8⅜, with two-color printing throughout. **They buy appropriate poetry up to 12 lines.** *Purpose* uses 3-4 poems/week, receives about 2,000/year of which they use 150, has a 10- to 12-week backlog. Send SASE for guidelines and free sample. Mss should be typewritten, double-spaced, one side of sheet only. Simultaneous submissions OK. Reports in 6-8 weeks. Pays $5-15/poem plus 2 copies. *On the Line*, edited by Mary C. Meyer, another "monthly in weekly parts," is for children 10-14, a "story paper that reinforces Christian values," circulation 8,500. It is 7×10, saddle-stapled, with 2-color printing on the cover and inside, using art and photos. **Sample free with SASE. Wants poems 3-24 lines. Submit "as many as desired, but each should be typed on a separate 8×11½ sheet." Simultaneous submissions and previously published poems OK. Reports in 1 month. Pays $5-15/poem plus 2 copies.** *Story Friends*, edited by Marjorie Waybill, is for **children 4-9**, a "story paper that reinforces Christian values," also a "monthly in weekly issues," circulation 9,000, uses poems **3-12 lines. Send SASE for guidelines/sample copy. Pays $5-10.** *With*, Editorial Team, Box 347, Newton KS 67114, phone (316)238-5100, is for **"senior highs, ages 15-18,"** focusing on helping "high school youth make a commitment to Christ in the context of the church amidst the complex and conflicting values they encounter in their world," circulation 6,100, uses **poetry dealing with youth in relation to their world, nature and light verse. Poems should be 4-50 lines. Pays $10-25.**

MERLYN'S PEN: THE NATIONAL MAGAZINES OF STUDENT WRITING, GRADES 7-12 (IV-Students, young adults), Dept. PM, Box 1058, East Greenwich RI 02818, phone (800)247-2027, founded 1985, editor R. Jim Stahl, one for grades 7-10, the other ('senior edition') for grades 9-12. Each edition is 40 pgs., magazine-sized, professionally printed with glossy paper color cover. Press run is 30,000 for 25,000 subscriptions of which 5,000 are libraries. Subscription: $18.95. **Sample postpaid: $3. Send SASE for guidelines. Reports in 3 months. Pays 3 copies.**

METAMORPHOUS PRESS (V), P.O. Box 10616, Portland OR 97210-0616, phone (503)228-4972, founded 1982, publishes and distributes books, cassettes and videotapes on **neurolinguistic programming,** health and healing education, business and sales, women's studies, and children's books. **They currently do not accept unsolicited poetry.**

METRO SINGLES LIFESTYLES (I), Box 28203, Kansas City MO 64118, phone (816)436-8424, founded 1984, editor Robert L. Huffstutter. *MSL* is a tabloid publication for women and men of all ages: single, divorced, widowed or never-married. Not a lonely hearts type of publication, but positive and upbeat, it is published 4 times/year and has a circulation of 25,000 (approximately 5,000 subscribers in Kansas City and throughout the USA), newsstand, bookstore sales and limited complimentary copies to clubs, organizations and singles groups. Interested in seeing **"free verse, lite verse, philosophical, romantic, sentimental and Frost-type poetry. All subjects considered."** They have published poetry by Patricia Castle, Milton Kerr and Mary Ann McDonnell. As a sample, the editor selected these lines from "The Women of Cairo" by Phillip Slattery:

> *Eyes made of the Egyptian night*
> *Sparkling like an oasis pool*
> *Skin the color of the endless sand*
> *Beauty of forgotten goddesses lives on.*

Each issue is about 36 pgs. and printed on Webb Offset press. Each issue features at least 12 poems by poets living throughout the USA. "Poets are invited to send a photo and a brief paragraph about their goals, single status and lifestyle. This is optional and does not influence selection of poetry, but does add interest to the publication when space for this extra feature permits." **Sample copy of current issue is $2 postpaid. Ms should be typewritten, double-spaced or written in easy-to-read format. "Prefer to look at original poetry. No simultaneous or previously published work." Reports in 6-8 weeks. Pays from $5/poem or in subscriptions plus complimentary copies.** The editor says, "We do not limit or restrict subject of poems, but insist they convey an emotion, experience or exercise the reader's imagination."

METROPOLITAIN (II, IV-Regional), 6307 N. 31st St., Arlington VA 22207, founded 1991, editor J.L. Bergsohn, is a quarterly designed to showcase the talents of **Washington area poets, writers and artists. "Will consider well-crafted poetry of any form."** They have published poetry by Elisavietta Ritchie and Hilary Tham. As a sample the editor selected these lines from "Washington Harbor" by M.A. Schaffner:

> *When the blood seeps sweet as grenadine,*
> *is it our loss or the NBA's, or*
> *one less cause for us to flinch*
> *when we walk at night?*
>
> *Brown hands lay linen on the tabletop.*
> *Black hands finger powder and steel.*
> *White hands pour on cold as milk:*
> *snap, crackle, die.*

Metropolitain is about 50 pgs., digest-sized, laser printed, saddle-stapled with card cover varying in color each issue and b&w drawings throughout. They receive about 750 poems a year, accept approximately 50. Press run is 200 for 50 subscribers, 100 shelf sales. Single copy: $2; subscription: $8. Sample postpaid: $3. **Previously published poems and simultaneous submissions OK. Cover letter, including bio, required.** Time between acceptance and publication is 6-12 months. **Reports in 4-6 weeks. Pays 1 copy. Acquires one-time rights.** The editor says, "The urban poet has never had a greater task than that which is currently at hand: to evaluate, condemn, clarify and ultimately rejoice in and preserve mankind's greatest cultural resource—the city."

MICHIGAN QUARTERLY REVIEW (III), Dept. PM, 3032 Rackham Bldg., University of Michigan, Ann Arbor MI 48109, phone (313)764-9265, founded 1962, editor-in-chief Laurence Goldstein, is "an interdisciplinary, general interest academic journal that publishes mainly essays and reviews on subjects of cultural and literary interest." They use **all kinds of poetry except light verse. No specifications as to form, length, style, subject matter or purpose.** Poets they have published include Tess Gallagher, Robert Hass, Amy Gerstler and Cathy Song. As a sample the editor chose these lines by Donald Hall:

> *Daylilies go from the hill; asters return; maples redden again*
> *as summer departs for winter's virtuous deprivation.*
> *When we stroll the Pond Road at nightfall, western sun stripes*
> *down through dust raised by a pickup ten minutes ago:*
> *vertical birches, hilly road, sunlight slant and descending.*

The *Review* is 6×9, 160+ pgs., flat-spined, professionally printed with glossy card cover, b&w photos and art, has a circulation of 2,000, with 1,500 subscriptions of which half are libraries. They receive 1,500 submissions/year, use 30, have a 1-year backlog. Single copy: $5; subscription: $18. **Sample postpaid: $2.50. They prefer typed mss. Reports in 4-6 weeks. Pays $8-12/page. Buys first rights only.** Reviews books of poetry. "All reviews are commissioned." Poetry published in the *Michigan Quarterly Review* was also selected for inclusion in **Best American Poetry 1992.** Laurence Goldstein advises, "There is no substitute for omnivorous reading and careful study of poets past and present, as well as reading in new and old areas of knowledge. Attention to technique, especially to rhythm and patterns of imagery, is vital."

MID-AMERICAN REVIEW; JAMES WRIGHT PRIZE FOR POETRY (II, IV-Translations), Dept. of English, Bowling Green State University, Bowling Green OH 43403, phone (419)372-2725, founded 1980, editor-in-chief George Looney, poetry editor Edward Dougherty, appears twice a year. **"Poetry should emanate from strong, evocative images, use fresh, interesting language, and have a consistent sense of voice. Each line must carry the poem, and an individual vision should be evident. We encourage new as well as established writers. There is no length limit."** They have published poetry by Silvia Curbelo, Mark Doty, Fleda Brown Jackson, Pat Mora, Frankie Paino and Ronald Wallace. The following lines are the closing of "Hopalong Cassidy" by Dionisio D. Martinez:

> *West, she says, is what you tell*
> *yourself when every word has lost its name.*
>
> *West is where you go when you run out of sky.*

The review is 200 pgs., flat-spined, offset, professionally printed, using line drawings, laminated card cover. They receive 1,000 mss a year, use 60-80 poems. Press run is 1,000. Single copy: $5; subscription: $8. **Sample postpaid: $4. Reads submissions September 1 through May 30 only. Send SASE for guidelines. Pays $7/printed page plus 2 copies. Rights revert to authors on publication.** Reviews books of poetry. Open to unsolicited reviews. Poets may also send books to Andrea Van Vorhis, reviews editor, for review consideration. **Also publishes chapbooks in translation.**

MIDDLE EAST REPORT (IV-Regional, ethnic, themes), Suite 119, 1500 Massachusetts Ave. NW, Washington DC 20005, phone (202)223-3677, founded 1971, editor Joe Stork, is "a magazine on contemporary political, economic, cultural and social developments in the Middle East and North Africa and U.S. policy toward the region. We occasionally publish **poetry that addresses political or social issues of Middle Eastern peoples."** They have published poetry by Dan Almagor (Israeli) and Etel Adnan (Lebanese). It is 48 pgs., magazine-sized, saddle-stapled, professionally printed on glossy stock with glossy paper cover, 6 issues/year. Press run is 7,500. "We published 9 poems last year, all solicited." Subscription: $25. **Sample postpaid: $6 domestic; $8 airmail overseas. Simultaneous submissions and previously published poems OK. Reports in 6-8 weeks.** "We key poetry to the theme of a particular issue. Could be as long as 6 months between acceptance and publication." Editor sometimes comments on submissions. **Pays 3 copies.**

MIDNIGHT ZOO; ABERATIONS (I, IV-Horror/science fiction/fantasy), 544 Ygnacio Valley Rd. #13, P.O. Box 8040, Walnut Creek CA 94596, phone (510)682-9662 or (510)825-4434, *MZ* founded 1990, *Aberations* founded 1992, editor/publisher Jon L. Herron. *MZ* appears monthly using **poems of 4-75 lines, "horror, science fiction, fantasy. No haiku, no mainstream. Submit up to 20 poems. Light verse, traditional, experimental OK."** They have recently published poetry by Bruce Boston, Holly Day,

Denise Dumars, John Grey, Herb Kauderer, John Piwarski and Sue Storm. *MZ* is 64 + pgs., magazine-sized, saddle-stapled with 3-color glossy cover. They accept 100-240 of 400-600 poems received. Press run is 2,850 for 497 subscribers of which 27 are libraries, 1,900 shelf sales. Subscription: $40. **Sample postpaid: $6. Short cover letter with bio and telephone number required with submissions. Send SASE for guidelines. Reports within 4 months. Editor usually comments on rejections. Pays $1-3/poem plus 1 copy or copies only. Buys first North American serial rights.** Reviews books, magazines and videos. Open to unsolicited reviews. Poets may also send books for review consideration, attn. Bobbi Senha. *Midnight Zoo* ranked #6 in the "Open Markets" category of the June 1993 *Writer's Digest* Poetry 60 list. This category ranks those publications most open to both free and formal verse. Herron's other publication, *Aberations*, appears monthly using **poems of 4-36 lines, "*adult* horror, science fiction, *dark* fantasy. Submit up to 10 poems. Work that is too hot for other publications — too erotic, too gory, too profane, too cutting edge."** They have recently published poetry by Holly Day, Francis DiPietro, John Grey, KL Jones, David Kopaska-Merkel and Wade Robertson. *Aberations* is 64 pgs., digest-sized, saddle-stapled with 3-color glossy cover. They accept 72-100 of 200-300 poems received. Press run is 1,500 for 129 subscribers of which 7 are libraries, 900 shelf sales. Subscription: $31. **Sample postpaid: $4.75. Short cover letter with bio and telephone number required with submissions. Send SASE for guidelines. Editor usually comments on rejections. Reports within 4 months. Pays "1 copy to $2 plus 1 copy." Buys first North American serial rights.**

MIDSTREAM: A MONTHLY JEWISH REVIEW (IV-Ethnic), 110 E. 59th St., New York NY 10022, phone (212)339-6021, editor Joel Carmichael, associate editor M.S. Solow, is a national journal appearing monthly except February/March, June/July and August/September, when it is bimonthly. They want **short poems with Jewish themes or atmosphere.** They have published poetry by Yehuda Amichai, James Reiss, Abraham Sutzkever, Liz Rosenberg and John Hollander. The magazine is 48 pgs., approximately 8½ × 11, saddle-stapled with colored card cover. Each issue includes 4 to 5 poems (which tend to be short, lyric and freestyle expressing cogent ideas). They receive about 300 submissions/year, use 5-10%. Circulation: 10,000. Single copy: $3; subscription: $21. **Reports in 1 month. Pays $25/poem. Buys all rights.**

MIDWEST POETRY REVIEW; MIDWEST POETRY LIBRARY SERIES; RIVER CITY PUBLICATIONS (IV-Subscribers), P.O. Box 4776, Rock Island IL 61201, founded 1980, poetry editors Tom Tilford, Grace Keller and Jilian Roth, is a "subscriber-only" quarterly, with no other support than subscriptions — that is, **only subscribers may submit poetry and/or enter their contests.** Subscribers may also get help and criticism on 1 poem/month. "We are attempting to encourage the cause of poetry and raise the level thereof by giving aid to new poets, to poets who have lapsed in their writing and to poets who desire a wider market, by purchasing the best of modern poetry and giving it exposure through our quarterly magazine. We want **poetry from poets who feel they have a contribution to make to the reader relating to the human condition, nature and the environment. Serious writers only are sought. No jingly verses or limericks. No restrictions as to form, length or style. Any subject is considered, if handled with skill and taste."** They have recently published poetry by Tom McFadden, John Thomas Baker, B.R. Culbertson, Martin Musick, Nancy Graham and Maude Paro. One of their latest features is The Festival of States salute to poets. Each issue features the poets of a selected state writing about natural beauties, historical features and heroes of that state. Kimberly Courtright, in her poem "Drought," writes of California in the April 1993 issue:

> Each slow and
> snowless month-to-a-minute
> day lies sluggish on
> brittle hills where grass no longer
> grows (the clouds are
> Ebenezer-stingy here).

The digest-sized, saddle-stapled magazine is 52 pgs., professionally printed in various type styles, with matte card cover and some b&w art. They have quarterly and annual contests plus varied contests in each issue, with prizes ranging from $25-500 (the latter for the annual contest), with "unbiased, non-staff judges for all competitions. Paid-up subscribers enter the contests with fees." **Sample postpaid: $5. Subscription fee of $20 ($25 Canadian, $30 foreign, both in US funds) must accompany first submission. Send SASE and $1 for guidelines. Reports in 2 weeks. Pays $5-500/poem. Buys first rights.** Staff reviews books of poetry in 400 words. Send books for review consideration. They are currently embarking on a project to publish subscribers' chapbooks under the auspices of the Midwest Poetry Library Series. They say, "The books will have matching covers, for an attractive shelf display. Poets will retain full editorial control and copyright but may benefit from the advice and help of the editorial staff. Books will be listed for sale in the magazine's register which will appear in each issue." *Midwest Poetry Review* ranked #7 in the "Nontraditional Verse" category of the June 1993 *Writer's Digest* Poetry 60 list. Tom Tilford advises, "We are interested in serious poets, whether new or published. We will help those who wish to consider serious criticism and attempt to improve themselves. We want to see the poet improve, expand and achieve fulfillment." He has developed a 20-point Self-Analysis Survey to assist poets in analyzing their own work. It is offered free to subscribers.

THE MIDWEST QUARTERLY (II), Pittsburg State University, Pittsburg KS 66762, phone (316)235-4689, founded 1959, poetry editor Stephen Meats, "publishes articles on any subject of contemporary interest, particularly literary criticism, political science, philosophy, education, biography, sociology and each issue contains a **section of poetry from 10-30 pages in length. I am interested in well-crafted, though not necessarily traditional poems that see nature and the self in bold, surrealistic images of a writer's imaginative, mystical experience of the world. 60 lines or less (occasionally longer if exceptional)."** They have published poetry by Charles Bukowski, Marguerite Bouvard, Jared Carter, Lyn Lifshin, Harold Witt and Greg Kuzma. As a sample the editor selected these lines from "Resurrection" by Andrea Moorhead:

> *tear the ice from dirt*
> *the arms from stone*
> *electric and cold*
> *when the voice runs along the ground*
> *murmuring in the soil, murmuring along the bent cut wood.*

The magazine is 130 pgs., digest-sized, flat-spined, matte cover, professionally printed. A nice mix of poems appears here, most of it free verse with room for an occasional formal or narrative piece. Circulation is 650, with 600 subscriptions of which 500 are libraries. They receive approximately 3,200 poems annually; publish 60. "My plan is to publish all acceptances within 1 year." Subscription: $10. **Sample: $3. Mss should be typed with poet's name on each page, 10 poems or fewer. Submit an original and copy. Simultaneous submissions accepted, but first publication in** *MQ* **must be guaranteed. Reports in 1 month, usually sooner. Pays 3 copies. Acquires first serial rights. Editor comments on rejections "if the poet or poems seem particularly promising."** Reviews books of poetry by *MQ* published poets only. He says, "Keep writing; read as much contemporary poetry as you can lay your hands on; don't let the discouragement of rejection keep you from sending your work out to editors."

‡MIDWEST VILLAGES & VOICES (V, IV-Regional, membership), 3220 Tenth Ave. S., Minneapolis MN 55407, founded 1979, is a cultural organization and small press publisher of **Midwestern poetry.** They have published books of poetry by Ethna McKiernan, Florence Chard Dacey, Kevin FitzPatrick and Sue Doro. They have also recently published a collection of poetry and prose by Irene Paull. As a sample here is "Divorced" by Carol Connolly:

> *I am alone, single, solitary,*
> *separated, celibate.*
> *I have borne eight children.*
> *I worry now*
> *that I will die*
> *a virgin.*

The flat-spined books are 48+ pgs., professionally printed with glossy card covers, selling for $5-6. **"We encourage and support Midwestern writers and artists. However, submissions are accepted by invitation only."**

MIDWIFERY TODAY (IV-Themes), P.O. Box 2672, Eugene OR 97402, phone (503)344-7438, founded 1986, editor Jan Tritten, is a quarterly that "provides a voice for midwives and childbirth educators. **We are a midwifery magazine. Subject must be birth or profession related."** They do not want poetry that is "off subject or puts down the subject." As a sample the editor selected these lines by Karen Hope Ehrlich:

> *you get to keep the baby*
> *not the midwife*
> *she is a fickle lover*
> *merged and passing*

ALWAYS include a self-addressed, stamped envelope (SASE) when sending a ms or query to a publisher within your own country. When sending material to other countries, include a self-addressed envelope and International Reply Coupons (IRCs), available for purchase at most post offices.

MT is 52 pgs., approximately 8½×11, offset, saddle-stapled, with glossy card cover with b&w photo and b&w photos, artwork and ads inside. They use about 1 poem/issue. Press run is 3,000 for 1,500 subscribers, 1,000 shelf sales. Subscription: $30. Sample postpaid: $7.50. No previously published poems or simultaneous submissions. Cover letter required. Time between acceptance and publication is 1-2 years. Seldom comments on rejections. Send SASE for writer's guidelines. Reports in 2-6 weeks. Pays 2 copies. Acquires first rights. The editor says, "With our publication *please* stay on the subject."

MILKWEED EDITIONS (II), Suite 505, 528 Hennepin Ave., Minneapolis MN 55403, phone (612)332-3192, founded 1979, poetry editor Emilie Buchwald. Three collections published annually. Unsolicited mss are only accepted from writers who have previously published a book-length collection of poetry or a minimum of 6 poems in commercial or literary journals. Rapidly becoming one of the leading literary presses in the country, Milkweed publishes some of the best poets composing today in well-made, attractively designed collections. Recent books of poetry include: **Astonishing World**, by Angel Gonzalez; **The Dead Get By With Everything**, by Bill Holm; and **Paul Bunyan's Bearskin**, by Patricia Goedicke. Unsolicited mss accepted in June and January; please include return postage. Catalog available on request, with 74¢ in postage.

MIND IN MOTION: A MAGAZINE OF POETRY AND SHORT PROSE (I, II), P.O. Box 1118, Apple Valley CA 92307, phone (619)248-6512, founded 1985, a quarterly, editor Céleste Goyer wants poetry "15-60 lines. Explosive, provocative. Images not cliched but directly conveyant of the point of the poem. Use of free association particularly desired. We encourage free verse, keeping in mind the essential elements of rhythm and rhyme. Traditional forms are acceptable if within length restrictions. Meaning should be implicit, as in the styles of Blake, Poe, Coleridge, Stephen Crane, Emily Dickinson, Leonard Cohen. Submit in batches of 5-6. Not interested in sentimentality, emotionalism, simplistic nature worship, explicit references." She has recently published poetry by Robert E. Brimhall, Jon Taylor, Ella Leber Grove, Kenneth Lamb and Jane McCray. As a sample she selected these lines from "Designedly Dropped" (poet unidentified):

> *A fine thought*
> *designedly dropped*
> *by one who flew above*
> *in years gone by*
> *is sighted now only by those*
> *who live the winged life too*
> *who seek meanings anew.*

MIM is 54 pgs., digest-sized, saddle-stapled, photocopied from photoreduced typescript with a heavy matte cover with b&w drawing. Of approximately 2,400 poems/year she accepts about 200. Press run is 525 for 350 subscribers. Subscription: $14. Sample postpaid: $3.50 (overseas: $4.50, $18/year). Unpublished works only. Simultaneous submissions OK if notified. "Please have name and address on each poem. We also use dates of composition; it would help if these were provided with submissions." Editor usually comments on rejected mss. Send SASE for guidelines. Reports in 1-6 weeks. Pays 1 copy "when financially possible." Magazine is copyrighted; all rights revert to author.

MIND MATTERS REVIEW (III), 2040 Polk St. #234, San Francisco CA 94109, founded 1988, editor Carrie Drake, poetry editor Lorraine A. Donfor (and submissions should be sent directly to her at 2837 Blue Spruce Lane, Silver Spring MD 20906) is a "literary quarterly with emphasis on use of science as a tool for responsible organization of information; analysis of the role of language in consciousness, knowledge and intelligence; and social criticism particularly of metaphysics. Also includes book reviews, poetry, short stories, art and essays." They want "short poems for fillers. Would like to see inspirational poetry; but open to satire and contemporary subjects that reflect the struggle between the 'inner voice' and external pressures. Rhythm important, but rhyme isn't." They have recently published poetry by Terry Williams, Michael Edward Burczynski and Simon Perchik. As a sample the editor selected these lines from "Inaccessible" by Nancy Worsham:

> *We are all alone*
> *Inaccessible is the interior*
> *The key to another's soul*
> *isn't known to mortal, the inferior*
> *To cut into the gem*
> *is not a gift burdened upon men*
> *Grasp your soul, and you have done well.*

MMR is magazine-sized, desktop published, includes graphics, sketches, b&w photos. Subscription: $12 US, $15 foreign. Sample postpaid: $3.50. Simultaneous submissions and previously published poems OK. Cover letter required; include publishing credits and note if submissions have been previously published or accepted for publication elsewhere. **Send SASE for guidelines. Pays 1 copy. Poets are encouraged to buy a copy before submitting.** Staff reviews books of poetry. Send books for review consideration to David Castleman, 512 Tamalpais Dr., Mill Valley CA 94941. The editor says, "Poetry should reflect the deeper layers of consciousness, its perceptions, observations, joys and sorrows; should reflect the independence of the individual spirit. Should not be 'trendy' or 'poetic' in a forced way."

THE MINNESOTA REVIEW (II), English Dept., East Carolina University, Greenville NC 27858, phone (919)757-6388, founded 1960, editor Jeffrey Williams, poetry editor Mary Jo Mahoney, is a biannual literary magazine wanting **"poetry which explores some aspect of social or political issues and/or the nature of relationships. No nature poems, and no lyric poetry without the above focus."** As a sample the editors selected these lines from "Hotel Kitchen" by Jonathan Holden:

> *Downstairs in those steel kitchens, in the loud*
> *bucket-brigade of order, pots and shuttling*
> *of dishes hand-to-hand, you couldn't hear*
> *the murmurous conversation of the rich . . .*

TMR is 160 pgs., digest-sized, flat-spined, with b&w glossy card cover and art. Mostly free verse (lyric and narrative), poems here tend to have strong themes and powerful content, perhaps to coincide with the magazine's subtitle: "a journal of committed writing." Circulation: 1,200 for 700 subscriptions. Subscription: $10 to individuals, $20 to institutions. **Sample postpaid: $6. Cover letter including "brief intro with address" preferred with submissions. Reports in 2-4 months. Pays 2 copies. Acquires all rights. Returns rights upon request.** Reviews books of poetry in single or multi-book format. Open to unsolicited reviews.

MINORITY LITERARY EXPO (IV-Membership, ethnic, regional), 216 Avenue T, Pratt City, Birmingham AL 35214, phone (205)798-9083, founded 1990, editor/publisher Kervin Fondren, is an annual literary professional publication featuring minority poets, novices and professionals. **"Organization membership open to all minority poets nationally. I want poems from minority poets that are holistic and wholesome, less than 24 lines each, no vulgar or hate poetry accepted, any style, any form, any subject matter. Poetry that expresses holistic views and philosophies is very acceptable. Literary value is emphasized.** Selected poets receive financial awards, certificates, honorable mentions, critiques and special poetic honors." No fee is charged for inclusion. As a sample the editor selected these lines from his poem "Rain and Pain":

> *Do I Dare*
> *As A Man*
> *Dance in My Backyard*
> *In the Rain*

An annual national literary expo, implemented in Birmingham, Alabama, features many entertainers, stars, health fairs, health runs, writing and poetry workshops, concerts, etc. Write for details. *Minority Literary Expo* ranked #7 in the "New Poets" category of the June 1993 *Writer's Digest* Poetry 60 list. This category ranks those markets who often publish poets whose work is new to their publication.

MINOTAUR PRESS; MINOTAUR (II), #11, 95 Harbormaster Rd., S. San Francisco CA 94080, founded 1974, editor Jim Gove. *Minotaur* is a "small press literary quarterly **with emphasis on contemporary and experimental styles. Must be relevant. No rhymed and/or traditional verse."** They have published poetry by Judson Crews, Ed Mycue and Julia Vinograd. As a sample the editor selected these lines from "For Jack Spicer" by William Talcott:

> *No one listens to poetry*
> *Jack Spicer.*
> *Salt & Pepper*
> *Are just another passida laugh*
> *in the mashed potatoes*

The editor describes it as digest-sized, perfect-bound, photocopied, "stock cover—cover graphics—sometimes use interior graphics, but rarely." They publish about 12 of 100 poems received. Press run is 400 for 300 subscribers of which 50 are libraries. Subscription: $18. **Sample postpaid: $3.50. Send SASE for guidelines. Submit 4-8 poems with name and address on each page. Pays 1 copy. "Best of issue from subscribing contributors receives 1-year subscription. You do not need to subscribe to be published." Editor comments on submissions "if requested only."** Reviews books of poetry. Open to unsolicited reviews. Poets may also send books for review consideration. Minotaur Press publishes a "Back to Back" chapbook with each issue. **"We ask for mss from regular magazine contributors." Pays 40 copies of chapbooks.** They "never" subsidy publish. The editor says, "Subscribe to the magazines that publish your work. Few poetry magazines run in the black."

MIORITA: A JOURNAL OF ROMANIAN STUDIES (IV-Ethnic), Department of Foreign Languages Literatures and Linguistics, University of Rochester, Rochester NY 14627, is a scholarly annual, 100 pgs., digest-sized, circulation 200, focusing on **Romanian culture and using some poetry by Romanians or on Romanian themes. Sample: $5. Pays copies.** Reviews books of poetry "occasionally; must be Romanian-connected."

THE MIRACULOUS MEDAL (IV-Religious), 475 E. Chelten Ave., Philadelphia PA 19144-5785, phone (215)848-1010, founded 1928, editor Rev. John W. Gouldrick, C.M., is a religious quarterly. "**Poetry should reflect solid Catholic doctrine and experience. Any subject matter is acceptable, provided it does not contradict the teachings of the Roman Catholic Church. Poetry must have a religious theme, preferably about the Blessed Virgin Mary.**" They have published poetry by Gladys McKee. The editor describes it as 32 pgs., digest-sized, saddle-stapled, 2-color inside and cover, no ads. *The Miraculous Medal* is no longer circulated on a subscription basis. It is used as a promotional piece and is sent to all clients of the Association. The circulation figure is now 340,000. **Sample and guidelines free for postage. Poems should be a maximum of 20 lines, double-spaced. No simultaneous submissions or previously published poems. Reports in 6 months-3 years. Pays 50¢ and up/line, payable on acceptance. Buys first North American rights.**

MIRIAM PRESS; UP AGAINST THE WALL, MOTHER (I, IV-Women, theme), 9114 Wood Spice Lane, Lorton VA 22079, phone (703)690-2246, founded 1980, poetry editor Lee-lee Schlegel. The quarterly is "**concerned with poetry as therapy first, literary excellence second.** Our philosophy is that there are many good literary markets but few who 'help' those in trouble." They want **anything on women in crisis ("we deal with the darker side here—death, rape, abuse, the frustrations of mothering/wives, etc.").** *Mother* has published poetry by Jill DiMaggio, Serena Fusek, Joan Payne Kincaid, John Fiore and John Grey. Each issue of the digest-sized magazine has 39-52 pgs. of poetry. It has a circulation of about 500 with 400 subscriptions of which 25 are university libraries. It is inexpensively produced, laser, card covers with simple art. They receive about 6,000 submissions/year, use 800. **Subscription: $12. Sample: $3.50. Submit 4-6 poems. Simultaneous submissions OK. Send SASE for guidelines. Usually reports within one month. No pay, not even a copy. Acquires one-time rights.** "We are a friendly press open to all. We are also very poor and appreciate support. Our immediate goals include being able to pay poets in copies, eventually money. Advice: 1) study your market, 2) always send SASE, 3) please don't tell me how good your poetry is!"

‡MIRRORS; AHA BOOKS (IV-Form, subscribers), P.O. Box 1250, Gualala CA 95445, AHA Books, P.O. Box 767, founded 1987 (out of Humidity Productions, Hamburg, Germany), editor Jane Reichhold. *Mirrors* is a "**subscriber-produced haiku magazine.** Each subscription entitles the author to the use of one 8½×11 page each issue. Each author is totally in control of page for choice of material, layout, artwork, copyrights, taste, quality and readability. **The author should be familiar enough with the form that he/she can publish with the top authors in this field. Beginners are not encouraged. No poetry set into 3 lines and labeled haiku. Haiku is different and the author should know the rules— before breaking them.**" They have published poetry by Marlene Mountain, Anne McKay, Joe Nutt and Charles Dickson. As a sample the editor selected this haiku by Penny Crosby:

> *reflections*
> *in a quiet pool*
> *the room once white*

The magazine-sized publication is 90-100 pgs., perfect-bound with matte card cover, appearing biannually. Press run 300 for 200 subscriptions of which 10 are libraries, about 35 shelf sales. **Subscription: $10. Sample postpaid: $5. Send SASE for guidelines. Submit camera-ready work with 1″ gutter for binding on plain white paper with black ink.** "**Author is responsible for copyrights on artwork or quotes.**" **Simultaneous submissions and previously published poems OK,** "but most are new and experimental. Only the timid who cannot trust their own judgment use previously published poems." **No report on submissions:** "I reject only material that is not haiku or related." **Pays nothing, not even copies. Open to unsolicited reviews.** Poets may also send haiku-related books for review consideration. *Mirrors* sponsors a yearly tanka contest. Send SASE for guidelines. AHA Books publishes 5 flat-spined paperbacks/year averaging 200 pgs. **They accept submissions for books *only* during October.** "Only interested in Japanese genre!"

MISNOMER (II), P.O. Box 1395, Prestonsburg KY 41653, founded 1990, editors Eric Cash and Jeff Weddle, associate editor Randy Burruss, appears twice a year. "**We like to see poetry that is vibrant and honest, poetry that communicates the human experience by dancing on the matchhead of reality, yet conveys true human compassion. We want real images, real situations. If your head is in the clouds, leave it there. Send us those poems that you would be afraid to show your mother, poems that scream to the reader. If it's good, we'll publish it. We need good poetry and would like more political and imagist poetry. No religious, light verse, rhymed, overly sentimental pieces about your grandmother,**

your dog or your grandmother's dog." They have recently published poetry by Charles Bukowski, Lyn Lifshin, A.D. Winans, Neeli Cherkovski, B.Z. Niditch, Arthur Winfield Knight and Paula Creasy-Fontaine. As a sample the editors selected "abstract and concrete" by Gerald Locklin:

> how thick is a line?
> can a line be a color?
> can a line not be linear?
> can a line cast a shadow?
>
> a line may catch a fish.
> a line may catch a critic.
> refugee families catch fish
> to feed their families.
> a critic feeds a line to feed his.

The editor describes it as 40-60 pgs., digest-sized, saddle-stapled, photocopied from typescript. They use about 5% of work submitted. Press run is 300. Subscription: $8. **Sample postpaid: $5.** **"Need short bio to be included with cover letter: tell us who you are (no bearing on acceptance)."** **Pays 1 copy.** Reviews books, chapbooks and other magazines. Open to unsolicited reviews. Poets may also send books for review consideration. "*Misnomer* is running a chapbook contest for 1994. Deadline is March 1994. Entry fee is $10 per manuscript. Manuscript should be from 15-25 pgs. Winner receives 20 copies of chapbook. All entrants receive one copy of winning chapbook."

‡**MISSISSIPPI MUD (III)** 1336 SE Marion St., Portland OR 97202, phone (503)236-9962, founded 1973, editor Joel Weinstein, is an irregular publication that features fiction, poetry and artwork that "portray life in America at the twilight of the 20th century." As for poetry they want **"lively, contemporary themes and forms, free verse preferred."** They do not want "anything stodgy, pathetic or moralistic; the self-consciously pretty or clever; purely formal exercises." They have recently published poetry by Ivan Arguelles, Christy Sheffield Sanford and Simon Perchik. *MM* is 48 pgs., 11×17, saddle-stitched, with 4-color glossy paper cover, full-page graphics and display ads. They receive 100-200 poems a year, accept less than 10%. Press run is 1,500 for 150 subscribers of which 16 are libraries, 1,000 shelf sales, about 200 distributed free to galleries, museums and critical media. Single copy: $5; subscription: $19 for 4 issues. **Sample postpaid: $6. Submit no more than 6 poems at a time. No previously published poems; simultaneous submissions OK.** Time between acceptance and publication is 1 year. Seldom comments on rejections. **Reports in 4-6 months. Pays $25 and 2 copies. Buys first North American serial rights.**

MISSISSIPPI REVIEW (II), University of Southern Mississippi, Box 5144, Hattiesburg MS 39406-5144, phone (601)266-4321, editor Frederick Barthelme, managing editor Rie Fortenberry. Literary publication for those interested in contemporary literature. Poems differ in style, length and form, but all have craft in common (along with intriguing content). **Sample: $8.80. Does not read manuscripts in summer. Pays copies.**

MISSISSIPPI VALLEY REVIEW (II), English Dept., Western Illinois University, Macomb IL 61455, phone (309)298-1514, founded 1973, editors John Mann and Tama Baldwin, is a literary magazine published twice a year. They want **poems of high quality, no specifications as to form, length, style, subject matter or purpose.** They have published poetry by Denise Levertov, David Citino, A.E. Stringer, William Heyen, David Ray, Ronald Wallace, Patricia Henley and Edward Allen. *MVR* is handsomely printed, digest-sized, flat-spined, 90+ pgs. with glossy color cover. They have about 25 pgs. of poetry in each issue, receive 1,000-2,500 submissions/year, use about 30, and have a 6-12 month backlog. Press run is 400. Subscription: $12. **Sample postpaid: $6. Submit 5 poems or less. No simultaneous submissions.** Editor comments on rejections "occasionally, particularly if we are interested in the ms. Send us poems of high quality which speak authentically from human experience." **Reports in 4 months. Pays 2 copies and a year's subscription.** Occasionally reviews books of poetry.

UNIVERSITY OF MISSOURI PRESS; DEVINS AWARD (II), 2910 LeMone Blvd., Columbia MO 65201, phone (314)882-7641, founded 1958, editor Clair Willcox. The press accepts poetry mss from both published and unpublished authors throughout the year. Query first with 5-6 sample poems (not a complete ms), a table of contents and a cover letter stating the ms length. The Devins Award is given for an outstanding poetry manuscript, not necessarily a first book, already accepted for publication by the University of Missouri Press during the year.

MISSOURI REVIEW (II), 1507 Hillcrest Hall, University of Missouri, Columbia MO 65211, phone (314)882-4474, founded 1978, poetry editor Greg Michalson, general editor Speer Morgan, is a quality literary journal, 6×9, 208 pgs., which appears 3 times a year, **publishing poetry features only—6-12**

pages for each of 3 to 5 poets/issue. By devoting more editorial space to each poet, *MR* provides a fuller look at the work of some of the best writers composing today. However, the number of poets whose work appears here has decreased significantly, limiting your chances in a prestigious market where competition has become even keener than in the past. **Sample: $6. No simultaneous submissions. Reports in 8-10 weeks. Pays $125-250/feature. Buys all rights. Returns rights "after publication, without charge, at the request of the authors."** Reviews books of poetry. "Short, inhouse reviews only." Awards the Tom McAfee Discovery Feature once or twice a year to an outstanding young poet who has not yet published a poem; poets are selected from regular submissions at the direction of the editors. Also offers the Editor's Prize Contest in Poetry. Deadline: October 15. $500 first prize and publication. Three finalists named in addition. Write for details. The editors add, "We think we have enhanced the quality of our poetry section and increased our reader interest in this section. We remain dedicated to publishing at least one younger or emerging poet in every issue."

MR. COGITO PRESS; MR. COGITO (II), Humanities Division, Pacific University, Forest Grove OR 97116 or 3314 SE Brooklyn, Portland OR 97202, founded 1973, poetry editors John M. Gogol and Robert A. Davies. *Mr. Cogito*, published 2-3 times/year, is a tall, skinny (4½ × 11) magazine, 24-26 pgs. of poetry. The editors want **"no prose put in lines. Yes: wit, heightened language, craft. Open to all schools and subjects and groups of poets."** They have published poetry by Norman Russell, Ann Chandonnet, John Minczeski, Peter Wild and Zbigniew Herbert. As a sample the editors selected these lines from "ghost poem" by Bill Shields:

> *I don't think the country is ever going to forgive us*
> *for throwing up our hands and dying in Vietnam*

They use poems in both English and translation, **"preferably representing each poet with several poems."** The magazine has a circulation of 400. Subscription for 3 issues: $9. **Sample: $3. Submit 4-5 poems. Simultaneous submissions OK. Reports in 2 weeks-2 months. Pays copies. Acquires first rights and anthology rights.** Mr. Cogito Press publishes collections by poets they invite from among those who have appeared in the magazine. Send SASE for catalog to buy samples. They also conduct special theme and translation contests with prizes of $50 or $100. The editors advise, "Subscribe to a magazine that seems good. Read ours before you submit. Write, write, write."

‡MIXED MEDIA (I, II), 33 Aspen Rd., West Orange NJ 07052, founded 1992, executive editor Paul Semel, is an annual "outlet for all forms of expression—poetry, short stories, drama, art and photography. They want **poetry up to 50 lines, any style.** They prefer not to see poetry that is "unrealistically **happy or overly mushy, but good poetry is good poetry. Because of the range of taste our editors have—we are all diverse individuals—the magazine has no theme; anything goes."** They have recently published poetry by Roddy Potter, Steve Dalachinsky and Kevin Powell. As a sample we selected these lines from "Himalayan Trek" by Raj Merchant:

> *we rested at sherpa stops*
> *manmade hovels*
> *carved*
> *into the sides of the earth*
> *thick hot tea and rice*
> *brewed under charcoals and*
> *shivering stars*

Mixed Media is 32 pgs., 8½ × 11, saddle-stapled with card cover. Press run is 150. **Sample postpaid: $3. Submit up to 3 poems, typed, with short bio. Previously published poems and simultaneous submissions OK. Reporting time varies. Pays 1 copy. All rights revert to author upon publication.**

MOBIUS (I, II), Orion Art Center, P.O. Box 563, Lake Orion MI 48361, phone (313)693-4986, founded 1982, editor Jean Hull Herman. The editor looks for "the informed mind responding to the challenges of reality and the expression of the imagination in poetry with intelligence and wit. **Open to examples of the forms of poetry (quatrain, free verse, limericks, etc.). General topics include response to art and to nature; the philosophical questions; love and romance; relationships; war; the events of and thoughts about everyday life; science and technology; and humor (for which the editor has a weakness). Shorter poems as well as longer ones will be considered."** They have published poetry by John Williams, Stephen Gill, G.C. Mahan, Daniel Green, B.Z. Niditch, Richard Davignon, Lyn Lifshin, Dawn Zapletal, Linda Nemec Foster, Sylvia Bailey and Denise Lerew-Evans. As a sample the editor selected these lines from "Love Is A Season," a sonnet by Jaye Giammarino:

> *And as I grieve the death of autumn leaves,*
> *My own lost love—which Time does not forsake—*
> *Returns to haunt my aching heart that grieves*
> *So much, that in its loneliness will break*

> *Unless remembering, despite the pain,*
> *A flame that flickers in the autumn rain.*

Mobius is published twice a year, at Memorial Day and Thanksgiving. It is magazine-sized, 80+ pgs., professionally printed, saddle-stapled with matte card cover. Subscription: $10/year. Sample postpaid: $6. Send SASE for guidelines. "Response time is two weeks to two months, as editor does read submissions all year round. Printed authors receive one copy free. Editor will comment on all rejections."

MODERN BRIDE (IV-Love/romance), 249 W. 17th St., New York NY 10011, phone (212)779-1999, managing editor Mary Ann Cavlin, a slick bimonthly, occasionally buys **poetry pertaining to love and marriage. Pays $30-40 for average short poem.**

"Haiku poetry is the journal's concern," says Robert Spiess, editor and publisher of Modern Haiku, *"both directly by publishing haiku, and indirectly by publishing essays, articles and book reviews that relate to haiku." The Wisconsin-based publication, originally founded by Kay Titus Mormino, appears three times a year, in February, June and October. The cover of this issue, entitled "Chrysanthemums and Bamboo," was created by John R. Reynolds, Modern Haiku's art editor who is trained in Oriental painting techniques.*

MODERN HAIKU; KAY TITUS MORMINO MEMORIAL SCHOLARSHIP; MARGARET DUFFIELD MEMORIAL SCHOLARSHIP (IV-Form, students), P.O. Box 1752, Madison WI 53701, founded 1969, poetry editor Robert Spiess, "is the foremost international journal of English language haiku and criticism. We are devoted to publishing only the very best haiku being written and also publish articles on haiku and have the most complete review section of haiku books. Issues average over 100 pages." They use **haiku only. No tanka or other forms. "We publish all 'schools' of haiku, but want the haiku to elicit intuition, insight, felt-depth."** They have recently published haiku by William J. Higginson, James Kirkup, Elizabeth Lamb and Alexis Rotella. As a sample the editor selected this haiku (poet unidentified):

> *the field's evening fog—*
> *quietly the hound comes*
> *to fetch me home*

The digest-sized magazine appears 3 times a year, printed on heavy quality stock with cover illustrations especially painted for each issue by the staff artist. They receive 16,000-18,000 freelance submissions/year, use 800. There are over 260 poems in each issue, circulation 650. Subscription: $13.75; single copy: $4.85. Sample postpaid: $4.50. **No simultaneous submissions. Submit on "any size sheets, any number of haiku on a sheet; but name and address on each sheet." Send SASE for guidelines. Reports in 2 weeks. Pays $1/haiku (but no contributor's copy). Buys first North American serial rights.** Staff reviews books of haiku in 350-1,000 words, single format. Send books for review consideration. The Kay Titus Mormino Memorial Scholarship of $500 is for the best haiku by a high school senior, deadline early March. They also offer the Margaret Duffield Memorial Scholarship of $200. Send SASE for rules. *Modern Haiku* ranked #2 in the "New Poets" category of the June 1993 *Writer's Digest* Poetry 60 list. This category ranks those markets who often publish poets whose work is new to their publication. As for the journal's editor, Robert Spiess received a third place 1992 Merit Book Award from The Haiku Society of America for his book **The Cottage of Wild Plum.** He says "Haiku achieve their effect of felt-depth, insight and intuition through juxtaposition of perceived entities, not through intellective comment or abstract words."

MOKSHA JOURNAL; VAJRA PRINTING & PUBLISHING OF YOGA ANAND ASHRAM (IV-Spiritual), 49 Forrest Pl., Amityville NY 11701, phone (516)691-8475, founded 1984, is a "small press publisher of spiritual and/or philosophical literature, poetry, nonfiction and poetry pertaining to the concept of 'Moksha,' defined by Monier-Williams as a 'liberation, release' (A Sanskrit-English Dictionary, 1899). Perspectives include, but are not limited to: Yoga, various schools of Buddhism, Sufism, Mystical Christianity, etc." *Moksha Journal* appears twice a year, and is 40-55 pgs., 7¼ × 9½, offset, litho. Press run is 400-500 for that many subscribers. Subscription: $8. **Sample: $4. Pays 2 copies. Simultaneous submissions OK. Reports in 4-6 weeks.** The press publishes flat-spined paperbacks.

MONOCACY VALLEY REVIEW (II), Department of English, Mount Saint Mary's College, Emmitsburg MD 21727, founded 1985, poetry editor Mary Noel, editor William Heath, is an annual literary review. Submissions should be received by January 15th. "In general, we cannot publish longer poems; we also publish short stories, nonfiction prose, book reviews and artwork. We pride ourselves in being a review that is always local but never provincial. If we have a bias, it is in favor of clarity of vision and eloquence of language. We dislike poems that 'hurt the ear and unfit one to continue.'" *MVR* is magazine-sized, 60 pgs., saddle-stapled, high quality paper. "We reject over 95% of submissions, publish 15-20 poems an issue." Their press run is 500 with 200 subscriptions of which 10 are libraries. Subscription: $8. **Sample postpaid: $5. Include a 50-word or less biographical statement with all submissions. All submissions are judged anonymously and there is no backlog. If mss are sent in December and early January, response time is 6-8 weeks. Pays $10-25/poem plus 2 copies.** The editor says they "prefer reviews of major writers in the area."

‡THE MONTANA POET MAGAZINE (IV-Regional); GOLDEN STAR AWARD FOR POETRY (II), P.O. Box 100, Three Forks MT 59752, founded 1987, editor Don "Cheese" Akerlow. *TMP* is a bimonthly publication using "cowboy poetry and poetry from all walks of life." They are interested in poems about Montana or from poets who live in Montana. They also use cartoons and philosophies. They have published poetry by Greg Keeler and Sandy Seaton. As a sample the editor selected these lines from his own poem "Want Ads":

> *I've been writin' poems for some 25 years*
> *Written cowboy poems about shootin', Ridin', and drinkin' beers*
> *Kickin' up my heels and once at the moon I did howl*
> *Guess that Chicken Factory is still with me cause my poems are still just plain foul.*

TMP is 16 pgs., magazine-sized, saddle-stapled. Their press run is 1,000. Subscription: $10. **Sample postpaid: $2. Guidelines available for SASE. Submit up to 5 poems at a time, with name and address on each page. Considers simultaneous submissions and previously published poems. Cover letter required; include bio and photo. Reports in 4-6 weeks. Pays $5/poem plus 1 copy upon publication.** The magazine annually sponsors the Golden Star contest, entries accepted January 1 through May 15, entry fee $1/each poem, prizes of $50, $25, $15, $10, and 6 honorable mentions. The *TMP* Membership offers 1-year subscription plus the *TMP* T-shirt (which sells for $10), plus 5 poems entered in the Golden Star competition, for $20. They also sponsor the Montana Poets' Hall of Fame. *The Montana Poet Magazine* ranked #5 in the "New Poets" category of the June 1993 *Writer's Digest* Poety 60 list. This category ranks those markets who often publish poets whose work is new to their publication. The editor says, "I feel that poetry has too long been enjoyed by a select few. It is the purpose of *TMP* to get more people involved in reading and enjoying poetry; to make reading poetry as commonplace as reading any other type of literature. Advice to beginning poet: Don't be discouraged. Believe in your work because, if it comes from within, you are pleasing at least one person, and keep sending your work to editors. I do not judge poetry on perfect grammar or structure but on feeling and that's what I look for when selecting poems for the magazine."

‡THE MOODY STREET REVIEW (I, II), Apt. 19L, 205 E. 78th St., New York NY 10021, founded 1988, editor David Gibson, appears twice a year publishing "poetry informed by the lyrical and inspirational traditions of the 20th century, i.e. symbolism, imagism, objectivism, projective verse, beat generation, etc. No out-and-out sexual poetry, no poems disguised as political or religious sermons (or vice versa), no metered verse, nothing boring." They have recently published poetry by Arthur Winfield Knight, B.Z. Niditch, Joy Walsh, George Bowering and Raymond Radiguet. The editor says *MSR* is 50-100 pgs., 5½ × 8, saddle-stitched, quality photocopy, with b&w artwork in drawings, linoleum prints, some photographs. "Some color work now being accepted." They receive 20-80 submissions of poetry/month, "publish no more than 20% of all material received." Press run is 300. Subscription: $10. **Sample postpaid: $4. Previously published poems and simultaneous submissions OK. Cover letter required.** "We like to get an overview of a poet's work, so send at least five poems. Also, if there is no SASE, or only a postcard to be filled out, the submission will probably get tossed." Often comments on rejections; "sometimes I critique or suggest other markets." **Reports in 2 weeks to 2 months. Pays 2 copies, more at a discount. Acquires one-time rights.** The editor says, "Persistence is an admirable trait, but know when to stop sending to any one publication. Be educated about poetry. Read, read, read! Blank verse is not the end all, be all. Know the metered forms, if not practice them. Their importance is only in the discipline they teach. Editors will appreciate this self-conscious approach to your craft."

WILLIAM MORROW AND CO. (V), 1350 Avenue of the Americas, New York NY 10019, phone (212)261-6500, publishes poetry on standard royalty contracts **but accepts no unsolicited mss. Queries with samples should be submitted through an agent.**

(m)ÖTHÊR TØÑGUÉS (II, IV-Translations), RR#2 Alders C-14, Ganges, British Columbia V0S 1E0 Canada, founded 1990, editor/publisher Mona Fertig, is a literary magazine of poetry, fiction and essays appearing twice a year. She wants **"unpublished, new, volatile, political, well-written poetry, no clichés or unstimulating poetry,"** includes translations from many languages. They have published poetry by Thich Tue Sy, Erin Mouré, Dorin Tudoran and Ann Diamond. *MT* is magazine-sized, 70 pgs., photocopied. Press run 500. Subscription: $12 Canadian, $14 USA, $18 international. **Sample postpaid: $7. Include "Writers Notes" with submissions. Reports in 3 months. Pays 1-year subscription.**

‡MOVING PARTS PRESS; MUTANT DRONE PRESS (V), 220 Baldwin St., Santa Cruz CA 95060, phone (408)427-2271. Moving Parts founded 1977, Mutant Drone, 1982. Poetry editor Felicia Rice says they are a "fine arts literary publisher using letterpress printing and printmaking to produce handsome and innovative books, broadsides and prints in limited editions." Moving Parts has published books of poetry by Ellen Bass, William Pitt Root, Katharine Harer and William Everson. Mutant Drone "the One-&-Only-Wholly-Owned Subsidiary, is free to laugh and throw punches at the whole predicament," and has published books by Charles Bukowski and Nick Zachreson. As a sample here is the opening lines of "On a Darkening Road" by Robert Lundquist from **before/ THE RAIN,** Moving Parts Press:

> *This evening the tide is low,*
> *Ducks walk through bunched beds of kelp*
> *Looking for insects.*

They accept no unsolicited mss. Pay 10% of the edition in copies.

MS. MAGAZINE (V), 7th Floor, 230 Park Ave., New York NY 10169, founded 1972, is a bimonthly "feminist source of national and international news, politics, arts, scholarship and book reviews." **They are currently not accepting unsolicited poetry.** They have published poetry by Alice Walker, Maya Angelou and May Swenson. Circulation is 150,000. Single copy: $5 (available on newsstands); subscription: $30. They say, "Due to the volume of the material received, we cannot accept, acknowledge or return unsolicited poetry or fiction. We cannot discuss queries on the phone and cannot be held responsible for manuscripts sent to us."

MUDFISH; BOX TURTLE PRESS (I, II), 184 Franklin St., New York NY 10013, phone (212)219-9278, founded 1983, poetry editor Jill Hoffman. *Mudfish*, published by Box Turtle Press, is a journal of poetry and art that appears once a year and is looking for **"energy, intensity, and originality of voice, mastery of style, the presence of passion." Considers sexually explicit material.** They have published poetry by Charles Simic, Harvey Shapiro, Nicholas Kolumban, Denise Duhamel and John Ashbery. Press run is 1,500. Single copy: $10. **Sample copies are available, include $1.50 shipping and handling. They will not consider simultaneous submissions or previously published poems. Reports from "immediately to 6 months." Pays 2 copies.**

MULBERRY PRESS (I, II), 105 Betty Rd., East Meadow NY 11554, founded 1991, publisher G.M. Frey. This is an arrangement for publishing chapbooks only. mulberry press (they prefer lowercase) will **consider chapbooks (any length) for a $5 reading fee, for which you get 2 sample chapbooks in return if your ms is rejected, 50 copies if accepted (additional copies at cost). Press run 150-200 copies, and additional printings. Poems may be previously published. Make checks payable to G.M. Frey.** They are also open to co-op publishing: Poet pays "a modest fee to cover cost of their copies only and receives 50 copies." They have recently published chapbooks by Nate Tate, Steve Ullmann, Bob Balo, Richard Swiss, Todd Moore, Tony Moffeit, Lyn Lifshin and many others. As a sample here is a complete poem, "Communion In Venice," from **White Horse Cafe** by Gina Bergamino:

> *he told me time was running out*
> *so I loved him*
> *dropping to my knees*
> > *and walls became clouds*
> > *the pigeons listened*
> > *from rooftops*

They also offer an annual chapbook contest. Entry fee: $5. All entrants receive copy of winning chapbook. Winner receives 100 copies. **Send SASE for guidelines.** The editor advises, "Take your art seriously, make it a priority in your life. Be persistent and patient and eventually you will endure and prevail. If you keep on writing, you can only get better."

‡**MUSE PORTFOLIO (I, II)**, 25 Tannery Rd., Box 8, Westfield MA 01085, founded 1992, editor Haemi Balgassi, appears 2-4 times a year. *Muse Portfolio* is a "casual magazine for sincere, eloquent, earnest writers who crave forum to share work with others." They want **poetry of "any structure, formal or free, 50 lines maximum. No forced rhymes, nothing profane.** We also publish short stories and nonfiction, as well as cartoons and art sketches." They have recently published poetry by Bobbi Sinha, Conny Jakoboski and Jordan Faris. As a sample the editor selected these lines from "Red Shift" by E.J. Cherhavy-Shumak:

> I pull back the shield and am inundated with a hue
> a hue and vision I betray by describing it here
> it is at once all colors and no color
> it is at once the presence of light
> and the absence of light

Muse Portfolio is 20-28 pgs., 5½ × 8½, saddle-stapled, printed on 20 lb. paper with heavier stock cover, b&w artwork, occasional ads. They receive about 100 poems a year, accept 10-25%. Press run is 150 for 100+ subscribers. Subscription: $4. **Sample postpaid: $2. Previously published poems OK; no simultaneous submissions. Cover letter required.** "Include a biographical paragraph—need not list published credits if author prefers to write something else." Seldom comments on rejections. **Send SASE for guidelines. Reports in 1-2 months. Pays 1 copy. Acquires one-time rights.** The editor says, "Remember the three P's: Be professional, persistent and patient."

MUSICWORKS (IV-Themes), 1087 Queen St. W., Toronto, Ontario M6J 1H3 Canada, phone (416)533-0192, founded 1978, editor Gayle Young, is a tabloid triannual journal of contemporary music. The editor says, "**The poetry we publish only relates directly to the topics discussed in the magazine or relates to contemporary sound poetry**—*usually* it is poetry written by the (music) composer or performers we are featuring." Poets published include bpnichol, Colin Morton and Jackson Mac Low. The magazine is 64 pgs., with b&w visuals, b&w photography, some illustrative graphics and scores and accompanied by 60-minute cassette. Circulation is 1,600, of which 500 are subscriptions. Price is $5/issue or $12 for the paper plus cassette. **Sample postpaid: $4. Considers simultaneous submissions. They report on submissions within 2 months, and there is no backlog before publication. The magazine pays Canadian contributors $20-50/contribution plus 2-3 free copies.**

MY LEGACY (I); OMNIFIC (I); FELICITY (I, IV-Themes); THE BOTTOM LINE, HC-13, Box 21-AA, Artemas PA 17211-9405, phone (814)458-3102, editor/publisher Kay Weems. *My Legacy* is a quarterly of poetry and short stories using **36-line, sometimes longer, poems, "anything in good taste"** with an Editor's Choice small cash award for each issue. No contributor copies. Subscription: $12/year; $3.50/copy. *Omnific,* a "family-type" quarterly publishes poetry only, 36 lines, sometimes longer; readers vote on favorites, small cash award or copy to favorites. **Send SASE for guidelines.** No contributor copies. Subscription: $12/year; $3.50/copy. *Felicity,* founded 1988, is a bimonthly newsletter for contests only, 30-40 pgs. They offer 10 contests/flyer including a bimonthly theme contest, 36 lines. Other contests may be for theme, form, chapbook, etc. Entry fees vary. **Send SASE for guidelines** and upcoming themes. Payment for contest winners is small cash award and/or publication. No work is returned. They consider simultaneous submissions and previously published poems. All winning entries including honorable mentions are printed in the newsletter which also publishes market and other contest listings. Subscription: $15/year; $2.50/copy. She also publishes an annual **Christmas anthology. Poetry only, published/unpublished, 36 lines maximum, Christmas themes. Address to "Christmas Anthology." Deadline: August 31.** *The Bottom Line,* founded 1988, is a monthly newsletter listing over 50 publications and contests for writers, reproducing guidelines of still others. Information is presented in chronological order by deadline date, and then in alphabetical order. Circulation 50-100. Subscription: $21/year; $2.50/copy.

MYSTERY TIME (I, IV-Themes), P.O. Box 2907, Decatur IL 62526, poetry editor Linda Hutton, founded 1983, is an annual containing 1-2 pages of **humorous poems about mysteries and mystery writers** in each issue. As a sample the editor selected her own poem, "Agatha's Jane":

> Miss Marple holds orthodox views
> On murder and all of its clues.
> She disapproves strongly
> Of those who do wrongly
> And evil, to her, is no news.

Mystery Time is 44 pgs., digest-sized, plastic ring bound with heavy stock cover. They receive up to 15 submissions a year, use 4-6. Circulation 100. **Sample: $3.50. Does not read mss in December. No guidelines available. Pays 25¢/line on acceptance.**

‡THE MYTHIC CIRCLE; THE MYTHOPOEIC SOCIETY (I, IV-Fantasy), P.O. Box 6707, Altadena CA 91001, editor Tina Cooper. *The Mythic Circle* is a "writer's workshop in print, appearing 2-3 times a year, publishing fantasy short stories and poems. They want **"poetry with a mythic or fairy-tale theme."** They have recently published poetry by Angelee Anderson and Gwyneth Hood. They receive approximately 100 poetry submissions/year, accept 10%. Press run is 230 for 200 subscribers. Subscription: $18/year for non-members of sponsoring organization, the Mythopoeic Society; $13/year for members. **Sample postpaid: $6.50. No previously published poems or simultaneous submissions.** Time between acceptance and publication is 2 years. Seldom comments on rejections. Send SASE for guidelines. **Reports in 2-4 months. Pays 1 copy for 3 poems.** The editor says, "Subscribers are heavily favored, since they provide the critical review which our authors need in their letters of comment."

NADA PRESS; BIG SCREAM (II, IV-Themes, bilingual), 2782 Dixie SW, Grandville MI 49418, phone (616)531-1442, founded 1974, poetry editor David Cope. *Big Scream* appears annually and is **"a brief anthology of mostly 'unknown' poets. We are promoting a continuation of objectivist tradition begun by Williams and Reznikoff. We want objectivist-based short works; some surrealism; basically short, tight work that shows clarity of perception and care in its making. Also poems in Spanish—*not* translations."** They have published poetry by Antler, James Ruggia, Richard Kostelanetz, Andy Clausen, Allen Ginsberg, John Steinbeck, Jr., Bob Rixon and Janet Cannon. *Big Scream* is 35 pgs., magazine-sized, xerograph on 60 lb. paper, side-stapled, "sent gratis to a select group of poets and editors." They receive "several hundred (not sure)" freelance submissions/year, use "very few." Press run is 100. Subscription to institutions: $6/year. **Sample postpaid: $3. Submit after July. Send 10 pgs. No cover letter. "If poetry interests me, I will ask the proper questions of the poet." Simultaneous submissions OK.** Comments on rejections "if requested and ms warrants it." **Reports in 1-14 days. Pays as many copies as requested, within reason.** The editor advises: "Read Pound's essay, 'A Retrospect,' then Reznikoff and Williams; follow through the Beats and NY School, especially Denby & Berrigan, and you have our approach to writing well in hand. I expect to be publishing *BS* regularly 10 years from now, same basic format."

NAHANT BAY (II), #2, 29 Front St., Marblehead MA 01945, founded 1990, editors Kalo Clarke and Kim A. Pederson, appears once a year. **"Open submissions; submit a maximum of 6 poems."** They have recently published poetry by Jody Savin, Lyn Lifshin and Jonathan Gillman. As a sample the editor selected these lines from "Batman's Secret Passion for Limbo" by Glen Armstrong:

> There are severed heads inside me,
> memories that need a punch
> in the nose and undercurrents strong
> enough to suck a church
> through a pipe bomb.

The handsome magazine contains mostly free verse (some selections more structured than others) and is digest-sized, 60-100 pgs., saddle-stapled, professionally printed, with matte card cover, b&w photos and illustrations. Subscription: $5. **Sample postpaid: $5. Reports in 1-3 months. Pays 1 copy.**

NASHVILLE HOUSE (IV-Themes, science fiction/fantasy/horror), P.O. Box 60072, Nashville TN 37206, founded 1991, publishes books, including poetry, relating to the South, Old West and Civil War. They are also interested in science fiction, fantasy and horror poetry and have published **Poems of the Divided Self** by Gothic poet and scholar Gary William Crawford, introduced by Joey Froehlich. **Query with letter only.** As a sample the director, Steve Eng, selected these lines from one of Crawford's poems, "My Thoughts Conceive":

> Days pass, infinitely stretching my
> Brain cells to the rings of Saturn.
> Forever travelling in the emptiness of Time,
> I see a grain of dust floating
>   and never settling.

Market categories: (I) Beginning; (II) General; (III) Limited; (IV) Specialized; (V) Closed.

NASSAU REVIEW (II), English Department, Nassau Community College, Garden City NY 11530, phone (516)222-7186, founded 1964, managing editor Dr. Paul A. Doyle, is an annual "creative and research vehicle for Nassau College faculty and the faculty of other colleges." They want "serious, intellectual poetry of any form or style. No light verse or satiric verse." Submissions from adults only. "No college students; graduate students acceptable." They have published poetry by Patti Tana, Dick Allen, Louis Phillips and David Heyen. As a sample the editor selected these lines from "Chekhov, For Beginners" by Barbara Novack:

> Chekhov said
> throw out the first three pages;
> it takes that long
> to get to the beginning.
>
> And I may say
> put aside the first three decades
> sweep away their debris
> cast off versions of the self . . .

NR is about 150 pgs., digest-sized, flat-spined. They receive 400-450 poems a year, use approximately 20. Press run is 1,000 for about 1,000 subscribers of which 600 are libraries. **Sample free. No previously published poems or simultaneous submissions. Submit only 3 poems at a time. Reads submissions September 1 through December 1 only. Reports in 2-3 months. Pays in copies.** They sponsor occasional contests with $100 or $200 poetry awards, depending on college funding. Well-edited and visually appealing, *Nassau Review* tends to publish free verse emphasizing voice in well-crafted lyric and narrative forms.

THE NATION; LEONORE MARSHALL/NATION PRIZE FOR POETRY; DISCOVERY/THE NATION (III), 72 Fifth Ave., New York NY 10011, founded 1865, poetry editor Grace Schulman. *The Nation*'s only requirement for poetry is "excellence," which can be inferred from the list of poets they have published: Marianne Moore, Robert Lowell, W.S. Merwin, Maxine Kumin, Donald Justice, James Merrill, Richard Howard, May Swenson, Garrett Hongo and Amy Clampitt. The editor chose this as a sample from a poem in *The Nation*, 1939, by W.B. Yeats:

> Like a long-legged fly upon the stream
> His mind moves upon silence.

Pay for poetry is $1/line, not to exceed 35 lines, plus 1 copy. The magazine co-sponsors the Leonore Marshall/Nation Prize for Poetry which is an annual award of $10,000 for the outstanding book of poems published in the U.S. in each year; and the "Discovery/The Nation" ($200 each plus a reading at The Poetry Center, 1395 Lexington Ave., New York NY 10128. Deadline: mid-February. Send SASE for application.

NATIONAL ENQUIRER (II, IV-Humor), Lantana FL 33464, assistant editor Michele Cooke, is a weekly tabloid, circulation 4,550,000, which uses **short poems, most of them humorous and traditional rhyming verse. "We want poetry with a message or reflection on the human condition or everyday life. Avoid sending obscure or 'arty' poetry or poetry for art's sake. Also looking for philosophical and inspirational material. Submit seasonal/holiday material at least 3 months in advance." Requires cover letter from first-time submitters; include name, address, social security and phone numbers. Pays $25 after publication; original material only. Buys first rights.**

NATIONAL FORUM (III), 129 Quad Center, Mell St., Auburn University AL 36849-5306, phone (205)844-4000, founded 1915, editor Stephen W. White, is the quarterly of Phi Kappa Phi using **quality poetry, no "profanity, brutality, love poems."** They have published poetry by William Stafford, Bin Ramke, Mary Oliver and Marge Piercy. As a sample the editor selected these lines from "In Spite of Everything, the Stars" by Edward Hirsch:

> Like a stunned piano, like a bucket
> of fresh milk flung into the air
> or a dozen fists of confetti
> suddenly thrown hard at a bride
> stepping down from the altar, the stars
> surprise the sky.

NF is 48 pgs., magazine-sized, professionally printed, saddle-stapled, with full-color paper cover. They publish about 20 poems of 300 received a year. Their press run is 118,000 with 115,000 subscriptions of which 600 are libraries. Subscription: $10. **Sample postpaid: $2.75. Submit 3-5 poems. Reads submissions January and September only. Reports in 4-6 weeks, publishes within 9-12 months. Pays "small honorarium" and 10 copies.** The editor advises, "Do not send out work that has not been proofread by a couple of helpfully critical friends. Enclose a biographical sketch with recent publications. We do not include comments on rejected work."

NAUGHTY NAKED DREAMGIRLS; NAUGHTY LINGERIE; SEX COMIX (I, IV-Erotica, science fiction, humor), Suite 253, 5960 S. Land Park Dr., Sacramento CA 95822, phone (916)429-8522, founded 1986, editor Andrew L. Roller. These newsletters appear "approximately monthly." They want **erotic poetry**. Also willing to look at **"weird, occult or science fiction, or humorous poetry (political or comics related)."** They have published poetry by Cheryl Townsend, P.D. Wilson, William Dockery, Norma Lee Edwards, Arthur Winfield Knight and Scott C. Holstad. As a sample the editor selected these lines:

> At first I think
> There's a turd in the toilet
> I'm not wearing my glasses
> And it's one a.m.
> I tell my wife,
> "You forgot to flush"

The newsletters are saddle-stitched, 16 pgs. Press run is 105 for 20 subscribers of which 2 are libraries. **Sample postpaid: $2 US, $3 Canada, $4 foreign. "Poems should be well typed for camera ready reproduction." Reports "at once." Pays 1 copy ("2 for regulars"). Acquires first North American serial rights.** Reviews books of poetry. Open to unsolicited reviews. Poets may also send books for review consideration to William Dockery, P.O. Box 3663, Phenix City AL 36868. The editor says, "As for poetry submissions, **don't send me more than a few pages of poems.** I'm getting more poems than I can handle right now. I prefer to send 'rejected' poems on to other potential publishers and respond with an informative letter on self-publishing."

NAZARENE INTERNATIONAL HEADQUARTERS; STANDARD; WONDER TIME; LISTEN; BREAD; TEENS TODAY; HERALD OF HOLINESS (IV-Religious, children), 6401 The Paseo, Kansas City MO 64131, phone (816)333-7000. Each of the magazines published by the Nazarenes has a separate editor, focus and audience. *Standard*, circulation 177,000, is a weekly **inspirational "story paper" with Christian leisure reading for adults. Send SASE for free sample and guidelines. Uses a poem each week. Submit maximum of 5, maximum of 50 lines each. Pays 25¢ a line.** *Wonder Time*, editor Lois Perrigo, a publication of the Children's Ministries Department, Church of the Nazarene, **"is committed to reinforcement of the Biblical concepts taught in the Sunday School curriculum, using poems 4-8 lines, simple, with a message, easy to read, for 1st and 2nd graders. It should not deal with much symbolism."** As a sample the editors selected this poem, "God's Word," by Joyce Lindberg:

> The Bible stories help me know
>   What God wants me to do.
> I'll learn the lessons from God's Word,
>   And I'll obey it too.

Wonder Time is a weekly 4-page leaflet, magazine-sized, newsprint, circulation 37,000. **Sample free for SASE. Also send SASE for guidelines. Reports in 2-3 months. Pays minimum of $3 – 25¢/line – and 4 contributor's copies.** For *Listen, Bread, Teens Today* and *Herald of Holiness*, write individually for guidelines and samples.

NCASA JOURNAL (NEWSLETTER OF THE NATIONAL COALITION AGAINST SEXUAL ASSAULT) (IV-Themes, social issues, women/feminism), Suite 500, 123 S. Seventh, Springfield IL 62701, founded 1986, editor Becky Bradway. Appears 3 times/year using **"well-written poetry by survivors of rape, child sexual abuse and incest. Poems may deal with aspects of the sexual assault experience or recovery from sexual assault."** It is 16 pgs., magazine-sized, professionally printed, with matte card cover, saddle-stapled. Press run 700 for 600 subscribers. Subscription: $12; or with NCASA membership: $25. **Sample postpaid: $4. Previously published poems and simultaneous submissions OK. Pays 3 copies. Acquires first rights.** Accepts reviews of books relevant to feminism and the anti-rape movement – up to 1,000 words. Poets may also send books relating to sexual assault for review consideration. The editor says, "*NCASA Journal* is a nationally circulated magazine. Its 'Voices of Survivors' section includes poetry and fiction by survivors of sexual assault."

NEBO: A LITERARY JOURNAL (II), English Dept., Arkansas Tech University, Russellville AR 72801-2222, phone (501)968-0256, founded 1982, poetry editor Michael Ritchie, appears in May and December. Regarding poetry they say, **"We accept all kinds, all styles, all subject matters and will publish a longer poem if it is outstanding. We are especially interested in formal poetry."** They have published poetry by Jack Butler, Turner Cassity, Wyatt Prunty, Charles Martin, Julia Randall and Brenda Hillman. *Nebo* is digest-sized, 50-70 pgs., professionally printed on quality matte stock with matte card cover. Press run "varies." **Sample postpaid: $6. Simultaneous submissions OK. "Please no onion skin or offbeat colors." Cover letter with bio material and recent publications required. Do not submit mss between May 1 and August 15 of each year.** Editor comments on rejections **"if the work has merit but requires revision and resubmission; we do all we can to help." Reports at the end of November and February respectively. Pays 1 copy.** Staff reviews books of poetry. Send books for review consideration.

THE NEBRASKA REVIEW; TNR AWARDS (II), ASH 212, University of Nebraska, Omaha NE 68182-0324, phone (402)554-2771, founded 1973, coeditor Art Homer, is a semiannual literary magazine publishing fiction and poetry with occasional essays. The editor wants **"Lyric poetry from 10-200 lines, preference being for under 100 lines. Subject matter is unimportant, as long as it has some. Poets should have mastered form, meaning poems should have form, not simply 'demonstrate' it."** He doesn't want to see **"concrete, inspirational, didactic or merely political poetry."** They have published poetry by Patricia Goedicke, Mary Swander, Roger Weingarten and Billy Collins. As a sample, he selected these lines from "The Twins Visit a Farm" by Mary Crow:

> *The heavy black bulk of the draft horse*
> *lay in the heat, circled by lime. Too huge*
> *to bury, it was left for flies, night animals.*
> *We walked around the gleaming hill*
> *of its flanks, the tulip-blue nostrils,*
> *the tiny terrain of the pink gums,*
> *the belly mushrooming sweetness.*

The magazine is 6×9, nicely printed, 60 pgs., with flat-spined, glossy card cover. It is a publication of the Writer's Workshop at the University of Nebraska. Some of the most exciting, accessible verse is published in this magazine. All styles and forms are welcome here, although relatively few long poems are used. Circulation is 400, of which 260 are subscriptions and 80 go to libraries. Single copy: $3.50; subscription: $6/year. **Sample postpaid: $2. "Clean typed copy strongly preferred." Reads submissions August 15 through March 31 only. Reporting time is 3-4 months and time to publication 3-6 months. Pays 2 copies and 1-year subscription. Acquires first North American serial rights.** The TNR Awards of $300 each in poetry and fiction are published in the spring issue. Entry fee: $6 subscription. You can enter as many times as desired. Deadline: November 30. The editor says, "Your first allegiance is to the poem. Publishing will come in time, but it will always be less than you feel you deserve. Therefore, don't look to publication as a reward for writing well; it has no relationship."

NEGATIVE CAPABILITY; NEGATIVE CAPABILITY PRESS; EVE OF ST. AGNES COMPETITION (II), 62 Ridgelawn Dr. E., Mobile AL 36608-2465, founded 1981, poetry editor Sue Walker. *Negative Capability* is a tri-quarterly of verse, fiction, commentary, music and art. The press publishes broadsides, chapbooks, perfect-bound paperbacks and hardbacks. They want **both contemporary and traditional poetry. "Quality has its own specifications—length and form."** They have published poetry by John Brugaletta, Rita Dove, Richard Moore, Marge Piercy, William Stafford and John Updike. As a sample Sue Walker selected these lines from "Flakey Blake" by Dorothy Moseley Sutton:

> *I asked Billy Blake*
> *to come out and play with me*
> *and while we was out there playin'*
> *he said he seen a buncha angels*
> *settin' up in a tree.*
> *There wasn't no angels*
> *settin' up in a tree.*
> *I ain't playin with that flakey Blake no more.*

The editor says, "Reaching irritably after a few facts will not describe *Negative Capability*. Read it to know what quality goes to form creative achievement. Shakespeare had negative capability, do you?" In its short history this journal has indeed achieved a major prominence on our literary scene. It is a flat-spined, elegantly printed, digest-sized format of 130+ pgs., glossy card color cover with art, circulation 1,000. About 60 pgs. of each issue are devoted to poetry. They receive about 1,200 unsolicited submissions/year, use 350. Subscription: $15; single copy: $5. **Sample postpaid: $4. Reads submissions September 1 through May 30 only. Send SASE for guidelines. Reports in 6-8 weeks. Pays 2 copies. Acquires first rights. For book publication, query with 10-12 samples and "brief letter with major publications, significant contributions, awards. We like to know a person as well as their poem." Replies to queries in 3-4 weeks, to submissions (if invited) in 6-8 weeks. Payment arranged with authors.** Editor sometimes comments on rejections. Reviews books of poetry. They offer an Annual Eve of St. Agnes Competition with major poets as judges. *Negative Capability* ranked #3 in the "New Poets" category of the June 1993 *Writer's Digest* Poetry 60 list. This category ranks those markets who often publish poets whose work is new to their publication.

NEW CHICANA/CHICANO WRITING (IV-Bilingual/ethnic), (formerly *New Chicano Writing*), Dept. of Spanish & Portuguese, Mod. Lang. Bldg. 545, Univ. of Arizona, Tucson AZ 85721, founded 1991, phone (602)621-7347, editor Chuck Tatum, is an annual anthology, uses **"poetry in Spanish or English or a combination of the two languages. Send an original and a photocopy of ms and return postage."** It is 6×9, flat-spined, hardback and paperback, professionally designed. Press run is 1,000. **Sample:**

$15-17. Cover letter required with submissions. Editors seldom comment on rejections. Editorial board reports in 3-5 months. Pays contributor's copies and a small fee.

NEW CICADA (IV-Form), 40-11 Kubo, Hobara, Fukushima, 960-06 Japan, phone 0245-75-4226, founded 1984, editor Tadao Okazaki. *New Cicada* is "the first and only magazine introducing the universal definition of haiku that is applicable to all languages. Of all existing Japanese haiku magazines in English, it has the longest history of publication." As a sample the editor selected this haiku from an unidentified poet:

> *One dead moth*
> *The only listener left for*
> *the balding bluesman*

The purpose of the magazine, which appears twice yearly in March and September, is "to introduce to the world, and define, haiku." Volumes 1 through 5 of *Cicada* were published in Toronto, Canada, by Eric W. Amann, founding editor, and later by the Haiku Society of Canada. The digest-sized publication is offset from dot-matrix copy with a b&w frontispiece; one-color matte card cover, saddle-stapled. Price is $4/issue, $6 for a 1-year subscription. Sample: $4 postpaid by US personal check or 7 international reply coupons. The editor requests a self-addressed postcard and an IRC for reports. No mss returned. It will take up to approximately 6 months to get a report. No payment in any form is offered for published poems. All rights revert to the author after publication. Open to unsolicited reviews. The editor who says he "introduced the universal definition of haiku for the first time" maintains that "(1) the traditional Japanese haiku is recited in an iambic trimeter—tetrameter—trimeter triplet form, and is rhythmically identical with the last three lines of a ballad stanza and (2) the free-verse (jiyuh-litsu) haiku in any language in the three lines (triplet) or less can be classified as a legitimate variant of haiku. The old definition of haiku as a form of syllabic verse is wrong. Haiku is a Japanese ballad, i.e., an unrhymed, non-narrative triplet consisting alternately of 3-4-3 mostly iambic beats."

‡NEW COLLAGE MAGAZINE (II), 5700 N. Tamiami Trail, Sarasota FL 34243-2197, phone (813)359-4360, founded 1970, poetry editor A. McA. Miller. *New CollAge* provides "a forum for contemporary poets, both known and undiscovered. We are partial to fresh slants on traditional prosodies and poetry with clear focus and clear imagery. No greeting card verse. We prefer poems shorter than five single-spaced pages. We like a maximum of 3-5 poems per submission." They have published poetry by Peter Meinke, Yvonne Sapia, Lola Haskins, J.P. White, Peter Klappert, Peter Wild, Stephen Corey and Malcolm Glass. The editor selected these sample lines from "The Palm at the Edge of the Bay" by Daniel Bosch:

> *I would need a ship to moore here, really,*
> *if I were to earn this girth of fibrous hemp,*
> *round-waisted, tall, leaning a head*
> *into the corner a cross-breeze walls itself against . . .*

The magazine appears 3 times a year, 28-32 pgs. of poetry in each issue, circulation 500 with 200 subscriptions of which 30 are libraries. They receive about 5,000 poems/year, use 90. Subscription: $6. Sample: $2. Simultaneous submissions not read. Reports in 6 weeks. Pays 2 copies. Editor sometimes comments on rejections. Editor "Mac" Miller advises, "Sending a ms already marked 'copyright' is absurd and unprofessional, unless your name is Robert Lowell. Mss may be marked 'first North American serials only,' though this is unnecessary."

THE NEW CRITERION (III), The Foundation for Cultural Review, Inc., 850 7th Ave., New York NY 10019, poetry editor Robert Richman, is a monthly (except July and August) review of ideas and the arts, which uses poetry of high literary quality. They have published poetry by Donald Justice, Andrew Hudgins, Elizabeth Spires and Herbert Morris. It is 90+ pgs., 7×10, flat-spined. Poems here truly are open, with structured free verse and formal works highlighted in the issues we critiqued. Much of it was excellent, and book reviews were insightful. Sample: $4.75 plus postage. Cover letter required with submissions. Reports in 2-3 months. Pays $2.50/line ($75 minimum). Poetry published in this review was selected for inclusion in **Best American Poetry 1992**, and *The New Criterion* ranked #3 in the "Top Pay" category of the June 1993 *Writer's Digest* Poetry 60 list. The editor says, "To have an idea of who we are or what we stand for aesthetically, poets should consult back issues."

NEW DELTA REVIEW; THE EYSTER PRIZE (II), English Dept., Louisiana State University, Baton Rouge LA 70803-5001, editors Randi Gray, Nicola Mason and Catherine Williamson, say, "We call ourselves a 'breakthrough magazine'; we publish work of merit by writers who for one reason or another are still slightly outside the mainstream. Most of them are younger writers who are building a reputation. We are wide open: poets who are brave enough to take chances and fly in the face of the poetic conventions of the late twentieth century are welcome." They have published poetry by Laura

New *Delta* Review

"NDR strives to publish works by artists outside of the mainstream and to present poetry and literature that reflect a multicultural worldview," says Catherine Williamson, coeditor-in-chief of New Delta Review, a biannual magazine published by Louisiana State University. "We publish a great deal of poetry, and we like to think we are both accessible to new writers and amenable to innovation in poetry." The illustration on this cover is the work of New Orleans artist Louise Mouton.

Kasischke, Eve Shelnutt, Sue Standing, David Trinidad and Gary Duehr. As a sample the editors selected these lines from "Camping Beside Lost Creek" by Kay Bache-Snyder:

> *We flow*
> *with the creek — [. . .]*
> *until it plunges underground*
> *and leaves us,*
> *drying ourselves*
> *upon a granite boulder:*
> *larvae of the morning,*
> *with wings unfolding.*

NDR appears twice a year, 6×9, flat-spined, 90-120 pgs., typeset and printed on quality stock with glossy card cover with art. Its press run is 500, with 100 subscriptions of which 20 are libraries, the rest for shelf sales. Subscription: $7. Sample postpaid: $4. **No simultaneous submissions or previously published poems. Cover letter required. Mss read in summer. Poetry editor "sometimes" comments on rejections. "Often I will return a piece and ask for revision." Reports in 1-3 months. Pays 2 copies. Acquires first North American serial rights.** Reviews books of poetry in "no more than 2,000 words," single or multi-book format. Open to unsolicited reviews and interviews. Poets may also send books to poetry editor for review consideration. The Eyster Prize of $50 is awarded to the best story and best poem in each issue.

NEW DIRECTIONS PUBLISHING CORPORATION (III, IV-Translations), 80 Eighth Ave., New York NY 10011, founded 1936, poetry editor Peter Glassgold. New Directions is "a small publisher of 20th-Century literature with an emphasis on the experimental," publishing about 36 paperback and hardback titles each year. "We are looking for highly unusual, literary, experimental poetry. We can't use traditional poetry, no matter how accomplished. Ninety-five percent of the time we publish poets who have built up a reputation in the literary magazines and journals. It is generally not financially feasible for us to take on unknown poets." They have published poetry by William Carlos Williams, Ezra Pound, Denise Levertov, Jerome Rothenberg, Robert Creeley, Michael McClure, Kenneth Rexroth, H.D., Robert Duncan, Stevie Smith, David Antin, Hayden Carruth, George Oppen, Dylan Thomas, Lawrence Ferlinghetti, Jimmy Santiago Baca, Rosmarie Waldrop and Gary Snyder. "Please send a sampling of about 10 typed, photocopied poems, preferably not a simultaneous submission. Include a cover letter with publishing history and any academic information or affiliations with poets or poetic institutions." They look at all submissions but "chances are slight." Reports on submissions in 4 months; **may be 2 years until publication. Terms for book publication "all depend."** To see samples, try the library or purchase from their catalog (available), local bookstores or their distributor, W.W. Norton. New Directions advises, "Getting published is not easy, but the best thing to do is to work on being published in the magazines and journals, thus building up an audience. Once the poet has an audience, the publisher will be able to sell the poet's books. Avoid vanity publishers and read a lot of poetry."

NEW EARTH PUBLICATIONS; CO-PRESS; UTOPIAN WORKER (IV-Spiritual, political, transla-tions), P.O. Box 4790, Berkeley CA 94704, phone (510)549-0575, founded 1990, editor Clifton Ross, publishes "**book-length collections (up to 96 pgs.) dealing with the struggle for peace and justice, well-crafted poetry, prose and translations. Some publications are author subsidized.**" They publish 1-2 paperbacks, 2-3 chapbooks/year. **Reports on queries in 2 weeks, on mss in 6 weeks. Pays 10% royalties or 10% of press run.** Also publishes *Utopian Worker*, an annual magazine of revolutionary spiritual culture.

NEW ENGLAND REVIEW (II), Middlebury College, Middlebury VT 05753, phone (802)388-3711, ext. 5075, founded 1978, editor T.R. Hummer, associate editor Devon Jerslid. *New England Review* is a prestigious literary quarterly, 6×9, 160+ pgs., flat-spined, elegant make-up and printing on heavy stock, glossy cover with art. All styles and forms are welcome in this carefully edited publication. Poets published include Toi Derricotte, Albert Goldbarth, Norman Dubie, Philip Booth and Carol Frost. Subscription: $18. **Sample postpaid: $4. Response times can be exceptionally slow here, far exceeding published limits of 6-8 weeks. Pays.** Also features essay-reviews. Publishers may send books for review consideration. Work published in this review was included in **Best American Poetry 1992.** In addition, *New England Review* ranked #7 in the "Poets' Pick" category of the June 1993 *Writer's Digest* Poetry 60 list. This category ranks those publications in which poets said they would most like to see their work published.

NEW ERA MAGAZINE (I, IV-Religious, teen/young adult), 50 E. North Temple St., Salt Lake City UT 84150, phone (801)240-2951, founded 1971, managing editor Richard M. Romney, appears monthly. *New Era* is an "official publication for youth of The Church of Jesus Christ of Latter-day Saints; it contains feature stories, photo stories, fiction, news, etc." They want "**short verse in any form — must pertain to teenage LDS audience (religious and teenage themes). No sing-songy doggerel, gushy love poems or forced rhymes.**" As a sample we selected these lines from "Open Windows" by Lani Berry:

> No "to dos" on
> My list. Sit
> And watch.
> It would be so
> Nice to see your face
> Instead of
> Your words.

New Era is 50 pgs., approximately 8×10½, 4-color offset, saddle-stitched, quality stock, top-notch art and graphics, no ads. They receive 200-300 submissions, purchase 2-5%. Press run is 220,000 for 205,000 subscribers, 10,000 shelf sales. Single copy: 75¢; subscription: $8/year. **Sample: 75¢ plus postage. No previously published poems or simultaneous submissions. Send no more than 5 poems at one time.** Time between acceptance and publication is a year or longer. "We publish one poem each month next to our photo of the month." **Sometimes comments on rejections. Send SASE for writer's guidelines. Reports in 6-8 weeks. Pays $10 minimum. Buys all rights. "LDS church retains rights to publish again in church publications — all other rights returned."** They also offer an annual contest — including poetry — for active members of the LDS church between ages 12-23. Poetry entries should consist of one entry of 6-10 different original poems reflecting LDS values, none of which exceeds 50 lines. Deadline: January. Winners re-ceive either a partial scholarship to BYU or Ricks College or a cash award. Send SASE for rules. The editor says, "Study the magazine before submitting. We're a great market for beginners, but you must understand Mormons to write well for us. Just because a subject is noble or inspirational doesn't mean the poetry automatically is noble or inspirational. Pay attention to the craft of writing. Poetry is more than just writing down your thoughts about an inspirational subject. Poetry needs to communicate easily and be readily understood — it's too easy to mistake esoteric expression for true insight."

NEW HOPE INTERNATIONAL (II), 20 Werneth Ave., Gee Cross, Hyde, Cheshire SK14 5NL United Kingdom, founded 1969, editor Gerald England, includes "*NHI Writing*, publishing poetry, short fiction, translations, artwork, literary essays and reports. All types of poetry from traditional to avant-garde, from haiku to long poems. *NHI Review* carries reviews of books, magazines, cassettes, CDs, records, PC software, etc. Special Edition Chapbooks with a theme or individual collections also included." They have recently published poetry by Louie Crew, J.W. Curry, Brian Daldorph, Jean Jorgensen, Thomas Kretz and Florentin Smarandache. As a sample the editor selected these lines from "Behind your Back" by Penny Windsor:

> the plants are already marching.
> in these places
> there is a revolution underway

behind your back

The digest-sized magazine, 36-40 pgs., is printed offset-litho from computer typesetting, saddle-stapled, color card cover, using b&w artwork. Press run is 600 for 300 subscribers of which 25 are libraries. $25 for 6 issues (*NHI Writing, NHI Review* and **S.E. Chapbooks** as published). **Sample postpaid: $5 cash (add $5 to cover bank charges if paying by check). Put name and address on each sheet; not more than 6 at a time; simultaneous submissions *not* encouraged. Cover letter required. Translations should include copy of original. Full guidelines available for IRC (3 for airmail). Send 1 IRC for reply if return of mss not required. Reports "usually fairly prompt, but sometimes up to 4 months." Pays 1 copy. Acquires first British serial rights. Staff reviews books of poetry. Send books for review consideration. For chapbooks, query first.** The editor advises, "Long lists of previous publications do not impress; perceptive, interesting, fresh writing indicative of a live, thinking person makes this job worthwhile."

NEW HORIZONS POETRY CLUB (II, IV-Membership), Box 5561, Chula Vista CA 91912, phone (619)474-4715, founded 1984, poetry editor Alex Stewart. This organization offers poetry contests of various sorts for experienced writers, publishing winners in an anthology. They also offer newsletters and critiques and publish anthologies of members' poetry. Membership (includes 4 newsletters): $10/year. They have published poetry by Alice Mackenzie Swaim, Glenna Holloway, Pegausus, Buchanan and Thelma Schiller. Prizes in their Annual Poetry Day Contest are "$250 and down. We offer other cash awards, prizes and trophies, and certificates for honorable mentions. 'Mini-manuscript' winners are offered trophies, cash prizes and free anthologies." Entry fees are $5/2 poems, $10/5 poems. **"We expect poets to know technique, to be familiar with traditional forms and to be able to conform to requirements regarding category, style and length and to show originality, imagery and craftsmanship. Nothing amateurish, trite or in poor taste."** Alex Stewart offers critiques at reasonable rates. (Discounts on critiques and books to members.) She says, "Poets need to study technique before *rushing to get published! (Where* is what counts!) The current trend seems to be a healthy blend of traditional forms and comprehensible free verse." NHPC publishes 3 books annually, 2 in the NHPC Poets' Series (4 poets/book) and 1 anthology of prizewinning and selected poems from the semiannual contests. (Book list, including **The Poet's Art**, the editor's complete handbook on the craft of poetry writing, available on request.)

THE NEW KENT QUARTERLY-LUNA NEGRA (I), Box 26, Student Activities, Kent State University, Kent OH 44240, is a student-run, biannual literary and art magazine of the KSU main campus, **open to all forms of poetry.** The editor says it is 40-50 pgs., 5½ × 8½, with art and photography throughout. They receive 400-450 poems a year, accept 40 or 50. Press run is 2,000, most distributed to KSU students. **Simultaneous submissions OK. Reads submissions September 1 through March 30 only. Seldom comments on rejections. Reports in 1 month or so ("depending on school calendar"). Pays 1 copy. "All rights revert to author immediately after publication."** The editor adds, "We are also interested in any b&w reproducible artwork or photographs."

THE NEW LAUREL REVIEW (II, IV-Translations), 828 Lesseps St., New Orleans LA 70117, founded 1971, editor Lee Meitzen Grue, "is an independent nonprofit literary magazine dedicated to fine art. Each issue contains poetry, translations, literary essays, reviews of small press books, and visual art." They want **"poetry with strong, accurate imagery. We have no particular preference in style. We try to be eclectic. No more than 3 poems in a submission."** They have published poetry by Jane McClellan, Kalamu Ya Salaam, Melody Davis, Sue Walker and Keith Cartwright. As a sample the editor selected these lines by Quo Vadis Gex-Breaux:

> *She had a kind of classy coarseness*
> *like raw silk*
> *a kind of open earthiness*
> *without being dirt*
> *a way of saying things*
> *that made them seem something*
> *more than she meant*
> *(sometimes a little less)*

The *Review* is 6 × 9, laser printed, 115 pgs., original art on cover, accepts 30 poems of 300 mss received. It has a circulation of 500, subscription: $9; per copy: $7. **Sample (back issue) postpaid: $5. Accepts simultaneous submissions. Submit 3-5 poems with SASE and a short note with previous publications. Reads submissions September 1 through May 30 only. Guidelines for SASE. Reports on submissions in 3 months, publishes in 8-10 months. Pays contributor's copies. Acquires first rights.** Reviews books of poetry in 1,000 words, single or multi-book format.

NEW LETTERS; NEW LETTERS POETRY PRIZE (II), University of Missouri-Kansas City, Kansas City MO 64110, phone (816)235-1168, founded 1934 as *University Review*, became *New Letters* in 1971, managing editor Bob Stewart, editor James McKinley, "is dedicated to publishing the best short fiction, best contemporary poetry, literary articles, photography and artwork by both established writers and new talents." They want **"contemporary writing of all types — free verse poetry preferred, short works are more likely to be accepted than very long ones."** They have published poetry by Joyce Carol Oates, Hayden Carruth, John Frederick Nims, Louise Glück, Louis Simpson, Vassar Miller and John Tagliabue. The flat-spined, professionally printed quarterly, glossy 2-color cover with art, 6×9, uses about 65 (of 120+) pgs. of poetry in each issue. Circulation 1,845 with 1,520 subscriptions of which about 40% are libraries. They receive about 7,000 submissions/year, use less than 1%, have a 6-month backlog. Poems appear in a variety of styles exhibiting a high degree of craft and universality of theme (rare in many journals). Subscription: $17. Sample postpaid: $5. Send no more than 6 poems at once. No simultaneous submissions. **"We strongly prefer original typescripts and we don't read between May 15 and October 15. No query needed."** They report in 4-10 weeks, pay a small fee plus 2 copies. Occasionally James McKinley comments on rejections. The New Letters Poetry Prize of $750 is given annually for a group of 3-6 poems, entry fee $10 (check payable to New Letters Literary Awards). Send SASE for entry guidelines. Deadline: May 15. They also publish occasional anthologies, selected and edited by McKinley. Work published in *New Letters* appeared in **Best American Poetry 1992**.

NEW MEXICO HUMANITIES REVIEW (II, IV-Regional), Humanities Dept., New Mexico Tech, Socorro NM 87801, phone (505)835-5200, founded 1978, editors Jerry Bradley and John Rothfork. *NMHR*, published twice a year, invites mss **"designed for a general academic readership and those that pursue Southwestern themes or those using interdisciplinary methods." There are no restrictions as to type of poetry; "*NMHR* publishes first class, literary poetry,"** but does not want "sentimental verse, shallow, pointlessly rhymed ideas." They have published poetry by George Garrett, Ralph Mills, Jr., Grace Butcher, Peter Wild and Walter McDonald. The review is 180 pgs., digest-sized, printed by offset on white stock, with an embossed, one-color matte card cover, flat-spined; there are graphics and ads. Circulation is 650, of which 350 are subscriptions; other copies are sold at poetry readings, writers' workshops, etc. Single copy: $6; subscription: $11/year. **No simultaneous submissions.** Time between acceptance and publication is 6 months. **Reports in 6-10 weeks. Pays one year's subscription. Acquires first serial rights.** Reviews books of poetry in 750 words, single or multi-book format. Open to unsolicited reviews. Poets may also send books for review consideration to Jerry Bradley. Also has a poetry contest supported by Witter Bynner Foundation for Poetry. Best three poems from two issues. Past judges have been Mark Strand and Fred Chappell. Awards: 1st prize $500, 2nd $300, 3rd $200.

NEW ORLEANS POETRY JOURNAL PRESS (III), 2131 General Pershing St., New Orleans LA 70115, phone (504)891-3458, founded 1956, publisher/editor Maxine Cassin, coeditor Charles deGravelles. **"We prefer to publish relatively new and/or little-known poets of unusual promise or those inexplicably neglected — 'the real thing.' "** They do not want to see **"cliché or doggerel, anything incomprehensible or too derivative, or workshop exercises. First-rate lyric poetry preferred (not necessarily in traditional forms)."** They have published books by Vassar Miller, Everette Maddox, Charles Black and Martha McFerren. Their most recent book is **Illuminated Manuscript** by Malaika Favorite. As a sample the editor selected these lines from "Missing Z and Nola" in **Hanoi Rose** by Ralph Adamo:

> *Nobody owns the bright blue dawn for long.*
> *You can be there day after day, raking it in,*
> *and still there'll be a palm under your token,*
> *and the palm won't be yours. And the animal*
> *you traded power with will contrive to be*
> *given away. In the barracks where the last*
> *detachment waits, beauty won't show her face.*

Query first. They do not accept freelance submissions for chapbooks, which are flat-spined paperbacks. The editors report on queries in 2-3 months, mss in the same time period, if solicited. Simultaneous submissions will possibly be accepted. Pay is in author's copies, usually 50 to 100. Ms. Cassin does not subsidy publish at present and does not offer grants or awards. For aspiring poets, she quotes the advice Borges received from his father: "1) Read as much as possible! 2) Write only when you *must*, and 3) Don't rush into print!" As a small press editor and publisher, she urges poets to read instructions in **Poet's Market** listings with utmost care! She says, "Most poets do not query first surprisingly!"

NEW ORLEANS REVIEW (II), Box 195, Loyola University, New Orleans LA 70118, phone (504)865-2294, founded 1968, poetry editor John Biguenet. It is 100 pgs., perfect-bound, elegantly printed with glossy card cover using a full-color painting. Poems are set off from prose with plenty of white space in this 8½×11 magazine and tend toward free verse establishing a milieu and appealing to the senses (via voice). Circulation is 750. **Sample postpaid: $10. Reports in 3 months. Acquires first North American serial rights.**

THE NEW POETS SERIES, INC.; CHESTNUT HILLS PRESS (II); STONEWALL SERIES (IV-Gay/lesbian), 541 Piccadilly, Baltimore MD 21204, phone (301)830-2863 or 828-0724, founded 1970, editor/director Clarinda Harriss Raymond. The New Poets Series, Inc. brings out **first books by promising new poets. They want** "excellent, fresh, nontrendy, literate, intelligent poems. Any form (including traditional), any style. No poetry riding any one particular political, social, sexual or religious hobbyhorse." Provides 20 copies to the author, the sales proceeds going back into the corporation to finance the next volume (usual press run: 1,000). "It has been successful in its effort to provide these new writers with a national distribution; in fact, The New Poets Series was named an Outstanding Small Press by the prestigious Pushcart Awards Committee, which judges some 5,000 small press publications annually." Chestnut Hills Press publishes author-subsidized books — "High quality work only, however. CHP has achieved a reputation for prestigious books, printing only the top 10% of mss CHP and NPS receive." The New Poets Series also publishes an occasional anthology drawn from public reading series. They have published books by Nuala Archer, Richard Fein, Shelley Scott, Carole Glasser Langille, Peter Wessel, Charles Stuart Roberts, Elaine Erickson, Steven Sills, Gail Wronsky and Tony Esolen. Clarinda Harriss Raymond selected "Calling Canada," a complete poem by Irish writer Medbh McGuckian, as a sample:

> I talk to the darkness as if to a daughter
> Or something that once pressed from inside
> Like a street of youth. My striped notebook
> Is just a dress over my body, so I will waken
> At a touch, or for no reason at all. In it
> I learn how to cut into other people's dreams,
> How to telephone them Paris-style and how
> Like sunshine, a tenderness roughened
> Because there was so little time for snow-months
> To paint my woman's walls into sea.

Query with 50- to 55-page manuscript and cover letter giving publication credits and bio. Simultaneous submissions OK. Editor sometimes comments briefly on rejections. Reports in 6 weeks-8 months. Mss "are circulated to an editorial board of professional, publishing poets. NPS is backlogged, but the best 10% of the mss it receives are automatically eligible for Chestnut Hills Press consideration," a subsidy arrangement. **Send $5 for a sample volume.** Stonewall Series offers a chapbook contest whose winner is published by NPS. Send 20-25 poems with $20 entry fee. Stonewall is for gay, lesbian and bisexual writers. Entrants in chapbook contest may send full ms to Stonewall or NPS *without* the normal $10 readers' fee.

THE NEW PRESS LITERARY QUARTERLY; THE NEW PRESS POETRY CONTEST (I, II), 53-35 Hollis Ct. Blvd., Flushing NY 11365, founded 1984, poetry editor Harry Ellison, is a quarterly magazine using poems **"less than 200 lines, accessible, imaginative. No doggerel, sentimentality."** They have published poetry by Les Bridges, Gina Bergamino, Barbara Weekes and Robert Parody. As a sample the editor selected these lines by R. Nikolas Macioci:

> a conversation he has
> with himself as he thinks now
> of hinges he must oil
> before old doors will open
> quietly onto another year's
> garden and the scent
> of newly spaded soil.

It is magazine-sized, 28 pgs., desktop published, with glossy cover, saddle-stapled. They accept about 10% of 700 poems received/year. Press run 1,200 for 200 subscribers of which 1 is a library, 1,000 shelf sales. Subscription: $15. **Sample postpaid: $4. "Include name and address on the top of each page." Reports in 2 months. Pays 3 copies. Acquires first-time rights.** The New Press Poetry Contest is semiannual, deadlines are January and July 1, entry fee of $4 for up to 3 poems or 200 lines, has prizes of $150, $75 and ten 2-year subscriptions.

THE NEW QUARTERLY (II, IV-Regional), ELPP University of Waterloo, Waterloo, Ontario N2L 3G1 Canada, phone (519)885-1211, ext. 2837, founded 1981, managing editor Mary Merikle, is a "literary quarterly—new directions in Canadian writing." For the poetry they want, the editors have **"no preconceived conception—usually Canadian work, poetry capable of being computer typeset—4½" line length typeset lines. No greeting card verse."** The editor describes it as 120 pgs., flat-spined, 6×8½, with a photograph on the cover, no graphics or art, some ads. Of 2,000 poems received/year, they use 100. Press run is 600 for 300 subscriptions (10 of them libraries) and additional shelf sales. Subscription:

$15 (add $2 for US or overseas subscriptions). **Sample postpaid: $4 Canadian, $4 US. Submit no more than 5 poems at a time. Cover letter with short bio required. Send SASE for guidelines. Reports in 3-6 months.** No comments on rejections of poetry. **Pays $20/poem plus 3 copies.**

THE NEW REPUBLIC (II), 1220 19th St. NW, Washington DC 20036, phone (202)331-7494, founded 1914, poetry editor Mary Jo Salter. *The New Republic*, a weekly journal of opinion, is magazine-sized, printed on slick paper, 42 pgs., saddle-stapled with 4-color cover. Subscription: $69.97/year. Back issues available for $3.50 postpaid. **They provide no submission or payment information.**

NEW RIVERS PRESS; MINNESOTA VOICES PROJECT, INC. (II, IV-Regional, translations), Suite 910, 420 N. 5th St., Minneapolis MN 55401, founded 1968, publishes collections of poetry, translations of contemporary literature, collections of short fiction, and is also involved in publishing Minnesota regional literary material. **Write for free catalog or send SASE for guidelines/inquiries.** New and emerging authors living in Iowa, Minnesota, North and South Dakota and Wisconsin are eligible for the Minnesota Voices Project. Book-length mss of poetry, short fiction, novellas or familiar essays are all accepted. **Send SASE for entry form.** Winning authors receive a stipend of $500 plus publication by New Rivers. Second and subsequent printings of works will allow 15% royalties for author.

‡**NEW VIRGINIA REVIEW (II)**, 2A, 1306 E. Cary St., Richmond VA 23219, phone (804)782-1043, founded 1978, poetry editor Margaret Gibson, appears 3 times a year publishing both fiction and poetry. They want **"seriously written poetry addressing any subject matter, in any variety of styles. No greeting card verse or haiku."** They have recently published poetry by Mona Van Duyn, Mary Oliver, Philip Booth and Norman Dubie. *NVR* is 160 pgs., 6¾ × 10, offset, perfect-bound, with color cover, no graphics. They receive over 6,000 mss a year, accept approximately 10%. Press run is 2,500 for 1,500 subscribers of which 20% are libraries, 250 shelf sales. Subscription: $15. **Sample postpaid: $6. No previously published poems; simultaneous submissions OK. Reads submissions September 1 through May 31 only. Seldom comments on rejections. Send SASE for guidelines. Reports in 3-6 weeks. Pays $25/poem on publication, plus $10 for additional printed pages. Buys first North American serial rights.**

NEW VOICES IN POETRY AND PROSE; NEW VOICES SPRING/FALL COMPETITIONS (I), P.O. Box 52196, Shreveport LA 71135, founded 1990, editor Cheryl White, is a semiannual that publishes new poets and writers and reviews collected works. **"All types of poetry welcome. However, prefer poetry that makes a statement about the emotions of the writer."** The editor says it is 12-16 pgs., 8½ × 11. Press run is 500 for 100 subscribers. Subscription: $8. **Sample postpaid: $5.** "All submissions are also considered for annual anthology." **Seldom comments on rejections. Send SASE for guidelines. Reports in approximately 1 month. Pays 1 copy.** Offers semiannual poetry and short fiction competitions. Small entry fees. Cash prizes.

NEW WELSH REVIEW (II, IV-Ethnic), 49, Park Place, Cardiff CF1 3AT Wales, United Kingdom, phone 0222-665529, founded 1988, editor Robin Reeves. *NWR* is a literary quarterly publishing articles, short stories and poems. They have published poetry by Joseph Clancy, Gillian Clarke, Lawrence Ferlinghetti, John Heath-Stubbs, Michael Longley, Les A. Murray, Peter Porter and Anne Stevenson. The editor describes it as 88 pgs., glossy paper in three colors, laminated cover, using photographs, graphics and ads. Their press run is 1,100. Subscription: £15. **Sample postpaid: £4.20. Submit double-spaced. No simultaneous submissions or previously published poems. Reports in 6 weeks. Publication within 1-7 months.** Reviews books of poetry.

‡**NEW WRITER'S MAGAZINE (I, II, IV-Humor, themes)**, P.O. Box 5976, Sarasota FL 34277, phone (813)953-7903, founded 1986, editor George J. Haborak, is a bimonthly magazine "for aspiring writers, and professional ones as well, to exchange ideas and working experiences." **They are open to free verse, light verse and traditional, 8-20 lines, reflecting upon the writing lifestyle. "Humorous slant on writing life especially welcomed."** They do not want poems about "love, personal problems, abstract ideas or fantasy." As a sample the editor selected this poem, "Lucky Who?" by Vera Koppler:

> I wish I were Anonymous
> When I send out a rhyme
> For lucky old Anonymous
> Gets published all the time.

NWM is 28 pgs., 8½ × 11, offset, saddle-stapled, with glossy paper cover, b&w photos and ads. They receive about 300 poems a year, accept approximately 10%. Press run is 5,000. Single copy: $2; subscription: $14 for 1 year, $25 for 2 years. **Sample postpaid: $3. Submit up to 3 poems at a time. No previously published poems or simultaneous submissions.** Time between acceptance and publication is 1 year maximum. **Send SASE for guidelines. Reports in 1-2 months. Pays $5/poem. Buys first North American serial rights.** Each issue of this magazine also includes an interview with a recognized author, articles on writing and the writing life, tips and markets.

NEW YORK QUARTERLY (II), P.O. Box 693, Old Chelsea Station, New York NY 10113, founded 1969, poetry editor William Packard, appears 3 times a year. They seek to publish "a cross-section of the best of contemporary American poetry" and, indeed, **have a record of publishing many of the best and most diverse of poets,** including W.D. Snodgrass, Gregory Corso, James Dickey and Judson Jerome. It appears in a 6×9, flat-spined format, thick, elegantly printed, color glossy cover. Subscription: $15 to 305 Neville Hall, University of Maine, Orono ME 04469. (This address is for subscriptions *only*. Poetry mss should be submitted to above New York address.) **Submit 3-5 poems. Reports within 2 weeks. Pays copies.** This magazine is sponsored by the National Poetry Foundation, listed under Organizations Useful to Poets.

THE NEW YORKER (III, IV-Translations, humor), 20 W. 43rd St., New York NY 10036, founded 1925, poetry editor Alice Quinn, circulation 640,000, uses **poetry of the highest quality (including translations). Sample: $1.75 (available on newsstands). Mss are not read during the summer. Replies in 6-8 weeks. Pays top rates.** Seven poems appearing in *The New Yorker* were selected for inclusion in **Best American Poetry 1992.** In addition, *The New Yorker* itself ranked #2 in the "Poets' Pick" category of the June 1993 *Writer's Digest* Poetry 60 list. This category ranks those publications in which poets said they would most like to see their work published.

NEWSLETTER INAGO (I), P.O. Box 26244, Tucson AZ 85726-6244, phone (602)294-7031, founded 1979, poetry editor Del Reitz, is a monthly newsletter, 4-5 pgs., corner-stapled. **"Free verse preferred although other forms will be read. Rhymed poetry must be truly exceptional (nonforced) for consideration. Due to format, 'epic' and monothematic poetry will not be considered. Cause specific, political or religious poetry stands little chance of consideration. A wide range of short poetry, showing the poet's preferably eclectic perspective is best for** *NI*. **No haiku, please."** They have recently published poetry by Jack Coulehan, Patricia Hock, Valery Brackenridge, Carter McKenzie, Joel Kuper, Elizabeth Dossa, Nola Perez, Albert Huffstickler, Marilyn Click and John Grey. The editor says, "Since editorial taste in poetry especially is such a subjective and narrow thing," a short selection cannot be chosen "with any fairness to either that taste or the poet whose material might be quoted." However, as a sample the editor selected these lines from "The Swindle" by Charles Webb:

> *I was to have a place where*
> *I could forget to fear*
> *that some fly-speck of life*
> *might be wasted on me. There*
> *I could stop struggling*
> *to make each second "count"*

Their press run is approximately 200 for that many subscriptions. **No price is given for the newsletter, but the editor suggests a donation of $3 an issue or $17 annually (overseas: $4 and $19). Guidelines available for SASE. They consider simultaneous submissions and previously published poems. Editor sometimes comments on rejections. Reports ASAP (usually within 2 weeks). Pays 4 copies.** Staff reviews books of poetry. Send books for review consideration.

NEXUS (I), English Dept., Simon Fraser University, Burnaby, British Columbia V5A 1S6 Canada, founded "198-something," editor Simon Thompson, appears 2 times/year, using short fiction, graphic art and poetry. **"No specifications other than quality; nothing sentimental, derivative. Most submissions have a fairly belligerent tone; we won't print sentimental material. For a very small journal, we've managed to establish a reputation for publishing the best work of new writers, as well as that of established artists."** They have recently published poetry by Scott C. Holstad, Martin Gray and Robert Nagler. *Nexus* is 40-50 pgs., digest-sized, saddle-stapled, with matte card cover. They accept about 30% of poetry received. Press run 200 for 150 shelf sales. **Sample postpaid: $3.50. Cover letter with short bio information required with submissions. "Please, no long lists of publications; we don't really care." Reports in 2 months. Pays 2 copies. Acquires first Canadian publication rights.** Open to unsolicited reviews. Poets may also send books for review consideration.

NEXUS (II), 006 University Center, Wright State University, Dayton OH 45435, phone (513)873-2031, founded 1967. *"Nexus* is a student operated magazine of mainstream and street poetry; also essays on environmental and political issues. **We're looking for truthful, direct poetry.** Open to poets anywhere.

Use the General Index to find the page number of a specific publisher. If the publisher you are seeking is not listed, check the " '93-'94 Changes" list at the end of this section.

We look for contemporary, imaginative work." Issues have featured themes on Japan and American West. *Nexus* appears 3 times a year—fall, winter and spring, using about 40 pgs. of poetry (of 80-96) in each issue, circulation 1,000. They receive 1,000 submissions/year, use 30-50. For a sample, send a 10×15 SASE with 5 first class stamps and $4 for first copy, $3 for each additional issue. Submit up to 6 pgs. of poetry, with bio, September through May. Simultaneous submissions OK. Editor sometimes comments on rejections. Send SASE for guidelines. Reports in 10-12 weeks except summer months. Pays 2 copies. Acquires first American serial rights.

NIGHT ROSES (I, IV-Teen/young adult, love/romance, nature, students, women/feminism); **MOONSTONE BLUE** (I, IV-Anthology, science fiction/fantasy), P.O. Box 393, Prospect Heights IL 60070, phone (708)392-2435, founded 1986, poetry editor Allen T. Billy, appears 2-4 times a year. "*Moonstone Blue* is a science fiction/fantasy anthology, but we have no set dates of publication. We do an issue every 14-24 months as items, time and funds allow. We look for women/feminism themes for our *Bikini* series." For *Night Roses* they want "poems about dance, bells, clocks, nature, ghost images of past or future, romance and flowers (roses, wildflowers, violets, etc.). Do not want poems with raw language." They have recently published poetry by Mary R. DeMaine, Dwight C. DeMaine, Arlene L. Mandell, Deloris Selinsky and Emma Blanch. As a sample the editor selected these lines from "Girl In The Attic Picture" by Peter A. Flessas:

> Frozen in time under years of dust,
> alone in a Victorian attic.
> I wiped away one hundred years
> and gazed at a forgotten face.

Night Roses is 44 pgs., saddle-stapled, photocopied from typescript on offset paper with tinted matte card cover. Press run 200-300. Subscription: $8 for 3 issues, $3/copy. Sample postpaid: $2.50 for *Night Roses*, $2.75 for *Moonstone Blue*. "Desire author's name and address on all sheets of mss. If previously published—an acknowledgment must be provided by author with it." No simultaneous submissions; some previously published poems used. "I prefer submissions between March and September." Reports in 6-12 weeks. "Material is accepted for current issue and 2 in progress." Pays 1 copy. Acquires first or reprint rights. Staff reviews books of poetry. Send books for review consideration. The editor says, "We are more interested in items that would be of interest to our teen and women readers and to our readership in the fields of dance, art and creative learning. We are interested in positive motives in this area."

‡**NIGHT SONGS** (IV-Horror), 4998 Perkins Rd., Baton Rouge LA 70808-3043, founded 1991, editor Gary William Crawford, is a quarterly newsletter that publishes "supernatural horror poetry in the great tradition of supernatural verse. Poems that modernize themes explored in the poetry of Poe, Baudelaire, H.P. Lovecraft." They want "horror poetry in a variety of forms. However, not interested in strict imitations of such poets as Edgar Allan Poe or H.P. Lovecraft. In general, themes of terror and darkness, madness and death should be present. Poems that explore the underlying horror of civilization." They have recently published poetry by Bruce Boston, Lisa Lepovetsky, Keith Allen Daniels and Joey Froehlich. As a sample the editor selected these lines from "Indianapolis Rising" by John David Christensen:

> city spires emaciated
> insubstantial remnants
> no more than a wraith: transitory phantom
> ghost ship sailing
> seas of waving grass.

Night Songs is 6 pgs., 8½×11, neatly photocopied with line drawings and stapled at the corner. They receive about 30 poems/month, use approximately 5. Press run is 75 for 45 subscribers. Subscription: $3/year. Sample postpaid: $1. No previously published poems or simultaneous submissions. Time between acceptance and publication is 6 months. Often comments on rejections. Reports in 2 weeks. Pays $1/poem. Buys first rights.

NIGHTSUN (II), Dept. of English, Frostburg State University, Frostburg MD 21532, founded 1981, editor Douglas DeMars, is a 64-page, digest-sized literary annual. They want "highest quality poetry." Subject matter open. Prefers poems not much longer than 40 lines. Not interested in the "extremes of sentimental, obvious poetry on the one hand and the subjectless 'great gossamer-winged gnat' school of poetry on the other." They have published poetry by William Stafford, Linda Pastan, Marge Piercy, Diane Wakoski, Dennis Brutus and Philip Dacey. Interviews include Carolyn Forché, Grace Cavalieri, Lucille Clifton and Sharon Olds. As a sample the editor selected these lines from "The Digs in Escondido Canyon" by Walter McDonald:

> If they dreamed of gods

> and hid from enemies at night

> *without fires, time fast as the wind*
> *was enough to fear under the same blue dome,*
> *the vast tornado skies we worship.*

Nightsun, an attractive journal on good stock paper, features well-known poets alongside relative newcomers. Editors take free verse mostly with attention paid to line, stanza and shape of poem. They accept about 1% of poetry received. **Sample postpaid: $6.50. Do not submit mss during summer months. "Contributors encouraged to subscribe." Reports within 3 months. Pays 2 copies. Acquires first rights.**

NIMROD INTERNATIONAL JOURNAL OF CONTEMPORARY POETRY AND FICTION; RUTH G. HARDMAN AWARD: PABLO NERUDA PRIZE FOR POETRY (II), 2210 S. Main St., Tulsa OK 74114, phone (918)584-3333, founded 1956, poetry editor Fran Ringold, "is an active 'little magazine,' part of the movement in American letters which has been essential to the development of modern literature. *Nimrod* publishes 2 issues per year: an awards issue in the fall featuring the prize winners of our national competition and a thematic issue each spring." They want **"vigorous writing that is neither wholly of the academy nor the streets, typed mss."** They have published poetry by Pattiann Rogers, Denise Levertov, Willis Barnstone, Alvin Greenberg, Francois Camoin, Tess Gallagher, McKeel McBride, Bronislava Volek, Josephine Jacobsen, William Stafford and Ishmael Reed. The 6×9 flat-spined, 160+ pgs., journal, full-color glossy cover, professionally printed on coated stock with b&w photos and art, uses 50-90 pgs. of poetry in each issue. It is an extraordinarily lovely magazine with one of the best designs in the lit world. Poems in non-award issues range from formal to freestyle with several translations. Circulation 3,500, 500 subscriptions of which 100 are public and university libraries. Subscription: $10/year plus $1.50 inside USA; $3 outside. They use about 1% of the 2,000 submissions they receive each year, have a 3-month backlog. **Sample postpaid: $6.90 for a recent issue, $5 for an issue more than 2 years old. Reports in 3 weeks-4 months. Pays $5/page up to $25 total/issue. "Poets should be aware that during the months that the Ruth Hardman Awards Competition is being conducted, reporting time on non-contest manuscripts will be longer."** Send business-sized SASE for guidelines and rules for the Ruth G. Hardman Award: Pablo Neruda Prize for Poetry ($1,000 and $500 prizes). Entries accepted January 1 through April 1 each year with $10 entry fee for which you get one copy of *Nimrod*. This annual poetry contest is considered one of the most prestigious in the publishing world, and your material is still considered for publication if you lose in the contest!

‡NINETY-SIX PRESS (V, IV-Regional), P.O. Box 30882, Furman University, Greenville SC 29613, founded 1991, editors William Rogers and Gilbert Allen, publishes 1 paperback book of poetry/year. "The name of the press is derived from the old name for the area around Greenville, South Carolina—the Ninety-Six District. The name suggests our interest in the writers, readers and culture of the region. **We currently accept submissions by invitation only. At some point in the future, however, we hope to be able to encourage submissions by widely published poets who live in South Carolina."** They have recently published poetry by William Aarnes and Bennie Lee Sinclair. As a sample the editor selected these lines from "Who Can Show the Child as She Is?" in Aarnes' book, **Learning to Dance**:

> *Truth is, she's just too ridiculous,*
> *my daughter standing naked in her pool,*
> *her swimming suit tossed into the grass,*
> *and over her head the tilted hose spouting*
> *a putto's wing. She commands, imperious:*
> *"Take your shorts off; take them off now!"*

That book is 58 pgs., 6×9, professionally printed and perfect-bound with coated stock cover. **For a sample, send $10.**

9TH ST. LABORATORIES; MODOM; THE EXPERIODDICIST (IV-Form), P.O. Box 3112, Florence AL 35630, phone (205)760-0415, founded 1986, "front man" Jake Berry. *"9th St. Laboratories* is a noncommercial enterprise publishing *experimental* poetry, fiction, graphics and audio material in broadsheets, booklets, postcards, objects, chapbooks and audiotapes. *MODOM* is an ongoing series of any of the above. *The Experioddicist* is a newsletter of poetry, deviant theory and graphics. **The key words are *experiment* and *explore*. Poetry that breaks new ground for the poet personally, that comes from the commitment to a vision. Also graphic poetry. Poetry using devices other than straight linear narrative, that makes use of things otherwise considered nonsensical or absurd."** They have published poetry by Jack Foley, Chris Winkler, Malok, Richard Kostelanetz, Mike Miskowski and John M. Bennett. As a sample the editor selected these lines by Harry Polkinhorn:

> *to challenge your balance drastic yet nuclear ocean*
> *urgent to implement an unwilling shifty murder victim*
> *subject I say a minister question of what she meant*

MODOM and *The Experioddicist* appear irregularly: "something appears 4 times a year." They use about 10 of 150 submissions received a year. Press run is 100-200. **Sample postpaid: $4. "All** checks or money orders should be made out to Jake Berry, not the name of the mag and not to *9th St. Laboratories*. Of course poems submitted for the tape mag should be on tape and include a SASE for its return." No simultaneous submissions. They use some previously published work. Considers submissions January 1 through October 31 only. They pay 1 copy. They publish chapbooks by invitation only. Pay 15-20 copies. Editor sometimes comments on rejections. He says, "We publish as much as we can as often as we can, attempting to expand the area of poetic, visionary concentration. Going to the mailbox to find it full of work that ignores conventional limitations and is highly involved with exploring new ideas, provoking unusual insights, is what makes us happy."

‡NOCTURNAL LYRIC (I), P.O. Box 77171, San Francisco CA 94107-7171, phone (415)621-8920, founded 1987, editor Susan Moon, is a quarterly journal "featuring bizarre fiction and poetry, primarily by new writers." They want "poems dealing with the bizarre: fantasy, death, morbidity, horror, gore, etc. Any length. No 'boring poetry.' " They have recently published poetry by D. Castleman, Ray E. Reents and Andre Scheluchin. As a sample the editor selected these lines from "Moondeath" by Len Whitney:

> *The sickening sound of bone splintering agony,*
> *jugular burst,*
> *severed spine.*
> *Man, Wolf, the entity must hunt,*
> *a singular pack and blood will flow.*

NL is 40 pgs., digest-sized, photocopied, saddle-stapled, with trade ads and staff artwork. They receive about 140 poems a year, use approximately 70%. Press run is 250 for 25 subscribers. Subscription: $7. **Sample postpaid: $1.50 through December 1992, $2 for more recent issues. "Make checks payable to Susan Moon." Previously published poems and simultaneous submissions OK. Seldom comments on rejections. Reports in 3 months. Pays 50¢ "discount on subscription" coupons.** Acquires one-time rights. The editor says, "Please send us something really wild and intense!"

NOMAD'S CHOIR (II), (formerly *Smoke Signals*), % Meander, P.O. Box 232, Flushing NY 11385-0232, founded 1989, editor Joshua Meander, is a quarterly. **"No curse words in poems, little or no name-dropping, no naming of consumer products, no two-page poems, no humor, no bias writing, no poems untitled. 9-30 lines, poems with hope. Simple words, careful phrasing. Free verse, rhymed poems, sonnets, half-page parables, myths and legends, song lyrics. Subjects wanted: love poems, protest poems, mystical poems, nature poems, poems of humanity, poems with solutions to world problems and inner conflict."** They have published poetry by Brenda Charles, Joseph Gourdji, Dorothy Wheeler and Jeff Swan. As a sample the editor selected these lines from "Loves Giant Piano" by Connie Goodman:

> *Walk a giant piano . . .*
> *Destination, the stars*
> *Along love's entrancing melody;*
> *The night, it is ours.*

Nomad's Choir is 10 pgs., 8½ × 11, typeset and saddle-stapled with 3 poems/page. They receive 150 poems/year, use about 50. Press run 400, all distributed free. Subscription $5; per copy $1.25. **Make check payable to Joshua Meander. Reports in 6-8 weeks. Pays one copy.** The editor says, "Stick to your guns; however, keep in mind that an editor may be able to correct a minor flaw in your poem. Accept only minor adjustments. Go to many open poetry readings. Respect the masters. Read and listen to other poets on the current scene. Make pen pals. Start your own poetry journal. Do it all out of pure love."

NOMOS PRESS INC.; NOMOS: STUDIES IN SPONTANEOUS ORDER (IV-Political), 9421 S. Longwood, Chicago IL 60620, phone (312)233-8684, poetry editor John Enright, editorial contact person Carol B. Low. *Nomos* is a quarterly magazine "dedicated to individual freedom and responsibility." One page of each issue is devoted to poetry up to 24 lines, "although longer pieces are considered. Poetry must promote individual freedom and responsibility, skepticism toward government solutions for economic and social ills and/or celebrate the human condition. No contrived rhymes, pedestrian prose or cryptic charades. Clarity of meaning and direct emotional appeal are paramount; form should contribute to, not detract or distract from these." They have published poetry by John Harllee and Christopher Brockman. "*Nomos*' purpose is to call attention to the erosion of civil and economic rights, much of which erosion has government as its catalyst." The editor describes it as magazine-sized, generally 40 pgs. in length, offset, matte cover occasionally printed 2-color. Ad copy, line art for cover and article illustrations are solicited. It has a circulation of 1,000 with 450 subscriptions of which 10 are libraries, 300 sent out to potential subscribers. Subscription: $18. **Sample postpaid: $4.50. Submit poems with name and address on each page. Send SASE for guidelines.** Reporting time varies, up to

1 year to publication. Pays 3 copies. "Reviewing sample copies strongly encouraged."

THE NORTH CAROLINA HAIKU SOCIETY PRESS (V); NCHSI CONTEST (IV-Form), 326 Golf Course Dr., Raleigh NC 27610, phone (919)231-4531, founded 1984, editor/publisher Rebecca Rust. The North Carolina Haiku Society International Contest has a $1 entry fee for each haiku. Eleven awards. Deadline in hand is December 31. Send SASE for copy of rules. **The press, temporarily closed and not currently accepting submissions,** was established "solely as a vehicle for publishing books by those authors who have received a grant from the North Carolina Haiku Society." They publish flat-spined paperbacks of, or about, haiku only.

NORTH DAKOTA QUARTERLY (III), Dept. PM, Box 7209, University of North Dakota, Grand Forks ND 58202, phone (701)777-2703, fax (701)777-3650, founded 1910, poetry editor Jay Meek, is a literary quarterly published by the University of North Dakota Press that includes material in the arts and humanities — essays, fiction, interviews, poems and visual art. **"We want to see poetry that reflects an understanding not only of the difficulties of the craft, but of the vitality and tact that each poem calls into play."** Poets published include Donald Hall, Elizabeth Libbey and Alane Rollings. As a sample, the editor selected lines from "Dog Days" by Mark Vinz:

> *The apartment swells with August heat,*
> *an old jazz man on the radio —*
> *we climb the slippery stairs of each piano riff*
> *and wonder out loud if some day*
> *we'll ever do anything that well.*

The editor says *North Dakota Quarterly* is 6 × 9, 261 pgs., flat-spined, professionally designed and printed with full-color artwork on the white matte card cover and b&w photographs inside. You can find almost every kind of poem here — avant-garde to traditional — in a trademark array of fonts. Typically the work of more than 60 poets is included in each issue. Circulation of the journal is 850, of which 650 are subscriptions and 200 go to libraries, 100 are newsstand sales. Subscription: $15/year. **Sample available for $5 postpaid. No simultaneous submissions. Reporting time is 4-6 weeks and time to publication varies. Pay is 2 copies and a year's subscription.** Reviews books of poetry in 500-5,000 words, single or multi-book format. The press does not usually publish chapbooks, but "we will consider."

NORTH EAST ARTS MAGAZINE; BOSTON ARTS ORGANIZATION, INC. (III), P.O. Box 6061 J.F.K. Station, Boston MA 02114, founded 1990, editor/president Mr. Leigh Donaldson, is a quarterly using **poetry that is "honest, clear, with a love of expression through simple language, under 30 lines. Care for words and craftsmanship are appreciated."** They have recently published poetry by Otto Laske, Meleta Murdock Baker, Jennifer Smith and Win Travassos. As a sample the editor selected this poem, "How I Gained Knowledge of the World," by Thomas Wiloch:

> *So I traded an eye for a drink of*
> *water, Then she told me, go ahead,*
> *pick one of those apples too.*

It is digest-sized, 32 or more pgs., professionally printed with 1-color coated card cover. They accept 20-25% of submissions. Press run 500-1,000 for 150 subscribers of which half are libraries, 50 to arts organizations. An updated arts information section and feature articles are included. Subscription: $10. **Sample postpaid: $4.50. Reads submissions September 1 through May 30 only. "A short bio is helpful."** Send SASE for guidelines. **Reports in 1-2 months. Pays 2 copies. Acquires first North American serial rights.**

UNIVERSITY OF NORTH TEXAS PRESS; TEXAS POET SERIES (IV-Regional), P.O. Box 13856, Denton TX 76203-3856, phone (817)565-2142, series editor Richard Sale, has published work by these Texas poets: Naomi Nye, William Davis, R.S. Gwynn and Jan Seale. As a sample the editor selected these lines from "Driving at Night Through Texas" from **Rafting the Brazos** by Walt McDonald:

> *Tonight we race the quarter moon,*
> *counting the miles by pelts on a highway*
> *black as a Bible and seldom used.*
> *Truckers don't even blink their brights,*
> *our low beams shining no more*
> *than fifty feet ahead, nothing to see*

Books in the series average 120-128 pgs. **Query with sample poems, bio and list of publications. Simultaneous submissions OK. Reports on queries or mss in 8-10 weeks. Pays 10% of net sales in royalties plus 5 copies.** To buy samples, request the Texas A&M University Press catalog, Drawer C, College Station TX 77843.

NORTHEAST JOURNAL (II, IV-Regional), P.O. Box 2321, Providence RI 02906, phone (401)751-4383, founded 1969, editor Gil Poulin, is a literary annual published by The Poetry Mission, a nonprofit literary arts organization. The journal is **"open to conventional-experimental poetry."** They have published poetry by John Grey and Janet Gray. As a sample the editor selected these lines from "The Surface and Depths of Southern Friendship" by Janet McCann:

> *I wait, Alice poised*
> *on the giant chair, an obedient child.*
> *Men in brown suits discuss the Kuwait War*
> *and problems with their software. I don't*
> *snicker.*

The purpose of *NJ* is "to encourage local (state and area) writers while remaining open to national submissions." It is digest-sized, flat-spined, 100 pgs., typeset, with glossy card cover. Circulation is 500, with 200 subscriptions of which 100 are libraries. **Sample postpaid: $6. Reports in 3-6 months. Pays 1 copy.** Reviews books of poetry.

NORTHEASTERN UNIVERSITY PRESS; SAMUEL FRENCH MORSE POETRY PRIZE (III), Northeastern University, 360 Huntington Ave., Boston MA 02115. The Samuel French Morse Poetry Prize, % Prof. Guy Rotella, Editor, Morse Poetry Prize, English Dept., 406 Holmes, Northeastern University, Boston MA 02115, for book publication (ms 50-70 pgs.) by Northeastern University Press and an **award of $500, entry fee $10. Deadline of August 1 for inquiries, September 15 for single copy of ms. Ms will not be returned. Open to US poets who have published no more than 1 book of poetry.**

‡**THE NORTHERN CENTINEL (II)**, Suite 7B, 115 E. 82nd St., New York NY 10028-0833, founded 1788, poetry editors Ellen Rachlin and Lucie Aidinoff, is a newspaper appearing 5 times a year focusing on "political/cultural essays and analyses on matters of national interest." **They will publish 2 poems each issue.** It is 16-24 pgs., 11×17, offset on newsprint, with b&w artwork, photos, engravings, woodcuts, political cartoons and ads. Press run is 13,000. Subscription: $12.50. **Sample postpaid: $2.50. No previously published poems; simultaneous submissions OK. Cover letter with SASE required.** Time between acceptance and publication is up to one year. **Seldom comments on rejections. Reports within 3 months. Pays $40 plus 1 copy.**

‡**NORTHERN PERSPECTIVE (II)**, Northern Territory University, P.O. Box 41246, Casuarina NT 0811 Australia, founded 1977, managing editor Dr. Lyn Riddett, appears twice a year. This liberal arts journal is magazine-sized, 115-125 pgs., using a full-color cover, professionally printed. Press run 600 for 250 subscribers of which 20 are libraries, including university and public libraries in the US, UK, Europe and Africa. 300 shelf sales. **Sample postpaid: $7.50 AUD. Submit in March and September. Editor often comments on rejections. Reports "hopefully within 10 weeks." Pays minimum of $20 AUD/poem.** Reviews books of poetry in 300-500 words. "Review articles are 1,500-2,500 words. *NP* reviews are *not* solicited; review articles, however, may be submitted."

NORTHWEST REVIEW (II), 369 PLC, University of Oregon, Eugene OR 97403, phone (503)346-3957, founded 1957, poetry editor John Witte. They are "seeking excellence in whatever form we can find it" and use **"all types" of poetry.** They have published poetry by Alan Dugan, Olga Broumas, William Stafford and Richard Eberhart. *NR*, a 6×9, flat-spined magazine, appears 3 times a year and uses 25-40 pgs. of poetry in each issue. They receive 3,500 submissions/year, use 4%, have up to a 4-month backlog. Press run is 1,300 for 1,200 subscribers of which half are libraries. **Sample postpaid: $3. Submit 6-8 poems clearly reproduced. No simultaneous submissions. The editor comments "whenever possible" on rejections. Send SASE for guidelines. Reports in 8-10 weeks. Pays 3 copies.** He advises poets to "persist."

NORTHWOODS PRESS; DAN RIVER PRESS; NORTHWOODS JOURNAL: A MAGAZINE FOR WRITERS; C.A.L. (II), P.O. Box 298, Thomaston ME 04861-0298, phone (207)354-0998, Northwoods Press founded 1972, Dan River Press 1978, C.A.L. (Conservatory of American Letters) 1986 and *Northwoods Journal* 1993. *Northwoods Journal* is a quarterly literary magazine, incorporating a brief version of the C.A.L. newsletter. **"The journal is interested in all poets who feel they have something to say and who work to say it well. We have no interest in closet poets, or credit seekers. All poets seeking an audience, working to improve their craft and determined to 'get it right' are welcome here. Please request submission guidelines (with SASE) before submitting."** Subscription: $10/year, free to C.A.L. members. **Sample: $4. Deadlines are the 1st of March, June, September and December for seasonal publication. Reports within 2 weeks after deadline, sometimes sooner. Pays $5/page, average, on acceptance.** "Northwoods Press is designed for the excellent *working poet* who has a following which is likely to create sales of $3,000 or more. Without at least that much of a following and at least that level of sales, no book can be published. Request 15-point poetry program. **Northwoods Press will pay a minimum of $250 advance on contracting a book.** C.A.L. is a nonprofit tax-exempt literary/educational foundation; up to four anthologies of poetry and prose are published each year. **There is a $1 (cash — no checks) reading fee for each poetry submission to their anthologies, which goes to readers, not to the publisher. Poets are paid $5/page on acceptance, shorter poems pro-rata page rate. Payment is advance against 10% royalties on all sales we can attribute to the influence of the author."** Robert Olmsted regards his efforts as an attempt to face reality and provide a sensible royalty-contract means of publishing many books. He says, **"If you are at the stage of considering book publication, have a large number of poems in print in respected magazines, perhaps previous book publication, and are confident that you have a sufficient following to insure very modest sales, send 8½ × 11 SASE (3 oz. postage) for descriptions of the Northwoods Poetry Program and C.A.L."** His advice is, **"Poetry must be non-trite, non-didactic. It must never bounce. Rhyme, if used at all, should be subtle. One phrase should tune the ear in preparation for the next. They should flow and create an emotional response."** Query with cover letter dealing with publication credits and marketing ideas. Submit "entire ms as desired for final book form." No simultaneous submissions; no previously published poems. **Pays 10% royalties. Bob Olmsted "rarely" comments on rejections, but he offers commentary for a fee. Query. Membership in C.A.L. is $24 a year, however, membership is not required.** Members receive the quarterly *Northwoods Journal* plus 10% discount on all books and have many services available to them. C.A.L. sponsors an annual writers' conference with no tuition, only a $20 registration fee. Dan River Press, which publishes books of prose, also publishes an annual **Dan River Anthology**, using short fiction and poetry. **Pays $5/page on acceptance.**

NOSTALGIA: A SENTIMENTAL STATE OF MIND (II), P.O. Box 2224, Orangeburg SC 29116, founded 1986, poetry editor Connie Lakey Martin, appears spring and fall using **"nostalgic poetry, style open, prefer *non* rhyme, but occasional rhyme OK, relatively short poems, never longer than one page, no profanity, no ballads."** *Nostalgia* is digest-sized, 24 pgs., saddle-stapled, offset typescript, with matte card cover. Press run is 1,000. Subscription: $5. **Sample postpaid: $3. "Most poems selected from contest." Guidelines available for SASE.** There are contests in each issue with award of $100 and publication for outstanding poem, publication and 1-year subscription for Honorable Mentions. Entry fee of $3 reserves future edition, covers 3 entries. Deadlines: June 30 and December 31 each year. **No simultaneous submissions or previously published poems. All rights revert to author upon publication.** Reviews books of poetry. Open to unsolicited reviews. Poets may also send books for review consideration. Connie Martin says, "I offer criticism to most rejected poems and feature a poet each edition as 'Poet of the Season.' I suggest sampling before submitting."

NOSUKUMO (III), GPO Box 994-H, Melbourne, Victoria 3001 Australia, founded 1982, editor Javant Biarujia, publishes 1-2 chapbooks/year. **"We publish language-oriented and experimental poetry, but not exclusively so. We are particularly interested in prose poems. Our program is curtailed by recession in Australia — please inquire before sending ms."** Their products are characterized by elegant printing on quality paper in sewn chapbooks. **Pays 5-10% royalties plus 30 copies. Buys first option rights for new editions or new titles.**

NOTUS: NEW WRITING; OTHERWIND PRESS (V), 541 Lakeview Ave., Ann Arbor MI 48103, phone (313)665-0703, poetry editor Pat Smith, managing editor Marla Smith. *Notus* appears twice a year, using **experimental writing and translations. However, they are currently not accepting poetry submissions.** They have published poetry by Robert Creeley, Robert Kelly, Leslie Scalapino, Kenneth Irby and Gerrit Lansing. As a sample the editor selected these lines from "Dear Friend" by Elizabeth Robinson:

> *As though Sunday's letters*
> *excessively long*
>
> *procure this*
>
> *Pronunciation does change*
>
> *Ascribe the letter to its softness*

Notus is 6 × 9, 96 pgs., flat-spined, professionally printed on heavy cream stock with glossy b&w cover with photo. No ads. Press run is 500 for 50 subscriptions of which 10 are libraries. **Sample postpaid: $6.** Reviews books of poetry in 500-750 words, single format.

NOW AND THEN (IV-Regional, themes), P.O. Box 70556, ETSU, Johnson City TN 37614-0556, phone (615)929-5348, founded 1984, poetry editor Jo Carson, is a regional magazine that deals with Appalachian issues and culture. **The editor does not want any poetry not related to the region. Issues have themes** — previous issues have focused on Appalachian veterans, working Cherokees, blacks, children, rural life, media, Scottish-Appalachian connection, sports and recreation, and education. Themes for issues coming up: the Civil War and storytelling. **"No haiku or sentimental, nostalgic,**

romantic or religious poems." They have published poetry by Fred Chappell, Michael McFee, Michael Chitwood, Jim Wayne Miller and George Ella Lyon. As a sample the editor selected these lines from "Flannel Pajamas" by Ruth Moose:

> You never had a fabric in your life
> worthy of your fingers. You made
> leftovers, castoffs, bargains better.
> Stitched each seam twice and straight.
> I marvel at your craft
> on something so nightly,
> utility, this poor man's warmth.
> Pajamas Eve would have made Adam
> if she'd owned a needle.

Now and Then appears three times a year and is 48 pgs., magazine-sized, saddle-stapled, professionally printed, with matte card cover. Its press run is 2,000 for 900 subscriptions of which 200 are libraries. Of 200 poems received they accept 6-10 an issue. Subscription: $10. Sample: $3.50 plus $1.50 postage. They will consider simultaneous submissions but "not usually" previously published poems. Submit up to 5 poems, with cover letter including "a few lines about yourself for a contributor's note and whether work has been published or accepted elsewhere." Deadlines: March 1, July 1 and November 1. Guidelines available for SASE. Reports in 3-4 months. Pays 2 copies plus subscription. Acquires one-time rights. Reviews books of poetry in 750 words. Open to unsolicited reviews. Poets may also send books for review consideration to Pat Arnow, editor.

NUTSHELL (I, II), 8 George Marston Rd., Binley, Coventry CV3 2HH United Kingdom, founded 1988, editor Tom Roberts, is a quarterly using poetry "all subjects considered, any length. Nothing hateful, pornographic, badly assembled." They have published poetry by Amryl Johnson, Ian MacDonald, Avril Redman, Kenneth Pobo and Carol Lee Saffiotti. The editor describes *Nutshell* as "A5 size, stapled, card cover, 64 pgs." They accept about 10% of some 500 poems submitted/year. Press run is 200 for 130 subscribers. Sample postpaid: £2.50. Editor comments on submissions when requested. Pays £1.50, extra copy or reduced rate subscription. Buys first serial rights. Reviews books of poetry in 100-200 words.

THE OAK (I); THE ACORN (I, IV-Children); THE GRAY SQUIRREL (I, IV-Senior citizens), 1530 7th St., Rock Island IL 61201, phone (309)788-3980, poetry editor Betty Mowery. *The Oak*, founded 1991, is a "publication for writers with short articles, poetry, fiction (no more than 500 words) and writers conferences." They want poetry "no more than 32 lines. No restrictions as to types and style but no pornography." *The Oak* appears 6 times/year. They take more than half of about 100 poems received each year. Press run is 200, with 10 going to libraries. Subscription: $10. Sample: $2. Simultaneous submissions and previously published poems OK. Reports in 1 week. Pays 1 copy. Acquires first or second rights. *The Acorn* is a "newsletter for young authors and teachers or anyone else interested in our young authors. Takes mss from kids K-12th grades or from adults if it is slanted to grades K-12. Poetry no more than 32 lines. It also takes articles and fiction, no more than 500 words." It appears 6 times/year and "we take well over half of submitted mss." Press run 100, with 6 going to libraries. Subscription: $10. Sample postpaid: $2. Simultaneous submissions and previously published poems OK. Reports in 1 week. Pays 1 copy. Acquires first or second rights. Young authors, submitting to *The Acorn*, should put either age or grade on manuscripts. *The Gray Squirrel* takes poetry of no more than 20 lines only from poets 60 years of age and up. The publication is new with a press run of about 50. Six issues: $10. Sample: $2. Make checks for *Squirrel* payable to *The Oak*. Pays copy. *The Oak* holds an Orange Blossom Poetry Contest February 1 through August 1. *The Acorn* has the Shawna Poetry Contest and the Peri Poetry Contest for adults who write for children February 1 through August 1. *The Gray Squirrel* sponsors the Minnie Chezum Memorial Contest December through May. Editor Betty Mowery advises, "Beginning poets should submit again as quickly as possible if rejected. Study the market: don't submit blind. Always include a SASE or rejected manuscripts will not be returned."

OASIS BOOKS; OASIS (II), 12 Stevenage Rd., London SW6 6ES England, founded 1969, editor and publisher Ian Robinson. *Oasis* is a bimonthly magazine of short fiction and poetry as well as occasional reviews and other material. "No preference for style or subject matter; just quality. No long poems; *Oasis* is a very short magazine. Also, usually no rhyming poetry." They have published poetry by John Ash, Lee Harwood, George Evans and Roy Fisher. The editor says *Oasis* is international A5 size, litho, folded sheets. They receive 500-600 poems a year, use about 4 or 5. Press run is 500 for 400 subscribers of which 5 are libraries. Sample postpaid: $2.50. Previously published poems sometimes OK; no simultaneous submissions. Include SAE and 4 IRCs for surface mail return. Seldom comments on rejections. Reports in 1 month. Pays 4 copies. Staff reviews books of poetry. Send books for review consideration. Oasis Books publishes 2-3 paperbacks and 2-3 chapbooks/year. Replies to queries and mss in 1 month. For sample books or chapbooks, write for catalog. Ian Robinson says, "One IRC is not enough to ensure return postage; four will, provided manuscript is not too thick. No return postage will ensure that the ms is junked."

OBLATES (IV-Religious, spirituality/inspirational), Missionary Association of Mary Immaculate, 15 S. 59th St., Belleville IL 62223-4694, phone (618)233-2238, editor Jacqueline Lowery Corn, is a magazine circulating free to 500,000 benefactors. "We use well-written, perceptive traditional verse, average 16 lines. Avoid heavy allusions. Good rhyme and/or rhythm a must. We prefer a reverent, inspirational tone, but not overly 'sectarian and scriptural' in content. We like to use seasonal material. We like traditional poetry (with meter) and are always on the lookout for good Christmas poetry." They have published poetry by Raymond A. Schoeder, Joy Lee Holman and Claire Puneky. *Oblates* is 20 pgs., digest-sized, saddle-stapled, using color inside and on the cover. Sample and guidelines for SAE and 52¢ postage. Six back issues: $1.44. Considers simultaneous submissions. Time to publication "is usually within 1 to 2 years." Editor comments "occasionally, but always when ms 'just missed or when a writer shows promise.' " Reports within 4-6 weeks. Pays $30 plus 3 copies. Buys first North American serial rights. She says, "We are a small publication very open to mss from authors—beginners and professionals. We do, however, demand professional quality work. Poets need to study our publication, and to send no more than one or two poems at a time. Content must be relevant to our older audience to inspire and motivate in a positive manner."

OBSIDIAN II: BLACK LITERATURE IN REVIEW (IV-Ethnic), Box 8105, North Carolina State University, Raleigh NC 27695-8105, phone (919)515-4153, founded 1975, editor Gerald Barrax, is a biannual publication "for the study and cultivation of creative works in English by Black writers worldwide, with scholarly critical studies by all writers on Black literature." They are open as to subject matter but want poetry (as well as fiction and drama) from Black writers only. The editor says *Obsidian II* is 126 pgs., 6×9. Lyric and narrative free verse appear here for the most part and, typically, several poems by each author are featured. Press run is 700 for 500 subscriptions of which an eighth are libraries. Subscription: $12; single issue: $5. Sample postpaid: $11. Submit double-spaced ms on 8½ ×11 paper. Send SASE for guidelines. "See copy of journal for more detailed submission guidelines." Reports in 3-4 months. Pays 2 copies and 1-year subscription.

OCCIDENT MAGAZINE; OCCIDENT PRESS; OCCIDENT POETRY COMPETITION; BERKELEY POETRY PRIZE BOOK CONTEST (II), 700 Eshelman Hall, U. of CA, Berkeley CA 94720, founded 1868, editor P. Michael Campbell, a small press publisher of books (poetry, stories, prose) and an annual magazine, *Occident*. They want "good poetry of any sort." They have published poetry by Robert Pinsky, Thom Gunn, Michael Palmer, Charles Bernstein, August Kleinzahler, Charles Simic, Brenda Hillman, Susan Howe, Leslie Scalapino and Lyn Hejinian. The magazine is 300 pgs., 6×10, flat-spined, professionally printed with glossy card cover. Press run is 750-1,000. Sample postpaid: $3.50. They prefer no simultaneous submissions. Previously poems accepted, but "depends on where they were published." Reports in 3-12 months. Pays 1 copy. They publish 2 poetry chapbooks/year. Their annual contest has prizes of $75, $50, $25, and publication in the magazine. Deadline in April. Fee: $2/poem. Send SASE for information about the Berkeley Poetry Prize Book Contest.

‡OFFICE NUMBER ONE (I), 1708 S. Congress Ave., Austin TX 78704, founded 1988, editor Carlos B. Dingus, appears 4 times a year. *ONO* is a "zine of news information and events from parallel and alternate realities." They want "haiku and limericks, mostly. However well-crafted poetry of other kinds also acceptable. Poems should be short (2-12 lines), make a definite point, have meter and rhyme. No long rambling poetry about suffering and pathos." As for a sample, the editor says "No one poem will provide a fair sample of what I accept." *ONO* is 12 pgs., 8½×11, computer set in 10 pt. type, saddle-stitched, with graphics and ads. They use about 12 poems a year. Press run is 1,000 for 75 subscribers, 50 shelf sales, 600 distributed free. Single copy: $1.85; subscription: $8.82/6 issues. Sample postpaid: $2. Previously published poems and simultaneous submissions OK. "Will comment on rejections if comment is requested." Send SASE for guidelines. Reports in 1 month. Pays "27¢" and 1 copy. Buys "one-time use, and use in any *ONO* anthology." The editor says, "Say something that has the power to change someone's life. Know who that person is, the change you seek, and how what you write can accomplish this."

The Subject Index, located before the General Index, can help you narrow down markets for your work. It lists those publishers whose poetry interests are specialized.

THE OHIO REVIEW (II); OHIO REVIEW BOOKS (V), 209C Ellis Hall, Ohio University, Athens OH 45701-2979, phone (614)593-1900, founded 1959, editor Wayne Dodd, attempts "to publish the best in contemporary poetry, fiction and reviews" in the *Review* and in chapbooks, flat-spined paperbacks and hardback books. They use **"all types"** of poetry and have published poems by David Baker, William Matthews, Lynn Emanuel and Robin Behn. As a sample the editor selected these lines from "Alba" by Pamela Kircher:

> The lovers rise from bed and leave
> the fire banked in ashes,
> stars dim and disappearing
> as night unpins and drops
> its faded cloth.

The *Review* appears 3 times a year in a professionally printed, flat-spined format of 140+ pgs., matte cover with color and art, circulation 2,000, featuring about 18 poets/issue. One of the respected "credits" in the literary world, this magazine tends to publish mostly lyric and narrative free verse with an emphasis on voice. Content, structure and length seem open, and voices tend to complement each other, evidence of careful editing. Moreover, you'll find top-name writers appearing with relative newcomers. They receive about 3,000 freelance submissions/year, use 1% of them, and have a 6- to 12-month backlog. Subscription: $12. **Sample postpaid: $4.25. Reads submissions September 1 through June 30 only. Send SASE for guidelines. Reports in 1 month. Pays $1/line for poems and $5/page for prose plus copies. Buys first North American serial rights. Editor sometimes comments on rejections.** Reviews books of poetry in 5-10 pgs., single or multi-book format. Send books to Robert Kinsley for review consideration. **They are not presently accepting freelance submissions of book mss. Query with publication credits, bio.** Work published in *The Ohio Review* has been included in **Best American Poetry** and **Pushcart Prize** anthologies.

OHIO STATE UNIVERSITY PRESS/JOURNAL AWARD IN POETRY (II), 180 Pressey Hall, 1070 Carmack Rd., Columbus OH 43210-1002, phone (614)292-6930, poetry editor David Citino. Each year *The Journal* (see that listing) selects for publication by Ohio State University Press for the Ohio State University Press/Journal Award **one full-length (at least 48 pgs.) book ms submitted during September, typed, double-spaced, $15 handling fee (payable to OSU). Send SASE for return of ms; self-addressed, stamped postcard for notification of ms receipt. Some or all of the poems in the collection may have appeared in periodicals, chapbooks or anthologies, but must be identified. Along with publication,** *The Journal* Award in Poetry pays **$1,000 cash prize from the Helen Hooven Santmyer Fund "in addition to the usual royalties."** Each entrant receives a subscription (2 issues) to *The Journal*.

OLD HICKORY REVIEW (I), P.O. Box 1178, Jackson TN 38302, founded 1969, president Bill Nance, poetry editor Edna Lackie, is now a "literary triannual publishing 2-4 short stories and approximately 75-80 poems each issue. **No more than 24-30 lines, any form, any subject.** We publish poets from Maine to California and several foreign countries." It is digest-sized, 120+ pgs., professionally printed with matte card cover. Press run is about 450 for 400 subscribers of which 17 are libraries. Subscription: $12/year. **Sample postpaid: $3.50. Guidelines available for SASE. Pays 1 copy/poem.** Poets may send books for review consideration, but *must query first.* Bill Nance says, "We are very open to submissions from new poets, although you should be aware that competition is fierce. We receive over a thousand submissions annually for our two hundred-some-odd places. I strongly suggest a sample copy be obtained. Also, omission of SASE from submissions pretty much guarantees your work won't be considered."

THE OLD RED KIMONO (I, II), P.O. Box 1864, Rome GA 30163, phone (706)295-6312, founded 1972, poetry editors Ken Anderson and Jon Hershey, a publication of the Humanities Division of Floyd College, has the "sole purpose of putting out a magazine of original, high-quality poetry and fiction. *ORK* is looking for submissions of 3-5 short poems. Poems should be very concise and imagistic. Nothing sentimental or didactic." They have recently published poetry by Walter McDonald, Peter Huggins, Kim Thomas, Kathleen Condon, Paul Rice and David Huddle. As a sample the editors selected these lines by T. Sheehan:

> Wet leaves
> at the bottom
> of a leaf pile
> shine
> like new shoes.

The magazine is an annual, circulation 1,200, 8½ × 11, 64 pgs., professionally printed on heavy stock with b&w graphics, colored matte cover with art, using approximately 40 pgs. of poetry (usually 1 or 2 poems to the page). They receive 1,000 submissions/year, use 60-70. **Reading** period is September 1 through March 1. Reports in 3 months. Pays copies. Acquires first publication rights.

THE OLIVE PRESS PUBLICATIONS (V), Box 99, Los Olivos CA 93441, phone (805)688-2445, founded 1979, editor Lynne Norris, is a general small press publisher for whom "poetry is incidental effort at this time. We specialize in local and family history." They have recently published **It Don't Hurt to Laugh**, a collection of cowboy poetry by Jake Copass.

‡OLYMPIA REVIEW (II), 1727 E. 4th Ave., Olympia WA 98506, founded 1988, revived 1992, first issue fall 1993, editor Michael McNeilley, appears twice annually, publishing "the best available contemporary writing, without regard for rules, conventions or precedent. **No taboos, beyond reasonably good taste; style and talent, significance and artistry are our only criteria. Seldom use rhyme. Nothing incidental, religious or sentimental. Prefer poems under 50 lines or so.** Also publish stories, essays and cartoons." They have recently published poetry by James Garvey, Frederic Silbey and Frank Till. As a sample the editor selected his own poem, "Postcard":

> *The memory of*
> *your last touch,*
> *like the red telephone*
> *you left behind*
> *rings, but is*
> *never you.*

The editor says *OR* is 40+ pgs., digest-sized, saddle-stapled, with occasional 2-color card cover, art, graphics, photos and ads. Press run is 300+ for 50 subscribers, 100 shelf sales. Single copy: $3.95; subscription: $6.95. **Sample postpaid: $4.25. Submit up to 6 poems at a time. Previously published poems ("tell us where") and simultaneous submissions OK. Cover letter required. Seldom comments on rejections. Send SASE for guidelines. Reports in 1-2 months. Pays 1 copy. Acquires first North American serial or one-time rights.** Reviews books of poetry and magazines in up to 700 words, single or multi-book format. The editor advises poets to "start with the classics, to see where poetry has been. Then read more poetry, and fiction, in the little magazines, where today's writing is found. Develop your own voice, master the language of your readers, write a clean line, edit mercilessly, and you may help determine where poetry is going. We look for poetry, prose and things between that illuminate archetypal hopes, fears, dreams and understandings. We want every issue of *OR* to connect with every reader, in as visceral a way as possible."

‡ONCE UPON A WORLD (IV-Science fiction/fantasy), Route 1, Box 110A, Nineveh IN 46164, founded 1988, editor Emily Alward. **"All poetry submitted should relate to science fiction or fantasy in concept and/or imagery. This does not mean it has to be 'about' space travel or dragons. None with a nihilistic outlook, extremely avant-garde style or formats."** They have recently published poetry by John Grey, W. Gregory Stewart and Laura Vess. As a sample the editor selected these lines by Mark L. Ridge:

> *Flashing swords,*
> *and dented shields,*
> *what our blood and bodies build.*

Once Upon A World is magazine-sized, 80-100 pgs. with heavy card-stock colored covers, spiral-bound. They accept 5-10 of 50+ submissions received. Press run 120. **Sample postpaid: $8. Checks payable to Emily Alward. Reports in 1-4 months. Pays 1 copy. "We strongly recommend purchase of a copy before submitting both to give some idea of the content and tone and to help keep the magazine solvent. But this is not a requirement."** The editor says, "Our major interest is in presenting science fiction and fantasy *short* stories with well-worked-out alternate world settings and an emphasis on ideas and/or character interaction. We use poetry for fillers. Where possible we try to match a poem with an adjacent story that it somewhat resembles in subject matter or tone. As the editor's major interest is fiction, she does not feel qualified to give in-depth critiques of poetry."

ONE EARTH: THE FINDHORN FOUNDATION & COMMUNITY MAGAZINE (II, IV-Spiritual/inspirational, ecology), The Park, Findhorn, Forres, Morayshire 1V36 0TZ Scotland, phone (03094)574, founded 1974, contributing editor Vidura LeFeuvre, is a quarterly which "reflects awakening of consciousness throughout the world and also developments and life of the spiritual community at Findhorn." They want **poetry that is "spiritual, inspirational, about personal/social awakening or ecological. Not overly long—15 lines maximum. Nothing sentimental, negative or partisan; no poetry that is** *too* **subjective."** As a sample the editor selected these lines by Dana Finch:

> *Will my death leave a trace*
> *in the world*

> *Will the invisible be shattered*
> *into fragments of sight.*

One Earth is 48 pgs., A4, offset litho, saddle-stapled, with full-color cover, recycled paper throughout, line art and photos; 20% ads. They receive about 50 poems a year, accept approximately 30%. Press run is 4,000 for 1,700 subscribers of which 10 are libraries, 2,300 shelf sales. Single copy: $4.50; subscription: $20 surface, $26 airmail. **Sample postpaid: $3, surface mail. Previously published poems and simultaneous submissions OK. Cover letter required.** Time between acceptance and publication is 2-6 months. **Comments on rejections "only if asked." Pays 2 copies.**

ONIONHEAD; ARTS ON THE PARK, INC. (THE LAKELAND CENTER FOR CREATIVE ARTS); WORD-ART, THE NATIONAL POETS COMPETITION; ESMÉ BRADBERRY CONTEMPORARY POETS PRIZE (II), 115 N. Kentucky Ave., Lakeland FL 33801-5044, phone (813)680-2787. Arts on the Park founded 1979; *Onionhead* founded 1988. *Onionhead* is a literary quarterly. **"Our focus is on provocative political, social and cultural observations and hypotheses. Controversial material is encouraged. International submissions are welcome. We have no taboos, but provocation is secondary to literary excellence. No light verse please."** They have published poetry by Jessica Freeman, Arthur Knight, Lyn Lifshin, B.Z. Niditch and A.D. Winans. As a sample we selected these lines from "Paying Back Karma" by Jo Ann Lordahl:

> *This bed I made*
> *will haunt me*
>
> *Until I burn it*
> *bury it, or defuse it.*

The magazine is 40-50 pgs., digest-sized, photocopied from typescript with glossy card cover. Their press run is 250. Complimentary distribution to universities, reviews and libraries worldwide. They use 100 of 2,500 submissions received/year. Subscription: $8 US, $16 other. **Sample postpaid: $3. Poet's name and title of poems should appear on the upper right-hand corner of each page. Poem "should be submitted exactly as you intend it to appear if selected for publication."** Editor comments on rejections "rarely." Poems are reviewed by an Editorial Board and submissions are reported on within 2 months. If accepted, poems will normally appear within one year. **Pays 1 copy.** WORDART, The National Poets Competition, established 1983, is open to all American authors. Cash awards, "including the prestigious Esmé Bradberry Contemporary Poets Prize, are announced at a reading and reception during the first part of March." $8 reading fee. For guidelines and specific dates send SASE to the sponsoring organization, Arts on the Park, Inc., at the above address.

ONTARIO REVIEW; ONTARIO REVIEW PRESS (V), 9 Honey Brook Dr., Princeton NJ 08540, founded 1974. The *Ontario Review* appears twice a year. They have published poetry by William Heyen, Alice Ostriker, Albert Goldbarth and Jana Harris. *OR* is 112 pgs., 6×9, offset, flat-spined. Press run is 1,200 for 650 subscribers of which 450 are libraries. 250 shelf sales; 75 direct sales. Subscription: $10. **Sample postpaid: $4.95. Currently not accepting unsolicited poetry. Ontario Review Press is also not currently considering new poetry mss.** They publish 1-2 hardbacks and that many paperbacks/year, paying 10% royalties plus 10 copies.

ONTHEBUS; BOMBSHELTER PRESS (II), 6421 ½ Orange St., Los Angeles CA 90048, founded 1975. *ONTHEBUS* editor Jack Grapes. Bombshelter Press poetry editors Jack Grapes and Michael Andrews. *ONTHEBUS* uses **"contemporary mainstream poetry—no more than 6 poems (10 pgs. total) at a time. No rhymed, 19th Century traditional 'verse.'"** They have published poetry by Charles Bukowski, Albert Goldbarth, Ai, Norman Dubie, Kate Braverman, Stephen Dobyns, Allen Ginsberg, David Mura, Richard Jones and Ernesto Cardenal. *ONTHEBUS* is a magazine appearing 2 times/year, 200 pgs. offset, flat-spined, with color card cover. Press run 3,500 for 600 subscribers of which 40 are libraries, 1,200 shelf sales ("500 sold directly at readings"). Subscription: $24 for 3 issues; Issue #8/9, special double issue: $15. **Sample postpaid: $10. Send SASE for guidelines. Simultaneous submissions and previously published poems OK, "if I am informed where poem has previously appeared and/or where poem is also being submitted. I prefer cover letters with list of poems included plus poet's bio." Do not submit mss between November 1 and March 1 or between June 1 and September 1. Submissions sent during those times will be returned unread.** Reports in "anywhere from 2 weeks to 6 months." **Pays 1 copy.** Acquires one-time rights. No comments on rejections. Reviews books of poetry in 400 words (chapbooks in 200 words), single format. Open to unsolicited reviews. Poets may also send books for review consideration. This exciting and relatively new journal seems a cross between *The Paris Review* and *New York Quarterly* with a distinct West Coast flavor that puts it in a league of its own. Editor Jack Grapes jampacks each issue with dozens upon dozens of poems, mostly free verse (lyric, narrative, dramatic)—some tending toward avant-garde and some quite accessible—that manages somehow to reach out and say: "Read Me." Bombshelter Press publishes 4-6 flat-spined paperbacks and 5 chapbooks/year. **Query first. Primarily interested in Los Angeles poets. "We publish very few unsolicited mss." Reports in 3 months. Pays 50 copies.** Jack Grapes says, "My goal is to publish a democratic range of American poets and insure they are read by striving to circulate the magazine as widely as possible. It's hard work and a financial drain. I hope the mag is healthy for poets and writers, and that they support the endeavor by subscribing as well as submitting."

OPEN HAND PUBLISHING INC. (V), P.O Box 22048, Seattle WA 98122, phone (206)447-0597, founded 1981, publisher P. Anna Johnson, is a "literary/political book publisher" bringing out flat-spined paperbacks as well as cloth cover editions designed "to promote understanding between the world's people." They have published **Puerto Rican Writers at Home in the USA,** "an anthology of seventeen of the most well-known Puerto Rican writers," and **Where Are the Love Poems for Dictators?** by E. Ethelbert Miller. **They do not consider unsolicited mss. Send SASE for catalog to order samples.**

ORACLE POETRY; ASSOCIATION OF AFRICAN WRITERS; RISING STAR PUBLISHERS (I, IV-Ethnic), 2105 Amherst Rd., Hyattsville MD 20783, phone (301)422-2665, founded 1989, editorial director Obi Harrison Ekwonna. *Oracle Poetry* and *Oracle Story* appear quarterly using works **"mainly of African orientation; must be probing and must have meaning—any style or form. Writers must have the language of discourse and good punctuation. No gay, lesbian or erotic poetry."** As a sample the editor selected these lines from "War of 1968" by Greggette Soto:

> *Twenty-three years ago*
> *A son went off to war*
> *It wasn't to fight*
> *Communism in Vietnam*
> *But to fight*
> *Racism in his own backyard.*

Membership in the Association of African Writers is $20/year. The editor describes *Oracle Poetry* as digest-sized, saddle-stapled, print run 500. Subscription: $20/year. **No previously published poems or simultaneous submissions. Reports in 4-6 weeks. Pays copies. Acquires first North American serial rights.** Reviews books of poetry. The editor says, "Read widely, write well and punctuate right."

ORBIS: AN INTERNATIONAL QUARTERLY OF POETRY AND PROSE (II), 199 The Long Shoot, Nuneaton, Warwickshire CV11 6JQ England, founded 1968, editor Mike Shields, considers **"all poetry so long as it's genuine in feeling and well executed of its type."** They have published poetry by Sir John Betjeman, Ray Bradbury, Seamus Heaney and Naomi Mitchison, as well as a recent US issue including Bukowski, Levertov, Piercy, Stafford and many others, "but are just as likely to publish absolute unknowns." The quarterly is 6 × 8½, flat-spined, 64 pgs., professionally printed with glossy card cover, circulation 1,000 with 600 subscriptions of which 50 are libraries. They receive "thousands" of submissions/year, use "about 5%." Single copy: £3.50 ($7.50); subscription: £14 ($30). **Sample postpaid: $2 (or £1). Submit typed on 1 side only, one poem/sheet. No bio, no query. Enclose IRCs for reply, not US postage. Reports in 1-2 months. Pays $10 or more per acceptance plus 1 free copy automatically. Each issue carries £50 in prizes paid on basis of reader votes.** Editor comments on rejections "occasionally—if we think we can help. *Orbis* is completely independent and receives no grant-aid from anywhere."

ORCHISES PRESS (II), P.O. Box 20602, Alexandria VA 22320-1602, founded 1983, poetry editor Roger Lathbury, is a small press publisher of literary and general material in flat-spined paperbacks. **"Although we will consider mss submitted, we prefer to seek out the work of poets who interest us."** Regarding poetry he states: "No restrictions, really; but it must be sophisticated—i.e., no religious versification, arty nonsense, etc. I find it increasingly unlikely that I would publish a ms unless a fair proportion of its contents has appeared previously in respected literary journals." He has recently published poetry by Timothy Houghton and Richard Foerster. Asked for a sample, he says, "I find this difficult, but . . ." (from Joe David Bellamy):

> *And the sea extends for miles, blank from above,*
> *white and brittle, encircled by blank trees, the ice*
> *as hard and heavy as iron, though suffused with light,*
> *opalescent beneath the surface, then, deeper. . . .*

He publishes about 2 flat-spined paperbacks of poetry a year, averaging 64 pgs. **When submitting, "tell where poems have previously been published." Reports in 1 month. Pays 36% of money earned once Orchises recoups its initial costs.** Roger Lathbury says, "Real poets persist and endure."

ORE (II, IV-Themes), 7 The Towers, Stevenage, Hertfordshire, SG1 1HE England, founded 1955, editor Eric Ratcliffe, a magazine that appears 2-3 times/year. They want work that is or relates to **"folk, legend, Celtic, Arthurian, fairy, spiritual, religious. No obscenities or too much materialism."** They have published poetry by Jay Ramsay and James Kirkup. As a sample the editor selected these lines (poet unidentified):

> *Ashurnasipal worships the sun-god Shamash*
> *in front of the Sacred Tree*
> *priest of Ashur*
> *beloved of Anu and Dagan*
> *son of Tukulti-Ninurta.*

They receive about 1,000 poems/year, accept 5%. **Sample: £1.75 or 5 IRCs. Simultaneous submissions OK. Brief cover letter noting "items forwarded and successes elsewhere" required. Editor "always" comments—"no curt rejection slips." Pays 1 copy, others at half price.** Staff reviews books of poetry. Send books for review consideration. Query regarding unsolicited reviews. He advises: "1.) Realize what your type of interest is and your educational and expression limits. 2.) Read lots of poetry consistent with 1. Dwell internally on imagery, etc. 3.) Write poetry when something comes in the head—don't intend to write first. 4.) Put it away for a week and rewrite it."

OREGON EAST (II, IV-Regional), Hoke Center, Eastern Oregon State College, La Grande OR 97850, founded 1950, editor changes yearly, is the "literary annual of EOSC, 50% of magazine open to off-campus professional writing." Their preferences: **"Eclectic tastes in poetry with the only requirement being literary quality work for off-campus submissions. Chances of publication are better for short poems (one page) than longer ones. No 'greeting card' verse."** They have recently published poetry by Ling Wen Yuan, Heather Pankl, Thomas Madden, Sarah E. Witte and Lucinda Van Handel. It is flat-spined, book format, typeset, with end papers, 6×9, approximately 100 pgs., using graphics and b&w art. Circulation 1,000 (300 off-campus) with 100 subscriptions of which 30-40 are libraries. Content tends toward free verse lyrics. Editors try to give readers an overview of art in each issue, from poetry to prose to graphics. **Single copy: $5. Special 35-year issue available for $9.95 (256 pgs.). Submit only 3-5 poems. No simultaneous submissions. All submissions must be accompanied by SASE and cover letter with brief bio and phone number. Reads submissions September 1 through March 1 only. Notification by June. Pays 2 copies. Acquires all rights. Returns rights "with condition that *Oregon East* may reprint in any upcoming anthology."** The editor says, "In terms of content, we like to see/read tangible images. If something doesn't make sense to us, it won't make sense to our readers."

ORIEL BOOKSHOP (IV-Regional), The Friary, Cardiff, Wales CF2 5AT United Kingdom, phone 0222-395548, founded 1974, head of bookshop Peter Finch, publishes **Anglo-Welsh poetry, nothing else.** They have published poetry by Dylan Thomas, T. Harri Jones and R.S. Thomas. As a sample the editor selected these lines from Dannie Abse's "Return to Cardiff":

> *No sooner than I'd arrived the other Cardiff had gone,*
> *smoke in the memory, these but tinned resemblances,*
> *where the boy I was not and the man I am not*
> *met, hesitated, left double footsteps, then walked on.*

That poem is handsomely printed on a large color poster.

ORPHIC LUTE (II), 1713 14th Ave., Seattle WA 98122-2624, founded 1950, now published by Dreamcatcher Multiple Arts, Inc., editor David Sparenberg, is a literary quarterly. *"Orphic Lute* **seeks quality lyric and narrative poems (40-line limit), as well as haiku and short prose (500 words maximum). Themes of special interest are deep ecology, mythology, folklore, dreamwork, healing, pathos of the human condition, experiences of love and beauty, Native American and world tribal traditions."** Each issue now includes a "Featured Poet" centerfold and "Mythopoesis" section. They have recently published poetry by Antler, Mary de LaValette, Wendy Burch and Victoria Lena Manyarrows. *Orphic Lute* is 40-48 pgs., 7×10½. The magazine has a circulation of 750. **Subscription: $12. Sample: $3.50. SASE required with all submissions. "Editor is internationally publishing poet/short story author who personally replies to all contributors." Pays copies.** He says, *"Orphic Lute* is dedicated to the preservation and extension of those sensibilities and sensitivities that make us more humane in our humanity, and to the poetic and storytelling arts and their practicioners."

ORTALDA & ASSOCIATES (V), 1208 Delaware St., Berkeley CA 94702, phone (510)524-2040, fax (415)527-3411, founded 1985, poetry editor Floyd Salas, director/editor Claire Ortalda, publishes quality flat-spined paperbacks of poetry but **is not accepting submissions at this time.** They have published poetry by Czeslaw Milosz, Robert Hass, Ishmael Reed, Gary Soto, Jack Micheline and Carolyn Kizer.

OSIRIS, AN INTERNATIONAL POETRY JOURNAL/UNE REVUE INTERNATIONALE (II, IV-Translations, bilingual), P.O. Box 297, Deerfield MA 01342, founded 1972, poetry editor Andrea Moorhead, is a 6×9, saddle-stapled, 40-page semiannual that **publishes contemporary poetry in English, French and Italian without translation and in other languages with translation, including Polish, Danish and German**. They also publish graphics and photographs. They want poetry which is **"lyrical, non-narrative, multi-temporal, well crafted."** They have recently published poetry by Robert Dassanowsky-Harris, Simon Perchik, Helen Dorion (Quebec), Robert Marteau (France) and Eugenio de Andrade (Portugal). As a sample the editor selected these lines (poet unidentified):

> *i see Niagara above Aachen*
> *falling so gold in early light*
> *the sky has turned to blood*
> *what pact is made here*
> *in silence, at the narrow*
> *waters where the heart stills*

There are 12-18 pgs. of poetry in English in each issue of this intriguing publication. They have a print run of 500 and send 50 subscription copies to college and university libraries, including foreign libraries. They receive 50-75 freelance submissions/year, use 12. Single copy: $5; subscription: $10. **Sample postpaid: $2. Include short bio with submission. Reports in 1 month. Pays 5 copies.** If you translate poems from other countries or want to gain an international perspective on the art, you should send for a sample copy. Two poems published in *Osiris* have received Honorable Mentions from **The Pushcart Prize**. The editor advises, "It is always best to look at a sample copy of a journal before submitting work, and when you do submit work, do it often and do not get discouraged. Try to read poetry and support other writers."

THE OTHER SIDE MAGAZINE (II, IV-Political, religious, social issues), 300 W. Apsley St., Philadelphia PA 19144, phone (215)849-2178, founded 1965, poetry editor Rod Jellema, is a "magazine (published 6 times a year) concerned with **social justice issues from a Christian perspective. The magazine publishes 1-2 poems per issue. We will consider no more than 4 poems at one time from the same author.** Submissions should be of high quality and must speak to and/or reflect the concerns and life experiences of the magazine's readers. We look for **fresh insights and creative imagery in a tight, cohesive whole. Be warned that only 0.5% of the poems reviewed are accepted.** Seldom does any **published poem exceed 40-50 lines. Do not want to see pious religiosity, sentimental schlock, haiku."** They have published poetry by Eric Ormsby, Elisabeth Murawski, Nola Garrett and Mark Mitchell. *The Other Side* is magazine-sized, professionally printed on quality pulp stock, 64 pgs., saddle-stapled, with full-color paper cover, circulation 13,000 to that many subscriptions. Subscription: $29.50. **Sample postpaid: $4.50. No simultaneous submissions. Previously published poems rarely used. Editor "sometimes" comments on rejections. Send SASE for guidelines (material pertaining to poetry is quoted above). Pays $15 plus 4 copies and free subscription.**

OTTER (IV-Regional), Parford Cottage, Chagford, Devon TQ13 8JR United Kingdom, founded 1988, editor Christopher Southgate, appears 3 times/year **using poetry by contributors associated with the County of Devon, "poems concerned with local community and with issues — social, political, religious. Like poems in strict forms."** They have published poetry by Lawrence Sail, Ron Tamplin, Harry Guest and Jane Beeson. As a sample, here are lines from "The Yellow and Green Daughter" by Sandra McBain:

> *She dances like a daffodil*
> *or wind driven forsythia*
> *like a petal whirled in water*

It is digest-sized, 48 pgs., stapled with glossy card cover, professionally printed. They accept about 25% of 400-500 poems/year. Press run 300 for 70 subscribers of which 5 are libraries. Subscription: £5. **Sample postpaid: £2 (or $5 US; dollar checks OK). "Those not resident in Devon should indicate in their cover letter their connection with the county." Editor always comments on rejections. Reports within 3 months. Pays contributors 1 copy.** Staff reviews books of Devon poetry only.

OUR FAMILY (IV-Religious), Box 249, Battleford, Saskatchewan S0M 0E0 Canada, phone (306)937-7771, fax (306)937-7644, founded 1949, editor Nestor Gregoire, o.m.i., is a monthly religious magazine **for Roman Catholic families. "Any form is acceptable. In content we look for simplicity and vividness of imagery. The subject matter should center on the human struggle to live out one's relationship with the God of the Bible in the context of our modern world. We do not want to see science fiction poetry, metaphysical speculation poetry, or anything that demeans or belittles the spirit of human beings or degrades the image of God in him/her as it is described in the Bible."** They have published poetry by Nadene Murphy and Arthur Stilwell. *Our Family* is magazine-sized, 40 pgs., glossy color paper cover, using drawings, cartoons, two-color ink, circulation 13,500 of which 48 are libraries. Single copy: $1.95;

subscription: $15.98 Canada/$21.98 US. **Sample postpaid: $2.50. Send SASE or SAE with IRC or personal check (American postage cannot be used in Canada) for writer's guidelines. Will consider poems of 4-30 lines. Simultaneous submissions OK. Reports within 1 month after receipt. Pays 75¢-$1/line.** The editor advises, "The essence of poetry is imagery. The form is less important. Really good poets use both effectively."

OUT LOUD: THE MONTHLY OF LOS ANGELES AREA POETRY EVENTS (IV-Regional), 1318 Third St. Promenade, Santa Monica CA 90401, founded 1988, editor Carrie Etter, "is distributed at poetry venues throughout the greater Los Angeles area: performance spaces, theaters, bookstores, etc." and accepts poetry from poets living in Los Angeles or Orange County, up to 20 lines. No "work that demonstrates that the writer is not an avid reader of modern poetry." Format is an 11×17 sheet, printed and folded in half. Circulation 4,000, all copies distributed free except subscriber copies. **Subscription: $9/year. Sample postpaid: 75¢.** Previously published poetry OK if cover letter indicates when and where it was published. **"Otherwise cover letters are not necessary." Reports within 1-2 months. Pays 2 copies** "unless poet requests more."

OUTERBRIDGE (II), English A324, The College of Staten Island, 715 Ocean Terrace, Staten Island NY 10301, phone (718)390-7654, founded 1975, editor Charlotte Alexander, publishes "the most crafted, professional poetry and short fiction we can find (unsolicited except special features—to date rural, urban and Southern, promoted in standard newsletters such as *Poets & Writers, AWP, Small Press Review*), interested in newer voices. **Anti loose, amateurish, uncrafted poems showing little awareness of the long-established fundamentals of verse; also anti blatant PRO-movement writing when it sacrifices craft for protest and message. Poems usually 1-4 pgs. in length."** They have published poetry by Craig S. Brown, Kay Murphy and Naomi Rachel. As a sample the editor selected these lines from "How to Imagine Deafness" by Kim Roberts:

> *Darken your ears until the tunnels*
> *with their intricate clockwork*
> *are sheathed in pitchy calm.*
> *Hum a little blue, to yourself,*

> *but keep it secret.*

The digest-sized, flat-spined annual is 100+ pgs., about half poetry, circulation 500-600, 150 subscriptions of which 28 are libraries. They receive 500-700 submissions/year, use about 60. **Sample postpaid: $5. Submit 3-5 poems anytime except June and July. Include name and address on each page. "We dislike simultaneous submissions and if a poem accepted by us proves to have already been accepted elsewhere, a poet will be blacklisted as there are many good poets waiting in line." Cover letter with brief bio preferred. Reports in 2 months. Pays 2 copies (and offers additional copies at half price). Acquires first rights.** The editor says, "As a poet/editor I feel magazines like *Outerbridge* provide an invaluable publication outlet for individual poets (particularly since publishing a book of poetry, respectably, is extremely difficult these days). As in all of the arts, poetry—its traditions, conventions and variations, experiments—should be studied. One current 'trend' I detect is a lot of mutual backscratching which can result in very loose, amateurish writing. Discipline!"

OUTREACH: FOR THE HOUSEBOUND, ELDERLY AND DISABLED (IV-Senior citizens, specialized: disabled, religious), 7 Grayson Close, Stocksbridge, Sheffield S30 5BJ England, editor Mike Brooks, founded 1985, is a quarterly using **"semi-religious poetry and short articles. This is a magazine for the housebound, elderly and disabled who need cheering up, not made more depressed or bored!"** It is photocopied from typescript on ordinary paper, folded and saddle-stapled. As a sample, here are lines from "Stairs to God" by Helen S. Rice:

> *Prayers are the stairs*
> *We must climb every day,*
> *If we would reach God*
> *There is no other way.*

OUTRIDER PRESS (II, IV-Women), #2, 937 Patricia Lane, Crete IL 60417, founded 1988, president Phyllis Nelson, publishes 1-2 chapbooks/year. They want **"poetry dealing with the terrain of the human heart and plotting inner journeys; growth and grace under pressure. No bag ladies, loves-that-never-were, please."** As a sample the editor selected these lines from "Elegy" in *Listen to the Moon* by Whitney Scott:

> *He slipped*
> *Away,*
> *Gently as the rustle of silk*
> *He so favored in his shirts.*

That chapbook is digest-sized, 16 pgs., photocopied from typescript with matte card cover, $4. **Responds to queries in 3 months, to submissions in 6 months. Pay negotiable.**

THE OVERLOOK PRESS; TUSK BOOKS (V), 149 Wooster St., New York NY 10012, phone (212)477-7162, founded 1972, are trade publishers with about 8 poetry titles. They have published books of poetry by David Shapiro and Paul Auster. Tusk/Overlook Books are distributed by Viking/Penguin. **They publish on standard royalty contracts with author's copies. Not accepting poetry submissions.**

OWL CREEK PRESS; OWL CREEK POETRY BOOK AND CHAPBOOK COMPETITIONS (II), 1620 N. 45th St., Seattle WA 98103, founded 1979, poetry editor Rich Ives. "Owl Creek Press is a nonprofit literary publisher. Selections for publication are based solely on literary quality." They publish full-length poetry books, chapbooks, anthologies. **"No subject or length limitations. We look for poetry that will endure."** They have published poetry by Angela Ball, Art Homer and Laurie Blauner. As a sample here are the opening lines of "Ordinance on Returning" by Naomi Lazard:

> We commend you on your courage.
> The place you have chosen to revisit
> is as seductive as ever.
> It has been in that business for centuries.

Owl Creek Press accepts books and chapbooks for publication only through its annual contests for each. The *book* competition selects 1-3 books for publication. Mss should be a minimum of 50 typed pages and should include an acknowledgments page for previous publications. Deadline: January 31; entry fee: $9; winners receive 100 copies of published book. The *chapbook* competition chooses 1-3 chapbooks for publication. Mss should be under 40 pages and should include an acknowledgments page for previous publications. Deadline: July 15; entry fee: $5; winners receive 50 copies of published chapbook. Additional payment for reprinting. Send SASE for information on Owl Creek Poetry Book and Chapbook Contests. The editor says, "It is clear that many would-be poets do not read enough. A hungry mind is a valuable asset. Feed it."

‡OXALIS; STONE RIDGE POETRY SOCIETY ANNUAL POETRY CONTEST; DAY OF THE POET (II), P.O. Box 3993, Kingston NY 12401, founded contest 1983, *Oxalis* (a literary quarterly) 1988. **"We are generally open as to form and subject matter. Usually would not take over 50 lines per poem. No gratuitous sex, violence, ugh types."** They have recently published poetry by Stephen Dunn, Elizabeth Hahn and Albert Huffstickler. As a sample the editor selected these lines from "Positive Self Images" by Michael S. Smith:

> Looking only on the bright side
> became so natural
> we could walk around in the dark
> and feel enlightened.

Oxalis is 40+ pgs., magazine-sized, saddle-stapled, desktop published with matte card cover using some b&w art. Their press run is 300 with 70 subscriptions of which 15 are libraries. They receive about 700 poems a year, use 120. Single copy: $6; subscription: $18 for 3 issues, $14 for members of Stone Ridge Poetry Society. **Sample postpaid: $5. Submit poems double-spaced with cover letter including a brief bio (2 or 3 sentences to use on contributor's page if work is accepted). "We return unread anything that comes without adequate postage. Please send SASE for our reply even if you don't want your poems returned." Send SASE for guidelines and contest rules. Pays 2 copies.** Reviews books of poetry only if poet has already been published in *Oxalis*. Stone Ridge Poetry Society sponsors weekly poetry readings March through September. They seldom pay readers. They co-sponsor, with *Home Planet News* (a literary tabloid based in Brooklyn), an annual Day of the Poet in early October, at Ulster County Community College. The day features a poetry reading contest, open readings, a book fair, music and refreshments. They have a paid featured poet for that event, and the $5 entry fees for poets participating in the contest are used for winners' prizes (as well as to benefit *Oxalis* and *Home Planet News*). SRPS also sponsors an annual poetry contest.

OXFORD MAGAZINE (II), 302C Bachelor Hall, Miami University, Oxford OH 45056, phone (513)529-5256, founded 1984, appears twice a year. **"We are open in terms of form, content, length and subject matter."** They have recently published poetry by Eve Shelnutt and Lyn Lifshin. As a sample here are lines from "Burning the Fields" by C.L. Rawlins:

> Between the grass and rolling flame, a pact;
> the farmers with their torches: custom, wisdom, lore.
> The fierce green rises blind above the black.
> Dry orchard prunings blaze in bony stacks
> at equinox, the land bare of snow and poor.
> Between the grass and rolling flame, a pact.

Oxford Magazine

Fall/Winter 1992

Steve Barthleme Lyn Lifshin
Sandra Kolankiewicz Ellen Smith

Editor Keith Banner says poetry plays a major—and sometimes sole—role in Oxford Magazine, the biannual publication of Miami University in Oxford, Ohio. "When we put an issue together, the philosophy shifts but orbits the same idea: What is new, stark, original, interesting?" he says. The artwork on this cover, created by Bill Ross, is entitled "A World of Touch." It was chosen, Banner says, because "we liked its strangeness and poetic surrealism. This dreaminess hinted at the poetry and fiction inside."

It is 6×9, 80-100 pgs., flat-spined, professionally printed with matte card cover. Press run 500. Sample postpaid: $5. "We accept submissions from September 1 until May 1 only." No simultaneous submissions or previously published poems. Cover letter with a short (one or two-line) bio required. Reports in 8-10 weeks. Pays copies. Buys first North American serial rights.

OXFORD UNIVERSITY PRESS (V), 200 Madison Ave., New York NY 10016, phone (212)679-7300, founded 1478, poetry editor Jacqueline Simms (U.K.), is a large university press publishing academic, trade and college books in a wide variety of fields. Not accepting any poetry mss. "Our list includes Conrad Aiken, Richard Eberhart, Robert Graves, Geoffrey Hill, Peter Porter, M.L. Rosenthal, Stephen Spender, Anne Stevenson and Charles Tomlinson. These indicate our direction."

PABLO LENNIS (IV-Science fiction/fantasy), 30 N. 19th St., Lafayette IN 47904, founded 1976, editor John Thiel, appears irregularly, is a "science fiction and fantasy fanzine preferring poems of an expressive cosmic consciousness or full magical approach. I want poetry that rimes and scans and I like a good rhythmic structure appropriate to the subject. Shorter poems are much preferred. I want them to exalt the mind, imagination, or perception into a consciousness of the subject. Optimism is usually preferred, and English language perfection eminently preferable. Nothing that is not science fiction or fantasy, or which contains morbid sentiments, or is perverse, or does not rime, or contains slang." They have recently published poetry by Scott Francis, Paul Humphrey, David Hundley and Anne Valley. As a sample the editor selected these lines from "We are All Travellers Together in Space" by James Musheneaux:

> *Did you ever sit down, pause and think*
> *Relative to what the universe actually is?*
> *Let us put a few words on this paper*
> *To try to give it some thought, analysis.*

> *Let us begin with our solar system,*
> *With the Sun the center and heartbeat,*
> *A tremendous ball of hot glowing gas,*
> *Source of all Earth's light and heat.*

It is magazine-sized, 30 pgs., side-stapled, photocopied from typescript, with matte card cover, using fantastic ink drawings and hand-lettering. "I get maybe fifty poems a year and have been using most of them." Press run "up to 100 copies." Subscription: $12/year. Sample postpaid: $1. Pays 1 copy, 2 if requested. Reports "at once. I generally say something about why it was not used, if it was not. If someone else might like it, I mention an address." Reviews books of poetry if they are science fiction or fantasy. Open to unsolicited reviews. Poets may also send books for review consideration. The editor says, "Poetry is magic. I want spells, incantations, sorceries of a rhymic and rhyming nature, loftily and optimistically expressed, and I think this is what others want. People buy poetry to have something that will affect them, add new things to their lives. If they want something to think about, they get prose. See how much magic you can make. See how well-liked it is."

‡PAGE 5 (II), 1455 W. Prospect Ave., Appleton WI 54914, founded 1990, editor and publisher R. Chris Halla, who says *Page 5* is an irregular publication designed "to publish what I feel like publishing regardless of the opinions of others. **Nothing poorly written, poorly cultivated, poorly nurtured and poorly harvested.**" They have recently published poetry by Gary Busha, Bruce Taylor, John Judson and Robert Schuler. *Page 5* is one 11×17 sheet, folded twice so the cover is 5½×8½. It usually contains the work of one author. The editor accepts 1% of poetry received. Press run is 250, all distributed free. **Sample free with 6×9 or larger SASE. Due to format, poets should submit work to fit two 5½×8½ pages and one 11×17 page spread. No previously published poems or simultaneous submissions. Cover letter required.** "**Submissions unaccompanied by SASE will be fed to the perch.**" Seldom comments on rejections. **Reporting time varies. Pays 25-50 copies. Acquires first and reprint rights.** Staff reviews books of poetry "if something comes in that knocks us out of our saddles." Send books for review consideration.

PAINTBRUSH: A JOURNAL OF POETRY, TRANSLATIONS, AND LETTERS (III), Division of Language & Literature, Northeast Missouri State University, Kirksville MO 63501, founded 1974, editor Ben Bennani. *Paintbrush* appears 2 times/year and is 5½×8½, 64+ pgs., using **quality poetry.** Circulation is 500. **Sample: $7. No submissions June, July and August. Send SASE with inquiries and request for samples.** Reviews books of poetry.

PAINTED HILLS REVIEW (II, IV-Regional), P.O. Box 494, Davis CA 95617-0494, founded 1990, editors Michael Ishii and Kara Kosmatka, appears 3 times/year using "**well-crafted poetry. Poems must sustain themselves. Rather than abstractly generalizing, make a poem detailed and real—full of 'real' people and 'real' situations. Nothing abstract, general, sloppy and unsustained, trite, 'greeting card' verse, no philosophy or dogmatism. Special interest in poetry of West Coast.**" They have published work by Patricia Goedicke, Roland Flint, William Stafford, Ingrid Wendt, Lia Smith and Omar S. Castañeda. As a sample the editors selected these lines from "Swimming After Birds" by Laurie O'Brien:

> *Over water it is easier to understand. They*
> *need some angle of light on the silver*
> *backs of fish, they must have a line*
> *of descent before the plunge. The child*
> *in the green waves chases every rocking*
> *trough, the fish which spiral and disperse,*
> *the feathers just above foam. The world tilts*
> *and we see her swimming with a little flutter*
> *kick out into the territory of summer air.*

PHR is 48 pgs., digest-sized, professionally printed and typeset, saddle-stapled, with matte card cover, all on recycled paper. Press run 250-300. **Subscription: $10 (add 7.5% tax in California). Sample postpaid: $3. Send no more than 6 poems at a time, no more than 100 lines/poem.** "**We would also like biographical information on the author.**" **Reports in 4-6 weeks. Pays 1-2 copies. Acquires first North American serial rights.** Reviews books of poetry in 250-500 words, single or multi-book format. Open to unsolicited reviews. Poets may also send books (marked attn. Reviews) for review consideration. Sponsors "Paintbrush Award in Poetry," yearly contest. Deadline is in May. Send SASE for information. Winners win up to $100 cash prize and are published in *PHR*. One of the poems published in this review was included in a **Pushcart Prize** anthology. The editors advise, "Read other poets; revise and revise again; keep trying."

PAISLEY MOON (II), Box 2373, Santa Cruz CA 95063, founded 1990, editors Michael Spring and P. Notzka, is a triannual magazine. "**Prefer poems around 35 lines or less, but will consider longer poems if exceptional. Open to all forms/style, even haiku! Editors prefer strong imagery, rich language and explorative verse, original twists in vision and metaphor. No didactic, greeting-cardish, cliche-ridden verse.**" They have recently published poetry by Joyce Odam, Antler, Wm. Everson, Sheila E. Murphy, Errol Miller, Francisco X. Alarcon, B.Z. Niditch, Stephen Kessler and John Grey. As a sample the

Market conditions are constantly changing! If you're still using this book and it is 1995 or later, buy the newest edition of Poet's Market at your favorite bookstore or order directly from Writer's Digest Books.

editor selected these lines from "Companion" by Martha M. Vertreace:

> The chapel carillon crashes over wild seas
> you fingerpaint in cobalt, thick pigment
> cresting in noble-savage waves.
> When you leave,
> the gibbous moon floats on its side . . .

PM is digest-sized, 32-40 pgs., photocopied from typescript on ordinary paper with matte card cover (with art). Press run is 300. They accept about 15% of 1,000 poems received. Subscription: $9. **Sample postpaid: $3. Will consider previously published poems and simultaneous submissions. Reports in 1 day to 2 months. Pays 1 copy.** They sponsor an annual contest. All poems in contest are considered for publication. Winners are featured in additional issue. Prizes of $100, $50, $25, 5 honorable mentions; fee $2/poem, limit 35 lines. Deadline: November 1. The editors advise, "Read past and present masters (critically); read everything you can on poetry; read enough to know what is and isn't a cliche. Write and rewrite often. Be patient and persistent with your craft and vision."

‡**PALANQUIN; PALANQUIN POETRY SERIES (II)**, 11 Inverness St. W., Aiken SC 29803-5962, founded 1989, editor Phebe Davidson. The Palanquin Poetry Series has **an issue every 2 months consisting of 3 columns of poetry showcasing a single poet, professionally printed on a folded card.** She does not want "sentimental, religious, clotted academic" poetry. They have published poetry by Jean Hollander, Joe Weil and Patricia Celley Groth. As a sample the editor selected these lines from "Harp" by Lois Harrod:

> This gentle plucking of all my strings now,
> these ferns like green fingers when
> I walk the road, these vines like wild serpents
> tongues like threads, this thrush nagging me

The card we received, featuring poems by Sander Zulauf, is printed on heavy recycled paper. Press run is 100 for 50 subscribers. Subscription: $12.50. **Sample postpaid: $2. No previously published poems. "I read January through March for the following year." Reports in 2 months. Pays one-half press run.** She also holds an annual fall chapbook contest for spring publication. Send SASE for information.

PANCAKE PRESS (V), 163 Galewood Circle, San Francisco CA 94131, phone (415)665-9215, founded 1974, publisher Patrick Smith, a small press publisher of hand-bound paperbacks with sewn signatures. "**Current projects are selected. At present we can consider only solicited mss for publication. Unsolicited mss will be returned with brief comment and thanks.**" The editor publishes "**poetry aware of its own language conventions, tuned to both the ear and eye, attentive to syntax, honest about its desires, clear about something, spoken or written as a member of the species.**" He has published books by John Logan, David Ray and Stephen Dunning.

PANDORA; PANDORA'S ALL YOUTH ISSUE (I, IV-Science fiction/fantasy), 2844 Grayson, Ferndale MI 48220. Contact Ruth Berman, 2809 Drew Ave. S., Minneapolis MN 55416. *Pandora*, founded 1978, editor Meg Mac Donald, poetry editor Ruth Berman, appears 2 times yearly (hoping to return to quarterly), publishing 6-12 poems in each issue of "**science fiction, fantasy, offbeat, any form. No horror! Long poems of extremely high quality. Most under 30 lines.**" They have recently published poetry by John B. Rosenman, Monica Nehm Cook, W. Gregory Stewart and Ann K. Schwader. As a sample these lines are from "three steps" by Roger E. Moore:

> will i lay down in the
> wet long grass of heaven, to
> breathe the loam and sleep
> under the blue forever?

It is digest-sized, 72 pgs., offset, on white stock with glossy card stock cover in b&w and 1 additional color, perfect-bound, using b&w graphics and ads, circulation 500, including some libraries, newsstand and bookstore sales. Subscription: $10 for 2 issues (US); $12 for 2 issues (Canada); $18 for 2 issues overseas. **Sample postpaid: $5 (US); $6 (Canada); $10 overseas. All payments must be made in US funds.** *Pandora's* All Youth issue publishes poetry by those in grades K-12 of the current year. Cover letter not required but you can include "a few *relative* credits or a note about age if author is very young." Send SASE for guidelines. They advise, "Researching your market is probably the most valuable time you will spend as a poet. You've already spent precious time in the creation process; don't waste time and postage on blind submissions. Send for guidelines. Better yet, acquire a few issues of the magazine you are interested in submitting to. Spend some serious time scrutinizing the contents. Watch for trends, for changes in editorial tastes. Be careful not to send work that only repeats what you've seen recently. Trying to win the editor over with what you already know 'isn't quite right' is risky.

When an editor can't use your work, take any comments to heart. Above all, don't be discouraged and never take rejection personally. Poetry is a very personal thing for many editors — it may not be the technical form that makes or breaks it, it may just be a gut reaction to that particular poem on that day. Take whatever clues you're given to improve your chances — or your poetry — in the future."

THE PANHANDLER (II), Dept. PM, English Dept., University of West Florida, Pensacola FL 32514, phone (904)474-2923, founded 1976, editors Michael Yots and Stanton Millet, appears twice a year, using **poetry "grounded in experience with strong individual 'voice' and natural language. Any subject, no 'causes.' Length to 200 lines, but prefer 30-100. No self-consciously experimental, unrestrained howling, sophomoric wailings on the human condition."** They have published poetry by Malcolm Glass, Lyn Lifshin, Donald Junkins, David Kirby and Joan Colby. As a sample here is the first stanza of "York, Maine" by Leo Connellan:

> *Through the Cutty Sark motel room 21 picture window now*
> *the gray waves coming into York Beach like*
> *an invasion of plows pushing snow. Tomorrow*
> *the sun will scratch its chin and bleed along the skyline*
> *but today everything is gray poached in a steam of fog.*

The handsomely printed magazine is digest-sized, 64 pgs., flat-spined, large type on heavy egg-shell stock, matte card cover with art. Circulation is 500 for 100 subscribers of which 10 are libraries and 200 complimentary copies going to the English department and writing program. Subscription: $5. **Sample postpaid: $2. No simultaneous submissions. Submit maximum of 7 poems, typewritten or letter-perfect printout. Reports in 1-2 months, 6-12 months to publication. Pays 2 copies.** They sponsor a national chapbook competition each year, October 15 through January 15. Submit 24-30 pgs. with $7 reading fee. Send SASE for details. The editor advises: "(1) take care with ms preparation. Sloppy mss are difficult to evaluate fairly; (2) send only poems you believe in. Everything you write isn't publishable; send finished work."

PANJANDRUM BOOKS; PANJANDRUM POETRY JOURNAL (III, IV-Translations), 6156 Wilkinson Ave., North Hollywood CA 91606, founded 1971, editor Dennis Koran, associate editor David Guss. **The press publishes a distinguished list of avant-garde books. They are interested in translations (especially European) of modern poetry, surrealism, dada and experimental poetry and accept book-length mss only with SASE; query first. Cover letter listing previous publications is required.** *Panjandrum Poetry Journal* **is published occasionally. Submit no more than 10 poems at a time.** Staff also reviews books of poetry. Send books for review consideration to Dennis Koran.

PANTHEON BOOKS INC., 201 E. 50th St., New York NY 10022. Prefers not to share information.

THE PAPER BAG (I, II), Box 268805, Chicago IL 60626-8805, phone (312)285-7972 (an answering service), founded 1988, editor M. Brownstein, is a quarterly using **poetry "any kind, any style. We look for strong and original imagery. No love poems at the beach, by water, across from candlelight."** As a sample the editor selected this complete poem, "Road Kill," by Michael Scott:

> *In the cool light of summer*
> *morning, the possum seems*
> *almost alive, no blood or guts*
> *spilled in the road, white*
> *fur tipped with gray,*
> *looking like the dirty*
> *snow of early spring.*

The Paper Bag is 24 pgs., digest-sized, saddle-stapled, photocopied from typescript, with matte card cover. They publish about 30 of 200 poems received/issue. "Our circulation varies from 20-300+ and we sell out every issue." Subscription: $12/4-5 issues plus "anything else we publish." **Sample postpaid: $3. Typed mss only, address and phone number on each submission. Cover letter with brief bio required. Editor comments on submissions "always." Send SASE for guidelines. Pays copies.** All checks or money orders should be made out to M. Brownstein. The editor says, "Be persistent. Because we reject one group of submissions does not mean we will reject another batch. Keep trying."

PAPER RADIO (IV-Form/style), P.O. Box 4646, Seattle WA 98104-0646, founded 1986, poetry editor Serge Lecomte **(and submissions should be sent directly to him at P.O. Box 82052, Fairbanks AK 99708)**, is a literary journal appearing 3 times a year. **"Actually what we want doesn't have a descriptive monicker because it is at the vanguard but not yet a movement. Suffice it to say, we are more in the line of descent from Wallace Stevens and the French dadaist and surrealists than from, say, W.C. Williams. Length: up to 100 lines. Style: from** *ambient* **to** *grand mal.* **Do not want to see mainstream**

theocratic bathos." They have published poetry by Sheila E. Murphy, Bradley Goldman, Judson Crews and Stacey Sollfrey. The editor describes *Paper Radio* as intended for "pointedly experimental poetry, fiction, graphics and criticism." It is 8¼×10⅞, "mixed printing (computer-generated, run on a web press), generally ½ words and ½ graphics." They receive about 3,000 poems/year, accept 25-50. The circulation is 3,000, 350+ subscriptions of which 20 are libraries. Subscription: $19. **Sample postpaid: $3. "No specifications (we're anarchists) but more than 5-6 poems seems pointless or downright unstrategic (makes us feel Sisyphean)." Simultaneous submissions OK. On rejections, "we try to give some indication that a human read the work, but it depends on its quality and our workload." Reports in 1-2 months, 1-8 months delay till publication. Pays 1 copy.** Reviews books of poetry "sometimes." The editor says, "Always remember Borges' comment: 'I write for myself and my friends, and to ease the passing of time.' Greed and mundane equivocation would seem, fortunately, to have no place in poetry—it's the useless utterance that is our greatest fulfillment."

THE PAPER SALAd POETRY JOURNAL (II), 627 E. 100 S. #A, Salt Lake City UT 84102, founded 1990, editor R.L. Moore (who has dropped the pen name Eldon Holt), is an annual using **"poetry by poets who work rigorously on their poetry, who make every poem an attempt at the 'perfect' poem, and who know that the meaning of a poem is always secondary to the music of the poem."** They have recently published poetry by Richard Cronshey, Lyn Lifshin, Robert Nagler, Errol Miller, John M. Bennett and Gayle Elen Harvey. As a sample the editor selected these lines from "Spring is the Season of Looking" by Glenn Parker:

> *There is a man with blue eyes*
> *standing in the darkness*
> *that surrounds me. He can*
> *feel the subterranean winds*
> *of the interior. He fills*
> *my waterclock with rain from Jerusalem*
> *until my voice becomes as rainy*
> *as the cold brown foothills of China.*

The editor describes it as 80-110 pgs., flat-spined, digest-sized. Press run is 200. **Sample: $6.50 ("An additional dollar will help with postage, but is optional"). Submit no more than 6 poems, one poem to a page, name and address on each. Seldom comments on rejections. Replies within 2 months. Pays 1 copy.** The editor says, "Poetry is a craft. Although it is a historical record of your interior, it should not simply be such. This means you should spend time and energy working the lines until they have *that sound*, you know the one. *Every single line* should be placed on the page with purpose and with a certain degree of thought and attention! If you are going to ask the reader to spend any time at all looking at your poem, you better give them something to look at. Lie, and after you have lied, you might find that you have really said what you intended in the first place."

PAPIER-MACHE PRESS (IV-Themes, anthologies), 795 Via Manzana, Watsonville CA 95076, phone (408)726-3105, fax (408)726-1255, founded 1984, editor Sandra Martz, is a small press publisher of anthologies, poetry and short fiction in flat-spined paperbacks and casebound books. They typically **"work on specialized projects that explore a particular aspect of women's experience, e.g., sports, aging, parental relationships, work, etc. Any length acceptable; primarily interested in well-written, accessible material."** They have published poetry by Sue Saniel Elkind, Shirley Vogler Meister, Sue Doro, Patti Tana and Janet Carncross Chandler. As a sample the editor selected these lines from "It Is Enough" by Ruth Daigon, in the anthology **If I had my life to live over I would pick more daisies:**

> *We invent a lifetime out of small things,*
> *free the air between our fingers,*
> *diagram the stars   dream them into*
> *daylight and admit the future*
> *which is here   always here*
> *like a clock that runs forever.*

They publish 1-2 poetry collections each year and one anthology every two years. Each anthology contains 30-40 poems; poetry collections contain 70-80 poems. **Query before submission to obtain current themes and guidelines. They report on queries in 6 weeks, on mss in 3 months. Simultaneous submissions must be identified as such. Cover letter required; include name, address, phone and fax numbers (if available) as well as length and subject of submission. Pays 2 copies on work accepted for anthologies.** Royalties and modest advances are negotiated on individual collections. Send SASE for book list to buy samples, typically $4-10. *"Papier-Mache's* primary objective is to publish anthologies, poetry and fiction books by, for and about mid-life and older women. Material from socially aware men is welcome. Our strategy is to select subjects of particular importance to women, find well-written, accessible material on those themes, develop attractive, high quality book formats and market them to an audience that might not otherwise buy books of poetry. We take particular pride in our reputation for dealing with our contributors in a caring, professional manner."

PARAGON HOUSE PUBLISHERS (III), Dept. PM, 90 5th Ave., New York NY 10011, phone (212)620-2820, founded 1983, editor-in-chief Arthur Samuelson, has published books of poetry by Louis Simpson and Leo Connellan.

PARANOIA PRESS (II, IV-Regional), 35 Percy St., Middlesbrough, Cleveland TS1 4DD United Kingdom, founded 1984, managing editor Kate More, publishes 4-5 paperbacks/year. **"We are inclined towards winners of the Cleveland Writearound festival for first collections of local writers. Contemporary mainstream poetry, but quality is the main thing."** As a sample the editor selected "Lovebite," by Pauline Plummer:

> Today
> Sat in a conference of teachers
> Your lovebite blushed
> In the crook of my elbow

> I folded it away
> But everytime I reached for a pen
> It gave a bruised smile.

Cover letter with name and address required with submissions. Pays 7-10% royalties, honorarium of £50 and 6 copies. Buys publication rights. Their poets "will usually have published in a quality press previously—e.g. *Stand, London Magazine, Iron,* etc."

THE PARIS REVIEW; BERNARD F. CONNORS PRIZE; JOHN TRAIN HUMOR PRIZE (III, IV-Humor), 45-39 171st Pl., Flushing NY 11358, founded 1952, poetry editor Richard Howard. (**Submissions should go to him at 541 E. 72nd St., New York NY 10021**). This distinguished quarterly (circulation 10,000, digest-sized, 200 pgs.) has published many of the major poets writing in English. Though form, content and length seem open, free verse—some structured, some experimental—tends to dominate recent issues. Because the journal is considered one of the most prestigious in the world, competition is keen and response times can lag. **Sample: $8. Study publication before submitting.** The Bernard F. Connors prize of $1,000 is awarded annually for the best previously unpublished long poem (over 200 lines), submitted between April 1 and May 1. The John Train Humor Prize of $1,500 is awarded annually for the best previously unpublished work of humorous fiction, nonfiction or poetry submitted before March 31. **All submissions must be sent to the 541 E. 72nd St., New York NY 10021 address.** Poetry published in *The Paris Review* was selected for inclusion in **Best American Poetry 1992.** As for the publication itself, *The Paris Review* ranked #4 in the "Poets' Pick" category of the June 1993 *Writer's Digest* Poetry 60 list. This category ranks those publications in which poets said they would most like to see their work published.

‡PARIS/ATLANTIC, INTERNATIONAL MAGAZINE OF CREATIVE WORK (II, IV-Translations), 31 Avenue Bosquet, 75007 Paris, France, founded 1982. The magazine appears twice a year, published by the American University of Paris. It includes poetry, prose and b&w artwork. "Recent poets have been from a wide variety of countries—U.S., U.K., France, Ireland, Canada, Russia, the Netherlands and Taiwan, among others. **We encourage both published and unpublished writers and artists."** The magazine is 90 pgs., 6×9. Circulation 1,000. **Submit up to 10 poems, typed. Cover letter with short bio ("approximately 30 words") required. Sufficient postage for reply—in the form of either French stamps or IRCs—should also be included. Contributors receive 1 copy of the magazine. Copyright reverts to authors after publication.** They say, "We offer a unique bilingual, international medium for publication and would like to establish links with poets from as wide a variety of backgrounds as possible."

PARNASSUS LITERARY JOURNAL (I, II), P.O. Box 1384, Forest Park GA 30051, founded 1975, edited by Denver Stull: "Our sole purpose is to promote poetry and to offer an outlet where poets may be heard. **We are open to all poets and all forms of poetry, including Oriental, 24-line limit, maximum 5 poems."** They have published poetry by C. David Hay, Diana K. Rubin, T.K. Splake, Ann Gasser and Alan Renfro. As a sample the editor selected these lines by Rod Farmer:

> The strong are few and though
> they speak in the same language
> as the weak, the masses, it is
> in a different voice. Often the
> majority muffles the free few with
> fashion, conformity, market appeal

> *being America's chief censors in*
> *art, literature, politics, religion.*
> *And the fashion now is nothing new.*

PLJ is 84 pgs., saddled-stapled, photocopied from typescript, with an occasional drawing. The magazine comes out 3 times a year with a print run of 300 copies. Subscribers presently number 200 (5 libraries). They receive about 1,500 submissions/year, of which they use 350. Currently have about a 12-month backlog. Circulation includes: Japan, England, Greece, India, Korea, Germany and Netherlands. **Sample: $3.50** (regularly $4.25/copy, $12/subscription). **Make checks or money order payable to Denver Stull. Include name and address on each page of ms. "Definitely" comments on rejections. Reports within one week. Pays 1 copy. Acquires all rights. Returns rights.** Readers vote on best of each issue. Also conducts a contest periodically. Staff reviews books of poetry by subscribers only. *Parnassus Literary Journal* ranked #2 in the "Open Markets" category of the June 1993 *Writer's Digest* Poetry 60 list. This category ranks those publications most open to both free and formal verse. The editor advises: "Write about what you know. Study what you have written. Does it make sense? A poem should not leave the reader wondering what you are trying to say. Improve your writings by studying the work of others. Be professional."

PARNASSUS: POETRY IN REVIEW; POETRY IN REVIEW FOUNDATION (V), Room 804, 41 Union Square W., New York NY 10003, phone (212)463-0889, founded 1972, poetry editor Herbert Leibowitz, provides "comprehensive and in-depth coverage of new books of poetry, including translations from foreign poetry. **We publish poems and translations on occasion, but we solicit all poetry. Poets invited to submit are given all the space they wish; the only stipulation is that the style be non-academic.**" They have published work by Alice Fulton, Eavan Boland, Ross Feld, Debora Greger, William Logan, Tess Gallagher, Seamus Heaney and Rodney Jones. They do consider unsolicited essays. In fact, this is an exceptionally rich market for thoughtful, insightful, technical essay-reviews of contemporary collections. However, it is strongly recommended that writers study the magazine before submitting. **Multiple submissions disliked. Cover letter required. Reports on essay submissions within 4-10 weeks (response takes longer during the summer). Pays $25-250 plus 2 gift subscriptions—contributors can also take one themselves. Acquires all rights. Editor comments on rejections—from 1 paragraph to 2 pages.** Send for a sample copy (prices of individual issues can vary) to get a feel for the critical acumen needed to place here. Subscriptions are $23/year, $46/year for libraries; they have 1,100 subscribers, of which 550 are libraries. The editor comments, "Contributors should be urged to subscribe to at least one literary magazine. There is a pervasive ignorance of the cost of putting out a magazine and no sense of responsibility for supporting one."

PARTING GIFTS; MARCH STREET PRESS (II), 3413 Wilshire, Greensboro NC 27408, founded 1987, poetry editor Robert Bixby. **"I want to see everything.** I'm a big fan of Jim Harrison, C.K. Williams, Amy Hempel and Janet Kauffman. If you write like them, you'll almost certainly be published. But that's pretty useless advice unless you're one of those people." He has published poetry by Eric Torgersen, Lyn Lifshin, Elizabeth Kerlikowske and Russell Thorburn. *PG* is digest-sized, 36 pgs., photocopied, with colored matte card cover, press run 200, appearing twice a year. Subscription: $8. **Sample postpaid: $4. Submit in groups of 3-10 with SASE. No previously published poems, but simultaneous submissions OK. "I like a cover letter because it makes the transaction more human. Best time to submit mss is early in the year." Send SASE for guidelines. Reports in 1-2 weeks. Pays 1 copy.** March Street Press publishes chapbooks; $10 reading fee.

PARTISAN REVIEW (III, IV-Translations, themes), Dept. PM, 236 Bay State Rd., Boston MA 02215, phone (617)353-4260, founded 1934, editor William Phillips, is a distinguished quarterly literary journal (6×9, 160 pgs., flat-spined, circulation 8,200 for 6,000 subscriptions and shelf sales), using **poetry of high quality.** They have published poetry by Joseph Brodsky, Eavan Boland, W.S. Merwin and C.H. Sisson. **Sample postpaid: $6.50. Submit maximum of 6. No simultaneous submissions. Editor "occasionally" comments on rejections. Reports in 2 months. Pays $50 and 50% discount on copies.** "Our poetry section is very small and highly selective. We are open to fresh, quality translations but submissions must include poem in original language as well as translation. We occasionally have special poetry sections on specified themes."

PASQUE PETALS; SOUTH DAKOTA STATE POETRY SOCIETY, INC. (I, IV-Regional, subscribers), 909 E. 34th St., Sioux Falls SD 57105, phone (605)338-9156, founded 1926, editor Barbara Stevens. This is the official poetry magazine for the South Dakota State Poetry Society, Inc., but it is open to non-members. **Those not residents of SD are required to subscribe when (or before) submitting. They use "all forms. 44-line limit, 50-character lines. Count titles and spaces.** Lean toward SD and Midwest themes. No rough language or porno—magazine goes into SD schools and libraries." As a sample the editor chose her poem "The Errol Flynn Look-Alike":

> *His tongue was as smooth as honey on a spoon.*
> *Went from job to job,*
> *Fooled everyone at first meeting*
>   *talked great projects completed by others.*
> *Fooled his wife all the time,*
> *she grew fat and comfortable*
>   *He left her*
>   *for a size five.*

PP appears 10 times a year (no August or November issues) and is digest-sized, 16-20 pgs., using small b&w sketches. Circulation is 250 to member/subscribers (16 to libraries). Subscription: $15/year. Sample postpaid: $1.50. Submit 3 poems at a time, 1 poem (or 2 haiku)/page, seasonal material 3 months ahead. Editor "always" comments on rejections. Send SASE for guidelines. Reports in 3 months. 2-3 month backlog. Pays non-members only 1 copy. Acquires first rights. Reviews books of poetry by members only. $5 prize for the best poem in every issue. They also sponsor a yearly contest with 10 categories. Entry fees vary. Prizes total $600. Send SASE for details.

"Passager *is 50% poetry and 50% fiction or prose," says Editor Kendra Kopelke. "We feature not only the work, but also the writer, by including photos and interviews so readers can 'meet' the writers," she says. Subtitled "A Journal of Remembrance and Discovery," this quarterly also has a special interest in older writers. Featured on this cover—and in this issue—is Will Inman, a poet who has been submitting to Passager since its beginning. Cover design: Sally Darnowsky. Cover photo: LaVerne H. Clark.*

PASSAGER: A JOURNAL OF REMEMBRANCE AND DISCOVERY (I, II, IV-Senior citizen, themes), English and Communications Design Dept., University of Baltimore, 1420 N. Charles St., Baltimore MD 21201-5779, phone (410)625-3041, founded 1989, editors Kendra Kopelke and Sally Darnowsky. *Passager* is published quarterly and publishes fiction, poetry and interviews that give voice to human experience. "We seek powerful images of remembrance and discovery from writers of all ages. One of our missions is to provide exposure for new older writers; another is to function as a literary community for writers across the country who are not connected to academic institutions or other organized groups." The journal is 8×8, 32 pgs., printed on white linen, saddle-stitched. Includes photos of writers. Poetry, 30 lines maximum; fiction, 3,000 words maximum. Simultaneous submissions acceptable if notified. No reprints. Do not submit mss in August. Occasionally does special issues. Send SASE for guidelines. Reports in 2 months. Pays 1 year's subscription. They sponsor an annual poetry contest for poets over 50 years old. Prize is $100 and publication in *Passager*.

PASSAGES NORTH (II), Kalamazoo College, 1200 Academy St., Kalamazoo MI 49006-3295, founded 1979, editor Michael Barrett, poetry editor Conrad Hillberry, is a semiannual magazine containing fiction, poetry, essays, interviews and visual art. "The magazine publishes quality work by established and emerging writers." They have recently published poetry by Mark Halliday, William Matthews, Thomas Lux, Cynthia Huntington, Jo Anne Rawson, Mark Doty, Nancy Eimers and John Rybicki. As a sample the editor selected these lines from "The Waves Roll In" by Susan Wylie:

> *I lay flat over the engine, the thrum*
> *of the motor in my chest and belly,*

> *the close sun hot on my head,*
> *and memorized the roadside blur:*
> *dried brush and trash, a blue inverted*
> *sky cradling the dunes.*

Passages North is 100 pgs., perfect-bound. Circulation is at 1,000 "and growing." Single copy: $5; subscription: $10 for 1 year, $18 for 2 years. **Prefers groups of 4-6 poems, typed single-spaced. Simultaneous submissions OK. Reads submissions September through May only. Reports in 6-8 weeks, delay to publication 6 months. Pays copies.**

PATH PRESS, INC. (IV-Ethnic), Dept. PM, Suite 724, 53 W. Jackson Blvd., Chicago IL 60604, phone (312)663-0167, fax (312)663-5318, founded 1969, president Bennett J. Johnson, executive vice president and poetry editor Herman C. Gilbert, a small publisher of books and poetry primarily "by, for and about African American and Third World people." The press is open to all types of poetic forms except "poor quality." Submissions should be typewritten in manuscript format. Writers should send sample poems, credits and bio. The books are "hardback and quality paperbacks."

THE PEACE FARM ADVOCATE (IV-Social issues), HCR 2 Box 25, Panhandle TX 79068, phone (806)335-1715, founded 1986, editor Mavis Belisle, is a quarterly which promotes peacemaking through information, commentary and reflection. **"We consider only poetry related to peace, environmental and social justice issues."** As a sample the editor selected these lines from "Packing for Saudi Arabia" by Mary Carter Rak:

> *I stare at the empty green bag*
> *I must fill in the next fifteen minutes*
> *with things most important*
> *to you. Underwear, T-shirts,*
> *your St. Christopher medal*
> *wrapped in tissue.*

The Peace Farm Advocate is 40 pgs., 8½×11, printed on recycled paper. Press run is 1,000 for 800 paid subscribers. The rest are distributed free. Subscription: $5. **Previously published poems and simultaneous submissions OK.** Time between acceptance and publication is 3-6 months. **Reports in 6 months. "We do not pay for published poems."** Open to unsolicited reviews. Poets may also send books for review consideration. The editor says, "Because of downsizing, opportunity will be very limited; we do not expect to be able to accept more than 1-2 short to medium-length poems per issue."

THE PEACE NEWSLETTER (IV-Social issues, political), Dept. PM, Syracuse Peace Council, 924 Burnet Ave., Syracuse NY 13203, founded 1936, is magazine-sized, 24 pgs., circulating 12 times a year to 5,000 people mostly in upstate and central NY with news about the peace movement and using some poetry relating to that movement. Subscription: $12/year. **Sample free for SASE. Considers simultaneous submissions. Unable to pay.**

‡PEACEMAKING FOR CHILDREN (IV-Children, social issues, themes), 2437 N. Grant Blvd., Milwaukee WI 53210, phone (414)445-9736, founded 1983, editor Jacqueline Haessly, is a magazine appearing 5 times a year, covering **peace education themes *for* children**. "We are a peace education center. The magazine is highly specialized in this field. Writers must have a sensitivity to interdependence of justice and peace issues, a commitment to non-violence, and an ability to write for children's level of comprehension." All issues have a single-focus theme such as the environment, handicapped, "all the ways we are family, space exploration vs. exploitation, understanding racism, our Latin friends." They do not want "Bible-related" or avant-garde poetry. Poems 5-20 lines only. Circulation is 10,000 and growing, "includes schools, libraries, churches, families on 6 continents." **Sample: $2. Send SASE for themes and guidelines. Pays 2 copies.**

PEARL; PEARL CHAPBOOK CONTEST (II), 3030 E. Second St., Long Beach CA 90803, phone (310)434-4523 or (714)968-7530, founded 1974, folded after 3 issues, resurrected in 1987, poetry editors Joan Jobe Smith, Marilyn Johnson and Barbara Hauk, is a literary magazine appearing three times a year. "We are interested in accessible, humanistic poetry that communicates and is related to real life. Humor and wit are welcome, along with the ironic and serious. No taboos stylistically or subject-wise. Prefer poems up to 35 lines, with lines no longer than 10 words. We don't want to see sentimental, obscure, predictable, abstract or cliché-ridden poetry. Our purpose is to provide a forum for lively, readable poetry that reflects a wide variety of contemporary voices, viewpoints and experiences—that speaks to *real* people about *real* life in direct, living language, profane or sublime." They have recently published poetry by Charles Bukowski, Edward Field, Lisa Glatt, Jennifer Olds and Gerald Locklin. As a sample they selected these lines from "Cafes of Childhood" by R. Nikolas Macioci:

> *He used to build salt effigies*
> *atop glossy barroom tables. He rivered*
> *salt with a nine-year-old finger,*
> *swirled it, fanned it from side to side,*
> *shaped it, gave it the perspective*
> *and proportion of escape routes.*

Pearl is digest-sized, 72 pgs., saddle-stapled, professionally printed (offset from camera-ready copy). Their press run is 500 with 70 subscriptions of which 7 are libraries. Subscription: $12/ year. **Sample postpaid: $5. "Handwritten submissions and unreadable dot-matrix print-outs are not acceptable." No simultaneous submissions or previously published poems. "Cover letters appreciated." Guidelines available for SASE. Reports in 6-8 weeks. Pays 2 copies. Acquires first serial rights.** Each issue contains the work of 40-50 different poets and a special 10-15 page section that showcases the work of a single poet. Staff reviews books of poetry. Send books for review consideration to Marilyn Johnson. "We sponsor an annual chapbook contest, judged by one of our more well-known contributors. Winner receives publication, $100 and 50 copies, with an introduction by the final judge. (To date, judges have been Gerald Locklin, Laurel Speer, Robert Peters and Donna Hilbert). Entries accepted during the months of May and June. There is a $10 entry fee, which includes a copy of the winning chapbook." Send SASE for complete rules and guidelines. *Pearl* ranked #8 in the "Nontraditional Verse" category of the June 1993 *Writer's Digest* Poetry 60 list. The editors add, "Advice for beginning poets? Just write from your own experience, using images that are as concrete and sensory as possible. Keep these images fresh and objective, and always listen to the music. . . ."

PECKERWOOD (I), 1503-1465 Lawrence W., Toronto, Ontario M6L 1B2 Canada, phone (416)248-2675, founded 1987, editor Ernie Ourique, appears 3 or 4 times/year. **"It could be any style you wish, any length. Haiku—yes. Rhymes—yes. Beauty—yes. Ugliness—yes. No clones of good poets, creative writing class crap or poems written by television housewives."** They have published poetry by Chris Wood, Stan Rogal, John Bennett, Ibi Kaslik, Charles Bukowski and Allen Ginsberg. As a sample the editor selected these lines from "Unlike Mine" by Yuki Hayashi:

> *duckweed*
> *pond*
> *no whale*
> *just another carp*
> *with eyes like hers*

It is 30-40 pgs., saddle-stapled, photocopied from typescript with matte card cover. They accept about 30% of poems received. Press run is 150, 60 shelf sales. **Sample postpaid: $1. Editors always provide comments on rejections. Pays 5 copies. Acquires all rights.** Ernie Ourique says, "The poems should have tongues and hearts. No one can teach you how to write poetry. Don't accept the 'masters' of poetry (Pound, Eliot, Yeats) as the greatest. Explore poetry from all over the world. This means reading more than writing. Also get a job that doesn't involve brains: construction, washing toilets. You'll meet the greatest and worst human beings in the working class. Never insult people."

PEGASUS (II), 525 Ave. B., Boulder City NV 89005, founded 1986, editor M.E. Hildebrand, is a poetry quarterly "for serious poets who have something to say and know how to say it using sensory imagery." **Submit 3-5 poems, 3-40 lines. Avoid "religious, political, pornographic themes."** They have published poetry by Stan Moseley, Gayle Elen Harvey, Robert K. Johnson and Elizabeth Perry, who provides the opening lines of "The Meeting Hour" as a sample:

> *Before Dawn drops*
> *her luminous petals*
> *I wake and listen*
> *for your muted voice*
> *to break the silence*
> *of our worlds*
> *like rustlings*
> *in the deep woods.*

Pegasus is 32 pgs., digest-sized, saddle-stapled, offset from typescript with colored paper cover. Publishes 10-15% of the work received. Circulation 200. Subscription: $12.50. **Sample postpaid: $4.50. Previously published poems OK, provided poet retains rights, but no simultaneous submissions. Send SASE for guidelines. Reports in 2 weeks. Publication is payment. Acquires first or one-time rights.**

THE PEGASUS REVIEW (I, II, IV-Themes), P.O. Box 134, Flanders NJ 07836, founded 1980, is a 14-page (counting cover) pamphlet entirely in calligraphy, illustrated on high-quality paper, some color overlays. Poetry editor Art Bounds says, "This magazine is a bimonthly, based on specific themes. Those for 1994 are: January/February—Beginnings; March/April—Environment; May/June—Family; July/August—War; September/October—Creativity; and November/December—Future. Uses poetry not more than 24 lines (the shorter the better); fiction that is short short (3 pages would be ideal); essays and cartoons. All material must pertain to any or all of the indicated themes." Poets recently published include Pamela Portwood, Joanne Seltzer, Robert Loudin and Jeanpaul Ferro. As a sample the editor selected these lines from "October Gold" by Marcia A. Kassel:

> From my mountain house,
> Plumes of leaf-smoke
> Shadow the sky with pewter smudges.
> Leaves drying, leaves dying
> Over sun-flowered fields of October Gold
> Tinged with topaz.
> While willows weep yellow-green leaf tears.

158 copies are printed for 150 subscriptions, of which 4 are libraries. Subscription: $8. **Sample: $2. Submit 3-5 poems with name and address on each page. Cover letter with brief background and list of publishing credits helpful. "If a beginner—no problem." Query if additional information is needed. Reports within a month, often with a personal response. Pays 2 copies.** Occasional book awards throughout the year. The editor advises, "Immerse yourself into all kinds, all forms of poetry. Write daily and market your work. Great benefits can be derived by becoming an active member of a poetry society or writers' group. Use **Poet's Market** as a marketing tool as well as informative reading."

PELICAN PUBLISHING COMPANY (V, IV-Children, regional, religious), Box 3110, Gretna LA 70054, phone (504)368-1175, founded 1926, editor Nina Kooij, is a "moderate-sized publisher of cookbooks, travel guides, regional books and inspirational/motivational books," which accepts poetry for "hardcover children's books *only*, preferably with a Southern focus. However, our needs for this are very limited; we do fewer than 5 juvenile titles per year, and most of these are prose, not poetry." **They are currently not accepting unsolicited mss. Query first with cover letter including "work and writing backgrounds, plot summary and promotional connections." No simultaneous submissions. Reports on queries in 1 month, on mss (if invited) in 3 months. Pays royalties. Buys all rights. Returns rights upon termination of contract.** These are 32 pgs. large-format (magazine-sized) books with illustrations. Two of their popular series are prose books about Gaston the Green-Nosed Alligator by James Rice and Clovis Crawfish by Mary Alice Fontenot. They have a variety of books based on "The Night Before Christmas" adapted to regional settings such as Cajun, prairie, and Texas. Typically their books sell for $14.95. **Write for catalog to buy samples.** The editor says, "We try to avoid rhyme altogether, especially predictable rhyme. Monotonous rhythm can also be a problem."

PEMBROKE MAGAZINE (II), Box 60, Pembroke State University, Pembroke NC 28372, founded 1969 by Norman Macleod, edited by Shelby Stephenson, is a heavy (252+ pgs., 6×9), flat-spined, quality literary annual, which has published poetry by Fred Chappell, Stephen Sandy, A.R. Ammons, Barbara Guest and Betty Adcock. Press run is 500 for 125 subscribers of which 100 are libraries. **Sample postpaid: $5. Sometimes comments on rejections. Reports within 3 months. Pays copies.** Stephenson advises, "Publication will come if you write. Writing is all."

PENDRAGON (II), VSC Box 7110, Valdosta GA 31698, founded 1983 under the name *Odradek*, is a biannual literary publication of Valdosta State College. "We publish the best fiction and poetry we can find. No particular preferences. Send your best. No more than 3 pages usually. No poorly-crafted work." They have recently published poetry by Trent Busch, Marvin Evans and Susan Ludvigson. As a sample the editor selected these lines from "Georgia Evening" by Faye Altman:

> Light the fire.
> There will be time tonight for neighbors
> and guitar picking.
> Someone will tell a story of their childhood

Pendragon is about 85 pgs., digest-sized, perfect-bound and publishes approximately 15% of poetry received. Press run is 700. **Subscription: $8. Sample postpaid: $4. No previously published poems or simultaneous submissions. Cover letter with brief bio required. Reads submissions September 15 through June 15. Seldom comments on rejections. Reports in 2-3 months. Pays 2 copies. Acquires first rights.** The editors award an annual $50 prize for the best poetry of the year. Contributions here are not only from English departments but also from poets with varied careers and backgrounds (i.e. counselors, political scientists, journalists). The work is appealing because the authors focus on a number of critical concerns, including racism and diversity, from differing viewpoints.

PENNINE INK (I, II), % MPA The Gallery Downstairs, Burnley BB10 3JJ Great Britain, founded 1985, appears approximately every 9 months using mainly poems, a few short prose items and a few b&w illustrations. "Local and dialect items welcome plus worldwide." They want **"poetry up to 40 lines maximum. Consider all kinds. Contributions from poets having links with Lancashire/N. England welcome. This does not exclude others."** As a sample the editor selected these lines (poet unidentified):

> *Between her quick pillow and the world*
> *Between the deeper secret and the shore*
> *Colliding waves shattered glass mountains hurled*
> *And heaved their burden from the ocean floor.*

The editor says it is 44 pgs., A3, with b&w illustrated cover, a few small local ads and 3 or 4 b&w graphics. They receive about 300 items a year, use approximately 40. Press run is 300. Single copy: £1 sterling. **Sample postpaid: £1 and SAE. Previously published poems and simultaneous submissions OK. Cover letter preferred. Seldom comments on rejections. "Contributors whose works are accepted receive one free copy if SAE sent."** Reviews small press poetry books in about 200 words. Open to unsolicited reviews. Poets may also send books for review consideration.

PENNINE PLATFORM (II), Ingmanthorpe Hall Farm Cottage, Wetherby, W. Yorkshire LS22 5EQ England, phone 0937-64674, founded 1973, poetry editor Brian Merrikin Hill, appears 3 times a year. The editor wants **any kind of poetry but concrete ("lack of facilities for reproduction"). No specifications of length, but poems of less than 40 lines have a better chance. "All styles — effort is to find things good of their kind. Preference for religious or sociopolitical awareness of an acute, not conventional kind."** They have published poetry by Elizabeth Bartlett, Anna Adams, John Ward, Ian Caws, John Latham and Geoffrey Holloway. As a sample the editor selected these lines from "A Vision of Cabez De Vaca" by Cal Clothier:

> *Blanched to a skin manned by bones,*
> *we have blood and our breathing*
> *to prove we are men, and the hungry light*
> *jerking our eyes. We are down to mercy,*
> *gratitude, love, down to humanity.*

The 6×8, 48-page journal is photocopied from typescript, saddle-stapled, with matte card cover with graphics, circulation 400, 300 subscriptions of which 16 are libraries. They receive about 300 submissions/year, use about 30, have about a 6-month backlog. Subscription: £7 for 3 issues (£10 abroad; £25 if not in sterling). **Sample postpaid: £2. Submit 1-6 poems, typed. Reports in about a month. No pay. Acquires first serial rights. Editor occasionally comments on rejections.** Reviews books of poetry in 2,500 words, multi-book format. Open to unsolicited reviews. Poets may also send books for review consideration. Brian Hill comments, "It is time to avoid the paradigm-magazine-poem and reject establishments—ancient, modern or allegedly contemporary. Small magazines and presses often publish superior material to the commercial hyped publishers."

PENNSYLVANIA ENGLISH (II), Penn State-Erie, Erie PA 16563, founded 1988 (first issue in March, 1989), contact poetry editor, is "a journal sponsored by the Pennsylvania College English Association." They want poetry of **"any length, any style."** The journal is magazine-sized, saddle-stapled, and appears twice a year. Press run is 300. Subscription: $15, which includes membership in PCEA. **Submit 4-5 typed poems. Do not submit mss in the summer. They consider simultaneous submissions but not previously published poems. Reports in 1 month. Pays 2 copies.**

THE PENNSYLVANIA REVIEW (II), English Dept., 526 CL, University of Pittsburgh, Pittsburgh PA 15260, phone (412)624-0026, founded 1985, editor Julie Parson-Nesbitt. This ambitious semiannual journal was described by *Choice* as "a fine small literary magazine." **There are no restrictions on subject matter, style or length, although they do not want to see "light verse or greeting card verse."** They have published poetry by Nance Van Winckel, Jim Daniels, Maggie Anderson, Sharon Doubiago, Lawrence Joseph, Debra Bruce, Sonia Sanchez and translations of Karl Krolow by Stuart Friebert. As a sample the editor selected these lines from "Live Remote" by Dorothy Barresi:

> *. . . Me? I hate myself.*
> *I could be me at thirteen or eighteen*
> *but I am fat, six,*
> *deeply aware that we are given the world and each other*
> *and no wonder we're lonely.*

It is a handsome magazine, 7×10, 80 pgs., flat-spined, professionally printed on heavy stock with graphics, art and ads, glossy card cover with b&w illustration. Circulation is approximately

1,000 with 350 subscriptions. Subscription: **$10 for 2 issues. Sample postpaid: $5. Writers should submit 3-6 poems, typewritten only. Cover letter with brief 3-line bio (publishable if work is accepted) required. Submission deadlines are November 30 for Spring issue, April 1 for Fall issue. Submissions are not accepted between May 1 and September 1. Submissions are reported on in 2-3 months. Pays 2 copies.** Staff reviews books of poetry and fiction. Send books for review consideration.

THE PENUMBRA PRESS (II), 920 S. 38th St., Omaha NE 68105, phone (402)346-7344, founded 1972, poetry editors Bonnie O'Connell and George O'Connell, publishes "contemporary literature and graphics in the tradition of fine arts printing." Their books are "designed, illustrated (unless otherwise indicated), hand printed from hand-set type, and bound by the proprietor," Bonnie O'Connell. All are limited editions, including hard and soft cover books, chapbooks, postcards and theme anthologies. They have published poetry by David St. John, Sam Pereira, Brenda Hillman, Debora Greger, Peter Everwine, Laura Jensen, Norman Dubie and Rita Dove. As a sample the editor selected these lines from "Cool Dark Ode" by Donald Justice:

> *When the long planed table that served as a desk*
> *was recalling the quiet of the woods*
> *when the books, older, were thinking farther back,*
> *to the same essential stillness . . .*

Query with 5-6 samples, some personal background and publication credits. Simultaneous submissions OK. Editor sometimes comments on rejections. Send SASE for catalog to order samples or inquire at university libraries (special collection) or through the distributor, Nebraska Book Arts Center, 124 Fine Arts Bldg., University of Nebraska-Omaha, Omaha NE 68182.

PEOPLENET (I, IV-Specialized, love/romance), P.O. Box 897, Levittown NY 11756, phone (516)579-4043, founded 1987, editor/publisher Robert Mauro, is a newsletter **for disabled people focusing on dating, love and relationships.** The editor wants **"poetry on relationships, love and romance only. The length should remain 10-20 lines. 3 or 4 poems at a time. We publish beginners, new poets. Prefer free verse, a lot of good imagery—and very little rhyme."** As a sample the editor chose these lines from his poem "When All That Blooms Are Roses":

> *Mornings are not mornings*
> *when all that blooms are roses:*
> *dewy petals opening, blushing*
> *in the wind; a hand*
> *plucks a flower, a finger*
> *touches a bud that didn't*
> *bloom and never will.*

Peoplenet appears 3 times a year and is 12-16 pgs., magazine-sized, offset, using graphics and ads. Press run is about 200, with that many subscriptions. **Subscription: $18. Sample copy: $3. Poems should be double-spaced with name and address on each page. No simultaneous submissions. Editor comments on good but rejected mss. Reports "immediately." Pays tearsheets only. Acquires first rights.** (Copies of the newsletter, which contains personal ads, go to subscribers only. Free brochure available.) He says, "We want to publish poems that express the importance of love, acceptance, inner beauty, the need for love and relationship, and the joy of loving and being loved."

PEP PUBLISHING; LOVING MORE (I, IV-Themes, group marriage), P.O. Box 6306, Captain Cook HI 96704-6306, founded 1984, editor Ryam Nearing. *Loving More* is a quarterly that "publishes articles, letters, poems, drawings and reviews related to polyfidelity, group marriage and multiple *intimacy*." They use **"relatively short poems, though a quality piece of length would be considered, but topic relevance is essential. Please no swinger or porno pieces. Group marriage should not be equated with group sex."** It is 14 pgs., magazine-sized, few ads. Circulation 500. **Subscription: $30 a year. Sample: $4 to poets. Ms should be "readable." Considers simultaneous submissions. Editor comments on rejections "sometimes—if requested." Responds "ASAP," delay to publication is 2-6 months.** Open to unsolicited reviews. Poets may also send books for review consideration. **Pays 1 copy.** The editor says, "Writers should read our publication before submitting, and I emphasize no swinger or porno pieces will be published."

PEQUOD: A JOURNAL OF CONTEMPORARY LITERATURE AND LITERARY CRITICISM (III, IV-Translations), Dept. of English, Room 200, New York University, 19 University Place, New York NY 10003, contact poetry editor, is a semiannual literary review publishing **quality poetry, fiction, essays and translations.** They have published poetry by David Baker, Lynda Hull and Sam Hamill. It is a professionally-printed, digest-sized, 200+ pgs., flat-spined magazine with glossy card cover. Subscription:

$12 annually. **Sample postpaid: $5. Reads submissions September 15 through May 15 only.** Staff reviews books of poetry.

PERCEPTIONS (IV-Women), 1530 Phillips, Missoula MT 59802, founded 1982, poetry editor Temi Rose, is a "small prize-winning **women's poetry magazine for the promotion and development of women's consciousness of peace and hope and freedom to be."** They have recently published poetry by Chocolate Waters, Lyn Lifshin and Edna Kovacs. As a sample the editor selected these lines by Marcia Arrieta:

> eyes like birds
> and hips for babies
> a woman who is
> not afraid to wander
> into mountains alone

Perceptions is 30 pgs., digest-sized, photocopied from typescript with colored paper cover and comes out 3 times a year. They publish about 250 of 1,000 poems received/year. Press run is 100 for 30 subscribers of which 3 are libraries. Subscription: $15. **Sample postpaid: $5. They consider simultaneous submissions and previously published poems. Guidelines available for SASE. Reports in 1-3 months. Pays 1 copy.** *Perceptions* ranked #1 in the "Open Markets" category of the June 1993 *Writer's Digest* Poetry 60 list. This category ranks those publications most open to both free and formal verse.

PEREGRINE: THE JOURNAL OF AMHERST WRITERS & ARTISTS (II); AWA CHAPBOOK SERIES (V), Box 1076, Amherst MA 01004, *Peregrine* founded 1983, Amherst Writers & Artists Press, Inc., 1987. **Open to all styles, forms and subjects except greeting card verse.** They have published poetry by Jane Yolen, Walter McDonald and Barbara Van Noord. As a sample the editors selected these lines by Carol Edelstein:

> Nothing winged at the hummingbird feeder
> But us girls, taking the sun, and notes.
> We lean, like young broccoli, slightly forward
> Under green whirligig hats, ready
> To catch words, and if possible, whole sentences
> As they dart up from the ground.
> Shrubbery tells only the truth,
> For this we are grateful . . .

Peregrine is 70+ pgs., digest-sized, flat-spined, professionally printed, with matte card cover. Their press run is 500. **Sample postpaid: $4.50. Cover letter required with submissions.** "We try to publish twice a year, but sometimes cannot because of finances. We may hold poems for several months, so we encourage simultaneous submissions." **Pays contributor's copies.** The AWA Chapbook Series publishes handsome collections on a cooperative basis. **"No unsolicited chapbook manuscripts, please. Query only."**

PERMAFROST (II, IV-Regional), Dept. PM, English Dept., University of Alaska, Fairbanks AK 99775-0640, phone (907)474-5237, founded 1977. "Editors change annually." *Permafrost* is a biannual journal of poems, short stories, essays, reviews, b&w drawings and photographs. "We survive on both new and established writers, and hope and expect to see your best work (we are not the Siberia of mediocre poetry). We publish any style of poetry provided it is conceived, written, revised with care; favor poems with strong, unusual images or poems with abstraction backed up by imagery; both must have universal applications. We discourage 'tourist poetry' which rarely works because of its hackneyed imagery and lack of universal theme; encourage poems about Alaska and by Alaskans, but they are works and writers at ease with their setting. We also encourage poems about anywhere and from anywhere. We are not a regional publication, but in order to support contemporary Alaskan literature, we publish reviews only of work by Alaskan authors or publishers." They have published poetry by Wendy Bishop, Jerah Chadwick, Leslie Leyland Fields, Linda Gregg, Patricia Monaghan, John Morgan, Peggy Shumaker and Kim Stafford. The digest-sized journal is 100+ pgs., flat-spined, professionally printed, two-color paper cover with b&w graphics and photos, has a circulation of 500 with 100 subscriptions of which 20 are libraries. Subscription: $7. **Sample postpaid: $4. Submit no more than 5 poems, neatly typed; considers simultaneous submissions but "expects to be told." Does not accept submissions between April 1 and August 1. Deadlines are December 1 and April 1.** Editors comment only on mss that have made the final round and then are rejected. Depth of comments vary. **Guidelines available for SASE** ("although most are listed here"). Return time is 1-3 months; "longer if work was submitted well before deadline and is under serious consideration." **Pays 2 copies, reduced contributor rates on others.**

‡PERMEABLE PRESS; PUCK: THE UNOFFICIAL JOURNAL OF THE IRREPRESSIBLE (III), 900 Tennessee #15, San Francisco CA 94107-3014, phone (415)648-2175, founded 1984, editor Brian Clark, associate editor Kurt Putnam. *Puck* is a biannual designed to "provoke thought, dialog. Contents: reviews, stories, essays, poems." **As for poetry they want "radical reinterpretations of the 'accepted.' No restrictions as to style, length, etc. No love poems."** They have recently published poetry by B. Subraman and Hugh Fox. As a sample they selected these lines from "Tarot of Nature" by Susan Luzarro:

> Yesterday the queen of wands came to me. She was painted with honey-colored locks
> to perpetuate the myth that nature, like christ, was blonde. Lay me down, *she said.*
> Do not reverse me & I will offer you this sunflower, beneath it—a promise—the
> bud of an unknown flower. I spit on the solace of nature, *I said*, give me a happy life.

The editors describe *Puck* as 80 pgs., 8½×11, offset and saddle-stapled with color covers. They accept 1% or less of poetry received. Press run is 500 for 200 subscribers of which 4 are libraries, 100 shelf sales. Single copy: $6.50; subscription: $12/2 issues. **Previously published poems OK; no simultaneous submissions. Cover letter required. "SASE must be big enough to accomodate return of all material submitted."** Send SASE for guidelines. Reports in 1-4 weeks. Pays 2 copies. Acquires first North American serial or reprint rights. "Subsequent publication should mention *Puck*." They add, "Current issue contains 30 (out of 80) pages of reviews. We review anything, everything." Permeable Press also publishes 2 paperbacks and **4 chapbooks/year. Query first with sample poems and cover letter with brief bio and publication credits. Replies to queries in 1 month, to mss in 1-2 months. Pays 50+ author's copies for chapbooks.**

PERSEA BOOKS (III), 60 Madison Ave., New York NY 10010, phone (212)779-7668, editor Michael Braziller, publishes books of **"serious" poetry.** They have published poetry by Thylias Moss, Paul Blackburn and Les Murray. They publish 4-6 paperbacks and the same number of hardbacks/year. **Reports in 4-6 weeks. Payment "negotiable."**

THE PET GAZETTE (IV-Themes), 1309 N. Halifax, Daytona Beach FL 32118, phone (904)255-6935, founded 1984, editor Faith A. Senior, a quarterly journal that wants **"poems about animals, nature and/or ecology. Simple and easily understood, in behalf of animals overall, short poems preferred."** She does not want "haiku, and ultra-contrived and/or highly intellectual poetry." Poets frequently in *The Pet Gazette* are Vincent Hathaway, John Coulbourn, Rhoda Rainbow, Johnathan Russell, C. David Hay and S. Mary Ann Henn. As a sample the editor selected "Fat" (poet unidentified):

> I walked into a house
>   full of fat people
> to find hungry/skinny
>   cats & a dog
>   ribs showing
>
>   no food or water
>   for them in sight

The Pet Gazette is magazine-sized, offset on 60 lb. opaque paper, in many type styles with b&w photos and drawings, saddle-stapled with b&w photos on cover, inserts from various pro-animal organizations. Circulation is 300. Subscription: $12.50 yearly. **Sample postpaid: $2.50. Cover letter required with submissions. Reporting time is "upon receipt," and time to publication is** "sometimes a year, though usually much sooner." Pays copies.

PETRONIUM PRESS (V, IV-Regional), 1255 Nuuanu Ave., 1813, Honolulu HI 96817, founded 1975, editor Frank Stewart. Petronium is a small press publisher of poetry, fiction, essays and art—**"primarily interested in writers in and from Hawaii, but will publish others under special circumstances.** Interested in fine printing, fine typography and design in limited editions." They publish chapbooks, trade books, limited editions, broadsides and "other ephemera," but they **"are not accepting unsolicited material at this time."** They publish 3-6 poetry chapbooks/year, with an average page count of 32, flat-spined paperbacks. The editor says, "Query letters are welcome, with SASE." He replies to queries within 3 weeks and reports on mss in the same amount of time. He has "no special requirements," but will not accept photocopied or dot-matrix mss or discs. "Payment of authors is negotiated

The double dagger before a listing indicates that the listing is new in this edition. New markets are often the most receptive to submissions.

differently for each book." Buys all rights. Returns rights by request. The editor does not comment on rejections "unless the material is exceptionally good." He says, "We are not really for beginners nor, in general, for people outside the Pacific region. We are not strict regionalists, but believe in nurturing first the writers around us. Beginning writers might do well to look for publishers with this same philosophy in their own cities and states rather than flinging their work to the wind, to unknown editors or to large publishing houses. All writers should consider supporting quality publishing in their own region first." Some of Petronium's books are distributed by the University of Hawaii Press (2840 Kolowalu St., Honolulu HI 96822) and may be obtained from them; "send for their literature catalog or ask for our titles specifically."

PHASE AND CYCLE (II); PHASE AND CYCLE PRESS (V), 3537 E. Prospect, Fort Collins CO 80525, phone (303)482-7573, founded 1988, poetry editor Loy Banks. *Phase and Cycle* is a poetry magazine published semiannually. **"We look for short-to-moderate-length poems of all kinds, especially those that set out 'the long perspectives open at each instance of our lives' (Larkin). We are looking for poetry that will pass technical inspection in the academic community."** They have recently published poetry by Steven Reese, Rhina Espaillat, Kenneth Pobo, Therese Arceneaux, Rod Farmer, David Starkey and Mary Balazs. The magazine is digest-sized, 48 pgs., saddle-stapled. **Sample postpaid: $2.50. Guidelines available for SASE. "A brief bio note may accompany poems." No simultaneous submissions or previously published poems. Editor sometimes comments on rejections. Reports in 5-10 weeks. Pays 2 copies. Acquires first rights only.** Open to unsolicited reviews. Poets may also send books for review consideration. Phase and Cycle Press has published two poetry chapbooks, **Breathing In The World** by Bruce Holland Rogers and Holly Arrow and **Out of Darkness** by Mary Balazs. **"At present we accept inquiries only. No book manuscripts."**

PHILOMEL BOOKS (III), 200 Madison Ave., New York NY 10016, phone (212)951-8700, an imprint founded in 1980, editor-in-chief Paula Wiseman. Philomel Books publishes 2-3 paperbacks, 40-45 hardbacks and 5-10 chapbooks/year. They say "since we're a children's book imprint, **we are open to individual poem submissions—anything suitable for a picture book. However, publication of poetry collections is usually done on a project basis—we acquire from outside through permissions, etc. Don't usually use unpublished material."** They have published poetry by Edna St. Vincent Millay and Walt Whitman. **Previously published poems and simultaneous submissions OK. Cover letter—including publishing history—required. Replies to queries in 1 month, to mss in 2. Pay is negotiable.**

‡THE PHLEBAS PRESS (V), 2 The Stables, High Park, Oxenholme, Kendal, Cumbria LA9 7RE United Kingdom, founded 1990, publishes **up to 3 chapbooks/year.** They publish **"poems that take an independent or imaginative view of the human condition and human spirit. No middle-class sentimentality or poems that could double as adverts."** They have recently published chapbooks of poetry by A.C. Evans and Martin A. Hibbert. As a sample the editor selected these lines from "Vertical Time" in In the Absence of a Summit by Norman Jope:

> Every dome of crystal, however distantly, reflects a
> murder. White and red, the tissues line the spotless aisles
> of supermarkets. Muzak 'happens'— a theme from Offenbach,
> played digitally, asserts the act of liquidation.

> Now, we work to work, we live to live, and only
> cheque-cards hold us to our promises . . .

"Unfortunately we cannot accept any submissions at present. Recommended poets are asked for submissions." Phlebas normally expects authors to buy back, and distribute, most of the print run.

‡PHOEBE (IV-Women/feminism), Women's Studies Dept., S.U.N.Y. College at Oneonta, Oneonta NY 13820, phone (607)431-2014, founded 1988, editor Kathleen O'Mara, is a biannual feminist journal containing scholarly articles, short fiction and poetry, book reviews and occasional artwork. **As for poetry, they have "no specifications vis-a-vis form, length, etc. Seek material describing, either directly or vaguely, women's experiences/realities. Nothing sexist, racist or homophobic."** They have recently published poetry by Lyn Lifshin, Wanda Coleman, Rita Ann Higgins, Zoe Angelesey, Edith Pearlman and Kyoko Mori. *Phoebe* is 130-140 pgs., approximately 7×9, professionally printed and perfect-bound, coated card cover with artwork. They receive about 220 poems a year, use approximately 18-20%. Press run is 500 for 125 subscribers of which 25% are libraries, 100 shelf sales. **Single copy: $7.50; subscription: $15. Sample postpaid: $5. Previously published poems OK; no simultaneous submissions. Submissions preferred August 15 through April 15. Seldom comments on rejections. Send SASE for guidelines. Reports within 3 months. Pays 2 copies.** Reviews books of poetry in 500-2,000 words.

PHOENIX BROADSHEETS; NEW BROOM PRIVATE PRESS (II), 78 Cambridge St., Leicester, England LE 3 0JP, founded 1968, poetry editor Toni Savage, publishes chapbooks, pamphlets and broadsheets on a small Adana Horizontal Hand Press. The editor wants poetry which is **"descriptive—not too modern, not erotica or concrete, up to 12 lines (for the sheets)**. Also some personal background of the poet." He has published poems by Spike Milligan, Sue Townsend, Sue Mackrell, Lucy Banwell, Chris Challis, Roger McGough and Arthur Caddick. Toni Savage selected these sample lines from "All" by Alix Weisz:

> one dragonfly
> one heart peering behind
> one alcoved shore
> one universe awaiting
> one sunrise more

The broadsheets are letterpress printed on tinted paper (about 5×8) with graphics. "Some sheets are hand coloured." **Submit no more than 3 poems with cover letter giving "personal backgrounds and feelings." Poet receives 20-30 copies.** "My *Broadsheets* are *given* away in the streets. They are given away to Folk Club, Jazz Club and theater audiences. The broadsheets started as a joke and now are up to 380+. Now much sought after and collected. This is my hobby and is strictly part-time. Each small booklet takes 1-3 months, so it is impossible to ascertain quantities of publications." *Phoenix Broadsheets* may be obtained by sending adequate postage, approximately $1.50.

‡PHOENIX PRESS (V), 22 Pintail Dr., Pittsburgh PA 15238, founded 1982, poetry editors Heywood Ostrow and Robert Julian, publishes 2-3 books a year **but accepts no unsolicited mss.** They have published poetry by Robert Julian and Sebastian Barker. As a sample here are the opening lines from **XII** by George Barker:

> Ah most unreliable of all women of grace
> in the breathless hurry of your leave taking
> you forgot, you forgot for ever, our last embrace

PIEDMONT LITERARY REVIEW; PIEDMONT LITERARY SOCIETY (II, IV-Form), Rt. 1, Box 512, Forest VA 24551, founded 1976; poetry editor Gail White, 1017 Spanish Moss Lane, Breaux Bridge LA 70517 (and **poetry submissions should go to her address**). If you join the Piedmont Literary Society, $12 a year, you get the quarterly *Review* and a quarterly newsletter containing much market and contest information. Gail White says, **"I consider all types of poems—am partial to rhyme—up to 48 lines. Each issue has a special section for oriental forms with an emphasis on haiku."** Each also includes short fiction. She does *not* want: "smut or overly romantic verse." She has published poetry by Harold Witt, Julie Kane, John Brugaletta and Jared Carter. As a sample the editor selected these lines by Martha Bosworth:

> Our lives fall open, all that's left of them,
> under the gulls' wing-scattered requiem;
> building on waste, for wastrels to destroy,
> the landfill cities rise: here is my Troy,
> and my Jerusalem.

The quarterly is digest-sized, saddle-stapled, offset from typescript, matte card cover, using b&w graphics, with 40-50 pgs. of poetry in each issue, circulation 300 with 200 subscriptions of which 10 are libraries. It's a modest-looking publication with well-made formal and free verse poems. **Sample postpaid: $3. Welcomes all submissions.** She "sometimes" **comments on rejections. Send SASE for guidelines. Reports within 3 months. Pays copies. Acquires first rights.** Briefly reviews "a few" books of poetry, "mostly contributors' books," in accompanying newsletter. They sponsor occasional contests; write to Forest, VA address for rules and dates. Gail White advises, "Strive for clarity first, then beauty, then profundity. Poems must have meaning for people who can't see inside your head."

PIG IRON (II, IV-Themes), Dept. PM, P.O. Box 237, Youngstown OH 44501, phone (216)747-6932, founded 1975, poetry editor Jim Villani, is a literary annual devoted to special themes. They want poetry **"up to 300 lines; free verse and experimental; write for current themes."** Forthcoming themes: The Family: Tradition & Possibility and Jazz Tradition. **They do *not* want to see "traditional" poetry.** They have recently published poetry by Wayne Hogan, Laurel Speer, Louis McKee, Lloyd Mills, Marian Steele, Hugh Fox and John Pyros. As a sample the editor selected these lines by Joan Kincaid:

> I'm yelling my goose call
> bahonk bahonk
> to make her laugh

> *because there are no geese*
> *when we're surprised*
> *by an eerie screech-purr*
> *echoing across the dark water*
> *I bahonk again*
> *and a white swan launches*
> *into the night a song*
> *I've never heard.*

Pig Iron is magazine-sized, flat-spined, 128 pgs., typeset on good stock with glossy card cover using b&w graphics and art, no ads, circulation 1,000. They have 200 subscriptions of which 50 are libraries. Single copy: $10.95. Subscription: $9/1 year, $16/2 years. **Sample postpaid: $4. No simultaneous submissions. Send SASE for guidelines. Reports in 3 months, 12-18 months delay to publication. Pays $5/poem plus 2 copies. Buys one-time rights.** They sponsor the annual Kenneth Patchen Competition. Send SASE for details. The editor says, "We want tomorrow's poetry, not yesterday's."

THE PIKESTAFF FORUM; PIKESTAFF PUBLICATIONS, INC.; THE PIKESTAFF PRESS; PIKESTAFF POETRY CHAPBOOKS (II, IV-Children, teens), P.O. Box 127, Normal IL 61761, phone (309)452-4831, founded 1977, poetry editors Robert D. Sutherland, James R. Scrimgeour and James McGowan, is "a not-for-profit literary press. Publishes a magazine of national distribution, *The Pikestaff Forum*, and a poetry chapbooks series." They want "substantial, well-crafted poems; vivid, memorable, based in lived experience—Not: self-indulgent early drafts, 'private' poems, five finger exercises, warmed over workshop pieces, vague abstractions, philosophical woolgathering, 'journal entries,' inspirational uplift. The shorter the better, though long poems are no problem; we are eclectic; welcome traditional or experimental work. We won't publish pornography or racist/sexist material."** They have published poetry by Gayl Teller, J.W. Rivers, Lucia Cordell Getsi, Frannie Lindsay and Fritz Hamilton. *The Pikestaff Forum* is an annual newsprint tabloid, 40 pgs., "handsome, open layout. Trying to set a standard in tabloid design. Special features: poetry, fiction, commentary, reviews, young writers (7-17 in a special section), editors' profiles (other magazines), The Forum (space for anyone to speak out on matters of literary/publishing concern)." Circulation 1,100 with 200 subscriptions of which 5 are libraries. They receive 2,000-3,000 submissions/year, use 3%, have a year's backlog. Subscription: $10/6 issues. **Sample postpaid: $2. "Each poem should be on a separate sheet, with author's name and address. We prefer no simultaneous submissions—but if it is, we expect to be informed of it." No more than 6 poems/submission. Send SASE for guidelines. Reports within 3 months. Pays 3 copies.** Reviews books of poetry if published by small presses or self-published. Open to unsolicited reviews. Poets may also send books to Jim Elledge, Review Editor, Dept. of English, Illinois State University, Normal IL 61761 for review consideration. This is a lively publication and editors typically comment on rejected work that has merit. All forms and styles appear here, but published verse usually displays a high degree of craft that somehow enhances content (always insightful or unusual). **Query with samples and brief bio for chapbook submission. Replies to queries in 2 weeks, to submission (if invited) in 3 months. Pays 20% of press run for chapbooks.** They advise, "For beginners: don't be in a hurry to publish; work toward becoming your own best editor and critic; when submitting, send only what you think is your very best work; avoid indulging yourself at the expense of your readers; have something to say that's worth your readers' life-time to read; before submitting, ask yourself, 'Why should *any* reader be asked to read this?'; regard publishing as conferring a responsibility."

PIKEVILLE REVIEW (II), Humanities Dept., Pikeville College, Pikeville KY 41501, founded 1987, editor James Alan Riley, who says: **"There's no editorial bias though we recognize and appreciate style and control in each piece. No emotional gushing."** *PR* appears once yearly, accepting about 10% of poetry received. Press run is 500. **Sample postpaid: $3. No simultaneous submissions or previously published poetry. Editor sometimes comments on rejections. Send SASE for guidelines. Pays 5 copies.** They also sponsor contests.

PINCHGUT PRESS (V), 6 Oaks Ave., Cremorne, Sydney, NSW 2090 Australia, founded 1948, publishes Australian poetry but is not currently accepting poetry submissions. **Send SASE for catalog to order samples.**

THE PINEHURST JOURNAL; PINEHURST PRESS (I, II), P.O. Box 360747, Milpitas CA 95036, founded 1990, editor Michael K. McNamara, is a quarterly. **"Generally open, 24-line limit. Some sort of rhyme, meter, assonance, consonance or alliteration is a plus as well as good haiku. No religious, porno or dire despair. Work should be original, no reprints."** They have recently published poetry by Lyn Lifshin and Joanna M. Weston. As a sample the editor selected these lines from "Edges And Imprints" by Pearl Bloch Segall:

> *In the eternity*

of this ocean
whose waves crash
to defy the edge of sound
even as we whisper
in the night, I
detect the imprint
of wind-whipped shore.

It is magazine-sized, 44 pgs., offset from typescript, saddle-stapled. Of 600 poems/year received they use 100. Press run 225 for 100 subscribers of which 1 is a library, 20 shelf sales. Subscription: $17. Sample postpaid: $4.75. Submit no more than 6 poems at a time. "We feel a cover letter is an asset/vehicle of introduction for all contributors and should be employed. It is not a requirement, however." Send SASE for guidelines. Reports in 6-8 weeks. Pays 1 copy. Acquires one-time rights. Staff reviews books of poetry. Send books for review consideration.

THE PIPE SMOKER'S EPHEMERIS (I, IV-Themes), 20-37 120th St., College Point NY 11356, editor/ publisher Tom Dunn, who says, "The *Ephemeris* is a limited edition, irregular quarterly for pipe smokers and anyone else who is interested in its varied contents. Publication costs are absorbed by the editor/publisher, assisted by any contributions—financial or otherwise—that readers might wish to make." They want poetry with themes related to pipes and pipe smoking. Recent issues range from 76-96 pgs., offset from photoreduced typed copy, colored paper covers, with illustrations, saddle-stitched. The editor has also published a collection covering the first 15 years of the *Ephemeris*. It is 41 pgs., hardcover. Cover letter required with submissions; include any credits. Staff also reviews books of poetry. Send books for review consideration.

‡PIRATE WRITINGS; PIRATE WRITINGS PUBLISHING (I, II, IV-Science fiction/fantasy), 53 Whitman Ave., Islip NY 11751, founded 1992, editor and publisher Edward J. McFadden. *Pirate Writings* is a biannual "collection of contemporary, energetic, socially relevant, imaginative poems and short stories by 'under' published writers. Our theme is anything from the down deep to the way out." They want all forms and styles of poetry "within our genres—literary (humorous or straight), fantasy, science fiction, mystery/suspense and adventure. Best chance is 20 lines or less. No crude language or excessive violence. No pornography, horror, western or romance. Poems should be typed with exact capitalization and punctuation suited to your creative needs." They have recently published poetry by John Grey, Richard Novak and Jacie Ragan. As a sample the editor selected these lines from "Changes" by Herb Kauderer:

modern man
changed the world
to fill his needs

Someday man
must find the strength
to mold both
to match his dreams

Pirate Writings is 40-50 pgs., digest-sized and perfect-bound with coated card cover with art and b&w art throughout. They receive about 100 poetry submissions a year, use approximately 15-25 poems. Press run varies. Single copy: $3.50; subscription: $6.50 for 2 issues. Sample postpaid: $3. Previously published poems accepted from "well established poets only." Simultaneous submissions OK. Cover letter required; include credits, if applicable. Often comments on rejections. Send SASE for guidelines. Reports in 1-2 months. Pays 1-2 copies. Acquires first North American serial or one-time rights. Also "reserves the right to print in anthology." Query regarding reviews of chapbooks. Pirate Writings Publishing publishes chapbooks through various arrangements. Query first. Replies to queries in 1 month, to mss in 6 months. Poets may have to share publication costs. For sample chapbooks, write for flyer.

PITT POETRY SERIES; UNIVERSITY OF PITTSBURGH PRESS; AGNES LYNCH STARRETT POETRY PRIZE (II), 127 N. Bellefield Ave., Pittsburgh PA 15260, founded 1968, poetry editor Ed Ochester, publishes "poetry of the highest quality; otherwise, no restrictions—book mss minimum of 48 pages." Simultaneous submissions OK. They have recently published books of poetry by Richard Garcia, Larry Levis, Sharon Doubiago, Robley Wilson and Liz Rosenberg. Their booklist also features such poets as Peter Meinke, Leonard Nathan, Sharon Olds, Ronald Wallace, David Wojahn and Belle Waring. "Poets who have not previously published a book should send SASE for rules of the Starrett competition ($12.50 handling fee), the *only* vehicle through which we publish first books of poetry."

The Starrett Prize consists of cash award of $2,500 and book publication. Poets who have previously published books should query.

THE PITTSBURGH QUARTERLY (II), 36 Haberman Ave., Pittsburgh PA 15211-2144, phone (412)431-8885, founded 1990, editor Frank Correnti, who says, "Our first criterion is good writing with the variety of content that is common to a broad community interest. Generally, writing with narrative and real-life elements. We don't want doggerel or most rhyme." They have recently published poetry by Marc Jampole, Ellen Smith, Kristin Kovacic, Robert Cooperman and Lynne Hugo de Courcy. As a sample the editor selected these lines from "Tender Meat" by June Hopper Hymas:

> . . . the sounds and the smells of the lives of the poet
> and the poet's ancestors. I haven't thought

> to ask my children if they talk to janitors or sometimes feel
> like sawdust: null brown bits, cellulose without form.

> Tonight is a hot night; when you hung up on me,
> I did not call you back. I am reclaiming myself.

It is digest-sized, 76 pgs., professionally printed, saddle-stapled with matte card cover. Press run 700 for 250 subscribers of which 10 are libraries, 300 shelf sales. Subscription: $12 ($14 Canadian). **Sample postpaid: $5. "We will reply by letter to queries." Editor often comments on submissions. Reports in 2-3 months. Pays 2 copies. Acquires first North American serial rights.** Published books are reviewed as space is available, 1-2/issue. Accepts reviews of 4-6 pages, double-spaced. Send books for review consideration. "We are responding in part to the network of writers whose crafted creativity made the magazine possible, but also we are attempting to provide a readership that will connect more strongly to the community of poets and writers through this quarterly." *The Pittsburgh Quarterly* now sponsors an annual prize for poetry: The Sara Henderson Hay Prize. Entry requires current subscription or renewal and is limited to 3 poems up to 100 lines each. Deadline: July 1. Winner receives a cash award and publication of the winning poem in the fall issue.

PIVOT (II), 250 Riverside Dr. #23, New York NY 10025, phone (212)222-1408, founded 1951, editor Martin Mitchell, is a poetry annual that has published poetry by Philip Appleman, William Matthews, Eugene McCarthy, Craig Raine, W.D. Snodgrass and Robert Wrigley. It is a handsome 6×9, flat-spined, professionally printed magazine with glossy card cover. Press run is 1,200. Single copy: $5. **Reads submissions January 1 through June 1 only. Reports in 2-4 weeks. Pays 2 copies.**

THE PLACE IN THE WOODS; READ, AMERICA! (I, IV-Children), 3900 Glenwood Ave., Golden Valley MN 55422, phone (612)374-2120, founded 1980, editor and publisher Roger A. Hammer, publishes *Read, America!*, a quarterly newsletter for reading coordinators. They want **"poems for children that are understandable, under 500 words, unusual views of life. Also, foreign-language poems with English** X **translation. Nothing vague, self-indulgent, erotic. No navel introspection."** As a sample we selected these lines from "Circus" by Eugene C. Baggott:

> Did you ever watch the bareback riders
> As they lovingly groomed their steeds?
> Or the trapeze artist practice his catch
> While hanging by his knees?

Read, America! is 8 pgs., magazine-sized, professionally printed on yellow paper. "Pages 1-4 are distributed free to some 10,000 programs. Four additional pages go only to readers who support us as subscribers." Most poems appear in the "Subscribers only" insert but poets do not have to be subscribers to submit. Subscription: $20. **No previously published poems; simultaneous submissions OK.** Cover letter "optional and appreciated for insight into poet's background and interests or goals." **Always comments on rejections. Pays $10 on publication. Buys all rights.**

PLAINS POETRY JOURNAL; STRONGHOLD PRESS (II, IV-Form), P.O. Box 2337, Bismarck ND 58502, founded 1982, editor Jane Greer, publishes "meticulously crafted, language-rich poetry which is demanding and accessible. We love rhyme and meter and poetic conventions used in vigorous and interesting ways. I strive to publish unpublished poets as well as old pros. I do *not* want broken-prose 'free verse' or greeting card-type traditional verse. I want finely-crafted poetry which uses the best poetic conventions from the past in a way that doesn't sound as if it were *written* in the past. No specifications. I'm especially interested in compelling long poems and essays on poetry. Our credo is, 'no subject matter is taboo; treatment is everything.' " They have recently published poetry by Julia Budenz, Rhina P. Espaillat, Harold McCurdy, Jack Butler, Johnny Wink, Paul Ramsey and Frederick Turner. As a sample, Jane Greer selected these lines from "Species: Zealot" by Gerald George:

> His handshake is tarantular,

> *his stance is antlike and his eyes*
> *glow the way a wasp's abdomen*
> *glows before its victim dies*

Plains Poetry Journal is semiannual, digest-sized, 44 pgs. (of which about 40 are poetry), saddle-stapled, professionally printed on tinted paper with matte card cover, graphics, circulation 500, 400 subscriptions of which 50 are libraries. They receive 1,500-2,000 submissions/year, use about 100, seldom have more than a 6-month backlog. Subscription: $9/year, $18/5 issues. Sample postpaid: $4.50. Submit "not less than 3 poems, not more than 10 at a time. Hand-written and simultaneous submissions OK." Comments on rejections "occasionally, especially if the ms is especially promising or if I think the poet is a child or teen." Send SASE for guidelines. Reports in 1 week to 3 months. Pays copies. Acquires first or reprint rights. Has ceased book publishing. This remains one of the best outlets for formal poetry and otherwise well-crafted free verse displaying verve, energy and insight. If unfamiliar with this publication, request a sample copy. Editor Jane Greer also has a clear vision of what she wants expressed frankly in her writer's guidelines. She comments, "An author is *crazy* not to submit simultaneously. Do enclose a SASE, and *don't* enclose an explanation of the poems. Above all understand that a poet never 'gets good,' he or she just keeps *working* at it. If you're willing to do this, I am, too."

PLAINSONG (II), Box 8245, Western Kentucky University, Bowling Green KY 42101, phone (502)745-5708, founded 1979, poetry editors Frank Steele, Elizabeth Oakes and Peggy Steele, is an occasional poetry journal. "Our purpose is to print the best work we can get, from known and unknown writers. This means, of course, that we print what we like: poems about places, objects, people, moods, politics, experiences. We like straightforward, conversational language, short poems in which the marriage of thinking and feeling doesn't break up because of spouse-abuse (the poem in which ideas wrestle feeling into the ground or in which feeling sings alone—and boringly—at the edge of a desert). Prefer poems under 20 lines in free verse. No limits on subject matter, though we like to think of ourselves as humane, interested in the environment, in peace (we're anti-nuclear), in the possibility that the human race may have a future." They have published poetry by William Matthews, Ted Kooser, William Stafford, Del Marie Rogers, Betty Adcock, Julia Ardery and Abby Niebauer. The magazine is 48-56 pgs., 6×9, professionally printed, flat-spined, matte color card cover with photos and graphics, print run 600 with 250 subscriptions of which 65 are libraries. They use about 100 of the 2,000 submissions received each year. Subscription: $7. Sample postpaid: $3.50. "We prefer poems typed, double-spaced. Simultaneous submissions can, of course, get people into trouble, at times." Send SASE for guidelines. Reports "within a month, usually." Pays copies. Staff reviews books of poetry. Send books for review consideration to Frank Steele.

PLAINSONGS (II), Dept. PM, Dept. of English, Hastings College, Hastings NE 68902, phone (402)463-2402, founded 1980, editor Dwight C. Marsh, a poetry magazine that "accepts manuscripts from anyone, considering poems on any subject in any style." They have recently published poetry by Robert Cooperman, Mary D'Angelo, Allison Joseph and William Stafford. As a sample the editor selected these lines from "Only One Promise" by Mary Winters:

> *Stay please stay with us so*
> *begged early people of fire*
> *here's your favorite dry straw*
> *bark peeling tiniest of twigs*

Plainsongs is digest-sized, 40 pgs., saddle-stapled, set on laser, printed on thin paper with b&w illustrations, one-color matte card cover with black logo. The magazine is financed by subscriptions, which cost $9 for 3 issues/year. Sample copies: $3. Submit poems with name and address on each page. Ms deadlines are August 15 for fall issue; November 15 for winter; March 15 for spring. Notification is mailed about three weeks after deadlines. Pay is two copies and a year's subscription, with three award poems in each issue receiving small monetary recognition. "A short essay in appreciation accompanies each award poem." Acquires first-time rights.

PLANTAGENET PRODUCTIONS (V), Westridge, Highclere, Nr. Newbury, Royal Berkshire RG15 9PJ England, founded 1964, director of productions Miss Dorothy Rose Gribble. Plantagenet issues cassette recordings of poetry, philosophy and narrative (although they have issued nothing new since 1980). Miss Gribble says, "Our public likes classical work . . . We have published a few living poets, but this is not very popular with our listeners, and we shall issue no more." They have issued cassettes by Oscar Wilde, Chaucer and Pope, as well as Charles Graves, Elizabeth Jennings, Leonard Clark and Alice V. Stuart. The recordings are issued privately and are obtainable only direct from Plantagenet Productions; write for list. Miss Gribble's advice to poets is: "If intended for a listening public, let the meaning be clear. If possible, let the music of the words sing."

THE PLASTIC TOWER (II), P.O. Box 702, Bowie MD 20718, founded 1989, editors Carol Dyer and Roger Kyle-Keith, is a quarterly using **"everything from iambic pentameter to silly limericks, modern free verse, haiku, rhymed couplets — we like it all! Only restriction is length — under 40 lines preferred."** They have published poetry by "more than 325 different poets. It wouldn't be fair to single anyone out!" As a sample we selected these lines from "After Mother's Day" by Linda Ashear:

> *I am tipsy on tulips,*
> *high on hibiscus,*
> *bombed on baby's breath.*
> *Out of control, I collide*
> *with an African violet in the vestibule,*
> *down dahlias on the deck,*
> *tipple begonias masquerading as camelias.*

It is digest-sized, 38-54 pgs., saddle-stapled; "variety of typefaces and b&w graphics on cheap photocopy paper." Press run is 200. Subscription: $8/year. Copy of current issue: $2.50. **"We'll send a back issue free for a *large* (at least 6 × 9) SAE with 75¢ postage attached."** Simultaneous submissions OK. **Editors comment on submissions "often." Send SASE for guidelines. Reports in 2 months. Pays 1-3 copies.** Open to unsolicited reviews. Poets may also send books for review consideration. Roger Kyle-Keith says, *"The Plastic Tower* hurtles into a fifth year of publication as the same old unpretentious little rag. Our advice remains the same, too: don't put more importance on those rejection or acceptance slips than the paper they're photocopied on. So let's laugh and shout and have fun and especially enjoy the incredible coolness of cognitive thought."

PLOUGHSHARES (III), Emerson College, 100 Beacon St., Boston MA 02116, phone (617)578-8753, founded 1971. **The magazine is "a journal of new writing edited on a revolving basis by professional poets and writers to reflect different and contrasting points of view."** Recent editors have included Carolyn Forché, Gerald Stern, Rita Dove and M.L. Rosenthal. They have published poetry by Donald Hall, Li-Young Lee, Robert Pinsky, Brenda Hillman and Thylias Moss. The triquarterly is 5½ × 8½, 250 pgs., circulation 4,200. They receive approximately 2,000 poetry submissions/year. Since this influential magazine features different editors with each issue, content varies. The issue edited by Carolyn Forché, for example, displays a variety of styles and forms with strong voices and messages. As always with prestigious journals, competition is keen. Response times can be slow because submissions are logged inhouse and sent to outside guest editors. Subscription: $19 domestic; $24 foreign. **Sample postpaid: $8.95. "Due to our revolving editorship, issue emphasis and submission dates will vary. We suggest you read a few issues and send a #10 SASE for writer's guidelines before submitting." Simultaneous submissions acceptable. Do not submit mss from April 1 to August 1. Reports in 3-5 months. Pays $20 minimum per poem, $10/printed page per poem, plus 2 contributor copies and a subscription.** Work published in *Ploughshares* appears in **Best American Poetry 1992.** The magazine itself ranked #10 in the "Poet's Pick" category of the June 1993 *Writer's Digest* Poetry 60 list. This category ranks those publications in which poets said they would most like to see their work published.

THE PLOWMAN (I, II), Box 414, Whitby, Ontario L1N 5S4 Canada, phone (416)668-7803, founded 1988, editor Tony Scavetta, appears 3 times/year using **"didactic, eclectic poetry; all forms."** As a sample we selected the beginning lines of "The Cancer Victim" by Bonnie Colby:

> *The stones on the plains*
> *Don't think about the ones on the sidehills,*
> *Who rest precariously at best,*
> *Gripping to earth, forcing their wills*
> *To hang on even when one by one*
> *The stones around them fall away*

The Plowman is a 56-page, newsprint tabloid which accepts 70% of the poetry received. Press run is 15,000 for 1,200 subscribers of which 500 are libraries. Single copy: $7.50; subscription: $10. **Sample free. Previously published poems and simultaneous submissions OK. Cover letter required. No SASE necessary. Always comments on rejections. Guidelines available free. Reports in 1 week.** Reviews books of poetry. They offer monthly poetry contests. Entry fee: $2/poem. 1st prize: 50% of the proceeds; 2nd: 25%; 3rd: 10%. The top poems are published. "Balance of the poems will be used for anthologies." **They also publish 125 chapbooks/year. Replies to queries and mss in 1 week. Requires $20 reading fee/book. Pays 20% royalties.**

THE PLUM REVIEW (II), P.O. Box 3557, Washington DC 20007, founded 1990, editors M. Hammer and Christina Daub, appears twice a year. **"We are open to original, high quality poetry of all forms, lengths, styles and subject matters. Our only criterion is excellence."** They have recently published poetry by Robert Bly, Laurie Sheck, Donald Hall, Marge Piercy, Billie Collins, Larry Levis, Jon

Stallworthy and William Stafford. As a sample the editor selected these lines from "Erythronium Americanum" by Brooks Haxton:

> *What-was-to-be kept coming back with leaves*
> *to the willow, with late sleet, with a familiar smell*
> *of bark, with mud between the frost and the old ice.*
>
> *Downed-over scales of pussy willow bud now broke,*
> *first into tatters, then full catkins of white silk,*
> *and all, all that much sooner for it, fell apart.*

It is approximately 100 pgs., flat-spined, professionally printed, 6 × 9. Editors seem to favor well-made free verse, emphasizing voice and line. Press run is 1,000. **Sample postpaid: $5. "Absolutely no simultaneous submissions. Include a brief bio indicating previous publications and/or awards." Seldom comments on rejections. Send SASE for guidelines. Reports in 1 month. Pays 1 copy.** They welcome unsolicited reviews (up to 15 pgs., single or multi-book format) of recently published books of poetry and interviews with prominent poets. Poets may also send books for review consideration. They sponsor a reading series and creative writing workshops for the elderly and the handicapped. This magazine says that it is "so delicious" — a takeoff on William Carlos Williams' famous lyric "This Is Just To Say"? — and it is, too, featuring the best work of top-name poets and relative newcomers. In addition, *The Plum Review* was awarded a grant from the Council of Literary Magazines and Presses for outstanding content and design.

POCAHONTAS PRESS, INC.; MANUSCRIPT MEMORIES (V), P.O. Drawer F, Blacksburg VA 24063-1020, phone (703)951-0467, founded 1984, president Mary C. Holliman, publishes chapbook collections of poetry, but is temporarily not considering new mss "because I am trying to finish those already accepted." Inquire before submitting. **"Most of the poetry books I have published have been subsidized to some extent by the author. So far one of those authors' books has sold enough copies that the author has received a significant reimbursement for his investment. We continue to market all of our books as aggressively as possible. The idea is to make a profit for both of us (though we have yet to do so)."** She offers editorial critiques for $40/hour. She has published books by Leslie Mellichamp, Lynn Kozma, Mildred Nash, Preston Newman and Elaine Emans. As a sample the editor selected these lines by Cecil J. Mullins:

> *In the East, time has been divorced*
> *From things. No clocks hem the hours*
> *In, and time, not being firmly forced,*
> *Slops around.*

Pays 10% royalties on all sales receipts, 10 free copies of book, and any number of copies at 50% for resale or "whatever use author wishes. If author helps with printing costs, then an additional percentage of receipts will be paid." Mary Holliman adds, "There's much more good poetry being written than is getting published, and I only wish I could publish more of it."

POEM; HUNTSVILLE LITERARY ASSOCIATION (II), English Dept., University of Alabama at Huntsville, Huntsville AL 35899, founded 1967, poetry editor Nancy Frey Dillard, appears twice a year, consisting entirely of poetry. **"We are open to traditional as well as non-traditional forms, but we favor work with the expected compression and intensity of good lyric poetry and a high degree of verbal and dramatic tension. We welcome equally submissions from established poets as well as from less known and beginning poets. We do not accept translations or previously published works. We prefer to see a sample of 3-5 poems at a submission, with SASE. We generally respond within a month. We are a nonprofit organization and can pay only in copy to contributors. Sample copies are available at $5."** They have published poetry by Robert Cooperman, Andrew Dillon and Scott Travis Hutchison. As a sample the editor selected these lines from "Mister Varsey" by Sally Jo Sorensen:

> *With the myths*
> *his methods excelled:*
> *The Odyssey, for instance,*
> *became more than just the same old song*
> *about some guy who'd left his wife and kid*
> *for the guys. Mr. Varsey fetched a bow*
> *out of his great, fabled closet*
> *and asked the gentlemen of the class —*
> *as he called them — to see who might be*
> *Penelope's true suitor. None could*
> *match the task, so he exclaimed*
> *blind Homer walks again!*
> *until I raised my hand*

Poem is a flat-spined, 4⅜ × 7¼, 90-page journal that contains more than 60 poems (mostly lyric free verse under 50 lines) generally featured one to a page on good stock paper with a clean design and a classy matte cover. Circulation is 400 (all subscriptions of which 90 are libraries). Overall, it's a good market for beginners and experienced poets who pay attention to craft.

POEMS FOR A LIVABLE PLANET (I, IV-Nature/ecology, translations), 1235½ N. Larrabee St., Los Angeles CA 90069, founded 1990, editor Jeffrey Dellin, appears "once or twice a year" using "**poems dealing with the beauty/peril of the Earth & Her creatures. Any form, language given equal consideration; length limit 50 lines. Non-English should include translation.**" As a sample the editor selected these lines from "1989 Last Day" by C.B. Follett:

> *Tossed on a corner at rite's end.*
> *Nailed to a cross. Forlorn*
> *and dying among curbside fellows.*
> *5, 10, 15 years grown.*
> *Cut off at the knees.*

Sample postpaid: $3.75. No previously published material. Reads submissions January 1 through April 30 only. Reports in 2-3 months. Pays 1 copy. The ecology theme of this publication is one of the most important of our time. The poetry is insightful and, overall, well-executed; craft does not suffer because of politics. If you have environmentally sound verse, consider this a good market. The editor says, "I rely on my passion. Try not to be too obvious, yet do say something. Irony is very welcome. We strive for the fine line."

POET; COOPER HOUSE PUBLISHING INC.; JOHN DAVID JOHNSON MEMORIAL POETRY AWARDS; IVA MARY WILLIAMS INSPIRATIONAL POETRY AWARDS; AMERICAN CHAPBOOK AWARDS; AMERICAN COLLEGE & UNIVERSITY POETRY AWARDS; AMERICAN HIGH SCHOOL POETRY AWARDS; THE AMERICAN LITERARY MAGAZINE AWARDS (I, II), P.O. Box 54947, Oklahoma City OK 73154, founded 1984, managing editor Peggy Cooper, editor Joy Hall, poetry editor Michael Hall. "*Poet* is one of the largest commercial publishers of poetry in the U.S. and is **open to submissions from writers at all levels of experience. Contributors receive a free copy of the issue in which their work appears.**" Michael Hall says, "I look for poems that **display wit, knowledge and skill . . . verse that employs arresting images, poems that make the reader think or smile or even sometimes cry.**" They have recently published poetry by Lewis Turco and H.R. Coursen. As a sample the editor selected the opening stanzas of "Marshwind Song" by Patricia A. Lawrence:

> *The music of the marsh has my heart pinned*
> *To tidal flats and skittle dancing crabs.*
> *A hanging gull is tossed on beats of wind.*
>
> *Her lonely mewing, plaintive, swordlike, stabs*
> *Each note that wells to fullness like a tide*
> *Until she streaks the sky. A talon grabs*
>
> *Another note that haunts me . . .*

It is magazine-sized, professionally printed, 56-80 pgs. with glossy cover, saddle-stitched. Of about 7,000-10,000 submissions, they use a little fewer than 5%. Subscription: $20/year. Subscribers receive free the giant "Forms of Poetry" poster and the quarterly *Poet's Digest* newsletter. **Sample copy of *Poet*, postpaid: $5.50 or "call your bookstore where you can purchase it for $4 ($5 Canada) if it's in stock." For guidelines, send 1 loose first class stamp with request.** For poetry publishing kit (while supplies last), send 3 loose first class stamps with request. **Previously published poems and simultaneous submissions OK. Editor sometimes comments on rejections. Reports within 3-6 months. Pays 1 copy.** Reviews books of poetry. Open to unsolicited reviews. Poets may also send books for review consideration to Joy Hall, P.O. Box 22047, Alexandria VA 22304. They sponsor annual chapbook awards (up to 30 pgs., $20 entry fee, grand prize: publication in book form and 50 copies). John David Johnson Memorial Poetry Awards (prizes of $200, $100, $50, special merit and honorable mention awards, award certificates, publication and a copy of the magazine in which the winning poems appear to all winners. Additionally, all contestants receive the "Forms of Poetry" poster. Entry fee: $5/poem. March 1 and September 1 deadlines). Iva Mary Williams Inspirational Poetry Awards (prizes of $100, $50, $25, special merit and honorable mention awards, award certificates, publication and a copy of the magazine in which the winning poems appear to all winners. Additionally, all contestants receive the master form for a "Submission Journal." Entry fee: $3/poem. February 1 and August 1 deadlines). American College & University Poetry Awards (prizes of $200, $100, $50, each divided equally between winning student and teacher, special merit and honorable mention awards, award certificates, publication and copy of the magazine in which the winning poems appear to all winners. Additionally, all teachers receive the "Forms of Poetry" classroom poster. No entry fee. Rules and official entry forms may be requested with 3 loose first class stamps). American

CLOSE-UP

Let Your Muse Be Tuned

"For the Piano Tuner"

He deserves something better than money
for making the wires waver
like sitars or ring keen as thin glass.
Again and again his wrench twists each note
higher, and again a little higher,
and again, until the voice begins to test itself
against the tightening steel and the throat
feels the awful stress of music, the strain
of each perfect sound held waiting,
as if without effort, the way a small stem
holds its heavy flower,
the room filling with sprays and bouquets,
cups humming on their hooks in the pantry,
everything testing its pitch—pictures and
windowpanes, the silverware in its muffled case—
the whole house coming into tune
as he finishes by playing something new,
something he says he just made up,
and I begin to dance.

Neal Bowers

Photo by Douglas E. Smith

(originally published in *The Hudson Review*)

"I've often suspected that much of my poetry comes from a kind of musical frustration," says premier poet and editor Neal Bowers. "I don't play an instrument. Consequently, I find myself trying to make music with language."

He has been hugely successful in that endeavor. Bowers' poems appear regularly in such prestigious publications as *The New Yorker, Poetry, Harper's* and *The Sewanee Review.* Among the awards he has received are a National Endowment for the Arts fellowship in poetry, the Frederick Bock Prize (from *Poetry*) and the *Yankee* Poetry Prize. He has three collections of poems: **The Golf Ball Diver** (New Rivers Press, 1983), **Lost in the Heartland** (Cedar Creek Press, 1990) and **Night Vision** (BkMk Press, 1992).

The above poem, "For the Piano Tuner," appears in his last book. His goal in this composition was to replicate "the sustained, repetitive process of tuning the piano," Bowers says. "Consequently, most of the poem is a single sentence."

He came up with the idea for the poem when a professional tuner worked on his wife's piano. "The whole job usually takes about two hours, and Nancy usually leaves me to monitor the operation. This means she escapes the repetitive key-pounding and wire-tightening while I drift about the house unable to hear or think of anything else. On the occasion of this poem, it occurred to me that I was being tuned along with the piano, rude instrument that I am. In fact, the entire house seemed to be involved somehow in the search for tone and key."

In addition to composing poems, Bowers teaches English and poetry workshops at Iowa State University and edits *Poet & Critic*, a well-respected journal. In workshops and at the magazine, Bowers is open to any style or topic, as long as the work conveys a sense of discovery.

The most common weakness, he says, is the poet's failure to trust the writing process. "Too often," he notes, "writers seem bent on willing a poem to happen, and it shows.

"The poems that work best are those that surprise the writer during the process of composition, that take her somewhere she couldn't have imagined if she hadn't written the poem. In short, the poem is not a repository of thought—it is the *thought* itself."

To guard against verse that sounds forced, Bowers advises poets to compose "without having the slightest idea what you may write about. Be patient, and let the process engage."

The editorial process at *Poet & Critic* is vigorous and competitive but also humane, Bowers says. "Although it's hard for many writers to believe, editors typically view themselves as helpers, and most take no pleasure in rejecting manuscripts. For me, writing rejection notes is demoralizing, and it's the one part of the business I truly dislike."

Bowers says he reads submissions closely and tries to write a personal note in response to each writer. "It's a time-consuming approach, but I believe editors and writers ought to be engaged in a dialogue."

You can find that dialogue in any issue of *Poet & Critic*, which was founded on the concept of being "a workshop in print." The magazine used to publish poems accompanied by brief critiques. In the 1960s and early 1970s, "workshops were not the norm," Bowers says. When he took over the editorship in 1987, however, the "workshop" concept began to dominate American poetry, particularly in creative writing departments. Bowers saw no need to duplicate the concept in the magazine, so he changed the focus.

To live up to the "critic" part of the magazine's name, Bowers accepts one or two critical essays for each issue. "Their focus is on the contemporary scene, and they usually take the form of essay reviews of current collections or commentaries on poetics," he says.

Without exception, essayists and reviewers are poets *and* critics. "This reflects a personal bias," says Bowers, "a belief on my part that poets are better qualified than theoreticians or 'pure' scholars to talk about poetry."

At *Poet & Critic*, the dialogue begins between poet and editor . . . and ends in each issue with the critic having the last word.

—*Michael J. Bugeja*

> 66 The poems that work best are those that surprise the writer during the process of composition, that take her somewhere she couldn't have imagined if she hadn't written the poem. 99
>
> —Neal Bowers

High School Poetry Awards (prizes of $100, $50, $25, each divided equally between winning student and teacher, special merit and honorable mention awards, award certificates, publication and copy of the magazine in which the winning poems appear to all winners. Additionally, all teachers receive the "Forms of Poetry" classroom poster. No entry fee. Rules and official entry forms may be requested with 3 loose first class stamps). The American Literary Magazine Awards are engraved plaques for Best Overall, Best Editorial Content and Best Cover Design. Special merit and honorable mention award certificates may also be given. The top three winners will also receive free advertising in *Poet*. All contestants receive a T-shirt. $30 entry fee/title. Deadline: December 31. Send 1 loose first class stamp with request for rules and entry form.

POET & CRITIC (II), 203 Ross Hall, Iowa State University, Ames IA 50011, phone (515)294-2180, founded 1961, editor Neal Bowers, appears 3 times a year. This is one of the best literary magazines for the money; it is packed with some of the most readable poems being published today—all styles and forms, lengths and subjects. The editor shuns elite-sounding free verse with obscure meanings and pretty-sounding formal verse with obvious meanings. *Poet & Critic* is 6×9, 48 pgs., staple bound, professionally printed, matte card cover with color, circulation 400, 300 subscriptions of which 100 are libraries. Subscription: $18. **Sample postpaid: $8. "We don't require a cover letter, but we prefer one." Submit 4-6 poems. "We do not read mss between the end of May and mid-August." Reports in 2 weeks (often sooner). Pays 1 copy. Acquires first rights.** The magazine also includes review-essays usually focusing on the works of one poet. "We assign reviews following a query." Poets may also send books for review consideration.

POET LORE (II), The Writer's Center, 4508 Walsh St., Bethesda MD 20815, founded 1889, managing editor Sunil Freeman, executive editor Philip Jason, is a quarterly dedicated "to the best in American and world poetry and objective and timely reviews and commentary. We look for **fresh uses of traditional form and devices, but any kind of excellence is welcome. The editors encourage narrative poetry and original translations of works by contemporary world poets."** They have published poetry by Sharon Olds, John Balaban, William Heyen, Walter McDonald, Reginald Gibbons and Howard Nemerov. *Poet Lore* is 6×9, 80 pgs., perfect-bound, professionally printed with matte card cover. Circulation includes 600 subscriptions of which 200 are libraries. Editors are open to all styles (as long as the work is well-crafted and insightful), leaning toward lyric and narrative free verse with an emphasis on voice. They receive about 3,000 poems in freelance submissions/year, use about 125. Subscription: $15. Single copy: $4.50 plus $1 postage. **Sample postpaid: $4. Submit typed poems, author's name and address on each page. Reports in 3 months. Pays 2 copies.** Reviews books of poetry. Open to unsolicited reviews. Poets may also send books for review consideration.

‡POET PAPERS; THE RECORD SUN (II, IV-Subscribers), P.O. Box 528, Topanga CA 90290, founded 1969. *The Record Sun* is a 3- to 6-page quarterly tabloid which uses **quality poetry, mostly by its 7,000 subscribers. Sample: $2.** Poet Papers publishes collections of poetry, mostly solicited. **Always send SASE if you want a reply.**

THE POETIC KNIGHT: A FANTASY ROMANCE MAGAZINE (I, IV-Fantasy, romance), 110 S. West St., Columbiana OH 44408, founded 1990, editor Michael While, appears 4 times/year. **They want "fantasy poetry that exemplifies the classical romantic in all of us. Accept poetry from haiku to ballad length as well as fiction under 5,000 words. No profanity or explicit sex. Like to see work based on very human characters. Looking for more poetry with action bent to it and something that tells a specific story."** They have recently published poetry by Carl Heffley and William Robertson. As a sample the editor selected these lines from "The Ocean Tryst" by Jessica Amanda Salmonson:

> There standing in the gate or crack
> A damsel clad in green and black
> Her eyes half shut, her hair adrift-
> Around her brilliant rainbows shift.

It is 40-52 pgs., magazine-sized, laser set with full color cover, saddle-stapled. They accept on a "30 to 1 ratio and we get 50-60 submissions a week." Press run 300 for 100 subscribers of which 10 are libraries, 150 shelf sales. Subscription: $20/4 issues. **Sample postpaid: $5. Submit 3-5 poems with cover letter. Send SASE for guidelines. Pays 1 copy. Acquires first North American serial rights.** Editor "tries to comment on all submissions and make everyone who writes to us feel at home."

‡POETIC LICENSE; HATHAWAY-MILLER PUBLICATIONS (I), 13 Cebold Dr., Montgomery IL 60538, phone (708)897-3363, Hathaway-Miller Publications founded 1992, *Poetic License* founded 1993, editor/publisher Deena Miller. *Poetic License* appears 4 times a year using all kinds of poetry, articles, book reviews, b&w line drawings, photos and ads. It also includes a mailbox section for correspondence. They are **"open to all forms of poetry. Keep it under 40 lines, any genre. 'Make me feel!'** Nothing obscene or anything so abstract that it becomes obscure. I like analytical stuff." As a sample of the kind of poetry she is seeking, the editor selected these lines from her own poem, "Vulnerable," published in *Poetic Page*:

> Rock me
> Gently in your lyings —
> Let hypocrisy rest east
> On your careless fingertips or
> Thrusts of weaknesses and dyings —
> Leave my belly soft with white/ Blinding
> As an act of birth.

The editor describes *PL* as 8½×11, desktop-published and comb bound with cover art and graphics. Press run is 100. Single copy: $3; subscription: $12/year. **Sample postpaid: $4. Submit poems with $1/poem reading fee. Previously published poems and simultaneous submissions OK. Cover letter with brief bio and credits required. Often comments on rejections. For an additional $1/poem the editor will provide "a private written critique containing suggestions and/or offering helpful advice." Send SASE for guidelines. Reports in 4-6 weeks. Pays 1 copy. Acquires first or reprint rights.** Reviews chapbooks of poetry in 250 words or less, single format. Open to unsolicited reviews. Poets may also send books for review consideration. Hathaway-Miller Publications is a chapbook publishing service. **"You pay costs, books are yours." Query first with sample poems and cover letter with brief bio and publication credits. Replies to queries and mss in 4-6 weeks. If interested, write for samples.** The editor says, "Spend time developing your craft. Read as much poetry as you can! Learn the basics. Attend workshops or public readings. Best yet, find a writers group! Writers groups offer support and feedback — two important elements for a writer's growth! I am after quality, not quantity. I watch for depth and conciseness. Make me think and feel! Don't be trite or didactic, ever."

POETIC PAGE (I); OPUS LITERARY REVIEW (II), P.O. Box 71192, Madison Heights MI 48071-0192, phone (313)548-0865, *Poetic Page* founded 1989, *Opus Literary Review* founded 1993, editor Denise Martinson. *Poetic Page* appears bimonthly. **Each issue has a contest, $1/poem fee, prizes of $30, $20 and $10. All poetry published is that of contest winners, and some poets receive invitations to appear on their own page. "All forms are used except explicit sex, violence and crude. 30 lines."** They have published poetry by Marian Ford Park, Pearl Bloch Segall, Alice Mackenzie Swaim, Phil Eisenberg, T. Kilgore Splake, Glenna Holloway and John Grey. As a sample the editor selected her poem "Edward Scissorhands":

> He usually cuts pieces from the whole,
> reveals hidden hearts and love.
> Once he found frozen fragments
> laced with confusion. A cold
> reminder that truth can sting,
> burn a dry-ice awareness
> on the verge of his extinction.
> But he lives and learns,
> continues to shape his world
> in whatever form fits illusion.

Poetic Page is 36 pgs., magazine-sized, desktop-published. Press run is 250-350, sent to libraries, universities, editors and subscribers. Subscription: $15. **Sample postpaid: $3. Simultaneous submissions and previously published poems OK. Cover letter required. Send SASE for guidelines. Nonsubscribers receive 1 copy.** The editor says, "We look for poetry that has something to say. No trite rhyme. Only the very best poems are selected each issue. First place is featured on its own page. We now use more articles, tidbits, poet interactions and fillers. We pay $5 for articles, $10 for cover art, but must be of the highest quality. We ask poets to send us copies of their poetry books for our 'Review' section. Just because we are listed under the I category, does not mean that we are an easy magazine to be published in. We want poetry that is well written, poetry that demands to be read. Send your best." *Opus Literary Review* is a biannual that publishes **poetry only. No specifications as to form, length, style, subject matter or purpose.** They have recently published poetry by Rudy Zenker, Leonard Cirino, Daniel Gallik, John Grey and Patricia A. Lawrence. As a sample, the editor selected these lines from "My Mother's Third Call On A Day Of Sleet And December Falling" by Lyn Lifshin:

> as if the whiteness was
> gauze wrapped over the
> mouth of someone dying
> and she had to slash it
> with a last word, or
> Monday was a blank

> *sheet of paper only my*
> *words would cling to.*

Opus Literary Review is digest-sized, saddle-stitched, desktop-published, with matte cover. Subscription: $10. **Sample postpaid: $5. No previously published poems or simultaneous submissions. Cover letter required. All accepted poets are listed with bio. Editor often comments on rejections. Send SASE for guidelines. Reports in 1 month. Pays 1 copy. Acquires first rights.** The editor says: "We want poetry that will last the ages. Poetry that is intelligent, well thought out. Use strong verbs and nouns and let your reader feel your work by showing, not telling. If you want to write a poem about a flower, go ahead. But make that flower unique—surprise us. Give us your best work; we want to publish it. But beginners beware, no trite rhyme here. However, we will publish a well-written rhyme if the rhyme is the poem, not the word endings. Free verse is what we prefer."

POETIC SPACE: POETRY & FICTION (I), P.O. Box 11157, Eugene OR 97440, founded 1983, editor Don Hildenbrand, is a literary magazine with emphasis on contemporary poetry, fiction, reviews, interviews and market news. Accepts poetry and fiction that is **"well-crafted and takes risks. We like poetry with guts. Would like to see some poetry on social and political issues. Erotic and experimental OK."** They have recently published poetry by Crawdad Nelson, Sesshu Foster, Spenser Reese, Keith A. Dodson, Susan Holahan, Albert Huffstickler, Arthur W. Knight, Patricia McDonald and Thomas Strand. As a sample the editor selected these lines by Robert Bixby:

> *Her shooting clears her.*
> > *The voice hears the war again.*
> > *To tolerate well*
> *is standing next to a broken arm.*
> > *The stray water was exterminating*
> *upon her pure shark.*

The magazine is 8½ × 11, saddle-stapled, 20-24 pgs., offset from typescript and sometimes photo-reduced. It is published twice a year. They use about 25% of the 200-300 poems received/year. Press run: 800-1,000 with 50 subscriptions of which 12 are libraries. Subscription: $10/one year, $18/two years. **Sample: $3. Send SASE for list of available back issues ($4). No simultaneous submissions or previously published poems. Ms should be typed, double-spaced, clean, name/address on each page. Editor provides some critical comments. Guidelines for SASE. Reports in 2-4 months. Pays 1 copy, but more can be ordered by sending SASE and postage.** Reviews books of poetry in 500-1,000 words. Open to unsolicited reviews. Poets may also send books for review consideration. Publishes one chapbook each spring. Recently published an Anthology: **1987-1991 Best of Poetic Space, $5.** Don Hildenbrand says, "We like poetry that takes risks—original writing that gives us a new, different perspective."

‡POETICAL HISTORIES (IV-Regional, style), 27 Sturton St., Cambridge CB1 2QG United Kingdom, founded 1985, editor Peter Riley, is a "small press publishing **poetry only.**" They publish poetry that is "British, modernist," not "concrete, experimental, translated, homely." They have recently published poetry by J.H. Prynne, John James, Denise Riley and Nicholas Moore. **They publish 8-10 hand-printed chapbooks/year averaging 8 pgs. each.** *PH* is also a contact address for The Cambridge Conference of Contemporary Poetry, which takes place annually in late April.

POETPOURRI; COMSTOCK WRITERS' GROUP INC.; SUMMER SIZZLER CONTEST (II), 907 Comstock Ave., Syracuse NY 13210, phone (315)475-0339, founded 1987, published by the Comstock Writers' Group, Inc., coeditors Jennifer B. MacPherson and Kathleen Bryce Niles, appears biannually. **They use "work that is clear and understandable to a general readership, that deals with issues, ideas, feelings and beliefs common to us all—well-written free and traditional verse. No obscene, obscure, patently religious or greeting card verse."** They have published poetry by Gayle Elen Harvey, Katharyn Howd Machan, Robert Cooperman, Susan A. Manchester and R. Nikolas Macioci. As a sample they selected these lines from "In The Blizzard" by Robert Edwards:

> *Not snow falling between us*

ALWAYS *include a self-addressed, stamped envelope (SASE) when sending a ms or query to a publisher within your own country. When sending material to other countries, include a self-addressed envelope and International Reply Coupons (IRCs), available for purchase at most post offices.*

> *but a sinking sorrow of stars—*
>
> *whole galaxies dissolving at a breath*
> *in your hair . . .*

Poetpourri is 100 pgs., digest-sized, professionally printed, perfect-bound, raised cover. Circulation 550. Subscription: $8. Sample postpaid: $4. Poems may be submitted anytime for possible publication, 3-6 at a time, name and address on each page, unpublished poems only. Cover letter with short bio of poet preferred. Return time: about 6 weeks. Editors usually comment on returned submissions. Pays copies. Acquires first North American serial rights. They offer a yearly Summer Sizzler contest with over $400 in prizes, $2/poem fee, 30-line limit.

POETRY; THE MODERN POETRY ASSOCIATION; BESS HOKIN PRIZE; LEVINSON PRIZE; OSCAR BLUMENTHAL PRIZE; EUNICE TIETJENS MEMORIAL PRIZE; FREDERICK BOCK PRIZE; GEORGE KENT PRIZE; UNION LEAGUE PRIZE; RUTH LILLY POETRY PRIZE (III), 60 W. Walton St., Chicago IL 60610, founded 1912, editor Joseph Parisi, "is the oldest and most distinguished monthly magazine devoted entirely to verse," according to their literature. "Founded in Chicago in 1912, it immediately became the international showcase that it has remained ever since, publishing in its earliest years— and often for the first time—such giants as Ezra Pound, Robert Frost, T.S. Eliot, Marianne Moore and Wallace Stevens. *Poetry* has continued to print the major voices of our time and to discover new talent, establishing an unprecedented record. There is virtually no important contemporary poet in our language who has not at a crucial stage in his career depended on *Poetry* to find a public for him: John Ashbery, Dylan Thomas, Edna St. Vincent Millay, James Merrill, Anne Sexton, Sylvia Plath, James Dickey, Thom Gunn, David Wagoner—only a partial list to suggest how *Poetry* has represented, without affiliation with any movements or schools, what Stephen Spender has described as 'the best, and simply the best' poetry being written." Although its offices have always been in Chicago, *Poetry*'s influence and scope extend far beyond, throughout the US and in over 45 countries around the world. Asked to select 4 lines of poetry "which represent the taste and quality you want in your publication" Joseph Parisi selected the opening lines of "The Love Song of J. Alfred Prufrock" by T.S. Eliot, which first appeared in *Poetry* in 1915:

> *Let us go then, you and I,*
> *When the evening is spread out against the sky*
> *Like a patient etherized upon a table;*
> *Let us go, through certain half-deserted streets . . .*

Poetry is an elegantly printed, flat-spined, 5½×9 magazine. They receive over 70,000 submissions/year, use 300-350, have a 9-month backlog. Circulation 7,000, 6,000 subscriptions of which 65% are libraries. Subscription: $25; $27 for institutions; per copy: $2.50. Sample postpaid: $3.50. Submit no more than 4 poems. Send SASE for guidelines. Reports in 2-3 months. Longer for mss submitted during the summer. Pays $2 a line. Buys all rights. Returns rights "upon written request." Reviews books of poetry in 750-1,000 words, multi-book format. Open to unsolicited reviews. Poets may also send books to Stephen Young, associate editor, for review consideration. This is probably the most prestigious poetry credit in the publishing business. In fact, *Poetry* ranked #1 in the "Poets' Pick" category of the June 1993 *Writer's Digest* Poetry 60 list. (This category ranks those publications in which poets said they would most like to see their work published.) Consequently, competition here is extraordinarily keen with more poems received in a year than there are people in some cities in your state. Yet Joseph Parisi is one of the most efficient (and discerning) editors around, and he does much to promote poetry. This is a magazine that you can buy straight off the newsstand to get a feel for the pulse of poetry each month. Seven prizes (named in heading) ranging from $100 to $1,000 are awarded annually to poets whose work has appeared in the magazine that year. *Only verse already published in Poetry is eligible for consideration and no formal application is necessary. Poetry* also sponsors the Ruth Lilly Poetry Prize, an annual award of $25,000, and the Ruth Lilly Collegiate Poetry Fellowship, an annual award of $15,000 to undergraduates to support their further studies in poetry/creative writing. Work published in *Poetry* was also selected for inclusion in **Best American Poetry 1992.**

‡POETRY & AUDIENCE; PELICANS POETRY MAGAZINE; GREAT NORTHERN UNION (I, II), School of English, University of Leeds, Leeds, West Yorkshire LJ2 9JT England, founded 1953, editor Antony Rowland. *P&A* and *PPM* each appear 2-3 times/year. Both are "general poetry journals accepting work from new and established poets. We do not discriminate against any form of poetry although there is a general move towards a more lyrical style. This said, we have and will continue to publish even the most obscure poetic forms." They have recently published poetry by Carol Ann Duffy, Ian Duhig, Peter Porter and Seamus Heaney. As a sample the editor selected these lines from "Cowrie Shells" by Graham Mort:

> *We hold our hands under water, let*

Them touch like drifting fish-bones;
The sun falls and its flattened light
Catches your eyes for a moment, blue as dusk . . .

The editor describes the 2 publications simply by saying "*P&A* is somewhat larger and more elegant." Both have press runs of 200-300 for 50 subscribers of which 10 are libraries. Subscription for either: £10 (overseas). **Sample: £1.50. "Poetry must be sent either to *P&A* or *PPM*, not both. Indicate on envelope which. Please double or at least use 1.5 spacing for all lines with triple-line spacing of stanzas. Please give birth date and place in any correspondence as well as previous publications, if applicable. No comments on rejections."** The editor of *P&A* has a small consultative council. *Pelicans* is a more personal magazine with a rotating or sometimes joint editorship. **Replies for either: 2 months. Pays 1 copy.** Open to unsolicited reviews. Poets may also send books for review consideration. They founded Great Northern Union, "which brings together the university poets of Northern England."

POETRY BREAK; BEING (I, IV-Spirituality, occult, horror), P.O. Box 891510, Temecula CA 92589-1510, founded 1988, (*Poetry Break* formerly *The Creative Urge*, founded 1984), editors and publishers Peggy and Richard Navarro. *Poetry Break* is a bimonthly magazine that publishes poetry and sometimes articles and short stories. **All subjects and styles of poetry are welcomed. There is a Youth Poetry Page for ages 5-12 and a Young Adult Poetry Page for ages 13-18.** *Being* is a quarterly "New Age, Metaphysical, magickal, wholistic health and healing journal." For *PB* the editor wants **rhyming, traditional, haiku, experimental poetry. No restriction in length.** For *Being*, "**poems, prose, haiku, experimental poetry, up to 45 lines. Poems can be erotic; no porno, however.**" They have recently published poetry by Pete McGovern, Michael R. Roth, Linda Maupin, Diane Krueger and Tom McFadden. As a sample the editors selected these lines from "Rem . . ." by Richard Navarro:

My significant other . . . Goddess Extraordinaire,
The sun in her face, gentle breeze in golden hair;
Eyes aglow with laughter and content
The wealth of pleasure . . . As God so meant.

Poetry Break is digest-sized, 32-36 pgs., sometimes illustrated with pen and ink drawings; it uses 80 to 100 poems bimonthly. Circulation is about 375. **Subscription for *Poetry Break* is $14/year. Sample postpaid: $3.50. Subscription for *Being* is $18/year. Sample postpaid: $4.50. Please make checks/money orders for samples/subscriptions payable to Peggy Talarico-Navarro. There is a reading fee for non-subscribers (refundable) of $2 (1-6 poems). "We accept handwritten submissions (legible, please)." Guidelines for both magazines are available for SASE. Reporting time is 8-14 weeks and time to publication is 4-6 months. Pays discounted copies. Acquires first North American serial rights.** The editor says, "Beginning poets are most welcome . . . surprise me . . . bend your imaginations and tell me in a cover letter why you write and your hopes and dreams. Dare to share. Read and heed the information in **Poet's Market** and you will be published eventually."

THE POETRY CONNEXION (II, IV-Specialized), Wanda Coleman and Austin Straus, co-hosts, P.O. Box 29154, Los Angeles CA 90029-0154, contact person Austin Straus. "**The Poetry Connexion" is a radio program, usually live; poets coming to the Los Angeles area make contact several months in advance and send work with SASE just as though the program were a press. "We are especially interested in poets who are planning to do readings in the Los Angeles area. Please notify us at least 1-3 months in advance for consideration as a guest on our program. Always include at least 6 poems, cover letter and vita in any submission.**" The program is heard on the first, third and fifth Saturdays of each month from 6 to 7 p.m. Its purpose is "to broaden the audience, reading and listening, for poetry in the Southern California area which is now experiencing a cultural 'boom' of sorts. We are volunteer Pacifica Radio broadcasters and do not pay." The co-hosts say, "We have a preference for the 'serious' poet who has published in recognized magazines. The poet may not necessarily have a book but must be on the verge of publishing, participating in workshops, readings, residencies, etc. We are also always most interested in poets whose lives are as committed and intense as their work."

POETRY DURHAM (II), English Dept., University of Durham, New Elvet, Durham DH1 3JT England, edited by David Hartnett, Michael O'Neill and Gareth Reeves, founded 1982, appears 3 times a year using **quality poetry and essays on modern poetry**. It is 44 pgs., digest-sized, professionally printed on good stock with glossy card cover. Circulation 300. **Subscription: £5 for 3 issues. All overseas subscriptions by international money order. Pays £12/poem.** Reviews books of poetry.

POETRY EAST (II), Dept. of English, DePaul University, 802 W. Belden Ave., Chicago IL 60614, phone (312)341-8330, founded 1980, editor Richard Jones, "is a biannual international magazine publishing poetry, fiction, translations and reviews. We suggest that authors look through back issues of the magazine before making submissions. **No constraints or specifications, although we prefer open form.**"

They have published poetry by Tom Crawford, Thomas McGrath, Denise Levertov, Galway Kinnell, Sharon Olds and Amiri Baraka. The digest-sized, flat-spined journal is 100+ pgs., professionally printed with glossy color card cover. Circulation 1,200, 250 subscriptions of which 80 are libraries. They use 60-80 pgs. of poetry in each issue. They receive approximately 4,000 freelance submissions/year, use 10%, have a 4-month backlog. Single copy: $8; subscription: $12. **Sample postpaid: $4.50. Reports in 4 months. Pays copies. Editors sometimes comment on rejections.** Open to unsolicited reviews. Poets may also send books for review consideration. This is one of the best-edited and de-signed magazines being published today. Award-winning editor Richard Jones assembles an exciting array of accessible poems, leaning toward lyric free verse with room for narrative and otherwise well-structured poems in all traditions. He occasionally schedules theme issues and selects poems accordingly. Because competition is keen, response times can exceed stated limits, particularly in the spring. *Poetry East* ranked #8 in the "Open Markets" category of the June 1993 *Writer's Digest* Poetry 60 list. This category ranks those publications most open to both free and formal verse.

THE POETRY EXPLOSION NEWSLETTER (THE PEN) (I), P.O. Box 2648, Newport News VA 23609-0648, phone (804)874-2428, founded 1984, editor Arthur C. Ford, Sr., is a "quarterly newsletter dedi-cated to the preservation of poetry." Arthur Ford wants **"poetry—40 lines maximum, no minimum. All forms and subject matter with the use of good imagery, symbolism and honesty. Rhyme and non-rhyme. No vulgarity."** He has published poetry by Veona Thomas and Rose Robaldo. *The Pen* is 12-16 pgs., saddle-stitched, mimeographed on both sides. He accepts about 80 of 300 poems received. Press run 450 for 300 subscribers of which 5 are libraries. Subscription: $12. **Send $3 for sample copy and more information. Submit maximum of 5 poems. Include $1 for reading time. Simultaneous submissions and previously published poems OK. Editor comments on rejections "sometimes, but not obligated."** Pays 1 copy. He will criticize poetry for 15¢ a word. Open to unsolicited reviews. Poets may also send books for review consideration. The editor comments: "Even though free verse is more popular today, we try to stay versatile."

POETRY FORUM (I); THE JOURNAL (IV-Subscription), 5713 Larchmont Dr., Erie PA 16509, phone (814)866-2543 (also fax: 8-10 a.m. or 5-8 p.m.), poetry editor Gunvor Skogsholm, appears 3 times a year. **"We are open to any style and form. We believe new forms ought to develop from intuition. Length up to 50 lines accepted. Would like to encourage long themes. No porn or blasphemy, but open to all religious persuasions."** As a sample the editor selected these lines (poet unidentified):

> Is it anger I see in your eyes
> When they look at mine?
> Because I see no smile or happiness
> there—merely a blank stare.
>> Is it anger I see
>> Or is it Longing for me?

The magazine is 7 × 8½, 38 pgs., saddle-stapled with card cover, photocopied from photoreduced typescript. **Sample postpaid: $3. They will consider simultaneous submissions and previously published poems. Editor comments on poems "if asked, but respects the poetic freedom of the artist." Send SASE for guidelines.** They give awards of $50, $25, $10 and 3 honorable mentions for the best poems in each issue. Acquires one-time rights. *The Journal* appears twice a year, accepts experimental poetry of any length from subscribers only. Sample: $3. Reviews books of poetry in 250 words maximum. Open to unsolicited reviews. Poets may also send books for review consideration. They offer a poetry chapbook contest. Entry fee: $9. Prize is publication and 20 copies. Send SASE for information. The editor says, "I believe today's poets should experiment more and not feel stuck in the forms that were in vogue 300 years ago. I would like to see more experimentalism—new forms will prove that poetry is alive and well in the mind and spirit of the people."

POETRY KANTO (V), Kanto Gakuin University, 1641 Kamariya-cho, Kanazawa-Ku, Yokohama 236, Japan, founded 1984, editor William I. Elliott. *Poetry Kanto* is a literary annual published by the Kanto Poetry Center, which sponsors an annual poetry conference. It publishes **well-crafted original poems in English and in Japanese.** The magazine publishes **"anything except pornography, English haiku and tanka, and tends to publish poems under 30 lines."** They are not reading mss until further notice, however, as **"special numbers are planned."** They have published work by Seamus Heaney, Desmond Egan, Shuntaro Tanikawa and Les Murray. As a sample, here is the final stanza from "A Suite . . ." by Serge Gavronsky:

> Is it perverse to be inspired
> by poems when outside
> a pine tree
> waits
> for my pen to move

in a respectful manner?

The magazine is digest-sized, nicely printed (the English poems occupy the first half of the issue, the Japanese poems the second), 60 pgs., saddle-stapled, matte card cover. Circulation is 700, of which 400 are complimentary copies sent to schools, poets and presses; it is also distributed at poetry seminars. The magazine is unpriced. **Pay is 3-5 copies.** The editor advises, "Read a lot. Get feedback from poets and/or workshops. Be neat, clean, legible and polite in submissions. *SAE with international reply coupons absolutely necessary when requesting sample copy.*"

POETRY MOTEL; SUBURBAN WILDERNESS PRESS, BROADSIDES AND CHAPBOOKS (I, II), 1619 Jefferson, Duluth MN 55812, founded 1984, editors Pat McKinnon, Bud Backen and Jennifer Willis-Long aim **"to keep the rooms clean and available for these poor ragged poems to crash in once they are through driving or committing adultery."** No specifications. They have recently published poetry by Jesse Glass, Robert Peters, Ellie Schoenfeld, Albert Huffstickler, Susan Hauser, Ligi and Todd Moore. As a sample they selected these lines from "Family Traditions" by Will Lahti:

> *when great-grandfather was 4 years old*
> *he and his brothers would play funeral.*
>
> *since matti was the youngest*
> *he had to be the corpse.*
>
> *he played this role so well that*
> *one day his brothers buried him alive . . .*

Poetry Motel appears "every 260 days" as a 7 × 8½ digest, with various covers, including wallpaper (issue 16) and chrome plated mylar (issue 10), circulation 800 (to 600 subscriptions), 52 pgs. of poetry, prose, essays and reviews. They receive about 1,000 submissions/year, take 250, have a 6- to 12- month backlog. **Sample $5.95. Submit 3-5 pgs., name and address on upper half of each page. Simultaneous submissions OK. Informal cover letter with bio credits required. Reports in 1-3 weeks. Payment varies. Acquires one-time rights.** Editors are "always glad to comment, on request." Reviews books of poetry. Open to unsolicited reviews. Poets may also send books for review consideration. They advise, "Poets should read as much poetry as they can lay their hands on. And they should realize that although poetry is no fraternal club, poets are responsible for its survival, both financially and emotionally. Join us out here—this is where the edge meets the vision. We are very open to work from 'beginners.'"

POETRY NEW YORK: A JOURNAL OF POETRY AND TRANSLATION (II, IV-Translations, themes), P.O. Box 3184, Church Street Station, New York NY 10008, founded 1985, editors Burt Kimmelman and Cheryl Fish, is an annual. They have published poetry by Wanda Coleman, Jerome Rothenberg, Enid Dame, Amiel Alcalay and Ann Lauterbach, and translations of Mallarme, Hesiod and Makoto Ooka. As a sample the editors selected these lines from "The Second Month of Separation" by Corinne Robins:

> *I don't hear or see,*
> *an ocean and your drugs are*
> *in between.*
> *The beautiful garbage birds fly the island ferry,*
> *and ocean planes criss-cross*
> *while I dream you grow beyond closed doors.*

The editors describe it as 6 × 9, perfect-bound, 80 pgs. They accept about 20% of "blind submissions." Press run: 500 for 300 shelf sales. **Some issues are on themes. "Query us first to see whether we are currently reading manuscripts. If so, send no more than five poems per submission."** Editor comments on submissions "at times." Reports in 3-4 months. Pays 1 copy. They sometimes sponsor readings.

POETRY NIPPON PRESS; THE POETRY SOCIETY OF JAPAN; POETRY NIPPON; POETRY NIPPON NEWSLETTER (II, IV-Form, translations), Ishikawa-cho 3-3-2, Mizuho-ku, Nagoya 467 Japan, phone (052)841-1714, founded 1967, poetry editors Atsuo Nakagawa and Yorifumi Yaguchi (and guest editors). *Poetry Nippon*, a quarterly, uses **translations of Japanese poems into English, poems by Western and Japanese poets, tanka, haiku, one-line poems, essays on poetry and poets, poetry book reviews, poetry news, home and abroad. They want tanka, haiku, one-line poems and poems on contemporary themes and on Japan.** They have published poetry by Toshimi Horiuchi, Naoshi Koriyama, Cliff Fyman and Alexis Rotella. As a sample the editor selected these lines by Marian Chow:

> *How much makes a lifetime?*
> *How far is birth from death?*
> *Between heaven and earth,*
> *What day is today?*

> *My cup I raise*
> *Singing a sad song to my soul.*

Poetry Nippon has a press run of 300 for 200 subscriptions of which 30 are libraries. They use 25% of the 400 submissions they receive each year, have a 6- to 12-month backlog. Single copy: $8; subscription: $29. **Sample free for 4 IRCs. Submit 2 poems, 5 tanka or 6 haiku, unpublished and not submitted elsewhere. Include name and address on each page. "Deadline March 31 for nonmembers." Send SAE with 2 IRCs for guidelines. Reports in 6 months for members. Pays copies.** Open to unsolicited reviews. Poets may also send books for review consideration. Apparently you can join the Poetry Society of Japan, receive the *Newsletter* and *Poetry Nippon* and have other benefits. For example, **the editors provide criticism "on members' mss only."** They sponsor contests for tanka and haiku and publish collections by individuals and anthologies.

POETRY NORTHWEST (II), 4045 Brooklyn NE, Seattle WA 98105, phone (206)685-4750, founded 1959, poetry editor David Wagoner, is a quarterly. The magazine is 48 pgs., 5½ × 8½, professionally printed with color card cover. It features all styles and forms. For instance, in two recent issues, lyric and narrative free verse was included alongside a sonnet sequence, minimalist sonnets and stanza patterns—all accessible and lively. They receive 20,000 poems in freelance submissions/year, use 160, have a 3-month backlog. Circulation 1,500. Subscription: $10. **Sample postpaid: $3. Occasionally editor comments on rejections. Reports in 1 month maximum. Pays 2 copies. They award prizes of $100, $50 and $50 yearly, judged by the editors.**

POETRY NOTTINGHAM; LAKE ASKE MEMORIAL OPEN POETRY COMPETITION (II); NOTTINGHAM POETRY SOCIETY (IV-Regional); QUEENIE LEE COMPETITION (IV-Membership/subscription), 39 Cavendish Rd., Long Eaton, Nottingham NG10 4HY England, founded 1941, editor Martin Holroyd, poetry editor Claire Piggott. Nottingham Poetry Society meets monthly for readings, talks, etc., and publishes quarterly its magazine, *Poetry Nottingham: The International Magazine of Today's Poetry*, which is open to submissions from all-comers. **"We wish to see poetry that is intelligible to and enjoyable by the intelligent reader. We do not want any party politics or religious freaks. Poems not more than 30 lines in length."** They have published poetry by Bert Almon, William Davey and Nikolas Macioci from the US. As a sample the editor selected these lines from "Half-Term" by Maurice Rutherford:

> *And if you've ever wondered what goes on*
> *inside the heads of men who sit on seats*
> *and ogle passers-by, come, sit with me,*
> *it's marvelous . . . fantastic's more the word!*
> *I chose at will, make this one rich, that poor . . .*

There are 30 pgs. of poetry in each issue of the 6 × 8, 36-page magazine, professional printing with occasional essays and b&w graphics, glossy art paper cover, circulation 325 for 200 subscriptions of which 20 are libraries. They receive about 1,500 submissions/year, use 120, usually have a 1- to 3-month backlog. Subscriptions: £8 ($60 for 2 years US); per copy: £2 ($8 US). **Sample postpaid: $8 or £1.75. Submit at any time 3 poems, not more than 30 lines each, not handwritten, and previously unpublished. Send SAE and 3 IRCs for stamps. No need to query but requires cover letter. Reports "within 2 months plus mailing time." Pays one copy.** Staff reviews books of poetry, but space allows only listings or brief review. Send books for review consideration. **Nottingham Poetry Society publishes collections by individual poets who were born, live or work in the East Midlands of England.** The Lake Aske Memorial Open Poetry Competition offers cash prizes, annual subscriptions and publication in *Poetry Nottingham*. Open to all. The Queenie Lee Competition is for members and subscribers only, offers a cash prize and publication.

POETRY OF THE PEOPLE (I, IV-Humor, love/romance/erotica, nature, fantasy, themes), P.O. Box 13077, Gainesville FL 32604, founded 1986, poetry editor Paul Cohen. *Poetry of the People* is a leaflet that appears once a month. **"We take all forms of poetry but we like humorous poetry, love poetry, nature poetry and fantasy. No racist or highly ethnocentric poetry will be accepted. I do not like poetry that lacks images or is too personal or contains rhyme to the point that the poem has been destroyed."** *Poetry of the People* is 8-16 pgs., about 5½ × 4⅛, stapled, sometimes on colored paper. Issues are usually theme oriented. It has a circulation between 300 and 2,300. Copies are distributed to Gainesville residents for 25¢ each. Subscription: $8/year. **Samples $4 for 11 pamphlets. Cover letter with biographical information required with submissions. "I feel autobiographical information is important in understanding the poetry." Poems returned within 3 months. Editor comments on rejections "often." Pays 5 copies. Acquires first rights.** He advises, "Be creative; there is a lot of competition out there."

POETRY PLUS MAGAZINE; GERMAN PUBLICATIONS (I, IV-Subscribers), Route 1, Box 52, Pulaski IL 62976, founded 1987, publisher/editor Helen D. German. *PPM* is a quarterly with articles about poetry, stories and poems. "**We accept all styles. Length should be no more than 24 lines. Poets can write on any subject that offers a meaningful message. We want our poets to write poems that will make the reader really think about what has been said. Reader should not have to guess at what was said. We do *not* want any holiday poems, obscene poems or sexual poems. Poems should not be indecent.**" As a sample the editor selected this poem by Robert R. Hentz:

> *Scientific thought is a process*
> *By which you reproduce*
> *In a sequence of words or symbols*
> *A chain of events in reality*
> *In such a way that when you come*
> *To the end of a train of thought*
> *You have arrived at the station.*

PPM is magazine-sized, 25-35 pgs., photocopied from typescript, bound with tape, paper cover. Subscription: $20 (includes the booklet **Poetry Profits: How to Turn Your Poems into Dollars**). Sample postpaid: $3. "**Please submit at least 5 poems for consideration.**" Send SASE for guidelines. Subscribers are paid up to $5 for outstanding poems; no payment to nonsubscribers. Offers editorial/critique service for $6/poem. They also offer two other booklets to poets and writers: **Make and Sell Your Own Line of Greeting Cards** and **How to Operate a Poetry Telegram Service.** Cost is $10 each. The editor says, *"Poetry Plus* is a fresh magazine that offers poets and writers the opportunity to see their poems in print. We want poems that are written to stimulate the deeper side of the reader. Rhymed or unrhymed, poems should offer a message that is meaningful. They should leave a memorable impression. Always send a large SASE with sufficient postage to return your unused poems. We publish both the work of our subscribers and nonsubscribers. Of course, due to limited space in each issue, subscribers get their poems published first. If you haven't been published yet or if you have, order a sample copy today and see what you've been missing in literary refreshment."

POETRY: USA QUARTERLY; NATIONAL POETRY ASSOCIATION (II, IV-Themes, translations, children/teen/young adult), 2569 Maxwell Ave., Oakland CA 94601, founded 1985, editor Jack Foley. *Poetry: USA Quarterly* is the literary organ of the National Poetry Association. "**We want poems that exhibit a depth of insight, imagination, awareness and compassion—not self-indulgent, trivial material.**" Every issue has a thematic focus: for example, love and experience, four dozen ways of looking at the moon, in praise of other muses, etc. Send SASE for upcoming themes. They have published poetry by Amy Gerstler, Mary Mackey, Diane di Prima, Neeli Chekovski and Robert Bly. As a sample the editor selected these lines from "In the Laboratory" by Ok-Koo Kang Grosjean, translated from the Korean by the author and Glen Grosjean:

> *I recite*
> *continuously*
> *the name of Amida Buddha*
> *as a zen priest*
> *suggested I should do*
> *to relieve the pain*

It is a typeset unstapled tabloid, 24 pgs., with photos, graphics and ads, circulation 10,000, distributed free "to reach 40,000 literati in the Bay Area" and available to others by subscription at $10/year. Sample postpaid: $2. **Previously published poems OK (if the editor knows). "Big backlog, active file for a year. Suggest poems under 32 lines. No SASEs. Just send photocopies— if published, contributor will get copies."** No other pay "as yet. Suggest that contributors subscribe to maintain good contact." One section of the tabloid, "Young Poets Speak Up," is devoted to poetry by children of elementary and high school age. Cover letter required with submissions for this section. Send SASE for guidelines. They are also assembling an anthology of contemporary world poetry from 6 continents, published quarterly in fine English translations and entitled *Uniting the World Through Poetry*, editor Herman Berlandt. Send SASE for information to the National Poetry Association, Bldg. D, Fort Mason Center, San Francisco CA 94123.

POETRY WALES PRESS; POETRY WALES (II, IV-Ethnic), Andmar House, Trewsfield Ind. Estate, Tondu Rd., Bridgend, Mid-Glamorgan CF31 4LJ Wales, founded 1965. *Poetry Wales*, a 72-page, 253×185mm quarterly, circulation 1,000, has a primary interest in Welsh and Anglo-Welsh poets but also considers submissions internationally. Send submissions (with SAE and IRC) to Richard Poole, editor, Glan-y-Werydd, Llandanwg, Harlech LL46 2SD Wales. Overseas subscription: £18/year. Sample: £2.50. One-page cover letter required with name, address and previous publications. Pays. Staff reviews books of poetry. Send books for review consideration to Amy L. Waek, reviews editor, Andmar House address. The press publishes books of primarily Welsh and Anglo Welsh poetry, also biography, critical works and some fiction, distributed by Dufour Editions, Inc., Box 449, Chester Springs PA 19425. They have received several Welsh Arts Council "Book of the Year" Prizes.

POETRY WLU (I, II), Department of English, Wilfrid Laurier University, Waterloo, Ontario N2L 3C5 Canada, phone (519)884-1970, ext. 2308, founded 1979, editorial contact E. Jewinski, is an annual literary magazine "with emphasis on *all* poetry and *all* prose *under* 1,000 words. **20-30 lines are ideal; but all kinds and lengths considered."** As a sample the editor selected the opening lines from "Katherine's Eye" by Bruce Bond:

> *It's the faithfulness that fools us,*
> *how its fine red vein*
> *slips under the living seam*
>
> *When Katherine lost her glass eye*
> *in the deep-end of her uncle's pool,*
> *her brothers scouted the blue*

Poetry WLU is 6½ × 8, saddle-stapled, typeset, with matte card cover using b&w art. They receive about 100-120 submissions a year, use approximately 15-20%. Press run 300. **Sample postpaid: $3. Cover letter preferred. Reads submissions September 1 through January 30 only. "When the editorial board has time, comments are made." Reports in 6-8 months. Pays 1 copy.** Staff reviews books of poetry. The magazine is published every March.

POETS AT WORK (I, IV-Subscribers), VAMC 325 New Castle Rd., Box 113, Butler PA 16001, founded 1985, editor/publisher Jessee Poet, **all contributors are expected to subscribe.** Jessee Poet says, **"Every poet who writes within the dictates of good taste and within my twenty-line limit will be published in each issue. I accept all forms and themes of poetry, but no porn, no profanity."** He has published poetry by Jaye Giammarion, Katherine Krebs, James Webb, Phil Eisenberg and Ernestine Gravely. As a sample he selected his poem "An Old Romance":

> *I almost loved you . . . did you know?*
> *Sometimes you still disturb my dreams.*
> *A summer romance long ago*
> *I almost loved you . . . did you know?*
> *We danced to music soft and low*
> *Just yesterday . . . or so it seems*
> *I almost loved you . . . did you know?*
> *Sometimes you still disturb my dreams.*

Poets at Work, a bimonthly, is generally 36-40 pgs., magazine-sized, saddle-stapled, photocopied from typescript with colored paper cover. Subscription: $16. **Sample: $3. Simultaneous submissions and previously published poems OK. Reports within 2 weeks. Pays nothing, not even a copy.** "Because I publish hundreds of poets, I cannot afford to pay or give free issues. Every subscriber, of course, gets an issue. Subscribers also have many opportunities to regain their subscription money in the numerous contests offered in each issue. Send SASE for flyer for my separate monthly and special contests." He also publishes chapbooks. Send SASE for details. Jessee Poet says, "These days even the best poets tell me that it is difficult to get published. I am here for the novice as well as the experienced poet. I consider *Poets at Work* to be a hotbed for poets where each one can stretch and grow at his or her own pace. Each of us learns from the other, and we do not criticize one another. The door for poets is always open, so please stop by; we probably will like each other immediately."

POETS ON: (IV-Themes), 29 Loring Ave., Mill Valley CA 94941, phone (415)381-2824, founded 1976, poetry editor Ruth Daigon, is a poetry semiannual, **each issue on an announced theme (such as *Poets On: Regrets*). "We want well-crafted, humanistic, accessible poetry. We don't want to see sentimental rhymed verse. Length preferably 40 lines or less, or at the very most 80 lines (2-page poems)."** They have published poetry by Marge Piercy, Charles Edward Eaton, Walter Pavlich, Barbara Crooker and Lyn Lifshin. As a sample we selected these lines from "Widow's Walk" by Lisa Lepovetsky in *Poets On: Remembrance*:

> *Memory casts me too far adrift*
> *and old currents swallow me deep*
> *in turmoils of damp debris and*
> *dreams, till I'm worn smooth*
> *as a whelk half-buried in sand.*
> *Years bend me leeward, clinging*
> *to the sides of these rocky fists.*

Poets On: is 48 pgs., digest-sized, professionally printed, matte card cover with b&w graphics. Circulation is 450, 350 subscriptions of which 125 are libraries. They use about 5% of the 800 submissions they receive each year, have a 2- to 3-month backlog. Daigon tends to accept strong and well-structured lyric free verse, although you are apt to find any style or form with exciting or insightful content. Subscription: $8. Sample postpaid: $4. Query with SASE for upcoming themes and deadlines. Submit 1-4 poems (40 lines or shorter). No handwritten mss. Include short bio. "It's a good idea to read the magazine before submitting poetry." Submit only September 1 through December 1 or February 1 through May 1. Reports in 2-3 months. Pays 1 copy. Editor sometimes comments on rejections. She has designed a rejection slip that has several categories explaining why your work didn't make it into the magazine, and yet she'll often add a comment to encourage good work. Ruth Daigon says, "We are not interested in poetry that is declamatory, sloganeering, bathetic or opaque. Nor are we concerned with poetry as mere word-games or technical exercises."

POETS. PAINTERS. COMPOSERS; COLIN'S MAGAZINE (II), Dept. PM, 10254 35th Ave. SW, Seattle WA 98146, phone (206)937-8155, founded 1984, editor Joseph Keppler, who says *"Poets. Painters. Composers.* is an avant-garde arts journal which publishes poetry, drawings, scores, criticism, essays, reviews, photographs and original art. **If poetry, music or art is submitted, the work should be exciting, knowledgeable and ingenious.**" The journal, which appears once or twice a year, has published such artists as Carla Bertola, Fernando Aguiar, Ana Hatherly and Sarenco and such poets as Carol Barrett, Carletta Wilson and D. Bauer. "We also publish *Colin's Magazine, A Special Review from Poets. Painters. Composers.* with a focus on the interface of literature and computer technology." As a sample the editor selected these lines from "Carpenter Mondrian" by Gregory Jerozal:

> . . . *Forget*
> *Green fields: they are*
> *The summer places of*
> *Regret, forgetfulness,*
> *The past we watch with others*
> *Reassembled on the screen.*

The journal is magazine-sized, 86 pgs. Each cover has an original painting on it. Mr. Keppler says, "each odd-numbered issue appears in an 8½×11 format; each even-numbered issue changes format: No. 2, for example, is published as posters; No. 4 appears on cassettes. No. 6 will be an exhibition of sculpture with a catalog and a collection of multiples." Circulation is 300, no subscriptions. Each issue of the magazine carries an individual price tag. A copy of *Poets. Painters. Composers.* No. 5 is $50. Sample of No. 2 available for $10.50 postpaid. Sample of *Colin's Magazine* is available for $7. "Contributors' poetry receives great care. All material is returned right away unless (a) it's being painstakingly examined for acceptance into the journal or (b) it's being considered as right for some other way of publishing it or (c) we died." Contributors receive 1 copy. Acquires one-time rights. "We prefer short (500-800 word) reviews unless we already have asked for a longer piece from a poet/reviewer because of his or her interest in the book." He expects to publish 3 chapbooks of poetry a year and will accept freelance submissions. **For chapbook publication poets should query first "if poet prefers," sending credits, 7 sample poems, bio, philosophy and poetic aims. Pay for chapbooks will be in author's copies, number negotiable ("We're generous"); honorariums are given whenever possible.** Format of the chapbooks is expected to be "small, avant-garde, distinguished, exciting, experimental." Joseph Keppler says, "Poets' work is important work, and poetry is a most difficult art today. We maintain absolutely high standards, yet offer a hopeful critique . . . . We want to develop the avant-garde here and everywhere. We expect to last well into the 21st century and to change the way this culture understands literature. We intend to transform the role of poets in society. Advice for beginning poets? We're all beginning poets today."

POETS PEN QUARTERLY; M&M PUBLISHING (I, IV-Children/teens/young adults), (formerly Algilmore), Dept PM, 125 N. Main St., Galena IL 61036, phone (815)777-2979, is a quarterly poetry publication including a Children's Corner and a Featured Poet in each issue. "Poetry types/form open but no smut or slander. No epics. Children and young writer submittals encouraged. It is approximately 50-60 pgs., 8½×11, tape-bound with glossy paper cover. Sample postpaid: $6. No previously published poems. Cover letter with bio and photo preferred. Send SASE for guidelines. Reports within 2 weeks, international takes longer. "No payment for published submittals."

POET'S REVIEW (I, IV-Subscribers), P.O. Box I, 806 Kings Row, Varnell GA 30756, phone (706)694-8441, founded 1988, publisher Bob Riemke, is a monthly booklet, digest-sized, 20 pgs., photocopied from typescript with paper cover, using poetry by subscribers and making cash awards monthly and annually on basis of votes by subscribers. "Prefer rhyme. 44 lines or less. Any subject. No porn! No foreign languages." They have published poetry by Helen Webb, Ashley Anders and J. Alvin Speers. Subscription: $36. Sample postpaid: $4. "Subscribers are sent a ballot along with their monthly booklet to vote for the poems they believe to be the best." Monthly prizes are $75, $50 and $25, plus 7 honorable mentions. "All $75 winners are presented to the subscribers again at the end of the year and compete for a $500, $250 and $100 prize." 20-30 poems are printed each month along with the names of winners for the previous month. *Poet's Review* ranked #4 in the "Open Markets" category of the June 1993 *Writer's Digest* Poetry 60 list. This category ranks those publications most open to both free and formal verse.

POETS' ROUNDTABLE; POETS' STUDY CLUB OF TERRE HAUTE; POETS' STUDY CLUB INTERNATIONAL CONTEST (I, IV-Membership), 826 S. Center St., Terre Haute IN 47807, phone (812)234-0819, founded in 1939, president/editor Esther Alman. Poets' Study Club is one of the oldest associations of amateur poets. It publishes, every other month, *Poets' Roundtable*, a newsletter of market and contest information and news of the publications and activities of its members in a mimeographed, 10-page bulletin (magazine-sized, stapled at the corner, on colored paper), circulation 2,000. They have also published an occasional chapbook-anthology of poetry by members "but do not often do so." **Dues: $6 a year. Sample free for SASE. Uses short poems by members only. Simultaneous submissions and previously published poems OK.** They offer an annual Poets' Study Club International Contest, open to all, with no fees and cash prizes—a $25 and $15 award in 3 categories: traditional haiku, serious poetry, light verse. Deadline: February 1. Also contests for members only each two months. "We have scheduled criticism programs for members only."

POINT JUDITH LIGHT (IV-Form/style), 39 East Ave., Westerly RI 02891, founded 1992, editor Patrick Frank, is a quarterly publishing individual haiku/senryu, sequences and statements of aesthetic philosophy. They want haiku/senryu **"which explore the relation of the poet to his/her environment and which focus on life as truly lived; 13 syllables maximum."** They have recently published haiku/senryu by H.F. Noyes, Elizabeth St. Jacques and Mark Arvid White. As a sample the editor selected these haiku/senryu by George Ralph and the editor respectively:

> at the campfire's
> edge
> the void

> a gull passes
> over the court—
> winter dusk

The editor says *PJL* is desktop published in a newsletter format, 20 pgs. maximum. Press run is 500. Subscription: $12/year. **Sample postpaid: $3. Previously published poems OK; no simultaneous submissions. Send 20 haiku/senryu maximum. Submissions should be typed. Cover letter with bio required.** "I want to have some knowledge of the poet behind the work and publish a brief bio." **Often comments on rejections. Send SASE for guidelines. Reports within 1 month. Pays 1 copy. Acquires first rights.** The editor says, "Focus on the aspects of life that are immediately before you. Be yourself. Follow your intuition and be willing to explore and experiment. With James J.Y. Liu, I see poetry as a vehicle to explore external and internal worlds, as well as the language in which it is written. I am particularly interested in promoting the development of haiku/senryu sequencing in English. I am also exploring the connection between haiku, Eastern philosophy and the scientific imagination. Children's haiku are welcome. Politically relevant haiku are welcome, if they are imagistic and grounded in concrete experience. I also publish sports-related haiku."

THE POINTED CIRCLE (II), 705 N. Killingsworth, Portland OR 97217, phone (503)244-6111, ext. 5230, founded 1980, advisor Rachel Stevens, is an annual. They want poems **"under 60 lines, mostly shorter. 1-page poems on any topic of any form."** They have published poetry by Judith Barrington, William Stafford, Dianne Averill and Barbara Drake. As a sample the editor selected these lines from "Jessie" by Michael Ishii:

> She folds her hands like a dry dish towel,
> remembers leftover rain from last evening,
> unexpected, the smell of wet bark and turned-up
> dirt. Her bread drawer, full. She bends over dishes.
> The sky out her window is rough like a cutting board;
> it opens in anger, each raindrop finding
> its target, collecting in drainpipes.

It is 80 pgs., flat-spined, with b&w glossy card cover, professionally printed. Press run 400. **Sample postpaid: $3.50. Cover letter required. Submit mss from December 1 through February 15 only. "Place name, address, etc., on cover sheet only, listing titles of submissions. Limit 5 poems/poet. All submissions are read anonymously by student editorial staff; notification about June 1 for submissions received by February 15." Send SASE for guidelines. Pays 1 copy. Acquires one-time rights.**

POLYPHONIES (III, IV-Translations), BP189, Paris 75665 CEDEX 14 France, founded 1985, editor Pascal Culerrier. Editorial committee: Laurence Breysse, Emmanuelle Dagnaud, Jean-Yves Masson and Alexis Pelletier. Appears twice a year. **"Every case is a special one. We want to discover the new**

"About 80% of submissions are poems," says Rachel Stevens, faculty advisor of The Pointed Circle, an annual magazine of art, poetry and prose published by the Cascade Campus of Portland Community College in Portland, Oregon. "This cover is an interpretation of the seemingly oxymoronic figure, the pointed circle," Stevens says. The design is nanduti, "a fine lace found nowhere else in the world but Paraguay." The artwork was created by Carole Woik, a student in the university's graphic design program.

important voices of the world to open French literature to the major international productions. For example, we published Brodsky in French when he was not known in our country and had not yet the Nobel Prize. No vocal poetry, no typographic effects." They have published poetry by Mario Luzi (Italy), Jeremy Reed (Great Britain), Octavio Paz (Mexico) and Claude Michel Cluny (France). It is about 110 pgs., 6½×9½, flat-spined, with glossy card cover, printed completely in French. Press run: 850 for 300+ subscriptions. **They use translations of previously published poems. Pays 2 copies.** The editor says, "Our review is still at the beginning. We are in touch with many French editors. Our purpose is to publish together, side-by-side, poets of today and of yesterday."

PORTABLE WALL (III), 215 Burlington, Billings MT 59101, phone (406)256-3588, founded 1977, publisher Daniel Struckman. He wants, as Ezra Pound described, **"words that throw the object on to the visual imagination and that induce emotional correlations by the sound and rhythm of the speech."** He has published poetry by Dave Thomas and Joe Salerno. As a sample he selected these lines by Kathleen Taylor:

> Lightning rams down
> a cloud-clotted sky;
> the red moon is wasted.

PW is published twice a year. It is 40 pgs., saddle-stapled, on heavy tinted stock with 2-color matte card cover. Press run is 200. Subscription: $15 for 2 years. **Sample postpaid: $5. Reports in 6 weeks, 6 months between acceptance and publication. Pays 3 copies. Acquires one-time North American rights.**

‡UNIVERSITY OF PORTLAND REVIEW (II), 5000 N. Willamette, Portland OR 97203, phone (503)283-7144, appears twice a year—"a commentary on the contemporary scene intended for the college educated layman." As a sample of their poetry here is the first stanza of "Un-Just Spring" by Mary Comstock:

> Nothing is right this year.
> Rain is beating Spring back to the ground.
> Grass drowns about us.
> Buds never blossom

The 6×9, saddle-stapled, 44-page magazine uses about 10 pgs. of poetry in each issue, has 200 subscribers of which 200 are libraries and sends out 600 complimentary copies. They receive about a hundred submissions of poetry/year, use half, have a 1-year backlog. Subscription: $1. **Sample postpaid: 50¢. Submit up to 4 poems any time. Reports within 6-12 months. Pays 5 copies. The editors sometimes comment on rejections.** Open to unsolicited reviews.

POST-INDUSTRIAL PRESS (III), P.O. Box 265, Greensboro PA 15338, founded 1989, publishes 1-3 paperbacks/year. They have recently published poetry by Georges Perec and Johannes Poethen. **Replies to queries in 1 month.**

POTATO EYES; NIGHTSHADE PRESS (II), P.O. Box 76, Troy ME 04987, phone (207)948-3427, founded 1988, editors Roy Zarucchi and Carolyn Page, is a semiannual literary arts journal "with a focus on writers who write about the land and/or quality of life close to the earth. We now accept submissions from throughout the U.S. and Canada, although much of our poetry is from Appalachian states." They have published poetry by Gayle Elen Harvey, Robert Morgan, Nzadi Keita, Willie James King, Cynthia Lelos, Karen Blomain and Melody Davis. As a sample the editors selected these lines from Michael Chitwood's **Martyrdom of the Onions**, the title poem from a 1991 chapbook:

> *In a garden, they are knots along a rope of dirt.*
> *Pulled out and hung in a bundle on the back porch,*
> *they chime in deep tones against the wood frame.*
> *I have seen my father rub a half on the lintel*
> *of a rabbit trap, to erase the smell of his hands.*

PE is 5½×8½, 100+ pgs., flat-spined, professionally printed, with block cut matte paper cover. Circulation is 800. Subscription: $11 (Canadian $14). **Sample postpaid: $6 (back issue $5), or $7 Canadian.** The editors say, "those who submit receive a handwritten rejection/acceptance. We are open to any form other than rhymed, in batches of 3-5, but we tend to favor poetry with concrete visual imagery, solid intensity and compression. We respect word courage and risk-taking, along with thoughtful lineation. We prefer rebellious to complacent poetry. We prefer a cover letter with brief bio along with SASE." Reports in 1-2 months. Acquires first North American serial rights. Reviews books of poetry in less than 500 words. Open to unsolicited reviews. Poets may also send books for review consideration. Nightshade Press is the imprint under which they publish about 6 chapbooks/year, each 24-48 pgs., "usually with block print or pen-and-ink covers, endsheets and recycled 60 lb. text, 80 lb. covers. **Chapbooks are selected from competitions, mainly, but a few may be from poets who appear first in our magazine.**" Send SASE for catalog, information and/or $5 for sample chapbook. They advise, "Beginning poets should devour as much good poetry as possible in order to delineate their own style and voice. Look for a match between substance and sound."

POTPOURRI (II), P.O. Box 8278, Prairie Village KS 66208, founded 1989, poetry editor Pat Anthony, haiku editor Carl Bettis, is a monthly tabloid "to publish works of writers, **including new and unpublished writers. No religious, confessional, racial, political, erotic, abusive or sexual preference materials unless fictional and necessary to plot or characterization. No concrete/visual poetry (because of format)."** They have recently published poetry by Bernard Morris, David Ray and Gabriel Neruda. As a sample the editor selected these lines from "That Thief Burns" by Robert Cooperman:

> *My mother-in-law claimed an ancestor*
> *wrote the songs Burns became famous for.*
> *When the three of us visited Scotland,*
> *we tracked down the old estate,*
> *her disappointment bitter as poisoned stew . . .*

It is 28 pgs. Press run is 6,000-10,000 for 550 subscribers of which 20 are libraries, 5,000 distributed free to other publications, libraries, bookstores, universities, hospitals, community centers and others. Subscription: $15. **Sample postpaid: $1. Submit no more than 3 poems, no more than 1/page, length to 75 lines (approximately 30 preferred). Submit seasonal themes 6 months in advance. Address haiku and related forms to Carl Bettis.** "*Potpourri* publishes reprints of exceptional materials only from submissions by other magazines." **Send SASE for guidelines.** Reports in 8-10 weeks at most. Pays 1-20 copies (poet's request). Acquires first North American serial rights. The David Ray Poetry Award is given annually for best of volume. They also publish a line of *Potpourri Petites*, 20-24 pgs., 4×8, set in 9.5 pt. type. "At present, we do not accept unsolicited submissions. New poets can establish themselves for consideration by solid acceptances in *Potpourri* and through other credits." The editor advises, "Keep your new poems around long enough to become friends with them before parting. Let them ripen, and, above all, learn to be your own best editor. To borrow from William Carlos Williams, strive to let your particular 'specific' idea or poem be window to universality for your reader. Let them *in* to your work and write *for* an audience in terms of professionalism and clarity. Unrequited love, favorite pets and description that seems to be written for its own sake find little chance."

POULTRY, A MAGAZINE OF VOICE (IV-Humor), P.O. Box 4413, Springfield MA 01101, founded 1979, editors Jack Flavin, Brendan Galvin and George Garrett, is a tabloid (2-3 times a year) of **"parody, satire, humor and wit, particularly of the modern literary scene." They do not want to see**

Market categories: (I) Beginning; (II) General; (III) Limited;
(IV) Specialized; (V) Closed.

"serious" poetry. They have recently published poetry by Carol Poster, David McCleery, Scott Owens, Charles O'Neill, Kelly Anspaugh, B.J. Buckley and Dennis Hammes. As a sample the editors selected these lines by Bruce Berlind:

> Yes, scorn the critic, for I've read
> The collected Merrill Moore. The sonnet's dead.

The 11½×17 tabloid, 8 pgs., unstapled, professionally printed on newsprint, uses b&w photos, graphics, drawings, press run 500, 250 subscribers of which 35 are libraries. Subscription: $6. **Sample postpaid: $3. Pays 10 copies. Acquires first rights. Simultaneous submissions OK, "rarely" uses previously published poems.** Jack Flavin calls for "a little more humor and light, please, in the deadly serious (and oftentimes deadly) business of being a poet, a writer and getting published. Beginning poet? Get it down while it's hot, let it cool and consider it with a cold eye a bit later. Learn to write by doing it, if you're lucky, under the watchful eye and with encouragement from a good critic."

POWER ANIMAL (I), Joe Skyfoot Word and Music Creations, Suite 528, 5468 Dundas St. W., Etobicoke, Ontario M9B 6E3 Canada, phone (416)582-7414, editor Phillip Boucher, is a semiannual magazine-sized newsletter, 5-10 double-sided pgs., of **"poetry, humour and the New Age. Needs all types of poetry: inspirational, New Age, pagan, horror, children's, fantasy and anything else you could think of. Nonsense verse or unintelligible poetry gets trashed. I love poems that make sense on the first reading. Poems must be short, unpublished, 15 lines or less."** They have recently published works by Nina Silver, M.L. Krolak and Sherry Keown. As a sample, the editor selected this short poem, "Haiku #4," by C.M. Lana:

> The wind tickles ears,
> speaking to my soul, mourning.
> Where have all the days gone?

It is photocopied from typescript, side stapled. Subscription: $5/year. **Sample postpaid: $3. Send 1-3 poems. Cover letter with short bio required. Reads submissions February through May and August through November. Reports in 4-6 months. Pays 1 copy. Acquires first North American serial rights.**

PRAIRIE FIRE (III), Room 423, 100 Arthur St., Winnipeg, Manitoba R3B 1H3 Canada, phone (204)943-9066, founded 1978, editor Andris Taskans, is a quarterly magazine of new writing including fiction, poetry and reviews. They want **"poetry that articulates a connection between language and ethics, an aesthetic of writing 'from the body', and open to the nuances of orality, ethnic and racial differences and feminism. No haiku, sonnets or other rhyming forms, nor political or religious treatises in verse form."** They have recently published poetry by Douglas Barbour, Di Brandt and Erin Mouré. As a sample the editor selected these lines from "Divining for Aunt Amelja's Origins" by Andrew Suknaski:

> so tell me aunt amelja
> here where i float sleepless on the eve of my brother's burial
> this side of luminous constellations
> as berlin's wall crumples
> where so many in their glasnost dream
> fantasize about a european common home

Prairie Fire is 128+ pgs., 6×9, offset, perfect-bound, glossy card cover, illustrations and ads. They receive 300-400 submissions (average 6 poems each), accept approximately 3%. Press run is 1,400 for 900+ subscribers of which 100+ are libraries, 150+ shelf sales. Single copy: $7.95; subscription: $24 Canadian, $28 US. **Sample postpaid: $8 Canadian. No previously published poems or simultaneous submissions. Cover letter required. Include other publications, brief biographical information, list of poems submitted, name, address and phone number. Submissions should be typed, double-spaced, one poem to a page, name and address on each page, no more than 6 poems at a time. Reads submissions September 1 through June 30 only.** Time between acceptance and publication is 18 months. Seldom comments on rejections. **Send SASE for guidelines. Reports in 3-4 months. Pays $35 for first page, $20 for each additional page, plus 1 copy. Buys first Canadian serial rights only.** Staff reviews books of poetry in 500-2,000 words, single or multi-book format. Send books for review consideration. The editor says, "Be patient!"

THE PRAIRIE PUBLISHING COMPANY (III, IV-Regional), Dept. PM, Box 2997, Winnipeg, Manitoba R3C 4B5 Canada, phone (204)885-6496, founded 1963, publisher Ralph E. Watkins, is a "small press catering to regional market, local history, fantasy, poetry and nonfiction," with flat-spined paperbacks. They want **"basically well-crafted poems of reasonable length"** and do not want to see **"the work of rank amateurs and tentative and time-consuming effort."** They have published collections of poetry by Brian Richardson and Brian MacKinnon. Their books are handsomely produced, 6×9, using b&w photos and art along with the poems, glossy card covers. They publish about 1 a year, 68 pgs. **Samples available at a 20% discount—send SASE or SAE and IRC for catalog. Query with samples. Simultane-**

ous submissions OK. Do not submit mss during summer. Responds to queries in 6 weeks. Nancy Watkins notes, "Robert E. Pletta's point that most poets need to do more reading is well taken. We would endorse this suggestion."

PRAIRIE SCHOONER; STROUSSE PRIZE; SLOTE PRIZE; FAULKNER AWARD; STANLEY AWARD; READERS' CHOICE AWARDS (II), 201 Andrews, University of Nebraska, Lincoln NE 68588-0334, phone (402)472-3191, founded 1927, editor Hilda Raz; "one of the oldest literary quarterlies in continuous publication; publishes poetry, fiction, personal essays, interviews and reviews." They want "**poems that fulfill the expectations they set up.**" No specifications as to form, length, style, subject matter or purpose. No simultaneous submissions. They have recently published poetry by Carl Dennis, Albert Goldbarth, Sharon Hashimoto, Joan Murray, Alicia Ostriker, David Slavitt and Marcia Southwick. As a sample the editor selected these lines from "How to Get in the Best Magazines" by Eleanor Wilner:

> it is time to write
> the acceptable poem—
> ice and glass, with its splinter
> of bone, its pit
> of an olive,
> the dregs
> of the cup of abundance,
> useless spill of gold
> from the thresher, the dust
> of it filling the sunlight, the chum
> broadcast on the black waters
> and the fish
> —the beautiful, ravenous fish—
> refusing to rise.

The magazine is 6×9, flat-spined, 176 pgs. and uses 70-80 pgs. of poetry in each issue. They receive about 4,000 mss (of all types)/year from which they choose 300 pgs. of poetry. Press run is 3,100. Subscription: $20/year; $6.45/copy. **Sample postpaid: $3.50. Submit 5-7 poems. "Clear copy appreciated.**" Send SASE for guidelines. Reports in 2-3 months; "sooner if possible." Pays copies. Acquires all rights. Returns rights upon request without fee. Reviews books of poetry. Open to unsolicited reviews. Poets may also send books for review consideration. One of the most influential magazines being published today, often named as such in independent surveys of creative writers, this publication is genuinely open to excellent work in any form: lyric, narrative, dramatic, traditional, etc. Send only your best work, as competition is keen. Brief reviews are an excellent way to break into the journal. Editor Hilda Raz also promotes poets whose work has appeared in her pages by listing their continued accomplishments in a special section (even when their work does not concurrently appear in the magazine). The $500 Strousse Prize is awarded to the best poetry published in the magazine each year, the Slote Prize for beginning writers ($500), the Stanley Award for Poetry ($300) and six other *PS* prizes are also awarded, as well as the Faulkner Award for Excellence in Writing ($1,000). Also, each year 5-10 Readers' Choice Awards ($250 each) are given for poetry, fiction and nonfiction. Editors serve as judges. *Prairie Schooner* ranked #1 in the "New Poets" category of the June 1993 *Writer's Digest* Poetry 60 list. This category ranks those markets who often publish poets whose work is new to their publication. Hilda Raz comments, "*Prairie Schooner* receives a large number of poetry submissions; we're not unusual. We don't have time to comment on mss, but the magazine's reputation is evidence of our careful reading. We've been dedicated to the publication of good poems for a very long time and have published work early in the career of many successful poets."

‡**PRAIRIE WINDS (II)**, Box 159, Dakota Wesleyan University, 1200 University Ave., Mitchell SD 57301, phone (605)995-2633, editor Joseph M. Ditta, is an annual of poetry, fiction, short essays, photos and art. **They are open to all forms, lengths, styles and subjects of poetry except pornographic.** They have recently published poetry by Simon Perchik, Aaron Kramer, David Ignatow and Henry Hughes. The editor says *PW* is 50-60 pgs., 7½×9¼, offset, bound, gloss litho, no ads. They accept approximately 25% of the poetry received each year. Press run is 500 for 50 subscribers of which 10 are libraries. The rest are distributed free to professors and students. **Sample postpaid: $4. No previously published poems; simultaneous submissions OK. Cover letter required.** "We are an annual, published in spring. All submissions must arrive by January 15." Reads submissions January 15 through February 15 only. Seldom comments on rejections. Send SASE for guidelines. Reports by end of February. Pays 1 copy.

PRAKALPANA LITERATURE; KOBISENA (I, IV-Bilingual, form), P-40 Nandana Park, Calcutta 700034, West Bengal, India, *Kobisena* founded 1972, *Prakalpana Literature* press founded 1974, magazine 1977, editor Vattacharja Chandan, who says, "We are small magazines which publish only *Prakalpana* (a mixed form of prose and poetry), Sarbangin (whole) poetry, essays on Prakalpana movement and Sarbangin poetry movement, letters, literary news and very few books on Prakalpana and Sarbangin literature. **Purpose and form: for advancement of poetry in the super-space age, the poetry must be really experimental and avant-garde using mathematical signs and symbols and visualizing the pictures inherent in the alphabet (within typography) with sonorous effect. That is Sarbangin poetry. Length: within 30 lines (up to 4 poems). Prakalpana is a mixed form of prose, poetry, essay, novel, story, play with visual effect and it is not at all short story as it is often misunderstood. Better send 4 IRCs to read *Prakalpana Literature* first and then submit. Length: within 16 pages (up to 2 prakalpanas) at a time. Subject matter: society, nature, cosmos, humanity, love, peace, etc. Style: own. We do not want to see traditional, conventional, academic, religious and poetry of prevailing norms and forms."** They have recently published poetry by Dilip Gupta, Gopal Mondal, Richard Kostelanetz and Susan Smith Nash. As a sample the editor chose these lines by Charlene Mary Cath Smith:

> tiny poem
>   tin   poe
> ti   po
>   t   p
> -------
>   . .

Prakalpana Literature, an annual, is 70 pgs., digest-sized, saddle-stapled, printed on thin stock with matte card cover. *Kobisena*, which appears at least twice a year, is 16 pgs., digest-sized, a newsletter format with no cover. Both are hand composed and printed by letterpress. Both use both English and Bengali. They use about 10% of some 400 poems received/year. The press run is 1,000 for each, and each has about 450 subscriptions of which 50 are libraries. **Samples: 6 rupees for *Prakalpana*, 4 rupees for *Kobisena*. Overseas: 4 IRCs and 2 IRCs respectively or exchange of avant-garde magazines. Simultaneous submissions OK. Previously published poetry OK. Cover letter with short bio and small photo/sketch of poet required. Publication within a year.** After being published in the magazines, poets may be included in future anthologies with translations into Bengali/English if and when necessary. **"Joining with us is welcome but not a pre-condition." Editor comments on rejections "if wanted." Send SAE with IRC for guidelines. No reporting time given. Pays 1 copy.** Reviews books of poetry, "but preferably experimental books." Open to unsolicited reviews. Poets may also send books for review consideration. He says, "We believe that only through poetry, the deepest feelings of humanity as well as nature and the cosmos can be best expressed and conveyed to the peoples of the ages to come. And only poetry can fill up the gap in the peaceless hearts of dispirited peoples, resulted from the retreat of god and religion with the advancement of hi-tech. So, in an attempt, since the inception of Prakalpana Movement in 1969, to reach that goal in the avant-garde and experimental way we stand for Sarbangin poetry. And to poets and all concerned with poetry we wave the white handkerchief saying (in the words of Vattacharja Chandan) 'We want them who want us.'"

THE PRESBYTERIAN RECORD (IV-Inspirational, religious), 50 Wynford Dr., Don Mills, Ontario M3C 1J7 Canada, phone (416)441-1111, founded 1876, is "the national magazine that serves the membership of The Presbyterian Church in Canada (and many who are not Canadian Presbyterians). We seek to stimulate, inform, inspire, to provide an 'apologetic' and a critique of our church and the world (not necessarily in that order!)." They want **poetry which is "inspirational, Christian, thoughtful, even satiric but *not* maudlin. No 'sympathy card' type verse a la Edgar Guest or Francis Gay. It would take a *very* exceptional poem of epic length for us to use it. Shorter poems, 10-30 lines, preferred. Blank verse OK (if it's not just rearranged prose). 'Found' poems. Subject matter should have some Christian import (however subtle)."** They have published poetry by Jean Larsen, Jeanne Davis, Joan Stortz, Marlow C. Dickson, Len Selle and J.R. Dickey. The magazine comes out 11 times a year. Press run is 64,000. Subscription: $11. **Submit seasonal work 6 weeks before month of publication. Simultaneous submissions OK. Poems should be typed, double-spaced. Pays $20-50/poem. Buys onetime rights.** Staff reviews books of poetry. Send books for review consideration. *The Presbyterian Record* has won several Canadian Church Press Awards.

THE PRESS OF MACDONALD & REINECKE (II); PADRE PRODUCTIONS (I), P.O. Box 840, Arroyo Grande CA 93421-0840, phone (805)473-1947, founded 1974, poetry editor Lachlan P. MacDonald. Padre Productions prints books on a fee basis, as a book packager. MacDonald & Reinecke **requires the poet to "purchase 200 copies of an edition (at liberal discounts)" but they do not consider themselves subsidy publishers. They publish under the M&R imprint only work they consider of merit and in which they, like the poet, must invest.** "The press is a division of Padre Productions bringing together under one imprint drama, fiction, literary nonfiction and poetry. We publish poetry in broadsides, flat-spined paperbacks, chapbooks and hardcover. We are looking for **poetry of literary merit and also poetry suitable for travel and nature photo books. We are averse to tightly rhymed conventional poetry unless designed to appeal to the general humor market."** They have published Terre Ouwehand's **Voices from the Well**, Steven Schmidt's **Avigation and Other Poems** and Phyllis K. Collier's **Daughters**

of Cain. Query with 5-6 samples, publication credits, bio. The editor also wants to know "do they give readings or have marketing opportunities? Some authors distribute flyers to build up pre-publication orders sufficient to justify the print order." Replies to queries in 2-4 weeks, to submissions (if invited) in 2-6 months. Simultaneous submissions OK. Ms should be double-spaced. Pays minimum of 4% royalties, 6 copies. The editor "frequently makes brief comments" on rejections. Send 6×9 SASE for catalog. The editor advises, "Poets who have not published 10 or 20 poems in literary magazines are unlikely to have developed the craft we require. We also prefer books with a unifying theme rather than a sampling reflecting the author's virtuosity."

‡**THE PRESS OF THE NIGHTOWL (V)**, 320 Snapfinger Dr., Athens GA 30605, phone (706)353-7719, founded 1965, owner Dwight Agner, publishes 1-2 paperbacks and 1-2 hardbacks each year. They have recently published poetry by Paul Zimmer, Stephen Corey, Mary Anne Coleman and C.K. Williams. However, they are currently not accepting unsolicited poetry submissions. Pays author's copies. Sample books may be ordered directly from the publisher or located through bookstores.

THE PRESS OF THE THIRD MIND (IV-Form), 65 E. Scott St. #6P, Chicago IL 60610, phone (312)337-3122, founded 1985, poetry editor Rasta Purina, is a small press publisher of artist books, poetry and fiction in glass bottles, tape measures, paperbacks, broadsides, T-shirts and Tarot cards. **"We are especially interested in the cut-up/fold-in technique, concrete poetry, translations, collaborative** *(Exquisite Corpse)* **poetry, found poems, dada, surrealism, etc."** They have published poetry by "Pessoa, Spiro, Cesariny, Mansour and Lamantia." As a sample the editor selected these lines from "Frisco Spleen" by G. Sutton Breiding:

> *Dark city*
> *I have stripped shadows of*
> *   concrete*
> *From your flesh*
> *To find my face*

Asked how much poetry they typically receive per year and how much they accept, he said, "We get about 6 metric tons and accept it all for fireplace logs." They have a press run of 1,000 with 100 subscriptions of which 38 are libraries. Sample postpaid: $5. *"No dot matrix!!!"* Simultaneous submissions OK, if noted. Cover letter preferred. They have sometimes used previously published poetry and have simultaneously published with *Exquisite Corpse*. Pay? *"Surely you jest!"* But contributors can have all the copies they can photocopy. Reviews books of poetry. Press of the Third Mind publishes 2 flat-spined paperbacks, 56 pgs., per year. They recently published **Concave Buddha and Other Public Disservice Announcements** (paperback). For book publication submit 20 sample poems, bio and credits. Responds to queries in 1 week, mss in 3 weeks. **"Just ask for free samples and include a substantial 'love offering.' "** Editor comments on rejections. His advice: "Absolute zero corrupts absolutely; Absolut Vodka boils at Fahrenheit 491."

PRIMAVERA (II, IV-Women), Dept. PM, P.O. Box #37-7547, Chicago IL 60637, phone (312)324-5920, founded 1975, coeditor Ruth Young, is "an irregularly published but approximately annual magazine of poetry and fiction reflecting the experiences of women. We look for strong, original voice and imagery, generally prefer free verse, fairly short length, related, even tangentially, to women's experience." They have published poetry by Donna Jackson, Neile Graham, Pamela Miller, Claire Nicolas White and Lynne H. deCourcy. As a sample the editors selected these lines by Ann Gearen:

> *playing tea party underwater*
> *while we held our breath,*
> *gestures slowed, deliberate,*
> *our conversation bubbling to the surface*
> *in vowels only, oohs and ahs.*

The elegantly printed publication, flat-spined, generously illustrated with photos and graphics, uses 30-35 pgs. of poetry in each issue. Circulation is 1,000. They receive over 1,000 submissions of poetry/year, use 32. Single copy: $9. **Sample postpaid: $5. No simultaneous submissions. Submit no more than 6 poems anytime, no queries. Editors comment on rejections "when requested or inspired."** Send SASE for guidelines. Reports in 1-2 months. Pays 2 copies. Acquires first-time rights.

PRINCETON UNIVERSITY PRESS; LOCKERT LIBRARY OF POETRY IN TRANSLATION (IV-Translations, bilingual), 41 William St., Princeton NJ 08540, phone (609)452-4900, literature editor Robert E. Brown. "In the Lockert Library series, we publish simultaneous cloth and paperback (flat-spine) editions for each poet. Clothbound editions are on acid-free paper, and binding materials are chosen for strength and durability. Each book is given individual design treatment rather than stamped into a series mold. We have published a wide range of poets from other cultures, including well-known writers such as Hölderlin and Cavafy, and those who have not yet had their due in English translation, such as Ingeborg Bachmann and Faiz Ahmed Faiz. Manuscripts are judged with several criteria in mind: the ability of the translation to stand on its own as poetry in English; fidelity to the tone and spirit of the original, rather than literal accuracy; and the importance of the translated poet to the literature of his or her time and country." The editor says, "All our books in this series are heavily subsidized to break even. We have internal funds to cover deficits of publishing costs. We do not, however, publish books chosen and subsidized by other agencies, such as AWP. Our series is an open competition, for which the 'award' is publication." Simultaneous submissions OK if you tell them. Cover letter required. Send mss only during respective reading periods stated in guidelines. "We comment on semifinalists only." Send SASE for guidelines to submit. Reports in 2-3 months. Pays royalties (5% or more) on paperback and 12 author's copies. In 1993 the press published A Child Is Not a Knife: Selected Poems of Göran Sonnevi, translated from the Swedish by Rika Lesser, who was awarded the 1992 American-Scandinavian Foundation Translation Prize for her work.

PRINTED MATTER (II), Hikari Biru 303, 3-7-10 Takadanobaba, Shinjuku-ku, Tokyo 169 Japan, phone (03)3362-7589, founded 1977, editor Stephen Forster, is a quarterly literary journal featuring poetry, fiction, reviews, essays, interviews and artwork. It has published poetry by Jon Silkin, Cid Corman, Shuntaro Tanikawa, Xavier Villaurrutia, Harry Guest and La Loca. As a sample, the editor selected these lines by Simon Armitage:

> United mainly,
> every odd Saturday
> or White Hart Lane for a worthwhile away game.
> Down in the crowds at the grounds where the bread is:
> the gold, the plastic,
> the chequebooks, the readies

Printed Matter is 58 pgs. in professionally printed A5 format. Press run is 600. The magazine appears four times/year plus one special issue. Subscription: 3,000 yen (US $25). Sample postpaid: 600 yen (US $5). Unless otherwise arranged, submissions to *Printed Matter* are accepted on condition that they have not previously been published and that the material is not under consideration elsewhere. Submissions should be accompanied by the usual materials, including cover letter with bio. Editor comments on rejections. Reports in 2-3 months. Acquires all rights. "I return rights to the author on request; I only ask for *Printed Matter* citation in other published works." Reviews books of poetry in 1,000-1,500 words, single or multi-book format. Open to unsolicited reviews. Poets may also send books for review consideration. "Printed Matter Press publishes chapbooks. Printed Matter Press is also associated with the Tokyo-based SARU Press, which publishes collections of poetry." The editor says, "Poets need to study what they are submitting to. *Printed Matter* is published in Japan, but I'm not especially out to promote haiku, tanka or cherry blossoms—that is done very capably by other magazines."

PRISM INTERNATIONAL (I, II), Dept. of Creative Writing, University of British Columbia, Vancouver, British Columbia V6T 1Z1 Canada, phone (604)822-2514, founded 1959, executive editors Anna Nobile and Vigeland Rubin. "*Prism* is an international quarterly that publishes poetry, drama, short fiction, imaginative nonfiction and translation into English in all genres. We have no thematic or stylistic allegiances: excellence is our main criterion for acceptance of mss. We want poetry that shows an awareness of the tradition while reiterating its themes in a fresh and distinctive way. We read everything." They have published poetry by Daphne Marlatt, Al Purdy, Diana Hartog, Roo Borson and Bill Bissett. As a sample the editor selected these lines by Michael Ondaatje:

> This is for people who disappear
> for those who descend into the code
> and make their room a fridge for Superman
> —who exhaust costume and bones that could perform flight
> who shave their moral so raw
> they can tear themselves through the eye of a needle

Prism is elegantly printed in a flat-spined, 6×9 format, 80 pgs., original color artwork on the glossy card cover, circulation to 1,000 subscribers of which 200 are libraries. They receive 1,000 submissions/year, use 125, have 1-2 special issues/year, and a 1- to 3-month backlog. Subscription: $16. Sample postpaid: $5. Submit a maximum of 6 poems at a time, any print so long as it's typed. Cover letter with brief introduction and previous publications required. Send Canadian SASE or SAE with IRCs for guidelines. Reports in 6-12 weeks ("or we write to poets to tell them we're holding onto their work for a while"). Pays $20/printed page plus subscription. Editors often comment on rejections. *Prism International* is known in literary circles as one of the top journals in Canada. It contains good poems, mostly free verse with a leaning toward lyric. The editors say, "While we don't automatically discount any kind of poetry, we prefer to publish work that challenges the writer as much as it does the reader."

PRISONERS OF THE NIGHT; MKASHEF ENTERPRISES (IV-Psychic/occult, science fiction/fantasy/ horror, erotica), P.O. Box 688, Yucca Valley CA 92286-0688, poetry editor Alayne Gelfand. *Prisoners of the Night*, founded 1987, focusing on vampire erotica, uses poetry that is "erotic, unique, less horrific and more romantic, non-pornographic, original visions of the vampire." Poets who have appeared recently in *POTN* include Jacie Ragan, G. Sutton Breiding and Ernie Hilbert Jr. As a sample the editor selected these lines from "Cryptic Dreams" by Alex Grayton:

> Cool rain on my lips,
> the taste of damp seeping into my throat,
> the breath of fog stale in my lungs.
>
> Outside my crystal crypt,
> a boy with a rock—
> jagged, intentional.

The intent of *POTN* is "to show the erotic, the romantic, rather than the horrific aspects of the vampire." It is 70-90 pgs., magazine-sized, perfect-bound, with color cover, produced by high-speed photocopying. Most poems are illustrated. It appears annually, usually in June. Of over 300 poems received/year they use between 10 and 25. It has an initial print run of 3,000, but each issue is kept in print. Sample postpaid: $15 (for #1-4), $12 (#5), $9.95 (#6). Send SASE for guidelines. No more than 6 poems per submission. No simultaneous submissions or previously published poems. Reading schedule: September 15 through March 31 annually. Editor sometimes comments on rejections. Reports "within 3 months." Pays $5/poem plus 1 copy. Buys first serial rights. *POTN* wants unusual visions of the vampire, not the standard, stereotypical characterizations. "We prefer non-rhyme and find most humor too subjective to appeal to our readers. The startling, unique, ethereal usage of words will catch our eye much more than the expected, mundane. Be original, surprise us!"

PROOF ROCK PRESS; PROOF ROCK (I, II, IV-Humor), Box 607, Halifax VA 24558, founded 1982, poetry editors Serena Fusek and Don R. Conner. "We try to wake up a passive readership. We challenge our writers to search for something new under the sun and improve on the old." The poetry they want is: "adventure, contemporary, humor/satire, fantasy, experimental. Avoid overt sentimentality. Poems up to 32 lines. All subjects considered if well done." The digest-sized magazine appears 2-3 times/year, is offset from typescript copy, colored matte card cover, with 30-40 pgs. in each issue. They receive 800-1,000 submissions/year, use 120-150, have a 3- to 6-month backlog. Press run is 300 for 100 subscribers of which 8-10 are libraries. Subscription: $4. Sample postpaid: $2.50. Submit no more than 6 pieces, year round. No query needed, though some issues are on announced themes. Simultaneous submissions OK. Send SASE for guidelines. Reports "usually within 1 month." Pays 1 copy. Proof Rock Press publishes an occasional anthology and collections by individuals. Query with 8-10 samples, bio and publishing credits. Reply to queries in 1 month, to submissions (if invited) in 1-3 months. Simultaneous submissions OK. Pays copies. Send $2.50 for a sample chapbook. Editor sometimes comments on rejections. His advice is, "Be introspective. Accept the challenge of looking within and write from experience."

PROPHETIC VOICES; HERITAGE TRAILS PRESS (II), 94 Santa Maria Dr., Novato CA 94947, founded 1982, poetry editors Ruth Wildes Schuler, Goldie L. Morales and Jeanne Leigh Schuler. "Our goal is to share thoughts on an international level. We see the poet's role as that of prophet, who points the way to a higher realm of existence." They publish *Prophetic Voices* twice a year and chapbooks. They want "poetry of social commentary that deals with the important issues of our time. Poetry with beauty that has an international appeal. Do not want religious poetry or that with a limited scope. Open to any kind of excellent poetry, but publish mostly free verse. Limited number of long poems accepted due to lack of space." They have published Jack Brooks, Hazel F. Goddard, A. Manoussos, B.Z. Niditch, H.F. Noyes, Gloria H. Procsal and Bo Yang. *Prophetic Voices* is digest-sized, 144 pgs., perfect-bound, offset from typescript with matte card cover, colored stock with graphics. They have 100 pgs. of poetry in each issue, circulation to 400 subscribers of which 10 are libraries. They receive 4,000 submissions/year, use 800, have a 5-year backlog. Single copy: $7; subscription: $14; $16 to libraries. Sample postpaid: $5. Submit 4 poems or less. Reports in 1-8 weeks. Pays 1 copy. Heritage Trails now considers unsolicited mss. The editors advise, "Be aware of what is going on in the world around you. Even the personal poem should have universal appeal if it is to survive the test of time."

THE PROSE POEM (II, IV-Form), 1004 Sycamore, San Marcos TX 78666, phone (512)353-4998, founded 1990, editor Steve Wilson, is an annual using prose poems only. "I hope and pray the author knows what prose poetry is before submitting to me. For me 'prose poems' run from margin to margin, with no line breaks, and use intense, compact language." The have recently published poetry by Linda Foster, Barry Silesky, Ray Gonzalez, Tom Whalen, Harriet Zinnes, Robert Bly and George Myers, Jr. The editor describes *TPP* as 60 pgs., professionally printed with card stock cover, saddle-stapled.

Most selections are one paragraph or a few small ones, each about (or under) 200 words. Press run is 200. **Sample postpaid: $3. Reads submissions January 1 through March 31 only. Reports by 1 month after deadline. Pays 1 copy. Acquires first North American serial rights.** Staff reviews books of poetry. Send books for review consideration. The editor says, "*TPP* is a journal focusing on one particular genre and publishing only the best work done in that genre. This does not mean an author cannot experiment. I encourage it. It also does not mean I don't want to see work from new writers. Please send, but only your best. I publish this magazine with my own money, so sales are very important. I won't take grants. I like my freedom. If you think prose poetry matters and like the idea of a journal dedicated to it, please help me keep it going by sending great work and subscribing."

PROSETRY: NEWSLETTER FOR, BY AND ABOUT WRITERS (I), The Write Place, P.O. Box 117727, Burlingame CA 94011, phone (415)347-7613, editor P.D. Steele, founded 1985. *Prosetry* is a monthly newsletter featuring "new and newly published poets and prose writers with a 'guest writer' column each month. Includes original poetry, new markets, contests, seminars, workshops and **general poetry potpourri gleaned from our subscribers.**" 50% freelance. **Sample for 52¢ postage. Invites new writers. Send up to 3 poems, no more than 20 lines, English only. No profanity. Cover letter required with 2-line bio plus latest credits ("tell us if you've never been published"). Guidelines available for SASE. Reports in less than 1 month. Pays one-year subscription. Acquires one-time rights; release required.** Reviews books of poetry in 150 words. Open to unsolicited reviews. Poets may also send books (chapbooks only) for review consideration. "For 'guest writer' column we would prefer information relevant to the beginning or newly published writer/poet." Also publishes "How-to" *CLIPS©* for writers, $2.50 each. Free list for SASE. The Write Place will critique poetry for a nominal fee.

PROVINCETOWN ARTS; PROVINCETOWN ARTS PRESS (II), 650 Commercial St., Provincetown MA 02657, phone (508)487-3167, founded 1985, editor Christopher Busa, is an elegant, flat-spined annual, 170+ pgs., with full-color glossy cover, using quality poetry. "*Provincetown Arts* focuses broadly on the artists and writers who inhabit or visit the tip of Cape Cod and seeks to stimulate creative activity and enhance public awareness of the cultural life of the nation's oldest continuous art colony. Drawing upon a century-long tradition rich in visual art, literature and theater, *Provincetown Arts* publishes material with a view towards demonstrating that the artists' colony, functioning outside the urban centers, is a utopian dream with an ongoing vitality." They have published poetry by Bruce Smith, Franz Wright, Sandra McPherson and Cyrus Cassells. As a sample the editor selected these lines from "Sky of Clouds" by Susan Mitchell:

> *And after heavy rains, when the egrets*
> *settle on the gardens, cramming*
> *their beaks with the shrill*
> *cries of the frogs, I think*
> *I could do that too, I could be gorgeous and cruel.*

Press run 10,000 for 500 subscribers of which 20 are libraries, 6,000 shelf sales. **Sample postpaid: $7.50. Reads submissions August through February. Reports in 2-3 months. Pays $25-100/poem. Buys first rights.** Reviews books of poetry in 500-3,000 words, single or multi-book format. Open to unsolicited reviews. Poets may also send books for review consideration. The Provincetown Arts Press published 4 volumes of poetry in 1993. Two poems by Susan Mitchell ("Sky of Clouds" and "Rapture"), published in *Provincetown Arts*, have been included in **Best American Poetry** (1991 and 1993, respectively).

PSYCHOPOETICA (II, IV-Themes), Dept. of Psychology, University of Hull, Hull HU6 7RX England, founded 1979, editor Dr. Geoff Lowe uses "**psychologically-based poetry.**" That is not a very narrow category, though many of the poems in *Psychopoetica* are explicitly about psychology or psychological treatment. But most good poetry is in some sense "psychologically based," as the editor seems to recognize in these comments (from his guidelines): "**I prefer short, experimental, rhymed and unrhymed, light verse, haiku, etc., (and visual poems). I will read and consider any style, any length, providing it's within the arena of 'psychologically-based' poetry. I'm not too keen on self-indulgent therapeutic poetry (unless it's good and original), nor 'Patience Strong' type stuff. I like poetry that has some (or all!) of the following: humor, vivid imagery, powerful feelings, guts and substance, originality, creative style, punch or twist, word-play, good craftsmanship, etc.**" Published poets include Sheila E. Murphy, Wes Magee, R. Nikolas Macioci and Ruth Wildes Schuler. The magazine appears 2-3 times/year, circulating to "several hundred and increasing." It is A5, saddle-stitched. **Sample: £1 ($2). Send SASE for guidelines. Considers simultaneous submissions. Editor "always" comments on rejections. Reports within 1 month. Pays 1 copy.** Occasionally reviews books of poetry in 25 words, single format. Open to unsolicited reviews. Poets may also send books for review consideration. He says, "Careful presentation of work is most important. But I continue to be impressed by the rich variety of submissions, especially work that shifts boundaries. Also, we now welcome interesting juxtapositions of words and graphics."

THE PUCKERBRUSH PRESS; THE PUCKERBRUSH REVIEW (IV-Regional), 76 Main St., Orono ME 04473, phone (207)581-3832, press founded 1971, *Review* founded 1978, poetry editor Constance Hunting, is a "small press publisher of a literary, twice-a-year magazine focused on Maine and of flat-spined paperbacks of literary quality." The editor **does not want to see "confessional, dull, feminist, incompetent, derivative" poetry.** They have published poetry by Amy Clampitt, and the editor selected these sample lines from "Not a Navigable River" by Muska Nagel:

> *flow seaward, seaward*
> *my river, filled to the brink—*
> *(but no king's horses, no more*
> *will ever come to drink).*

For book publication, query with 10 samples. Prefers no simultaneous submissions. Editor comments on rejections. She offers criticism for a fee: $100 is usual. Pays 10% royalties plus 10 copies.

PUDDING HOUSE PUBLICATIONS; PUDDING MAGAZINE: THE INTERNATIONAL JOURNAL OF APPLIED POETRY; PUDDING WRITING COMPETITIONS; PUDDING HOUSE BED & BREAKFAST FOR WRITERS; OHIO POETRY THERAPY CENTER & LIBRARY (II, IV-Political, social issues), 60 N. Main St., Johnstown OH 43031, phone (614)967-6060 (after 7 p.m.), founded 1979, poetry editor Jennifer Welch Bosveld, provides "a sociological looking glass through poems that provide 'felt experience' and shares intense human situations. Speaks for the difficulties and the solutions. Provides a forum for poems and articles by people who take poetry arts into the schools and the human services." They publish *Pudding* every several months, also chapbooks, anthologies, broadsides. They **"want experimental and contemporary poetry—what hasn't been said before. Speak the unspeakable. Don't want preachments or sentimentality. Don't want obvious traditional forms without fresh approach. Long poems are happily considered too, as long as they aren't windy."** They have published poetry by James Belcher, Lowell Jaeger, Edward Boccia and Alan Catlin. The editor selected these sample lines from "The Stroke" by Douglas M. Swisher:

> *His sense takes hold in its accustomed niche*
> *Like a gimballed compass righted from awry.*

Pudding **is a literary journal with an emphasis on poetry arts in human service. They use about 80 pgs. of poetry in each issue—**5½ × 8½, 80 pgs., offset composed on IBM 1st choice, circulation 1,500, 1,400 subscriptions of which 50 are libraries. Subscription (3 issues): $15.75. **Sample postpaid: $5. Submit 5-10 poems. No simultaneous submissions. Previously published submissions OK but include credits. Likes cover letter. Send SASE for guidelines. Reports on same day (unless traveling). Pays 1 copy—to featured poet $10 and 4 copies. Buys negotiable rights, usually first North American or all rights. Returns rights "with** *Pudding* **permitted to reprint simultaneously."** For chapbook publication, no query. $5 reading fee. Send complete ms and cover letter with publication credits and bio. Editor often comments, will critique on request for $3/page of poetry or $35 an hour in person. Staff reviews books of poetry. Send books for review consideration. Jennifer Welch Bosveld shares, "Editors have pet peeves. I won't respond to postcards or on them. Don't individually-fold rather than group-fold poems. I don't like cover letters that state the obvious." The Pudding Writing Competitions are for single poems (deadline September 30, fee $1/poem) and for chapbook publication (deadline June 30, $9 entry fee). Pudding House Bed & Breakfast for Writers offers "luxurious rooms with desk, electric typewriter and all the free paper you can use." Free breakfast, large comfortable home ½ block from post office. Location of the Ohio Poetry Therapy Center and Library. $55 single/night, discounts available. Reservations recommended 3 months in advance. Send SASE for details.

PUEBLO POETRY PROJECT (IV-Regional), Dept. PM, 1501 E. 7th St., Pueblo CO 81001, phone (719)584-3401, director Tony Moffeit, founded 1979, **publishes poets from the Pueblo area only. If you qualify, inquire.**

PUERTO DEL SOL (II, IV-Translations, regional), New Mexico State University, Box 3E, Las Cruces NM 88003, phone (505)646-3931, founded 1972 (in present format), poetry editors Joseph Somoza and Kathleene West (on alternate years). "We publish a literary magazine twice per year. Interested in poems, fiction, essays, photos, originals and translations from the Spanish. Also (generally solicited) reviews and dialogues between writers. We want **top quality poetry, any style, from anywhere. We are sympathetic to Southwestern work, but not stereotype (cactus and adobe). Anything that is interesting and/or moving. Poetry, of course, not verse (light or otherwise)."** They have published poetry by Bill Evans, Naton Leslie, Anselm Hollo, Philip Garrison, Cecelia Hagen, J.B. Goodenough and Marilyn Hacker. The 6 × 9, flat-spined, professionally printed magazine, matte card cover with art, has a circulation of 650, 300 subscriptions of which 25-30 are libraries. 40-50 pgs. are devoted to poetry in each 150-page issue, which also includes quite a lot of prose. They use about 60 of the 700 submissions (about 3,500 poems) received each year to fill up the 90 pgs. of poetry two issues encompass. "Generally no backlog." You won't find many literary journals as attractive as this one. It has an award-caliber design (from the selection of fonts to the use of rules and type-size to enhance content). Furthermore, the journal features readable, thought invoking verse in all styles including translations. It's an exceptional publication. Single copy: $5, subscription: $7.75. **Sample postpaid: $3. Submit 5-6 pgs., 1 poem to a page. Simultaneous submissions not encouraged. Reports within 10 weeks. Pays copies. Editor comments "on every ms."** They advise: "Be true to yourself rather than worrying about current fashions—but *do* read as much of the best of contemporary poetry as you can find."

PURDUE UNIVERSITY PRESS; VERNA EMERY POETRY COMPETITION (II), 1532 S. Campus Courts-B, West Lafayette IN 47907-1532, phone (317)494-2038, founded 1960. They select 1 book/year to publish through the Verna Emery Poetry Competition. **There is a reading fee. Those interested are urged to send SASE for guidelines as particulars vary from year to year.** They have published poetry by Jim Barnes, editor of *Chariton Review*, and Fleda Brown Jackson, whose book, **Fishing With Blood**, won the GLCA New Writers Award.

PURPLE PATCH; THE FIRING SQUAD (I, II), 8 Beaconview House, Charlemont Farm, West Bromwich B7I 3PL England, founded 1975, editor Geoff Stevens, a bimonthly poetry and short prose magazine with reviews, comment and illustrations. The editor says, **"All good examples of poetry considered, but prefer 40 lines max. Do not want poor scanning verse, non-contributory swear words or obscenities, hackneyed themes."** They have recently published poetry by Ana Christy, Derek Kortlandt, Roger A. Ball, Maureen Weldon, Susanna Roxman and John Ward. As a sample the editor selected "Ely Cathedral" by Gordon Mason:

> *Pitched black like a Mogul tent*
> *it hangs its tattered anthems.*
> *It's a raven chimed to the*
> *village green. It's prostrate*
> *Gulliver arched finger-tips*
> *tentering the grass pool-table*
> *tight.*

Purple Patch is 14-20 pgs., magazine-sized, offset on plain paper, cover on the same stock with b&w drawing, side-stapled. Circulation "varies." Price is 3 issues for £2.50; US price is $5/issue (submit dollars). **Cover letter with short self-introduction preferred with submissions. Time to publication is a maximum of 4 months. Reporting time is 1 month to Great Britain, can be longer to US. Overseas contributors have to buy a copy to see their work in print. Acquires first British serial rights.** Staff reviews poetry chapbooks, short stories and tapes in 30-300 words. Send books for review consideration. *The Firing Squad* is a broadsheet of **short poetry of a protest or complaint nature,** published at irregular intervals. The editor says, "I have started to issue a broadsheet, *Purple Patch USA,* consisting of poems by U.K. poets and distributed in the U.S. only. All inquiries, submissions of work, etc., must include SASE or SAE and IRCs or $1 U.S./Canadian for return postage/reply."

PYGMY FOREST PRESS (II), P.O. Box 591, Albion CA 95410, founded 1987, editor/publisher Leonard Cirino, publishes flat-spined paperbacks. **"Forms of any kind/length to 64 pgs., subject matter open; especially ecology, prison, asylum, Third World, anarchist to far right. Prefer Stevens to Williams. I like Berryman, Roethke, Jorie Graham; dislike most 'Beats.' Open to anything I consider 'good.' Open to traditional rhyme, meter, but must be modern in subject matter."** He has published **The Sixth Day** by James Doyle; **Fresh Water** by Crawdad Nelson; **for you/on stones** by L. Cirino; **The Elk Poems** by Kate Dougherty; **Low Tech In the Great Northwest** by Gordon Black; **Obeli** by Sheila Murphy; **Windows** by Philip Corwin. **Submit 10-15 poems with bio, acknowledgements, publications. Simultaneous submissions and previously published material OK. Reports on queries in 1-3 weeks, submissions in 2-4 weeks. Pays 10% of run—about 30-50 copies. Buys first rights.** He comments on "almost every" ms. They also publish (on a subsidized basis) poetry on 30- to 60-minute audiotapes: $200-250 fee for production costs, for which author gets 60 copies of the tape. Leonard Cirino says, "I am basically an anarchist. Belong to no 'school.' I fund myself. Receive no grants or private funding. Generally politically left, but no mainline Stalinist or Marxist. Plan to publish 3-8 books yearly."

QUARRY MAGAZINE; QUARRY PRESS; POETRY CANADA (II, IV-Regional), P.O. Box 1061, Kingston, Ontario K7L 4Y5 Canada. Quarry Press founded 1952, *Poetry Canada* founded 1979, managing editor Melanie Dugan, poetry editor Barry Dempster. "Quarry Press is designed to extend the range of material, poetry and prose, generally handled by *Quarry Magazine*—that is, to represent, as accurately as may be, the range of contemporary writing. We publish chapbooks, soft-bound books of stories and poetry collections ranging from 60-150 pgs., in addition to the quarterly *Quarry Magazine.* **We are interested in seeing any and all forms of contemporary verse.** *Quarry Magazine* **maintains a practical limit on length of submissions—that we cannot consider any single piece or series by one**

author that would print at more than 10 pages. Quarry Press considers mss on an individual basis." They have published poetry by Roo Borson, Kim Maltman, Roger Nash, Jane Munro, Fred Cogswell and Don Bailey. *Quarry* is 130+ pgs., digest-sized, flat-spined, professionally printed on eggshell stock. There are 40-50 pgs. of poetry in each issue. An interesting mix of poems appears here: rhymed sequences, couplets and lyric free verse—ranging from the accessible to the experimental—all with an emphasis on voice. Press run is 1,000 for 600 subscribers of which 140 are libraries. They use about 70 of over a thousand submissions of freelance poetry received each year. "We are prompt. Very small backlog if any. 3- to 6-month lead time." Single copy: $5.95; subscription: $19. **Sample postpaid: $6.** No limit on number or time of submissions; prefers typed (or WP) double-spaced; query not necessary, though it will be answered. Cover letter with any previous publication credits required. Send SASE for guidelines. Reports in 6-8 weeks. Pays $10/poem plus 1-year subscription. Buys first North American serial rights. For book consideration, query with 6-10 samples, publication credits, brief bio and current projects. "We give priority to Canadians because of our Arts Council funding and our own interest in promoting Canadian writing." Replies to queries in 1 month, to submissions (if invited) in 6-8 weeks. Contract is for 10% royalties, 10 author's copies. Send 5×7 SASE for catalog to order samples. Editor "frequently" comments on rejections. *Poetry Canada* is a quarterly magazine featuring interviews, essays, international criticism and comprehensive reviews of every Canadian poetry book published. Each issue features a major Canadian poet on the cover and center spread (issues have featured Marlene Nourbese Philip, Di Brandt and Don McKay). Press run is 1,800 for 600 subscribers, 600 newsstand. Subscription: $16/year ($32/year institutions). **Sample postpaid: $4.55. Submit average 10 poems with SAE and IRC. Reports within 1-2 months. Pays $100/page of poetry (usually 100 lines). Buys first North American serial rights.**

THE QUARTERLY (III), 201 E. 50th St., New York NY 10022, phone (212)572-2128 or 872-8231, founded 1987, editor Gordon Lish, is a literary quarterly publishing poetry, fiction, essays and humor. They want **poetry of the "highest standards."** They have published poetry by Sharon Olds, Bruce Beasley, Jack Gilbert and Thomas Lynch. It is 256 pgs., digest-sized, flat-spined, with glossy card cover. Circulation: 15,000. Subscription: $40. **Pays contributor's copies. "Do not submit a batch of poems folded separately!"**

QUARTERLY REVIEW OF LITERATURE POETRY SERIES; QRL PRIZE AWARDS (II, IV-Subscription, translation), 26 Haslet Ave., Princeton NJ 08540, founded 1943, poetry editors T. Weiss and R. Weiss. After more than 35 years as one of the most distinguished literary journals in the country, *QRL* now appears as the *QRL Poetry Series*, in which 4-6 books, chosen in open competition, are combined in one annual volume, each of the 4-6 poets receiving $1,000 and 100 copies. The resulting 300 to 400-page volumes are printed in editions of 3,000-5,000, selling in paperback for $10, in hardback for $20. Subscription—2 paperback volumes containing 10 books: $20. **Manuscripts may be sent for reading during the months of November and May only. The collection need not be a first book. It should be 50-80 pgs. if it is a group of connected poems, a selection of miscellaneous poems, a poetic play or a work of poetry translation, or it can be a single long poem of 30 pgs. or more. Some of the individual poems may have had magazine publication. Also considers simultaneous submissions. Manuscripts in English or translated into English are also invited from outside the US. Only one ms may be submitted per reading period and must include a SASE.** "Since poetry as a thriving art must depend partly upon the enthusiasm and willingness of those directly involved to join in its support, the editors require that **each ms be accompanied by a subscription to the series.**"

‡**QUARTOS MAGAZINE (IV-Subscription)**, BCM-Writer, London WC1N 3XX United Kingdom, founded 1987, editor Suzanne Riley, appears every other month. This is a "creative writers publication which includes reviews usually submitted by subscribers. **Poems included are usually those previously accepted by other editors or competition judges to help other readers establish a clear idea of editorial requirements. Submissions accepted are the work of our readers.**" The newsletter is magazine-sized, 28 pgs. folded. Press run is 1,200 for that many subscribers, of which 20 are libraries. Subscription: $25. **Sample postpaid: $2. Pays 1 copy.** "The Writers Handbook lists us as the 'best single source of UK poetry competitions anywhere. We would accept articles of 800 words on poetry writing from any source." **Pays $10.**

Use the General Index to find the page number of a specific publisher. If the publisher you are seeking is not listed, check the " '93-'94 Changes" list at the end of this section.

QUEEN OF ALL HEARTS (IV-Religious), 26 S. Saxon Ave., Bay Shore NY 11706, phone (516)665-0726, founded 1950, poetry editor Joseph Tusiani, is a magazine-sized bimonthly that uses **poetry** "**dealing with Mary, the Mother of Jesus—inspirational poetry. Not too long.**" They have published poetry by Fernando Sembiante and Alberta Schumacher. The professionally printed magazine, 48 pgs., heavy stock, various colors of ink and paper, liberal use of graphics and photos, has approximately 5,000 subscriptions at $15/year. Single copy: $2.50. **Sample postpaid: $3.** They receive 40-50 submissions of poetry/year, use 2/issue. **Submit double-spaced mss. Reports within 3-4 weeks. Pays 6 copies (sometimes more) and complimentary subscription. Sometimes editor comments on rejections.** His advice: "Try and try again! Inspiration is not automatic!"

‡**ELLERY QUEEN'S MYSTERY MAGAZINE (IV-Themes)**, 1540 Broadway, New York NY 10036, founded 1941, appears 13 times a year, primarily using short stories of mystery, crime or suspense. "**We also publish short limericks and verse pertaining to the mystery field.**" As a sample the editor selected these lines from "Another Grave Tone" by James Holding:

> *Here lies a hitman, David Stout,*
> *Whose major talent was rubbing out*
> *Whoever you wanted to turn up dead*
> *With a thirty-eight-caliber hole in the head.*
> *David was expert—a pro, of course,*
> *A cold-blooded killer without remorse—*

EQMM is 160 pgs., 5 × 7¾, professionally printed newsprint, flat-spined with glossy paper cover. Subscription: $31. **Sample: $2.25 (available on newsstands). No previously published poems; simultaneous submissions OK. Reports in 3 months. Pays $5-20.**

QUEEN'S QUARTERLY: A CANADIAN REVIEW (II, IV-Regional), Queen's University, Kingston, Ontario K7L 3N6 Canada, phone (613)545-2667, founded 1893, editor Boris Castel, is "a general interest intellectual review featuring articles on science, politics, humanities, arts and letters, extensive book reviews, some poetry and fiction. **We are especially interested in poetry by Canadian writers. Shorter poems preferred.**" They have published poetry by Evelyn Lau, Sue Nevill and Raymond Souster. There are about 12 pgs. of poetry in each issue, 6 × 9, 224 pgs., circulation 3,500. They receive about 400 submissions of poetry/year, use 40. Subscription: $20 Canadian, US subscribers may pay either $20 US or $25 Canadian. **Sample postpaid: $5 US. Submit no more than 6 poems at once. No simultaneous submissions. Reports in 1 month. Pays usually $50 (Canadian)/poem, "but it varies," plus 2 copies.**

QUICK BROWN FOX (II); MAD DOG PRESS (V), P.O. Box 47, Youngwood PA 15697, founded 1987, editor K.K. Shields, publisher Bill Shields. **Mad Dog Press does not accept unsolicited mss.** *Quick Brown Fox* is a broadsheet of 1-3 pgs. which appears irregularly using "**informed contemporary poems. Shorter poems (20 lines or less) have a better chance, although a solid longer poem will be considered.**" As for sample lines of poetry, the editor says, "I continue to resist including sample lines because it may prejudice people one way or another. And, six lines cannot truly indicate the breadth or depth of what I'll accept." **She will consider simultaneous submissions and previously published poems. Sometimes comments on rejections. Pays 5 copies. Authors retain rights.** She advises: "Read poetry incessantly, from Catullus to Bukowski and everything in between and beyond. Read, read, read. It's the only way to find your *own* style." They add, "We became disillusioned with the alternative press for awhile, but we are beginning to publish *qbf* and selected one-shot 'zines from time to time. Your work may fit our publications if you write poetry that sets the heart or soul on fire. That is our only criterion. We remain cautious but hopeful."

‡**RACKHAM JOURNAL OF THE ARTS AND HUMANITIES (RAJAH) (II, IV-Students, themes)**, 411 Mason Hall, The University of Michigan, Ann Arbor MI 48109, phone (313)763-2351, founded 1971, editor Thomas Mussio, is "primarily a forum for the critical and **creative work of graduate students of the University of Michigan**" but each year they include three contributions by others. It is an annual journal with emphasis on criticism, fiction, poetry and translation. **Open to all varieties of poetry, but usually limited to 1-2 pgs. in length. Nothing "pornographic or grotesque."** They have published poetry by Duchess Edmée de la Rochefoucauld and John Ditsky. The editor selected these sample lines by David L. Labiosa:

> *The small dog makes me think*
> *of our island in Puerto Rico:*
> *confronted with the ponderous*
> *importer, person government . . .*

RAJAH is 6 × 9, professionally printed, 120 pgs., flat-spined, with b&w glossy card cover, using illustrations, photos, ads. Of 50 submissions from non-university graduate students they accept three. Press run is 400 for 200 subscriptions of which 150 are libraries. It sells for $3 to individuals,

$6 to institutions. **Sample postpaid: $1.75. Include cover letter with short bio (previous publications), address and telephone number with submissions. No simultaneous submissions, but previously published poems OK. Reports in 4-6 months. Pays 2 copies. Editor sometimes comments on rejections.**

RADCLIFFE QUARTERLY (IV-Specialized), 10 Garden St., Cambridge MA 02138, phone (617)495-8608, editor Ruth Whitman, is an alumnae quarterly that **publishes alumnae and college-related poets.** They have published poetry by Patricia Filipowska and Rhea Kovar Sossen. *RQ* is magazine-sized, with glossy full-color paper cover. They receive about 50 poems/year, use 3 poems/issue. Press run is 31,000 for 30,500 subscribers. **Samples free to anyone. No pay.** "Radcliffe College holds copyright on most poems." Reviews books of poetry in 250 words, single format. The Dean's office sponsors a contest for poets, winners printed in the quarterly. Must be a Radcliffe student to enter.

RADDLE MOON (II, IV-Form), Dept. PM, 2239 Stephens St., Vancouver, British Columbia V6K 3W5 Canada or 9060 Ardmore Dr., Sidney, British Columbia V8L 3S1 Canada, phone (604)736-9769, founded 1985, editor Susan Clark, appears twice a year using **"language-centered and 'new lyric' poetry."** They have published poetry by Claude Royet-Journoud, Lyn Hejinian, Rosmarie Waldrop and Leslie Scalapino. The editor describes it as 6×9, flat-spined, 100+ pgs. Press run 700. **Sample postpaid: $5. Reports in 2-3 months. Pays subscription.**

RADIANCE: THE MAGAZINE FOR LARGE WOMEN (I, IV-Women), P.O. Box 30246, Oakland CA 94604, phone (510)482-0680, founded 1984, publisher/editor Alice Ansfield, appears quarterly. **"Keeping in mind that our magazine is geared toward large women, we look for poetry from women of any size who don't accept society's stereotypical standards of beauty and weight—but who celebrate women's bodies, sexuality, search for self-esteem and personal growth."** As a sample she quotes "Homage to My Hips" by Lucille Clifton:

> these hips are big hips
> they need space to
> move around in.
> they don't fit into little
> petty places. these hips
> are free hips.
> they don't like to be held back.
> these hips have never been enslaved,
> they go where they want to go
> they do what they want to do.
> these hips are mighty hips.
> these hips are magic hips.
> i have known them
> to put a spell on a man and
> spin him like a top!

Radiance is magazine-sized, professionally printed on glossy stock with full-color paper cover, 60 pgs., saddle-stapled, 2-color graphics, photos and ads, circulation 10,000 to 4,000 subscriptions, 2,500 selling on newsstands or in bookstores, 1,000 sent as complimentary copies to media and clothing stores for large women. Subscription: $15/year. **Sample postpaid: $3.50. Submit double-spaced, typed ms. Editor usually comments on rejections. Send SASE for guidelines. Reports in 2-3½ months. Pays $10-30. Buys one-time rights.** Reviews related books of poetry in 500-800 words.

RAG MAG; BLACK HAT PRESS (I, II), P.O. Box 12, Goodhue MN 55027, phone (612)923-4590, founded 1982, poetry editor Beverly Voldseth, accepts **poetry of** "any length or style. No pornographic SM violent crap." They have published poetry by Bill Keith, James Lineberger, Laurel Mills and JoAnne Makela. As a sample the editor selected these lines from "Life Here & Hereafter; a Phototropism" by Gayle Nordling:

> Looking inside an immense home on a woody,
> back-lit lot you see a woman lying
> beside the kitchen door. She is slaughtered.
> One eye bulges, two gunshot holes in her
> skull gleam copper-bright as new pennies.
> Her hands lie open—they are unclouded and
> turning blue at the edges, like an
> advancing morning sky.

Rag Mag, appearing twice a year, is 80-112 pgs., perfect-bound, 6×9, professionally printed in dark type with ads for books, matte colored card cover. The editor says she accepts about 10%

of poetry received. Press run is 250 for 80 subscriptions of which 8 are libraries. Subscription: $10. **Sample postpaid: $6. "Send 6-8 of your best with brief bio. Something that tells a story, creates images, speaks to the heart." Pays 1 copy.** Reviews books of poetry. Open to unsolicited reviews. Poets may also send books for review consideration. **They may publish chapbook or paperback collections of poetry under the imprint of Black Hat Press. Query first. Simultaneous submissions and previously printed material OK. Reports in 6 weeks. Detailed comments provided "sometimes." Financial arrangements for book publication vary.** They have published Riki Kölbl Nelson's English/German poems about living in 2 worlds/2 languages, **Borders/Grenzen**, 128 pages plus the author's artwork. In addition, they published two books of poems by Karen Herseth Wee in 1993.

RAINBOW CITY EXPRESS (II, IV-Spiritual, nature, women, aesthetics), P.O. Box 8447, Berkeley CA 94707-8447, founded 1988, editor Helen B. Harvey, is a semiannual journal using **"excellent evocative material pertaining to individual spiritual insights and experiences, God-in-nature, women's issues and creative unfolding. 30 lines maximum. No rhyming poems! No infantile beginners.** Please obtain and study at least one issue of *RCE* prior to submitting any manuscript." The editor describes it as 60-80 pgs., magazine-sized, side-stapled, with "exquisite art and graphics, uplifting essays and poems." They accept about 25-45 poems/year. Press run 500-1,000. Subscription: $12. **Sample postpaid: $7. Pays 1 copy.** They offer "sporadic contests with cash prizes and publication of winners."

RAMBUNCTIOUS PRESS; RAMBUNCTIOUS REVIEW (II, IV-Regional), 1221 W. Pratt, Chicago IL 60626, founded 1982, poetry editors Mary Dellutri, Richard Goldman, Beth Hausler and Nancy Lennon. *Rambunctious Review* appears once yearly in a handsomely printed, saddle-stapled, 7 × 10 format, 48 pgs. They want **"spirited, quality poetry, fiction, photos and graphics. Some focus on local work, but all work is considered."** They receive 500-600 submissions a year and use 50-60. They have a circulation of about 500 with 200 subscriptions. Single copy: $3.50. **Sample postpaid: $4. Will consider simultaneous submissions. No submissions accepted June 1 through August 31. No queries.** Occasionally comments on mss. **Reports in 9 months. Pays 2 copies.** They run annual contests in poetry, fiction and short drama.

RANGER INTERNATIONAL PRODUCTIONS; LION PUBLISHING; ROAR RECORDING (III), P.O. Box 71231, Milwaukee WI 53211-7331, phone (414)332-7474, founded 1969, editor Martin Jack Rosenblum, publishes **"objectivist/projectivist poetry, primarily with action subjects by adventurers – such as the Harley poetry –** in flat-spined paper and hardcover chapbooks." They have published poetry by Karl Young, Howard McCord, Toby Olson and Carl Rakosi. They publish about 3 books a year. **Query with cover letter including "something interesting to say regarding your work." Payment "negotiable." Editor comments on submissions "always."** He says, "Poetry has been swept into an academic corner and dusted off of daily living spaces and this is what Ranger International Productions works against: we want to bring poetry out of academics and back into life's daily platform. Write hard, accept no public money and achieve honesty and integrity personally while studying the master poets in school or out. Control of the forms is essential. Control of the life is absolutely required."

RANGER RICK MAGAZINE (III), 8925 Leesburg Pike, Vienna VA 22184, founded 1967, associate editor Deborah Churchman, is a monthly nature magazine for children aged 6-12. **They want "short, funny verses for children about nature and the environment. No religious, preachy or difficult poetry."** They have recently published poetry by John Ciardi and Charles Ghigna. *RR* is 46 pgs., full color. They receive 100-200 submissions/year, "may accept one." Press run is 850,000. Subscription: $15. **Sample postpaid: $2. Previously published poems OK; no simultaneous submissions.** Time between acceptance and publication is 2-5 years. **Seldom comments on rejections. Send SASE for guidelines. Reports in 2 months. Pays $5/line plus 2 copies. Buys all rights. Return is "negotiable."** The editor says, "Think: Will kids understand these words? Will it hook them? Will an 8-year-old want to read this instead of playing Nintendo?"

RARACH PRESS (V), 1005 Oakland Dr., Kalamazoo MI 49008, phone (616)388-5631, founded 1981, owner Ladislav Hanka, is a "small bibliophilic press specializing in hand-printing, hand-binding with original artwork. The material is either in Czech or, if English, dealing with environmentalist subject matter." He has printed books of poetry by James Armstrong, Richard Neugebauer, Bennet Mitchell and Rainer Maria Rilke. "Authors tend to be friends, acquaintances or dead. They are given a portion of the books or a portion of sales after the fact. **I do not care to receive unsolicited mss.** I pity the lot of you. I fully expect most of my books to eventually be taken apart and sold for the artwork when they pass from the present collector of bibliophili to some philistine. This means the poetry will be lost . . . I really sell my books for the price of the binding and artwork."

RARITAN QUARTERLY (III), Dept. PM, 31 Mine St., New Brunswick NJ 08903, phone (908)932-7887, founded 1982, editor Richard Poirier. "We publish very little poetry. We publish *almost* no unsolicited poetry, so it would be misleading to encourage submissions." They have published poetry by J.D. McClatchy, James Merrill, Richard Howard and Robert Pinsky. It is 6×9, flat-spined, 150+ pgs., with matte card cover, professionally printed. The few poems appearing here (including sequences and translations) tend toward free verse. Press run 4,000 for 3,500 subscriptions of which 800 are libraries. Subscription: $16. **Sample postpaid: $5. Pays $100/submission if accepted.** They review recent poetry books and chapbooks. Poetry published in this quarterly was included in **Best American Poetry 1992**.

RASHI (IV-Ethnic), Box 1198, Hamilton, New Zealand, founded 1985, editor Norman Simms, uses poetry on "Jewish topics in English or any Jewish language such as Hebrew, Yiddish, Ladino, etc." They do not want poetry that is "pompous, self-indulgent nonsense." They have published poems by Anne Ranasinghe and Simon Lichman. *Rashi* is the literary supplement of the monthly *New Zealand Chronicle*. They accept about 25 of 40 poems received/year. Circulation is over 2,000. Subscription: $30. **Sample postpaid: $4. Subscription "recommended, but not necessary." Cover letter with some background on the author required. Reports in 1 month. Pays 1 copy. Editor comments on rejections for $5/page.** Open to unsolicited reviews. Poets may also send books for review consideration. He says, "This is a special part of our overall projects. We would like to see multilingualism develop, reinterpretation of ancient and medieval traditions."

THE RAVEN (I, IV-Science fiction/fantasy/horror), Route 5 Box 504, Union SC 29379, founded 1990, editor Micheal Nave, is a quarterly magazine of poetry and fiction which "publishes fantasy science fiction with a slant toward soft horror." They want **poetry of a "mystical, thought-provoking nature. 20 lines or less. 5 poems/submission. Any style or form. No witches, chants, gore, sex or nursery rhymes."** They have published poetry by John Grey, Shannon Riley and Anita Barnard. As a sample the editor selected these lines from "Ruined Birds" by Robert Dunbar:

> *Across a broken pillar*
> *Floats the shadow of a raven*
> *How romantic*
> *And in the shattered shadows,*
> *The phantoms of this dusty heat*
> *Watch me . . . and wait.*

The Raven is 40-45 pgs., digest-sized, laser-printed, saddle-stapled, with b&w artwork. They accept about 30-40% of the poetry received each year. Press run is 500 for 100 subscribers of which 5 are libraries. Subscription: $12. **Sample postpaid: $4. No previously published poems or simultaneous submissions. Always comments on rejections. Send SASE for guidelines. Reports in "usually 2 weeks." Pays 2 copies.** "Each issue has a feature poet on the center pages—poet featured receives a free year's subscription." They also offer a poetry contest in each issue. Entry fee: $3 for each 5-poem submission. 1st prize: $25; 2nd prize: $10; 3rd prize: $5. Winners published in the magazine. The editor says, "My goal is to see new talent in print. I enjoy working with under-published poets and try to encourage, try to build on strong points, without harsh criticism—never use form rejection slips. Please read guidelines—nearly 30-40% of my rejections are for not following guidelines. If you have just fallen in love with Mary Lou and have written a beautiful poem all about the moon-in-June, please send it to her. I don't want it. Buying a sample copy encouraged but not required."

RAW DOG PRESS; POST POEMS (IV-Humor), 128 Harvey Ave., Doylestown PA 18901, phone (215)345-6838, founded 1977, poetry editor R. Gerry Fabian, "publishes Post Poems annual—a post-card series. **We want short poetry (3-7 lines) on any subject. The positive poem or the poem of under-stated humor always has an inside track. No taboos, however. All styles considered. Anything with rhyme had better be immortal."** They have published poetry by ave jeanne, Lyn Lifshin, Philip Miller, Conger Beasley, Jr. and the editor, R. Gerry Fabian, who selected his poem, "Arc Welder," as a sample:

> *After years of burning*
> *he pressed his lips against hers*
> *and sealed out any doubt.*

Send SASE for catalog to buy samples. The editor "always" comments on rejections. Pays copies. Acquires all rights. Returns rights on mention of first publication. Sometimes reviews books of poetry. He says he will offer criticism for a fee; "if someone is desperate to publish and is willing to pay, we will use our vast knowledge to help steer the ms in the right direction. We will advise against it, but as P.T. Barnum said . . . . Raw Dog Press welcomes new poets and detests second-rate poems from 'name' poets. We exist because we are dumb like a fox, but even a fox takes care of its own."

REAL (RE ARTS & LETTERS) (II, IV-Bilingual, translations, humor), Dept. PM, Box 13007, Stephen F. Austin State University, Nacogdoches TX 75962, phone (409)568-2101, founded 1968, editor Lee Schultz, is a "Liberal Arts Forum" using short fiction, drama, reviews and interviews; contains editorial notes and personalized "Contributors' Notes"; printed in the winter and summer. They "hope to use from 15 to 35 pages of poetry per issue, one poem per page (typeset in editor's office). Last two issues had submissions from thirty-eight states, Great Britain, Italy and Israel." **They receive between 10-35 poems/week. "We presently do not receive enough formal or witty/ironic pieces. We need a better balance between open and generic forms. We're also interested in critical writings on poems or writing poetry and translations with a bilingual format (permissions from original author)."** As a sample the editor selected these lines from "Within the Womb of This Mountain" by Jenna Fedock:

> *We will not see him again,*
> *"Lord have mercy,"*
> *but only in the black box wedged in an aisle,*
> *heavy lid crushing our heads. We chant*
> *"Vichnaya pamyat, Vichnaya pamyat, Vichnaya pamyat,"*
> *trying to cast it off—but cannot.*

It is handsomely printed, "reserved format," perfect-bound with line drawings and photos. Simply one of the most readable literary magazines published today, *REAL* welcomes all styles and forms that display craft, insight and accessibility. Circulation approximately 400, "more than half of which are major college libraries." Subscriptions also in Great Britain, Ireland, Italy, Holland, Puerto Rico, Brazil and Canada. **Sample postpaid: $5. Submit original and copy. "Editors prefer a statement that ms is not being simultaneously submitted; however, this fact is taken for granted when we receive a ms."** Writer's guidelines for SASE. They acknowledge receipt of submissions and strive for a 1-month decision. Submissions during summer semesters may take longer. **"We will return poems rather than tie them up for more than a one-issue backlog (6-9 months)."** Pays copies. Reviews are assigned, but queries about doing reviews are welcome.

REALITY STREET EDITIONS (V), 4 Howard Court, Peckham Rye, London SE15 3PH United Kingdom, is the joint imprint of Reality Studios and Street Editions, editors Ken Edwards and Wendy Mulford. They publish 2 paperbacks/year. They have published books of poetry by Allen Fisher, Tom Raworth and Stephen Rodefer, but **currently do not accept unsolicited mss.** Their US distributor is Small Press Distribution, 1814 San Pablo Ave., Berkeley CA 94302.

RECONSTRUCTIONIST (IV-Ethnic), Church Rd. & Greenwood Ave., Wyncote PA 19095, founded 1935, poetry editor Jeremy Garber, is a Jewish cultural and intellectual review published 4 times/year. **"We publish about 4 poems per year—either on Jewish themes or in some other way related to Jewish spiritual quests—short poems up to about 30-35 lines."** They have published poetry by Gabriel Preil, Shulamis Yelin and Marcia Falk. As a sample the editor selected these lines (poet unidentified):

> *Come, share the watermelon I have sliced.*
> *My yearning for the hurricane*
> *fills yawning distance with our pain*

Reconstructionist is 32 pgs., magazine-sized, professionally printed on heavy stock with matte card cover, saddle-stapled. Subscription: $20. **Sample postpaid: $3. No simultaneous submissions. Editor sometimes comments on rejections. Reports in 1-2 months, delay to publication 1-2 years. Pays $36/poem plus 5 copies.**

THE RED CANDLE PRESS; CANDELABRUM (II), 9 Milner Rd., Wisbech PE13 2LR England, founded 1970, editor M.L. McCarthy, M.A., administrative editor Helen Gordon, B.A., was "founded to encourage poets working in **traditional-type verse, metrical unrhymed or metrical rhymed.** We're more interested in poems than poets: that is, we're interested in what sort of poems an author produces, not in his or her personality." They publish the magazine, *Candelabrum*, twice yearly (April and October), occasional postcards, paperbound staple-spined chapbooks and occasional poetry leaflets. For all of these they want **"good-quality metrical verse, with rhymed verse specially wanted. Elegantly cadenced free verse is acceptable. No weak stuff (moons and Junes, loves and doves, etc.) No chopped-up prose pretending to be free verse. Any length up to about 50 lines for *Candelabrum*, any subject, including eroticism (but not porn)—satire, love poems, nature lyrics, philosophical—any subject, but nothing racist or sexist."** They have published poetry by Jon Taylor, John Laycock, David Castleman, William Davey, Ann Keith and Tony Esolen. The editors offer these lines by Paris Flammonde as a sample:

> *Tomorrow is a place where dreams begin*
> *To flutter like a fancy; feather-kissed*
> *Flamingo, arc'd awake and to its tryst;—*
> *A field whereon the vanquished always win.*

The digest-sized magazine, staple-spined, small type, exemplifies their intent to "pack in as much as possible, wasting no space, and try to keep a neat appearance with the minimum expense." They get in about 44 pgs. (some 60 poems) in each issue. Circulation: 900 with 700 subscriptions of which 22 are libraries. **Sample: $4 in bills only; checks not accepted.** They receive about 2,000 submissions/year, use approximately 5% of those, sometimes holding over poems for the next year or longer. **"Submit any time. IRCs essential if return wished, and please check the weight—each poem on a separate sheet please, neat typescripts or neat** *legible* **manuscripts.** *Please* **no dark, oily photostats, no colored ink (only black or blue). Author's name and address on each sheet, please."** No simultaneous submissions. Reports in about 2 months. Pays one contributor's copy. Staff occasionally reviews books of poetry in 500 words, single format. Send books for review consideration. The books published by **Red Candle Press** "have been at our invitation to the poet, and at our expense. We pay the author a small royalty-advance, but he/ she keeps the copyright." The editor comments, "Traditional-type poetry is much more popular here in Britain, and we think also in the United States, now than it was in 1970, when we founded *Candelabrum*, though some people are still rather scared of it. We always welcome new poets, especially traditionalists, and we like to hear from the U.S.A. as well as from here at home. General tip: Study the various outlets at the library, or buy a sample, or borrow a copy from a subscriber, before you go to the expense of submitting your work."

‡**RED CEDAR REVIEW (II)**, 17C Morrill Hall, Dept. of English, Michigan State University, East Lansing MI 48824, editor Jackie Justice, founded 1963, is a literary biannual which uses poetry—"any subject, form, length; the only requirement is originality and vision." The editors encourage work "beyond animal poems, flora and fauna poems, etc. No pornography." They have recently published poetry by Diane Wakoski, Margaret Atwood and Stuart Dybek. As a sample the editor selected these lines by Matt Marinovich:

> *Beats Times Square, Jeff says,*
> *where once we squeezed into*
> *a sticky peep show booth*
> *to watch a naked woman cry*
> *because it was Christmas Eve*
> *and she was coming down.*

The review is 80 pgs., digest-sized. They receive about 400 submissions/year, use 30. Press run is 400 for 200 subscribers of which 100 are libraries. Subscription: $10. **Sample postpaid: $2. Current issue: $5. Submit only previously unpublished works. Reports in 2 months, sometimes longer. Pays 2 copies.** Editor sometimes comments on rejections. Reviews books of poetry. Open to unsolicited reviews. Poets may also send books for review consideration. They also offer an annual writing contest. Entry fee: $5/poem, $10/short story. Prizes: $150 poetry, $300 fiction. Winners are published in *Red Cedar Review*, finalists mentioned. All entrants receive copy. Send SASE for deadline information.

RED DANCEFLOOR (I, II); RED DANCEFLOOR PRESS (III), P.O. Box 7392, Van Nuys CA 91409-7392, phone (818)785-7650, founded 1989, editor David Goldschlag, appears 3 times/year (in September, January and May) publishing poetry, fiction, interviews, profiles, reviews, photos and art. "No restrictions on form, length or subject matter. We want poetry that is well thought out—not a first draft. If you send us rhyme it should have a specific purpose and work; would consider a good sestina." They have published poetry by Michael C Ford, David Lake, Glenn Bach, Mario René Padilla and Charles Webb. As a sample the editor selected these lines from "Moments in the Real World" by Virginia Anderson:

> *He pinched her nose,*
> *pulled her face into his hands,*
> *a soft scarf.*
> *leaving the rest of her at loose ends.*

The magazine is digest-sized, 90-130 pgs., flat-spined, laser printed, with glossy card cover. Press run is 400. Single copy postpaid: $7. **Sample postpaid: $5. Previously published poems and simultaneous submissions OK,** "but please note. A short cover letter is appreciated. Submit 5-7 poems." **Reads submissions from September 1 through May 31 only. Send SASE for guidelines. Reports in 6-8 weeks. Pays 1 copy and % off additional copies.** Acquires one-time rights. Reviews books of poetry. Open to unsolicited reviews. Poets may also send books for review consideration. "Please send one copy to the press. The author will then be notified to whom/where to send another copy." Red Dancefloor Press publishes full-length books, chapbooks and poetry audiotapes. "The author may want to get a copy of a book, chap or tape before submitting to the press." Book: $7.95, chapbook: $3.50, audiotape: $8—plus $1 postage and handling for each. "**We openly accept submissions for books, chaps and tapes, but** *please* **query first with 10 samples and a cover letter explaining which area of our press you are interested in. Listing credits in a cover letter is fine, but don't go crazy."** They also publish the *International Contemporary Poets*

Directory. "It lists names, addresses and phone numbers of poets, coffeehouses, literary bookstores and presses throughout the world. It is very useful to publishers, editors and poets who would like to correspond with other poets. Send SASE with a note specifying it is for *ICPD*." The editor says, "The mag is of high quality and has been called one of L.A.'s best. We desperately need art for covers. Send SASE and a note for specs."

RED HERRING POETS; MATRIX; RED HERRING PRESS; RED HERRING CHAPBOOK SERIES; CHANNING-MURRAY FOUNDATION (IV-Membership), 1209 W. Oregon St., Urbana IL 61801, phone (217)344-1176, founded 1975, director of Red Herring Poets Ruth S. Walker. The Red Herring Poets is a workshop that publishes its members' work, after they have attended at least 5 meetings, in their annual magazine, *Matrix*, and, for those who have been members for at least 2 years and given 2 public readings, one chapbook/year.

RED RAMPAN' PRESS; RED RAMPAN' REVIEW (V); RED RAMPAN' BROADSIDE SERIES (IV-Form), 4707 Fielder St., Midland TX 79707-2817, phone (915)697-7689, founded 1981, poetry editor Larry D. Griffin. **"For 1994 we will consider long poems for Red Rampan' Broadside Series."** *RRR* is an "eclectic review quarterly." The editor says it is 6×9, 48-60 pgs., with a press run of 300, **"presently not accepting poetry and only using staff-written reviews."** The press plans to publish flat-spined paperback collections.

THE REDNECK REVIEW OF LITERATURE (I, IV-Regional), 2919 N. Downer Ave., Milwaukee WI 53211, phone (414)332-6881, founded 1975, editor Penelope Reedy, is a semiannual magazine publishing poetry, fiction, drama and essays **dealing with the contemporary West. The editor wants to see "any form, length or style."** She does not want **"ethereal ditties about nothing; obscure."** She has published poetry by R.M. Davis, C. Bukowski, Charlotte Wright, Lawson Inada, Ed Abbey and Suzanne Scollon. As a sample the editor selected these lines by Stephen Lyons:

> *When women go mad out*
> *west, they stack the*
> *bottles behind the*
> *dryer . . .*

The magazine, which appears in the spring and fall each year, is magazine-sized, offset, perfect-bound, some advertising. Circulation is 500, of which 200 are subscriptions and 100-150 are newsstand sales. **Sample postpaid: $7. Writers should submit "2-3 poems at a time, letter quality — don't like simultaneous submissions. Please send SASE with *enough* postage to return mss." Criticism is sometimes given. Rejected mss are reported on immediately, and no accepted mss are held beyond 3 issues. Pays 1 copy.** Reviews books of poetry. The editor says, "Rethink what 'the West' means to American culture — as a concept rather than merely a geographical area."

REFLECT (IV-Form/style), 3306 Argonne Ave., Norfolk VA 23509, founded 1979, poetry editor W.S. Kennedy. They use **"spiral poetry: featuring an inner-directed concern with sound (euphony), mystical references or overtones, and objectivity — rather than personal and emotional poems. No love poems, pornography, far left propaganda; nothing overly sentimental. (Don't write yourself into the poem.)"** They have published poetry by B.Z. Niditch, Joe Malone, Ruth Wildes Schuler and Stan Proper. As a sample the editor selected these lines from "Euphonies" by Marikay Brown:

> *The spring wind is a silver flute*
> *Piping lilac-hyacinth*
> *Passionatos of perfume.*
> *The summer wind — a green guitar*
> *Of fluttering leaves and grasses*
> *Strummed on fretted sunlight gold . . .*

The quarterly is digest-sized, 48 pgs., saddle-stapled, typescript. Subscription: $8. **Sample postpaid: $2. All submissions should be *single-spaced* and should fit on one typed page. Editor sometimes comments on rejections. Guidelines available for SASE. Reports within a month. No backlog. Pays 1 copy. Acquires first rights.** Occasionally reviews books of poetry in 50 words or more. *Reflect* ranked #5 in the "Open Markets" category of the June 1993 *Writer's Digest* Poetry 60 list. This category ranks those publications most open to both free and formal verse.

RENDITIONS: A CHINESE-ENGLISH TRANSLATION MAGAZINE (IV-Translations), Research Center for Translation, CUHK, Shatin, NT, Hong Kong, editor Dr. Eva Hung, appears twice a year. **"Contents exclusively translations from Chinese, ancient and modern."** They also publish a paperback series of Chinese literature in English translation. They have published translations of the poetry of Gu Cheng, Shu Ting, Mang Ke and Bei Dao. *Renditions* is magazine-sized, 180 pgs., flat-spined, elegantly printed, often with side-by-side Chinese and English texts, using some b&w and color drawings and photos, with glossy card cover. **Sample postpaid: $13. Reports in 2 months.** Pays "honorarium" plus 2 copies. Use British spelling. They "will consider" book mss, for which they would like a query with sample poems. Books pay 10% royalties plus 10 copies. Mss usually not returned. Editor sometimes comments on rejections.

RENEGADE (II), P.O. Box 314, Bloomfield Hills MI 48303, phone (313)972-5580, founded 1988, editors Miriam Jones and Michael Nowicki, appears twice a year using stories, essays and poems. "We are an eclectic publication. There is no preference for form or style; we simply wish to see polished work of good quality. Poems are generally of a length no more than 200 lines, no less than 10 lines. We try to avoid anything that is anarchistic, antifeminist or of a derogatory nature to any group of persons or individuals." They have published poetry by John Sinclair, M.L. Liebler, Linda Nemec Foster and Laurence Pike. *Renegade* is 32 pgs., digest-sized, laser-printed, with matte card cover, b&w drawings and graphics. Ads welcome. They accept about 5% of 300 mss of 5 poems or less. Press run is 200 for 20 subscribers, free to libraries and editors of other literary journals, 50 shelf sales. Subscription: $5.90. **Sample postpaid: $3. Editor comments on submissions "often." Reports in 3-6 months. Pays 1 copy, 2 on request. Acquires all rights. Returns rights to author free of charge.** Reviews books of poetry. Open to unsolicited reviews. Poets may also send books for review consideration to the attention of Larry Snell. "We put together Warlords of the Subculture Poetry Contest. People interested should inquire first."

RESPONSE (IV-Ethnic, students), 9th Floor, 27 W. 20th St., New York NY 10011, phone (212)675-1168, fax (212)929-3459, founded 1966, poetry editor Adam Margolis, is a "contemporary Jewish review publishing poetry, fiction and essays **by students and young adult authors." The only specification for poetry is that it be on a Jewish theme and have some significant Jewish content.** They have published poetry by Sharon Kessler, Sue Saniel Elkind and Shulamith Bat-Yisrael. As a sample the editor chose these lines from "Old Nazis Don't Die (They Move To South America)" by Sylvia Warsh:

> *The jungles of Brazil teem*
> *with a new strain of*
> *European animal, serpents of*
> *such camouflage that their own*
> *Bavarian mothers would not*
> *recognize them,*
> *insects that thrust hard*
> *consonants into a victim's*
> *heart and suck him dry,*
> *then use his shell*
> *for a livingroom.*

They look for "creative, challenging and chutzapadik writing" from young writers. The quarterly is 64 pgs., flat-spined, 6×9, professionally printed on heavy stock, with a glossy "varnished" cover with artwork. Circulation 1,600 with 600 subscribers of which 30% are libraries. 1,000 distributed through bookstores and newsstands. Subscription: $16 ($10 for students); $20 for institutions. **Sample postpaid: $2. Cover letter with bio and previous publications required with submissions. Reports in about 2 months. 6 months between acceptance and publication. Pays 2 copies/poem published. Acquires all rights.** Occasionally reviews books of Jewish poetry. Open to unsolicited reviews. Poets may also send books for review consideration.

THE REVIEW (I), (formerly *The Belladonna Review*), P.O. Box 3331, Montebello CA 90640, founded 1992, editor Paul Quintero, is a biannual which **"accepts all poetry; open to length, subject matter and style."** The editor says it is about 30 pgs., photocopied. Subscription: $7. **Sample postpaid: $4. Previously published poems OK; no simultaneous submissions. Submit 3-5 poems with $3 reading fee. Make checks or money orders payable to the editor. Reports in 1-2 weeks. Pays 1 copy. Acquires onetime rights. Rights revert to authors upon publication.** The editor says, "I encourage beginning poets to submit here, as they have a very good chance of getting published."

REVIEW: LATIN AMERICAN LITERATURE AND ARTS (IV-Ethnic, regional, translations), Dept. PM, 680 Park Ave., New York NY 10021, phone (212)249-8950, ext. 366, founded 1967, managing editor Daniel Shapiro, is a biannual magazine which serves as a "major forum for Latin American literature in English translation and articles on Latin American visual and performing arts." **They want contemporary Latin American poetry.** They have published poetry by Jose A. Mazzotti, Mateo Rosas de Oquendo and Gregorio de Matos. As a sample the editor selected these lines from "The Forest" by Mariela Dreyfus, translated from the Spanish by Alfred J. MacAdam:

> *Dark, I wander amid the uncertain*
> *I avoid the traces of the human*
> *silence is the king in this forest*
> *here, where only your breath protects me in winter.*

It is 100+ pgs., 8½ × 11, with b&w photos of Latin American art. They receive 50-100 submissions, accept the work of 1-2 poets. Press run is 10,000 for 6,000 subscribers of which 500 are libraries. Subscription: $16 for individuals, $25 for institutions. **Sample postpaid: $9. Previously published poems and simultaneous submissions OK. Cover letter required. Do not submit mss November 15 through March 1. Seldom comments on rejections. Reports in 2-3 months. Pays $100-300.** Reviews books of poetry by Latin Americans. The *Review* is published by the Americas Society, a not-for-profit organization.

REVISTA/REVIEW INTERAMERICANA (IV-Ethnic, regional), Inter-American University of Puerto Rico, Box 5100, San Germán, Puerto Rico 00683, phone (809)264-1912, ext. 373, editor Juan R. Gonzalez Mendoza. The *Revista/Review* is a bilingual scholarly journal oriented to **Puerto Rican, Caribbean and Hispanic American and *inter-American* subjects, poetry, short stories and reviews.** Press run is 750. **Submit at least 5 poems in Spanish or English, blank verse, free verse, experimental, traditional and avant-garde, typed double-spaced. No simultaneous submissions. Cover letter with brief personal data required. Pays 2 copies.** Open to unsolicited reviews. The editor says, "It is very difficult to really get the feel of a poet's merit when only one or two poems are submitted."

RFD: A COUNTRY JOURNAL FOR GAY MEN EVERYWHERE (I, IV-Gay), P.O. Box 68, Liberty TN 37095, founded 1974, poetry editor Steven Riel. *RFD* "is a quarterly for gay men with emphasis on lifestyles outside of the gay mainstream—poetry, politics, profiles, letters." They want **poetry with "personal, creative use of language and image, relevant to journal themes, political themes. We try to publish as many poets as we can so tend to publish shorter poems and avoid epics."** They have published poetry by Antler, James Broughton, Gregory Woods and Winthrop Smith. *RFD* has a circulation of 2,600 for 1,300 subscriptions. Single copy: $5.50; subscription: $25 first class, $18 second class. **Sample postpaid: $5. Submit up to 5 poems at a time. Simultaneous submissions OK. Send SASE for guidelines. Editor sometimes comments on rejections. Reports in 6-9 months. Pays copies.** Open to unsolicited reviews. The editor says, "*RFD* looks for interesting thoughts, succinct use of language and imagery evocative of nature and gay men and love in natural settings."

RHINO (II), 8403 W. Normal, Niles IL 60714, founded 1976, editors Kay Meier and Don Hoffman, "is an annually published poetry journal. **We seek well-crafted work with fresh insights and authentic emotion by known or new writers, poems which show careful attention to form and contain surprise. Poems no longer than 3 pgs. double-spaced.**" They have published poetry by Elaine Mott, Christopher Merrill and Mark Pawlak. The editors chose as a sample the opening lines of "Grandma and the Latch-Key Child" by Carol L. Gloor:

> *In 1916 my Irish grandma clutches*
> *her needlepoint satchel on the heaving*
> *ferry from Ellis Island. She has escaped*
> *the starched convent, and the wheeling*
> *seagull air screams fish, sweat and hope.*
> *She doesn't know in four years she will marry*
> *the Midwest and a man*
> *she doesn't love.*

Rhino is a 96-page journal, digest-sized, perfect-bound, matte card cover with art, offset from typescript on high-quality paper. They receive 1,000+ submissions a year, use approximately 50-60. Press run is 500 for 100 subscribers of which 10 are libraries. **Sample: $6 plus $1.15 postage. Submit 3-5 double-spaced poems. Submission period varies. Reports in 2 months. Pays one copy. Acquires first rights only.** They offer an annual *Rhino* poetry contest with $100 prize and publication in *Rhino*.

THE RIALTO (II), 32 Grosvenor Rd., Norwich, Norfolk NR2 2PZ England, founded 1984, poetry editors John Wakeman and Michael Mackmin, wants **"poetry of intelligence, wit, compassion, skill, excellence, written by humans. Potential contributors are strongly advised to read *The Rialto* before submitting."** They have recently published poetry by Peter Redgrove, Fleur Adcock and Kenneth Koch. As a sample the editors chose the last half of "Finnish Tango," an elegy by Hans Magnus Enzensberger for Felix Pollak, translated by Reinhold Grimm:

> *All is so bright   It was half dark*
> *The little boat will not always return*
> *It is the same and yet isn't*
> *No one's around   The rock is a rock*
> *The rock ceases being a rock*
> *The rock turns into a rock again*
> *It's always like that   Nothing*
> *dissolves and nothing remains   What existed*

> is and isn't and is   No one
> can grasp that   That which existed last night
> That's easy to say   How bright
> the summer here is and how brief

The Rialto, which appears 3 times a year, is magazine-sized, 48 pgs., saddle-stapled, beautifully printed on glossy stock with glossy b&w card cover, using b&w drawings. "U.S.A. subscription is now £15 (fifteen pounds sterling). If paying in dollars, please add £3 to cover bank charges, i.e. send dollar equivalent of £18 pounds sterling. **Single issue to U.S.A. is £5 sterling. If paying in dollars, send equivalent of £8 pounds sterling."** Submit up to 6 poems with SAE and IRCs. No simultaneous submissions or previously printed poetry. Editor "only rarely" comments on rejections. Reports within 3 months. Pays £10/poem.

"The Rialto is rigorously eclectic," says Coeditor John Wakeman. "We publish poems in free verse and in strict forms, by major poets and complete beginners." The drawing on this cover was created by Sandra Banks to illustrate a poem inside the issue, "Owl Time" by Christina Dunhill. "The drawing is skillful and witty, with a touch of menace, like the poem it illustrates. It reflects not so much The Rialto's philosophy," Wakeman says, "as the style it favors— tough-minded but imaginative."

RIDGE REVIEW MAGAZINE; RIDGE TIMES PRESS (IV-Regional), Dept. PM, Box 90, Mendocino CA 95460, phone (707)964-8465, founded 1981, poetry editors Jim Tarbell and Judy Tarbell, is a "bio-regional quarterly looking at economic, political and social phenomena of the area" which uses **only poets from Northern California.** They have published poetry by Michael Sykes and Judith Tannenbaum. The 7×10 magazine, saddle-stapled, $50+$ pgs., linen card cover with art, photos and ads with text, circulation 3,500, 1,000 subscriptions, uses about 1 page of poetry/issue. Subscription: $10. **Sample postpaid: $3.85. Considers simultaneous submissions. Reports in about a week. Usually pays $10/ poem.**

RIO GRANDE PRESS; SE LA VIE WRITER'S JOURNAL (I, IV-Themes); RIO GRANDE CHAPBOOK CLUB (I, IV-Membership), P.O. Box 371371, El Paso TX 79937, founded 1987, editor Rosalie Avara. *Se La Vie Writer's Journal* is a quarterly journal with articles and cartoons about poetry and writing and monthly contests in poetry, essays and short stories. Deadlines at end of each month. Prizes are $5-25 for poems, entry fee $5 for 3 poems. Publishes 70% of mss received/quarter, **"dedicated to encouraging novice writers, poets and artists; we are interested in original, unpublished mss that reflect the 'life' theme (La Vie). Poems are judged on originality, clarity of thought and ability to evoke emotional response."** They have published poetry by Marian Ford Park, Alice Mackenzie Swaim and Marianne McNeil. *SLVWJ* is 64 pgs., digest-sized, photocopied from typescript, with blue cover, saddle-stapled. **Sample postpaid: $4. Send SASE for guidelines.** Staff reviews books of poetry. Send books for review consideration. Those interested in the Rio Grande Chapbook Club "receive 4 free books for joining, then receive 4 more quarterly—original unpublished/published poems from new and experienced poets. Includes reviews in club newsletter. Send SASE for guidelines." *Se La Vie Writer's Journal* ranked #6 in the "Traditional Verse" category of the June 1993 *Writer's Digest* Poetry 60 list.

RIVER RAT REVIEW (II), Box 24198, Lexington KY 40524, phone (606)277-8601, founded 1987, editor Daryl Rogers, is published once a year, when possible, and is **"open to any poetry devoid of bullshit. If you haven't seen the magazine, don't submit."** They have recently published poetry by Charles

Bukowski, Elliot Richman and Joan Jobe Smith. As a sample the editor selected these lines from "Stench" by Lynne Savitt:

> perhaps it's midnight
> he's driving home
> the road black as betrayal
> he smells the fingers on his right hand

The review is 40 pgs., digest-sized, saddle-stapled, photocopied on 20 lb. stock with some b&w artwork. Single copy: $3. **Reports in "days or months." Pays 1 copy.**

RIVER STYX MAGAZINE; BIG RIVER ASSOCIATION (II), 14 S. Euclid, St. Louis MO 63108, phone (314)361-0043, founded 1975, executive director Anne Makeever, is "an international, multicultural journal publishing both award-winning and relatively undiscovered writers. We feature fine art, photography, interviews, poetry and short prose." They want **"excellent poetry—thoughtful."** They have published work by Diane Wakoski, Marge Piercy, Simon Ortiz, Toni Morrison and Donald Revell. As a sample the editor selected these lines by Eric Pankey:

> Contact and intersection, a communion
> With the unrisen moon,
> Trouble the sharp doubt that delves and disciplines
> His labor and purpose.

River Styx appears 3 times a year. The editor describes it as 90 pgs., digest-sized with b&w cover. They accept less than 10% of 750 mss received a year. **Sample postpaid: $7. Submit 3-5 poems, "legible copies with name and address on each page." Reading period September 1 through October 31. Guidelines available for SASE. Reports in 1 week to 2 months, publication within a year. Editor sometimes comments on rejections. Pays $8 a page plus 2 copies. Buys one-time rights.**

RIVERRUN (II), Glen Oaks Community College, Centreville MI 49032-9719, phone (616)467-9945, ext. 277, founded 1977, poetry editor David Bainbridge, is a literary biannual, using **30-40 magazine-sized pages of poetry in each issue—"no prejudices. We would like to receive more formal verse."** As a sample, the editor chose these lines from "The Trek for the Christmas Tree" by Gary J. Whitehead:

> Return strides leave a track
> like a wounded running buck, a
>
> bloodless trail of prints in the night,
> divergent, hurried, and intent on
> coming to that place where the burden
> drops, that place ending in light.

They have a print run of 600. **Sample postpaid: $4.** They receive 800-1,000 poems/year, use "as much as possible," have a 6- to 12-month backlog. **Reports immediately, except from June 15 through September 15. Pays 2 copies.** *Riverrun* ranked #2 in the "Traditional Verse" category of the June 1993 *Writer's Digest* Poetry 60 list.

‡**RIVERSIDE QUARTERLY (II, IV-Science fiction/fantasy)**, Box 958, Big Sandy TX 75755, phone (903)636-5505, founded 1964, editor Leland Sapiro, poetry editor Sheryl Smith **(and submissions should go directly to her at 515 Saratoga #2, Santa Clara CA 95050)**. *Riverside Quarterly* is **"aimed at the literate reader of science fiction and fantasy. If you've been reared on 'Startrek,' then** *RQ* **is not for you. We have no specific subject matter or style preferences. Length: 50 lines maximum. No didactic or 'uplifting' verse."** They have recently published poetry by George Gott, Sue Saniel Elkind, Julia Thomas and Denise Dumars. As a sample the editor selected these lines from "Ymir's Mirror/Eiseley's Glass" by Ace Pilkington:

> From the skull in the stone
> Eye sockets scrape the sky:
> Both are wayward worlds
> Aglint with stars.
> Black, bleak caverns
> Where the lightning grows

RQ is 68 pgs., approximately 5×8, offset, saddle-stapled with paper cover and b&w art. They receive about 1,100 poems a year, accept approximately 5%. Press run is 1,200 for 450 subscribers of which 150 are libraries. Subscription: $8. **Sample postpaid: $2.50. No previously published poems or simultaneous submissions. Cover letter required.** Time between acceptance and publication is 15 months. **Usually comments on rejections. Reports in 10 days. Pays 4 copies. Acquires all rights; rights released to contributor after publication.** "We print reviews of books, movies and magazines—no maximum length." They say, "We advise all contributors (of poetry or prose) to read a copy or two (available at any major public or college library) before sending a ms."

RIVERWIND (II, IV-Regional), General Studies, Hocking College, Nelsonville OH 45764, phone (614)753-3591, ext. 2375, founded 1982, poetry editor Cindy Yeager, is a literary annual publishing mainly writers from Appalachia. They want "work from serious writers. We are most open to work with serious content, though humor may be the vehicle. Do not want to see poetry from those who view it as a 'hobby.' We have not published limericks." They have published poetry by Naton Leslie, Gloria Ruth, Charles Semones, Walter McDonald, John Haines, John Aber, James Riley and Greg Anderson. *Riverwind* is 6 × 9, flat-spined, 80 pgs., typeset, offset, with 2-color semiglossy card cover. Of 500 poems received they accept approximately 60. Press run is 500. Per issue: $2.50. **Sample back issue postpaid: $1. Submit batches of 3-5, no previously published poems, no simultaneous submissions. Reads submissions September 15 through June 15 only. Submissions received after June 15 will be considered for the following year. Editor comments "particularly if we would like to see more of that person's work." Reports in 1-4 months. Response slow during summer months. Pays 2 copies.** Reviews books of poetry. They hope to begin publishing chapbook collections.

ROANOKE REVIEW (II), Roanoke College, Salem VA 24153, phone (703)389-2351, ext. 367, founded 1968, poetry editor Robert R. Walter, is a semiannual literary review which uses **poetry that is "conventional; we have not used much experimental or highly abstract poetry."** They have published poetry by Peter Thomas, Norman Russell, Alan Seaburg, Mary Balazs and Irene Dayton. *RR* is 52 pgs., 6 × 9, professionally printed with matte card cover with decorative typography, using 25-30 pgs. of poetry in each issue, circulation 250-300, 150 subscriptions of which 50 are libraries. They receive 400-500 freelance submissions of poetry/year, use 40-60, have a 3- to 6-month backlog. Subscription: $5.50. **Sample postpaid: $3. Submit original typed mss, no photocopies. Reports in 8-10 weeks. No pay.** The editor advises, "There is a lot of careless or sloppy writing going on. We suggest careful proofreading and study of punctuation rules."

‡ROCK FALLS REVIEW; AUTHOR'S INK (I), P.O. Box 104, Stamford NE 68977, phone (308)868-3545, founded 1989, editor Diana L. Lambson. *Rock Falls Review* is a quarterly that "started as a learning tool for our writer's group. We try to maintain a learning atmosphere. Much of what we publish is by new writers but we still insist on quality work submitted in a professional manner." They "prefer shorter poems—under 100 lines. Inspirational poetry is okay. No 'doomsday' or 'preachy' verse, though. Also okay: fantasy and science fiction, free verse, humor and traditional forms. No obscure, far out, experimental or pornographic verse. No horror or dark image. No violence. No obscene language! Concrete or shaped verse is nearly impossible for us to use." They have recently published poetry by R. Nikolas Macioci, Lyn Lifshin, Sheryl Nelms and John N. Miller. As a sample the editor selected these lines from "Waking Up" by Noel Smith:

> *Headfirst*
> *I drift down a silken thread*
> *Arms folded like wings.*

> *Voices of grand—*
> *Mothers and children who cannot follow*
> *Echo*
> *From far back at the beginning.*

RFR is 14-24 pgs., 8½ × 11, photocopied typescript, side-stapled with colored paper cover, clip art and original b&w line art and ads inside. They receive about 150 poems a year, use 115 to 120. Press run is 50 for 30 subscribers. Single copy: $3; subscription: $10. **Sample postpaid: $2.50. Previously published poems OK with release and proper credits. Simultaneous submissions also OK.** "While we do not require a cover letter it is nice to know something about the person submitting." **Often comments on rejections. Send SASE for guidelines. Reports in 6-12 weeks "usually." Pays 1 copy.** Reviews books of poetry. Open to unsolicited reviews. Poets may also send books for review consideration; "one of our group will review." The editor says, "We do not require purchase or subscription. However, because of space and funding restrictions, members of Author's Ink or the Great Plains Writer's Club and subscribers will be given first consideration. This should not discourage anyone, however, as 50-75% of our accepted submissions are non-subscribers. We prefer poetry that is *not* obscure. In order for most people to read and enjoy poetry, it should be understandable: something they can relate to."

The Subject Index, located before the General Index, can help you narrow down markets for your work. It lists those publishers whose poetry interests are specialized.

THE ROCKFORD REVIEW; TRIBUTARY (I, II), P.O. Box 858, Rockford IL 61105, *The Rockford Review* founded 1971, editor David Ross, is an annual publication of the Rockford Writers Guild, **publishing their poetry and prose, that of other writers throughout the country and contributors from other countries. "We look for the magical power of the words themselves, a playfulness with language in the creation of images and fresh insights on old themes, whether it be poetry, satire or fiction."** They have recently published poetry by Russell King, David Koenig and Christine Swanberg. As a sample the editor selected these lines by Olivia Diamond:

> The chill will nip us all in the end
> even fragile stems we brace in vases.
> The tips of petals curl in and bend
> toward the ground in stiff embraces.

TRR is 96 pgs., digest-sized, flat-spined, glossy cover with b&w photos. Circulation 550. Single copy: $6; subscription: $10 (2 issues). **Considers simultaneous submissions. Reports in 4-6 weeks. Pays 1 copy. Acquires first North American serial rights.** They offer Editor's Choice Prizes of $50 for prose, $50 for poetry. They also desktop publish triquarterly for the *Tributary*, 28 pages of poetry and very short prose featuring a reader poll to select the best work, which wins a $25 prize each edition. Circulation 200. **Poetry not accepted for** *The Rockford Review* **is automatically considered for** *Tributary*, **or poets may submit separately.**

ROCKY MOUNTAIN REVIEW OF LANGUAGE AND LITERATURE (IV-Membership, translations), Boise State University English Dept., Boise ID 83725, phone (208)385-1246, founded 1947, editor Carol Martin, poetry editor Marcia Southwick **(and submissions should go directly to her at English Dept., University of Nebraska, Lincoln NE 68588-0333). Contributors to the literary quarterly must be members of Rocky Mountain Modern Language Association. Poetry should be "generally relatively short"** and may be in English or other modern languages. The review has published poetry by Scott P. Sanders and translations of Antonio Cisneros and David Huerta. The 6×9, 276-page, flat-spined quarterly publishes work of interest to college and university teachers of literature and language. Circulation of the review is 1,100-1,200, all membership subscriptions. They accept a few ads from other journals and publishers. **Contributors are not paid and do not receive extra copies; contributors must be RMMLA members. Poets should submit 2 copies,** *without author's name.* **They report on submissions in 1-2 months and publish usually within 6 months but no more than 1 year after acceptance.**

‡**ROHWEDDER: INTERNATIONAL JOURNAL OF LITERATURE & ART (II, IV-Themes, translations)**, P.O. Box 29490, Los Angeles CA 90029, founded 1986, editors Robert Dassanowsky-Harris, Nancy Antell and Hans-Jurgen Schacht, who say their **"international journal seeks the highest quality poetry and prose. It is open to all styles and subject matter—foreign language with translation, multicultural, also experimental, open text and language-oriented poetry and prose.** We have published poetry from Lithuania, East and West Germany, Central America, Argentina, Portugal, Denmark, Poland, Canada and the U.S." Writers recently published in their Feminist issue include Michelle T. Clinton, Meredith Stricker, Judith Roche and Nicoletta Pireddu. As a sample the editors selected these lines from "Ancestry" by Natalie Safir:

> If it wasn't Emma Bovary's white thighs I slid from,
> then Tolstoi's Anna opened her legs to push me out.
> In the darkened room where flames choked, bearded,
> cloaked men stood mumbling, the stately clock
> declared its dominance—the rustle of silks
> was a dream shredded on the spokes of time.

Rohwedder (Rough Weather) is 50 pgs., 8½×11, saddle-stapled, offset from typesetter with b&w art inside and on the glossy card cover. About half the issue is poetry. Press run is 1,000. Single copy: $5. **"We often do theme issues; poets should check." Submit 5 poems. No simultaneous submissions or previously published poems. Cover letter with bio and credits preferred. Editor** sometimes comments on rejections. **Reports in approximately 3 months. Pays copies.**

THE ROLLING COULTER (II, IV-Religious, rural), Messiah College, Grantham PA 17027, phone (717)766-2511 (ext. 7026), founded 1988, editors William Jolliff and Harold Arnett, appears twice a year. **"We look for poetry that is not necessarily religious but which shows some evidence of being informed by a religious world-view. We're open to most forms, but work in traditional forms must be especially good to be printable. We don't want to see greeting card, calendar or bulletin cover stuff."** They have recently published poetry by Bertha Rogers, Gene Doty and Sofia Starnes. As a sample the editor selected these lines from "Sacred Women Lead Easy Lives" by Joanne Lowery:

> When their tongues are cut out they no longer stumble
> for words, they find new ways of humming.
> No one can accuse them of chatter

> *or of throwing themselves away for tenderness*
> *in the dustbins of masculine alleys.*
> *Instead, like Magi, they follow a star.*

The Rolling Coulter is 40-60 pgs., digest-sized, laser printed with glossy card cover. It features poems one to a page, and the work of well-knowns is placed alongside poems by lesser lights. Their press run is 400 with 100+ subscriptions. "We distribute to libraries at religious colleges, with or without charge." Subscription: $6/2 issues. **Sample postpaid: $3. Editor occasionally comments on rejections on request. Reports in 6-12 weeks. "We respond slowly in summer." Pays 1 copy. Acquires all rights. Returns rights after publication. "Mention us as first publisher in subsequent uses."** They say, "There's really no substitute for becoming familiar with a magazine before submitting work. We get in lots of work that we can enjoy reading, but far less that we can use. Tremendous variety exists in the little magazine scene, and poets should celebrate that fact by doing more reading of what is being written and published right now, *in addition to* what has been anthologized for their college courses. **We would like to receive more work on agrarian subjects and themes.**"

THE ROMANTIST (IV-Fantasy/horror/science fiction), Saracinesca House, 3610 Meadowbrook Ave., Nashville TN 37205, phone (615)226-1890, poetry editor Steve Eng, founded 1977, is a "literary magazine of nonfiction articles on fantasy, horror and romantic literature, using **lyrical poetry—prefer fantasy and horror content. No homespun, gushy, trite verse with forced rhyme.**" They have published poetry by Donald Sidney-Fryer, Joey Froehlich, Stephanie Stearns and Gary William Crawford. The annual is magazine-sized. Press run is 300 numbered copies for 150 subscriptions of which 50 are libraries. **Sample postpaid: $10. Contributors may purchase a copy for 50% of its price. They receive tearsheets. Submit no more than 3 poems at a time, double-spaced. Reports in 1 month. Editor sometimes comments on rejections.** Open to unsolicited reviews. Poets may also send books for review consideration; query first. He says, "Too much contemporary poetry is easy to write and hard to read. We resist the depressed, carefully jaded tone so often fashionable. We prefer lyric verse that reflects some knowledge of traditions of poetry, though we do not require the slavish adherence to any school."

‡ROOM OF ONE'S OWN (IV-Women), P.O. Box 46160 Station G, Vancouver, British Columbia V6R 4G5 Canada, founded 1975, is a quarterly using **"poetry by and about women, written from a feminist perspective. Nothing simplistic, clichéd."** It is 90 pgs., digest-sized. Press run is 1,000 for 420 subscribers of which 50-100 are libraries, 350 shelf sales. Subscription: $20 ($25 US or foreign). **Sample: $7 plus postage or IRCs. "We prefer to receive 5-6 poems at a time, so we can select a pair or group."** Send SASE or SAE with 1 IRC for guidelines. The mss are circulated to a collective, which "takes time." **Reports in 6 months. Pays honorarium plus 2 copies.** "We solicit reviews." Send books for review consideration, attn. book review editor.

ROPE BURNS (IV-Themes), Working Cowboy, P.O. Box 35, Gene Autry OK 73436, founded 1987, editor Bobby Newton, is "basically a bimonthly western heritage event publication with stories, poetry, etc. related to working cowboys. **I like to publish poems and stories about the average old cowboy, some good, some bad.**" As a sample, here is the opening of a full-page poem, "The Old Cowboy's Christmas," by Howard Norskog:

> *The cowboy woke up at the first light of day*
> *And anyone there would of heard the man say*
> *It's Christmas and time that all should relax*
> *And enjoy good tidings, now this is a fact*

Sample postpaid: 2 stamps. Pays copies. Reviews "some" books of poetry—"cowboy poetry only." Open to unsolicited reviews. Poets may also send books for review consideration. "Books will be returned if sufficient postage and instructions are included."

ROSE SHELL PRESS (I), (formerly Merging Media), 516 Gallows Hill Rd., Cranford NJ 07016, phone (908)276-9479, press originally founded in 1978 by D.C. Erdmann, current editor/publisher Rochelle L. Holt, who says she "will attempt to keep the press alive with Merging Media ideals as I believe there is still a need for presses open to women and a few sensitive men." She has recently published two books by Ruth Moon Kempher. As a sample, she selected these lines from Kempher's book **Mother Goose on Wheels:**

> *Hey Diddle Diddle*
> *The cat and the fiddle!*
> *Our cow jumped over the moon!*
>
> *She jumped at the clatter*
> *of a car coming at her*
> *and it wasn't a moment too soon.*

Interested poets should query first with 5 sample poems and a cover letter noting "how they heard of us and what they've read of Merging Media in the past." Include SASE and $10 "for criticism and/or suggestions."

THE ROUND TABLE: A JOURNAL OF POETRY AND FICTION (II), 375 Oakdale Dr., Rochester NY 14618, phone (716)244-0623, founded 1984, poetry editors Alan Lupack and Barbara Lupack. "We publish a journal of poetry and fiction. Currently, one issue a year. **Few restrictions on poetry — except high quality. We like forms if finely crafted. Very long poems must be exceptional.**" They have published poetry by Kathleene West, John Tagliabue, Wendy Mnookin and Paul Scott. *The Round Table* is 64 pgs., digest-sized, perfect-bound, professionally printed (offset) with matte card cover. Circulation 125, 75 subscribers of which 3 are libraries. Subscription: $7.50 regular issue, $10 special issue. **Sample postpaid: $5. "We like to see about 5 poems (but we read whatever is submitted but only from October 1 through June 30)."** Cover letter required. Simultaneous submissions OK. "**But we expect to be notified if a poem submitted to us is accepted elsewhere. Quality of poetry, not format, is most important thing.** We try to report in 3 months, but — especially for poems under serious consideration — it may take longer." Pays copies. "We are tending to focus more on Arthurian poetry and prose. Some years we will publish a volume of Arthurian poetry by one author."

THE RUGGING ROOM; RUGGING ROOM BULLETIN (IV-Themes), 10 Sawmill Dr., Westford MA 01886, founded as a press in 1983, periodical in 1987, poetry editor Jeanne H. Fallier, publisher of "how-to books **related to traditional rug hooking and related subjects of interest to people in fibre crafts.**" Verses of a philosophical theme or concerning nature are acceptable if they refer to hand works, wool or fibers, the therapeutic value of hand-made fiber crafts, etc. She accepts "**very short poems related to fibre arts (especially hooking) crafts — not more than ½ page.**" The *Rugging Room Bulletin* is a newsletter, 8-16 pgs., 8½ × 11, appearing 4 times a year, printed on white stock, with b&w illustrations, ads and graphics. Circulation 300 but widespread, coast to coast. Subscription: $11. **Sample postpaid: $2.50.** Simultaneous submissions OK. **Cover letter explaining what inspired your poem required.** Reports within about 2 weeks. Pays 3 copies plus 1-year subscription. Contributors are also expected to buy 1 copy. Acquires all rights. Returns rights after publication, by arrangement. Staff reviews related books of poetry. Send books for review consideration.

THE RUNAWAY SPOON PRESS (IV-Form), Box 3621, Port Charlotte FL 33949, phone (813)629-8045, founded 1987, editor Bob Grumman, is a "photocopy publisher of chapbooks of otherstream poetry & illumagery." He wants "**visual poetry, textual poetry mixed with visual matter, verbo-visual collages, burning poodle poetry — or anything insane. No work in which politics is more important than aesthetics.**" He has recently published poetry by Jonathan Levant, Marshall Hryciuk and Stephen-Paul Martin. As a sample the editor selected this poem by Guy R. Beining:

> *blue-prints of a dream*
> *in red*
>   *for the insomniac*

The books are usually about 4 × 5½, printed on good stock with matte card covers. He prints about 10 a year averaging 48 pgs. "**Query is a good idea but not necessary.**" Simultaneous submissions and previously published poems OK. **Editor comments on submissions "always."** Pays 25% of first edition of 100. Acquires all rights. Releases rights to author(s) upon publication. Sample books available for $3 apiece. The editor advises, "Don't let anti-intellectuals convince you the brain is less important than the heart in poetry."

RURAL HERITAGE (I, IV-Rural, humor), 281 Dean Ridge Lane, Gainesboro TN 38562-9685, founded 1975, editor Gail Damerow, **uses poetry related to rural living, Americana.** *RH* is magazine-sized, quarterly, using b&w photos, graphics and ads, 4-6 poems/issue. Circulation 3,000. Subscription: $14. **Sample postpaid: $5.50. Submit no more than 3 poems at a time, one/page. "Traditional meter and rhyme only. Preference is given to poems with a touch of humor or other twist."** 4-6 months between acceptance and publication. Guidelines available for SASE. Reports ASAP. Pays on publication $5 and up, depending on length, and 2 copies.

SACHEM PRESS (II, IV-Translations, bilingual), P.O. Box 9, Old Chatham NY 12136, phone (518)794-8327, founded 1980, editor Louis Hammer, a small press publisher of poetry and fiction, both hardcover and flat-spined paperbacks. **No new submissions, only statements of projects, until January 1994. Submit mss January through March.** The editor wants to see "**strong, compelling, even visionary work, English-language or translations.**" He has published poetry by Cesar Vallejo, Yannis Ritsos, 24 leading poets of Spain (in an anthology), Miltos Sahtouris and himself. As a sample, he selected the following lines from his book **Poetry at the End of the Mind:**

> *If the only paper you had*
> *was the flesh on your back*

between your shoulder blades
what would you write
with the motion of your body?

The paperbacks average 120 pgs. and the anthology of Spanish poetry contains 340 pgs. Each poem is printed in both Spanish and English, and there are biographical notes about the authors. The small books cost $6.95 and the anthology $11.95. **Royalties are 10% maximum, after expenses are recovered, plus 50 author's copies. Rights are negotiable.** Book catalog is free "when available," and poets can purchase books from Sachem "by writing to us, 33⅓% discount."

SACRED RIVER: BAY AREA WOMEN'S JOURNAL (I, IV-Women/feminism), P.O. Box 5131, Berkeley CA 94705, phone (510)658-2182, founded 1991, poetry editor Carla Kandinsky, is a monthly newspaper of news and inspiration for women. They want **short feminist poetry. No poetry from men.** It is 16-20 pgs., tabloid-sized newsprint, with b&w photos and graphics. They receive about 300 poems a year, use approximately 85. Press run is 10,000 for 100 subscribers; the rest placed in bookstores, cafes and health centers for women to pick up. Subscription: $18. **Sample postpaid: $2. Previously published poems and simultaneous submissions OK.** Time between acceptance and publication is 2-3 months. **Seldom comments on rejections. Reports within 3 months. Pays 1 copy "unless more are requested."** Reviews books of poetry in 200-800 words. Open to unsolicited reviews. Poets may also send books for review consideration.

SACRIFICE THE COMMON SENSE (I), c/o Gomez #15, 1251 S. Magnolia Ave., Los Angeles CA 90006, founded 1989, editor Humberto Gómez Sequeira-HuGóS, is a quarterly designed "to incite freedom of thought and expression." They want **poetry that is "strange. Any subject. Any length. Noncommercial. Nothing religious, patriotic or common."** They have recently published poetry by Sigmund Weiss, Paul Weinman, Robert Nagler, Rudy Sotelo and Horace Coleman. As a sample the editor selected these lines from "Children of the Moon" by Roxanna Gomez:

He crawls between
and around my legs.
With a vicious bite on my thigh
he proclaims my existence.
Then he offers to die with me.

STCS is 44 pgs., magazine-sized, saddle-stapled, with paper cover and b&w artwork, including collages. They receive 100 poems and short stories a year, accept approximately 98%. Press run is 100. Subscription: $20. **Sample postpaid: $5. No previously published poems or simultaneous submissions. Submit up to 3 poems. Include "$3 per work submitted."** Send SASE for guidelines. **Reports "when magazine is published. We can't return your material or inform you of our decision." Pays 1 copy. Acquires first rights.** Open to unsolicited reviews. Poets may also send books for review consideration.

ST. ANDREW PRESS (IV-Religious), P.O. Box 329, Big Island VA 24526, phone (804)299-5956, founded 1986, poetry editor Jean Horne, is a "small press publisher of religious material (worship materials, lyrics and music, etc.), **specializing in meditations, lifestyle, church renewal, spirituality, hunger, peace and justice issues."** Any form or style up to 64 lines on subjects listed. "No profanity for shock value only; no sickeningly sweet idealism." They say they will publish 3 chapbooks and flat-spined paperbacks, averaging 64 pgs., each year. **Submit 6 samples, bio, other publications. Simultaneous submissions and previously published poems OK. Reports in 2-4 weeks. Payment usually $10 minimum, averages more.** They will consider subsidy publishing. The editor says, "We are looking forward to doing more with poetry in the next couple of years. The amount we do will be largely determined by quality of submissions we receive. Poetry is not accepted if it is too 'sing-song' with trite rhymes, if it could be rewritten in paragraphs as prose, or if it is so 'stream-of-consciousness' that no one could possibly follow the thought or get any meaning from it."

ST. ANTHONY MESSENGER (IV-Religious), 1615 Republic St., Cincinnati OH 45210-1298, is a monthly 56-page magazine, circulation 350,000, for Catholic families, mostly with children in grade school, high school or college. In some issues, they have a **poetry page which uses poems appropriate for their readership. Their poetry needs are limited but poetry submissions are always welcomed.** As a sample here is "A Valentine for Darby" by Jean M. Syed:

Why do I love you, my potbellied love?
Not for your pregnant form or shiny pate.
Were these on tender those decades ago,
would I have been so indiscriminate
as to let you win my heart? No princess
from passion ever took a frog to mate.

"Submit seasonal poetry (Christmas/Easter/nature poems) several months in advance. Submit

a few poems at a time; do not send us your entire collection of poetry. We seek to publish accessible poetry of high quality." Send regular SASE for guidelines and 9 × 12 SASE for free sample. Pays $2/line on acceptance. Buys first North American serial rights. *St. Anthony Messenger* poetry occasionally receives awards from the Catholic Press Association Annual Competition.

ST. JOSEPH MESSENGER AND ADVOCATE OF THE BLIND (I, IV-Religious), 541 Pavonia Ave., P.O. Box 288, Jersey City NJ 07303, phone (201)798-4141, founded 1898, poetry editor Sister Ursula Maphet, C.S.J.P., is a quarterly (16 pgs., 8 × 11). They want **"brief but thought-filled poetry; do not want lengthy and issue-filled."** Most of the poets they have used are previously unpublished. They receive 400-500 submissions/year, use 50. There are about 2 pgs. of poetry in each issue. Circulation 20,000. Subscription: $5. **Editor sometimes comments on rejections. Send SASE for guidelines and free sample. Reports within 2 weeks. Pays $5-20/poem.**

ST. MARTIN'S PRESS, 175 5th Ave., New York NY 10010. Prefers not to share information.

SALMAGUNDI (III), Skidmore College, Saratoga Springs NY 12866, founded 1965, edited by Peggy Boyers and Robert Boyers, has long been **one of the most distinguished quarterlies** of the sciences and humanities, publishing poets such as Robert Penn Warren, Louise Gluck, John Peck, Howard Nemerov and W.D. Snodgrass. Each issue is handsomely printed, thick, flat-spined, priced at $5-10. Editors here tend to use more lyric free verse than any other style, much of it accessible and usually under 50 lines. Although the magazine is hefty, poems compete with prose (with the latter dominating). They use about 10-50 pages of poetry in each issue, receive 1,200 submissions/year, use about 20 and have a 12- to 30-month backlog. Paid circulation is 5,400 with 3,800 subscriptions of which about 900 are libraries. Subscriptions are $12 a year, $18 for two years. **Sample postpaid: $4. Submissions not accompanied by SASE are discarded. Reports in 3 months. Pays copies only.** Send books for review consideration. Work published in *Salmagundi* is selected annually for the **Pushcart Prize** anthology.

‡SALMON RUN PUBLISHERS (II), P.O. Box 231081, Anchorage AK 99523, founded 1991, editor/publisher John E. Smelcer, publishes 2-3 paperbacks/year, "only book-length poetry mss by well-known authors." They want **"quality poetry of any subject, any style. No poetry that is not representative of the highest achievement in the art."** They have recently published **The Bend Toward Asia** by Tom Sexton. As a sample the editor selected these lines from Sexton's "Trapper Creek":

> *Sitting down to write these lines for you*
> *I saw rainbows feeding on a hatch and went out*
> *to catch one for my breakfast.*
> *Its small bones white as prayers on my plate.*

Their books are flat-spined, with "high quality laser printed fonts appearing on heavy, natural-colored paper." **Query first with sample poems and cover letter with brief bio and publication credits. Previously published poems and simultaneous submissions OK. Often comments on rejections. Replies to queries within 1-2 weeks, to mss in 1-2 months. Pays 10-15% royalties and a negotiable number of author's copies.** They also sponsor an annual national poetry contest for book-length poetry mss of 48-64+ pgs. $10 reading fee and SASE required. Entries must be postmarked by May 1. The winning ms will be published in book form ("6 × 9, perfect-bound, glossy cover stock, laser fonts, with regional and national distribution and submissions for reviews"). All contestants receive a copy of the winning book. The editor says, "We are looking for poetry of the highest quality from known, published authors. Poetry, some say, has been in decline during the past few decades. We seek to publish only that poetry which re-establishes the craft's previous function and reverence in society."

SALT LICK; SALT LICK PRESS; SALT LICK SAMPLERS; LUCKY HEART BOOKS (II), #15, 1416 NE 21st Ave., Portland OR 97232-1507, phone (503)249-1014, founded 1969, poetry editor James Haining, publishes "new literature and graphic arts in their various forms." They have published poetry by Michael Lally, David Searcy, Julie Siegel, Paul Shuttleworth, Wm. Hart, Robert Slater, Gerald Burns and Sheila Murphy. The magazine-sized journal, 66 pgs., saddle-stapled, matte cover, experimental graphics throughout, appears irregularly, print run of 1,000. They receive 400-600 poems/year, use 1-2%. **Sample postpaid: $5. Reports in 1-6 weeks. Pays copies. To submit for book publication under the Lucky Heart Books imprint, send 20 samples, cover letter "open." Simultaneous submissions OK. Pays copies.**

SAN DIEGO POET'S PRESS; LA JOLLA POET'S PRESS; AMERICAN BOOK SERIES (II), P.O. Box 8638, La Jolla CA 92038. San Diego Poet's Press, a nonprofit press founded 1981 by editor/publisher Kathleen Iddings, has published collections and anthologies that include Galway Kinnell, Carolyn Kizer, Allen Ginsberg, Carolyn Forche, Tess Gallagher and Robert Pinsky, among others. Iddings began publishing individual poets in 1985 and has published approximately 20 poets to date. In 1989, she originated the "American Book Series" wherein she awards the winner $500 and publishes his/her first book of poetry. Past winners are Joan LaBombard, Regina McBride, Charles Atkinson and Michael Cleary. As a sample she selected these lines from "More Blessed to Receive" in Charles Atkinson's winning book **The Only Cure I Know:**

> More than anything I care for you
> *she said over the sink, and then*
> *I knew all the times I couldn't hear.*
> *It made me smile and start to cry.*
> *I cried into the waffle mix,*
> *in front of my children looking up*
> *asking why a man cries about waffles.*
> *What could be more perfect*
> *than arms around my neck*
> *and small ones clutching my knees?*
> *I couldn't give the love away*
> *and for once I didn't try.*

For either press, send 6-10 pgs. of poetry, cover letter (indicating "why work is being submitted"), bio and SASE. Poets may also send SASE for guidelines and further information. Sample of any winning book, postpaid: $11.50.

SAN FERNANDO POETRY JOURNAL; KENT PUBLICATIONS, INC.; CERULEAN PRESS (MINI AN-THOLOGY SERIES), (I, IV-Social issues, anthologies), 18301 Halsted St., Northridge CA 91325, founded 1978, poetry editors Richard Cloke, Shirley Rodecker and Lori Smith (and, for the Mini Anthology Series, Blair H. Allen, 9651 Estacia Court, Cucamonga CA 91730). *San Fernando Poetry Journal* uses **poetry of social protest.** According to Richard Cloke, "Poetry, for us, should be *didactic* in the Brechtian sense. It must say something, must inform, in the tenor of our time. We follow Hart Crane's definition of poetry as architectural in essence, building upon the past but incorporating the newest of this age also, including science, machinery, sub-atomic and cosmic physical phenomena as well as the social convulsions wrenching the very roots of our present world." **Send SASE for guidelines which explain this more fully.** For example, we quote this passage for its general usefulness for poets: "In some, the end-line rhyming is too insistent, seeming *forced;* in others the words are not vibrant enough to give the content an arresting framework. Others do not have any beat (cadence) at all and dsome are simply not well thought out—often like first drafts, or seem like prose statements. Please try reworking again to get some energy in your statement. If your poetry is to succeed in impelling the reader to act, it must electrify, or at least command interest and attention." **They welcome new and unpublished poets.** As a sample the editor selected this poem, "Paradise Lost," by Marian Steele:

> Adam trod the earth enraptured
> *When he was nearly alone on a younger land.*
> *His name was Muir . . . Bartram . . . Burroughs . . .*
>   *Audubon.*
> *It was not so long ago.*
> *We have seen to it;*
> *Whether in Saudi desert,*
> *Flaming Brazilian rain forest,*
> *In Detroit's blighted back streets*
> *Or South Bronx alleyways,*
> *In the belches from redbrick smokestack,*
> *Recoilless rifle, naval Big Gun,*
> *Or even Three-Mile-Island-Chernobyl—*
> *We have remodeled our planet*
> *In our own image.*

The flat-spined quarterly, photocopied from typescript, uses 100 pgs. of poetry in each issue. Press run is 400 for 350 subscribers of which 45 are libraries. They use about 300 of the 1,000 submissions (the editor rightly prefers to call them "contributions") each year. **Sample postpaid: $2.50. No specifications for ms form. Simultaneous submissions OK. Reports in 1 week. Pays copies.** The press, under its various imprints, also publishes a few collections by individuals. **Query with 5-6 pgs. of samples. For the Mini Anthology Series, query Blair Allen at the address above.**

SAN JOSE STUDIES; CASEY MEMORIAL AWARD (II), San Jose State University, San Jose CA 95192-0090, phone (408)924-4476, founded 1975, poetry editor John Engell. This "journal of general and scholarly interest, featuring critical, creative and informative writing in the arts, business, humanities, science and social sciences" uses poetry of **"excellent quality—with a focus on Bay Area and California**

cultures. Tend to like poems with something to say, however indirectly it may be communicated. Usually publish 7-12 pgs. of verse in each issue. We like to publish several poems by one poet—better exposure for the poet, more interest for the reader." They have published poetry by Leonard Nathan, Lyn Lifshin and James Sutherland-Smith. As a sample the editor chose these lines from "Mountain Woman" by Virginia de Araújo:

> . . . But place in her is deep root:
> hand, brain, nerve, tooth. Planted, she will
> spill upward in fern fronds, tight buds and fists.
> Overhead, winter and summer secretly will move,
> and she remain planted in true place.

SJS appears thrice yearly in a 6×9, flat-spined, 100+ pg. format, professionally printed, matte card cover, using b&w photos, circulation of 500-600 of which 70-75 are libraries. They receive about 200 submissions/year, use 8-10 authors, have a 1-year backlog. Subscription: $12 individuals, $18 institutions. **Sample postpaid: $5. No simultaneous submissions. Reports in 2-3 months. Pays 2 copies.** Annual award of a year's subscription for best poetry printed that year and a Casey Memorial Award of $100 for the best contribution in prose or poetry. Editor Emeritus O.C. Williams comments, "Poetry is both an art and a craft; we are not interested in submissions unless the writer has mastered the craft and is actually practicing the art."

‡SAN MIGUEL WRITER (II, IV-Bilingual/foreign language), Aldama 43, San Miguel de Allende, GTO 37700 Mexico, founded 1988, editor Carl Selph, appears twice a year publishing verse, short stories and essays. "About one-third of the magazine is in Spanish." **They want "well-crafted poetry. No effusions submitted in first draft."** They have recently published poetry by W.D. Snodgrass, Miller Williams and Nicholas A. Patricca. As a sample the editor selected these lines from "Quartering" by Charles Hasty:

> Reach where standing skies, like old faces,
> Awful floods blaze in Eden,
> Amber galleons of the nerve,
> In the firm lace of air, downwind.

San Miguel Writer is 88 pgs., 5⅞×8⅜, photo-offset, saddle-stapled, glossy card cover with drawings. They receive about 150 submissions a year, use approximately 25. Press run is 250. **Sample postpaid: $5. No simultaneous submissions. Cover letter required.** Mss are circulated and chosen by a two-thirds majority of the editorial board. **Often comments on rejections. Reports in 2-3 months. Pays 1 copy.** They also offer occasional prizes: "Currently $100 for both the best English and Spanish contributions annually."

SANDBERRY PRESS; DEBROSSE, REDMAN, BLACK & CO. LTD. (IV-Ethnic/nationality, regional, children), P.O. Box 507, Kingston 10, Jamaica, West Indies, founded 1986, managing director Pamela Mordecai, publishes 10 paperbacks and 5 hardbacks/year. **They want to see work from "poets born in the Caribbean or naturalized citizens of a Caribbean country or poets who have lived most of their lives in the region. Nothing racist, sexist or pornographic. Also interested in poetry for children."** They have recently published collections by Dennis Scott and Judith Hamilton. As a sample the director selected these lines from "Elemental" in *A Tale from the Rainforest* by Edward Baugh:

> I would have words as tenacious as mules
> to bear us, sure-footed
> up the mountain of night
>
> to where, at daybreak
> we would shake hands with the sun
> and breathe the breezes of the farthest ocean . . .

"Previously published poems may form part of a ms submission" but no simultaneous submissions. Cover letter required "to know whether, what and where the author has previously published. Also a brief bio note." Often comments on rejections. Replies to queries in 2 months, to mss in 6 months. Pays 10% royalties on net receipts, $200 (US) advance and 10 author's copies. Inquire about sample books.

SANDPIPER PRESS (V), P.O. Box 286, Brookings OR 97415, phone (503)469-5588, founded 1979, is a small press publisher of large print books. They have published **Poems from the Oregon Sea Coast; Unicorns for Everyone**, which includes some poetry; and **Walk With Me**, a book of prayers and meditations. However, they **currently do not accept unsolicited poetry.**

SANSKRIT (I), Cone Center, UNCC, Charlotte NC 28223, phone (704)547-2326, founded 1965, editor Jeff Byers, is a literary annual using poetry. **"No restrictions as to form or genre, but we do look for maturity and sincerity in submissions. Nothing trite or sentimental."** They have recently published poetry by Kimberleigh Luke-Stallings, Lance Phillips and Evan Smith. As a sample the editor selected these lines by Christy Beatty:

> *All I ever wanted*
> *was your lip*
> *your prophetic tongue*
> *your haggard arms*
> *about me*
>
> *A name to call my own.*

Their purpose is "to encourage and promote beginning and established artists and writers." It is 60-65 pgs., 9×12, flat-spined, printed on quality matte paper with heavy matte card cover. Press run is 3,500 for about 100 subscriptions of which 2 are libraries. **Sample postpaid: $6. Submit no more than 5 poems. Simultaneous submissions OK. Cover letter with biographical information and past publications required. Reads submissions September through October only. Editor comments on submissions "infrequently." Reports in 6-8 weeks. Pays 1 copy.**

SANTA MONICA REVIEW (III), 1900 Pico Blvd., Santa Monica CA 90405, founded 1988, poetry editor Jim Krusoe, appears twice a year. Single copy: $7; subscription: $12/year. **No submission information provided.**

SANTA SUSANA PRESS (V), CSU Libraries, 18111 Nordhoff St., Northridge CA 91330, phone (818)885-2271, founded 1973, a small press publisher of limited edition fine print books, history, literature and art, some poetry, all hardcover editions. **They do not accept unsolicited submissions of poetry. Poets should query first, and queries will be answered in 2 weeks. Honorariums paid depend on grant money.** The press has published books by George Elliott, Ward Ritchie and Ray Bradbury. Book catalog is free on request; prices are high. For instance, **Reaching: Poems by George P. Elliott**, illustrated, is published in an edition of 350 numbered copies at $35 and 26 lettered copies at $60.

SATURDAY EVENING POST (IV-Humor), 1100 Waterway Blvd., Indianapolis IN 46202, phone (317)636-8881, founded 1728 as the *Pennsylvania Gazette*, since 1821 as *The Saturday Evening Post*, Post Scripts editor Steve Pettinga, P.O. Box 567, Indianapolis IN 46206. *SEP* is a general interest, mass circulation monthly with emphasis on preventive medicine, using **"humorous light verse only. No more than 100 words per poem. Stay away from four-letter words and sexually graphic subject matter. No experimental verse (haiku, etc.) Morally, the *Post* is an anachronism of the early 50s; most of its readers are elderly. Other than that, anything goes, as long as it's in good taste." Payment is $15 for all rights.**

SATURDAY PRESS, INC.; EILEEN W. BARNES AWARD SERIES; INVITED POETS SERIES (V, IV-Women), Box 884, Upper Montclair NJ 07043, phone (201)256-5053, founded 1975, poetry editor Charlotte Mandel with guest editors for contest which have included Maxine Kumin, Colette Inez, Sandra M. Gilbert, Geraldine C. Little and Rachel Hadas. "Saturday Press, Inc., is a nonprofit literary organization. The press has a **special—though not exclusive—commitment to women's poetry, and by sponsoring the Eileen W. Barnes Award Competition for first books by women over 40 seeks to offer opportunity for new poets who have delayed their writing careers. Selection is by means of open competition or, in alternate years, by editorial board decision. Query for current information.** Not an annual event, the contest is widely posted when announced. The Invited Poets Series offers publication to established or less-known poets. We want **authoritative craft, strong, fresh imagery, sense of imagination and a good ear for syntax, sounds and rhythms. Language should lead the reader to experience a sense of discovery. Any form, content or style, but do not want polemic, jingles or conventional inspiration."** They have published books of poetry by Janice Thaddeus, Jean Hollander, Anne Carpenter, Anneliese Wagner and Doris Radin. As a sample the editor selected these lines from "Legacy" by Dixie Partridge:

> *Out on the plateau a ground hog,*
> *upright from his burrow, listens*
> *to the world. It is yesterday,*
> *or five centuries ago, and from dugouts*
> *on the hillside come monotones of prophecy*
> *that name us.*

"We are fully committed at present." Query first. Enclose 1-3 samples and minimum summary of publications. Replies to queries in 2 weeks. If invited, book ms may be photocopied; simultaneous submissions OK. "Prefer no binder, simple folder or paper clip." Pays 25-50 copies and possible honorarium ("depends on grants"). Send SASE for catalog to buy samples.

SCARP (II), School of Creative Arts, University of Wollongong, Locked Mail Bag 8844, South Coast Mail Centre 2521 Australia, phone (042)270985, founded 1982, editor Ron Pretty, "is a small press publisher of poetry, prose fiction and new art. *Scarp* also contains articles and reviews. Both new and established writers are encouraged to contribute." It appears twice a year. **"Not restricted by genre or form or subject matter or style or purpose, however we would prefer not to publish anything of an epic length."** They have published poetry by Marvin Bell, Bruce Beaver, John Millet, Shane McAuley and Debbie Westbury. As a sample the editor selected these lines by Lauren Williams:

> *After the reading I watch*
> *young male poets in rasta berets*
> *pant after her, old male poets*
> *pay serious attention to her*
> *opinions.*

Scarp is 64-80 pgs., A4 landscape format, perfect-bound, card cover, b&w graphics, some (mainly local) ads. There's a different flavor to poetry down under, but it is still mostly free verse bordering sometimes on what US poets would call the avant garde. Other poems are well-crafted and accessible, and the magazine is an odd rectangular shape but handsome and artistically designed. "*Scarp 19* received about 800 poems from 100+ contributors. We published 17 poems from these." Press run is 1,000 for approximately 300 subscribers of which 50 are libraries. Some shelf sales. Subscription: $24/4 issues. **Sample postpaid: $6. Subscription encouraged but not required. No more than 5 poems/submission. Poems previously unpublished in Australia OK. Cover letter required; include titles of poems, address and 2-3 line bio. Reads submissions January through March and July through September only. Editor comments on submissions. Send SASE for guidelines. Pays $20 (Aust.) plus 2 copies and 2-year subscription. Buys first Australian rights only.** Staff reviews books of poetry in 100-500 words, single or multi-book format. The editor says, "We're looking for poetry and prose that leaps off the page at you, and that usually means there's a lot of life in the language."

SCAT! (I, IV-Regional), Innis College, 2 Sussex Ave., Toronto, Ontario M5S 1J5 Canada, founded 1982, editors Claire Thompson, Donald Peters and Aub Glazer, is an annual, with **"dedication to new, wordy, smart poetry, any length, sure of speed and delivery, get to the point! Believe that 'It's all in the delivery.' Poet must be aware of the time and thought s/he's writing in."** They have published poetry by Brian Burke, Robbie Newton Drummond and Debbie Ferst. As a sample the editors selected these lines from "The Altar" by Jonathan Hyman:

> *It is night, wind*
> *and we storm together.*
> *There is nothing that binds*
> *like fury, nothing as quiet as air,*
> *The other corners*
> *are sunlit,*
> *holy.*

Scat! is published annually in the spring. **Sample postpaid: $10.** "Stress on Canadian representation and content." **Submit maximum of 5 poems. Cover letter required with $15 evaluation fee** (*postal money order only*). Editors comment "occasionally." No payment information provided.

SCAVENGER'S NEWSLETTER; KILLER FROG CONTEST (IV-Science fiction/fantasy/horror, mystery), 519 Ellinwood, Osage City KS 66523-1329, may seem an odd place to publish poems, but its editor, Janet Fox, uses 3-4 every month. The *Newsletter* is a 32-page booklet packed with news about **science fiction and horror publications** and printed at a quick printing shop. **Janet prefers science fiction/fantasy/horror and mystery poetry and will read anything that is offbeat or bizarre.** Writing-oriented poetry is occasionally accepted but "poems on writing must present fresh ideas and viewpoints. Poetry is used as filler so it must be 10 lines or under." Recently published poets include Lin Stein, Jacie Ragan, Steve Eng and Herb Kauderer. As a sample she selected this poem, "Junk Mail Fragment," by Ken Stone:

> *Of course*
> *the nose-cone*
> *fell into my house;*

Market conditions are constantly changing! If you're still using this book and it is 1995 or later, buy the newest edition of Poet's Market at your favorite bookstore or order directly from Writer's Digest Books.

> *thin air created*
> *highway to kitchen.*
> *Heavenly junk mail.*

Janet Fox says, "I have added mystery to the genres I cover, so I wouldn't mind seeing some mystery oriented poems in addition to those in the science fiction/fantasy/horror genres." She has around 800 subscribers. Subscription: $14/year; $7/6 months. **Sample copy plus guidelines for $2; guidelines alone for SASE. "I like poems with sharp images and careful craftsmanship." At last report was "accepting about 1 out of 10 poems submitted." You can use multiple submissions, simultaneous submissions (if informed) — even reprints if credit is given. Reads submissions all year "except for occasional overstock." No need to query. Reports in 1 month or less. Pays $2 on acceptance plus one copy. Buys one-time rights.** Staff reviews science fiction/fantasy/ horror and mystery chapbooks, books and magazines only. Send materials for review to either: Jim Lee, 801 - 26th St., Windber PA 15963 or Steve Sawicki, 186 Woodruff Ave., Watertown CT 06795. "I hold an annual 'Killer Frog Contest' for horror so bad or outrageous it becomes funny. There is a category for horror poetry. Has been opening April 1, closing July 1 of each year. Prizes $25 each in four categories: poetry, art, short stories and short short stories, plus the 'coveted' Froggie statuette." The last contest had no entry fee but entrants wanting the anthology pay $2.50 (postpaid). Winners list available for SASE.

SCIENCE FICTION POETRY ASSOCIATION; STAR*LINE (IV-Science fiction); THE RHYSLING ANTHOLOGY (V), %Mike Arnzen, P.O. Box 3712, Moscow ID 83843-1916, for membership information. **For poetry submissions:** Margaret Simon, 1412 NE 35th St., Ocala FL 34479. Founded 1978, the Association publishes *Star*Line*, a bimonthly newsletter and poetry magazine. The Association also publishes **The Rhysling Anthology**, a yearly collection of nominations from the membership "for the best science fiction/fantasy long and short poetry of the preceding year," along with a cassette tape anthology and a Science Fiction Poetry Handbook. The magazine has recently published poetry by Bruce Boston, Thomas Disch, Denise Dumars, John M. Ford, Robert Frazier and Steve Rasnic Tem. As a sample they selected this poem, "Moonwalking Surtsey," by Ann K. Schwader:

> *Here too, few traces:*
> *pale shell, gray feather*
> *laid against firebirth's lava image*
> *still warming infant skin*
>
> *fair warning*
> *of otherness stark as basalt sky/ocean,*
> *alien fragments forged for nothing*
> *further*
>
>   *not even footprints*

The digest-sized magazines and anthologies are saddle-stapled, photocopied, with numerous illustrations and decorations. They have 200 subscribers (1 library) paying $13 for 6 issues/year. **Sample postpaid: $1.50. Submissions to *Star*Line* only. They receive 200-300 submissions/year and use about 80 — mostly short (under 50 lines). They are "open to all forms — free verse, traditional forms, light verse — so long as your poetry shows skilled use of the language and makes a good use of science fiction, science, fantasy, horror or speculative motifs." Send 3-5 poems/submission, typed. Best time to submit is November. No simultaneous submissions, no queries. Reports in a month. Pays $1 for first 10 lines, 5¢/line thereafter, plus copy. Buys first North American serial rights.** Reviews books of poetry "within the science fiction/fantasy field" in 50-500 words. Open to unsolicited reviews. Poets may also send books for review consideration to William J. Daciuk, 304 N. Scott Ave., Glenolden PA 19036. A copy of **The Rhysling Anthology** is $3.

SCOP PUBLICATIONS, INC. (II, IV-Regional), Box 376, College Park MD 20740, phone (301)422-1930, founded 1977, president Stacy Tuthill, publishes approximately 2 paperbacks/year as well as an occasional anthology. They want "book-length regional manuscripts. No restrictions as to length or form but want well-crafted modern poetry with vivid imagery and skillful use of language with regard to sense impressions and fresh insights." They have recently published poetry by Ann Darr, Barbara Lefcowitz and Elisavietta Ritchie. **For sample book, send $5. Interested poets should query with sample poems. Previously published poems and simultaneous submissions OK. Cover letter should include a short biography and recent credits. Seldom comments on rejections. Replies to queries in 6 weeks, to mss in 2-3 months. Pays copies.**

SCORE MAGAZINE; SCORE CHAPBOOKS AND BOOKLETS (II, IV-Form), #B, 125 Bay View Dr., Mill Valley CA 94941-2627, phone (415)388-0578, poetry editors Crag Hill, Laurie Schneider and Bill DiMichele, is a "small press publisher of **visual poetry** in the magazine *Score*, booklets, postcards and broadsides. They want "poetry which melds language and the visual arts such as concrete poetry; experimental use of language, words and letters—forms. The appearance of the poem should have as much to say as the text. Poems on any subject; conceptual poetry; poems which use experimental, non-traditional methods to communicate their meanings." They don't want "traditional verse of any kind—be it free verse or rhymed." They have published poetry by Stephen-Paul Martin, Bruce Andrews, Karl Kempton, Larry Eigner and Bern Porter. They say that it is impossible to quote a sample because "some of our poems consist of only a single word—or in some cases no recognizable words." We strongly advise looking at a sample copy before submitting if you are not familiar with visual poetry. *Score* is 18-40 pgs., magazine-sized, offset, saddle-stapled, using b&w graphics, 2-color matte card cover, appearing once a year. Press run is 200 for 25 subscriptions (6 of them libraries) and about 40 shelf sales. Sample postpaid: $6. No simultaneous submissions. Previously published poems OK "if noted." Send SASE for guidelines. Pays 2 copies. Open to unsolicited reviews. Poets may also send books for review consideration. For chapbook consideration send entire ms. No simultaneous submissions. Almost always comments on rejections. Pays 8-16 copies of the chapbook. They subsidy publish "if author requests it."

SCRATCH (II, IV-Translations), 24 Nelson St., York Y03 7NJ England, founded 1989, editor Mark Robinson, now appears twice yearly using poetry, reviews (mainly books/chapbooks, some magazines) and some b&w graphics. As for poetry, the editor says **"We tend to the gritty, but mix styles, tones and subjects."** Recent issues have been "specials," including "Born in the 60s" featuring many leading young writers, such as Simon Armitage, Glyn Maxwell and Helen Kitson, and "Untitled Continent 1992," a European special featuring work in translation. As a sample the editor selected these lines from "Years like leaves" by Bo Carpelan, translated from Finland-Swedish by Anne Born:

> It's very possible I used to think
> that what I looked for was a "great" simplicity.
> Well, when the road wound through encroaching forests,
> all manner of ugly cottages strung across the fields,
> it was good to go down to the shore
> and see how sea and sky reflected each other.

Scratch is 80 pgs., A5 (5¹¹/₁₆ × 8¼), perfect-bound with card cover. Single copy: £3.50 ($10); subscription: £5.50 ($18). **No previously published poems or simultaneous submissions. Seldom comments on rejections. Reports in 2-3 weeks. Pays 2 copies.** Staff reviews books of poetry. Send books for review consideration. They have also started a chapbook series but are not currently accepting unsolicited chapbook mss. The editor says, **"Translations of younger poets especially welcome. Insufficient IRCs (a common U.S. failing) irk!"**

SEATTLE REVIEW (II), Padelford Hall GN-30, University of Washington, Seattle WA 98195, phone (206)543-9865, founded 1978, poetry editor Colleen McElroy, appears in the fall and spring using **"contemporary and traditional"** poetry. They have published poetry by William Stafford, Tess Gallagher, Marvin Bell and Walter McDonald. As a sample the editor selected these lines from "Car Mechanic Blues" by Jan Wallace:

> He lords his wrench over me like
> a magic wand. His ease with grease, the way
> he calms the speeding idle should convince
> me, this man's got the power. He wants
> to show me how the sparks fire. I say,
> No thanks, I'll get the book.

It is professionally printed, flat-spined, 110+ pgs., with glossy card cover. Press run is 800 for 250 subscribers of which 50 are libraries, 400 shelf sales. Single copy: $5; subscription: $8. **Sample postpaid: $3. Reads submissions September 1 through May 31 only. Send SASE for guidelines. Reports in 2-6 months. Pay "varies, but we do pay"** plus 2 copies. The editors offer these "practical suggestions: Cover letters with submissions do help. A cover letter provides something about the author and tells where and for what s/he is submitting. And don't let those rejection letters be cause for discouragement. Rejections can often be a matter of timing. The journal in question may be publishing a special issue with a certain theme (we've done a number of themes—'all-fiction,' 'all-poetry,' 'Asian-American,' 'Northwest,' 'science fiction,' etc.). Also, editorial boards do change, and new editors bring their individual opinions and tastes in writing. Good poetry will eventually be published if it is circulated."

SECOND AEON PUBLICATIONS (V), 19 Southminster Rd., Roath, Cardiff CF2 S4T Wales, phone 0222-493093, founded 1966, poetry editor Peter Finch, is a "small press concerned in the main with **experimental literary works."** He has published poetry by Bob Cobbing and himself. **Accepts no unsolicited mss. Pays copies.** Editor reviews poetry as a freelancer for a broad range of publications.

SECRETS FROM THE ORANGE COUCH (I, II), Box 688, Killam, Alberta T0B 2L0 Canada, founded 1988, appears twice a year. "We appreciate an eclectic range of styles: magic realism, traditional, experimental, deconstruction, cross-over writing etc. Above all, we insist on good quality writing." They have published poetry by Bert Almon, Scott Ellis, Elizabeth Haynes and Jay Henderson. As a sample the editor selected these lines from "Crescendo" by Catherine Thys:

> music I tell them every year
> is movement between tension
> and release

It is 48 pgs., magazine-sized, saddle-stapled, professionally printed (desktop) with matte card cover. Press run is 300 for 150 subscribers of which 3 are libraries, 100-150 shelf sales. Subscription: $10 plus $2.50 postage (Canadian). **Sample postpaid: $6. Cover letter with brief bio and list of submitted poems required. Reports within 4 months. Pays $12.50 (Canadian)/published page. Buys first North American serial rights.** Sponsors annual poetry and fiction contests. Poetry contest includes 2 categories: short poem (up to 48 lines) and long poem (up to 100 lines). Fiction entries may be up to 2,500 words. Entry fee for each contest: $10 (includes one-year subscription), plus $5 for each additional poem. Send SASE or SAE and IRC for contest rules. Deadline for poetry contest: February 28.

SEGUE FOUNDATION; ROOF BOOKS; SEGUE BOOKS (V), 303 E. 8th St., New York NY 10009, phone (212)674-0199, fax (212)254-4145, president James Sherry, is a small press publisher of poetry, literary criticism, and film and performance texts. Most of their books are flat-spined paperbacks, some hardcover. They have published books by Jackson MacLow, Charles Bernstein, Ron Silliman and Diane Ward, but they **do not consider unsolicited mss. Query first.** The Foundation is also a distributor of a number of prestigious small press magazines and books. Write for their catalog to buy samples.

"We focus exclusively on poetry," says Deborah Tall, editor of Seneca Review, the biannual publication of Hobart and William Smith Colleges in Geneva, New York. The special issue featured here, titled "Taking Note: From Poets' Notebooks," is an anthology of notebook excerpts. "They were solicited with the purpose of staying close to the craft and subject of poetry," says David Weiss in his introduction. The cover was designed by Gwen Butler, a member of the college's communications department.

SENECA REVIEW (II, IV-Translations), Hobart and William Smith Colleges, Geneva NY 14456-3397, phone (315)781-3349, founded 1970, editor Deborah Tall. They want "**serious poetry of any form, including translations. No light verse. Also essays on contemporary poetry.**" They have published poetry by Seamus Heaney, Rita Dove, Denise Levertov, Stephen Dunn and Hayden Carruth. *Seneca Review* is 100 pgs., 6×9, flat-spined, professionally printed on quality stock with matte card cover, appearing twice a year. You'll find plenty of free verse here—some accessible and some leaning toward experimental—with the emphasis on voice, image and diction. All in all, poems and translations complement each other and create a distinct editorial mood each issue. Of 3,000-4,000 poems received they accept approximately 100. Press run is 1,000 for 500 subscriptions of which half are libraries. About 250 shelf sales. Subscription: $8/year, $15/2 years. **Sample postpaid: $5. Submit 3-5 poems. No simultaneous submissions or previously published poems. Reads submissions September 1 through May 1 only. Reports in 6-12 weeks. Pays 2 copies.**

SEQUOIA (II), Storke Publications Building, Stanford CA 94305, founded 1892, poetry editor Carlos Rodriguez, appears twice a year. They have published poetry by Susan Howe, Seamus Heaney, Adrienne Rich, Rita Dove and James Merrill. *Sequoia* is 80-100 pgs., 6×9, professionally printed, flat-spined, with a glossy card cover with art. Their press run is 800 with 400 subscriptions, of which half are libraries. They publish a small percentage of hundreds of unsolicited submissions. Subscription: $10. Sample postpaid: $5. **They do not consider simultaneous submissions or previously published poems. Reads submissions September 15 through June 1. Reports in "2 months or more." Pays 2 copies.**

‡**SERPENT & EAGLE PRESS (II)**, RD#1, Box 29B, Laurens NY 13796, phone (607)432-2990, founded 1981, poetry editor Jo Mish. "Our aim is to print fine limited letterpress editions of titles worth printing in all subject areas." **In poetry they like "Imagist—Ezra Pound's not Amy Lowell's type."** They have published poetry by Charlotte Mendez, Robert Bensen and Mike Newell. Their chapbooks are elegantly designed and printed on handmade paper with hand-sewn wrappers. **For book consideration, query with 5 samples. No simultaneous submissions. Pays 10 copies and $100 honorarium.**

SEVEN BUFFALOES PRESS; AZOREAN EXPRESS; BLACK JACK; VALLEY GRAPEVINE; HILL AND HOLLER ANTHOLOGY SERIES (IV-Rural, regional, anthologies), Box 249, Big Timber MT 59011, founded 1973, editor Art Cuelho, who writes, "I've always thought that rural and working class writers, poets and artists deserve the same tribute given to country singers." These publications all express that interest. For all of them Art Cuelho wants poetry oriented **toward rural and working people, "a poem that tells a story, preferably free verse, not longer than 50-60 lines, poems with strong lyric and metaphor, not romantical, poetry of the head and not the heart, not poems written like grocery lists or the first thing that comes from a poet's mind, no ivory tower, and half my contributors are women."** He has published poetry by R.T. Smith, James Goode, Leo Connellan and Wendell Berry. *The Azorean Express* is 35 pgs., 5½×8½, side-stapled. It appears twice a year. Circulation 200. **Sample postpaid: $5. Submit 4-8 poems. No simultaneous submissions. Reports in 1-2 weeks. Pays 1 copy.** *Black Jack* is an anthology series on Rural America that uses rural material from anywhere, especially the American West; *Valley Grapevine* is an anthology on central California, circulation 750, that uses rural material from central California. **Sample postpaid: $5.** *Hill and Holler*, Southern Appalachian Mountain series, takes in rural mountain lifestyle and folkways. **Sample postpaid: $5. Seven Buffaloes Press does not accept unsolicited mss but publishes books solicited from writers who have appeared in the above magazines.** Art Cuelho advises, "Don't tell the editor how great you are. This one happens to be a poet and novelist who has been writing for 25 years. Your writing should not only be fused with what you know from the head, but also from what you know within your heart. Most of what we call life may be some kind of gift of an unknown river within us. The secret to be learned is to live with ease in the darkness, because there are too many things of the night in this world. But the important clue to remember is that there are many worlds within us."

SEVENTEEN (V), 850 3rd Ave., New York NY 10022, phone (212)759-8100, founded 1944, contact poetry/voice editor, is a slick monthly for teenage girls, circulation 1,750,000. They publish **"all styles of poetry up to 40 lines by writers 21 and under. However, due to a large backlog, *Seventeen* can no longer accept poetry submissions." Purchase sample ($1.75) at newsstands.**

THE SEWANEE REVIEW; AIKEN TAYLOR AWARD FOR MODERN POETRY (III), University of the South, Sewanee TN 37375, founded 1892, thus being our nation's oldest continuously published literary quarterly, editor George Core. Fiction, criticism and poetry are invariably of the **highest establishment standards. Most of our major poets appear here from time to time.** They have published poetry by William Logan, Howard Nemerov and Barry Spacks. Each issue is a hefty paperback of nearly 200 pgs., conservatively bound in matte paper, always of the same typography. Truly a magazine open to all styles and forms, issues we critiqued featured formal sequences, metered verse, structured free verse, sonnets, and lyric and narrative forms—all of it accessible and intelligent. Circulation: 3,400. **Sample: $5.75. Reports in 1-4 weeks. Pays 70¢/line.** Also includes brief, standard and essay-reviews. The Aiken Taylor Award for Modern Poetry is awarded by *The Sewanee Review* and its publisher, the University of the South in Sewanee, TN, "for the work of a substantial and distinguished career." Poetry published in *The Sewanee Review* was also selected for inclusion in **Best American Poetry 1992.**

SHAMAL BOOKS (IV-Ethnic, anthologies), Dept. PM, GPO Box 16, New York NY 10116, phone (718)622-4426, founded 1976, editor Louis Reyes Rivera. Shamal Books is a small press whose purpose is **"to promote the literary efforts of African-American and Caribbean writers, particularly those who would not otherwise be able to establish their literary credentials as their concerns as artists are with the people."** The press publishes individual and "anthological" books and chapbooks, mostly flat-spined paper texts. They have published poetry by SeKou Sundiata, Sandra Maria Esteves and Rashidah Ismaili. The editor wants to see **"poetry that clearly demonstrates an understanding of craft,**

content and intent as the scriptural source of the word guiding and encouraging the intellect of the people." He does not consider unsolicited submissions of individual mss, but will look at work only while anthologies are open. How many sample poems should you send? "Two is cool." The cover letter should include a "leaning toward personal goals and poetic principles." Mss of poetry should be "neat and single-spaced." The editor will reply to queries within 2 months. Royalties for book authors are 15%. The editor says that he will subsidy publish "delicately—depends on resources and interest in work." His projects include "an international anthology; drama; prison anthology; books on language as a weapon; a collectivized publisher's catalog of Third World presses working out of NYC." His advice to poets: "Certainly to study the craft more and to research more into the historical role that has been the hallmark of poetry across class and caste conscious lines that limit younger perspectives. Not to be as quick to publish as to be in serious study, then while looking to publish, looking as well into collective ventures with other poets for publication and distribution. Above all, *read!*"

SHARING THE VICTORY (IV-Spirituality/inspirational, sports), 8701 Leeds Rd., Kansas City MO 64129, phone (816)921-0909, founded 1959, editor John Dodderidge, assistant editor Robyne Baker, managing editor Don Hilkemeier. This monthly magazine is published September through May by the Fellowship of Christian Athletes. **They want free verse on themes of interest to Christian athletes (high school and college, male and female).** As a sample they selected these lines by Aileen L. Myers:

> *I am more than*
> *skill and conditioning*
> *More because*
> *I am a child of a loving God,*
> *who created me in His spiritual image,*
> *loves me for myself*
> *and promises me the eternal Victory.*

They use 2-3 poems/year. Press run is 50,000. **Sample available for $1 with 8½ × 11 SASE (first class stamps for 3 oz.). Reads submissions July 1 through March 1 only. Guidelines available free.** Reporting time is 2 weeks and time to publication averages 3-4 months. **Pays $25-50. Buys first or second rights.**

SHATTERED WIG REVIEW (II), 523 E. 38th St., Baltimore MD 21218, phone (410)243-6888, founded 1988, contact Fred Engels, is a semiannual using **"liquid, messy poetry, oozing the stuff of life. No frustrated English professor poetry."** They have published poetry by John M. Bennett, Eel Leonard, Lyn Lifshin and Dan Raphael. As a sample the editor selected these lines by Chris Toll:

> *A 10,000-year-old white man rules the world*
> *when he needs a new heart,*
> *he murders a 16-year-old boy*
> *His tanks may rumble through the cities*
> *My crack dealers will fight back to back with my crystal healers*
> *Every cell in my body knows the new world is coming*

SHW is approximately 70 pgs., 8½ × 8½, photocopied, side-stapled with cardstock covers with original artwork and art and graphics inside. They receive about 10 submissions/week, accept about 20%. Press run is 300 for 100 subscribers of which 10 are libraries, 100 shelf sales. Subscription: $7 for 2 issues. **Sample postpaid: $4. Previously published poems and simultaneous submissions OK. Seldom comments on rejections. Reports within a month. Pays 1 copy.** Acquires one-time rights. Occasionally reviews books of poetry in 100 words. Open to unsolicited reviews. Poets may also send books for review consideration. The editor says there are no requirements for contributors except "that the contributor include us in their nightly prayers."

HAROLD SHAW PUBLISHERS; WHEATON LITERARY SERIES (V), Box 567, Wheaton IL 60189, phone (708)665-6700, founded 1967, Director of Editorial Services Ramona Cramer Tucker, is "small publisher of the Wheaton Literary Series and Northcote Books, **works of Christian and literary merit** including fiction, poetry, literary criticism and original prose" in flat-spined paperback and hardback books. They have published poetry by Madeleine L'Engle, John Leax, Sister Maura Eichner and Luci Shaw. **They publish on a 10/5% royalty basis plus 10 author's copies.** They publish a volume of poetry approximately every 2 years. "Our work reflects **a Christian evangelical world-view**, though this need not be explicit. In the future we may publish an anthology, rather than single poets." **However, they are currently still not accepting poetry submissions.**

SHEILA-NA-GIG (II), 23106 Kent Ave., Torrance CA 90505, founded 1990, editors Hayley R. Mitchell and Kristine Sanders. For the next 2 years, *Sheila-na-gig* will appear once a year as a large general issue using **"all forms, styles and subject matter—length, use your own discretion (don't ramble!). No religious, 'ultra' traditional, i.e. rhyming, conservative."** They have recently published poetry by Eloise

Klein Healy, Lyn Lifshin, Gerald Locklin and Charles H. Webb. As a sample the editors selected these lines by Clifton Snider:

> We burn a tattoo,
> a flaming pink triangle on the body politic,
> on a governor who presses his lips
> to the asses of queer-haters,
> a president who sends a liar
> to the Supreme Court,
> who sends our brothers & sisters
> to fights in the Persian Gulf, afterwards
> excluding them for being queer,
> their lives so many campaign contributions.

It is digest-sized, flat-spined, 60-150 pgs., photocopied from laser prints with matte b&w card cover. Subscription: $15 for 3 issues. Sample postpaid: $5.75. **Cover letter preferred with submissions. Include brief bio and note whether poems are previously published or simultaneous submissions. 1994 Deadline: May 15. "We'll begin reading these submissions on June 1, and will report in 6-8 weeks. Submit up to 5 poems**, and/or short stories (1-10 pgs.), and/or b&w artwork (5×7 and easy to reproduce). **Please note that our yearly Women's Issue will be postponed until further notice." Pays copies. Acquires first rights.** They say, "We encourage new poets with new styles and a strong 'voice' and look especially for poets not afraid to speak out on issues such as: sexuality, politics and feminist issues. Looking for poetry on the edge. If in doubt, we suggest ordering a back issue. Please make checks payable to Hayley R. Mitchell."

SHENANDOAH (II), Box 722, Lexington VA 24450, phone (703)463-8765, founded 1950, editor Dabney Stuart, managing editor Lynn Williams. Published at Washington and Lee University, it is a quarterly literary magazine which has published poetry by Conrad Hilberry, Martha McFerren, Robert B. Shaw, Cathy Song and Jeanne Walker. As a sample the editor chose these lines from "The Lake of the Unconscious" by Geraldine Connolly:

> and everything was still,
> the deer frozen between two pines
>
> the way the child was caught
> between the two worlds, the air
>
> and the bottom of the lake
> bobbing there, amazed

The magazine is 6×9, 100 pgs., perfect-bound, professionally printed with full-color cover. Generally, it is open to all styles and forms but leans toward lyric and narrative free verse with an emphasis on voice. Circulation: 1,700. **Sample postpaid: $3.50. All submissions should be typed on one side of the paper only. Your name and address must be clearly written on the upper right corner of the manuscript. Include SASE. Reads submissions September 1 through May 30. Reports in 3 months. Payment includes a check, one-year subscription and one copy. Buys first publication rights.** Staff reviews books of poetry in 7-10 pages, multi-book format. Send books for review consideration. Some reviews are solicited.

SHIP OF FOOLS (II); SHIP OF FOOLS PRESS (V), Box 1028, University of Rio Grande, Rio Grande OH 45674, founded 1983, editor Gina Pellegrino-Pines, assistant editor Jack Hart, review editor James Doubleday, is "more or less quarterly." They want **"coherent, well-written, traditional or modern, myth, archetype, love, odd and/or whimsical poetry—most types. No concrete, incoherent or greeting card poetry."** They have published poetry by Rhina Espaillat, Carolyn Page, Denver Stull and T. Kilgore Splake. As a sample the editors selected these lines from "Following the Reaper" by Nancy Haas:

> I am here again;
> Gathering the heads
> With their wide astonished eyes
> And the hands
> With their silent fluttering fingers.

They describe *Ship of Fools* as digest-sized, saddle-stapled, offset printed with cover art and graphics. Press run is 275 for 36 subscribers of which 6 are libraries. Subscription: $7 for 4 issues. **Sample postpaid: $2. No previously published poems or simultaneous submissions. Cover letter preferred. Often comments on rejections. Reports in 2-4 weeks. "If longer than six weeks, write and ask why." Pays 1 copy.** Reviews books of poetry. Ship of Fools Press publishes chapbooks but does not accept unsolicited mss.

SHOFAR (IV-Children, ethnic, religious), 43 Northcote Dr., Melville NY 11747, founded 1984, publisher/editor Gerald H. Grayson, is a magazine for American Jewish children 9-13, appearing monthly October through May (double issues December/January and April/May). It is 32 pgs., magazine-sized, professionally printed, with color paper cover. Their press run is 17,000 with 16,000 subscriptions of which 1,000 are libraries. Subscription: $14.95. **Sample: $1.05 postage and SAE. They will consider simultaneous submissions and "maybe" previously published poems. Send SASE for guidelines. Reports in 6-8 weeks. Pays $25-50/poem.**

‡**SHOOTING STAR REVIEW; SHOOTING STAR WRITING CONFERENCE (II, IV-Themes, ethnic)**, 7123 Race St., Pittsburgh PA 15208-1424, phone (412)731-7464, founded 1986, publisher Sandra Gould Ford, "This is an adult-oriented magazine dedicated to the African American experience. Each issue explores a specific theme. In 1994, we are doing a series of regional issues: 'Best in the Northeast' (writers from Maine to Pennsylvania; deadline: September 1993), 'Best in the Southeast' (Maryland to Mississippi; deadline: December 1993), 'Best in the Midwest and Rockies' (deadline: March 1994) and 'Best in the West' (deadline: June 1994). Our spring 1995 issue will focus on 'The Erotic' (deadline: September 1994)." They have recently published poetry by Toi Derricote, Dennis Brutus, Terri Jewell and Pinkie Gordon Lane. As a sample Sandra Gould Ford selected these lines from "Budget Crunch" by Don W. Robinson:

> *I just lost my job*
> *My unemployment's zeroed out*
> *I'm reduced to eating' Budget Crunch*
> *This new thing they're talkin' bout!*
>
> *It's got fat tax raisin's*
> *And little pink slips . . .*

SSR is 64 pgs., saddle-stitched, offset with glossy cover and art, "illustrated with significant attention to design and graphics." It appears quarterly. They receive about 1,200 poems a year, accept approximately 40. Press run is 1,500 for 700 subscribers of which 50 are libraries, 350 shelf sales. Single copy: $3; subscription: $12/year. **Sample: $3 plus $1.21 in postage. Submit up to 6 poems/quarter, one poem/page. No previously published poems; simultaneous submissions OK. Seldom comments on rejections. Send SASE for guidelines. Reports in 3 months. Pays $10, "as funds permit," and 2 copies. Buys first North American serial rights.** The Shooting Star Writers Conference is usually held in the fall. Send SASE for information. The publisher adds, "Work by non-Black writers on the Black experience is welcome."

SIERRA NEVADA COLLEGE REVIEW (I), P.O. Box 4269, Incline Village NV 89450, founded 1990, editor June Sylvester, is an annual literary magazine featuring poetry and short fiction by new writers. They want **"high quality, image-oriented poems that suggest or surprise; no limit on length, style, etc. No light verse, sloppy sentiment, purposeful obscurity, cliches or cuteness."** They have published poetry by Marisella Veiga, Darrell G.H. Schramm, Ted Thompson and Terry Wright. As a sample the editor selected these lines from "Bee Song" by William Powley:

> *and the bee's open mouth*
> *swallows pollen: it is love*
> *without mistakes,*
>
> *only sweetness*
> *in a yellow fold,*
> *a bee song.*

The editor says *SNCR* is approximately 60 pgs., with cover art only, no ads. "We receive approximately 100-200 poems a year and accept approximately 25-35." Press run is 300. Subscription: $5/year. **Sample postpaid: $2.50. No previously published poems; simultaneous submissions OK. Include brief bio with submission. Reads submissions September 1 through April 1. Often comments on rejections. Reports in 2 weeks-2 months. Pays 1 copy.** The editor says, "We delight in publishing the unpublished or underpublished writer. We look specifically for subtlety and skill."

THE SIGNPOST PRESS; THE BELLINGHAM REVIEW; 49TH PARALLEL POETRY CONTEST (II), 1007 Queen St., Bellingham WA 98226, phone (206)734-9781, founded 1975, editor Knute Skinner, publishes *The Bellingham Review* twice a year, runs an annual poetry competition and publishes other books and chapbooks of poetry occasionally. **"We want well-crafted poetry but are open to all styles,"** no specifications as to form. Poets they have published recently include Jim Daniels, Val Gerstle, B.A. St. Andrews, Joseph Green and James Bertolino. As a sample, the editor selected these lines by Trish Rucker:

> *The woods are quiet.*

> *The beasts are not dead. They are sleeping.*
> *Each night I have to marry you,*
> *my evil side, the other half,*
> *The doubter.*

The *Review* is digest-sized, saddle-stapled, typeset, with art and glossy cover. Each issue has about 38 pgs. of poetry. They have a circulation of 700 with 500 subscriptions. **Sample postpaid: $2. Simultaneous submissions OK. Reads submissions September 1 through March 1 only. Reports in 1-4 months. Pays 1 copy plus a year's subscription. Acquires first North American rights.** Staff reviews books of poetry in 500-1,000 words, single or multi-book format. Send books for review consideration also between September 1 and March 1. Send SASE for rules for the next 49th Parallel Poetry Contest and query regarding book publication.

SILVER APPLES PRESS (V), P.O. Box 292, Hainesport NJ 08036, phone (609)267-2758, founded 1982, poetry editor Geraldine Little. "We're a very small press with very limited funds. Published our first chapbook in 1988; open contest for same. We plan to publish randomly, as things turn us on and as funds permit—pamphlets, chapbooks, a set of postcards. **We are over-committed at present. Not currently accepting unsolicited poetry submissions. Watch *Poets & Writers* for announcements.**" They publish **"first-class poetry by experienced poets. No greeting card verse, soupy sentimental verse or blatantly religious verse."** They have published **Contrasts in Keening: Ireland** by Geraldine C. Little, **Abandoned House** by Susan Fawcett and **The Verb to Love** by Barbara Horton. As a sample the editor selected these lines from **Keeping Him Alive** by Charlotte Mandel:

> *We do not cut it down.*
> *In winter,*
> *within the bitter scrabble*
> *of bared, practiced branches,*
> *the dead tree, too, promises.*

SILVER WINGS (IV-Religious, spirituality/inspirational), P.O. Box 1000, Pearblossom CA 93553-1000, phone (805)264-3726, founded 1983, published by Poetry on Wings, Inc., poetry editor Jackson Wilcox. "As a committed Christian service we produce and publish *Silver Wings*, a quarterly poetry magazine. We want **poems with a Christian perspective, reflecting a vital personal faith and a love for God and man. Will consider poems from 3-20 lines. Quite open in regard to meter and rhyme.**" They have published poetry by William T. Burke, Andrew Peterson, C. David Hay and Harriett Hunt. As a sample the editor selected these lines from "As a Thousand Years" by Elva McAllister:

> *You could never pack enough of doing*
> *into earth's rigid clock-bound now;*
> *for you,*
> *what a glory in the Glory*
> *of eternal-present timeless time.*

The magazine is 32-36 pgs., digest-sized, offset from typescript with hand-lettered titles on tinted paper with cartoon-like art, circulation 450 with 250 subscriptions. They receive 1,000 submissions/year, use 200. Subscription: $7. **Sample postpaid: $2. Submit typed mss, double-spaced. Reports in 3 weeks, providing SASE is supplied;** time to publication can be up to 2 years. **Pays $9 in subscription and copy value. Acquires first rights. Rarely comments on rejections.** They hold an annual contest with $200 in prizes and chapbook publication. Send SASE for details. *Silver Wings* ranked #10 in the "Open Markets" category of the June 1993 *Writer's Digest* Poetry 60 list. This category ranks those publications most open to both free and formal verse. The editor says, "While we will look at any poetry which is submitted, we do want to encourage Christian poets to master the techniques of quality poetry, remembering that this takes time and care. We are glad to look at poetry that has an uplift to it. The ecumenical nature of *Silver Wings* is guaranteed by a governing board with members representing six different Christian communions."

SILVERFISH REVIEW; SILVERFISH REVIEW PRESS (II), P.O. Box 3541, Eugene OR 97403, phone (503)344-5060, founded 1979, poetry editor Rodger Moody, is an irregularly appearing digest-sized, 48-page literary magazine, circulation 750. **"The only criteria for selection of poetry is quality. In future issues *Silverfish Review* also wants to showcase the short short story."** They have published poetry by Walter McDonald, Jon Davis, Dick Allen, Ivan Arguelles, D.M. Wallace, Walter Pavlich, Ralph Salisbury, Richard Jones, Christine Zawadiwsky and Susan Cobin. As a sample the editor selected these lines by Lauren Mesa:

> *This one, the tall boy with brown hair,*
> *the wicker creel's strap slung*
> *across his crest, is Great-Uncle Mickey,*
> *Michelangelo Cipolla, the uncle*

who dressed as Santa the years
my mother was a child.

There are 36-48 pgs. of poetry in each issue. The magazine is professionally printed in dark type on quality stock, matte card cover with art. They receive about 1,000 submissions of poetry/year, use 20, have a 6- to 12-month backlog. Subscription for institutions: $15; for individuals: $12. **Sample: $4, single copy orders should include $1.50 for postage and handling. Submit at least 5 poems to editor. No simultaneous submissions. Reports in 6-24 weeks.** Pays 2 copies and one-year subscription, plus small honorarium when grant support permits. Reviews books of poetry. Open to unsolicited reviews. Poets may also send books for review consideration. Silverfish Review Press will consider mss for chapbook publication and conducts an annual chapbook competition with an award of $100 and 25 copies (with a press run of 750). Send SASE for rules.

SING HEAVENLY MUSE! (IV-Feminist), Box 13320, Minneapolis MN 55414, founded 1977, editor Sue Ann Martinson, fosters "the work of women poets, fiction writers and artists. The magazine is feminist in an open, generous sense: we encourage women to range freely, honestly and imaginatively over all subjects, philosophies and styles. We do not wish to confine women to women's subjects, whether these are defined traditionally, in terms of femininity and domesticity, or modernly, from a sometimes narrow polemical perspective. We look for explorations, questions that do not come with ready-made answers, emotionally or intellectually. **We seek out new writers, many before unpublished.** The editors try to reduce to a minimum the common bureaucratic distance between a magazine and its readers and contributors. Although our staff is small, we encourage writers by discussing their work, and we solicit comments from our readers. This relationship makes *Sing Heavenly Muse!* a community where women with widely varying interests and ideas may meet and learn from one another." For poetry they have **"no limitations except women's writing or men's writing that reflects awareness of women's consciousness."** They have published poetry by Alexis Rotella, Jill Breckenridge and Amirh Bahati. The editor selected these sample lines from "Sons of Soweto" by June Jordan:

Words live in the spirit of her face
and that sound will no longer yield . . .
she will stand under the sun!
She will stay!

The magazine appears one or two times a year in a 6×9, flat-spined, 125-page format, offset from typescript on heavy stock, b&w art, glossy card color cover. They receive 1,500+ submissions/year, use 50-60. Press run is 1,000 for 275 subscribers of which 50 are libraries. Single copy: $7; subscription: $14 (2 issues). **Sample postpaid: $4. Submit 3-10 pgs., name and address on each page. No simultaneous submissions. Query for information about upcoming reading periods and themes.** Editors sometimes comment on rejections. **Send SASE for guidelines. Reports in 4-5 months.** Pays "usually $25 plus 2 copies."

‡SINGING HORSE PRESS (III), P.O. Box 40034, Philadelphia PA 19106, founded 1976, editor and publisher Gil Ott, publishes an average of 2 new titles/year, primarily poetry. **"We are most interested in work which explores the intersection of poetics and human relation, be that political, cultural or psychological."** Most recent titles: **S*PeRM**K**T** by Harryette Mullen and **Her Angel** by Karen Kelley. Press run is 1,000. Average page count: 48-64. Prices average $6. **Writers should become acquainted with their publications/editorial preferences and query before submitting. "Most work is solicited."**

SINGULAR SPEECH PRESS (V, IV-Translations), 10 Hilltop Dr., Canton CT 06019, phone (203)693-6059, founded 1976, editor Don D. Wilson. "Although initially a means of publishing the editor's verse translations, Singular Speech Press nonprofitably lives so that we may present to *some* public a few, fine examples of the thousands of real poets now at work, at play—probably our most unsupported artists. To this end, **we plan to publish at least 5-6 mss per annum, 32-88 pages. We have hardly any biases, are delighted by formal and informal verse, are made glad by unknown and well-known poets, and eschew only the egregiously confessional, so boring, and the patently prosy, in lines as though poetic."** They have published William Burns, Charles Fishman and Stephen Smith. Soon to publish Bulgarian poets, Michael Cadnum and Ron McFarland. "Impossible to find six representative and self-contained lines," but here are six from "Hush You Nightingales," translated by the editor from Andrey Filipov:

The double dagger before a listing indicates that the listing is new in this edition. New markets are often the most receptive to submissions.

> *The moon, springtime cool, is shining like a silver spoon.*
> *The widow leaves the gate ajar—*
> *probably for the Dream at night*
> *to slip in quietly*
> *with a bouquet of marigolds picked*
> *from the graveyard garden.*

The press is currently not accepting poetry submissions—"filled up with mss for next 2 years."

SISTER VISION PRESS (IV-Ethnic, woman), P.O. Box 217, Station E, Toronto, Ontario M6H 4E2 Canada, phone (416)533-2184, founded 1985, managing editor Makeda Silvera, publishes 10 paperbacks/year. They want "poetry that reflects our lives as women of color; not restricted by form or length." They have published poetry by ahdri zhina mandiela and Ramabai Espinet. As a sample the editor selected these lines from "Crebo" in Espinet's book **Nuclear Seasons**:

> *My hands had wrinkles*
> *But rims grew around my eyes*
> *My skin became ebony and rose*
> *And my tongue grew long beyond words*

Previously published poems and simultaneous submissions OK. Cover letter required. Submit a sample of work, to a maximum of 10 pages. Replies to queries in 2 weeks, to mss (if invited) in 2 months. Pays 10% royalties and 10 author's copies. Write for samples. They say, "Know the publisher you are submitting mss to. This saves the poet and publisher time, money and energy."

SISTERS TODAY (II, IV-Religious), The Liturgical Press, Collegeville MN 56321, phone (612)363-2213, poetry editor Sister Mary Virginia Micka, C.S.J., 1884 Randolph, St. Paul MN 55105, editor Sister Mary Anthony Wagner, has been published for about 60 years. Though it is a Roman Catholic magazine, not all of the poetry it uses is on religious themes, and the editors do not want poetry that is "overly religious." They want "short (not over 25 lines) poems on any topic, using clean, fresh images and appealing to the reader's feelings and thoughts in a compelling way." They do not want poetry that depends "heavily on rhyme and on 'tricks' such as excessive capitalization, manipulation of spacing, etc." They have published poetry by Irene Zimmerman, S.S.S.F., T. Kretz and Fredrick Zydek. As a sample, the poetry editor chose these lines from "Father's Lesson" by Frank Accuardi:

> *In that frozen moment I see his face*
> *Through the cloudy cold. Neck veins*
> *taut as tree limbs hold the heavy chin.*
> *Dark creases branch around knotted eyes.*

ST, appearing 6 times a year, is 6×9, 80 pgs., saddle-stapled, professionally printed with matte card cover. Press run is 9,000 for 8,500 subscribers. They receive about 100 poems/month, accept about 5. Subscription: $16 USA; $18 foreign. Sample postpaid: $3. No simultaneous submissions. Previously published poems OK with publisher's release, but original poems much preferred. They like you to put your "complete legal name, address and social security number typed in the upper right corner." Poetry editor comments when a poem has come close to being accepted. Send SASE to poetry editor at St. Paul, MN address (above) for guidelines. Reports within 1 month, 6-12 months until publication. Pays $10/poem and 2 copies. Buys first rights.

SKOOB BOOKS PUBLISHING LTD. (III, IV-Translations), 43 Old Bethnal Green Rd., London E2 6PR United Kingdom, founded 1987, editor Lucien Jenkins. "As a publishing house we are interested in translations, particularly from Modern European poetry." As a sample the editor selected these lines from Michael Hamburger's translation of "Inventory" by Gunter Eich:

> *This pencil lead*
> *is what I love most:*
> *by day it writes verses*
> *I thought up in the night*

Cover letter required; include publishing history and information about material submitted. Books pay 7% royalties plus 6 copies. "We run a major international poetry competition in partnership with *Index on Censorship*." Lucien Jenkins gives this advice to people who write: "It takes time, it takes work, it takes courage *and* it takes talent. Do not be buttered up by friends who reassure you otherwise. Expect no money, no fame, no gratitude, no respect, no success, no pleasure, no comfort. Do it *only* because not doing it is not a possibility."

SKYLARK (I, II, IV-Themes), Purdue University Calumet, 2200 169th St., Hammond IN 46323, phone (219)989-2262, founded 1972, editor Pamela Hunter, is "a fine arts annual, including **special theme**." They are looking for "original images, concise presentation and honesty; poems up to 30 lines. No horror, nothing extremely religious, no pornography." They have recently published poetry by Robert

Cooke, Richard Zabransky and Susan Landgraf. As a sample the editor selected these lines from "The Point of Poetry" by Joan Peternel:

> *Today the storm damage includes*
> *a pumpkin blown against a wall*
> *like the head of some soldier,*
> *like that part of my life*
> *shattered by the snipers hiding*
> *the other side of my biography.*

Skylark is magazine-sized, saddle-stapled, 100+ pgs., professionally printed, with matte card cover. Press run is 500-1,000 for 50 subscriptions of which 12 are libraries. Single copy: $6. **Sample postpaid: $3.50. "Typed or computer printout manuscripts OK. Simultaneous submissions discouraged. Inquire as to annual theme for special section." Do not submit mss between June 1 and November 1. Reports in 4 months. Pays 1 copy. Acquires first rights. Editor may encourage rejected but promising writers.** *Skylark* has won several awards for individual works from The Columbia Scholastic Press Association.

SLATE & STYLE (IV-Specialized), Dept. PM, 2704 Beach Dr., Merrick NY 11566, phone (516)868-8718, editor Loraine Stayer, is a **quarterly for blind writers available on cassette, in large print and Braille,** "including articles of interest to blind writers, resources for blind writers. Membership/subscription $5 per year, $8 for Braille only (specify format). Division of the National Federation of the Blind." **Poems may be "5-30 lines. Prefer contributors to be blind writers, or at least writers by profession or inclination. No obscenities. Will consider all forms of poetry. Interested in new talent."** They have recently published poetry by Mary McGinnis, Barbara Shaidnagle and Alice Chandler. As a sample the editor selected "Word Picture" by Jodie Hittle:

> *What if I could paint a picture with words so keen*
> *That I could make color, size and shape be seen?*
> *To say the sun looks like orange juice tastes,*
> *or that polka dots feel like an unshaven face;*
> *That blue is ice and red is fire;*
> *that water is lower and wind is higher. . .*

The print version is magazine-sized, 28-32 pgs., stapled, with a fiction and poetry section. Press run is 200 for 150 subscribers of which 4-5 are libraries. Subscription: $5/year, Braille $8. Single copy: $1.25 except Braille. **Sample postpaid: $2.50. No simultaneous submissions. Submit 6-7 poems once a year. Cover letter preferred. Do not submit mss in July. Editor comments on rejections "if requested." Send SASE for guidelines. Reports in "2 weeks if I like it." Pays 1 copy.** Reviews books of poetry. Open to unsolicited reviews. Poets may also send books for review consideration. They offer an annual poetry contest. Entry fee: $3/poem. Deadline: May 1. Loraine Stayer says, "Poetry is one of the toughest ways to express oneself, yet ought to be the easiest to read. Anything that looks simple is the result of much work."

‡SLIPPERY WHEN WET (IV-Erotica, humor), P.O. Box 3101, Berkeley CA 94703, founded 1991, editor Sunah Cherwin, is a quarterly magazine of "humor, liberation and the best sex I can find in two dimensions." **They want "2 kinds of poetry: hot and funny. If it's funny, I like it to rhyme and scan. No stream-of-consciousness, politics, romance. If it's not explicitly about sex I will throw it out."** They have recently published poetry by Trish Thomas, Jackie Weltman and Phil Buff. The editor says it is 48 pgs., saddle-stitched, offset, with art, graphics and ads. Press run is 2,000 for 50 subscribers, 1,600 shelf sales. Subscription: $19.50. **Sample postpaid: $7. Submit poems typed, double-spaced, or on disk. Previously published poems OK; no simultaneous submissions. Often comments on rejections. Reports in 1½ months. Pays 3 copies. Acquires one-time rights.** Reviews *"zines only"* in about 2 paragraphs. The editor says, "Read the magazine, any magazine, before you submit to it. I hope the idea of submitting your work to my magazine is kind of exciting and scary, because if it's not dangerous, I don't want it."

SLIPSTREAM; SLIPSTREAM AUDIO CASSETTES (II, IV-Themes), Box 2071, New Market Station, Niagara Falls NY 14301, phone (716)282-2616 (after 5pm, EST), founded 1980, poetry editors Dan Sicoli, Robert Borgatti and Livio Farallo. *Slipstream* is a "small press literary mag, uses about 70% poetry and 30% prose, also artwork. **The editors like new work with contemporary urban flavor. Writing must have a cutting edge to get our attention. Occasionally do theme issues. We like to keep an open forum, any length, subject, style. Best to see a sample to get a feel. Like city stuff as opposed to country. Like poetry that springs from the gut, screams from dark alleys, inspired by experience."** No "pastoral, religious, traditional, rhyming" poetry. They have recently published poetry by Fred Voss, Charles Safford, Gerald Locklin, Allan Catlin, Charles Bukowski, Patrick McKinnon, Jenifer Olds, Marael Johnson, Kurt Nimmo and M. Scott Douglass. As a sample the editors selected these lines from "Library Service" by Jennifer Lagier:

> *You are eleven years old*
> *and already pregnant,*
> *trusting me to provide*
> *a Walt Disney picturebook*
> *dealing with childbirth.*

Slipstream appears 1-2 times a year in a 7 × 8½ format, 128 pgs., professionally printed, saddle-stapled, using b&w graphics. More than 100 pgs. are devoted to poetry. The poems are of varying quality; all attempt to be lively with the focus on voice. It contains mostly free verse, some stanza patterns. They receive over 1,500 submissions of poetry/year, use less than 10%. Press run is 300 for 200 subscribers of which 10 are libraries. Subscription: $8.50/2 issues. **Sample postpaid: $5. Editor sometimes comments on rejections. Send SASE for guidelines. Reports in 2-8 weeks. Pays copies.** Some issues are on announced themes—e.g.,"working stiff," "erotic," "protest," "night life" and "ethnic" theme issues have been released in the past. Also producing an audio cassette series. "Spoken word, songs, audio experiments, etc. are all welcome. Query for current needs." Annual chapbook contest has December 1 deadline. Reading fee: $5. Submit up to 40 pgs. of poetry, any style, previously published work OK with acknowledgments. Winner receives 50 copies. All entrants receive copy of winning chapbook. Past winners have included Gerald Locklin, Serena Fusek, Robert Cooperman, Richard Amidon and Sherman Alexie. Dan Sicoli advises, "Do not waste time submitting your work 'blindly.' Sample issues from the small press first to determine which ones would be most receptive to your work."

SMALL POND MAGAZINE OF LITERATURE (II), P.O. Box 664, Stratford CT 06497, phone (203)378-4066, founded 1964, editor Napoleon St. Cyr, a literary triquarterly that features poetry . . . "and anything else the editor feels is original, important." Poetry can be **"any style, form, topic, so long as it is deemed good, except haiku, but limit of about 100 lines."** Napoleon St. Cyr wants **"nothing about cats, pets, flowers, butterflies, etc. Generally nothing under 8 lines."** Although he calls it name-dropping, he "reluctantly" provided the names of Marvin Soloman, Deborah Boe, Richard Kostela-netz, Fritz Hamilton and Emilie Glen as poets published. The magazine is digest-sized, offset from typescript on off-white paper, 40 pgs. with matte card cover, saddle-stapled, artwork both on cover and inside. Circulation is 300, of which about a third go to libraries. Subscription: $8 (for 3 issues). **Sample postpaid: $2.50 for a random selection, $3 current. Guidelines are available in each issue. The editor says he doesn't want 60 pages of anything; "dozen pages of poems max." He reports on submissions in 10-45 days (longer in summer), and publication is within 3-18 months. Pays 2 copies. Acquires all rights. Returns rights with written request including stated use. "One-time use per request." Staff reviews books of poetry. Send books for review consideration.** All styles and forms are welcome here. The editor usually responds quickly, often with comments to guide poets whose work interests him.

SMALL PRESS WRITERS & ARTISTS ORGANIZATION (SPWAO); SPWAO SHOWCASE; SPWAO NEWSLETTER (IV-Membership, Science fiction/horror/fantasy), 2131 S. 227th Dr., Buckeye AZ 85326, secretary Cathy Hicks, president Mike Olson, newsletter editor Dana Allen. The organization publishes a newsletter with emphasis on aiding members, advice columns, short poetry, art, reviews and short fiction and provides a poetry commentary service for members only. **They don't want to see** "mainstream, religious, highly sentimental, pornographic, racial or political poetry." They have published poems by Marge Simon, John Grey, D.M. Vosk, Anne Valley, Jacie Ragan and Mark Fewell. **Staff reviews books of poetry in 200-500 words, single format. Send books for review consideration** (with cover letter) to Panda England, 395 Meadow Lane, Hastings MI 49058. As for advice, Cathy Hicks offers this excerpt from "The Element of Fear in Horror Poetry" by Michael A. Arnzen (newsletter volume 14, number 1, February 1992): ". . . a poem must at least incorporate the emotion of fear in one way or another to qualify. The emotion of fear is a very personal one, and it can occur at a variety of levels in poetry."

THE SMITH; THE GENERALIST PAPERS (II), 69 Joralemon St., Brooklyn NY 11201, founded 1964, editor Harry Smith, publishes 3 to 5 books yearly. They have published poetry by Menke Katz, Lloyd Van Brunt, Richard Nason, Glenna Luschei and Karen Swenson. As a sample the editor selected these lines from "Hawk Forever in Mid-Dive" in Lance Lee's **Wrestling with the Angel:**

> *Her feet on the patio are leaves blown*
> *over flagstones. Aimed at her head,*
> *beak thrust out wings angled severely*
> *a hawk hangs frozen in mid-air,*
> *fanned to permanent fire in her sky.*

"Send 3-6 poem sampling with query. No jingles, no standard academic verse. The decision process is relatively slow—about three months—as many mss are offered. Readers' reports are often passed along and the editor often comments." Pays 15% royalties, $500 advance, 10 copies. Write for catalog (free) or send $2 for a "slightly irregular" book ("with bumped corners or a

little dust"). *The Generalist Papers*, appearing 6 times/year, consists of lively critical commentaries on contemporary poetry—more candor than you will find in most reviews. Subscription: $12. **Sample postpaid: $2.** Harry Smith received the 1992 Poor Richard Award, a lifetime achievement award for distinguished contribution to small press publishing from the Small Press Center. He advises, "Revert to earlier models. *Avoid* university wordshops where there are standard recent models leading to standard mod verse. A close reading of **The Pearl Poet** will be more nourishing than all the asparagus of John Ashbery or Robert Bly."

GIBBS SMITH, PUBLISHER; PEREGRINE SMITH POETRY COMPETITION (II), P.O. Box 667, Layton UT 84041, phone (801)544-9800, founded 1971, poetry series established 1988, assistant editor Dawn Valentine. **They want "serious, contemporary poetry of merit. No specs except book is only 64 pgs."** They have published books of poetry by David Huddle and Carol Frost. Books are selected for publication through competition for the Peregrine Smith Poetry Prize of $500 plus publication. **Entries are received in April only and require a $10 reading fee.** The judge for the series and editor is Christopher Merrill.

SMITHS KNOLL (II), 49 Church Rd., Little Glemham, Woodbridge, Suffolk IP13 0BJ England, founded 1991, coeditors Roy Blackman and Michael Laskey, is a magazine appearing 3 times a year printing **"poems of pity, indignation and celebration,"** with no other restrictions. They have recently published poetry by Geoffrey Holloway, John Latham, Carole Satyamurti, Myra Schneider, Frances Wilson and Patricia Pogson. As a sample the editors selected this poem by Peter Wyles, called "Image":

> Little blond kid
> straight out of the Mothercare catalogue.
> Tiny trainers, and trendy jeans,
> and your smart, dark and shiny jacket . . .
>
> across its back a flag, and a plane,
> and the slogan "Born to Kill."

The editors say it is 60 pgs., A5, offset-litho, perfect-bound, with card cover. They receive about 3,500 poems a year, "accept one in twenty-four." Press run is 600 for 250 subscribers. Single copy: £2.50; subscription: £6.50 for 3 issues (plus postage outside UK). **Sample postpaid: £3.** "**We would consider poems previously published in magazines outside the U.K.**" No simultaneous submissions. Poems only. Doesn't commission work. "**Constructive criticism of rejections where possible.**" Tries to report within 1 month (outside UK). Pays 1 copy/poem.

THE SNAIL'S PACE REVIEW (II, IV-Translations), Dept. PM, RR#2 Box 363 Brownell Rd., Cambridge NY 12816, founded 1990, editors Darby Penney and Ken Denberg, is a biannual of contemporary poetry. "We are committed to publishing the best work of all poetic genres by both well-known and emerging poets, as well as poetry in translation." They want "**work of all genres that has strong imagery, uses language imaginatively and contains an element of the unexpected. No religious, sentimental, patriotic and, in most cases, rhymed poetry.**" They have published poetry by Martha Collins, Stephen Dunn, Linda Pastan, Jerome Rothenberg and Fred Chappell. As a sample we selected these lines from "a reader considers the options" by A.J. Wright:

> know them by their options
> these people who study themselves
>
> one who memorizes lines
> and another making notes

It is 36 pgs., digest-sized, offset, saddle-stitched with cover illustration but no inside artwork. They receive about 3,000 poems a year. Press run is 350 for 100 subscribers of which 18 are libraries, 150 shelf sales. Subscription: $7; $12 libraries. **Sample postpaid: $3.50.** No previously published poems or simultaneous submissions. Cover letter, with brief bio, required. Time between acceptance and publication is 4 months. Sometimes comments on rejections. Send SASE for guidelines. **Reports in 10-16 weeks. Pays 2 copies.** Acquires first North American serial rights. Copyright reverts to author upon publication. As of 1994, they sponsor an annual chapbook competition.

SNAKE NATION REVIEW; SNAKE NATION PRESS (II), #2, 110 W. Force St., Valdosta GA 31601, phone (912)249-8334, founded 1989, editor Roberta George, appears 4 times a year. "**Any form, length of 60 lines or less.**" They have published poetry by Irene Willis and William Fuller. The handsome, 6×9, flat-spined magazine, 100 pgs., matte card cover, has a press run of 1,000 for 200 subscriptions of which 11 are libraries. Subscription: $15. **Sample postpaid: $6.** Editor comments on submissions sometimes. Send SASE for guidelines. Reports in 3 months. Pays 2 copies or prizes. Acquires first

rights. Snake Nation Press publishes books of poetry. **Submit 60-page ms with $10 reading fee. Pays $500 on publication.**

SNAKE RIVER REFLECTIONS (I, II), 1863 Bitterroot Dr., Twin Falls ID 83301, phone (208)734-0746, appears 10 times a year using **short (up to 20 lines) poems, any topic.** It is 8 pgs., stapled on the side. Press run is 100-200. Subscription: $6. **Sample postpaid: 25¢. Send SASE for guidelines. Pays 2 copies. Acquires first rights.** Reviews books of poetry. Send books for review consideration to editor Bill White.

SNOWY EGRET (II, IV-Nature), P.O. Box 9, Bowling Green IN 47833, founded 1922 by Humphrey A. Olsen, editors Karl Barnebey and Michael Aycock. **They want poetry that is "nature-oriented: poetry that celebrates the abundance and beauty of nature or explores the interconnections between nature and the human psyche."** As a sample of published poetry they selected the opening lines of "In a Climax Forest" by Conrad Hilberry:

> *The wooden past grows larger, I grow less*
> *and less convincing in this sullen air*
> *that wants a wind to stir its emptiness.*

Snowy Egret appears twice a year in a 48-page, magazine-sized format, offset, saddle-stapled, with original graphics. Of 500 poems received they accept about 20. Their press run is 800 for 500 subscribers of which 50 are libraries. **Sample postpaid: $8. Send #10 SASE for writer's guidelines. Reports in 1 month. Pays $4/poem or $4/page plus 2 copies. Buys first North American or reprint rights.** Open to unsolicited reviews. Poets may also send books for review consideration.

SOCIAL ANARCHISM (IV-Political, social issues, women/feminism), 2743 Maryland Ave., Baltimore MD 21218, phone (301)243-6987, founded (Vacant Lots Press) 1980, poetry editor Howard J. Ehrlich, is a digest-sized, 96-page biannual, print run 2,000, using about 10 pgs. of poetry in each issue which **"represents a political or social commentary that is congruent with a nonviolent anarchist, antiauthoritarian and feminist perspective."** They have published poetry by Jacqueline Elizabeth Letalien, L.M. Harrod, Mark Colasurdo, Bridget Balthrop Morton and Bert Hubinger. **Sample postpaid: $3; $3.50 outside U.S. Submit up to 5 poems. Considers simultaneous submissions. Cover letter with short (3-sentence) bio required. Reports in 4-6 weeks. Pays 3 copies.** Query regarding book reviews.

THE SOCIETY OF AMERICAN POETS (SOAP); IN HIS STEPS PUBLISHING COMPANY; THE POET'S PEN; THE POET'S PROGRESS (I, IV-Religious, membership), P.O. Box 120, Reidsville GA 30453, phone (912)557-4265, founded 1984, editor Dr. Charles E. Cravey. *The Poet's Pen* is a literary quarterly of poetry and short stories. In His Steps publishes religious and other books and publishes music for the commercial record market. **"Open to all styles of poetry and prose—both religious and secular. No gross or 'X-rated' poetry without taste or character."** They have published poetry by Carlton Cook, Lessie Perry and Joann Saulino. As a sample the editor selected these lines from "Grapevine" by Carol Ann Lindsay:

> *The withered winter vine*
> *of naked, knotted branches*
> *nailed to man-made fences,*
> *chains the cursing crosses to stolid, silent rows*
> *that betray the bitter sip*
> *of hollow human ways.*

The Poet's Pen uses **poetry primarily by members and subscribers.** (Membership: $20/year.) *The Poet's Progress*, a quarterly newsletter supplement to *The Poet's Pen*, **also uses poetry by members and subscribers. Each pays $2-25/poem. Query for book publication. 60/40 split of pay. Editor "most certainly" comments on rejections.** Sponsors various contests throughout the year. Editor's Choice Awards each quarter, prizes $25, $15 and $10. President's Award for Superior Choice has a prize of $50; deadline is November 1. They also publish an anthology that has poetry competitions in several categories with prizes of $25-100. *The Poet's Pen* ranked #3 in the "Open Markets" category of the June 1993 *Writer's Digest* Poetry 60 list. This category ranks those publications most open to both free and formal verse. The editor says, "We're looking for poets who wish to unite in fellowship with our growing family of poets nationwide. We currently have over 850 poets and are one of the nation's largest societies, yet small enough and family operated to give each of our poets individual attention and pointers."

SOJOURNERS (IV-Religious, political), P.O. Box 29272, Washington DC 20017, phone (202)636-3637, founded 1975, poetry editor Rose Berger, appears 10 times/year, "with approximately 40,000 subscribers. **We focus on faith, politics and culture from a radical Christian perspective. We publish**

1-3 poems/month depending on length. All poems must be original and unpublished. We look for seasoned, well-crafted poetry that reflects the issues and perspectives covered in our magazine. Poetry using noninclusive language (any racist, sexist, homophobic poetry) will not be accepted." As a sample the editor selected these lines by David Abrams:

> An eagle against a clear sky,
> A snake coming off a rock,
> A skiff in the center of a lake,
> And the Spirit slipping into bodies.

The editor describes *Sojourners* as 52 pgs., offset printing. It appears monthly except that there is one issue for August/September and February/March. Of 400 poems received/year they publish 8-10. Press run is 50,000 for 40,000 subscriptions of which 500 are libraries; 2,000 shelf sales. Subscription: $30. **Sample postpaid: $2.75. Submit no more than 3 poems at a time. Cover letter with brief bio required. Editor comments on submissions "sometimes." Send SASE for guidelines. Reports in 4-6 weeks. Pays $15-25/poem plus 5 copies.** "We assume permission to reprint unless the author requests otherwise. Staff reviews books of poetry in 600 words, single or multi-book format.

SOLEIL PRESS (IV-Ethnic), Box 452, RFD 1, Lisbon Falls ME 04252, phone (207)353-5454, founded 1988, contact Denis Ledoux, publishes and distributes **writing by and about Franco-Americans (AMericans of French-Canadian and Acadian descent)** in chapbooks and paperbacks. Not interested in the continental French experience. **Submit sample poems with cover letter noting how the material is Franco-North American. Pays copies.**

SOLO FLYER; SPARE CHANGE POETRY PRESS (IV-Regional), 2115 Clearview NE, Massillon OH 44646, Spare Change Poetry Press founded 1979, editor David B. McCoy. *Solo Flyer* is a 4-page flyer appearing 2-5 times/year featuring the work of a single poet in each issue. **"Submissions limited to Ohio poets."** They want **poetry using punctuation and capitalization. "Like to see poems with a common theme."** As a sample the editor selected "Absences" by Ruth V. Tams-Fuquen:

> Wordless
> we walked that hotel's midnight garden.
> The blossom you laid on my palm
>
> spoke
> for the song you hummed,
>
> suggested
> the words you chose
> not to sing.

The flyers are folded 8½ × 11 sheets of colored paper. **Sample free with #10 SASE. Previously published material OK. Pays 20-25 copies.** The editor says, "Submissions without SASE are not read."

SONOMA MANDALA (II), c/o English Dept., Sonoma State University, Rohnert Park CA 94928, phone (707)664-3902, founded 1973, faculty advisor Elizabeth Herron, is an annual literary review that publishes poetry, short fiction and some artwork. They are **"open to all styles. Preferably not over two pages."** They have published poetry by Lucille Clifton, Stephen Torre, Lyn Lifshin, Simon Perchik, Etheridge Knight and Maureen Hurley. As a sample the editor selected these lines (poet unidentified):

> There are people who are combustible, people that is
> who spontaneously burst into flames. We know this by
> their remains, the manner in which the body has been
> consumed. Always there is a small blackened area

She says *Sonoma Mandala* is 140 pgs., typeset, perfect-bound, no ads. They receive over 600 mss a year, accept approximately 10-15%. Press run is 500 for 10 subscribers of which 6 are libraries, 300 shelf sales. Subscription: $6. **Sample postpaid: $3. No previously published poems; simultaneous submissions OK. "Brief bio helps." Reads submissions August 1 through November 15 only. Comments on rejections "whenever possible." Send SASE for guidelines. Reports in 2-4 months. Pays 2 copies.** Acquires first North American serial rights. Elizabeth Herron says, "We are open to all schools of thought/poetics and seek fresh, original writing with life-affirming values."

SONORA REVIEW (II), Dept. of English, University of Arizona, Tucson AZ 85721, phone (602)626-8383 or 621-1836, founded 1980, address all work to Poetry Editor, is a semiannual literary journal that publishes "non-genre" fiction and poetry. **The editors want "quality poetry, literary concerns. Translations welcome. No overly cheerful and upbeat poetry; poetry without enough passion, i.e. too technical; swooping and universal sentiment." They have published poetry by Ricardo Pau-Llosa, Michael Collier, Barbara Anderson and Charlie Smith. As a sample, the editors chose the following lines by Laurie Blauner:

> Some days I spread myself out like butter
> on toast and hope for changes, how the body fades
> after dusk, how the architect of your house assumes
> you are now free of desire . . .

Sonora Review is a handsome magazine, 6×9, professionally printed on heavy off-white stock, 130 pgs., flat-spined, with 2-color glossy card cover. Recent issues have tended to include lyric and narrative free verse, with some metered poetry, translations and sequences rounding out selections. Circulation is 650, of which 250 are subscriptions and 45 go to libraries. Subscription: $10/year, $18/2 years. **Back issue available for $5 postpaid. Poets should submit typed copy; simultaneous submissions OK. "Brief cover letter helpful but optional." Reporting time is 2 months and time to publication 6 months. Pays 2 copies.** Send books for review consideration. The magazine sponsors annual poetry awards with prizes of $150 and $50. Send #10 SASE for deadlines and guidelines. In the past, contributors to *Sonora Review* have been listed in **Best of the West, Pushcart Prize, O. Henry** and **Best American Poetry** anthologies.

SOUNDINGS EAST (II), Salem State College, Salem MA 01970, phone (508)741-6270, founded 1973, advisory editor Claire Keyes. "*SE* is published by Salem State College and is staffed by students. We accept short fiction (15 pgs. max) and **contemporary poetry (5 pgs. max).** Purpose is to promote poetry and fiction in the college and beyond its environs. We **do not want graphic profanity.**" They have published poetry by Martha Ramsey, Walter McDonald and Linda Portnay as well as a feature section on "Incarcerated Poets." *SE* appears twice a year, 64-68 pgs., digest-sized, flat-spined, b&w drawings and photos, glossy card cover with b&w photo. Press run is 2,000 for 120 subscribers of which 35 are libraries. They receive about 500 submissions/year, use 40-60. **Sample postpaid: $3. Simultaneous submissions OK. Reads submissions September 1 through May 1 only. Fall deadline: November 20; Spring: April 20. Reports within 1-4 months. Pays 3 copies. Acquires all rights. Rights revert to the writers.** "We occasionally, when funding allows, publish an extra spring issue which features only poetry, fiction and artwork by Salem State College students."

‡**SOUTH ASH PRESS (I, II)**, 2311 E. Indian School Rd., Phoenix AZ 85016, founded 1991, publisher Chuck Hadd Jr., is a monthly poetry magazine sustained and distributed by community advertisers. **They want "well-crafted poems by beginning and established poets. 75 lines maximum. No doggerel."** They have recently published poetry by Denis Johnson. As a sample the publisher selected these lines from "Traveling Between Storms" by Albino Carrillo:

> Thunder is what wakes us all,
> the taste like salt and meat
> lingering as we pull on our clothes.
> And just before the evening's spent
> to wander with the gray constellations.
> To know this blackness, to know it well.

South Ash Press is 8 pgs., magazine-sized, saddle-stapled with card cover with b&w photo, numerous ads on same pages as poems. They receive about 1,000 poems a year, publish about 200. Each issue includes a number of poems by a "Featured Poet." Press run is 2,000 for 50 subscribers, the rest distributed free through advertisers. Subscription: $20/year. **Sample postpaid: $2. No previously published poems; simultaneous submissions OK.** "Three people select submissions. An acceptance by any one of them gets poem included. While we are glad to see work by beginners, we do not provide critiques and/or advice." **Reports in 4-6 weeks. Pays 2 copies. Acquires first rights.**

SOUTH CAROLINA REVIEW (II), English Dept., Clemson U., Clemson SC 29634-1503, phone (803)656-3229, founded 1968, editor Richard J. Calhoun, is a biannual literary magazine "recognized by the *New York Quarterly* as one of the top 20 of this type." They will consider **"any kind of poetry as long as it's good. No stale metaphors, uncertain rhythms or lack of line integrity. Format should be according to new MLA Stylesheet."** They have published poetry by Pattiann Rogers, J.W. Rivers and Claire Bateman. It is 200+ pgs., 6×9, flat-spined, professionally printed and uses about 8-10 pgs. of poetry in each issue. Reviews of recent issues back up editorial claims that all styles and forms are welcome; moreover, poems were accessible and well-executed, too. Circulation is 600, for 400 subscribers of which 250 are libraries. They receive about 1,000 freelance submissions of poetry/year, use 10, have a 2-year backlog. Subscription: $7. **Sample postpaid: $5. Do not submit during June, July, August or December. Reports in 6-9 months. Pays copies.** Staff reviews books of poetry.

SOUTH COAST POETRY JOURNAL (II), English Dept., California State University, Fullerton CA 92634, founded 1986, editor John J. Brugaletta. The twice-yearly (January and June) magazine publishes poetry only. "We'd like to see poems with strong imagery and a sense that the poem has found its best form, whether that form is traditional or innovative. We prefer poems under 36 lines, but we'll look at others. Any subject matter or style. We have published Marge Piercy, Mark Strand, X.J. Kennedy and Robert Mezey." As a sample, the editor selected these lines from "The Church Mouse's Trap" by Edward C. Lynskey:

> *I pamper a cranny in a church once*
> *charismatic Jesuit, now Episcopal,*
> *but cheese cuts the same way for me.*
> *Sleeping offdays with belfry bats;*
> *midnights I rouse with odd hymns*
> *hatched inside my head, "Have a Maria?"*

The journal is 60 pgs., digest-sized, perfect-bound, offset, heavy paper cover, some line art. Press run is 700 for 420 subscribers, 25 of which are libraries, 50 shelf sales. Subscription: $10, $6/issue. Sample postpaid: $3.50. No simultaneous submissions. Reads submissions September 1 through June 1 only. Every submission is read by at least 3 editors. Guidelines are available for SASE. Submissions are reported on in 6-8 weeks. Pays 1 copy. Acquires first North American serial rights. They conduct an annual poetry contest judged by eminent poets. Entry fee is $3/poem.

SOUTH DAKOTA REVIEW (II, IV-Regional, themes), University of South Dakota, Vermillion SD 57069, phone (605)677-5220 or 677-5966, founded 1963, editor John R. Milton, is a "literary quarterly publishing poetry, fiction, criticism, essays. When material warrants, an emphasis on the American West; writers from the West; Western places or subjects; frequent issues with no geographical emphasis; periodic special issues on one theme, or one place or one writer. Looking for originality, some kind of sophistication, significance, craft — i.e., professional work. Nothing confessional, purely descriptive, too filled with self-importance." They use 6-10 poems/issue, "receive tons, it seems." Press run is 650-900 for 450 subscriptions of which half are libraries. Subscription: $15/year, $25/2 years. Sample postpaid: $4. Editor comments on submissions "rarely." Reports in 1-12 weeks. Pays 1 copy/page. Acquires first and reprint rights. They have a distinct bias against personal or confessional poems, and generally publish free verse with a strong sense of place, a strong voice and a universal theme. Read the magazine — it's attractive and well-edited — to get a feel for the type of poetry that succeeds here. Milton advises, "Find universal meaning in the regional. Avoid constant 'I' personal experiences that are not of interest to anyone else. Learn to be less self-centered and more objective."

SOUTHEASTERN FRONT (II), 565 17th St. NW, Cleveland TN 37311, founded 1985, publisher Robin Merritt, is "an artists' and writers' presentation/representation service; a gallery in a magazine. No stylistic limitations, substantial human experience is a plus. Nothing devoid of artistic or literary merit, nor strictly commercially designed work." It is approximately 60 pgs., b&w, glossy, offset print with photos. Press run is 1,000 + . Inquire (with SASE) about availability of sample. Previously published poems ("if author retains all rights") and simultaneous submissions OK. Cover letter not required "but often beneficial." Often comments on rejections. Send SASE for guidelines. Reporting time varies. Pays "exposure, publication, referrals." Authors retain rights. Open to unsolicited reviews "as long as review is accompanied by a copy of the book." Poets may also send books for review consideration. *Southeastern FRONT* also offers short-run book printing and manufacturing services to individuals and institutions." Will print as few as fifty copies of perfect-bound or saddle-stitched books. Perfect for poets, teachers, catalogs, etc. Inquire for more information." They have recently published **Four Wheeler & Two Legged**, poems by Stephen Wing. "This author's first book was published due to his high quality submissions to our artists' & writers' presentation service. **Four Wheeler & Two Legged** is contemporary poetry with themes on hitchhiking, nature and earth awareness, international human rights and relationships. It is 112 pgs. and is available for $9.95 plus $1.05 postage from *Southeastern FRONT*." The editor says, "*Southeastern FRONT* offers its contributors exposure to selected publishers, reviewers, museums, galleries and individuals actively involved in the fine arts. We do not presently require submission or reading fees from our contributors; however, your purchase of Stephen Wing's excellent new collectionof poetry is the most effective way you can help us expedite the completion of our Artists' & Writers' showcase publications."

THE SOUTHERN CALIFORNIA ANTHOLOGY; ANN STANFORD POETRY PRIZES (III), c/o Master of Professional Writing Program, WPH 404, University of Southern California, Los Angeles CA 90089-4034, phone (213)740-3252, founded 1983, is an "annual literary review of serious contemporary poetry and fiction. Very open to all subject matters except pornography. Any form, style OK." They have published poetry by Robert Bly, John Updike, Denise Levertov and Peter Viereck. As a sample the editor selected these lines from "The Rivers of Paris" by James Ragan:

CLOSE-UP

Sharing One's Heritage Through Poetry

"Auntie"

It was the last time she saw him.

She remembers the buck wagon
The snow, like feathers, falling thick
The woven blanket across their laps.

She remembers eighty years back
The long rough trip on mother's lap
Shivering like a leaf between sleep.

She remembers the Black and sacred
Hills, the fear of being followed
The buck wagon unsure of the climb.

She remembers Grandfather coming
Down, smoke billowing from the nostrils
Of his horse. Snow muting the hills.

She remembers Grandfather, his horse,
The blanket wrapped around him,
His braids and earring, his warm smile

His hugs, his hugs, and the tears.

Charlene Blue Horse

The aunt depicted in Charlene Blue Horse's poem told stories that captured the imagination and Ogalala Lakota heritage of this well-known poet, writer and story-teller.

"We were standing in her kitchen," Blue Horse recalls. "She was washing the dishes and I was drying. She began to tell me her memories of when they knew they had to leave home."

The Reservation Era was beginning, and an extraordinary culture was being threatened.

In many of her poems, Blue Horse captures the harsh truths of the aftermath of the U.S.-Indian wars and passes them on in poems, continuing the story-telling tradition of Native Americans.

"My people are always very descriptive when they tell stories," Blue Horse explains. When her aunt shared the story about the great grandmother's leave-taking, she says, "I could put myself in her place. It was as though I had been there myself, and could feel everything that she had felt."

Blue Horse's "undeclared mentor" and friend was the late famous poet Richard Hugo. "He would talk to me about his writing and about the process he went through," she recalls. "He would discuss meter, imagination, how to rescue a poem.

He would write at my kitchen table when he came to visit, and when he liked a particular poem he had just written, he would share it with me."

Blue Horse completed undergraduate and advanced degrees at Portland State University, including a master's in liberal arts. (Her thesis was a book of poetry.) Currently, she is a member of both the Department of Minority Affairs and English department at the University of Wisconsin-La Crosse. In addition to counseling and advising, she teaches English and Native American Literature (along with Women's and Minority Studies classes). She also has been a workshop leader and speaker in several elementary and secondary schools and colleges.

In her classes and workshops, Blue Horse advises poets to slate a time to write every day. "Try the early morning," she says. She also advises poets to carry a notebook "to jot down pieces of dreams, conversations, descriptions, observations or lines that may come to you."

Keep a journal for longer descriptions and observations, she adds. "You will find that when you need to write, and have nothing to say, you can go back to your journal for an idea."

Most important, she stresses, learn the basics of craft. "Show what you're trying to say, instead of telling it."

Blue Horse practices what she preaches. As a result, her work has appeared in such publications as *Confluence, River Styx, The Louisville Review, Cafe Solo, Northwest Review, The Bellingham Review, The Native American Annual* and *The Oregonian*, among others.

She pays close attention to the craft and structure of a poem. In "Auntie," for instance, the chant-like "She remembers" generates the music of each stanza, and the lone first and last lines bookend those stanzas to form a circle or symbolic hoop on the page. Blue Horse says she revises until she is satisfied with every word, every image.

In this poem, she says, her goal was to keep her aunt's story fresh and immediate. When she had finished the last draft, she believed "you could not only see it, you could feel it; you could hear the music and choose to enter the hoop and keep it whole."

Finally, Blue Horse notes that in "Auntie," as in her other poems, her heritage plays a key role. "The philosophy of my people has everything to do with who I am and with my writing," she says. "Poetry is something almost sacred for Native Americans. Poetry is prayer; poetry is song; poetry is story and history."

—*Michael J. Bugeja*

❝Carry a notebook to jot down pieces of dreams, conversations, descriptions, observations or lines that may come to you.❞

—Charlene Blue Horse

> *The boulevards are the rivers wind owes*
> *to the eyes' reflections, light*
> *to the panes transparent*
> *in the domes of air wind weaves along Sacre Coeur*

The anthology is 144 pgs., digest-sized, perfect-bound, with a semi-glossy color cover featuring one art piece. A fine selection of poems distinguish this journal, and it has an excellent reputation, well-deserved. The downside, if it has one, concerns limited space for newcomers. Circulation is 1,500, 50% going to subscribers of which 50% are libraries. 30% are for shelf sales. **Sample postpaid: $5.95. No simultaneous submissions, no previously published poems. Submit 3-5 poems between September 1 and January 1. All decisions made by mid-February. Send SASE for guidelines. Reports in 4 months. Pays 3 copies. Acquires all rights.** The Ann Stanford Poetry Prizes ($750, $250 and $100) have an April 15 deadline, $10 fee (5 poem limit), for unpublished poems. Include cover sheet with name, address and titles and SASE for contest results. All entries are considered for publication. All entrants receive a copy of *SCA*.

SOUTHERN HUMANITIES REVIEW (II, IV-Translations), 9088 Haley Center, Auburn University AL 36849, poetry editor Scott Ward, coeditors Dan Latimer and R.T. Smith, founded 1967, is a 6×9 literary quarterly, 100+ pgs., circulation 800. **Interested in poems of any length, subject, genre. Space is limited, and brief poems are more likely to be accepted. "Translations welcome."** This journal continues to gain influence and prestige in the literary world by publishing a wide variety of verse that displays careful attention to image, theme, craft and voice. They have published poetry by Lars Gustaffson, Donald Hall, Reynolds Price, Mary Ruefle, Hayden Carruth, Robert Morgan and John Engels. Subscription: $15/year. Sample: $5. **"Several poems at a time recommended. Avoid sending faint computer printout." Responds in 1-2 months, possibly longer in summer. Pays 1 copy and $50 for the best poem published during the year. Buys all rights. "Poet has the right to publish *SHR* contribution in any volume consisting of his/her own work per our agreement."** Staff reviews books of poetry in approximately 750-1,000 words. Send books for review consideration. The editors advise, "For beginners we'd recommend study and wide reading in English and classical literature, and, of course, American literature – the old works, not just the new. We also recommend study of or exposure to a foreign language and a foreign culture. Poets need the reactions of others to their work: criticism, suggestions, discussion. A good creative writing teacher would be desirable here, and perhaps some course work too. And then submission of work, attendance at workshops. And again, the reading: history, biography, verse, essays – all of it. We want to see poems that have gone beyond the language of slippage and easy attitudes."

SOUTHERN POETRY REVIEW; GUY OWEN POETRY PRIZE (II), English Dept., University of North Carolina, Charlotte NC 28223, phone (704)547-4309, editors Lucinda Grey and Ken McLaurin, founded 1958, a semiannual literary magazine "with emphasis on effective poetry. **There are no restrictions on form, style or content of poetry; length subject to limitations of space."** They have published work by Linda Pastan, Judith Ortiz Cofer, David Ray, Stephen Sandy, Betty Adcock and Walter McDonald. *Southern Poetry Review* is 6×9, handsomely printed on buff stock, 78 pgs., flat-spined with textured, one-color matte card cover. Circulation is 1,000+. Subscription: $8/year. **Sample available for $2 postpaid; no guidelines, but will answer queries with SASE. Writers should submit no more than 3-5 poems. Reads submissions September 1 through May 31 only. Pays 1 copy. Acquires first-time rights.** Staff reviews books of poetry. Send books for review consideration. This is the type of literary magazine to settle back with in a chair and read, particularly during dry creative spells, to inspire one's muse. It is recommended as a market for that reason. It's a tough sell, though. Work is read closely and the magazine reports in a timely manner. There is a yearly contest, the Guy Owen Poetry Prize of $500, to which the entry fee is a subscription; submission must be postmarked in April.

THE SOUTHERN REVIEW (II), 43 Allen Hall, Louisiana State University, Baton Rouge LA 70803, phone (504)388-5108, founded 1935 (original series), 1965 (new series), poetry editors James Olney and Dave Smith, "is a literary quarterly which publishes fiction, poetry, critical essays and book reviews, with emphasis on contemporary literature in the U.S. and abroad, and with special interest in Southern culture and history. Selections are made with careful attention to craftsmanship and technique and to the seriousness of the subject matter." By general agreement this is one of the most distinguished of literary journals. Joyce Carol Oates, for instance, says, "Over the years I have continued to be impressed with the consistent high quality of *SR*'s publications and its general 'aura,' which bespeaks careful editing, adventuresome tastes and a sense of thematic unity. *SR* is characterized by a refreshing openness to new work, placed side by side with that of older, more established, and in many cases highly distinguished writers." The editors say they want **"No particular kinds of poetry. We are interested in any formal varieties, traditional or modern, that are well crafted, though we cannot normally accommodate excessively long poems (say 10 pgs. and over)."** They have recently published poetry by Norman Dubie, Margaret Gibson, Susan Ludvigson and Peter Schmitt. The editors selected these sample lines by Mary Oliver:

> *The story about Jesus in the cave*
> *is a good one,*
>   *but when is it ever like that*
>
> *as sharp as lightning,*
>   *or even the way the green sea does everything—*
>   *quickly,*
>   *and with such grace?*

The beautifully printed quarterly is massive: 6¾ × 10, 240+ pgs., flat-spined, matte card cover. They receive about 2,000 freelance submissions of poetry, use 10%. All styles and forms seem welcome, although accessible lyric and narrative free verse appear most often in recent issues. Press run is 3,100 with 2,100 subscriptions of which 70% are libraries. Subscription: $18. **Sample postpaid: $5. "We do not require cover letter but we prefer one giving information about author and previous publications." Prefers submissions of 1-4 pgs. Send SASE for guidelines. Reports in 2 months. Pays $20/printed page plus 2 copies. Buys first North American rights.** Staff reviews books of poetry in 3,000 words, multi-book format. Send books for review consideration. *The Southern Review* ranked #5 in the "Poets' Pick" category of the June 1993 *Writer's Digest* Poetry 60 list. This category ranks those publications in which poets said they would most like to see their work published.

SOUTHWEST REVIEW; ELIZABETH MATCHETT STOVER MEMORIAL AWARD (II), 307 Fondren Library West, Box 374, Southern Methodist University, Dallas TX 75275, phone (214)768-1037, founded 1915, editor Willard Spiegelman. *Southwest Review* is a literary quarterly that publishes fiction, essays, poetry and interviews. "It is hard to describe our preference for poetry in a few words. We always suggest that potential contributors read several issues of the magazine to see for themselves what we like. But some things may be said: We demand **very high quality in our poems; we accept both traditional and experimental writing, but avoid unnecessary obscurity and private symbolism; we place no arbitrary limits on length but find shorter poems easier to fit into our format than longer ones. We have no specific limitations as to theme.**" They have recently published poetry by Adrienne Rich, Amy Clampitt, Albert Goldbarth, John Hollander, Molly Peacock and Charles Wright. The journal is 6 × 9, 160 pgs., perfect-bound, professionally printed, with matte text stock cover, circulation 1,500 with 1,000 subscriptions of which 600 are libraries. They receive about 700 freelance submissions of poetry/year, use 24. Poems tend to be lyric and narrative free verse combining a strong voice with powerful topics or situations. Diction is accessible and content often conveys a strong sense of place. Subscription: $20. **Sample postpaid: $5. No simultaneous submissions, no previously published work. Send SASE for guidelines. Reports within a month. Pays cash plus copies.** The $150 Elizabeth Matchett Stover Memorial Prize is awarded annually for the best poem, chosen by editors, published in the preceding year. *Southwest Review* ranked #6 in the "Top Pay" category of the June 1993 *Writer's Digest* Poetry 60 list.

SOU'WESTER (II), Box 1438, Southern Illinois University, Edwardsville IL 62026, phone (618)692-3190, founded 1960, editor Fred W. Robbins, appears 3 times a year. "We like poetry **with imagery and figurative language that has strong associations and don't care for abstract poetry. We have no particular preference for form or length.**" They have published poetry by J.D. Smith, Walter Griffin and Douglas Leonard. As a sample the editor selected the final stanzas of "The Gleaners" by William Jolliff:

> *And even when their too-large coats are soaked*
> *with winter rains, I envy those children,*
> *the birds we were, kicking their buckles*
>
> *through the muddy dark. It would be a fair trade,*
> *a fair swap, for the work we turn to now,*

> *each grey and brittle season, seeking, digging,*
>
> *kicking the stalks for a blessing.*

There are 25-30 pgs. of poetry in each 6×9, 80-page issue. The magazine is professionally printed, flat-spined, with textured matte card cover, circulation 300, 110 subscriptions of which 50 are libraries. They receive some 2,000 poems (from 600 poets) each year, use 36-40, have a 2-month backlog. Subscription: $10 (3 issues). **Sample postpaid: $5. Simultaneous submissions OK. Rejections usually within 2 months. Pays 2 copies. Acquires all rights. Returns rights. Editor comments on rejections "usually, in the case of those that we almost accept."** He says, "Read poetry past and present. Have something to say and say it in your own voice. Poetry is a very personal thing for many editors. When all else fails, we may rely on gut reactions, so take whatever hints you're given to improve your poetry, and keep submitting."

THE SOW'S EAR (II, IV-Regional, children), 245 McDowell St., Bristol TN 37620, phone (703)628-2651, founded 1988, coeditors Errol Hess and Larry Richman, a quarterly. **"We are very open to form, style, length of poems. We see *TSE* as a three-ring circus—with a flair for the visual, which is very much lacking from most poetry journals.** The inside ring is the central Appalachian community focused in the area where Tennessee, Kentucky, North Carolina, West Virginia and Virginia come close together. The middle ring is the broader Appalachian region; a culture where we believe a poetry renaissance is beginning. The outer ring is the largest possible community, wherever the English language is spoken and written in poetic form. We encourage submissions from school-age children and plan to feature occasionally a previously unpublished poet." They have published poetry by Josephine Jacobsen and William Stafford. As a sample the editors selected these lines from "Loving Argument" by Margery A. Snyder:

> *When she was two*
> *Talk was female, its power*
> *Like the river spinning*
> *Grand Coulee's turbine,*
> *Words gathering, spilling,*
> *Tumbling, women's voices*
> *Piling up, tidal.*

TSE is 32 pgs., magazine-sized, saddle-stapled, with matte card cover, professionally printed. They accept about 150 of 4,000 poems submitted. Press run is 1,000 for 500 subscribers of which 15 are libraries. Shelf sales: 100-200. Subscription: $10. **Sample postpaid: $3.50. Simultaneous submissions OK if you tell them promptly when it is accepted elsewhere. Enclose brief bio. "We want to know if the poet has not yet been published or is a youth, as we have features for both." Editor comments on submissions "if poet specifically requests it." Send SASE for guidelines. Reports in 3-9 months. Pays 1 copy. Buys first publication rights.** Reviews books of poetry. Open to unsolicited reviews. Poets may also send books for review consideration "but only slight chance they'll get reviewed." Richman selects the kids' poems; others chosen by a 3-person board that meets quarterly. They offer an annual contest with fee of $2/poem, $500 prize. For contest, submit 1-5 poems October through November. Submissions with $10 receive 1-year subscription. 1992 judge: Amy Clampitt. Also sponsors a chapbook contest each April for 24 poems, maximum 24 pgs. Fee is $10; prize $500 and 50 copies.

SPARROW: THE POLITICALLY INCORRECT VERSE MAGAZINE (IV-Form), 103 Waldron St., West Lafayette IN 47906, editor and publisher Felix Stefanile, publishes "as material permits." They want **"formal sonnets *only*, 4 or 5 per submission. No subject restrictions. We don't publish poems in poor taste."** They have recently published poetry by Harold Witt, John Frederick Nims and Annie Finch. As a sample the editor selected these lines from R.S. Gwynn's sonnet on sonneteers:

> *Prefixing every phrase with Ah or O,*
> *They spoke as if the stems and stumps had ears,*
> *Letting the backwash of their idle tears*
> *Leave bathtub rings around the Vale of Woe.*

The editor says *Sparrow* is 9×12, using occasional graphics only by invitation. They receive about 1,000 pieces a year, use less than 1%. Press run is 500-750 for about 450 subscribers of which about 100 are libraries, 300 shelf sales. **Sample postpaid: $5. No simultaneous submissions. Typed copy only, 8½×11 bond. No material returned without SASE. "We have a very cynical attitude toward long cover letters." Seldom comments on rejections. "We are not in the business of offering criticism or advice." Send SASE with all queries. Reports "usually in a week." Pays $3 a sonnet plus 2 copies. Buys first and non-exclusive reprint rights.** "We also offer a $25 prize for the best sonnet each issue." Staff reviews books of poetry. Send books for review consideration. The editor says, "We are now essentially a 'new' magazine with a fine, old name. We pride ourselves on our liveliness and our currency. We also publish scores of musical settings for sonnets, by special arrangement with the composer. We are really not a market for beginners and the MFA degree does not impress us."

‡**SPECTACULAR DISEASES (II)**, 83B London Rd., Peterborough, Cambridgeshire PE2 9BS United Kingdom, founded 1974, Paul Green editor (various invited poetry editors). "The press presents **experimental writing with bias to the current French scene and to current, and past scenes, in the U.S. and Britain.** Most poetry is solicited by the editors. Long poems will be clearly accepted, if falling in the special categories." They have published poetry by Saúl Yurkievich, Jackson MacLow and Bernard Noël. *Spectacular Diseases* is "occasional," 40-60 pgs., digest-sized. **Sample postpaid: £1.75.** Query before submitting as most material is invited. Pays copies. Under the Spectacular Diseases imprint a number of books and anthologies are printed. For book consideration, **query with about 16 samples; letter helpful but not essential. Pays 10% of run. Send postage for catalog to buy samples.**

SPECTRUM (II), Anna Maria College, Box 72-D, Paxton MA 01612, phone (508)849-3450, founded 1985, editor Robert H. Goepfert, is a "multidisciplinary national publication with liberal arts emphasis," presenting 6-8 poems in each 64-page issue: **"poems of crisp images, precise language, which have something of value to say and say it in an authentic voice. Not the self-conscious, the 'workshop poem,' the cliché, the self-righteous."** They have published poetry by William Stafford. *Spectrum* appears twice a year in a 6×9, flat-spined format, professionally printed on quality stock with 2-color matte card cover, using b&w photos and art. Press run is 1,000 for 650 subscriptions (200 of them to libraries). Single copy: $4; subscription: $7 for 1 year, $13 for 2 years. **Sample: $3. No previously published poems or simultaneous submissions. Reads submissions September 1 through May 15 only.** Editor "occasionally" comments on rejections. Mss returned only with SASE. **Reports in 6 weeks. Pays $20/poem plus 2 copies. Buys first North American serial rights.** Open to unsolicited reviews.

SPECTRUM/OLD TIMES (IV-Seniors, regional, themes), (formerly *Senior Edition USA/Colorado Old Times*), Suite 218, 1385 S. Colorado Blvd., Denver CO 80222-3312, phone (303)758-4040, managing editor Rose Beetem, is a monthly tabloid "Colorado newspaper **for seniors (with national distribution)** emphasizing legislation, opinion and advice columns, local and national news, features and local calendar aimed at the over-50 community." They want **"usually no haiku, religious/inspirational.** Subject matter often to match *Old Times.*" Circulation 45,000. Sample copy: $1; writer's guidelines for SASE. Submit seasonal/holiday material 3 months in advance. Publishes ms an average of 1-6 months after acceptance. Pays on publication. Senior Overlook column features opinions of seniors about anything they feel strongly about: finances, grandkids, love, life, social problems, etc. (May be editorial, essay, prose or poetry). Buys 2-6 mss/year. Send complete ms. **Length: 250-900 words, poems shorter: optimal 12-40 lines. Pays $20, maximum.** Rose Beetem says, "Although we are not refusing manuscripts, the time to hear back from us has lengthened."

SPINDRIFT (II), Shoreline Community College, 16101 Greenwood Ave., Seattle WA 98133, founded 1962, faculty advisor varies each year, currently Carol Orlock, is **open to all varieties of poetry except greeting card style.** They have published poetry by James Bertolino, Edward Harkness and Richard West. *Spindrift*, an annual, is 125 pgs., handsomely printed in an 8" square, flat-spined. Circulation 500. Single copy: $6.50. Sample postpaid: $5. **"Submit 2 copies of each poem, 6 maximum. Include cover letter with biographical information. We accept submissions until February 1—report back in March."** Send SASE for guidelines. Pays 1 copy. Acquires first serial rights. The editors advise, "Read what the major contemporary poets are writing. Read what local poets are writing. Be distinctive, love the language, avoid sentiment."

THE SPIRIT THAT MOVES US; THE SPIRIT THAT MOVES US PRESS (II); EDITOR'S CHOICE (IV-Anthology), P.O. Box 820, Jackson Heights, Queens NY 11372-0828, phone (718)426-8788, founded 1974, poetry editor Morty Sklar. *"The Spirit That Moves Us* will be continuing its **Editor's Choice** series biennially and publishing regular issues only occasionally. **Editor's Choice** consists of reprints from other literary magazines and small presses, where our selections are made from nominations by the editors of those magazines and presses." They have published poetry by Julia Alvarez, Rita Dove, Czeslaw Milosz, Tom Disch and Grace Paley. As a sample the editor selected these lines from "Blood" by Naomi Shihab Nye:

> After that, my father told me who he was,
> "Shihab" — "shooting star" —
> a good name, borrowed from the sky.
> Once I said, "When we die, we give it back?"
> He said that's what a true Arab would say.

They offer **Editor's Choice III**, 336 pgs. covering 1984-1990, as a sample for $9 plus $1 postage (regularly $12.50 plus $1.50 postage). **Query first for plans and time frames.** The editor's advice: "Write what you would like to write, in a style (or styles) which is/are best for your own expression. Don't worry about acceptance, though you may be concerned about it. Don't just send work which you think editors would like to see, though take that into consideration. Think of the relationship between poem, poet and editor as personal. You may send good poems to editors who simply do not like them, whereas other editors might."

SPIT: A JOURNAL OF THE ARTS (I, II), 240 E. 9th St. #7, New York NY 10003, phone (212)505-9590, founded 1989, edited by Laurie Shapiro and Joan Dalin with collective input, appears twice a year using **poetry "judged on artistic merit rather than polemical intent."** They have recently published poetry by Gerald Burns, India Hixon, Ania Walwicz and Sparrow. As a sample the editors selected these lines from "Unlucky Sonnet" by Daniel O'Keefe:

> You go out there, nothing. Think of beyond
> The glass. The outer air. The sky. As black
> As anything there is, as old. Hear nothing.

It is 100 pgs./double issue, magazine-sized, flat-spined, with card cover, desktop published. Press run is 400. Subscription: $12. **Sample postpaid: $3. Previously pubilshed poems and simultaneous submissions OK, if so indicated. Include cover letter with name, address and short biographical statement. Do not print name on poems. Poems should be typed. Editors comment on rejections** "though not extensive. We are always willing to send more detailed comments if the writer requests." Reports in 1-9 months. Pays 1 copy.

SPITBALL; CASEY AWARD (IV-Sports), 6224 Collegevue Pl., Cincinnati OH 45224, phone (513)541-4296, founded 1981, poetry editor William J. McGill, is "a unique literary magazine devoted to poetry, fiction and book reviews *exclusively* about baseball. Newcomers are very welcome, but remember that you have to know the subject. We do and our readers do. Perhaps a good place to start for beginners is one's personal reactions to the game, *a* game, a player, etc. & take it from there." The digest-sized, 96-page quarterly is computer typeset and perfect-bound. Circulation is 1,000, 750+ subscriptions of which 25 are libraries. They receive about 1,000 submissions/year, use 40—very small backlog. "Many times we are able to publish accepted work almost immediately." Subscription: $16. **Sample postpaid: $5. "We are not very concerned with the technical details of submitting, but we do prefer a cover letter with some bio info. We also like batches of poems and prefer to use several of same poet in an issue rather than a single poem."** Pays 2 copies. "We encourage anyone interested to submit to *Spitball*. We are always looking for fresh talent. Those who have never written 'baseball poetry' before should read some first probably before submitting. Not necessarily ours. We sponsor the Casey Award (for best baseball book of the year) and the Casey Awards Banquet every January. Any chapbook of baseball poetry should be sent to us for consideration for the 'Casey' plaque that we award to the winner each year."

SPOKES (II), % The Orchard House, 45 Clophill Rd., Upper Gravénhurst, Bedford MK45 4JH England, founded 1985, editor Donald Atkinson, is a semiannual journal of new poetry, art and criticism, with an informational review of recent publications, called *SCAN*. The editor wants **"all types of poetry, 100-line limit. All kinds of subjects!"** *Spokes* is 7×10, perfect-bound, "offset litho printed," 72-80 pgs., with pictures, illustrated gloss cover. Its circulation is mainly Great Britain and USA, but some other countries. Single copy: £3.25 plus postage; subscription: £7.50/year (£9/year overseas). **There are no particular specifications for submissions. Reporting time is 6-8 weeks and time to publication** approximately 6-12 months.

THE SPOON RIVER POETRY REVIEW (III, IV-Regional, translations), English Dept., Illinois State University, Normal IL 61761, phone (309)438-7906, founded 1976, poetry editor Lucia Getsi, is a "poetry magazine that features newer and well-known poets from around the country and world"; features **one Illinois poet/issue** at length for the magazine's Illinois Poet Series among other national and international poets. "We want interesting and compelling poetry that operates beyond the ho-hum, so-what level, in any form or style about anything; language that is fresh, energetic, committed, filled with a strong voice that grabs the reader in the first line and never lets go. Do not want to see insipid, dull, boring poems, especially those that I cannot ascertain why they're in lines and not paragraphs; poetry which, if you were to put it into paragraphs, would become bad prose." They also use translations of poetry. They have published poetry by Frankie Paino, Tim Seibles, Paulette Roeske, Walter McDonald, Robin Behn, Elaine Terranova, Roger Mitchell and Katharine Soniat. As a sample Lucia Getsi selected these lines by Kay Murphy:

> This is as close as I can come to make what she says true:
> Inside, my uncle has his hand inside my aunt's blue dress.
> The fields are burning with a want I don't yet understand.
> The orchard has simply given up, as my cousin has.

TSRPR has moved to a twice a year double issue format. It is digest-sized, laser set with card cover using photos, ads. They accept about 2% of 1,000 poems received/month. Press run is 600 for 400 subscriptions (100 of them libraries) and shelf sales. Subscription: **$12. Sample: $8.** "No simultaneous submissions unless we are notified immediately if a submission is accepted elsewhere. Include name and address on every poem." Editor comments on rejections "many times, if a poet is promising." Reports in 2 months. Pays 2 copies. Acquires first North American serial rights only. Staff reviews books of poetry. Send books for review consideration. *The Spoon River Poetry Review* has received several Illinois Arts Council Awards and is one of the best reads in the poetry-publishing world. Editor Lucia Cordell Getsi jampacks the journal with poems of varied styles and presents them in a handsome, perfect-bound product. You'll want to order a sample issue to get a feel for this fine publication.

STAND MAGAZINE; NORTHERN HOUSE (I, II, IV-Translations), 19 Haldane Terrace, Newcastle on Tyne NE2 3AN England. US Editors: Daniel Schenker and Amanda Kay, Route #2, Box 122-B, Lacey's Spring AL 35754 **(all US contributions should be sent to US editors)**. *Stand*, founded by editor Jon Silkin in 1952, is a highly esteemed literary quarterly. Jon Silkin seeks more subscriptions from US readers and also hopes "that the magazine **would be seriously treated as an alternative platform to American literary journals.**" He wants "**verse that tries to explore forms. No formulaic verse.**" They have published poems by such poets as Peter Redgrove, Elizabeth Jennings and Barry Spacks. *Library Journal* calls *Stand* "one of England's best, liveliest and truly imaginative little magazines." Among better-known American poets whose work has appeared here are Robert Bly, William Stafford, David Ignatow, Philip Levine and Richard Eberhart. Poet Donald Hall says of it, "among essential magazines, there is Jon Silkin's *Stand*, politically left, with reviews, poems and much translation from continental literature." In its current format it is 6×8, flat-spined, 80 pgs., professionally printed in 2 columns, small type, on thin stock with glossy card cover, using ads. Circulation is 4,500 with 2,800 subscriptions of which 600 are libraries. Subscription: **$22. Sample postpaid: $6.50. Cover letter required with submissions, "assuring us that work is not also being offered elsewhere." Pays £30/poem (unless under 6 lines) and 1 copy (⅓ off additional copies). Buys first world serial rights for 3 months after publication. If work(s) appear elsewhere** *Stand*/Northern House must be credited. Reviews books of poetry in 3,000-4,000 words, multi-book format. Open to unsolicited reviews. Poets may also send books for review consideration. **Northern House "publishes mostly small collections of poetry by new or established poets. The pamphlets often contain a group of poems written to one theme. Occasionally larger volumes are published,** such as the full-length collection by Sorley Maclean, translated by Iain Crichton Smith."

STAPLE (I, II), Gilderoy East, Upperwood Rd., Matlock, Bath DE4 3PD United Kingdom, phone 0629-583867 and 0629-582764, founded 1982, coeditor Bob Windsor. This literary magazine appears 4 times a year including supplements. **"Nothing barred: Evidence of craft, but both traditional and modernist accepted; no totally esoteric or concrete poetry."** They have published poetry by Fleur Adcock, Jon Silkin, Patricia Pogson and Thomas Kretz. As a sample they selected these lines from "Flying with Mary" by Jennifer Olds:

> *We cruised relentlessly in her sports car and,*
> *in the sheer light heartedness of our last summer,*
> *each stretched an arm out*
> *the car's open windows and waved in unison*
> *so that it looked, to oncoming traffic,*
> *as if we were flying.*

Staple is professionally printed, flat-spined, 80 pgs., with card cover. Of 3,000 poems received/ year they accept about 5%. Their press run is 600 with 300 subscriptions. Subscription: £15 (sterling only). **Sample postpaid: £3. They consider simultaneous submissions but previously published poems only under special circumstances. Cover letter preferred.** Editors sometimes comment on rejections. Guidelines available for SASE. Submission deadlines are end of February, June and November. Response in up to 3 months. Pays modest fee plus complimentary copy (or free subscription). Send SASE (or SAE with IRC) for rules for their open biennial competitions and for *Staple First Editions* monographs (sample postpaid: £3). They now also produce (to order) poetry postcards of poetry *published* in the magazine.

STAR BOOKS, INC. (V); STARLIGHT MAGAZINE (I, IV-Spirituality/inspirational), 408 Pearson St., Wilson NC 27893, phone (919)237-1591, founded 1983, president Allen W. Harrell, who says they are **"very enthusiastically open to beginners. All of our poetry is specifically Christian, in line with the teachings of the Bible. We're looking for the fresh and the new. Can't use avant-garde and/or esoteric. For us the impact of the** *thought* **of a poem is paramount. Need more short poems, with short lines."** They have published books of poetry by Marilyn Phemister, Norma Woodbridge and Charlotte Carpenter. "Contributors to our *StarLight* magazine are largely previously unpublished." As a sample these lines were selected from Gennet Emery's "Lament for a Child" in her **Wayfarer:**

> *Some thought the pain was less*

Because I never saw you

But oh, I did!
My heart and mind wove textured skin,
Caressed your cheeks, touched finespun hair
And smelled sweet breath.

The book is 128 pgs., trade paperback size, flat-spined, professionally printed, with glossy card cover: $8. *StarLight* is a quarterly, digest-sized, 60 pgs., saddle-stapled, professionally printed, with matte card cover. The inspirational verse it contains is largely rhymed and free style (some of surprising good quality, considering this is billed mainly as a beginner's market). Some poems are illustrated with Bible excerpts, and the publication includes long bio notes about contributors. Subscription: $15. **Sample postpaid: $4. Guidelines available for SASE. Submit 5-6 poems, one poem/page, no cursive type, no erasable bond, no simultaneous submissions or previously published poems. Name and address on each page. "Don't submit poems in booklet form or center the lines. Title every poem. Include SASE." Reports in 1-4 weeks. Pays 3 copies of magazine; books pay 10% or more royalties. Acquires first serial rights for *StarLight*; all rights for Star Books. Not currently accepting book mss. Catalog available for #10 SASE with 2 first class stamps.** They hold an annual Star Books Writers' Workshop. Write for information.

STARMIST BOOKS (V), Box 12640, Rochester NY 14612, founded 1986, president Beth Boyd, publishes 2-4 paperbacks/year. They publish **"poetry that comes from the heart . . . that has the depth of true feeling. No pornography." They are currently not accepting poetry submissions: "We have reached our quota into 1995."** As a sample the editor selected these lines by jani johe webster:

shadows i
cannot reach
surround me

and there is
an aloneness
too deep to touch

even with

the gentle fingers
of love

Replies to queries in 2 weeks, to mss (if invited) in 3 weeks. Pay is negotiable. Inquire about samples. The editor advises poets, "To feel always the poetry within – to know it all about us."

STATE STREET PRESS (II), P.O. Box 278, Brockport NY 14420, phone (716)637-0023, founded 1981, poetry editor Judith Kitchen, "**publishes chapbooks of poetry (20-24 pgs.) usually chosen in an anonymous competition.** State Street Press hopes to publish emerging writers with solid first collections and to offer a format for established writers who have a collection of poems that work together as a chapbook. We have also established a full-length publication – for those of our authors who are beginning to have a national reputation. We want **serious traditional and free verse. We are not usually interested in the language school of poets or what would be termed 'beat.' We are quite frankly middle-of-the-road. We ask only that the poems work as a collection, that the chapbook be more than an aggregate of poems – that they work together.**" They have published poetry by Naomi Shihab Nye, Dionisio Martinez, Jeff Oaks, Cecile Goding and Marcia Hurlow. Chapbooks are beautifully designed and printed, 6×9, 30 pgs., with textured matte wrapper with art. **Send SASE for guidelines and chapbook contest rules. There is a $5 entry fee, for which you receive one of the chapbooks already published. Simultaneous submissions encouraged. Pays copies and small honorarium. Authors buy additional copies at cost, sell at readings and keep the profits.** Judith Kitchen comments, "State Street Press believes that the magazines are doing a good job of publishing beginning poets and we hope to present published and unpublished work in a more permanent format, so we do reflect the current market and tastes. We expect our writers to have published individual poems and to be considering a larger body of work that in some way forms a 'book.' We have been cited as a press that prints poetry that is accessible to the general reader."

THE STEELHEAD SPECIAL (I), P.O. Box 219, Bayside CA 95524, phone (707)445-1907, founded 1991, editor Crawdad Nelson, is a quarterly "Northwest working-class cultural and literary review." They want **"fresh, working-class, rugged, bold poetry. Nothing weepy, clichéd, sentimental."** They have published poetry by Albert Huffstickler, Jim Dodge and Leonard Cirino. As a sample the editor selected these lines from "Lonesome River" by C. Nelson:

They lie uneasy before dawn in very

> little water,
> someone has built a fire,
> someone else pukes their New Year's
> Eve on the weeds,
> And a third man slips his line in
> too early.

It is 40 pgs., 8½ × 11, newsprint, saddle-stapled, with art and graphics. They receive 500-600 poems a year, accept 10-20/issue. Press run is 3,500 for 100 subscribers, 500 shelf sales, rest distributed free to the general public and fishermen. Single copy: $1; subscription: $12. **Sample postpaid: $2. Previously published poems and simultaneous submissions OK. Often comments on rejections. Send SASE for guidelines. Reports in 1-8 weeks. Pays 3-4 copies.** Open to unsolicited reviews. Poets may also send books for review consideration. Crawdad Nelson says, "We see lots of good poetry. Hope to see more. Nothing bogged down in bourgeois ennui, please. Vitality helps, but stay alert. Subscriptions encouraged."

‡THE STEVAN COMPANY; SOCIETY OF ETHICAL AND PROFESSIONAL PUBLISHERS OF LITERATURE (II, IV-Translations), %A.T. Botkin, 1201 Larchwood Rd., Charleston WV 25314, founded 1980, publisher Kathryn Stewart-McDonald. "If you read *The New Yorker, The Atlantic*, and have read textbooks such as Voice Great Within Us, the major Mentor book of poems, e.e. cummings, R.H. Blyth, Li Po, William Blake, you're on track. Well-read poets usually write well. Our readers are very well read and read between 175-210 small press books per year. We prefer to work with experienced writers." They have published poetry by Jack Terahata (Japan), Nat Scammacca (Italy) and Dong Jiping (China). In addition to anthologies, they publish collections by individuals. **Query with no more than 5 samples, bio, publication credits.** "No lengthy cover letter; please do not inundate us with all 900 poems you have written. We prefer no previously published poems and usually not simultaneous submissions. No phone calls. Not necessary to subscribe or join SEPPL." Reading period June through August. **Reports in 6-8 weeks; publication within 1-2 years. Pays copies.** "We comment on rejections occasionally if requested. We will also accept foreign language poems with English translations." In 1992 they published collected essays about the violations of civil rights on Guam Island. **This year they plan to publish 3 chapbooks.** Kathryn McDonald says, "We are not a vanity press, sometimes try to solicit grants, will accept money from foundations. The Society of Ethical Publishers agrees to maintain a code of ethics, can make legal referrals, sometimes offers mechanical advice to poets and publishers. This is a private club of like-minded publishers who wish to continue traditions and facilitate rapport between publisher and writer. Board members share mailing lists, copyright attorney and networking information. Members receive free samples, parties and share trade information (i.e., grants available, distributors, printers information, etc.) All members have excellent references, personal and professional. Many can translate and all are committed to their craft."

THE WALLACE STEVENS JOURNAL (II, IV-Themes), Liberal Studies, Clarkson University, Potsdam NY 13699, founded 1977, poetry editor Prof. Joseph Duemer, appears biannually using **"poems about or in the spirit of Wallace Stevens or having some relation to his work. No bad parodies of Stevens' anthology pieces."** They have recently published poetry by Elizabeth Spires, Jorie Graham, Charles Wright, X.J. Kennedy and Robert Creeley. As a sample the editor selected these lines from "A World Without Desire" by Michael G. Gessner:

> Occurred tonight for an hour only,
> An hour spent around the back porch
> Where I was sent from the family, exiled
> From myself. It was a world of order,
> Order and presence, the final meaning
> Of forms conversing through the night
> As large as all thought must be
> This house a ragged piece of locale
> Torn adrift in the space of a dark mind.

The editor describes it as 80-120 pgs., 6 × 9, typeset, flat-spined, with cover art on glossy stock. They accept 10-15 poems of 50-75 received. Press run is 900 for 600 subscribers of which 200 are libraries. Subscription: $15. **Sample postpaid: $4. Reports in 2-8 weeks. Pays 2 copies. Acquires all rights. Returns rights with permission and acknowledgment.** Staff reviews books of poetry. Send books for review consideration "only if there is some clear connection to Stevens." *The Wallace Stevens Journal* is published by the Wallace Stevens Society. The editor says, "Brief cover letters are fine, even encouraged. Please don't submit to *WSJ* if you have not read Stevens. We like parodies, but they must *add* a new angle of perception. Most of the poems we publish are not parodies but meditations on themes related to Wallace Stevens and those poets he has influenced. Those wishing to contribute might wish especially to examine the Spring 1993 issue, devoted to prose and poetry by American poets."

STICKS; STICKS PRESS (III, IV-Form), P.O. Box 399, Maplesville AL 36750-0399, press founded 1989, journal 1991, editor/publisher Mary Veazey. *Sticks*, appearing irregularly, **publishes "the best short poems of experienced/established poets. All styles, subjects. But no haiku. Preferred length: 10 lines or less; width: 50 spaces per line."** She has published poetry by X.J. Kennedy and Richard Kostelanetz. As a sample the editor selected this poem, "Silent Vows," by Charles Ghigna:

> I kneel before
> you, you kneel
> before me.
>
> We pray
> at the altar
> of our egos.

The magazine is a 4¼×5½, saddle-stapled or saddle-sewn booklet, professionally printed on acid-free paper, 24 pgs. Press run is 250+. **"Permanent mailing list in lieu of subscriptions. Sample issue $1; issue with slight wrinkle for only first class stamp; sewn binding by request. No guidelines, just be a master of the short poem."** Seldom comments on rejections. Reports in 3 months or less. Pays 2 copies. Acquires first North American serial rights. The editor says, "*Sticks* will appear *only* when money for printing and a number of excellent small poems converge. **The Oxford Book of Short Poems is my touchstone here; write the poem that will outlast us all; many such poems have historically been brief."**

STILL WATERS PRESS (II, IV-Women), 112 W. Duerer St., Galloway NJ 08201-9402, phone (609)652-1790, founded 1989, editor Shirley Warren, is a "small press publisher of poetry chapbooks, short fiction chapbooks and poet's handbooks (contemporary craft). Especially interested in **works by, for and about women. We prefer poetry firmly planted in the real world, but equally mindful of poetry as art. The transformation from pain to perseverance, from ordinary to extraordinary, from defeat to triumph, pleases us. But we reject Pollyanna poetry immediately. Nothing sexist, in either direction, nothing sexually erotic. No rhymed poetry unless you're a master of form who can meticulously avoid strange manipulations of syntax simply to achieve end-rhyme. No patriarchal religious verse. Preferred length: 4 lines—2 pages per poem. Form: no restrictions—we expect content to dictate the form."** They have recently published poetry by Jeff Worley and Lance Olsen (a collaboration) and Wick Edelhauser. As a sample the editor selected these lines from "Molting," in Edelhauser's chapbook **Beneath the Wave**:

> Surely I have something to lose.
> My ears are marbled with mourning.
> Doves call from the black walnut tree,
> hazy shimmers hammer air
> while locusts drill a song of heat.
> I sit, clipped wings in a cage.

She publishes 4-8 chapbooks a year, averaging 28 pgs. **Send SASE for guidelines, then query. Simultaneous submissions and previously published poems OK. Pays 10% of the press run. Royalties on 2nd and subsequent press runs. Acquires first or reprint rights.** "Occasionally, will assist qualified authors with chapbook self-publication projects; send detailed query for price quote; these are independent projects and are not part of our booklist." Sample chapbooks: $5; writer's guide booklets: $3. They hold 2 annual contests, each with $10 reading fee; send SASE for detailed guidelines. The editor says, "Read other poets, contemporary and traditional. Attend workshops, establish rapport with your local peers, attend readings. Keep your best work in circulation. Someone out there is looking for you."

STOHLMBERG PUBLISHERS (II), (formerly listed as *Antipoetry and the Corruption of Muse*), P.O. Box 2043, Montgomery AL 36102-2043, founded 1993, editor Jake Stohlm, assistant editor Reb Gorjo, are publishers of books of poetry and literary magazines. They want **"poetry that many would feel is a perverted form of creative writing and poetry that escapes the realm of the physical. We don't want to see poetry about pretty flowers blooming or about people falling in love."** They have recently published poetry by Linda M. Horvath and Robert Hunter. They have also published **Journal of Dead Nuns**, a book of poetry by Kevin Redlake. As a sample the editor selected these lines from "Poems Mean Nothing To Me" by Bill Shields:

> I sleep
> face down
> facing
> the dead
> the revolver
> seeks a hand.

Their books and magazines are digest-sized, saddle-stapled, with card covers. Number of pages varies. Press run varies. **Sample book of poetry: $15.** Literary magazine subscription: $10. **Sample: $7. "Don't send more than five poems when submitting."** Time between acceptance and publication is 2 months. **Often comments on rejections. Reports in 2-3 weeks. Pays 1-2 copies. Acquires first North American serial rights.**

STONE CIRCLE PRESS (IV-Ethnic), P.O. Box 44, Oakland CA 94604, founded 1987, editor Len Irving, publishes books **"of a Celtic nature. Backgrounded in Scotland, Ireland, Wales, Isle of Man, Cornwall, Brittany. We welcome Stonehenge rather than Acropolis material. No non-Celtic material. All valid submissions are given serious consideration."** They publish about 2 flat-spined paperbacks/year, averaging 100 pgs. **Query with 6 samples. Responds to queries in 1 month. Pays 25 books.** "We are a nonprofit press associated with the Institute of Celtic Studies. We finance and publish the book. The author receives a stated number of books but no royalties." They also subsidy publish, providing "seed money and desktop publication," seeking donations from all available sources.

STONE PRESS (V), 9727 SE Reedway, Portland OR 97266, founded 1968, editor Albert Drake, publishes poetry postcards, posters, broadsides, chapbooks and books. He has published books by Earle Birney, Judith Goren, Lee Upton and James Kalmbach. **"However due to other publishing commitments, Stone Press is presently in limbo."**

STONE SOUP, THE MAGAZINE BY CHILDREN; THE CHILDREN'S ART FOUNDATION (IV-Children), P.O. Box 83, Santa Cruz CA 95063, founded 1973, editor Ms. Gerry Mandel. *Stone Soup* publishes writing and art by children through age 13; they want to see free verse poetry but no rhyming poetry, haiku or cinquain. The editor chose as a sample this poem, "Nightfall," by 7-year-old Jaiva Larsen:

> When the blackberry moon rises
> And the sky flies by like ocean waves
> And the chill of the evening
> Flies through your heart
> Run home
> Run home

Stone Soup, published 5 times a year, is a handsome 6 × 8¾ magazine, professionally printed on heavy stock with 4 full-color art reproductions inside and a full-color illustration on the coated cover, saddle-stapled. A membership in the Children's Art Foundation at $23/year includes a subscription to the magazine, each issue of which contains an Activity Guide. There are 4 pgs. of poetry in each issue. Circulation is 16,000, all by subscription; 2,000 go to libraries. **Sample postpaid: $4.50. Submissions can be any number of pages, any format, but no simultaneous submissions. Criticism will be given when requested.** The editor receives 5,000 poetry submissions/year and uses only 20. Guidelines are available for SASE. **Reports in 1 month. Pays $10 and 2 copies plus discounts. Buys all rights. Returns rights upon request.** Open to reviews by children. Children through age 13 may also send books for review consideration. *Stone Soup* has received both Parents' Choice and Edpress Golden Lamp Honor Awards.

‡**STONEVALE PRESS (II),** P.O. Box 484, Burkittsville MD 21718, phone (301)834-9380, founded 1991, editor Helen Vo-Dinh, publishes 2 paperbacks and 1 chapbook/year. **No specifications as to form, length, subject matter, style or purpose, "except no 'inspirational' verse or pornography."** They have recently published books of poetry by Mary Azrael and Kendra Kopelke. As a sample the editor selected these lines from "Girl Asleep At A Table" in Kopelke's book **Eager Street:**

> You see she is asleep
> so you want to turn away, embarrassed
> yet you feel
>
> strangely welcome, as if you
> are the subject of her inner gaze
> the stone that holds the plum . . .

That book is about 80 pgs., 5½ × 9, flat-spined with matte card cover, $8.95. **Query first with 10-15 pgs. of typed material and a cover letter with brief bio and publication credits. Previously published poems and simultaneous submissions OK, if indicated. Replies to queries in 1 month, to mss (if invited) in 2-3 months.** Time between acceptance and publication is 6 months to 1 year. **Occasionally comments on rejections. Pays 10% royalties after expenses and 25 author's copies.** Co-op publishing is also an option. **Sample book: $7.**

STORMLINE PRESS, INC. (V), Box 593, Urbana IL 61801, phone (217)328-2665, founded 1985, publisher Ray Bial, is an independent press publishing fiction, poetry and photography, **"only by invitation. Do not send unsolicited manuscripts. We publish both established and new poets, but in the latter case prefer to publish those poets who have been working some years to master their craft."** The press publishes 1-2 books each year with an average page count of 48-64. They are 6×9, some flat-spined paperbacks and some hardcover.

STORY LINE PRESS (V); NICHOLAS ROERICH POETRY PRIZE FOR FIRST BOOK OF POETRY (II), Three Oaks Farm, 27006 Gap Road, Brownsville OR 97327-9718, phone (503)466-5352, Story Line Press founded 1985, poetry editor Robert McDowell. Story Line Press publishes each year the winner of the Nicholas Roerich Poetry Prize for a First Book of Poetry ($1,000 plus publication and a paid reading at the Roerich Museum in New York City; a runner-up receives a full Story Line Press Scholarship to the Wesleyan Writers Conference in Middletown, CT; $15 entry and handling fee). Deadline for submissions: October 15. Send SASE for complete guidelines. The press also publishes books about poetry and has published collections by such poets as Colette Inez, Bruce Bawer and George Keithley. **They consider unsolicited mss only for the Nicholas Roerich Poetry Prize competition.**

STRAIGHT; STANDARD PUBLISHING CO. (IV-Religious, teens), 8121 Hamilton Ave., Cincinnati OH 45231, editor Carla J. Crane. Standard is a large religious publishing company. *Straight* is a weekly take-home publication (digest-sized, 12 pgs., color newsprint) **for teens. Poetry is *by* teenagers, any style, religious or inspirational in nature. No adult-written poetry.** As a sample the editor selected "Unseen" by Nicole Inman (16):

I've never seen the ocean,
And yet I know it's there.
I've never climbed any mountains,
But I've seen them everywhere.

I know I'm going to Heaven,
But I haven't yet been there
I don't need to see Christ Jesus,
To convince me that He cares!

Teen author must include birthdate. Simultaneous submissions OK. Guidelines available for SASE. Reports in 4-6 weeks, publishes acceptances in 9-12 months. Pays $10/poem plus 5 copies. Buys first or reprint rights. The editor says, "Many teenagers write poetry in their English classes at school. If you've written a poem on an inspirational topic, and your teacher's given you an 'A' on it, you've got a very good chance of having it published in *Straight*."

THE STRAIN (II), Box 330507, Houston TX 77233-0507, poetry editor Michael Bond, editor Norman C. Stewart, Jr. *The Strain* is a monthly magazine using **"experimental or traditional poetry of very high quality."** They do not include sample lines of poetry here as they "prefer not to limit style of submissions." **Simultaneous submissions and previously published poems OK. Guidelines issue: $5 and 8 first class stamps. Pays "no less than $5. We would prefer you submit before obtaining the guidelines issue which mostly explains upcoming collections and collaborations."** Send books for review consideration.

‡STREET NEWS (III), Suite 8040, 543 W. 43rd St., New York NY 10036, founded 1989, editor-in-chief John Conolley, is a semimonthly paper that is "sold to the homeless for a small price. They resell it for a nice profit." It contains "some work by the homeless, a lot of objectivist/libertarian philosophizing, some poetry and short fiction." They want **traditional or freestyle poetry. "Must have reference to something besides internal state of author. Very flexible on length. We especially appreciate poetry and fiction on the subject of homelessness or street life, but this is not a requirement. No haiku, senryu, limericks, etc."** They have recently published poetry by Patricia Landrum and Joe Cambi. As a sample the editor selected these lines from Cambi's poem, "Beneath the Windowsill":

So, save the whales, cause they're smarta than humans.
And when you go out, you dress to kill.
There's a mushroom cloud growing in our garden.
Beneath the windowsill.

Street News is a 20-page newsprint tabloid which features a full-color photo of a celebrity on the cover. Press run is 20,000 for about 200 subscribers. Single copy: $1; subscription: $18. **Sample postpaid: $2. Previously published poems and simultaneous submissions OK. Phone number required. Often comments on rejections. Reports in 2 weeks. Pays 3 copies. Acquires first or reprint rights.** John Conolley says, "This is not a literary magazine. The editor occasionally makes free to publish a poem if he really likes it. With the exception of submissions by the homeless, all poetry published since I took over has been by invitation."

‡STREET PRESS (V), P.O. Box 772, Sound Beach NY 11789-0772, founded 1974, editor Graham Everett. Street Press publishes an occasional limited edition book of poetry. Recent publications: **Much Cry Little Wool** by Ray Freed and **Endless Staircase** by Sandy McIntosh. **They are currently**

not accepting poetry submissions. "We're out looking and accept poetry from what we find." Send SASE for a list of available titles.

STRIDE PUBLICATIONS; TAXUS PRESS; APPARITIONS PRESS; TROMBONE PRESS (II), 37 Portland St., Newtown, Exeter, Devon EX1 2EG England, founded 1980, editor R.M. Loydell. Stride Publications publishes poetry, poetry sequences, prose and novels. **The editor wants to see any poetry that is "new, inventive, nothing self-oriented, emotional, no narrative or fantasy."** He has published work by Peter Redgrove, Alexis Lykiard, Sheila E. Murphy and David Miller. Stride Publications publishes paperbacks 60-100 pgs. of poetry, plus a few novels and anthologies. **Freelance submissions for book publication are accepted. Authors should query first, sending sample poems with return postage. Cover letter required with bio, summary and review quote. Queries will be answered in 3 weeks and mss reported on in 3 months or more. Pays author's copies.** Reviews books of poetry in 100-200 words, multi-book format. Send books for review consideration.

STRUGGLE: A MAGAZINE OF PROLETARIAN REVOLUTIONARY LITERATURE (I, II, IV-Political, themes, workers' social issues, women/feminism), Box 13261, Detroit MI 48213-0261, founded 1985, editor Tim Hall, is a "literary quarterly, content: the struggle of the working people against the rich. Issues such as: racism, poverty, aggressive wars, workers' struggle for jobs and job security, the overall struggle for a non-exploitative society, a genuine socialism." The **poetry and songs they use are "generally short, any style, subject matter must highlight the fight against the rule of the billionaires. No material unconnected to the fight to change society, but we welcome experimentation devoted to furthering such content."** They have recently published poetry by Mary R. De Maine, Lynda G. Araya, Vanessa Phillips, Willie Abraham Howard Jr. and Albert Chui Clark. As a sample the editor selected " 'Don't Make Me Do This, I Will' (Thursday At Nine, Eight Central Time)" by Greta Harris:

> There's a second-year law student
> up from me
> She watches television
> constantly
> She's watching "Police Beatbutt"
> She's watching "Guys on the Highway with Boots"
> She's watching "Win This Money, You Fool"
> She's watching "Idiots on Parade!"
> It's a thrill to hear her watch, I tell you
> She knows which side of the world
> her bread is on, well-buttered.

Struggle is 24-40 pgs., digest-sized, printed by photo offset using drawings, occasional photos of artwork, short stories, short plays and essays as well as poetry and songs (sometimes with their music). Subscription: $6 for 4 issues. **Sample postpaid: $1.50. Checks must be payable to "Tim Hall — Special Account." Accepted work usually appears in the next issue. Editor tries to provide criticism "with every submission." Tries to report in 1-3 months. Pays 2 copies.** Tim Hall says, "Show passion and fire. Formal experiments, traditional forms both welcome. Especially favor works reflecting rebellion by the working people against the rich, against racism, sexism, militarism, imperialism. We support the revolutions and rebellions in Eastern Europe and the Soviet Union, having always considered these regimes state-capitalist and not at all socialist. Especially interested now in material attacking both the Democrats and Republicans for bipartisan wars, job cutting, cutting social programs, material encouraging working people to see through the false hope promised by Clinton and instead to rely on a movement of the working class to bring change."

STUDENT LEADERSHIP JOURNAL (IV-Students, religious), Dept. PM, P.O. Box 7895, Madison WI 53707-7895, phone (608)274-9001, editor Jeff Yourison, is a **"magazine for Christian student leaders on secular campuses. We accept a wide variety of poetry. Do not want to see trite poetry. Also, we accept little rhymed poetry; it must be very, very good."** As a sample the editor selected the last stanzas of "A bird in the church" by Luci Shaw:

> and high and low and up again, through the sun's
> transfixing shafts, her wings test gravity
> in a bewilderment of interior air, opening
> and closing on her feathered restlessness
> until, as though coming home, she settles
>
> on the arm of the crucifix. Having found
> a nesting tree (even thine altars, O Lord!),
> she lodges at last, at the angle
> where vertex and horizon meet, resting

in the steady pain of Christ's left eye.

Student Leadership is a quarterly, magazine-sized, 32 pgs., 2-color inside, 2-color covers, with no advertising, 70% editorial, 30% graphics/art. Press run is 8,000 going to college students in the United States and Canada. Subscription: $12.50. Sample postpaid: $3. No simultaneous submissions. Previously published poems OK. "Would-be contributors should read us to be familiar with what we publish." Best time to submit mss is March through July ("We set our year's editorial plan"). Editor "occasionally" comments on rejections. Send SASE for guidelines. Reports in 2-3 months, 1-24 months to publication. Pays $25-50/poem plus 2 copies. Buys first or reprint rights. He says, "Try to express feelings through images and metaphor. Religious poetry should not be overly didactic, and it should never moralize!"

STUDIO, A JOURNAL OF CHRISTIANS WRITING (II, IV-Religious, spirituality), 727 Peel St., Albury, New South Wales 2640 Australia, founded 1980, publisher Paul Grover, a small press literary quarterly "with contents focusing upon the Christian striving for excellence in poetry, prose and occasional articles relating Christian views of literary ideas." In poetry, the editors want "shorter pieces but with no specification as to form or length (necessarily less than 3-4 pages), subject matter, style or purpose. People who send material should be comfortable being published under this banner: *Studio, A Journal of Christians Writing.*" They have published poetry by John Foulcher and other Australian poets. *Studio* is digest-sized, professionally printed on high-quality colored stock, 36 pgs., saddle-stapled, matte card cover, with graphics and line drawings. Circulation is 300, all subscriptions. Subscription: $40 (Aud) for overseas members. **Sample available (airmail from US) for $8 (Aud).** Submissions may be "typed copy or simultaneous." Cover letter required; include brief details of previous publishing history, if any. Reporting time is 2 months and time to publication is 9 months. Pays 1 copy. Acquires first Australian rights. Reviews books of poetry in 250 words, single format. Open to unsolicited reviews. Poets may also send books for review consideration. The magazine conducts a biannual poetry and short story contest. The editor says, "Trend in Australia is for imagist poetry and poetry exploring the land and the self. Reading the magazine gives the best indication of style and standard, so send a few dollars for a sample copy before sending your poetry. Keep writing, and we look forward to hearing from you."

SUB-TERRAIN; ANVIL PRESS (II, IV-Social issues, themes, form/style), P.O. Box 1575, Station A, Vancouver, British Columbia V6C 2P7 Canada, phone (604)876-8710, founded 1988, poetry editor Paul Pitre. Anvil Press is an "alternate small press publishing *Sub-Terrain* — a socially conscious literary quarterly whose aim is to produce a reading source that will stand in contrast to the trite and pandered — as well as broadsheets, chapbooks and the occasional monograph." They want "work that has a point-of-view; work that has some passion behind it and is exploring issues that are of pressing importance; work that challenges conventional notions of what poetry is or should be; work with a social conscience. No bland, flowery, uninventive poetry that says nothing in style or content." As a sample the editor selected these lines from "amber drive" by Pat McKinnon:

> *he must've carried some terrible sadness in his face*
> *which i was too young or too stoned to see*
> *some 8-legged hell crawling down his throat*
> *like maybe his dad held a magnifying glass*
> *between him & the blister sun or maybe*
> *he killed his sister or fucked his brother*
> *or his mom or the dog or . . .*

Sub-Terrain is 32 pgs., 7×10, offset, with a press run of 2,000. Subscription: $10. **Sample postpaid: $3.** They will consider simultaneous submissions, but not previously published poems. Reports in 4-6 weeks. Pays money only for solicited work; for other work, 4-issue subscription. Acquires one-time rights for magazine. "If chapbook contract, we retain right to publish subsequent printings unless we let a title lapse out-of-print for more than 1 year." Staff occasionally reviews small press poetry chapbooks. Sponsors Last Poems Poetry Contest; information for SASE. For chapbook or book publication submit 4 sample poems and bio, no simultaneous submissions. "We are willing to consider mss. But I must stress that we are a co-op, depending on support from an interested audience. New titles will be undertaken with caution. We are not subsidized at this point and do not want to give authors false hopes — but if something is important and should be in print, we will do our best." Editor provides brief comment and more extensive comments for fees. He says, "Poetry, in our opinion, should be a distillation of emotion and experience that is being given back to the world. Pretty words and fancy syntax are just that.

Market categories: (I) Beginning; (II) General; (III) Limited; (IV) Specialized; (V) Closed.

Where are the modern day writers who are willing to risk it all, put it all on the line? Young, new writers: show it all, bare your guts, write about what you fear! The last thing the world needs is soppy, sentimental fluff that gives nothing and says nothing."

THE SUCARNOCHEE REVIEW (II), Station 22, Livingston University, Livingston AL 35470, founded 1985, editor Joe Taylor, is an annual literary magazine which accepts poetry and fiction. "Sucarnochee (suke'nachi) is the Choctaw word for 'hog river' or 'a place where hogs bathe.' " **The editors have no specifications as to form, length, subject matter or style.** They have published poetry by R.T. Smith, Peter Huggins, Lewis Turco and Joseph Powell. As a sample the editor selected these lines from "Van Gogh at Saint Remy" by Wayne Cox:

> *Today, the poplars were on fire*
> *With autumn; tonight*
> *I see only an abyss of stars.*

> *Once again, I must point myself*
> *And take stock like a farmer*
> *At the end of another bad year.*

The editor says it is 70 pgs., perfect-bound. They receive about 500 poems a year, use approximately 10%. Press run is 500. Subscription: $10. **Sample postpaid: $5. No previously published poems; simultaneous submissions OK. Cover letter with short bio required.** Time between acceptance and publication is 6 months. **Seldom comments on rejections. Reports in "one week to four months." Pays 3 copies. Acquires first North American serial rights.** They award $50 for the best poem in each issue. Winning poems are chosen by the editors. You may want to order a sample copy of this magazine because its poetry, mostly structured free verse with emphasis on voice, has wide appeal. We found this a good read (with several poems as fine as what you might find in the best journals).

This cover was chosen because of "a deep fascination with the Irish Sheela-na-gig figure, receptive goddess over church lintels, most of whom were destroyed," says Sulfur Editor Clayton Eshleman. "The other figure, 'Wilma,' is Australian aboriginal work." The cover represents the "mythic-erotic vibrations/sympathies" of material in various issues of the magazine, he says. "Poetry is our stem, with off-branches into translation, archival materials, reviews, art and art criticism." Cover: Nancy Spero, "Sheela & Wilma," 1985. Courtesy Josh Baer Gallery, New York City.

SULFUR MAGAZINE (II, IV-Translations), Dept. of English, Eastern Michigan University, Ypsilanti MI 48197, phone (313)483-9787, founded 1981, poetry editor Clayton Eshleman, is a physically gorgeous and hefty (250+ pgs., 6×9, flat-spined, glossy card cover, elegant graphics and printing on quality stock) biannual that has earned a distinguished reputation. They have published poetry by John Ashbery, Ed Sanders, Gary Snyder, Jackson MacLow, Paul Blackburn and the editor (one of our better-known poets). As a sample the editor selected "Irish" by Paul Celan, translated by Pierre Fozis:

> *Give me the right of way*
> *across the grain ladder of your sleep,*
> *the right of way*

> *across the sleep trail,*
> *The right, for me to cut peat*
> *along the heart's hillside,*
> *tomorrow.*

Published by EMU, *Sulfur* has a circulation of 2,000, using approximately 100 pgs. of poetry in each issue. They use 5-10 of 600-700 submissions received/year. Free verse dominates here, much of it leaning toward the experimental. Subscription: $13. Sample postpaid: $6. **"We urge would-be contributors to *read* the magazine and send us material only if it seems to be appropriate."** Editor comments **"sometimes, if the material is interesting." Reports in 2-3 weeks. Pays $35-40/contributor.** Reviews 10-20 poetry books/issue. Open to unsolicited reviews. Poets may also send books for review consideration. *Sulfur* ranked #5 in the "Nontraditional Verse" category of the June 1993 *Writer's Digest* Poetry 60 list. Clayton Eshleman says, "Most unsolicited material is of the 'I am sensitive and have practiced my sensitivity' school—with little attention to language as such, or incorporation of materials that lead the poem into more ample contexts than 'personal' experience. I fear too many young writers today spend more time on themselves, without deeply engaging their *selves*, in a serious psychological way—and too little time breaking their heads against the Blakes, Stevens and Vallejos of the world. That is, writing has replaced reading. I believe that writing is a form of reading and vice versa. Of course, it is the quality and wildness of imagination that finally counts—but this 'quality' is a composite considerably dependent on assimilative reading (and translating, too)."

SULPHUR RIVER LITERARY REVIEW (III), P.O. Box 402087, Austin TX 78704-5578, founded 1978, reestablished 1987, editor/publisher James Michael Robbins, is a semiannual of poetry, prose and artwork. They have **"no restrictions except quality." They do not want poetry that is "trite or religious or verse that does not incite thought."** They have published poetry by Walt McDonald, Lyn Lifshin, Laurel Speer and Albert Huffstickler. As a sample we selected these lines from "Vegetable Garden" by J.B. Goodenough:

> *Now with a crooked back he tends*
> *Bean-rows straight as hoe-handles,*
> *Suspecting any of them*
> *Might be, suddenly,*
> *His last, perfected, effort.*

SRLR is digest-sized, perfect-bound, with glossy cover. They receive about 500 poems a year, accept about 20%. Press run is 400 for 200 subscribers, 100 shelf sales. Subscription: $7. **Sample postpaid: $4. No previously published poems or simultaneous submissions. "I enjoy receiving cover letters that acknowledge me as a human being rather than no letter or one that implies I am a machine that processes poems." Often comments on rejections. Reports in 1 month. Pays 2 copies.** The editor says, "Poetry is, for me, the essential art, the ultimate art, and any effort to reach the effect of the successful poem deserves some comment other than 'sorry.' This is why I try to comment as much as possible on submissions, though by doing so I risk my own special absurdity. So be it. However, there can be no compromise of quality if the poem is to be successful or essential art."

SUMMER STREAM PRESS (IV-Anthologies), P.O. Box 6056, Santa Barbara CA 93160-6056, phone (805)962-6540, founded 1978, poetry editor David D. Frost, publishes a series of books in hardcover and softcover, each presenting 6 poets, averaging 70 text pgs. for each poet. "The mix of poets represents many parts of the country and many approaches to poetry. The poets previously selected have been published, but that is no requirement. We welcome traditional poets in the mix and thus offer them a chance for publication in this world of free-versers. **The six poets share a 15% royalty. We require rights for our editions worldwide and share 50-50 with authors for translation rights and for republication of our editions by another publisher. Otherwise all rights remain with the authors."** They have published poetry by Virginia E. Smith, Sandra Russell, Jennifer MacPherson, Nancy Berg, Lois Shapley Bassen and Nancy E. Wallace. To be considered for future volumes in this series, **query with about 12 samples, no cover letter. Replies to query in 3 months, to submission (if invited) in 1 year. Previously published poetry and simultaneous submissions OK. Editor usually comments on rejections.** He says, "We welcome both traditional poetry and free verse. However, we find we must reject almost all the traditional poetry received simply because the poets exhibit little or no knowledge of the structure and rules of traditional forms. Much of it is rhymed free verse."

THE SUN (II), 107 N. Roberson St., Chapel Hill NC 27516, phone (919)942-5282, founded 1974, editor Sy Safransky, is "a monthly magazine of ideas" which uses **"all kinds of poetry."** They have recently published poetry by John Hodgen, Alison Luterman, David Budbill, Bertha Rogers, Edwin Romond, Karen Blomain, Chris Bursk and Barbara O'Brien. *The Sun* is magazine-sized, 40 pgs., printed on 50 lb. offset, saddle-stapled, with b&w photos and graphics, circulation 20,000, 10,000 subscriptions of which 50 are libraries. They receive 3,000 submissions of freelance poetry/year, use 25, have a 1- to 3-month backlog. Subscription: $30. **Sample postpaid: $3. Submit no more than 6 poems. Send SASE for guidelines. Reports within 3-5 months. Pays $25 on publication and in copies and subscription.** Buys first serial or one-time rights. *The Sun* received a 1991 *Utne Reader* Award for General Excellence.

SUN DOG: THE SOUTHEAST REVIEW (II), 406 Williams Bldg., English Department, Florida State University, Tallahassee FL 32306, phone (904)644-4230, founded 1979, poetry editor Michael Trammell. "The journal has a small student staff. We publish two flat-spined, 100-page magazines per year of poetry, short fiction and essays. As a norm, we usually accept about 12 poems per issue. **We accept poetry of the highest caliber, looking for the most 'whole' works. A poet may submit any length, but because of space, poems over 2 pages are impractical. Excellent formal verse highly regarded.**" They have published poetry by David Bottoms, David Kirby, Peter Meinke and Leon Stokesbury. *SD* is 6×9 with a glossy card cover, usually including half-tones, line drawings and color art when budget allows. Press run is 1,250. Subscription: $8 for 2 issues. **Sample postpaid: $4. Poems should be typed single-spaced. Send 2-5 submissions at a time. If simultaneous submission, say so. No previously published poems. Editor will comment briefly on most poems, especially those which come close to being accepted. Send SASE for guidelines. Reports in 3 months. Pays 2 copies. Acquires first North American serial rights.**

SUPERINTENDENT'S PROFILE & POCKET EQUIPMENT DIRECTORY (IV-Themes), 220 Central Ave., Box 43, Dunkirk NY 14048, phone (716)366-4774, founded 1978, poetry editor Robert Dyment, is a "monthly magazine, circulation 2,500, for town, village, city and county highway superintendents and Department of Public Works directors throughout New York State," and uses **"only poetry that pertains to highway superintendents and DPW directors and their activities." Submit no more than one page double-spaced.** They receive about 50 freelance submissions of poetry/year, use 20, have a 2-month backlog. Subscription: $10. **Sample: 80¢ postage. Reports within a month. Pays $5/poem.**

SYCAMORE REVIEW (II), Department of English, Purdue University, West Lafayette IN 47907, phone (317)494-3783, founded 1988 (first issue May, 1989), editor Linda E. Haynes, poetry editor is different for each issue. "We accept personal essays (25 pgs. max), short fiction (25 pgs. max), translations and **quality poetry in any form (6 pgs. max). There are no official restrictions as to subject matter or style.**" They have published poetry by Mary Oliver, John Updike, Marge Piercy, Russell Edson, Lee Upton and Brigit Pegeen Kelly. As a sample the editor selected the following lines by Fleda Brown Jackson:

> *... I must be in the middle*
> *of my life, the way I feel balanced*
> *between one thing and another. As if I have*

> *no hands or arms, parting the world*
> *as it reaches my face. Like a minnow, gone*
> *on little wings, a blush of sand from the bottom.*

The magazine is semiannual in a digest-sized format, 110 pgs., flat-spined, professionally printed, with glossy, color cover. Press run is 800 for 300 subscribers of which 50 are libraries. Subscription: $9. **Sample postpaid: $5. Cover letters not required but invited; include phone number, short bio and previous publications, if any. "We read August 15 through May 1." Editor comments on about 20% of rejections. Guidelines available for SASE. Reports in 3 months. Pays 2 copies.** Staff reviews books of poetry. Send books for review consideration. The editor says, "Poets who do not include SASE do not receive a response."

‡**TAILS OF WONDER (IV-Science fiction/fantasy)**, P.O. Box 23, Franklin Park NJ 08823, founded 1992, publisher Nicolas Samuels, editor Maritza DiSciullo, is a quarterly science fiction and fantasy literary magazine featuring short stories, poetry, reviews, articles, art and illustrations. As for poetry, they say, **"Length isn't so important, but poems must have some connection to science fiction or fantasy. Prefer poems under 40 lines."** They do not want "anything overly erotic or religious." They have recently published poetry by Troy Leaver and Peter Huge. The editor says *Tails* is 40-50 pgs., $8\frac{1}{2} \times 11$, high quality paper, glossy color cover with b&w illustrations and ads. They receive 5-10 poems/month, accept 4-6/issue. Press run is 500 for 200+ subscribers, 50+ shelf sales. Subscription: $18. **Sample postpaid: $5. Previously published poems and simultaneous submissions OK, if indicated. Cover letter required.** Time between acceptance and publication is 6-8 months. **Seldom comments on rejections. Send SASE for guidelines. Reports within 2 months. Pays 10¢/line ("no less than $1") plus 1 copy. Buys first North American serial or reprint rights.** Plans poetry contest. Send SASE for information. They say, "We love nothing better than great literary work, which is what we expect. Be innovative, challenge the 'cutting edge' and, above all else, write from your heart."

TAK TAK TAK (II, IV-Translations, themes), P.O. Box 7, Bulwell, Nottingham NG6 0HW England, founded 1986, editors Andrew and Tim Brown, appears occasionally in print and on cassettes, and, in addition, sometimes publishes collections of poetry. "No restrictions on form or style. However, each issue of the magazine is on a theme (i.e., 'Mother Country/Fatherland,' 'Postcards from Paradise'), and *all* contributions must be relevant. If a contribution is long it is going to be more difficult to fit in than something shorter. Write for details of subject(s), etc., of forthcoming issue(s)." They have published poetry by Michael Horowitz, Karl Blake, Keith Jafrate, Ramona Fotiade and Paul Buck. The editor describes it as "100 pgs., A5, photolithographed, board cover, line drawings and photographs, plus cassette of poetry, music, sounds. Of about 100 poems received in the past year we have used about 25." Press run 500. Subscription: £9, £11.80 postpaid to US surface rate (includes 2 issues with cassettes). **Sample postpaid to US: £10.90. Submit "a selection of 5 or 6 poems with a cover letter and bio of up to 30 words and a photograph suitable for publication."** They consider simultaneous submissions and previously published poems. Reports within 6 months. Pays 1 copy, sent surface rate. Editor sometimes comments on rejections. They also publish occasional flat-spined paperbacks averaging between 40 and 130 pgs. For chapbook consideration send as many as possible sample poems, bio, publications. Reports in 2 months. Pays a negotiated number of copies. The editors say, "Poetry is just one of the many creative forms our contributions take. We are equally interested in prose and in visual and sound media."

TAKAHE (II, IV-Translations), P.O. Box 13-335, Christchurch 1, New Zealand, phone (03)668659, founded 1989, poetry editors David Howard and Bernadette Hall, is a literary quarterly. "We have no preconceived specifications as to form, length, subject matter, style or purpose. We believe that poetry is, among other things, the art of significant silence. It demands an active reader whose trust in language matches that of the writer. No work that batters the reader about the head, that refuses to utilize silence and insists on spelling everything out—as if the reader was incapable of making connections." They have published poetry by Tatyana Shcherbina, Helen Trubek Glenn, Gregory O'Brien, Michael Harlow and Elizabeth Smither. As a sample the poetry editors selected these lines by Tony Beyer:

> *an indoors watery light and fetor*
> *and the hung sides of beef*
> *that acknowledge their classicism*
> *by dripping intermittently*
> *on the shoes of passers by*

The poetry editors describe it as 56 pgs., magazine-sized, desktop published with woodcut design on cover and some b&w graphics (including ads). They accept an average of 10% of 1,000 poems received a year. Press run is 300 for 189 subscribers of which 21 are libraries, 90 shelf sales. Subscription: $24 NZ. **Sample postpaid: $9 NZ. Submit up to 7 poems, name and address on each page. Simultaneous submissions and previously published poems OK (if not published in New Zealand). Cover letter with brief bio and publishing history required.** Editors comment on submissions "as a matter of course (particularly if the poem is potentially publishable but needs further work)." Reports in 2-3 months. Pays 1 copy plus small emolument at editors' discretion. Staff reviews books of poetry. Send books to David Howard for review consideration. The editors say, "In poetry (as in prayer) the essential thing is the degree to which the silences between words are charged with significance. 'Less is more'—but only if the less is carefully weighed."

TAL: A TORAH ART & LITERATURE REVIEW (I, IV-Religious, spirituality), 318 Ave. F, Brooklyn NY 11218, phone (718)871-1105, founded 1990, editor Y. David Shulman, appears irregularly using "poems by those engaged in Torah lifestyle." They have published poetry by Roberta Chester. As a sample the editor selected these lines by Yedidih Shalom:

> *A letter which swept through the nile-blue sky*
> *And splashed into my hand;*
> *A parchment in my reverent hand,*
> *A silver fish, alive in my wondering hand,*
> *A comet showering the paths of my hand,*
> *A cinder spinning fire in my hand,*

It is 7×8, offset, saddle-stapled, with matte card cover. Number of pages varies. Press run is 500. Subscription: $8. **Sample postpaid: $2. Pays 3 copies. Reports in 2 weeks.** Editor comments "upon request."

TALISMAN: A JOURNAL OF CONTEMPORARY POETRY AND POETICS (II), P.O. Box 1117, Hoboken NJ 07030, phone (201)798-9093, founded 1988, editor Edward Foster, appears twice a year. "Each issue centers on the poetry and poetics of a *major* contemporary poet and includes a selection of new work by other important contemporary writers. We are particularly interested in poetry in alternative (*not* academic) traditions. We don't want traditional poetry." They have published poetry by William

Bronk, Robert Creeley, Ron Padgett, Anne Waldman, Alice Notley, Edouard Roditi and Rosmarie Waldrop. As a sample the editor selected the following lines from "Opening Day" by Ann Lauterbach:

> *Locally a firm disavowal within the drift.*
> *Shaman of discourse said*
> *Or could have said*
> *These logics go teasingly forward*
> *Into capacities, and then the then.*

Talisman is digest-sized, flat-spined, 152+ pgs., photocopied from typescript, with matte card cover. Their press run is 650 with "substantial" subscriptions of which many are libraries. "We are inundated with submissions and lost track of the number long ago." Subscription: $9 individual; $13 institution. **Sample postpaid: $5. Reports in 1 month. Pays 1 copy. Acquires first North American serial rights.** Reviews books of poetry in 500-1,000+ words, single format.

TALISMAN LITERARY RESEARCH, INC. (V), P.O. Box 455, Georgetown CA 95634, founded 1965. They have published poetry collections by Kenneth Fields and Clinton Williams, but are **currently not accepting unsolicited mss.** As a sample they selected lines from "Cart Wheels" by William Burns:

> *And saw the caskets roll in Arlington,*
> *The heroes drawn through flags and guns to graves,*
> *And felt a stiffness give against the sun,*
> *A slouch of noon perhaps, a shrug of fate,*
> *Or sag of God in heavy sky revealed,*
> *And then a turn of mind, a spokeless reel.*

Pays 10% royalties. For sample books or chapbooks, write for brochure.

TAMPA REVIEW (III, IV-Translations), Dept. PM, University of Tampa, 401 W. Kennedy Blvd., Tampa FL 33606-1490, phone (813)253-3333, ext. 3621, founded 1964 as *UT Poetry Review*, became *Tampa Review* in 1988, editor Richard Mathews, poetry editors Kathryn Van Spanckeren and Donald Morrill, is an elegant semiannual of fiction, nonfiction, poetry and art (not limited to US authors) wanting **"original and well-crafted poetry written with intelligence and spirit. No greeting card or inspirational verse."** They have published poetry by Alberto Rios, Paul Mariani, Mark Halliday, Denise Levertov and Stephen Dunn. It is 78-96 pgs., flat-spined, 7½ × 10½ with a matte card color cover. They accept about 50-60 of 2,000 poems received a year. Their press run is 500 with 175 subscriptions of which 20 are libraries. **Sample postpaid: $5. Unsolicited mss are read between September and December. Reports by mid-February. Pays $10/printed page plus 1 copy and 40% discount on additional copies. Buys first North American serial rights.**

TANGRAM PRESS (III), Dept. PM, P.O. Box 2249, Granbury TX 76048, phone (817)579-1777, publisher Richard Fenker Jr. This very small press would like to publish more books such as their handsome coffee-table volume, 12 × 12, hardback, **Where Rainbows Wait for Rain: The Big Bend Country**, combining poems by Sandra Lynn and b&w photographs by Richard Fenker Jr., but "we have a limited staff. **While we do not discourage submissions, we cannot guarantee comments on same. We are not your standard poetry publisher."**

TAPJOE: THE ANAPROCRUSTEAN POETRY JOURNAL OF ENUMCLAW (II, IV-Nature, social issues), P.O. Box 632, Leavenworth WA 98826, founded 1987, is a biannual. **"We try to be very open-minded but have a definite preference for free verse poems, 10-50 lines, which yield a sense of place. 'Bioregionalism' and 'deep ecology' describe themes and ideals we hold close."** They have recently published poetry by David Edelman, Ron McFarland, Jess Mills and Linda Curtis Meyers. As a sample the editor selected these lines from "Siberia, the thin road to exile" by Donna Waidtlow:

> *We are the stripped larch, without*
> *hope of spring. Words are buried, even*
> *ravens have ceased to caw. A million*
> *bent spruce fence me from my home.*

The magazine is 28-35 pgs., digest-sized, saddle-stapled, offset from desktop with matte card cover. Accepts about 60 poems/year with 1,000+ submissions. Press run is 150-300. Subscription: $10 for 4 issues. **Sample postpaid: $3. "Cover letters appreciated but not necessary. Prefer 4-5 poems per submission." No simultaneous submissions or previously published poems. Initial reports in 2-8 weeks, final selections may take up to 6 months or so. Pays 1 copy for each accepted poem.** They say, "Submissions are circulated among several editors living hundreds of miles apart and working hectic jobs; sometimes this makes our responses very slow but we do the best we can. We lose $$$ on everything we print and appreciate purchases of our magazine—but mostly we enjoy receiving submissions of 'good' poetry! Read and buy poetry. The kinds of poets we admire: Linda Hogan, Mary Oliver, Lorna Dee Cervantes, Robert Sund, Czeslaw Milosz, William Stafford."

TAPROOT; BURNING PRESS; KRAPP'S LAST TAPE (II), P.O. Box 585, Lakewood OH 44107, founded 1980, editor Robert Drake, is a "micropress publisher of avant-garde and experimental literature and art. Also produces a weekly radio show (KLT) of music, noise, language-centered audio art and a series of audiocassettes." They want "**purposeful experiments with language in which form is the necessary outgrowth of content. No standard academic workshop slop.**" The editor describes *TapRoot*, a quarterly, as "typically 50 pgs., photocopied, handmade covers and binding." They accept less than 10% of 1,000-2,000 poems received/year. Press run is 250 typically for 50 subscriptions, 200 shelf sales. Sample postpaid: $5 when available. Submit "**no more than a dozen at a time unless previously contacted. No simultaneous submissions; previously published work is occasionally used.**" Pays 1 copy. "**Contributors may buy more at cost.**" Acquires first North American serial rights. Reviews books of poetry in 50-500 words. Burning Press publishes chapbooks averaging 50 pgs. **For chapbook publication query with no more than 12 samples. Pays 20% press run. Author may buy more at cost.** The editor says, "*Please* read us before submitting. We sponsor a yearly festival of micropress and alternative media and also a free 'dial-a-poem' service entitled 'in-yr-ear.' "

TAPROOT LITERARY REVIEW (I), 302 Park Rd., Ambridge PA 15003, phone (412)266-8476, founded 1986, editor Tikvah Feinstein, is an annual contest publication, very open to beginners. In addition to contest, each year a guest poet is selected; payment in copies. Writers recently published include Elizabeth R. Curry, Noel Valis, Rex Downie Jr., Judith R. Robinson and Gail Ghai. As a sample the editor selected the following lines from his own poem, "The Laundry":

> *Traffic passes and the soot-filled city breezes*
> *through the door, enters with me*
> *like the stooped, old men who come*
> *with their week's pile of soiled clothing*
> *and pick up their clean bundles of brown paper*
> *tied with string, like lunches.*

The review is approximately 80 pgs., printed by offset on white stock with one-color glossy cover, art and no ads. Circulation is 500, sold at bookstores, readings and through the mail. Single copy: $5.50. **Sample postpaid: $5. Nothing previously published or pending publication will be accepted. Cover letter with general information required. Submissions accepted between September 1 and December 31. There is a $5 entry fee for up to 5 poems, "no longer than 30 lines each."** All entrants receive a copy of *Taproot*; enclose $2 for postage and handling. Send books for review consideration.

TAR RIVER POETRY (II), English Dept., East Carolina University, Greenville NC 27858-4353, phone (919)752-6041, founded 1960, editor Peter Makuck, associate editor Luke Whisnant. "**We are not interested in sentimental, flat-statement poetry. What we would like to see is skillful use of figurative language.**" They have recently published poetry by William Matthews, Betty Adcock, William Stafford, Fred Chappell, Margaret Gibson, Susan Ludvigson, Philip Dacey, Neal Bowers and Elizabeth Dodd. As a sample the editors selected these lines from "Zuni Fetish" by Robert Cording:

> *This bear, its humped shoulders and backbone*
> *Scribed like the calm rise and fold*
> *Of oldest mountains, its upswept*
> *Ears and nose tracking some unseen presence,*
>
> *Was once half-seen in some common local stone*
> *Then freed, carved to the fetish I hold . . .*

Tar River appears twice yearly and is digest-sized, 60 pgs., professionally printed on salmon stock, some decorative line drawings, matte card cover with photo. They receive 6,000-8,000 submissions/year, use 150-200. Press run is 900+ for 500 subscribers of which 125 are libraries. Subscription: $8. Sample: $4.50. "**We do not consider simultaneous submissions. Double or single-spaced OK. We prefer not more than 6 pgs. at one time. We do not consider mss during summer months.**" **Reads submissions September 1 through April 15 only. Send SASE for guidelines. Reports in 4-6 weeks. Pays copies. Acquires first rights. Editors will comment "if slight revision will do the trick."** Reviews books of poetry in 4,000 words maximum, single or multi-book format. This is an especially good market for intelligent, concisely written book reviews. Poets may also send books for review consideration. *Tar River* is an "all-poetry" magazine that accepts dozens of poems in each issue, providing the talented beginner and experienced writer with an excellent forum that features all styles and forms of verse. Frequently contributors' works are included in the **Anthology of Magazine Verse & Yearbook of American Poetry**. The editors advise, "Read, read, read. Saul Bellow says the writer is primarily a reader moved to emulation. Read the poetry column in *Writer's Digest*. Read the books recommended therein. Do your homework."

TEAM (I, IV-Young Adults), Dept. PM, P.O. Box 7259, Grand Rapids MI 49510, phone (616)241-5616, editor Dale Dieleman. *Team* is a quarterly digest for volunteer youth workers. They want poetry "that reflects feelings and content to which young adults can relate in their personal lives and which will move them to a larger understanding of themselves and the world. We are looking for concise, fresh poetry, packed with images, contemporary in feel." No rhymed or erotic poetry. Sample $1 with SAE plus 2 first class stamps. Simultaneous submissions and previously published poems OK. Guidelines for SASE. Reports in 1 month. Pays $10-25/poem plus 1 copy. Specify "rights being offered."

TEARS IN THE FENCE (II), 38 Hodview, Stourpaine, Nr. Blandford Forum, Dorset DT11 8TN England, phone 0258-456803, founded 1984, general editor David Caddy, poetry editor Sarah Hopkins, a "small press magazine of poetry, fiction, interviews, articles, reviews and graphics. We are open to a wide variety of poetic styles. Work of a social, political, ecological and feminist awareness will be close to our purpose. However, we like to publish a balanced variety of work." The editors do not want to see "didactic rhyming poems." They have published poetry by Gerald Locklin, Ann Born, Sheila E. Murphy and Catherine Swanson. As a sample, they selected the following lines from "The Invisible Children" by Andrew Jordan:

> we found a well without a cover — its hollowness
> echoed with the movements of lost children,
>
> we heard their whisperings. There was a screaming
> in the rookery trees that leaned about the house

Tears in the Fence appears twice a year. It is magazine-sized, offset from typed copy on lightweight paper with b&w cover art and graphics, 60 pgs., matte card cover with black spiral binding. It has a press run of 600 copies, of which 141 go to subscribers. Price per issue is $5, sample available for same price. Writers should submit 5 typed poems with IRCs. Cover letter with brief bio required. Reporting time is 3 months. Time to publication 8-10 months "but can be much less." Pay is 1 copy. Reviews books of poetry in 200-250 words, single or multi-book format. Open to unsolicited reviews. Poets may also send books for review consideration. The magazine is informally connected with the East Street Poets literary event promotion. The editor says, "I think it helps to subscribe to several magazines in order to study the market and develop an understanding of what type of poetry is published. Use the review sections and send off to magazines that are new to you."

10TH MUSE (II), 33 Hartington Rd., Newtown, Southampton, Hants SO2 0EW England, founded 1990, editor Andrew Jordan, is a biannual of poetry, prose, book reviews and b&w artwork. "Generally radical rather than reactionary." They are **"particularly interested in human relationship stuff — sexuality/politics — wider subjects, too. No occasional verse."** They have published poetry by Peter Redgrove, Sheila E. Murphy and Belinda Subraman. As a sample the editor selected these lines from "Aliens" by Jeremy Reed:

> leaving a wife, a job, ditching a car
> to embrace the vision — holding to that
> and how its light breaks open like a star.

10th Muse is 48 pgs., A5, photocopied, saddle-stapled, with card cover, no ads. Press run is 200 for 20 subscribers of which 3 are libraries. Single copy: £2; subscription: £4 for 2 copies. Send a maximum of 6 poems. No previously published poems or simultaneous submissions. Often comments on rejections. Reports in 2-3 months. Pays 1 copy. Staff reviews books of poetry. Send books for review consideration. The editor says, "Poets should read a copy of the magazine first. *10th Muse* is a magazine that gets by on grant aid from my local city council — I need subscribers. A subscription taken out from a U.S. bank by check would have to be £12 for 2 issues or £6 for one issue. This is because of high bank charges levied in U.K. when cashing foreign currency checks. Alternatively people could send dollar notes equivalent to £4 (2 issues) or £2 (1 issue) plus IRCs to cover the number of issues ordered."

TESSERA (IV-Women, regional, bilingual, translations), 350 Stong, York University, 4700 Keele St., North York, Ontario M3J 1P3 Canada, founded 1984, revived 1988, managing editor Barbara Godard, appears twice a year: **"feminist literary theory and experimental writing by women in French and English, preference to Canadians."** It is 94 pgs., digest-sized, professionally printed, with glossy card cover. Subscription: $18. Sample postpaid: $10. Submit 4 copies. Deadlines are currently May 15 and November 15. Simultaneous submissions and previously published poems ("sometimes") OK. Editor comments on submissions "sometimes." Pays $10/page.

TESSERACT PUBLICATIONS (I), RR#1 Box 27, Fairview SD 57027-9719, phone (605)987-5070, founded 1981, publisher Janet Leih. **"All my books are subsidized publications. Payment is ⅓ in advance, ⅓ when book goes to printer, balance when book is complete. I help my poets with copyright,**

bar codes, listings and whatever publicity I can get for them. I have a number of mailing lists and will prepare special mailings for them, work with competent proofreaders, artists and a capable reviewer." They have helped publish books of poetry by Helen Eikamp, Fern Stuefen and Ellis Ovesen. As a sample Janet Leih selected these lines by Maria Bakkum:

> Love is
> a daughter's deserted room
> smiling back
> from love-worn Teddy bears
> and old doll faces.

They also hold occasional contests. Send SASE for information. Janet Leih adds, "I publish a catalog of books by South Dakota writers and take their books on consignment to fill orders. The catalog is new and modest at this time but the hope is to expand to a larger catalog and distribute it more widely."

TEXAS TECH UNIVERSITY PRESS (III, IV-Series), Lubbock TX 79409-1037, phone (806)742-2982, founded 1971, editor Judith Keeling, considers volumes of poetry in three categories only: **First-Book Poetry Series:** "Winning and finalist mss in an annual competition conducted by Poetry Editor Walter McDonald, who surveys some 20 literary journals throughout the year and invites up to 12 poets to submit mss for consideration in the competition"; **Invited Poets Series:** "Collections invited from established poets whose work continues to appear in distinguished journals"; and **TTUP Contemporary Poetry Series:** "Winning and finalist works in current national competitions." Mss should be submitted with cover letters and attachments to verify eligibility. Editors never comment on rejections. Books published on royalty contracts.

TEXTILE BRIDGE PRESS; MOODY STREET IRREGULARS: A JACK KEROUAC NEWSLETTER (IV-Themes), P.O. Box 157, Clarence Center NY 14032, founded 1978, poetry editor Joy Walsh. "We publish material by and on the work of Jack Kerouac, American author prominent in the fifties. Our chapbooks reflect the spirit of Jack Kerouac. We use poetry in the spirit of Jack Kerouac, poetry of the working class, poetry about the everyday workaday life. Notice how often the work people spend so much of their life doing is never mentioned in poetry or fiction. Why? **Poetry in any form.**" They have published poetry by Joseph Semenovich, Marion Perry, Bonnie Johnson, Boria Sax and Michael Basinski. *Moody Street Irregulars* is a 28-page, magazine-sized newsletter, biannual, circulation 700-1,000 (700 subscriptions of which 30 are libraries), using 3-4 pgs. of poetry in each issue. They receive about 50 freelance submissions of poetry/year, use half of them. Subscription: $7. **Sample postpaid: $3.50. Reports in 1 month. Pays copies.** Textile Bridge Press also publishes collections by individuals. For book publication, query with 5 samples. "The work speaks to me better than a letter." Replies to query in 1 week, to submission (if invited) in 1 month. Simultaneous submission OK for "some things yes, others no." Pays copies. Send SASE for catalog to buy samples. Editor comments on rejections "if they ask for it."

THALIA: STUDIES IN LITERARY HUMOR (I, IV-Subscribers, humor), Dept. of English, University of Ottawa, Ottawa, Ontario K1N 6N5 Canada, editor Dr. J. Tavernier-Courbin, appears twice a year using "humor (literary, mostly). Poems submitted must actually be literary parodies." The editor describes it as 7×8½, flat-spined, "with illustrated cover." Press run is 500 for 475 subscribers. Subscription: $20 for individuals, $22 for libraries. Sample postpaid: $8 up to volume 11, $15 and $20 for volumes 12 and 13 respectively (double issues). Contributors must subscribe. Simultaneous submissions OK but *Thalia* must have copyright. Will authorize reprints. Editor comments on submissions. Reviews books of poetry. "Send queries to the editor concerning specific books."

THEMA (II, IV-Themes), Thema Literary Society, P.O. Box 74109, Metairie LA 70033-4109, founded 1988, editor Virginia Howard, is a literary quarterly using poetry related to specific themes. "Each issue is based on an unusual premise. Please, please send SASE for guidelines before submitting poetry to find out the upcoming themes. For example: 'Mirror Image' was the theme for November 1, 1993 (submission deadline) and 'The Waiting Room' is for February 1, 1994. No scatologic language, alternate life-style, explicit love poetry." They have recently published poetry by Reva Sharon, Madeline Hoffer and Beryle Williams. As a sample the editor selected these lines by Shirley Vogler Meister:

> . . . I yearn to cry
> and cry
> until the birds halt their songs
> and listen with cocked heads
> in thronged stillness
> —and understand.

Thema is digest-sized, 200 pgs., professionally printed, with matte card cover. They accept about 10% of 320 poems received/year. Press run 500 for 250 subscriptions of which 30 are libraries.

Subscription: $16. Sample postpaid: $5. Submissions are accepted all year, but evaluated after specified deadlines. Editor comments on submissions. Pays $10/poem plus 1 copy. Buys one-time rights only.

THEMATIC POETRY QUARTERLY (I, IV-Themes), 4444 River Forest Rd., Marianna FL 32446, phone (904)482-3890, editor Wilbur I. Throssell, publishes loose-leaf portfolios of poetry on specific themes, limit 30 lines. Send SASE for list of themes.

THE THIRD HALF LITERARY MAGAZINE; K.T. PUBLICATIONS (I, II), 16, Fane Close, Stamford, Lincolnshire PE9 1HG England, founded 1987, editor Mr. Kevin Troop. *TTH* appears 3 times/year. K.T. Publications also publishes up to 6 other books, with a Minibooks Series, for use in the classroom. The editor wants **"meaningful, human and humane, funny poems up to 40 lines. Nothing obscene."** They have published poetry by Lee Bridges (Holland), Ann Keith (Amsterdam), Toby Litt (Prague) and Edmund Harwood, Michael Newman, Louise Rogers and Steve Sneyd (Britain). As a sample the editor selected this poem, "Fly," by Esther Gress (Denmark):

> *Like a butterfly*
> *we often fly in vain*
> *against the window pane*
> *and see not*
> *like the butterfly*
> *the open door*
> *to the sky*

TTH is 44 pgs., A5, printed on white paper with glossy cover. Press run is 200+. Individual booklets vary in length and use colored paper and card covers. **Cover letter required. Reports ASAP. Pays 1 copy. "Procedure for the publication of books is explained to each author; each case is different.** *The Third Half* is priced at £2.25 each; 2 issues for £4.25 and all three issues a year for £6.25, including postage and handling."

13TH MOON (II, IV-Women), English Department, SUNY-Albany, 1400 Washington Ave., Albany NY 12222, phone (518)442-4181, founded 1973, editor Judith Johnson, is a feminist literary magazine appearing yearly (one double issue) in a 6×9, flat-spined, handsomely printed format with glossy card cover, using photographs and line art, ads at $200/page. Beyond a doubt, a real selection of forms and styles is featured here. For instance, in recent issues free verse has appeared with formal work, concrete poems, long poems, stanza patterns, prose poems, a crown of sonnets and more. Press run is 2,000 for 690 subscriptions of which 61 are libraries, 700 shelf sales. Subscription: $10. **Sample postpaid: $10. Reads submissions September 1 through May 30 only. Send SASE for guidelines. Pays 2 copies. Acquires first North American serial rights.** Staff reviews books of poetry in 1,500 words "more or less." Send books to Sue Shaferzak, review editor, for review consideration.

THISTLEDOWN PRESS LTD. (V, IV-Regional), 668 East Place, Saskatoon, Saskatchewan S7J 2Z5 Canada, phone (306)244-1722, fax (306)244-1762, founded 1975, editor-in-chief Patrick O'Rourke, is "a literary press that specializes in **quality books of contemporary poetry by Canadian authors. Only the best of contemporary poetry that amply demonstrates an understanding of craft with a distinctive use of voice and language. Only interested in full-length poetry mss with 53-71 pgs. minimum."** They have published books of poetry by Glen Sorestad, George Whipple, Gary Hyland and John V. Hicks. Do not submit unsolicited mss. Canadian poets must **query first with letter, bio and publication credits.** Poetry ms submission guidelines available upon request. Replies to queries in 2-3 weeks, to submissions (if invited) in 3 months. **No authors outside Canada. No simultaneous submissions. "Please submit quality dot-matrix, laser-printed or photocopied material." Contract is for 10% royalty plus 10 copies.** They comment, "Poets submitting mss to Thistledown Press for possible publication should think in 'book' terms in every facet of the organization and presentation of the mss: poets presenting mss that *read* like good books of poetry will have greatly enhanced their possibilities of being published. We strongly suggest that poets familiarize themselves with some of our poetry books before submitting a query letter."

THORNTREE PRESS (II), 547 Hawthorn Lane, Winnetka IL 60093, founded 1986, contact Eloise Bradley Fink. This press publishes professionally printed, digest-sized, flat-spined paperbacks, 96 pgs., selected through competition January 1 through February 14 in odd-numbered years. **Sample postpaid: $6.95.** "Included in our 14 books are 21 poets." From **Troika IV** Helen Reed writes:

> *"The trap shuddered with blows of hissing prehistoric snouts, snapping turtles, heads big*
> *as knotted fists. They carried their past with them in mossy gouts of green and lightning-*
> *forked white scars on plated shells, pale markings of dark water gods . . . . We hid our*
> *eyes, shrank from monsters that could swim into our dreams that night . . ."*

Submit a stapled group of 10 pages of original, unpublished poetry, single or double spaced,

CLOSE-UP

View the Line as a Poetic Unit

"Words"

As air invisibly hugs chimneys, roofs,
running its fingers over gables, eaves,
let words embrace your wonder and return
it touch for touch — as fondled photographs
reward a lover's kiss with absent cheeks.

Are butterflies or flowers on that stem?
If flowers, air is galliard with the hazard
of their flight . . . all things are one and bloom
from the same shoot, the emblematic Word,
the solemn Om of which we are the breath.

We give ourselves away in what we write,
the harvest that has picked us, every choice
crisp appleword, root-cellar-cool and moist
and chaste to the ripe core if you should eat
— yet tasteless, withered, green, unless it's read.

George Whipple

George Whipple was reared in Toronto where he worked for more than 30 years as a postal clerk and then as a record clerk in city hall. He is known in his native Canada as a poet who possesses a surprising, alluring voice.

To illustrate, note the words in "Words" — 29 are nouns, averaging two or three per line in the first two stanzas. Some of them startle, especially when combined with unanticipated adjectives — "fondled photographs," "the emblematic Word," "the solemn *Om*," "crisp appleword." Moreover, music reverberates throughout — "Are butterflies or flowers on that stem?/ If flowers, air is galliard with the hazard/ of their flight. . . . "

Whipple says the above poem is based on "multiple and off-the-wall metaphysical conceits," controlled by uniform stanzas and off-rhyme. The final pun — words are green unless read (red) — caps the work.

The combination of metaphysical conceits (comparisons of unlike objects — "air" and "words," for example) and puns (witty word play) are hallmarks of Whipple's voice.

He has two collections to his credit, both widely praised in Canada. (Reviewers use such words as "amazing tour de force" and "technical brilliance.") His **Life Cycle: Selected Poems**, published by Hounslow Press (Toronto) in 1984, contains 99 poems and features such styles as traditional rhyme and meter, free verse and stanza patterns, and even shape poems. His **Passing Through Eden**, published by Thistledown (Saskatoon, Saskatchewan) in 1991, contains 68 poems and as many poetic forms and styles as his first book.

Whipple publishes individual poems almost exclusively in his homeland but is known in the United States by readers of such Canadian literary journals as *The Antigonish Review*, *The Fiddlehead*, *The Dalhousie Review* and *Poetry Canada*.

His poems display keen attention to the line as poetic unit. "A great line can support one bad line or three poor lines," Whipple says, "but it is better to cancel the bad line if it cannot be improved." He also recommends "one concrete noun per line," if possible, and "at least a third of all lines starting with a word other than a conjunction or indefinite article."

He advises poets to choose significant topics for their works—"although this can never represent more than 15% of a poem's value. The true subject of every poem is the poem itself, its images and especially its music."

Finally, he adds, "A poem is successful only inasmuch as it stimulates the reader's senses to complete the poem from his own imagination."

Successful poems, however, don't come easily. As a rule, Whipple usually revises each verse as many as 30 times before he is satisfied with sound and spontaneity. His goal is to find subtle rhythms in language and to suggest meanings for readers to discover and interpret on their own.

"Prose is poetry without music," he says. "Poetry without music is prose."

Whipple advises **Poet's Market** readers to befriend other poets for mutual encouragement. "You will need it," he says. "Double your enjoyment and knowledge of poetry by learning another language. Read 50 times as much as you write. When you revise, remember it is not what *you* feel that is important but what you can make *others* feel."

To be open to the experience of verse, Whipple also suggests that poets stop watching television. "It is anti-literate and destroys your imagination."

When asked how he spends his day without TV in Burnaby, located in the western province of British Columbia, he replies, "I spend mornings revising the poetry dictated the day before by the *genius loci* inhabiting the streams and rocks and trees of a neighboring wood. Usher at noon Mass. Patrol the aforesaid forest beat for poems and spend evenings in the local library with (currently) Browning, Merwin, C.S. Lewis."

—*Michael J. Bugeja*

66A great line can support one bad line or three poor lines, but it is better to cancel the bad line if it cannot be improved. **99**

—George Whipple

photocopied, with a $4 reader's fee. Mss will not be returned. (A SASE for winners' names may be included.) "The top fifteen finalists will be invited to submit a 30-page manuscript for possible publication in **Troika VI**."

THOUGHTS FOR ALL SEASONS: THE MAGAZINE OF EPIGRAMS (IV-Form, humor), % editor Prof. Em. Michel Paul Richard, 11530 SW 99th St., Miami FL 33176, founded 1976, "is an irregular serial: **designed to preserve the epigram as a literary form; satirical.** All issues are commemorative, e.g., **1976, 1984, 1989, 1992." Rhyming poetry will be considered although most modern epigrams are prose.** Prof. Richard has published poetry by Jack Hart and offers this sample:

> *Beware a cause: it is our fate*
> *To turn into the things we hate*

TFAS is offset from typescript on heavy buff stock with full-page cartoon-like drawings, card cover, 84 pgs., saddle-stapled. The editor accepts about 20% of material submitted. Press run is 500-1,000. There are several library subscriptions but most distribution is through direct mail or local bookstores and newsstand sales. Single copy: $4.75 plus $1.50 postage. **Simultaneous submissions OK, but not previously published epigrams "unless a thought is appended which alters it." Editor comments on rejections. Send SASE for guidelines. Reports in 1 month. Pays 1 copy.** He says, "This is the only magazine which is devoted to this literary form."

THREE CONTINENTS PRESS INC. (III, IV-Ethnic, translations), Suite 407, 1901 Pennsylvania Ave. NW, Washington DC 20006, phone (202)223-2554, founded 1973, poetry editor Donald Herdeck. **"Published poets only welcomed and only non-European and non-American poets ... We publish literature by creative writers from the non-western world (Africa, the Middle East, the Caribbean and Asia/Pacific) — poetry *only* by non-western writers or good translations of such poetry if original language is Arabic, French, African vernacular, etc."** They have published poetry by Derek Walcott, Khalil Hawi, Mahmud Darwish and Julia Fields. They also publish anthologies focused on relevant themes. **Query with 4-5 samples, bio, publication credits. Replies to queries in 5-10 weeks, to submissions (if invited) in 4-5 weeks. Offers 10% royalty contract (5% for translator) with $100-200 advance plus 10 copies. Buys worldwide English rights. Send SASE for catalog to buy samples.**

THE THREEPENNY REVIEW (II), P.O. Box 9131, Berkeley CA 94709, phone (510)849-4545, founded 1980, poetry editor Wendy Lesser, "is a quarterly review of literature, performing and visual arts, and social articles aimed at the intelligent, well-read, but not necessarily academic reader. Nationwide circulation. **Want: formal, narrative, short poems (and others); do not want: confessional, no punctuation, no capital letters. Prefer under 50 lines but not necessary. No bias *against* formal poetry, in fact a slight bias in favor of it."** They have published poetry by Thom Gunn, Frank Bidart, Robert Hass, Czeslaw Milosz and Brenda Hillman. There are about 9-10 poems in each 36-page tabloid issue. They receive about 4,500 submissions of freelance poetry/year, use 12. Press run is 7,500 for 6,000 subscribers of which 300 are libraries. Subscription: $18. **Sample: $6. Send 5 poems or fewer/submission. Send SASE for guidelines. Reports in 2-8 weeks. Pays $50/poem. Buys first serial rights.** Open to unsolicited reviews. "Send for review guidelines (SASE required)." *The Threepenny Review* ranked #7 in the "Top Pay" category of the June 1993 *Writer's Digest* Poetry 60 list.

THRESHOLD BOOKS (IV-Spirituality, translations), RD #4, Box 600, Dusty Ridge Rd., Putney VT 05346, phone (802)254-8300, founded 1981, poetry editor Edmund Helminski, is "a small press dedicated to the publication of quality works in metaphysics, poetry in translation and literature with some spiritual impact. **We would like to see poetry in translation of high literary merit with spiritual qualities, or original work by established authors."** They have published poetry by Rabia and Yunus Emre. As a sample the editor selected these lines by Jelaluddin Rumi, translated by John Moyne and Coleman Barks:

> *We've given up making a living.*
> *It's all this crazy love poetry now.*
>
> *It's everywhere. Our eyes and our feelings*
> *Focus together, with our words*

That comes from a collection, **Open Secret, Versions of Rumi,** published in a beautifully printed, flat-spined, digest-sized paperback, glossy color card cover, 96 pgs. Per copy: $9. **Query with 10 samples, bio, publication credits and SASE. Simultaneous submissions OK; discs compatible with IBM, hard copy preferred. Replies to queries in 1-2 months, to submissions (if invited) in 1-2 months. Publishes on 7% contract plus 10 copies (and 50% discount on additional copies). Send SASE for catalog to buy samples.**

THUMBPRINTS (I, IV-Themes, regional), 928 Gibbs, Caro MI 48723, phone (517)673-5563, founded 1984, editor Janet Ihle, is the monthly 8-page Thumb Area Writers' Club newsletter. They want **poetry about writers and writing, nothing "vulgar." Maximum 32 lines.** As a sample, the editor selected the last stanza of "My Pen's Words" by I. Wright:

> *Sometimes my pen is full of wit*
> *Sometimes it surprises me*
> *Sometimes its words become a poem*
> *For one and all to see.*

Press run is 45 for 30 subscriptions. **Sample postpaid: 75¢. Simultaneous submissions and previously published poems OK. Send SASE for guidelines. Editor comments on submissions "sometimes." Reports in about 3 months. Pays 1 copy.** They sponsor seasonal contests for Michigan amateur writers.

TIA CHUCHA PRESS (III, IV-Ethnic, regional, social issues), P.O. Box 476969, Chicago IL 60647, founded 1989, president Luis J. Rodriguez. Tia Chucha **generally discourages unsolicited mss.** They publish 2-4 paperbacks a year, **"multicultural, lyrical, engaging, passionate works informed by social, racial, class experience. Evocative. Poets should be knowledgeable of contemporary and traditional poetry, even if experimenting."** They have published poetry by David Hernandez, Michael Warr and editor Luis J. Rodriguez. As a sample the editor selected these lines from "The Poetry Widow" by Patricia Smith:

> *Tonight, I wished I was one of your poems;*
> *strong syllables curled in your throat*
> *awaiting a joyous delivery. I wished I*
> *was that clever, stilted script on the*
> *paper in your hand, words you sweat over.*

That's from her collection, **Life According to Motown**, published in a 6×9, flat-spined, professionally printed paperback, 74 pgs. with glossy card cover, $6.95. "We usually 'select' poets we'd like to publish, those active in a poetry environment (i.e., bar and cafe scene, magazines, etc.). We believe poetry matters. Although we publish in English, we do not limit our traditions to Western Culture. Poetry should draw on the richness of human cultures, with roots in African, Native American, Asian and Latin sensibilities. We believe in engaging poetry, socially necessary and shaped by political, economic and class realities. Redemptive and relevant. We believe poetry is an art. It needs to be crafted, thought-out and knowledgeable of contemporary and traditional poetics."

TICKLED BY THUNDER: WRITER'S NEWS & ROUNDTABLE (II, IV-Subscribers), 7385 129th St., Surrey, British Columbia V3W 7B8 Canada, founded 1990, publisher/editor Larry Lindner, appears 3 times/year, using poems about **"fantasy, about writing or whatever. Keep them short—not interested in long, long poems. Nothing pornographic, childish, unimaginative."** They have published poetry by Stephen Gill, Helen Singh, Victoria Collins and John Grey. As a sample the editor selected these lines (poet unidentified):

> *So she put a monkee in his tea*
> *marshmallows on the side . . .*

It is 16-20 pgs., digest-sized, published on Macintosh. Press run is 120 for 100 subscribers. **Subscription: $12 for 4 issues. Sample postpaid: $2.50. Send SASE for guidelines. Include samples of writing with queries. Cover letter required with submissions. Reports in 2 months. Pays 1 copy plus cash. Buys first rights. Editor comments on rejections "99% of the time."** Reviews books of poetry in up to 300 words. Open to unsolicited reviews. Poets may also send books for review consideration. They also offer a poetry contest 3 times/year. Deadlines: the 15th of March, July and November. Entry fee: $2 for 3 poems; free for subscribers. Prize: cash, publication and subscription. Send SASE for details.

TIDEPOOL (I, IV-Form), 4 E. 23rd St., Hamilton, Ontario L8V 2W6 Canada, phone (416)383-2857, founded 1984, publisher Herb Barrett, who says, **"We charge $10 entry fee. Money returned if poetry not used."** Send SASE for guidelines for details. He wants to see **"haiku and contemporary short verse, any style or theme (maximum 34 lines). No scatalogical vulgarity."** He has published poetry by Chris Faiers, Dorothy Cameron Smith and Jeff Seffinga. *Tidepool*, published each October, is 80+ pgs., digest-sized, saddle-stapled, professionally printed with matte card cover. Press run is 400 for 150 subscribers of which 60-70 are libraries. **Sample postpaid: $5. "Prefer unpublished material."** Cover letter required. Submit mss in May and June only. Sometimes comments on rejections. Reports on submissions in 2-3 weeks. Pays copies.

TIGER MOON PRESS; STAR TRIAD 'ZINE; TIGER MOON PRESS CATALOG (I, IV-Fantasy), P.O. Box 2371, Vero Beach FL 32961-2371, founded 1988, editor Sara Ryan. The press publishes cards, calendars and other products which use poetry. They also use poetry in their catalog and in *ST*, both of which appear 3 times/year. They want **"fantasy, metaphysical, inner growth experiences; I will look at others and have accepted a wide variety of poetry, including haiku. In the case of products, query for current theme."** As a sample, the editor selected these lines from "The Rain Staircase to Zenno" by Gregory L. Norris:

> There was a higher place
> of lilac breezes . . .
> A global place
> I've not forgotten
> at the end of your
> empty road.
> It was there, when
> we first met,
> somewhere atop
> the trees.

ST is magazine-sized, 28-60 pgs., desktop published. **Sample postpaid: $5 for current issue, $2.50 for special condensed sample edition.** Previously published poems and simultaneous submissions OK (if you notify the editor). Prefers a cover letter "with short line or two about the person." Guidelines for first class stamp. Reports in 10 days except between October and December, then it is 1 month. Pays $3-5/poem (depending on length). "I pay one-half in check, one-half in Tiger Moon Press products; payment also includes a copy of the publication." Buys first or reprint rights. She buys about 100 poems/year. Open to unsolicited reviews. Poets may also send books for review consideration. "Free service to all writers for a listing of any books or credits they want to share on the 'Writer's Preserve' page, which is in all publications." They have recently started publishing books of poetry. "No plans to publish more than one a year as yet." Current projects are by invitation only.

TIGHT (II), P.O. Box 1591, Guerneville CA 95446, founded 1990, editor Ann Erickson, appears 5 or 6 times a year. *"tight* **uses immediate poetry, favors fragmented, condensed, vivid form—direct experience or dream."** They have recently published poetry by Peter Layton, Keith Abbott, Sesshu Foster, Joel Dailey, Dan Nielsen, Grace Grafton, todd moore, Charlene Blue Horse, David Fisher, Patti Sirens and Ruth Marie Rignall. As a sample the editor selected these lines from "like the fawn in the clockwork" by Marcia Arrieta:

> desires grow
> in capsules, in clusters
> like segments of orange in sky

tight is 75 pgs., 7×8½, photocopied from typescript with 60 lb. matte cover. Press run 150 for 20 subscribers, 50 shelf sales. **Sample postpaid: $4.50.** Checks payable to Ann Erickson. Submit poetry for spring and summer of 1994. Reports in 2 months or sooner. Pays 1 copy. Acquires one-time rights.

TIGHTROPE (II); SWAMP PRESS (V), 323 Pelham Rd., Amherst MA 01002, founded 1977, chief editor Ed Rayher. Swamp Press is a small press publisher of poetry, fiction and graphic art in limited edition, letterpress chapbooks. *Tightrope*, appearing 1-2 times a year, is a literary magazine of varying format, circulation 300, 150 subscriptions of which 25 are libraries. Subscription: $10 for 2 issues. Sample of *Tightrope* postpaid: $6. No simultaneous submissions. Sometimes comments on rejections. Send SASE for guidelines. Reports in 2 months, 6-12 months until publication. Pays "sometimes" and provides 2 contributor's copies. Acquires first rights. Reviews books of poetry in one paragraph, single format. Swamp Press has published books by Edward Kaplan, editor Ed Rayher, Alexis Rotella (miniature, 3×3, containing 6 haiku), Sandra Dutton (a 4 foot long poem), Frannie Lindsay (a 10×13 format containing 3 poems), Andrew Glaze, Tom Hazo, Carole Stone and Steven Ruhl. Not presently accepting freelance submissions for chapbook publication but when he publishes chapbooks he pays 5-10%

Use the General Index to find the page number of a specific publisher. If the publisher you are seeking is not listed, check the " '93-'94 Changes" list at the end of this section.

of press run and, if there is grant money available, an honorarium (about $50). Sometimes comments on rejections. Send SASE for catalog.

TIMBERLINE PRESS (V), 6281 Red Bud, Fulton MO 65251, phone (314)642-5035, founded 1975, poetry editor Clarence Wolfshohl. "We do limited letterpress editions with the goal of blending strong poetry with well-crafted and designed printing. We lean toward **natural history or strongly imagistic nature poetry but will look at any good work. Also, good humorous poetry.** Currently, still not accepting submissions because we have a good backlog of mss to publish — enough for the next 2-3 years." They have published books of poetry by Walter Bargen and William Hart. **Sample copies may be obtained by sending $4 requesting sample copy and noting you saw the listing in Poet's Market. Reports in under 1 month. Pays "50-50 split with author after Timberline Press has recovered its expenses."**

TIMBERLINES (I), % Lake City Writers Forum, P.O. Box 38, Lake City CO 81235, founded 1990, contact Mary Stigall or Lynda Rivers, is an annual literary journal. They **"prefer poetry dealing with nature-man, out-of-doors, but not essential. Shorter poems have better chance of acceptance due to space limitations."** As a sample they selected these lines (poet unidentified):

> *When I was*
> *little, days were bright yellow blankets*
> *that warmed my words. Clouds were crowns*
> *that blessed mountain tops and brothers*
> *scrambled my eyes with mysteries. Night*
> *held the song of crickets in its palm . . .*

Sample postpaid: $5. Poems should be typed exactly as they should appear on the page if accepted. Deadline: March 1. Reads submissions September 1 through April 1 only. Seldom comments on rejections. Pays 1 copy.

TIMES CHANGE PRESS (V), P.O. Box 1380, Ojai CA 93024-1380, phone (805)646-8595, founded 1970, publisher Lamar Hoover, publishes nonfiction in areas of antiauthoritarian politics, feminism and gender issues, only rarely poetry. **They accept no unsolicited poetry.**

TIMES LITERARY SUPPLEMENT (II), Priory House, St. John's Lane, London EC1M 4BX England, founded 1902, is a weekly of book reviews which also accepts **poetry of all kinds ("shortness a virtue").** They have published poetry by Seamus Heaney, Thom Gunn, Joseph Brodsky and Paul Muldoon. It is 32 pgs., newsprint, folded with color cover, color and b&w illustrations, display and classified advertising. They receive about 5,000 poems a year, use approximately 2%. Press run is 27,000 for 20,000 subscribers, 7,000 shelf sales. Single copy: £1.75; subscription: £69.50 ($110 US). **No previously published poems or simultaneous submissions. Submit no more than 5 poems.** Time between acceptance and publication averages 1 month. **Reports in "1 day to 5 months." Pays £2.15/line. Buys first world rights.** "New poetry books reviewed constantly, mainly singly, in 300-3,000 words." Send books to F. Mount, editor, for review consideration.

TIN WREATH (II, III), P.O. Box 13401, Albany NY 12212-3401, founded 1985, "editor/janitor" David Gonsalves. "*Tin Wreath* is a triquarterly (March, July and November) gathering of writers and writing from the social, political, psychological, spiritual and linguistic margins of late 20th century America." The editor is looking for poetry **"that makes contact with the deeper forces at work in the world and poetry that explores the musical and sculptural qualities inherent in the language; I'd prefer to see abstract, minimalist, non-discursive or otherwise counter-traditional poetry."** He has published work by Geof Huth, Deborah Meadows, N. Sean William and Sheila E. Murphy. As a sample, he chose these lines from "The Lynching of J. Bro" by Michelle Perez:

> *quick his bonnet*
> *stepped, disrobed*
> *the wife*
> *half silent*
> *stately shook,*
> *a pattern, body*
> *as firm displayed —*
> *the patrons laughed.*

Tin Wreath consists of 10-12 unbound 8½×11 photocopied sheets. Circulation is 150. Subscription: $9 individuals, $15 institutions. **A sample copy with complete guidelines costs $2. Checks must be made payable to David Gonsalves. Writers should send 3-5 poems. Simultaneous submissions are OK. Reporting time is "13 days to 13 weeks" and time to publication is 3-6 months. Pays 3 copies. Acquires first North American serial rights.**

TOAD HIGHWAY (II), English Dept., University Hall, Bowling Green University, Bowling Green OH 43403, founded 1988, editor Grant Clauser. *Toad Highway* is a small magazine appearing irregularly using "all types of artwork, poetry, fiction, essays and reviews. **We want poetry which proves that the poet is obsessed by each sound, each stress, each image, each line. No 'happy poems' or work which shows that the poet has not studied contemporary poetry.**" They have recently published work by Donald Leverny, Peter Wild and Robert Peters. As a sample the editor selected these lines from "Hubbel Trading Post" by Robert Edwards:

> *The first time was the dust,*
> *bolts of calico and velvet,*
> *and Hopi and Pima baskets hanging*
> *by a shadow from the rafters.*
> *There were Navajo rugs of Ganado red,*
> *like flexible iron, on the floor,*
> *and the smell of dark leather*
> *glossed on the salt of many hands.*

TH is a 52-page pamphlet, saddle-stapled. Their press run is 250 with 20 subscriptions. "We accept about one in every 100 poems received." Subscription: $12/3 issues. **Sample: $2 back issues. Make checks payable to Grant Clauser. Submit maximum of 5 poems, single-spaced. Simultaneous submissions OK. Editor "seldom" comments on rejections. Responds to submissions "when I get to it." Pays 1 copy** (discount on others). He says, "We want to see strong imagistic narrative or descriptive meditation. Nothing experimental just for the sake of being different. No L.A. type poems. The poem must say something real, not just sit there and wet itself. *Toad Highway* aims to be an outlet for quality contemporary poetry at a low budget. I sometimes like to print short prose bits by the authors about their poetry."

‡TORNADO ALLEY QUARTERLY (II), P.O. Box 9390, St. Louis MO 63117, phone (314)758-7569, founded 1991, is a free coffeehouse tabloid containing poetry, fiction, articles on music and writing, book reviews and essays. They want **poetry "rich in imagery, with effective use of figurative language. Nothing sentimental, shaped or with forced rhyme. No poems about how beautiful one's lover is while he or she sleeps."** They have recently published poetry by Eric Pankey, Dina Ben-Lev, Lyn Lifshin and Qiu Xiaolong. As a sample the editor selected these lines from "Sunday Morning at the Edinburgh Zoo" by Ricardo DeUngria:

> *And after the Penguins have waddled their stuff*
> *in a soulful parade from their cages*
>
> *and back, and after the Sea Lions have been fed,*
> *and the crowd has trickled to the ice cream van,*
>
> *Barney the Polar Bear still swims in his pool*
> *and the world around him hangs, swinging in circles.*

TAQ is 24-32 pgs., 11×13, offset on newsprint with b&w photos. They receive about 100 unsolicited poems a year, use less than 10%. Press run is 5,000-7,500 for 32 subscribers of which 2 are libraries. The rest are distributed free in St. Louis, Chicago and Kansas City bookstores, bars, record stores, etc. Subscription: $16. **Sample postpaid: $4. No previously published poems; simultaneous submissions OK, but not preferred. Seldom comments on rejections. Send SASE for guidelines. Reports in 2-3 months. Pays 2 copies.** Reviews books and chapbooks of poetry in about 500 words.

TOUCH (IV-Religious, teens, themes), P.O. Box 7259, Grand Rapids MI 49510, phone (616)241-5616, founded 1970, poetry editor Carol Smith: "Our magazine is a 24-page edition written **for girls 7-14 to show them how God is at work in their lives and in the world around them. *Touch* is theme-orientated. We like our poetry to fit the theme of each. We send out a theme update biannually to all our listed freelancers. We prefer short poems with a Christian emphasis that can show girls how God works in their lives.**" They have published poetry by Janet Shafer Boyanton and Iris Alderson. As a sample we selected "Shall I Compare Myself to Others?" by May Richstone:

> *Better not. Such comparisons*
> *Most likely would become a strain—*
> *My betters could make me envious,*
> *The lesser tend to make me vain.*
>
> *Much better compare*
> *Yesterday's me*
> *With the tomorrow's*
> *I hope to be.*

Touch is published 10 times a year, magazine-sized, circulation 15,800 with 15,500 subscriptions. They receive 150-200 freelance submissions of poetry/year, use 2 poems in each issue, have a 6-month backlog. Subscription: $9 US, $10.50 Canada, $15 foreign. **Sample and guidelines free with 8 × 10 SASE. Poems must not be longer than 20 lines — prefer much shorter. Simultaneous submissions OK. Query with SASE for theme update. Reports in 2 months. Pays $10-15 and copies.**

TOUCHSTONE (I, II), Viterbo College, La Crosse WI 54601, phone (608)784-0268, founded 1950, moderator George Klawitter, is a literary quarterly using mostly poetry, short stories and artwork. **"Any form but no longer than 50 lines/poem. Nothing sentimental."** As a sample the editor selected these lines from "Outbound" by Kate Larkin:

> *Beware of the Park Street exit*
> *Where corners cross*
> *And weepy people*
> *Stare, pasty-faced.*

The magazine is digest-sized, 48 pgs., saddle-stapled, with semi-glossy card cover. Press run is 800 for 100 subscribers of which 25 are libraries. Subscription: $5. **Sample postpaid: $2.50. Submit 3-5 poems. Cover letter required; include "a note of origination"** (i.e. that the work is original). **Reads submissions August 1 through March 1 only. Send SASE for guidelines. Reports in 2 months. Best poem gets $20. All get 1 copy.** The editor says, "Write poetry that is rich in visual imagery. Strive to make your reader *see* what you are talking about. Do not philosophize. Do not moralize. Let the imagery carry the message."

TOUCHSTONE LITERARY JOURNAL; TOUCHSTONE PRESS (II), P.O. Box 8308, Spring TX 77387-8308, founded 1975, poetry editor William Laufer, is an annual publishing **"experimental or well-crafted traditional form, translations, no light verse or doggerel."** They have published poetry by Walter Griffin, Sheila Murphy, Michael L. Johnson, Walter McDonald and Joyce Pounds Hardy. *Touchstone* is digest-sized, flat-spined, 100 pgs., professionally printed in small, dark type with glossy card cover. Subscription: $7. **Sample postpaid: $3. Pays 1 copy.** Reviews books of poetry. Open to unsolicited reviews. Poets may also send books for review consideration, to Review Editor. Touchstone Press also **publishes an occasional chapbook. Send SASE for submission guidelines.**

TOWER POETRY SOCIETY; PINE TREE SERIES; TOWER (II), Dundas Public Library, 18 Ogilvie St., Dundas, Ontario L9H 2S2 Canada, founded 1951, editor-in-chief Joanna Lawson. "The Tower Poetry Society was started by a few members of McMaster University faculty to promote interest in poetry. We publish *Tower* twice a year and a few chapbooks. **We want rhymed or free verse, traditional or modern, but not prose chopped into short lines, maximum 35 lines in length, any subject, any comprehensible style."** They have published poetry by Sparling Mills, John Ferns, Kenneth Samberg and Catherine Bankier. The editor selected these sample lines by Tony Cosier:

> *From forging brass he took to forging soul,*
> *gave up plowing soil to plow his skull,*
> *ripped open the eye that never closed again*
> *and took for tongue the howl of the beast in pain.*

Tower is digest-sized, 40 pgs., circulation 150, 60 subscriptions of which 8 are libraries. They receive about 400 unsolicited submissions of poetry/year, use 30, no backlog. Subscription: $6 including postage. **Sample postpaid: $2. Limit submissions to 4 poems. Submit during February or August. "Comment if requested — no charge." Reports in 2 months. Pays 1 copy.** The editor advises, "Read a lot of poetry before you try to write it."

TOWNSHIPS SUN (IV-Rural/ecological, regional), 7 Conley St., P.O. Box 28, Lennoxville, Quebec J1M 1Z3 Canada, phone (819)566-7424, founded 1972, editor Patricia Ball, is a monthly newspaper in English "concerned with **history of townships, English community, agriculture and ecology and using poetry on these themes. Only poems about the area and people of Quebec ever accepted. Others need not submit."** The tabloid has a press run of 2,500 for 2,000 subscribers of which 20 are libraries, and 500 shelf sales. Subscription: $15/year Canada, $20/year outside Canada. **Sample postpaid: $2. Pays $10-30 plus 1 copy. "Will publish poems specifically about townships, townshippers, or of specific interest to townshippers."** Staff reviews books of poetry.

TRADESWOMEN MAGAZINE (IV-Women, themes), P.O. Box 40664, San Francisco CA 94140, founded 1982, poetry editor Sue Doro, editor Janet Scoll Johnson, is a national quarterly **"particular to women in blue collar non-traditional work"** and uses poetry **"pertaining to women in trades, tradeswomen as mothers, family and co-worker relationships."** Subscription: $35. **Sample postpaid: $2. Guidelines available for SASE. They consider simultaneous submissions and previously published poems. Cover letter with short bio — particularly about work history — required. Reports in 1 month.**

No backlog. Open to unsolicited reviews. Poets may also send books for review consideration.

TRANSLUCENT TENDENCY PRESS (III), 3226 Raspberry, Erie PA 16508, founded 1980 as *Northern Pleasure* magazine, publisher Ron Androla, publishes 2-3 chapbooks/year. **They want poetry that is "the reality of the edges. Nothing sanity-influenced."** They have published poetry by Kurt Nimmo, Paul Weinman and Belinda Subraman. As a sample the editor selected these lines (poet unidentified):

> . . . Hello Melville bruised by a bump
> from one angry whale the methadone
> stuffs cotton all around spiritual helplessness
> screaming on the top of a rupturing ocean hello
> ulysses . . .

No previously published poems or simultaneous submissions. Cover letter "with the soul of the poet" required. "Be enlightened or stay away." They want to hear from those "generally attuned to the agony of being a poet during the dissolution of America." **Replies to queries in "weeks." Often comments on rejections. Pays author's copies.** The editor says, "Poetry is a life-long curse. Either it's revolutionary, disturbing or wild, or it's worthless."

TRANSNATIONAL PERSPECTIVES (III), CP161, 1211 Geneva 16 Switzerland, founded 1975, editor René Wadlow, is a "journal of world politics with some emphasis on culture that crosses frontiers." Uses 4-6 poems/issue, usually illustrated by drawing or photo. They want **"poems stressing harmony of nature, human potential, understanding of other cultures — relatively short. No humor, nationalistic themes, nothing 'overly' subjective."** They have published poetry by Verona Bratesch and Janet Pehr. As a sample the editor selected these lines from "1989, A Pivot Year" by Brian Walker:

> This year, all bets are off.
> Unpredictable chances,
> expectations jilted;
> adepts will learn new dances.
> Watch old system hiccough,
> welcome new solutions
> in native phrase unstilted:
> in apt throughts, revolutions.

TP appears 3 times a year; it "is oriented toward making policy suggestions in international organizations, especially in the United Nations." It is 48 pgs., handsomely produced, magazine-sized, saddle-stapled with coated color paper cover. They receive about 100 poems/year, use 16. Press run is 5,000 for 4,000 subscribers of which half are libraries. **Sample back issue free on request. Simultaneous submissions OK. No previously published poems. Editor comments "rarely on quality, only why not for *TP*." Reports in 1 month. Pays 5 copies, more if desired.** René Wadlow says, "Poems in *TP* come from many countries, especially Eastern Europe, Scandinavia and India, often translated into English, usually 'upbeat' since most articles are on political and economic difficulties of the world."

TRESTLE CREEK REVIEW (II), 1000 West Garden, Coeur d'Alene ID 83814, phone (208)769-3300, ext. 384, founded 1982-83, poetry editor Chad Klinger et al, is a "2-year college creative writing program production. Purposes: (1) expand the range of publishing/editing experience for our small band of writers; (2) expose them to editing experience; (3) create another outlet for serious, beginning writers. **We favor poetry strong on image and sound, the West and country vs. city; spare us the romantic, rhymed clichés. We can't publish much if it's long (more than 2 pgs.)."** They have published poetry by Jesse Bier, Lowell Jaeger, Reja-e Busailah, Ray Mizer and Julia Thomas. As a sample Chad Klinger selected these lines by Ron McFarland:

> All around you the furious mines are closing
> like angry fists,
> their galvanized shells rusting too slowly
> to be a tourist attraction.
> Outside town a black bronze miner drills the sky.

TCR is a digest-sized, 57-page annual, professionally printed on heavy buff stock, perfect-bound, matte cover with art, circulation 500, 6 subscriptions of which 4 are libraries. This publication is well-designed and features both free and formal verse by relative newcomers. The editors receive freelance poetry submissions from about 100 persons/year, use 30. **Sample: $4. Submit before March 1 (for May publication), no more than 5 pgs., no simultaneous submissions. Reports by March 30. Pays 2 copies.** The editor advises, "Be neat; be precise; don't romanticize or cry in your beer; strike the surprising, universal note. Know the names of things."

TRIQUARTERLY MAGAZINE (II), 2020 Ridge Ave., Evanston IL 60208, phone (708)491-7614, founded 1964, editors Reginald Gibbons and Susan Hahn, is one of the most respected and visually appealing journals produced in the United States. Editors accept a wide range of verse forms and styles of verse (long poems, sequences, etc.) **with the emphasis solely on excellence,** and some issues are published as books on specific themes. They have published poetry by Tom Sleigh, Albert Goldbarth, Linda McCarriston, Pattiann Rogers and Theodore Weiss. *TriQuarterly's* three issues per year are 6×9, 200+ pgs., flat-spined, professionally printed with b&w photography, graphics, glossy card cover. There are about 40 pgs. of poetry in each issue. They receive about 3,000 freelance submissions of poetry/year, use 20, have about a year backlog. Press run is 4,500 for 2,000 subscribers of which 35% are libraries. Subscription: $18; single copy: $9.95. **Sample postpaid: $4. No simultaneous submissions. Reads submissions October 1 through April 30 only. Sometimes works with poets, inviting rewrites of interesting work. Reports in 10-12 weeks. Payment varies. Acquires first North American serial rights.** "We *suggest* prospective contributors examine sample copy before submitting." Reviews books of poetry "at times." Send books for review consideration. Work appearing in *TriQuarterly* has been included in the **Pushcart Prize** anthology.

TROUT CREEK PRESS; DOG RIVER REVIEW; DOG RIVER REVIEW POETRY SERIES; BACKPOCKET POETS (II), 5976 Billings Rd., Parkdale OR 97041-9610, founded 1981, poetry editor Laurence F. Hawkins, Jr., prefers **"shorter poems (to 30 lines) but will consider longer, book or chapbook consideration. No restrictions on form or content. No pornography or religious verse."** They have published poetry by Judson Crews, Gerald Locklin, Arthur Winfield Knight, Connie Fox, Nathaniel Tarn and Joseph Semenovich. As a sample the editor selected these lines from "Tales and Declarations" by Bruce Holland Rogers:

> *Glass is the voice of fire*
> *Speaking a tongue aphasiacs know*
> *But cannot translate*
> *Like the manifestoes of iron*
> *Known only to dead soldiers*
> *Or like the echo of copper*
> *In the ears of the drowned*

Dog River Review is a semiannual, digest-sized, 60 pgs., saddle-stapled, offset from computer typescript with b&w graphics. They receive about 500 freelance submissions of poetry/year, use 40-50. Press run is 300 for 40 subscribers of which 7 are libraries. Subscription: $7. **Sample postpaid: $2.50. Send SASE for guidelines. Reports in 1 week-3 months. Pays in copies. Acquires first North American serial rights.** *Dog River Review* is open to unsolicited reviews. Poets may also send books for review consideration. Backpocket Poets is a series of 4×5¼ chapbooks, professionally printed, 26 pgs., saddle-stapled with matte card cover, selling for $2.50 each, a drawing or photo of the author on the back. The Dog River Review Poetry Series consists of digest-sized, professionally printed, saddle-stapled chapbooks with matte card covers. **For book publication by Trout Creek Press, query with 4-6 samples. Replies to queries immediately, to submissions in 1-2 months. No simultaneous submissions. Editor sometimes comments on rejections. No payment until "material costs recovered. We also publish individual authors on cassette tape."** Send SASE for catalog to buy samples.

TUCUMCARI LITERARY REVIEW (II), 3108 W. Bellevue Ave., Los Angeles CA 90026, founded 1988, editor Troxey Kemper, assistant editor Neoma Reed, appears every other month. **"Prefer rhyming and established forms, 2-100 lines, but the primary goal is to publish good work. No talking animals. No haiku. The quest here is for poetry that will be just as welcome many years later, as it is now. Preference is for readable, understandable writing of literary and lasting quality."** They have recently published poetry by Kenneth W. Johnson, Elizabeth Dabbs, Ken MacDonnell, Jim Dunlap, Ruth Daniels, Fontaine Falkoff, Frances Smith and Patricia Higginbotham. As a sample the editor selected these lines from "The Release," a sonnet by Daniel Kaderli:

> *I jerked the rod just when the line went taut.*
> *The water swirled. The tail broke through and splashed.*
> *The hefty cat was angry. He was caught.*
> *Mud roiled, and bubbles surfaced as he thrashed.*

The magazine is digest-sized, 48 pgs., saddle-stapled, photocopied from typescript, with card cover. Their press run is 150-200. Subscription: $12, $20 for overseas. **Sample: $2, $4 for overseas. Submit no more than 4 poems at a time. Considers simultaneous submissions and previously published poems. Send SASE for guidelines. Reports within 1 month. Pays 1 copy. Acquires one-time rights.** This magazine is inexpensively produced but contains some good formal poems. If you're looking to place a particular sonnet or villanelle, try Troxey Kemper's magazine. He reports quickly, by the way, and may comment on rejections.

‡TURBULENCE (II), P.O. Box 40, Hockessin DE 19707, founded 1993, editor David Nemeth, aims to publish 4 times a year "to provide an alternative voice (in 40-60 pgs.) to the boring university press magazines or, as they call them, 'journals.' **I want to see poetry that goes along with the magazine's title.**" No previously published poems or simultaneous submissions. Cover letter required. **Send SASE for guidelines. Reports in 1-3 months. Pays 1 copy. Acquires first-time rights.** Reviews books, chapbooks and other mags. The editor says, "I want poets to push themselves to their limit and then some."

TURKEY PRESS (V), 6746 Sueno Rd., Isla Vista CA 93117, founded 1974, poetry editor Harry Reese along with his wife, Sandra Reese, "is involved with publishing contemporary literature, producing traditional and experimental book art, one-of-a-kind commissioned projects and collaborations with various artists and writers. **We do not encourage solicitations of any kind to the press. We seek out and develop projects on our own.**" They have published poetry by Thomas Merton, James Laughlin, Sam Hamill, Edwin Honig, Glenna Luschei, Tom Clark, Michael Hannon, Keith Waldrop, David Ossman, Peter Whigham, Jack Curtis, Kirk Robertson and Anne E. Edge.

TURNSTONE PRESS (II, IV-Regional), 607-100 Arthur St., Winnipeg, Manitoba R3B 1H3 Canada, phone (204)947-1555, founded 1975, is a "literary press publishing quality contemporary fiction, poetry, criticism" in flat-spined books (8/year), having a Canadian emphasis. They want **"writing based on contemporary poetics, but otherwise wide-ranging. Welcome experimental, graphic, long poems, the unusual. Nothing overly concerned with traditional rhyme and meter.**" They have published poetry by Di Brandt, Maara Haas and Kristjana Gunnars. **Submit complete ms with cover letter including bio and other publications. Poems previously published in magazines OK. Reports in 2-3 months. Pays $100-200 advance, 10% royalties and 10 copies.** Editor comments on rejections "if we believe it has promise." Send 9×12 SASE (or, from the US, SAE with IRCs) for catalog to buy samples.

TWISTED (IV-Horror, fantasy), P.O. Box 1249, Palmetto GA 30268-1249, phone (404)463-1458, founded 1985, editor/publisher Christine Hoard, is an annual using poetry of **"horror/dark fantasy; humor OK. Form and style open. Not more than 1 page long.**" They have published poetry by John Grey, Lisa Lepovetsky and Jeffery Lewis. As a sample the editor selected these lines by Jana Hakes:

> As a child takes
> to puddles of mud
> for play,
> I prefer puddles
> of blood
> every day;
> horror that stains
> the mind,
> never washes away.

Christine Hoard describes *Twisted* as "150 pgs., magazine-sized, offset, vellum bristol cover, much art, some ads, 60 lb. matte paper. I receive a lot of poetry submissions, use 30-50 per issue." Press run is 300 for single-copy sales. **Sample postpaid: $6, payable to Christine Hoard. "Don't submit more than four poems at a time. You should see a sample copy to get a 'feel' for what we publish."** No simultaneous submissions, but previously published poems are sometimes accepted. **Send SASE for guidelines. Reports within 3 months.** "We sometimes close when we are preparing next issue or are overstocked." Editor often comments on rejections. **Pays 1 copy.** She says, "Poets of science fiction, horror, fantasy will be pleased to know there are several markets in the small press and some organizations are available to offer support and market information."

2 AM MAGAZINE; 2 AM PUBLICATIONS (IV-Science fiction/fantasy/horror), P.O. Box 6754, Rockford IL 61125-1754, founded 1986, editor Gretta McCombs Anderson, a quarterly that wants **"fantasy, science fiction, heroic fantasy, horror, weird; any form, any style; preferred length is 1-2 pgs. We want poetry that leaves an after-image in the mind of the reader."** They have published poetry by Mark Rich, G.N. Gabbard, Bruce Boston and Leonard Carpenter. The editor describes it as 68 pgs., magazine-sized, offset on 60 lb. stock, cover printed on glossy stock, illustrations "by leading fantasy artists" and ads. Circulation 1,000 with 250 subscriptions. Single copy: $4.95; subscription: $19/year. **Sample postpaid: $5.95. Submit no more than 5 poems at a time.** "Prefer poems no more than 2 pages in length." **Send SASE for guidelines. Reports in 2 months, 6-12 months to publication. Pays 5¢/line or $1 minimum plus 1 copy, 40% discount for more. Buys one-time rights.** Reviews books of poetry in 250 words, single format. Open to unsolicited reviews. Poets may also send books for review consideration, attn. Irwin Chapman. For chapbook consideration (32 pgs., 4×5, saddle-stapled) query with 5 sample poems, bio, aesthetic or poetic aims. **"Poetry must have concrete images and patterned meter, evoke strong sense of mood and express horror, fantasy or science fiction themes." Pays royalties and copies. Negotiates individual contract.** Editor "sometimes" comments on rejections. Gretta M.

Anderson advises, "Read widely, be aware of what's already been done. Short poems stand a good chance with us. Looking for mood-generating poetry of a cosmic nature. Not interested in self-indulgent poetry."

THE TWOPENNY PORRINGER (II), P.O. Box 1456, Tacoma WA 98401, founded 1991, editor Adrian Taylor, is a quarterly containing poetry, art and short stories. They are **"very open to all forms and styles. However, poems which imply affiliation with organized religious groups and poems which are nursery-rhymish will be rejected."** The editor says it is 70-80 pgs., digest-sized, saddle-stitched, with glossy cover using b&w photo or artwork. "45% of material published is poetry, 10% art and photos, 45% short stories." Press run is 2,000 for 300 subscribers. Subscription: $8. **Sample postpaid: $2. No previously published poems; simultaneous submissions OK. "Limited staffing forces indefinite reporting time."** Pays 2 copies of issue in which published and 3 subsequent issues (5 total). The editor says, "We are looking for poems, short stories, b&w photography, and b&w or halftone images of original artwork. It is our wish to print contributions from artists who are new to their fields as well as works from those who have already established themselves. International submissions are encouraged. Non-English submissions are also encouraged, if typed and translated."

TYRO WRITERS' GROUP (I, IV-Membership), 194 Carlbert St., Sault Ste. Marie, Ontario P6A 5E1 Canada, phone (705)253-6402, founded 1984, editor Stan Gordon. Tyro Writers' Group only considers full-length mss for book publication. **Lifetime membership in the group costs $5, and you must be a member to submit. Query first with at least 6 sample poems. Mss should be in standard format. Send SASE for guidelines and further information.**

ULTRAMARINE PUBLISHING CO., INC. (II), Box 303, Hastings-on-Hudson NY 10706, founded 1974, editor C.P. Stephens, who says, "We mostly distribute books for authors who had a title dropped by a major publisher—the author is usually able to purchase copies very cheaply. We use existing copies purchased by the author from the publisher when the title is being dropped." Ultramarine's list includes 250 titles, 90% of them cloth bound, one-third of them science fiction and 10% poetry. **The press pays 10% royalties. "Distributor terms are on a book-by-book basis, but is a rough split." Authors should query before making submissions; queries will be answered in 1 week. Simultaneous submissions OK, but no discs.**

UNDERPASS; UNDERPASS PRESS (II), #574-21, 10405 Jasper Ave., Edmonton, Alberta T5J 3S2 Canada, founded 1986, editors Barry Hammond and Brian Schulze. *Underpass* is a literary annual. The press publishes chapbooks and flat-spined paperbacks of poetry. They want **"contemporary, urban, avant-garde, concrete or discursive prose-poems. Any length. No religious or nature poetry."** They have recently published poetry by Brian Burke, Errol Miller and Sheila E. Murphy. As a sample the editors selected these lines from "Alfred Jarry's Paris" by B.Z. Niditch:

> *from walls groomed with enemies*
> *begging for the sunlight*
> *when a prisoner of your own voice*
> *emerges up to the bedazzled mirror.*

Underpass is digest-sized. Their sixth issue was 80 pgs., but they hope to increase size and continue the flat-spined format. It is offset printed with a laminated card cover using b&w and color graphics inside. "This year we received about two hundred and fifty submissions and only used twenty-six poets." Press run is 100-300. **Sample postpaid: $6.95. No simultaneous submissions or previously published poems. Cover letter required; include one-paragraph bio. Reads submissions January 31 through August 31 only. Editor sometimes comments on rejections. Publication in late fall. Send SASE for guidelines. Pays $5/poem plus 2 copies. All rights remain with authors.**

UNDERWHICH EDITIONS (V), Box 262, Adelaide St. Station, Toronto, Ontario M5C 2J4 Canada, and, in western Canada, 920 9th Ave. N., Saskatoon, Saskatchewan S7K 2Z4 Canada, founded 1978, poetry editors Karl Jirgens, Steven Smith and Paul Dutton are "dedicated to presenting in diverse and appealing physical formats, new works by contemporary creators, **focusing on formal invention and encompassing the expanded frontiers of musical and literary endeavor**" in chapbooks, pamphlets, flat-spined paperbacks, posters, cassettes, records and anthologies. They have published poetry by Victor Coleman, Paula Claire and John Riddell. As a sample the editors selected these lines from "A Knife a Rope a Book" by Mari-Lou Rowley:

> *Prefers the body*
> *raw*
> *feeling*
> *his eye*
> *behind the lens*

They are currently not accepting poetry submissions. "We have all the mss we can handle for the foreseeable future."

UNITED METHODIST REPORTER; NATIONAL CHRISTIAN REPORTER; UNITED METHODIST REVIEW; UNITED METHODIST RECORD (IV-Religious), Box 660275, Dallas TX 75266-0275, phone (214)630-6495, founded "about 1840." *UMR* is a weekly broadsheet newspaper, circulation 500,000+, "aimed at United Methodists primarily, ecumenical slant secondarily." They use at most one poem a week. The poetry "must make a religious point—United Methodist or ecumenical theology; short and concise; concrete imagery; unobtrusive rhyme preferred; literary quality in freshness and imagery; not trite but easy to understand; short enough to fill 1- to 3-inch spaces. Do not want to see poems by 'my 13-year-old niece,' poems dominated by 'I' or rhyme; poems that are too long, too vague or too general; poems without religious slant or point." Managing Editor John A. Lovelace says they use about 50 of 1,000 poems received/year. Poems may appear in all publications. No simultaneous submissions or previously published poems. Send no more than 3-4 poems at a time. Time to publication can be up to a year. Editor comments on rejection. "if it is promising." Send SASE for guidelines. Pays $2/poem and 1 copy.

UNITY; DAILY WORD (IV-Religious), Unity School of Christianity, Unity Village MO 64065, founded 1889. "Unity periodicals are devoted to spreading the truth of practical Christianity, the everyday use of Christ's principles. The material used in them is constructive, friendly, unbiased as regards creed or sect, and positive and inspirational in tone. We suggest that prospective contributors study carefully the various publications before submitting material. Sample copies are sent on request. Complimentary copies are sent to writers on publication. We accept mss only with the understanding that they are original and previously unpublished. Mss should be typewritten in double space. Unity School pays on acceptance 5¢/word and up for prose and $1/line for verse." *Unity Magazine* is a monthly journal that publishes "articles and poems that give a clear message of Truth and provide practical, positive help in meeting human needs for healing, supply and harmony. Only 4 or 5 poems are published each month. We pay a $20 minimum." Buys first North American serial rights. *Daily Word* is a "monthly manual of daily studies" which "buys a limited number of short devotional articles and poems."

UNMUZZLED OX (IV-Themes, bilingual/foreign language), 105 Hudson St., New York NY 10013 or Box 550, Kingston, Ontario K7L 4W5 Canada, founded 1971, poetry editor Michael Andre, is a tabloid literary biannual. Each edition is built around a theme or specific project. The editor says, "The chances of an unsolicited poem being accepted are slight since I always have specific ideas in mind." He is assembling material for issues titled *Poems to the Tune*, "simply poems to old tunes, a buncha contemporary *Beggar's Opera*. The other is tentatively called *The Unmuzzled Ox Book of Erotic Verse*. Only unpublished work will be considered, but works may be in French as well as English." Subscription: $20.

‡UNSILENCED VOICE (I, IV-Political), 9333 N. Lombard #29, Portland OR 97203, founded 1990, editor Clint C. Wilkinson, is a bimonthly of "politically left (anarchist) and experimental art/literature." They want "anarchist poetry of one page or less. Nothing else." They have recently published poetry by Jon Brann. As a sample the editor selected these lines (poet unidentified):

> Single raindrop falls
> from a cloudless blue heaven
> maybe it was spit

UV is 20 pgs., digest-sized, typed, photocopied and saddle-stapled with cover art. They receive about 5 poems/issue, accept 1-2. Press run is 25-30 for 8 subscribers, 15-22 distributed free to coffee shops, etc. Subscription: $11.37 (14 issues). Sample postpaid: $1.50. Previously published poems and simultaneous submissions OK. Often comments on rejections. Send SASE for guidelines. Reports in 1 month. Pays 1 copy. Acquires one-time rights. The editor says, "Don't feel bound by conventional forms. Put your heart into your work and throw it at the world. If it's good, it'll stick."

URBANUS/RAIZIRR; URBANUS PRESS (III), P.O. Box 192561, San Francisco CA 94119, founded 1987, editors Peter Drizhal and Cameron Bamberger, is a twice-yearly journal of fiction and poetry. "Seeks post-modernist, experimental and mainstream poetry—with a social slant. Beginners would be advised to acquire a sample copy, particularly if unfamiliar with any of the poets we've published: Amy Gerstler, Charles Bukowski, Wanda Coleman, Terry Kennedy and Antler." As a sample the editors selected "Selling My Poems on the Street" by William Joyce:

> For the most part my buyers
> bought as quietly as I wrote.
> They smiled, they paid, they left
> with hardly a glance over their

shoulders—the same way I wrote.
It was the noisy ones—the ones
who spouted all sorts of appreciation
but who didn't put money on the table
who are so typical of the people
who fuck up our lives irrevocably.

The digest-sized, 48-64 page, perfect-bound magazine uses approximately 30 of the 1,000+ submissions they receive annually. Press run is 500. Subscription: $8 ($10 institutions). **Sample postpaid: $5. Reports in 2-8 weeks, 6-18 months till publication. Pays 1 copy.**

US1 WORKSHEETS; US1 POETS' COOPERATIVE (II), %Postings, P.O. Box 1, Ringoes NJ 08551-0001, founded 1973, is a literary biannual, 20-25 pgs., 11½×17, circulation 500, which uses **high quality poetry and fiction. Sample: $4. "We use a rotating board of editors; it's wisest to query when we're next reading before submitting. A self-addressed, stamped postcard to the secretary will get our next reading period dates."** Published poets include Alicia Ostriker, Toi Derricotte, Elizabeth Anne Socolow, Jean Hollander, Grace Cavalieri, Geraldine C. Little and David Keller. **"We read a lot but take very few. Prefer complex, well-written work. Requests for sample copies, subscriptions, queries, information about reading periods and all manuscripts should be addressed to the secretary, % POSTINGS (address above)."**

UTAH HOLIDAY MAGAZINE (II, IV-Regional), Suite 200, 807 E. South Temple, Salt Lake City UT 84102, phone (801)532-3737, founded 1971, is a "monthly magazine with a **strong regional focus that publishes poetry as space permits."** *UHM* says that none of our category designations really applies. **The poetry they use is not necessarily regional, and "We are very open to beginners' submissions. We** don't care if somebody has been published elsewhere or not. We will offer criticism and suggestions to writers, and will also consider accepting something after revision, if we are happy with the revision. But **we do not have much space to run poetry, so writers should be advised there is a high likelihood we will either not accept their poems, or that they will have to wait a considerable amount of time before they see them in print. There are no particular specifications except that the poetry be quality work and that it hasn't been published previously. We like poetry with a unique way of looking at experience or the world."** *UHM* is magazine-sized, 85-130 pages. "We look like any other regional magazine. We have b&w as well as 4-color pages and regular slick magazine quality paper." Its press run is 14,000 for 10,000 subscriptions, 4,000 shelf sales. Subscription: $15. **Sample postpaid: $2.50. They have "an extensive backlog." Simultaneous submissions OK. Editor sometimes comments on rejections. Reports "within 3 months." Pays $25-50 "usually,"** plus 2-3 copies. People from other regions are now encouraged to submit poetry.

‡UTAH STATE UNIVERSITY PRESS (V), Logan UT 84322-7800, phone (801)750-1362, founded 1972, editor John R. Alley, publishes poetry but is **not open for submissions.**

VANDELOECHT'S FICTION MAGAZINE (I), P.O. Box 515, Montross VA 22520, founded 1991, editor Mike Vandeloecht, is a quarterly publishing both fiction and poetry. They want **"free verse and traditional, 25 lines maximum. No pornography or vulgarity."** They have published poetry by E.V. Calloway and Hampton Creed. The editor says *VFM* is 8½×11, saddle-stapled. They accept about 10% of the poetry received/year. **Sample postpaid: $3. No previously published poems or simultaneous submissions. Submit no more than 5 poems. Always comments on rejections. Send SASE for guidelines. Reports within 10 days. Pays 1 copy. All rights revert to author upon publication.** The editor says, "My advice to poets? How does one teach a bird to sing? How does one teach a cricket to chirp? But seriously—I think a poet should write for himself, should write about those things that touch him deeply."

THE VANITAS PRESS (I, IV-Specialized, children), Platslagarevägen 4E1, 22730, Lund, Sweden, founded 1978, publisher (Mr.) March Laumer, who says, "The press is the shoestringyest in existence. We publish to an extremely enthusiastic but equally extremely tiny market. **No royalties can be paid, as we distribute volumes at rock-bottom cost of production/mailing (even then subscribers must pay circa $15 a volume; we just can't ask for more to cover royalties). But it is your chance to reach an audience of up to 2,000 readers. Currently we issue only 'latter-day novels' of the 'Oz' saga.** Please

---

The Subject Index, located before the General Index, can help you narrow down markets for your work. It lists those publishers whose poetry interests are specialized.

read the Oz books in your local public library, then send us short stories, outlines for novels, and/or Oz-oriented art; you're virtually certain to be published if material is promising at all." As a sample he selected these lines from **Charmed Gardens of Oz:**

> *Well said, indeed,*
> *And when you feed*
> *On things that bleed*
> *I hope you'll heed*
> *What Dot's decreed:*
> *It's only when you talk of flesh that's edible*
> *That you can mention 'meat' and still be credible!*

VEGETARIAN JOURNAL; THE VEGETARIAN RESOURCE GROUP (IV-Themes, children/teens), P.O. Box 1463, Baltimore MD 21203, founded 1982. *VJ* is a bimonthly. The Vegetarian Resource Group is a small press publisher of nonfiction, sometimes incorporating poetry. *VJ* is 36 pgs:, 8½×11, saddle-stapled and professionally printed with glossy card cover. Circulation is 20,000. **Sample: $3.** The Vegetarian Resource Group offers an annual contest for ages 18 and under, $50 savings bond in 3 age categories for the best contribution on any aspect of vegetarianism. "Most entries are essay, but we would accept poetry with enthusiasm." Deadline: May 1 postmark. Send SASE for details.

VEHICULE PRESS; SIGNAL EDITIONS (IV-Regional), Box 125 Station Place du Parc, Montreal, Quebec H2W 2M9 Canada, phone (514)844-6073, fax (514)844-7543, poetry editor Michael Harris, publisher Simon Dardick, is a "literary press with poetry series, Signal Editions, **publishing the work of Canadian poets only.**" They publish flat-spined paperbacks and hardbacks. Among the poets published are Erin Mouré, Don Coles, David Solway, Susan Glickman and Stephen Scobie. As a sample they selected these lines by Gérald Godin:

> *"What, you've forgotten my telephone number?"*
> *"Listen, old friend, I think you know*
> *they removed a tumour from my brain*
> *as big as a mandarine orange*
> *and I'm afraid*
> *your telephone number was in it . . . "*

They want Canadian poetry which is **"first-rate, original, content-conscious."** Query with 10 poems **("a good proportion of which should already have been published in recognized literary periodicals"),** bio, publication credits or poetic aims. Reports in 2 months. Pays 10% royalties plus 10 author's copies. Buys English-language world rights.

VERANDAH (II), c/o TAS, Deakin University, Toorak Campus, 336 Glenterrie Rd., Malvern Victoria, Australia 3144, founded 1986, is a handsome annual. **"We seek poetry of a high quality and literary kind, with no restrictions on length, subject or style."** They have published poetry by Lisa Dionofrio, Peter Bakowski, Adrian D'Ambra and Javant Biarujia. As a sample, a haiku by Duncan Richardson:

> *Along the cream*
> *beach they came four pelicans*
> *playing soft biplanes.*

It is flat-spined with full-color glossy card cover, professionally printed on glossy stock, 90+ pgs. **Sample postpaid: A$10.50. Annual deadline: May 31. Authors' names are deleted from mss before consideration by editors. Pays A$5-10/poem plus 2 copies. Buys first Australian publishing rights.**

VERSE (III), English Dept., College of William and Mary, P.O. Box 8795, Williamsburg VA 23187-8795, founded 1984, editors Henry Hart, Robert Crawford and David Kinloch, is a "poetry journal which also publishes interviews with poets, articles about poetry and book reviews." They want **"no specific kind; we only look for high quality poetry."** They have published poetry by A.R. Ammons, James Merrill, James Dickey, Galway Kinnell, Richard Kenney, John Hollander, Charles Wright, Robert Pinsky, Charles Simic and Wendell Berry. *Verse* is published 3 times a year. It is digest-sized, 90 pgs., saddle-stapled with card cover, using small type, professionally printed. They accept about 100 of 3,000 poems received. Press run is 700 for 600 subscribers of which 150 are libraries, 100 shelf sales. Subscription: $15 for individuals, $21 for institutions. **Sample postpaid: $5. Simultaneous submissions OK. Reports in 2 months, usually 4-5 months to publication. Pays 2 copies.** Open to unsolicited reviews. Poets may also send books for review consideration. Poetry published in this journal has appeared in **Best American Poetry 1992.** In addition, *Verse* itself ranked #7 in the "Open Markets" category of the June 1993 *Writer's Digest* Poetry 60 list. This category ranks those publications most open to both free and formal verse.

VERVE (II, IV-Themes), P.O. Box 3205, Simi Valley CA 93093, founded 1989, editor Ron Reichick, associate editors Mona M. Locke and Marilyn Hochheiser, is a quarterly **"open to contemporary poetry of any form which fits the theme of the issue; we look for fresh metaphor, unique ideas and language and imagery that informs."** They have recently published poetry by Marge Piercy, Michael Blake, Denise Levertov, Alberto Rios and Quincy Troupe. As a sample the editor selected these lines from "Imaging Cambodia" by David Oliveira:

> all with faces saved in family albums
> yet to be torn into pieces, thrown to the wind
> over bones whitening into brick
> for the new temples of Angkor;
> all with expectations
> yet to be peeled from those faces,
> abandoned in paddies to rot with their flesh
> into rice for the new order.
> You call it, "the sadness in my country," . . .

Verve is digest-sized, 40 pgs., saddle-stitched, using bios of each contributor. Press run is 700 for 100 subscribers of which 3 are libraries. Sample postpaid: **$3.50. Submit up to 5 poems, 2 pages maximum/poem; "36 lines or less has best chance." Simultaneous submissions, if noted, OK. Send SASE for guidelines and list of upcoming themes. Pays 1 copy. Acquires first rights.** Staff reviews books of poetry in 250 words, single format. Send books for review consideration. They sponsor 3 annual contests, each having prizes of $100, $50 and $25. Entry fee: $2 each poem. The editor advises, "Read a copy of *Verve* before you submit. Read good contemporary poetry — then write. Listen to criticism, but follow your instinct *and* the poem. *Then* — keep submitting."

‡VIET NAM GENERATION; BURNING CITIES PRESS (II, IV-Themes), 2921 Terrace Dr., Chevy Chase MD 20815, phone (301)608-0622, founded 1988, editor Kali Tal, is a quarterly that publishes "the best current fiction, poetry and nonfiction dealing with the Viet Nam War generation." **Poetry should deal with issues of interest to the Viet Nam War generation. "No POW/MIA poems, unless written by POWs. No racist or sexist poetry."** They have recently published poetry by W.D. Ehrhart, Maggie Jaffe, Gerald McCarthy and Jon Forrest Glade. As a sample the editor selected "Ralphie" by Leroy Quintana:

> Ralphie was signed up at seventeen
> by a fast-talking sergeant.
> Instead of the world got Georgia,
> "Airborne" tattooed on his scrawny biceps,
> the clap, and caught breaking into footlockers,
> another discharge, dishonorable.

The editor says it is 120-220 pgs., 8½ × 11, perfect-bound, with photos and graphics, no ads. They receive 200-300 submissions a year, accept about 40. Press run is 1,000 for 400 subscribers of which 200 are libraries. Subscription: $40. **Sample postpaid: $10 for single issues, $20 for double. Previously published poems OK; no simultaneous submissions. Often comments on rejections. Reports within 6-8 weeks. Pays 2 copies. Acquires "reprint rights for our own publications."** The Burning Cities Poetry Series publishes 4 paperbacks and 4 chapbooks/year. **Query first with sample poems and a cover letter with brief bio and publication credits. Replies to queries and submitted mss in 6-8 weeks. Pays 10% of press run. Sample book or chapbook: $10.**

VIKING PENGUIN, 375 Hudson St., New York NY 10014. Prefers not to share information.

THE VILLAGE IDIOT (II); MOTHER OF ASHES PRESS (V), P.O. Box 66, Harrison ID 83833-0066, *The Village Idiot* founded 1970, Mother of Ashes Press founded 1980, editor Joe M. Singer. They want **"poetry which breathes."** They have published poetry by Cynthia Hendershot and Georgia Axtell. *The Village Idiot* appears triannually in a 5½ × 8¾ format, saddle-stapled, 48 pgs., with cover. They receive about 500 poems/year, use less than 10%. Press run is 350 for 25 subscribers of which 4 are libraries. Subscription: $15 for 6 issues. **Sample postpaid: $3. "Previously published material and simultaneous submissions are not really appreciated." Editor sometimes comments on rejections. Send SASE for guidelines. Reports in 1 month. Pays copies. Acquires one-time rights.** Reviews books of poetry. Open to unsolicited reviews. Mother of Ashes Press **publishes books and chapbooks by invitation only.** The editor says, "We now **prefer poems to be submitted singly.** Poems used are set, as near as is humanly possible, as they appear in manuscript — this press does not proofread nor correct poetry manuscripts."

THE VILLAGER (II), Dept. PM, 135 Midland Ave., Bronxville NY 10708, phone (914)337-3252, founded 1928, editor Amy Murphy, poetry editor M. Josephine Colville, a publication of the Bronxville Women's Club for club members and families, professional people and advertisers, circulation 750, in 9 monthly issues, October through June. **Sample postpaid: $1.25. They use one page or more of poetry/**

issue, prefer poems less than 20 lines, "in good taste only," seasonal (Thanksgiving, Christmas, Easter) 3 months in advance. SASE required. Pays 2 copies. They copyright material but will release it to author on request.

THE VINCENT BROTHERS REVIEW (II, IV-Themes), 4566 Northern Circle, Mad River Township, Dayton OH 45424-5789, founded 1988, editor Kimberly A. Willardson, is a journal appearing 3 times a year. "We look for well-crafted, thoughtful poems that shoot bolts of electricity into the reader's mind, stimulating a powerful response. We also welcome light verse and are thrilled by unusual, innovative themes/styles. We do not accept previously published poems, simultaneous submissions or any type of bigoted propaganda. Sloppy mss containing typos and/or unintentional misspellings are automatically rejected. *TVBR* publishes 2 theme issues/year—poets should send us a SASE to receive details about our upcoming themes." They have recently published poetry by Diane Engle, Matthew J. Spireng and L.E. McCullough. As a sample the editor selected these lines from "Ménage à Trois (Plus One)" by Glenn Sheldon:

> And each of us awaits Allegheny
> spring, the thawing of pouches
> of the dried herbs hung delicately
> here, around us, in a claustrophobic
> corner of heaven's root cellar.

TVBR is digest-sized, 60-80 pgs., saddle-stapled, professionally printed, with matte card cover. Press run is 350. "We have 100 subscribers, 10 of which are libraries." Subscription: $12. **Sample postpaid: $4.50. Submit no more than 6 poems at a time, name and address on each page. Cover letter preferred; include recent publication credits and note "where author read or heard about *TVBR*. We do not read in December." Editor "often" comments on rejections. Send SASE for guidelines. Reports in 6-8 months (after readings by editor and 3 associate editors). Pays 2 copies. Acquires one-time rights.** Reviews books of poetry in 3,500 words maximum, single or multi-book format. Open to unsolicited reviews. Poets may also send books for review consideration. *The Vincent Brothers Review* ranked #9 in the "Traditional Verse" category of the June 1993 *Writer's Digest* Poetry 60 list. The editor advises, "*Don't* send your poetry to a magazine you haven't read. Subscribe to the little magazines you respect—they contain the work of your peers and competitors. Proofread your poetry carefully and read it aloud before sending it out."

VIRGIN MEAT (IV-Horror), 2325 West Ave. K-15, Lancaster CA 93536, phone (805)722-1758, founded 1986, editor Steve Blum, appears irregularly with fiction, poetry and art. "Fiction is non-violent horror. Subjects range from vampires and ghosts to magic and the occult. **Poetry: Similar subjects, short, emotionally dark and depressing. No rhyming poetry.**" The editor describes it as digest-sized. Press run is 300. **Sample postpaid: $2 or $7/4 issues. Send no less than 4 poems at a time. Simultaneous submissions and previously published poems OK. Reports in one week. Pays 1 copy for each poem printed.** Reviews books of poetry "only if it has a cover price."

THE VIRGINIA QUARTERLY REVIEW (III), 1 West Range, Charlottesville VA 22903, founded 1925, is one of the oldest and most distinguished literary journals in the country. **It uses about 15 pgs. of poetry in each issue, no length or subject restrictions.** Recent issues largely include lyric and narrative free verse, most of which features a strong message or powerful voice. The review is digest-sized, 220+ pgs., flat-spined, circulation 4,000. **Pays $1/line.**

VIRTUE: THE CHRISTIAN MAGAZINE FOR WOMEN (IV-Religious), P.O. Box 850, Sisters OR 97759-0850, founded 1978, editor Marlee Alex, is a slick magazine, appearing 6 times a year, which "encourages and integrates biblical truth with daily living." As for poetry, they look for "rhythmic control and metric effects, whether free or patterned stanzas; use of simile and metaphor; sensory perceptions, aptly recorded; and implicit rather than explicit spiritual tone." As a sample the editor selected these lines from "Bending" by Barbara Seaman:

> Down on my knees again, Lord
> and undignified as ever,
> (how to mop mud with grace?)
> attempting to confine the exuberance
> of yesterday's rain to the kitchen only . . .

Virtue is magazine-sized, 80 pgs., saddle-stapled, with full-color pages inside as well as on its paper cover. Press run is 150,000. Single copy: $2.95; subscription: $16.95. **Sample postpaid: $3. Submit "no more than 3 poems, each on separate sheet, typewritten; notify if simultaneous submission."** Send SASE for guidelines. Reports in 6-8 weeks, time to publication 3-9 months. **Pays $20-40/poem and 1 copy. Buys first rights.**

VIVO (II), 1195 Green St., San Francisco CA 94109, phone (415)885-5695, founded 1991, editor/publisher Carolyn Miller, is "an eclectic magazine of poetry, fiction, essays and art that combines humor and serious work," appearing once or twice a year. "We are open to almost any kind of poetry except the extremes of traditional and experimental work. We like poems that are fresh and alive and that show a love of language. We are interested in both unpublished and published poets." They do not want to see "poems that don't care about either depth of meaning or love of craft." As a sample the editor selected these lines from "Granite Under Water" by Jeanne Lohmann:

> *These places we live, we return to,*
> *the flowers, the durable river. I am crying*
> *for air I cannot breathe. It is luminous,*
> *this country where your death is granite*
> *under water, a single yellow iris*
> *standing clear from edges of stone.*

VIVO is 16 pgs., 11×17, printed web offset and unbound, with 2-color cover and centerfold, graphics and ads. You want to be seen in a cafe reading this artsy tabloid. Poetry competes with fiction and prose, but it gets the center spread and is eclectic, featuring all styles. Press run is 1,400 for 100 subscribers, 450 shelf sales. Single copy: $3; subscription: $8 for 2 issues. **Sample postpaid: $4. Previously published poems and simultaneous submissions OK, but not preferred.** Time between acceptance and publication is 12-18 months. **Seldom comments on rejections. Send SASE for guidelines. Reports in 6 weeks to 3 months. Pays 2 copies. Rights revert to author on publication.** Reviews books of poetry. Open to unsolicited reviews. Poets may also send books for review consideration. Carolyn Miller says, "The true goal is to live a creative life, to respond to the world as a poet. If you do this honestly and faithfully, and want your poems to have a larger life, keep sending them out, for their sake, not your own."

VOICES INTERNATIONAL (II), 1115 Gillette Dr., Little Rock AR 72207, editor Clovita Rice, is a quarterly poetry journal. "We look for poetry with a new focus, memorable detail and phrasing, and significant and haunting statement climax, all of which impel the reader to reread the poem and return to it for future pleasure and reference." As a sample the editor selected these lines from "The Crack Lines" by Marian W. Hurst:

> *I dreamt you sent me roses.*
> *Three apricot-colored roses*
> *In a blue vase.*
>
> *On the kitchen table I found*
> *Three withered, moldy apricots*
> *In a delft bowl . . .*

It is 32-40 pgs., 6×9, saddle-stapled, professionally printed with b&w matte card cover. Subscription: $10/year. **Sample postpaid (always a back issue): $2. Prefers free verse but accepts high quality traditional. Limit submissions to batches of 5, double-spaced, 3-40 lines (will consider longer if good). Cover letter preferred; include personal data. Publishes an average of 18 months after acceptance. Send SASE for guidelines. Pays copies.** The editor says, "Too many poets submit poetry without studying a copy to become familiar with what we are publishing. Our guidelines help poets polish their poems before submission."

VOICES ISRAEL (I, IV-Anthology); REUBEN ROSE POETRY COMPETITION (I); MONTHLY POET'S VOICE (IV-Members), P.O. Box 5780, 46157 Herzlia Israel, founded 1972, *Voices Israel* editor Mark L. Levinson, with an editorial board of 7, is an annual anthology of poetry in English coming from all over the world. **You have to buy a copy to see your work in print. Submit all kinds of poetry (up to 4 poems), each no longer than a sheet of typing paper.** They have published poetry by Yehuda Amichai, Eugene Dubnov, Alan Sillitoe and Gad Yaacobi. As a sample the editor selected these lines by Seymour Freedman:

> *This is a poem for all the silent poets,*
> *those who live in silence,*
> *and whose silence is eternal,*
> *For all those whose only poetry*
> *is the poem they have lived with their own lives.*

The annual *Voices Israel* is $6\frac{1}{4} \times 8$, offset from laser output on ordinary paper, approximately 121 pgs., flat-spined with varying cover. Circulation 350. Subscription: $13.50. **Sample back copy postpaid: $10; airmail extra. Contributor's copy: $13.50 airmail. Cover letter with brief biographical details required with submissions. Deadline end of February each year; reports in fall. Acquires first publication rights.** Sponsors the annual Reuben Rose Poetry Competition. Send poems of up to 40 lines each, plus $2/poem to P.O. Box 236, Kiriat Ata, Israel. Poet's name and address should be on a separate sheet with titles of poems. *The Monthly Poet's Voice*, a broadside edited by Ezra Ben-Meir, **is sent only to members of the Voices Group of Poets in English.** The *Voices Israel* editor advises, "Never let the reader guess what your next two or three words will be."

W.I.M. PUBLICATIONS (WOMAN IN THE MOON) (IV-Gay/lesbian, women/feminism), Dept. PM, Box 137, 2215-R Market St., San Francisco CA 94114, phone (408)253-3329, founded 1979, poetry editor SDiane Bogus, who says, "We are a small press with trade press ambitions. We publish poetry, business and writing reference books. We generally run 250-1,000 per press run and give the author half or a percentage of the books. We pay royalties to our established authors. We prefer a query and a modest track record." She wants poetry by "gay, black, women, prison poets, enlightened others—contemporary narrative or lyric work, free verse OK, but not too experimental for cognition. We prefer poems to be a page or less if not part of long narrative. No obviously self-indulgent exercises in the psychology of the poet. No sexual abuse themes. No gross sexual references. No hate poems." Send 2 first class stamps for guidelines/catalog. In addition to her own work, she has published poetry by Adele Sebastian. As a sample she selected these lines from "His Life" from **The Book of Lives** by Sherrylynn Posey:

> *I had 4 maybe 5 lovers*
> *in my life*
> *one of them*
> *lied to me*

SDiane Bogus publishes 2-4 chapbooks and flat-spined paperbacks a year each averaging 40-100 pages. **Submit 6 sample poems. Include cover letter with statement of "vision and poetics, theme selection of the work, poetic mentors, track record and $5 reading fee. New poets must take poetry test ($10 plus free critique). Submit between April 1 and June 30 each year. We** acknowledge submissions upon receipt. We report at end of reading season, July through September 7. Simultaneous submissions and previously published poems OK. Authors are asked to assist in promo and sales by providing list of prospective readers and promotional photos. To established authors we pay 5-10% royalties after costs; others half press run in copies. We may take advanced orders; no subsidy. We will accept subscriptions for a book in production at retail price. We fill orders author has provided and others our promo has prompted." They sponsor 2 poetry contests/year: The Woman in the Moon Poetry Prize (September 1 through November 17) and Pat Parker Memorial Poetry Award (March 1 through May 31). Write for guidelines. W.I.M. also offers a self-publishing and consultation criticism service for a fee. Bogus says, "W.I.M. promotes readings for its poets and encourages each poet who submits with a personal letter which discusses her or his strengths and weaknesses. Often we allow repeat submissions."

WAKE FOREST UNIVERSITY PRESS (IV-Bilingual/foreign language, ethnic/nationality), P.O. Box 7333, Winston-Salem NC 27109, phone (919)759-5448, founded 1976, director and poetry editor Dillon Johnston. **"We publish only poetry from Ireland and bilingual editions of French poetry in translation. I am able to consider only poetry written by Irish poets or translations of contemporary French poetry. I must return, unread, poetry from American poets."** They have published poetry by John Montague, Derek Mahon, Richard Murphy, Michael Longley, Paul Muldoon, Thomas Kinsella and Eilean N. Chuilleanain. **Query with 4-5 samples and cover letter. No simultaneous submissions. Replies to queries in 1-2 weeks, to submissions (if invited) in 2-3 months. Publishes on 10% royalty contract with $500 advance, 6-8 author's copies. Buys North American or US rights.** They say, "Because our press is so circumscribed, we get few direct submissions from Ireland. Our main problem, however, is receiving submissions from American poets, whom we do not publish because of our very limited focus here. I would advise American poets to read your publication carefully so that they do not misdirect to presses such as ours work that they, and I, value."

WARTHOG PRESS (II), 29 S. Valley Rd., West Orange NJ 07052, phone (201)731-9269, founded 1979, poetry editor Patricia Fillingham, publishes books of poetry **"that are understandable, poetic."** They have published poetry by Barbara A. Holland, Penny Harter and Marta Fenyves. **Query with 5 samples, cover letter "saying what the author is looking for" and SASE. Simultaneous submissions OK. Ms should be "readable."** Comments on rejections, "if asked for. People really don't want criticism." Pays copies, but "I would like to get my costs back." Patricia Fillingham feels, "The best way to sell poetry still seems to be from poet to listener."

WASHINGTON REVIEW; FRIENDS OF THE WASHINGTON REVIEW OF THE ARTS, INC. (II), P.O. Box 50132, Washington DC 20091, phone (202)638-0515, founded 1974, literary editor Joe Ross, is a bimonthly journal of arts and literature published by the Friends of the Washington Review of the Arts, Inc., a nonprofit, tax-exempt educational organization. *WR* is tabloid-sized, using 2 of the large pgs. per issue for poetry, saddle-stapled on high-quality newsprint, circulation 2,000 with 700 subscriptions of which 10 are libraries. **They publish local Washington metropolitan area poets as well as poets**

from across the US and abroad. "We have eclectic tastes but lean with more favor toward experimental work." Sample postpaid: $2.50. Cover letter with brief bio required with submissions. Pays 5 copies. Reviews books of poetry in 1,000-1,500 words, single format—multi-book "on occasion." Open to unsolicited reviews. Poets may also send books for review consideration.

WASHINGTON WRITERS' PUBLISHING HOUSE (IV-Regional), P.O. Box 15271, Washington DC 20003, phone (202)543-1905, founded 1975. An editorial board is elected annually from the collective. "We are a poetry publishing collective that publishes outstanding poetry collections in flat-spined paperbacks by **individual authors living in the greater Washington, DC area (60-mile radius, excluding Baltimore) on the basis of competitions held once a year.**" They have recently published poetry by Myra Sklarew, Ann Darr, Barbara Lefcowitz, Maxine Clair, Ann Knox, Nan Fry and Naomi Thiers. The editors chose this sample from "The Kidnapping of Science" in **From the Red Eye of Jupiter** by Patricia Garfinkel:

> Conception had been a quiet event, not
> the harsh strike of steel to flint,
> but an easing into fertile corners,
> patient as bacteria for the right conditions.

Submit 50-60 pgs. with SASE only between July 1 and September 30. $5 reading fee. Pays copies. Poets become working members of the collective. "Interested poets may write for a brochure of published poets and sheet of guidelines."

WATER MARK PRESS (V), 138 Duane St., New York NY 10013, founded 1978, editor Coco Gordon, proposes "to publish regardless of form in archival editions with handmade paper and hand done elements in sewn, bound books, broadsides, chapbooks and artworks. **I use only avant-garde material.**" Currently they accept no unsolicited poetry. They have published poetry by Barbara Roux and Alison Knowles. The editor selected this sample from "After Eden" by Michael Blumenthal:

> Once again the invasion of purpose
> into gesture: the stem towards the vase,
> the hands towards the dreaded morning music
> of predictability, Indian paintbrush fades

That's from a collection of his poetry, **Sympathetic Magic,** published by Water Mark in 1980, 96 pgs., flat-spined, with art by Theo Fried, printed on archival, matte card cover with colored art, $9. The Water Mark Book Awards are dormant now. Note: **Please do not confuse Water Mark Press with the imprint Watermark Press, used by other businesses.**

WATERWAYS: POETRY IN THE MAINSTREAM; TEN PENNY PLAYERS; BARD PRESS (I, IV-Themes, children/teen/young adult, anthologies), 393 St. Paul's Ave., Staten Island NY 10304, founded 1977, poetry editors Barbara Fisher and Richard Spiegel, "publishes **poetry by adult, child and young adult poets in a magazine that is published 11 times a year. We do theme issues** and are trying to increase an audience for poetry and the printed and performed word. The project produces performance readings in public spaces and is in residence year round at our local library with workshops and readings. We publish the magazine, *Waterways*; anthologies and chapbooks. **We are not fond of haiku or rhyming poetry; never use material of an explicit sexual nature.** We are open to reading material from people we have never published, writing in traditional and experimental poetry forms. While we do 'themes,' sometimes an idea for a future magazine is inspired by a submission so we try to remain open to poets' inspirations. Poets should be guided however by the fact that we are children's and animal rights advocates and are a NYC press." They have published poetry by Albert Huffstickler, Arthur Knight and Kit Knight. As a sample, the editors chose these lines by Ida Fasel:

> I try to find a word
> for the sound this inland water makes
> tirelessly washing up on shore,
> rippling on and on in the mild breeze
> in the restless serenity
> of light shadowing itself
> in valleys of cobalt blue.

Waterways is published in a 40-page, 4¼×7 format, saddle-stapled, photocopied from various type styles, using b&w drawings, matte card cover, circulation 150 with 58 subscriptions of which 12 are libraries. Subscription: $20. **Sample postpaid: $2.60. They use 60% of freelance poems submitted. Submit less than 10 poems for first submission. Simultaneous submissions OK. Send SASE for guidelines for approaching themes.** "Since we've taken the time to be very specific in our response, writers should take seriously our comments and not waste their emotional energy and our time sending material that isn't within our area of interest. Sending for our theme sheet and for a sample issue and then objectively thinking about the writer's own work is practical and wise. Without meaning to sound 'precious' or unfriendly, the writer should understand that small press publishers doing limited editions and all production work in house are working from their personal artistic vision and know exactly what notes will harmonize, effectively counterpoint and meld. Many excellent poems are sent back to the writers by *Waterways* because they don't relate to what we are trying to create in a given month or months. Some poets get printed regularly in *Waterways*; others will probably never be published by us, not because the poet doesn't write well (although that too is sometimes the case) but only because we are artists with opinions and we exercise them in building each issue. Manuscripts that arrive without a return envelope are not sent back." **Reports in less than a month. Pays 1 copy. Acquires one-time publication rights. Editors sometimes comment on rejections.** They hold contests for children only. **Chapbooks published by Ten Penny Players are "by children and young adults only — and not by submission; they come through our workshops in the library and schools. Adult poets are published by us through our Bard Press imprint, by invitation only. Books evolve from the relationship we develop with writers who we publish in *Waterways* and whom we would like to give more exposure.**" The editors advise, "We suggest that poets attend book fairs. It's a fast way to find out what we are all publishing."

WAYNE LITERARY REVIEW (I, II), Dept. of English, Wayne State University, 51 W. Warren, Detroit MI 48202, faculty advisor M.L. Liebler. Appears twice a year using **any kind of poetry except that using footnotes.** They have published poetry by Ken Mikolowski, Bob Hershon, Adam Cornford, Antler, Faye Kicknosway, Ed Sanders, and many up-and-coming student writers from across the country. It is 5½×8, perfect-bound and distributed free. **Samples are free. Submit 3-5 poems, nothing handwritten. Simultaneous submissions and previously published poems OK. "We only read from August through November — no summer reading." Reports in up to 5 months. Pays 1 copy and "eternal gratitude."**

WEBSTER REVIEW (II, IV-Translations), Webster University, 470 E. Lockwood, Webster Groves MO 63119, founded 1974, poetry editors Robert Boyd and Greg Marshall, is a literary annual. They want **"no beginners. We are especially interested in translations of foreign contemporary poetry."** They have recently published poetry by Georgi Belev, Antony Oldknow, Bruce Bond, Jane Schapiro and Ernest Kroll. As a sample the editor selected these lines from "That Day I Died" by James Finnegan:

> *This is my story of how I died and didn't.*
> *My body paralyzed suddenly*
> *while swimming in the Black River,*
> *you can find it on any map of Missouri,*
> *I sank on my back to the riverbed. Eyes open*
> *awash with all of the world above and around me, . . .*

Webster Review is 128 pgs., digest-sized, flat-spined, professionally printed with glossy card cover. They receive about 1,500 poems/year, use 90. Press run is 1,000 with 500 subscribers of which 200 are libraries. Single copy/subscription: $5. **Sample free for SASE. Editors comment on rejections "if time permits." Reports "within a month, usually." Contributors receive 2 copies.**

WELTER (I, II), Dept. PM, English and Communications Design Dept., University of Baltimore, 1420 N. Charles St., Baltimore MD 21201, founded 1963, is a literary annual **"extremely interested in beginners and lesser known writers. Let us know if you're a student."** It is flat-spined, digest-sized. Press run 500. **Sample postpaid: $2. Submit 3-5 poems no more than 30 lines each. Reads submissions September through January only; makes decisions in February through March. Send SASE for guidelines. Pays 2 copies. Acquires first-time rights.**

THE WESLEYAN ADVOCATE (IV-Religious), P.O. Box 50434, Indianapolis IN 46250-0434, founded 1843, is a monthly magazine using **"short religious poetry only; no long free verse or secular."** The editor describes it as 36 pgs., magazine-sized, offset, saddle-stapled, with 4-color cover. They use 10-15% of 100-200 poems received/year. Press run is 20,000 with "some" subscriptions of which 50 are libraries, no shelf sales (so it must be distributed free). Subscription: $12.50. **Sample: $2. Reports in 2 weeks. Pays $5-10 plus 4 copies on request. Buys first and/or one-time rights.**

WESLEYAN UNIVERSITY PRESS (III), 110 Mt. Vernon, Middletown CT 06459, founded 1957, editor Terry Cochran, is one of the major publishers of poetry in the nation. They publish 4-6 titles/year. They have published poetry by James Dickey, Joy Harjo, James Tate and Yusef Komunyakaa. **Send query and SASE. Considers simultaneous submissions. Responds to queries in 6-8 weeks, to mss in 2-4 months. Send SASE for guidelines. Pays royalties plus 10 copies.** Poetry publications from Wesleyan tend to get widely (and respectfully) reviewed.

WEST ANGLIA PUBLICATIONS (III), P.O. Box 2683, La Jolla CA 92038, phone (619)453-0706, founded 1982 by editor Helynn Hoffa, is a publishing company that **assumes the cost of putting out a book and pays author in royalties or in books. Author retains rights.** They have published poetry by Wilma

Lusk, John Theobald and Gary Morgan, among others. As a sample the editor chose lines from "Approach of Winter" in Kathleen Iddings' **Selected & New Poems, 1980-1990:**

> *We sit on the ancient porch swing, an eighty*
> *year old father and an aging daughter.*
> *I've never noticed how fast October's wind*
> *could strip an elm; leaves wing by like mallards*
> *heading south. I study the ancient barn,*
> *your escape that held a workshop, tractors, herds—*
> *and wonder when the snows will bring it down.*

To query send 6 pages of your work, a cover letter, bio and SASE.

WEST BRANCH (II), English Dept., Bucknell Hall, Bucknell University, Lewisburg PA 17837, founded 1977, is a literary biannual, using **quality poetry.** Free verse is the dominant form—lyric, narrative and dramatic—occasionally longer than one page, much of it accessible with the emphasis on voice and/ or powerful content. They have published poetry by D. Nurkse, Deborah Burnham, Jim Daniels, Anneliese Wagner, Betsy Sholl, David Citino, Barbara Crooker and David Brooks. It is 100-120 pgs., digest-sized, circulation 500. One-year subscription: $7. Two years (4 issues): $11. **Sample: $3. "We do not consider simultaneous submissions. Each poem is judged on its own merits, regardless of subject or form. We strive to publish the best work being written today." Reports in 6-8 weeks. Pays copies and subscription to the magazine. Acquires first rights.** Reviews books and chapbooks of poetry but only those by writers who have been published in *West Branch*.

WEST OF BOSTON (II), Box 2, Cochituate Station, Wayland MA 01778, phone (508)653-7241, founded 1983, poetry editor Norman Andrew Kirk, wants to see **"poetry of power, compassion, originality and wit—and talent, too." For book or chapbook submission, query with 5-10 sample poems, credits and bio. Simultaneous submissions and previously published poems OK. Editor "sometimes" comments on rejected mss. Pays 10% of press run.**

WEST WIND REVIEW (II, IV-Anthology), English Department, Southern Oregon State College, Ashland OR 97520, phone (503)552-6181, founded 1982, is an annual **"looking for sensitive but strong verse that celebrates all aspects of men's and women's experiences, both exalted and tragic. We are looking to print material that reflects ethnic and social diversity."** As a sample the editor selected these lines by Deanne Bayer:

> *to ethereality in the fire,*
> *solidifying again as our breaths*
> *bumped our words*
> *against ice-gilded walls, sharing*
> *our home with a roisterous wind*

WWR is handsomely printed, flat-spined, 140-160 pgs., digest-sized, appearing each spring. They receive about 600-700 submissions each year, publish 40-50 poems and 20-30 short stories. Press run is 500. **Sample "at current year's price. We take submissions—limit of 5 poems not exceeding 50 lines—year-round. Manuscripts should have poet's name and address on each page."** They will consider simultaneous submissions but not previously published poems. **Cover letter required; include brief bio and publication credits. Deadline: January 1 for publication in late May or early June. Send SASE for guidelines. Reports in 2-3 months after deadline. Pays 1 copy.** Offers awards for each category.

WESTERLY; PATRICIA HACKETT PRIZE (II), Centre for Studies in Australian Literature, University of Western Australia, Nedlands 6009, Australia, phone (09) 380-2101, founded 1956, editors Dennis Haskell, Delys Bird, Peter Cowan and Bruce Bennett. *Westerly* is a literary and cultural quarterly publishing quality short fiction, poetry, literary critical, socio-historical articles and book reviews. **"No restrictions on creative material. Our only criterion [for poetry] is literary quality. We don't dictate to writers on rhyme, style, experimentation, or anything else. We are willing to publish short or long poems. We do assume a reasonably well read, intelligent audience. Past issues of *Westerly* provide the best guides. Not consciously an academic magazine."** They have recently published work by Nicholas Hasluck, Bruce Dawe, Veronica Brady, Elizabeth Riddell and Alamgir Hashmi. The quarterly magazine is 7×10, "electronically printed," 96 pgs., with some photos and graphics. Press run is 1,000. Single copy: $6 (Aus.) plus overseas postage via surface mail; subscription: $24 (Aus.)/year. **Sample: $7 (Aus.) surface mail, $8 (Aus.) airmail. "Please do not send simultaneous submissions." Reporting time is 2-3 months and time to publication approximately 3 months. Minimum pay for poetry is $30 plus 1 copy. Buys first publication rights. Returns rights; requests acknowledgement on reprints.** Reviews books of poetry in 500-1,000 words. Open to unsolicited reviews. Poets may also send books to Reviews Editor for review consideration. The Patricia Hackett Prize (value approx. $500) is awarded in March for the best contribution published in *Westerly* during the previous calendar year. The advice

CLOSE-UP

Poetry from the Soul Finds its Way into Print

"The Mitchell Freeway"

Straight and smooth and stretched
over sand, scrub, hidden water,
flashing on, and on, the air never stilled
above the swift, purring laughter
of the tyres, mile after fierce mile
the stretched black sleeve
of the Mitchell; in modern style
the electric suburbs you leave
to each side of this plant-less, hill-less, stark
reminder of modern duty,
straight through the frantically floodlit dark
on this tight, efficient beauty,
where the erasure of time is the sincerest skill
and the greatest waste, time to kill.

Dennis Haskell

"The amount of poetry being written shows that in this visually-oriented, banality-laden society, poetry still answers some deep need in people," says Dennis Haskell, director of the Centre for Studies in Australian Literature at the University of Western Australia. "This is evident from the number of unsolicited manuscripts publishers receive."

Haskell coedits *Westerly*, Western Australia's main literary magazine, while keeping a finger on the pulse of poetry publishing in his homeland. "We actually receive more good poems than we can publish," he says, adding that the magazine's budget allows them to print only 100 pages per issue. "We receive 50-100 poems each week and publish approximately 2 percent."

In addition to poetry, this quarterly publication includes fiction, critical articles and book reviews. "We target a general, intelligent reading audience and cover literature and culture," says Haskell. "What prompts us to turn away a good poem is just the competition at the time. It's not fair to accept poems and then hold them for too long. The poet would be better off sending the poem(s) elsewhere. As it is, we have up to 12 months delay between acceptance and publication."

When deciding which poems will see "the dark of print," as he says, they look for poetry with something interesting to say. "We accept both free verse and formal poetry, though we receive many more submissions of free verse," says Haskell. "We try not to be prescriptive, as we do like to publish a variety of poetry—in form and content. It is true that beyond a certain length is impossible in the magazine. We could never have published **Paradise Lost**, unless Milton had got it down to about five or six pages.

"What we don't want to see is self-indulgence, including submissions accompanied by a long list of the author's achievements. It doesn't matter to us who you are or where you've been published before. We try to look at the poems on their own merits. At least two people read the poems, and normally three. To be published, a poem must be approved by all the readers without exception."

Though *Westerly* is known for its interest in Australia and the Indian Ocean region, the editors have published writers from many nations. Haskell estimates that 15-20 percent of their poetry submissions come from international sources, including Asia, Europe, South America, Africa, Arabia, Russia, Canada and the United States.

All poets interested in submitting to *Westerly should* read a copy of the magazine first. "If this seems impossible to do, contact us direct or contact the nearest Australian embassy or consulate and ask them. Nag them if necessary," he says.

Speaking about submissions from the United States, Haskell says they change American spellings, but American subjects are generally not a problem. "We've published poems about skunks and raccoons and snow and so on. I suppose there are sometimes subjects that we know little about, but they would have to be pretty specific and topical. Australia has been so bombarded with American culture that most American-ness is reasonably familiar."

Having never confessed to an interest in poetry until well into his 20s, Haskell has published poetry in a number of magazines and has three collections to his credit. His most recent book, **Abracadabra**, was published by Fremantle Arts Centre Press last year.

While many of Haskell's poems have found their way into print, he recognizes the fact that competition with other poets is growing. There are many more poets around, so getting published is still an achievement. Yet, he says, the material produced isn't always good. "Fashions, including intellectual ones, play a part. For example, in recent years there has been the publishing of a good deal of performance poetry or language poetry. On the page this works no better than Bob Dylan's songs, and mostly a lot worse.

"There is also, for ideological reasons, the publishing of pro-feminist or pro-Aboriginal or pro-other-perfectly-worthy-causes poetry. But moral virtue is not always matched with aesthetic skill."

He believes beginning poets can benefit from readings. "I find readings are a good way of testing your own poems, of feeling the words in your mouth and seeing if they fit properly, like good dentures.

"Of course, a lot of junk can be passed off as good at a reading and a lot of good poetry just doesn't work at a reading. But it is one way of keeping universities from having a stranglehold on poetry, and it can help make poetry seem a regular part of people's lives," he says.

"The fact that more poetry is written than is read says something about the importance of the activity itself to the human psyche. There's something about poetry that drives people to write it or to want to write it.

"My advice for good poets whose work is rejected is 'persist.' Persistence, even sheer pig-headed stubbornness, is one of the most important qualities a writer can have."

— *Christine Martin*

of the editors is: "Be sensible. Write what matters for you but think about the reader. Don't spell out the meanings of the poems and the attitudes to be taken to the subject matter—i.e. trust the reader. Don't be swayed by literary fashion. Read the magazine if possible before sending submissions. Read, read, read literature of all kinds and periods."

WESTERN PRODUCER PUBLICATIONS; WESTERN PEOPLE (IV-Regional), Box 2500, Saskatoon, Saskatchewan S7K 2C4 Canada, phone (306)665-3500, founded 1923, managing editor Michael Gillgannon. *Western People* is a magazine supplement to *The Western Producer*, a weekly newspaper, circulation 120,000, which uses **"poetry about the people, interests and environment of rural Western Canada."** As a sample the editor selected the entire poem "sky so heavy and low" by Marilyn Cay:

> it is November in Saskatchewan
> the sky so heavy and low
> I can feel the weight of it
> on my chest
> the days so short and getting shorter
> I can touch the sides of them
> at midday

The tabloid-sized supplement is 8 pgs., newsprint, with color and b&w photography and graphics. They receive about 600 submissions of freelance poetry/year, use 40-50. **Sample free for postage (2 oz.)—and ask for guidelines. One poem/page, maximum of 3 poems/submission. Name, address, telephone number upper left corner of each page. Reports within 2 weeks. Pays $15-50/ poem.** The editor comments, "It is difficult for someone from outside Western Canada to catch the flavor of this region; almost all the poems we purchase are written by Western Canadians."

WESTVIEW: A JOURNAL OF WESTERN OKLAHOMA (II, IV-Regional, themes), 100 Campus Drive, SOSU, Weatherford OK 73096, phone (405)774-3168, founded 1981, editor Fred Alsberg, is a quarterly using **themes related to Western Oklahoma, as well as non-thematic work of high quality by poets from elsewhere. "We publish free verse and formal poetry."** They have recently published poetry by Mark Sanders, Michael McKinney, Holly Hunt and Norman Arrington. As a sample the editor selected these lines from "Outlaw on Holiday" by Richard Plant:

> Palmer said that his hands looked like a millionaire's,
> so fine and hairless. He worked his spoon in that
> glass dish like you or I might play piano
> if only we knew how.

Westview is 44 pgs., magazine-sized, saddle-stapled, with glossy card cover in full-color. They use about 25% of 100 poems received a year. Press run is 1,000 for 500 subscribers of which about 25 are libraries, 150 shelf sales. Subscription: $10. **Sample postpaid: $4. Cover letter including biographical data for contributor's note required with submissions. "Poems on computer disk are welcome so long as they are accompanied by the hard copy and the SASE has the appropriate postage." Send SASE for themes. Editor comments on submissions "sometimes. Mss are circulated to an editorial board; we usually respond within a month." Pays 1 copy.**

WEYFARERS; GUILDFORD POETS PRESS (II), 9, White Rose Lane, Woking, Surrey GU22 7JA United Kingdom, founded 1972, administrative editor Margaret Pain, poetry editors Margaret Pain, Martin Jones and Jeffery Wheatley. They say, "We publish *Weyfarers* magazine three times a year. All our editors are themselves poets and give their spare time free to help other poets." They describe their needs as **"all types of poetry, serious and humorous, free verse and rhymed/metered, but mostly 'mainstream' modern. Excellence is the main consideration. NO hard porn, graphics, way-out experimental. Any subject publishable, from religious to satire. Not more than 40 lines."** They have recently published poetry by Susan Skinner, David Schaal, John Gallas and Michael Henry. As a sample the editors chose this extract from "In Sunlight" by Anne Smith:

> . . . The gin-trap lay
> where my father had set it, where foxes ran . . .
> . . . a young female, half-mad with rage and pain
> till my father beat her to death with a stick.
> Afterwards, we completed our check of the farm
> and came in home. But never entirely at home
> again my mind since that day. . . .

The digest-sized, saddle-stapled format contains about 28 pgs. of poetry (of a total of 32 pgs.). The magazine has a circulation of "about 300," including about 190 subscriptions of which 5 are libraries. They use about 125 of 1,200-1,500 submissions received each year. **Sample current issue: $5 in cash USA (or £1.60 UK) postpaid. Submit no more than 6 poems, one poem/sheet. No previously published or simultaneous submissions. Closing dates for submissions end of January, May and September.** They sometimes **comment briefly, if requested,** on rejections. **Pays**

1 copy. Staff reviews books of poetry briefly, in newsletter sent to subscribers. "We are associated with Surrey Poetry Center, which has an annual Open Poetry Competition. The prize-winners are published in *Weyfarers*." Their advice to poets is, "Always read a magazine before submitting. And read plenty of modern poetry."

WHETSTONE (I, II), Department of English, University of Lethbridge, 4401 University Drive, Lethbridge, Alberta T1K 3M4 Canada, appears twice a year with writing by beginners and published authors. **"Open to any kind of poetry, as long as it's of good quality."** They have published poems by Susan Musgrave and Rhonda McAdam. *Whetstone* is digest-sized, 80+ pgs., saddle-stapled, professionally printed in boldface type with 2-color matte card cover, circulation 500 with 200 subscriptions of which 25 are libraries. Single copy: $5 (Can.); subscription: $10. **Sample postpaid: $5. Any length of poetry OK. Editor sometimes comments on rejections. Send SASE for guidelines. Pays $10 and 1 copy.** "We have highly specialized poetry and short story competitions periodically. Writers should send $5 for sample copy, plus SASE for rules and regulations."

WHETSTONE; WHETSTONE PRIZE (II), P.O. Box 1266, Barrington IL 60011, phone (708)382-5626, editors Sandra Berris, Marsha Portnoy, Jean Tolle and Julie Fleenor, is an annual. **"We emphasize quality more than category. No erotica or haiku."** They have published poetry by Paulette Roeske, Lucia Getsi and Peyton Houston. As a sample the editor selected these lines by Robert Cooperman:

> *So what if Maggie and me*
> *made our spirit rappings*
> *by cracking our toe knuckles?*
> *Only men feed on facts*
> *like autumn turkeys on grain,*
> *on what they can touch and throttle.*

It is digest-sized, 96 pgs., professionally printed, flat-spined with matte card cover. Press run is 600+ for 100 subscribers of which 5+ are libraries, 350 shelf sales. **Sample postpaid: $3. Reports in 1-4 months. Pays 2 copies. Acquires first North American serial rights.** The Whetstone Prizes are cash awards ($50-$500) for the best work in each issue.

‡WHISPER; BROADSHEETS; ETHEREAL DANCES; SCREAM PRESS (II), 509 Enterprise Dr., Rohnert Park CA 94928, founded 1987, editor of *Whisper* and *Broadsheets* Anthony Boyd, editor of *Ethereal Dances* Sara Boyd. All are "publications promoting new and established literary thinkers. **Interested in any poetry well done, 50 lines or less, free verse, villanelles, haiku, etc. No 'guy' poems about beer, bars, hookers, etc. No juvenile love poetry. No 'shock value' poetry."** They have recently published poetry by Cheryl Townsend, Michael Estabook and Kathleen Iddings. As a sample the editors selected the complete poem, "Pine Trees Voodoo," by Walt Phillips:

> *the night kept whispering*
> *things i didn't want to hear*
>
>   *naturally i walked away*
>   *naturally it followed*

Whisper and *Ethereal Dances* are both biannual publications. *Whisper* is 16 pgs., 8 × 11, photocopied, saddle-stapled, color paper, art no ads. *Ethereal Dances* is 20 pgs., 5½ × 8½, photocopied, saddle-stapled, color paper, no art or ads. *Broadsheets* are 4 × 8, laser printed on special paper, some art, ad for press on back. Anthony Boyd says he receives about 750 poems from 200 poets for *Whisper* and *Broadsheets*. He accepts approximately 9%. Sara Boyd receives about 200 poems from 50 poets for *Ethereal Dances*. She accepts approximately 15%. Press run for their publications is 250 for 100 subscribers of which 5 are libraries. Subscription: $10. **Sample of either publication postpaid: $3. Submit 1 poem to a page. Previously published poems OK; no simultaneous submissions. Cover letter required. Often comments on rejections. Send SASE for guidelines. Reports in 1-3 months. Pays 1-2 copies. Acquires first or one-time rights.** Anthony Boyd reviews books of poetry in *Whisper*. Send books for review consideration to his attention. They say, "Anyone can send anything, but the acceptance rate for those who have seen a sample of our publications is double the rate for those who have not."

WHITE EAGLE COFFEE STORE PRESS (II); FRESH GROUND (IV-Anthology), P.O. Box 383, Fox River Grove IL 60021-0383, phone (708)639-9200, founded 1992, is a small press publishing 5-6 chapbooks/year. **"Alternate chapbooks are published by invitation and by competition. Author published by invitation becomes judge for next competition."** They are **"open to any kind of poetry. No censorship at this press. Aesthetic values are the only standard. Generally not interested in sentimental or didactic writing."** They have recently published poetry by Annie Davidovicz and Peter Blair. As a sample the editor selected these lines from "Hot Saws" by Paul Andrew E. Smith:

> *It's a metallic taste she has, sweet,*

my teeth are numb, my cheek bones.
Yes, by God in the treetops,
I'm beginning to see how these are
necessary skills, this lumberjacking.

Sample postpaid: $5. Submit complete chapbook ms (20-24 pages) with a brief bio, 125-word statement that introduces your writing and $10 reading fee. Previously published poems and simultaneous submissions OK, with notice. Competition deadlines: the 1st of September, January and May. Send SASE for guidelines. "Each competition is judged by the author of the most recent chapbook published by invitation." **Seldom comments on rejections. Reports 8-10 weeks after deadline. All entrants will receive a copy of the winning chapbook. Winner receives $100 and 25 copies.** *Fresh Ground* is an annual anthology that features "some of the best work of poets who have submitted chapbook manuscripts during the previous year. *Fresh Ground* is published in July. Poems for this annual are accepted during May." They say, "Poetry is about a passion for language. That's what we're about. We'd like to provide an opportunity for poets of any age who are fairly early in their careers to publish something substantial. We're excited by the enthusiasm shown for this new press and by the extraordinary quality of the writing we've received."

WHITE PINE PRESS (V), Suite 28, 10 Village Square, Fredonia NY 14063,, phone (716)672-5743, founded 1973, editor Dennis Maloney, managing director Elaine LaMattina, office manager Lisa Fuller. White Pine Press publishes poetry, fiction, literature in translation, essays—perfect-bound paperbacks. "At present we are **not accepting unsolicited mss. Inquire first.**" They have published poetry by William Kloefkorn, Marjorie Agosin, Miguel Hernandez, Peter Blue Cloud, Basho, Pablo Neruda, Maurice Kenny and James Wright. **Query with 4-5 samples, brief cover letter with bio and publication credits. Replies to queries in 2-4 weeks, to submissions (if invited) in 1 month. Simultaneous submissions OK. Pays 5-10% of run. Send $1 for catalog to buy samples.**

JAMES WHITE REVIEW: A GAY MEN'S LITERARY QUARTERLY (IV-Gay), Box 3356, Butler Quarter Station, Minneapolis MN 55403, phone (612)339-8317, founded 1983, poetry editor Clif Mayhood, **uses all kinds of poetry by gay men.** They have recently published poetry by Robert Peters, Jonathan Bracker and Joel Zizik. They receive about 1,400 submissions/year, use 100, have a 6-week backlog. Press run is 3,000 for 1,500 subscribers of which 50 are libraries. Subscription: $12/year (US). **Sample postpaid: $3. Submit a limit of 8 poems or 250 lines. A poem can exceed 250 lines, but it "better be very good." Send SASE for guidelines. Reports in 4 months. Pays $10/poem.** Reviews books of poetry. *James White Review* received the Lambda Publisher's Service Award in 1990.

‡**WHITE SANDS POETRY REVIEW (II)**, P.O. Box 10488, Pensacola FL 32524-0488, founded 1992, editor Sharon Noland Norred, appears 6 times/year. "Our purpose is to showcase the best poems we receive whether they come from new or established poets. **No restrictions on form, length, style, etc. We are looking for poetry with strong imagery that seems to pull us into the poet's heart and mind, evoking the same feelings in the reader that compelled the poet to write the poem. Nothing contrived. No occult. No sing-song rhyme.**" They have recently published poetry by Cheryl A. Townsend, R. Gerry Fabian and Jeannette Barnes Thomin. As a sample the editor selected these lines from "Dream On" (poet unidentified):

Still time expires
before we do,
but not before
we've seen perfection
through our faults
and found the courage
to imagine a world
only we can build.

The editor says it is 20-32 pgs., digest-sized, saddle-stapled with matte cover. They receive 1,000 poems a year, use approximately 150. Press run is 150-200 for 97 subscribers of which 2 are libraries, few shelf sales. Single copy: $2.50; subscription: $12. **Sample postpaid: $3. Previously published poems and simultaneous submissions OK. "Though a cover letter is not required, we appreciate one giving info on previous publications and interesting details for contributor's notes."** Time between acceptance and publication is 2-3 months. **Often comments on rejections. Send SASE for guidelines. Reports in 4-6 weeks. Pays 1 or 2 copies. Acquires one-time rights.** They also sponsor 1 or 2 poetry contests each year. No entry fees. First prize receives $25 (minimum) and publication in the magazine. Other top entries are also published. Send SASE for contest deadlines and guidelines (including special cover sheet to be completed by author and submitted with previously unpublished poems. The editor says, "Submit, submit, submit!

Support the small presses who love poetry as much as you do and exist with the sole purpose of getting your poetry into the hands of the general public."

WHITE WALL REVIEW (I), 63 Gould St., Toronto, Ontario M5B 1E9 Canada, phone (416)977-1045, founded 1976, editors change every year, is an annual using "**interesting, preferably spare art. No style is unacceptable. Should poetry serve a purpose beyond being poetry and communicating a poet's idea? Nothing boring, self-satisfied, gratuitously sexual, violent or indulgent.**" They have recently published poetry by Debora Bojman and Robert Hilles. As a sample the editor selected this poem, "the poet," by Arthur J. Scott:

> *the sadness of*
> *bent shadows struggling*
> *across pristine snows*
>
> *the uncharted course*
> *of lonely footprints*
> *now forever melted*
>
> *yet indelible the*
> *trail of the heart*
> *eternally beating*
> *in the pen's wake*

WWR is between 144-160 pgs., digest-sized, professionally printed, perfect-bound, with glossy card cover, using b&w photos and illustrations. Press run is 600. Subscription: $6. **Sample postpaid: $8. "Please do not submit between January and July of a given year." Cover letter required; include short bio.** Reports "as soon as we can. We comment on all mss, accepted or not." Pays 1 copy. They say, "Poets should send what they consider *their best work*, not everything they've got."

TAHANA WHITECROW FOUNDATION; CIRCLE OF REFLECTIONS (IV-Ethnic), Box 18181, Salem OR 97305, phone (503)585-0564, founded 1987, executive director Melanie Smith. The Whitecrow Foundation conducts **one spring/summer poetry contest on Native American themes in poems up to 30 lines in length. Deadline for submissions: May 31. No haiku, Seiku, erotic or porno poems. Fees are $2.75 for a single poem, $10 for 4.** Winners, honorable mentions and selected other entries are published in a periodic anthology, **Circle of Reflections.** Winners receive free copies and are encouraged to purchase others for $4.95 plus $1 handling in order to "help ensure the continuity of our contests." As a sample Melanie Smith selected these lines by Jack Iyall:

> *Today I'm dirty old man . .*
> *yesterday . . growing old*
>   *was beautiful . .*
> *today I'm a museum piece . .*
> *yesterday . . I could be*
>   *in line for Chief . .*
> *today I'm in the welfare line . .*
> *yesterday . . there was a place for me . .*

Reviews books of poetry for $10 reading fee (average 32 pages). Melanie Smith adds, "We seek unpublished Native writers. Poetic expressions of full-bloods, mixed bloods and empathetic non-Indians need to be heard. Future goals include chapbooks and native theme art. Advice to new writers — keep writing, honing and sharpening your material; don't give up — keep submitting."

WHOLE NOTES; WHOLE NOTES PRESS (I, II, IV-Children, translations), P.O. Box 1374, Las Cruces NM 88004, phone (505)382-7446, *WN* founded 1984, Whole Notes Press founded 1988, editor Nancy Peters Hastings. *WN* appears twice a year. Whole Notes Press publishes one chapbook/year by a single poet. "**All forms will be considered.**" They have recently published poetry by Stuart Friebert. As a sample the editor selected these lines from "Stone with Horseshoe" by Judita Vaiciunaite:

> *. . . and again through fog I hear*
>   *the horseshoe, hammered out on stone,*
>   *the wind in the rye,*

 The double dagger before a listing indicates that the listing is new in this edition. New markets are often the most receptive to submissions.

the steed barely tamed, neighing in the distance . . .

WN is 20-24 pgs., digest-sized, "nicely printed," staple bound, with a "linen 'fine arts' cover." Press run 400 for 200 subscriptions of which 10 are libraries. They accept about 10% of some 300-400 submissions/year. Subscription: $6. Sample postpaid: $3. **They prefer submissions of 3-7 poems at a time. Some previously published poems used. "We prefer not to receive simultaneous submissions." Reports in 2-3 weeks. Pays 2 copies. For 20-page chapbook consideration, submit 3-15 samples with bio and list of other publications. Pays 25 copies of chapbook. Editor sometimes comments on rejections.** The editor says, "In the fall of each even-numbered year I edit a special issue of *WN* that features writing by young people (under 21). We also welcome translations."

‡THE WICAZO SA REVIEW (IV-Ethnic), R.R.#8, Box 510, Rapid City SD 57702, phone (605)341-3228, founded 1985, poetry editor Elizabeth Cook-Lynn, is a "scholarly magazine appearing twice a year devoted to the developing of Native American Studies as an academic discipline, using **poetry of exceptional quality.**" They have used poetry by Simon Ortiz, Joy Harjo, Gray Cohoe and Earle Thompson. As a sample the editor chose these lines by Ray Young Bear:

> *With the Community's great "registered" Cottonwood*
> *Smoldering under an overcast sky*
> *no one will believe we are here*
> *in the middle & deepest part*
> *of the flood*

TWSR is magazine-sized, 40-46 pgs., saddle-stapled, professionally printed on heavy glossy stock with b&w glossy card cover, press run 500, using only 3-4 poems per issue. Once in a while they "feature" an exceptional poet. **Sample postpaid: $10. Cover letter required including credits and tribal enrollment affiliation. Pays 3 copies.** Reviews books of poetry. Open to unsolicited reviews. Poets may also send books for review consideration.

‡WICKED MYSTIC (IV-Horror), P.O. Box 3087, Astoria NY 11103, phone (718)545-6713, founded 1990, editor Andre Scheluchin, is a bimonthly of hardcore horror poetry and short stories. They want **"psychological horror, splatter-gore, death, gothic themes, vampires, etc. No safe, conventional, conservative poetry."** They have recently published poetry by Michael A. Arnzen, John Grey and Judson Crews. As a sample the editor selected this poem, "Alcohol," by Jonathan Yungkans:

> *In a giant glass vat, a man*
> *hangs by his ankles, drinks beer*
> *into his lungs. A child watches,*
> *walled in a block of ice*
> *stabbed many times, the reddened*
> *pieces dropped into the vat*
> *to keep the man's drink cold.*

Wicked Mystic is 80 pgs., digest-sized, saddle-stapled, with heavy stock colored cover and display ads. They receive about 1,000 poems a year, use approximately 20%. Press run is 2,000 for 500 subscribers of which 50 are libraries. Subscription: $21 for 6 issues, $39.95 for 12 issues. **Sample postpaid: $4. Submit typed poems, no longer than 30 lines. No previously published poems; simultaneous submissions OK. Cover letter required. Often comments on rejections. Reports within 2 months. Pays 1 copy. Acquires first North American serial rights.**

WIDENER REVIEW (II), Humanities Division, Widener University, Chester PA 19013, phone (215)499-4341, founded 1984, poetry editor Kenneth Pobo, is an annual that publishes poetry, fiction and nonfiction. **Form, length and subject matter open. "Greeting card verse is not welcome."** They have published poetry by Robert Cooperman, Eve Shelnutt and Peter Wild. *Widener Review* is approximately 100 pages. "We probably read 400 manuscripts per issue; we accept approximately 35 pages of poems." **No previously published poems or simultaneous submissions. Manuscripts must be typed. Reads submissions September 1 through April 1 only.** Time between acceptance and publication is 6 months. **Seldom comments on rejections. Send SASE for guidelines. Reports within 2 months. Pays 1 copy. Acquires first North American serial rights.** Sometimes publishes book reviews.

WILD EAST; THE POTTERSFIELD PORTFOLIO; SALAMANCA CHAPBOOK SERIES (II), 151 Ryan Court, Fredericton, New Brunswick E3A 2Y9 Canada, phone (506)472-9251, press founded 1988, magazine founded 1979. "Wild East's *The Pottersfield Portfolio* is a semiannual literary magazine of new English and French fiction, poetry, drama, artwork and essays **from Atlantic Canada** and elsewhere. Both new and more established writers are featured." **They do not accept "sexist, racist, homophobic, ageist or classist material and no erotica, limericks or haiku."** They have recently published poetry by Marc Arsenesu, Heather Browne Prince, Elizabeth Harvor, Don McKay and bill bissett. As a sample the editors selected these lines by Belinda Carney:

> *know your body as the sturdy root*
> *that has borne such red life, all alone:*
> *the votive lit, for sisters in the soul-house*
> *a candent contract*
> *between earth and memory*
> *the light at the centre of one red berry*
> *the eyes of an animal you meet on the road home*

TPP is 96 pgs., 6 × 9, perfect-bound, handsomely printed, with 2-color coated cover, b&w artwork and ads. Press run is 1,000 for 400 subscribers of which 50 are libraries, 200-300 shelf sales. Subscription (for individuals): $12/year Canadian, $15 US. Sample postpaid: $6. No previously published poems or simultaneous submissions. Cover letter with bio required. Editor seldom comments on rejections. Send SASE for guidelines. Reports in 3 months. Pays $10/published page plus 2 copies. Buys first Canadian serial rights. *TPP* sponsors an annual contest (poetry, fiction and nonfiction). Theme/subject changes each year. Send SASE for entry guidelines. Deadline: November 15. Wild East publishes 1-3 paperbacks and 5-7 chapbooks/year in the Salamanca Chapbook Series. Replies to queries in 1 month, to mss in 2-3 months. Pays 10% royalties. Sample chapbook: $4 postpaid.

WILDERNESS (II, IV-Nature/ecology), 5118 N. Princeton St., Portland OR 97203 (poetry submissions only should be sent to this address), founded 1935, poetry editor John Daniel, is a slick quarterly magazine of "The Wilderness Society, one of the oldest and largest American conservation organizations." Requests for sample and subscriptions should go to *Wilderness*, 900 17th St. NW, Washington DC 20006. They want **"poetry related to the natural world. Shorter poems stand a better chance than longer, but all will be read. Poetry in any form or style is welcome."** They have recently published poetry by Mary Oliver, Tom Sexton, Alison Deming, Paul Willis, William Stafford and Paulann Petersen. The magazine is published on slick stock, full-color, professionally printed, with full-color paper cover, saddle-stapled, 76 pgs. Their press run is 260,000 with 255,000 subscriptions. Subscription: $15. **Sample postpaid: $3.50. No simultaneous submissions or previously published material. Prefers cover letter with submissions indicating that "a human being has sent the poems." Editor comments on rejections "occasionally. Please understand that we have room for only about 15 poems a year." Responds in 2 months. Pays $100 plus 2 copies on publication. "We buy one-time rights and the right to anthologize the poem without further compensation."** *Wilderness* ranked #8 in the "Top Pay" category of the June 1993 *Writer's Digest* Poetry 60 list.

WILLAMETTE RIVER BOOKS (II), P.O. Box 605, Troutdale OR 97060, founded 1990, editor Douglas Allen Conner, publishes 2-3 chapbooks annually. "We run a yearly competition, advertised in *Poets & Writers*, for a 16- to 24-page chapbook. We are open to fresh new voices as well as established ones. We hope to publish chapbooks of newer poets who may not yet have published a chapbook but who have a publication history in magazines and small press. **Quality is our sole criterion."** They have recently published books by Dennis Saleh and Alana Sherman. As a sample the editor selected these lines from Sherman's **Everything is Gates:**

> *The banana trees are dusty,*
> *the donkeys*
> *the dogs*
> *the children are dusty.*
> *In richer towns, behind green*
> *Shuttered windows, the women shed*
> *their heavy black*
> *and dance for each other.*

No unsolicited mss. Query first with samples. Cover letter including **"publishing history and a little about the author"** required. Payment for publication arranged with author.

THE WILLIAM AND MARY REVIEW (II), Campus Center, College of William and Mary, P.O. Box 8795, Williamsburg VA 23187-8795, phone (804)221-3290, founded 1962, editor Stacy Payne, is a 112-page annual, **"dedicated to publishing new work by established poets as well as work by new and vital voices."** They have published poetry by Dana Gioia, Cornelius Eady, Amy Clampitt, Henri Cole, Julie Agoos, Diane Ackerman, Judson Jerome and Phyllis Janowitz. They accept 15-20 of about 5,000 poems submitted/year. Press run is 3,500. They have 250 library subscriptions, about 500 shelf sales. **Sample postpaid: $4.50. Submit 1 poem/page, batches of no more than 6 poems. Cover letter required; include address, phone number, past publishing history and brief bio note. Reads submissions September 15 through February 15 only. Reports in approximately 4 months. Pays 5 copies.** Open to unsolicited reviews. Poets may also send books to poetry editors for review consideration.

WILLOW REVIEW; COLLEGE OF LAKE COUNTY READING SERIES (II), 19351 W. Washington St., Grayslake IL 60030-1198, phone (708)223-6601, fax (708)223-9371, founded 1969, edited by Paulette Roeske. **"We are interested in poetry and fiction of high quality with no preferences as to form, style or subject."** They have published poetry by Lisel Mueller, Bruce Guernsey, John Dickson, Jill Breckenridge and Mark Perlberg. As a sample we selected these lines from "China" by David Jones:

> Not much of anything matches any more.
> Yet each one has an archeological fit
> to some era, and an expert could examine
> each round artifact and correctly say:
> Ah, early graduate school period,
> or: immediate post-divorce phase,
> followed by earthenware from
> the Fairfield Avenue site,
> characteristic of the time of Marlene.

The review is a 72-page, flat-spined annual, 6×9, professionally printed with a glossy cover featuring b&w art. Editors are open to all styles, free verse to form, as long as each poem stands on its own as art and communicates ideas. Circulation 1,000, with distribution throughout the Midwest. Subscription: $10 (3 issues). **Sample postpaid: $4. Submit up to 5 poems or short fiction up to 4,000 words, September through January for April publication. Cover letter required; include name, address, SS#, and information for contributor's notes. Pays 2 copies. Acquires first North American serial rights. Prizes of $100, $50 and $25 are also awarded to the best poetry and fiction in each issue.** The reading series, 4-7 readings/academic year, has included Angela Jackson, Ellen Bryant Voigt, Thomas Lux, Charles Simic, Gloria Naylor, David Mura, Galway Kinnell, Lisel Mueller, Amiri Baraka, Stephen Dobyns, Heather McHugh, Linda Pastan, Katha Pollitt, Tobias Wolff, William Stafford and others. One reading is for contributors to *Willow Review*. These are usually held on Thursday evenings, for audiences of about 150 students and faculty of College of Lake County and other area colleges and residents of local communities. They are widely publicized in Chicago and suburban newspapers.

WILLOW SPRINGS (II, IV-Translations), MS-1, Eastern Washington University, Cheney WA 99004, phone (509)458-6429, founded 1977. "We publish quality poetry and fiction that is imaginative, intelligent, and has a concern and care for language. **We are especially interested in translations from any language or period."** They have published poetry by Denise Levertov, Carolyn Kizer, Michael Burkard, Russell Edson, Dara Wier, Thomas Lux, Madeline DeFrees, Hayden Carruth, Al Young, Odysseas Elytis, W.S. Merwin, Olga Broumas, Kay Boyle and Lisel Mueller. *Willow Springs*, a semiannual, is one of the most visually appealing and designed journals being published. It is 98 pgs., 6×9, flat-spined, professionally printed, with glossy 2-color card cover with art. Circulation is 1,000, 400 subscriptions of which 30% are libraries. They use 1-2% of some 4,000 unsolicited poems received each year. Editors seem to prefer free verse with varying degrees of accessibility (although an occasional formal poem has appeared in recent issues). **Sample postpaid: $4. Submit September 1 through May 30 only. "We do not read in the summer months." Include name on every page, address on first page of each poem. Brief cover letter saying how many poems on how many pages preferred. No simultaneous submissions. Send SASE for guidelines. Reports in 1-3 months. Pays 2 copies, others at half price, and cash when funds available. Acquires all rights. Returns rights on release.** Reviews books of poetry and short fiction in 200-500 words. Open to unsolicited reviews. Poets may also send books for review consideration. They have annual poetry and fiction awards ($100 and $250 respectively) for work published in the journal.

WIND PUBLICATIONS; WIND MAGAZINE (II), P.O. Box 24548, Lexington KY 40524, phone (606)885-5342, *Wind Magazine* founded in 1971 by Quentin R. Howard, current editors/publishers Steven R. Cope and Charlie G. Hughes. "Although we publish poets of national repute, we are friendly toward beginners who have something to say and do so effectively and interestingly. **No taboos, no preferred school, form, style, etc. Our interests are inclusive.** Competition is keen; send only your best." They have published poetry by Locklin, Sarton, Turco, Semones, Chaffin, Etter, Tagliabue and Witt. *Wind* appears twice a year and is about 100 pgs., digest-sized, perfect-bound, containing approximately 40% poetry, also short fiction, essays and reviews ("Editor's Choice"). "We accept about 1% of submissions." Subscription: $10/year. **Sample postpaid: $3.50. Submit no more than 5 poems. No simultaneous submissions. "Cover letter optional; short bio desirable." Editor comments on submissions which are near misses. Reports in 1 month, publication within 1 year. Pays 1 contributor's copy plus discount on extras. "Your submission is understood to guarantee Wind Publications first North American serial rights and anthology reprint rights only."** Wind Publications sponsors yearly chapbook competitions. Reading fee: $15 (includes 1-year subscription to *Wind*). Send SASE for chapbook guidelines. Also publishes periodic anthologies; the **Best of Wind** anthology is $11.50 (including postage/handling).

GET YOUR WORK INTO THE RIGHT BUYERS' HANDS!

You work hard... and your hard work deserves to be seen by the right buyers. But with the constant changes in the industry, it's not always easy to know who those buyers are. That's why you'll want to keep up-to-date and on top with the most current edition of this indispensable market guide.

Keep ahead of the changes by ordering *1995 Poet's Market* today. You'll save the frustration of getting poems returned in the mail, stamped MOVED: ADDRESS UNKNOWN. And of NOT submitting your work to new listings because you don't know they exist. All you have to do to order the upcoming 1995 edition is complete the attached post card and return it with your payment or charge card information. Order now, and there's one thing that won't change from your *1994 Poet's Market* - the price! That's right, we'll send you the 1995 edition for just $19.95. *1995 Poet's Market* will be published and ready for shipment in September 1994.

Don't let another opportunity slip by...get a jump on the industry with the help of *1995 Poet's Market* . Order today! You deserve it!

(See other side for more books to help you get your poems published)

To order, drop this postpaid card in the mail.

☐ **Yes!** I want the most current edition of *Poet's Market*. Please send me the 1995 edition at the 1994 price - $19.95.* (NOTE: *1995 Poet's Market* will be ready for shipment in September 1994.) #10388

Also send me these books to help me get published:

_____(#1836) The Poet's Handbook $12.95 $10.95* (available NOW)

_____(#10209) Creating Poetry $18.95 $16.10* (available NOW)

_____(#10281) Freeing Your Creativity $17.95 $15.25 * (available NOW)

*Plus postage and handling: $3.00 for one book, $1.00 for each additional book. Ohio residents add $5 \frac{1}{2}\%$ sales tax.

Credit card orders call toll-free 1-800-289-0963

☐ Payment enclosed (Slip this card and your payment into an envelope)

☐ Please charge my: ☐ Visa ☐ MasterCard

Account #_____ Exp. Date_____

Signature _____ Phone (   ) _____

Name_____

Address_____

City _____State_____Zip_____

(This offer expires May 1, 1995)

| **30-Day Money Back Guarantee** |

W WRITER'S DIGEST BOOKS

Writer's Digest Books
1507 Dana Avenue
Cincinnati, OH 45207

6398

More Books for Poets!
Save Up To $2.85!

The Poet's Handbook
by Judson Jerome

Here's expert instruction on how to use figurative language, symbols, and concrete images; how to tune your ear to sound relationships; the requirements for lyric, narrative, dramatic, didactic, and satirical poetry. 244 pages/$12.95 $10.95/paperback

Creating Poetry
by John Drury

Designed to encourage budding poets to explore and practice poetry writing skills, Drury's nuts-and-bolts instruction addresses all elements of creating poetry. Each chapter offers an overview of each element discussed, a definition of terms. poetry examples, plus hands-on exercises. 224 pages/$18.95 $16.10/hardcover

Freeing Your Creativity: A Writer's Guide

Author Marshall Cook offers practical and inspirational instruction on how you can write more — and better — than you ever thought you could. Step by step, you'll learn to replace the fear, habits and excuses that inhibit creativity — and soon find your work more original, interesting and publishable than ever before! 176 pages/$17.95 $15.25/hardcover

Use coupon on other side to order today!

THE WINDHORSE REVIEW; SAMURAI PRESS (III), RR3, Box 3140, Yarmouth, Nova Scotia B5A 4A7 Canada, founded 1982, poetry editor John Castlebury, is a semiannual magazine that, according to its editor, **"seeks poetry with a place for the genuine, as per Marianne Moore. The truest poems no one writes yet they do still get written. Simply plucking notes out of the air and there is no one there doing that, and nobody gets to take credit."** They have published poetry by Janet McCann, Sam Hamill and Alan Napier. As a sample the editor selected the opening lines of "The Sadness of Windows" by Carole Glasser Langille:

> *Outside our window the river*
> *mirrors a white barn, floats lights up and down*
> *its other side. It soaks grey sky some days*
> *and leaves a blanket of fog*
> *to cover its deeds.*
> *They shoulder each other in old houses, these windows.*

TWR is handsomely printed, using artistic b&w photos and graphics. Press run is 500 and it is sold in bookstores in major cities. **Sample postpaid: $5. Submit 5-10 pgs. with brief bio and SAE with IRC or $1 US (US stamps invalid from Canada). Reports in 1 month. Pays copies. Acquires first North American serial rights.** Prisoner copies available free of charge. The editor says he often receives submissions from poets "whose ambitions to be 'published' are premature—too much ambition, not enough vision and maturity."

THE WINDHOVER PRESS (III), 102 EPB, The University of Iowa, Iowa City IA 52242, phone (319)335-0429, founded 1967, director K.K. Merker, publishes 3-4 hardbacks/year. They want **"poetry from writers who have studied serious literature and who want to add to it. 'There is nothing more dreadful than imagination without taste.' No inspirational, political or amateurish poetry; no doggerel."** They have published poetry by Charles Wright and Amy Clampitt. As a sample the director selected "The Midnight Club" by Mark Strand:

> *The gifted have told us for years that they*
> *   want to be loved*
> *For what they are, that they, in whatever*
> *   fullness is theirs,*
> *Are perishable in twilight, just like us.*
> *   So they work all night*
> *In rooms that are cold and webbed with the*
> *   moon's light;*
> *Sometimes, during the day, they lean on*
> *   their cars*
> *And stare into the blistering valley, glassy*
> *   and golden,*
> *But mainly they sit, hunched in the dark,*
> *   feet on the floor,*
> *Hands on the table, shirts with a bloodstain*
> *   over the heart.*

Poems previously published in magazines and simultaneous submissions OK. Cover letter required. Replies to queries in 2-3 weeks, to mss in 1-2 months. Seldom comments on rejections. Pays 10% royalties or 10% of edition. Sample books may be purchased from the press or examined in libraries.

THE WINDLESS ORCHARD; THE WINDLESS ORCHARD CHAPBOOKS (II), English Dept., Indiana University, Fort Wayne IN 46805, phone (219)481-6841, founded 1970, poetry editor Robert Novak, a "shoestring labor of love—chapbooks only from frequent contributors to magazine. Sometimes publish calendars." They say they want **"heuristic, excited, valid non-xian religious exercises. Our muse is interested only in the beautiful, the erotic and the sacred."** *The Windless Orchard* appears irregularly, 50+ pgs., digest-sized, offset from typescript, saddle-stapled, with matte card cover with b&w photos. The editors say they have 100 subscriptions of which 25 are libraries, a print run of 300, total circulation: 280. There are about 35 pgs. of poetry in each issue. They receive about 3,000 freelance submissions of poetry/year, use 200, have a 6-month backlog. Subscription: $10. **Sample postpaid: $4. Submit 3-7 pgs. Considers simultaneous submissions. Reports in 1 day-4 months. Pays 2 copies.** Chapbook submissions by invitation only to contributors to the magazine. Poets pay costs for 300 copies, of which The Windless Orchard Chapbook Series receives 100 for its expenses. **Sample: $4.** Editors sometimes comment on rejections. They advise, "Memorize a poem a day, do translations for the education."

UNIVERSITY OF WINDSOR REVIEW (II), University of Windsor, Windsor, Ontario N9B 3P4 Canada, phone (519)253-4232, ext. 2303, founded 1966, poetry editor John Ditsky, appears twice a year. **"Open to all poetry but epic length."** They have published poetry by Ben Bennani, Walter McDonald, Larry Rubin and Lyn Lifshin. As a sample the editor selected these lines (poet unidentified):

> *talking to white wolves*
> *talking to the first*
> *white wolves ever*
> *telling of how things are*
> *in his world.*

It is professionally printed, 100 pgs., digest-sized. They accept about 15% of 500 poems received/ year. Press run is 500. Subscription: $12 Canadian, $10 US. **Sample postpaid: $6 Canadian, $5 US. Reports in 6 weeks. Pays $10/poem.**

WINEBERRY PRESS (V, IV-Regional), 3207 Macomb St. NW, Washington DC 20008, phone (202)363-8036 or (416)964-2002, founded 1983, founder and president Elisavietta Ritchie, publishes anthologies and chapbooks of poems by **Washington area poets but is not currently accepting unsolicited mss.** She has published poetry by Judith McCombs, Elizabeth Follin-Jones and Beatrice Murphy. As a sample Elisavietta Ritchie selected these lines from "Through The Looking Glass" by Maxine Combs, included in **Swimming Out Of The Collective Unconscious:**

> *I drop a carton*
> *in someone else's shopping cart,*
> *kneel to comfort a weeping child*
> *I mistake for my own . . . . We start*
> *swimming out of the collective unconscious*
> *and end by resembling our lovers.*

THE WIRE; PROGRESSIVE PRESS (I, IV-Form), 7320 Colonial, Dearborn Heights MI 48127, phone (517)394-3736, founded 1981, editor Sharon Wysocki. *The Wire* is an "alternative arts" publication that appears 2-3 times a year. It publishes **"language and experimental poetry" but no sonnets. "We are also looking for short form erotic poems. Regarding all submissions, the poet has a much better chance for publication in *The Wire* if the poem is in short form."** Poets published include Ivan Argüelles, Paul Weinman and Joseph Raffa. *The Wire* is photocopied on 8½ × 11 offset paper, 9 pgs., with graphics, stapled at the top left corner. Single copy: $1; subscription: $3.75 (checks should be made out to Progressive Press). **Simultaneous submissions OK, but print must be dark enough for photocopying.** Criticism of rejected mss is provided "sometimes." Guidelines are available for SASE. **Submissions are reported on in 6 months and time to publication is the same. Contributors receive 1 copy.**

WISCONSIN ACADEMY REVIEW (IV-Regional), 1922 University Ave., Madison WI 53705, phone (608)263-1692, founded 1954, poetry editor Faith B. Miracle, "distributes information on scientific and cultural life of Wisconsin and provides a forum for **Wisconsin (or Wisconsin background) artists and authors."** They want **"good lyric poetry; traditional meters acceptable if content is fresh. No poem over 65 lines."** They have published poetry by Credo Enriquez, David Martin, Felix Pollak, Ron Wallace and John Bennett. As a sample we selected these lines from "J L Jones" by Art Madson:

> *Running before the wind*
> *on canvas wings,*
> *on lifting hands, empty spirits,*
> *I try, like flying fish*
> *sailing the Pacific,*
> *to transcend my element.*

Wisconsin Academy Review is a magazine-sized, 48-page quarterly, professionally printed on glossy stock, glossy card color cover. Press run is 1,500 for 1,200 subscribers of which 109 are libraries. They use 3-6 pgs. of poetry/issue. Of over 100 freelance submissions of poetry/year they use about 15, have a 6- to 12-month backlog. **Sample postpaid: $3. Submit 5 pgs. maximum, double-spaced, include SASE. Must include Wisconsin connection if not Wisconsin return address.** Editor sometimes comments on rejections. **Reports in 4-6 weeks. Pays 3 copies.** Staff reviews books of poetry with Wisconsin connection only. Send related books for review consideration.

UNIVERSITY OF WISCONSIN PRESS; BRITTINGHAM PRIZE IN POETRY (II), 114 N. Murray St., Madison WI 53715-1199, Brittingham Prize inaugurated in 1985, poetry editor Ronald Wallace. The University of Wisconsin Press publishes primarily scholarly works, but they offer the annual **Brittingham Prize of $1,000 plus publication. The contest is the only way in which this press publishes poetry.** Send SASE for rules. **Submit between September 1 and October 1, unbound ms volume of 50-80 pgs., with name, address and telephone number on title page. No translations. Poems must be previously unpublished in book form. Poems published in journals, chapbooks and anthologies may be included**

but must be acknowledged. There is a non-refundable $15 reading fee which must accompany the ms. (Checks to University of Wisconsin Press.) Mss will *not* be returned. Enclose SASE for contest results. Qualified readers will screen all mss. Winner will be selected by "a distinguished poet who will remain anonymous until the winner is announced in mid-February." Past judges include C.K. Williams, Maxine Kumin, Mona Van Duyn, Charles Wright, Gerald Stern, Mary Oliver, Donald Finkel, Donald Justice and Lisel Mueller. Recent winners are Jim Daniels, Patricia Dobler, David Kirby, Lisa Zeidner, Stefanie Marlis, Judith Vollmer, Renée A. Ashley, Tony Hoagland and Stephanie Strickland.

‡THE WISCONSIN RESTAURATEUR (IV-Themes), #300, 31 S. Henry, Madison WI 53703, phone (608)251-3663, founded 1933, poetry editor Jan LaRue, is a "trade association monthly (except November-December combined), circulation 4,200, for the promotion, protection, and improvement of the Wisconsin foodservice industry." They use "all types of poetry, but must have food service as subject. Nothing lengthy or off-color (length 10-50 lines)." They buy 6-12 poems/year. Sample: $1.75 plus postage. Send SASE for guidelines. Reports in 1-2 months. Pays $2.50-7.50/poem. Editor sometimes comments on rejections. She advises, "Study copies of the magazine before submitting."

"We believe writers, whether female or male, must be especially tuned into the world about them and the world as it translates to human existence," says Wisconsin Review *Editor Valerie Jahns. "The Renaissance quote (sometimes credited to da Vinci) sums this up very well: '[People are] but the cosmos in miniature.' " Jahns says they were struck by the overall emotional impact of this cover illustration by Jean Eglinton because "the woman sits in the natural world while also carrying the natural world inside her."*

WISCONSIN REVIEW

Volume 26, Number 2

WISCONSIN REVIEW; WISCONSIN REVIEW PRESS (II), Box 158, Radford Hall, University of Wisconsin-Oshkosh, Oshkosh WI 54901, phone (414)424-2267, founded 1966, editor Valerie Jahns, is published 3 times/year. "In poetry we publish mostly free verse with strong images and fresh approaches. We want new turns of phrase." They have published poetry by Laurel Mills, Joseph Bruchac, Kenneth Frost, Paul Marion, Dionisio Martinez, Stephen Perry, Margaret Randall, David Steingass, Brian Swann and Peter Wild. As a sample the editor selected these lines from "Early Morning of Another World" by Tom McKeown:

> After squid and cool white wine there is
> no sleep. The long tentacles uncurl
> out of the dark with all that was left behind.
> Promises expand promises. A frayed mouth
> loses its color in the dawn.

The *Review* is 48-64 pgs., 6×9, elegantly printed on quality white stock, glossy card cover with color art, b&w art inside. They receive about 1,500 poetry submissions/year, use about 75. They use 30-40 pgs. of poetry in each issue. Press run is 2,000, for 50 subscribers, 30 of which are libraries. Single copy: $3; subscription: $8. Sample postpaid: $2. Submit mss September 15 through May 15. Offices checked bimonthly during summer. Editor requests no more than 4 poems/submission, one poem/page, single-spaced with name and address of writer on each page. Simultaneous submissions OK, but previously unsubmitted works preferable. Cover letter also preferred; include brief bio. Send SASE for guidelines. Reports within 1-4 months. Pays 2 copies.

THE WISE WOMAN (I, IV-Feminist), 2441 Cordova St., Oakland CA 94602, founded 1980, editor and publisher Ann Forfreedom, is a quarterly journal "focusing on feminist issues, feminist spirituality, Goddess lore and Feminist Witchcraft." They want "mostly shorter poetry—by both women and men—

dealing with these themes." They have published poetry by Maura Alia Bramkamp and Viviane Lerner. As a sample the editor selected these lines from "Arise O Women" by Kathleen Weinschenk:

> O Women of the world,
> Catch a vision
> Of your own true self.
> Discover the power
> Within . . .

TWW is magazine-sized, approximately 52 pgs., offset. "At least 20 poems received/year; accept about 30% of appropriate poems." Subscription: $15. **Sample postpaid: $4. Ms should be typed, double-spaced, with writer's name and address on each page. Cover letter not required, "but it is appreciated." They will consider previously published poems. Pays 1 copy.** Ann Forfreedom says, "I prefer poems that are active, come from the writer's deep experiences or feelings, are brief and are applicable to many kinds of people. A focus on Goddess culture, nature or feminist issues is helpful. Good spelling is deeply appreciated."

WITHOUT HALOS; OCEAN COUNTY POETS COLLECTIVE (II), P.O. Box 1342, Point Pleasant Beach NJ 08742, founded 1983, editor-in-chief Frank Finale, an annual publication of the Ocean County Poets Collective; it prints "good contemporary poetry." The magazine **"accepts all genres, though no obscenity. Prefers poetry no longer than 2 pages. Wants to see strong, lucid images ground in experience." They do not want "religious verse or greeting card lyrics."** They have recently published poetry by Diana Der-Hovanessian, William Doreski, Marvin Solomon and Madeline J. Tiger. "Issue X features Alicia Ostriker with three poems and a brief essay on teaching." As a sample, the editor selected these lines from "Clearer than the moon" by Gayle Elen Harvey:

> Even the pond's scummed
> and mysterious. Colors won't stop
> bleeding.
>
> Thunder clouds of hot, magenta blossoms roamed
> these landscapes. Haystacks bloomed like peonies
> and there were flying buttresses of wind
> and poplars.

Without Halos is digest-sized, handsomely printed with b&w artwork inside and on the cover, 112 pgs. flat-spined with glossy card cover. Circulation is 1,000, of which 100 are subscriptions and 100 are sold on newsstands; other distribution is at cultural events, readings, workshops, etc. Single copy: $5. **Sample (back issue) postpaid: $4. The editors "prefer letter-quality printing, single or double-spaced, no more than 5 poems. Name and address should appear in top left-hand corner. Reads submissions January 1 through June 30 only. No manuscript returned without proper SASE. Sloppiness tossed back." Reports in 2-4 months and all acceptances are printed in the next annual issue, which appears in the winter. Pays 1 copy; discount on extras. Acquires first North American serial rights.** For the last seven years, *Without Halos* has received modest grants from the New Jersey State Council on the Arts.

‡WITWATERSRAND UNIVERSITY PRESS (IV-Foreign languages), University of the Witwatersrand, Johannesburg, WITS 2050 South Africa, phone (011)716-2023, **publishes poetry in African languages only.** In their Black Writers Series, for instance, they have published poems in Zulu, Xhosa, and Southern Sotho. Send SAE with IRCs for catalog to buy samples.

WOLSAK AND WYNN PUBLISHERS LTD. (II), Box 316, Don Mills Post Office, Don Mills, Ontario M3C 2S7 Canada, phone (416)222-4690, founded 1982, poetry editors Heather Cadsby and Maria Jacobs, publishes 5 flat-spined literary paperbacks/year (56-100 pgs.). They have published collections of poetry by Richard Harrison and Anne Marriott. Here is a sample from **Impromptu Feats of Balance** by Michael Redhill:

> (for lesley)
> putting on this sweater is like going underwater, this territory
> that is only yours, the place where your breasts come to a slow
> fall where your skin touches. your scent is stitched into its
> pattern, but now my skin, my hair, everything rises unfamiliar
> from the wool. and still later i might think i have walked the
> day out almost in your skin, but there is nothing of you in
> here at all. only the fabric's bad rendition of the shape you
> left, its apparent willingness to leave all of you behind.

The books are handsomely printed. **Sample: $8 US or $10 Canadian. Send sample poems with query, bio, publications. No simultaneous submissions. Reports on queries in 4 months. Pays**

10% royalties. **Buys first rights.** Maria Jacobs says, "W&W prefers not to prescribe. We are open to *good* writing of any kind."

‡WOMEN'S EDUCATION DES FEMMES (IV-Regional, women/feminism), 47 Main St., Toronto, Ontario M6J 2G6 Canada, phone (416)960-4644, founded 1982, editor Christina Starr, is a quarterly using **"feminist poetry, about women, written by Canadian women only."** They have recently published poetry by Elizabeth Brewster, Dianne Reid, Barbara Wood and Zoë Landale. As a sample the editor selected these lines by Gillian Harding-Russell:

> I could not set
> and set the table, practise not doing
> and doing. Not eating and eating,
> the meal not getting and getting
> cold, depending on how
> you look at it.

The editor describes it as 48 pgs., magazine-sized, web offset, saddle-stapled, with one-color cover. Subscription: $17 individual, $30 institution. **Sample postpaid: $2.50. Reports in 2-3 months. Pays $25/poem plus 2 copies.** Occasionally reviews books of poetry. Open to unsolicited reviews.

WOMEN'S PRESS (CANADA) (IV-Women/feminism, lesbian), #233, 517 College St., Toronto, Ontario M6G 4A2 Canada, founded 1972, co-managing editors Ann Decter and Martha Ayim, publishes **"minimum ms 48 pgs. Women of colour, feminist, political content, lesbian, modern or postmodern form. No haiku."** As a sample the editor selected these lines by Dionne Brand:

> this is you girl, this is the poem no woman
> ever write for a woman because she 'fraid to touch

They publish 1 flat-spined paperback/year. **Query first with cover letter and sample poems. Reports in 6 months. Pays 10% royalties, $150 advance, 6 copies.**

WOMEN'S STUDIES QUARTERLY; THE FEMINIST PRESS AT CUNY (IV-Women, feminist, bilingual), Dept. PM, 311 E. 94th St., New York NY 10128, phone (212)360-5790. *Women's Studies Quarterly*, founded 1972, publisher Florence Howe, is a nonfiction quarterly using **"poetry that focuses on current issues of importance to women; emphasis on education or activism preferable."** They have published poetry by Mila Aguilar. The editor describes it as 5½ × 8½, 150-200 pgs. They use 1-5 poems in each issue. Their press run is 1,500. **Sample postpaid: $13. Simultaneous submissions and previously published poems OK. Editor rarely comments on rejections. Pays 1 copy.** The Feminist Press publishes primarily both historical and contemporary fiction and nonfiction (12-15 titles/year), but it also publishes some poetry, such as the series, **The Defiant Muse,** bilingual volumes (Hispanic, French, Italian and German) of poetry by women from the Middle-Ages to the present.

WOMENWISE (III, IV-Women, feminist), 38 South Main St., Concord NH 03301, phone (603)225-2739, founded 1978, run by an editorial committee, is "a quarterly newspaper that deals specifically with issues relating to women's health—research, education, and politics." They want **"poetry reflecting status of women in society, relating specifically to women's health issues."** They do not want **"poetry that doesn't include women or is written by men; poetry that degrades women or is anti-choice."** *WomenWise* is a tabloid newspaper, 12 pgs., printed on quality stock with b&w art and graphics. Press run is 3,000 +. Single copy: $2.95; subscription: $10/year. **Sample: $2.95. Submissions should be typed double-spaced. Reads submissions March, June, September and December only. Reporting time and time to publication varies. Pays 1-year subscription. Acquires first North American serial rights.** Staff reviews books of poetry in "any word count," single format. They say they often receive mss with no SASE. "We throw them away. Please remember that we are a nonprofit organization with limited resources."

WOODLEY MEMORIAL PRESS; THE ROBERT GROSS MEMORIAL PRIZE FOR POETRY (IV-Regional), English Department, Washburn University, Topeka KS 66621, phone (913)231-1010, ext. 1448, founded 1980, editor Robert Lawson, publishes 1-2 flat-spined paperbacks a year, **collections of poets from Kansas or with Kansas connections, "terms individually arranged with author on acceptance of ms."** They have published poetry by Craig Goad, Michael L. Johnson, Bruce Bond and Harley Elliott. As a sample the editor selected these lines from "In the Old House" by William Stafford:

> Inside our Victrola a tin voice, faint
> but somehow both fragile and powerful, soared
> and could be only Caruso, all the way from
> Rome: I traced my fingers on the gold letters
> and listened my way deeper and deeper

"We charge $5 reading fee for unsolicited mss." Replies to queries in 2 weeks, to mss in 2 months,

published 1 year after acceptance. Samples may be individually ordered from the press for $5. Send SASE for guidelines for Robert Gross Memorial Poetry and Fiction Prize ($100 and publication).

WORCESTER REVIEW; WORCESTER COUNTY POETRY ASSOCIATION, INC. (II, IV-Regional), 6 Chatham St., Worcester MA 01609, phone (508)797-4770, founded 1973, managing editor Rodger Martin. *WR* appears annually with emphasis on poetry. New England writers are encouraged to submit, though work by other poets is used also. They want "work that is crafted, intuitively honest, and empathetic, not work that shows the poet little respects his work or his readers." They have published poetry by Richard Eberhart, William Stafford and Walter McDonald. *WR* is 6×9, flat-spined, 64+ pgs., professionally printed in dark type on quality stock with glossy card cover, press run of 1,000 for 300 subscriptions (50 of them libraries) and 300 shelf sales. Subscription: $15 (includes membership in WCPA). Sample postpaid: $4. Submit maximum of 5 poems. "I recommend 3 or less for most favorable readings." Simultaneous submissions OK "if indicated." Previously published poems "only on special occasions." Editor comments on rejections "if ms warrants a response." Send SASE for guidelines. Reports in 4-6 months. Pays $10/poem, depending upon grants, plus 2 copies. Buys first rights. They have an annual contest for poets who live, work, or in some way (past/present) have a Worcester County connection. The editor advises, "Read some. Listen a lot."

WORDS OF WISDOM (II, IV-Humor), 612 Front St. East, Glendora NJ 08029-1133, founded 1981, editor J.M. Freiermuth, appears monthly using **"short, pithy poetry, the stuff that brings a smile to the reader's face on first reading. No religious."** They have published poetry by Darcy Cummings, Jim DeWitt, Patrick Cauchi, Virginia Hlavsa and Robert Dunn. It is 30-44 pgs., photocopied with plain paper cover. They publish about 50 of 300 submissions received. Press run is 150 for 110 subscribers. Subscription: $15. Sample postpaid: $2. Make checks payable to J.M. Freiermuth. Will publish simultaneous and previously published material only if submitted on floppy disk in ASCII format. Cover letter required with submissions; include "names of lit mags author subscribes to." No submissions accepted December 1 through January 31. Reports usually within 2 months. Pays 1 copy. Acquires one-time rights. Staff reviews books of poetry.

WORDSMITH (I), Box 891, Ft. Collins CO 80522-0891, founded 1991, editor Judith Kaufman, poetry editor Brian Kaufman, appears annually. **"We are open to all styles of prose and poetry. Most subject matter is OK, but we steer clear of erotica and gay or lesbian work. Also, no greeting card poetry."** They have recently published poetry by Lyn Brown and Claire J. Baker. As a sample the poetry editor selected these lines from his own poem, "Metalhead":

> Like animals crouched over
> A fresh kill, we grab
> The throat of the world
> And tear it open. Violence is easy,
> The colors are splendid,
> And we are easily amused.

Wordsmith is 64-80 pgs., digest-sized, perfect-bound, with glossy cover. Uses 20-30 poems each issue. Press run is 400 for 200 subscribers of which 2 are libraries, 200 shelf sales. Single copy: $5; subscription: $5/year, $9/2 years. Sample postpaid: $3. No previously published poems or simultaneous submissions. Submit up to 100 lines, single-spaced, one poem/page. "We no longer personally respond to every submission. (We can't; too many!)" Send SASE for guidelines. Pays $5. Buys one-time rights. Offers $25 for the best poem in each issue; editor's choice. The editors seem to prefer free verse dealing with risky topics (i.e. politics, art). They feature poems of varying lengths (some long, others only a few lines), all trying to find the precise words to depict intriguing ideas. If you send here, focus on message and craft. Brian Kaufman says, "Tell the truth. Speak in images. Keep writing."

WORDSONG; BOYDS MILLS PRESS (IV-Children), 815 Church St., Honesdale PA 18431, phone (717)253-1164, founded 1990, editor-in-chief Dr. Bernice E. Cullinan, is the imprint under which Boyds Mills Press (a *Highlights for Children* company) publishes books of poetry for children of all ages. **"Wordsong encourages quality poetry which reflects childhood fun, moral standards and multiculturalism. We are not interested in poetry for adults or that which includes violence or sexuality or promotes hatred."** They have recently published poetry by Beverly McLoughland and John Ciardi. As a sample the editor selected these lines from **Somebody Catch My Homework** by David L. Harrison:

> Billy brought his snake to school
> For show and tell today.
> "This snake belongs to me," he said.
> "It's gentle as can be," he said.
> "It wouldn't hurt a flea," he said.

> *But it swallowed him anyway.*

"Wordsong prefers original work but will consider anthologies and previously published collections. We ask poets to send collections of 30-50 poems with a common theme; please send complete book manuscripts, not single poems. We buy all rights to collections and publish on an advance-and-royalty basis. Wordsong guarantees a response from editors within one month of our receiving submissions or the poet may call us collect to inquire. Please direct submissions to Beth Troop, manuscript coordinator." Dr. Cullinan says, "Poetry lies at the heart of the elementary school literature and reading program. In fact, poetry lies right at the heart of children's language learning. Poetry speaks to the heart of a child. We are anxious to find outstanding poetry—rhyme, free verse and songs—that will appeal to children."

WORKS MAGAZINE (IV-Science fiction), 12 Blakestones Rd., Slaithwaite, Huddersfield, Yorks HD7 5UQ United Kingdom, founded 1989, editor Dave W. Hughes, is a biannual using "speculative and imaginative fiction or poetry favoring science fiction." They want **"surreal/science fiction poetry. Nothing more than 50 lines. No romance or general work."** They have published poetry by Andy Darlington, Steve Sneyd, Paul Weinman and Brian Aldiss. The editor says *Works* is 52 pgs., A5, stitched with texture cover. They receive about 150 poems/year, use 36. Press run is 400 for 200 subscribers of which 4 are libraries, 50 shelf sales. Single copy: £1.60 sterling (£2.50 for US); subscription: £5.50 sterling. **No simultaneous submissions. Disk submissions acceptable: IBM (5¼ or 3½-inch) or Atari 520ST (3½-inch); ASCII files only. Seldom comments on rejections. Send SASE for guidelines. Reports within a month. Pays 1 copy.** "Reviews of books and magazines are handled in *Works Study*, a free supplement for subscribers." The editor says, "Study the market."

WoRM fEASt!; TAPE WoRM; KNIGHTMAYOR PRODUCTIONS (II, IV-Erotica, occult), P.O. Box 519, Westminster MD 21158-0519, *WoRM fEASt!*, an underground monthly, founded 1989, editors Llori Steinberg and Blaire Presley. *Tape WoRM* is an audio series featuring music, poetry, comedy and more. For *Wf* they want **"weird/strange poetry; no traditional verse, no rhyme (unless it's way off the keister), no haiku, no love poems, no religious or Christian poetry. Robert Frost is a no-no! Bukowski, Bennett, Kross and Bridgewater a must!"** They have recently published poetry by Nielsen, Moore, Bryant and Lifshin. The editors say *Wf* is usually 32 pgs., if not more, digest-sized, saddle-stitched, with artwork and photos (from subscribers). Press run 500. "The digest is different colors every time." **Sample postpaid: $5. Previously published poems OK. Cover letter required; include short bio with credits and picture. Always comments on rejections. Send SASE for guidelines. "We report rather quickly." Pays 1 copy of *WoRM fEASt!* No payment on *Tape WoRM* audio series; contact for submissions guidelines.** Reviews books of poetry. Open to unsolicited reviews. Send books to Llori Steinberg for review consideration. "Sometimes we publish chapbooks for poets' personal use. They buy and they sell." The editors say, "We want weird shock therapy poetry, erotica, poems about politics or drugs. No censorship. Don't be afraid to send the weirdest works. The more shock you induce, the better your chances."

WORMWOOD REVIEW PRESS; THE WORMWOOD REVIEW; THE WORMWOOD AWARD (II), P.O. Box 4698, Stockton CA 95204-0698, phone (209)466-8231, founded 1959, poetry editor Marvin Malone. "The philosophy behind *Wormwood*: (i) avoid publishing oneself and personal friends, (ii) avoid being a 'local' magazine and strive for a national and international audience, (iii) seek unknown talents rather than establishment or fashionable authors, (iv) encourage originality by working with and promoting authors capable of extending the existing patterns of Amerenglish literature, (v) avoid all cults and allegiances and the you-scratch-my-back-and-I-will-scratch-yours approach to publishing, (vi) accept the fact that magazine content is more important than format in the long run, (vii) presume a literate audience and try to make the mag readable from the first page to the last, (viii) restrict the number of pages to no more than 40 per issue since only the insensitive and the masochistic can handle more pages at one sitting, (ix) pay bills on time and don't expect special favors in honor of the muse, and lastly and most importantly (x) don't become too serious and righteous." They want **"poetry and prose poetry that communicate the temper and range of human experience in contemporary society; don't want religious poetry and work that descends into bathos; don't want imitative sweet verse. Must be original; any style or school from traditional to ultra experimental, but *must* communicate; 3-600 lines."** They have published poetry by Ron Koertge, Gerald Locklin, Charles Bukowski, Edward Field and Lyn Lifshin. As a sample the editor selected these lines by Phil Weidman:

> Life tests '
> *our mettle.*
> *Everyday.*
> *Unending.*
> *Life is what*
> *the dying*
> *pray for.*

> *What the*
> *healthy curse.*

Wormwood is a digest-sized quarterly, offset from photoreduced typescript, saddle-stapled. Press run is 700 for 500 subscribers of which 210 are libraries. Yellow pages in the center of each issue feature "one poet or one idea." Subscription: $8. **Sample postpaid: $4. Submit 2-10 poems on as many pages. Send SASE for guidelines. Reports in 2-8 weeks. Pays 2-10 copies of the magazine or cash equivalent ($6-30). Acquires all rights.** Returns rights on written request, without cost, provided the magazine is acknowledged whenever reprinted. Reviews books of poetry. **For chapbook publication, no query; send 40-60 poems.** "Covering letter not necessary—decisions are made solely on merit of submitted work." **Reports in 1-2 months. Pays 35 copies or cash equivalent ($105). Send $4 for samples or check libraries.** They offer the Wormwood Award to the Most Overlooked Book of Worth (poetry or prose) for a calendar year, judged by Marvin Malone. Comments on rejections if the work has merit. The editor advises, "Have something to say. Read the past and modern 'master' poets. Absorb what they've done, but then write as effectively as you can in your own style. If you can say it in 40 words, do *not* use 400 or 4,000 words."

WRIT (II, IV-Translations), 2 Sussex Ave., Toronto, Ontario M5S 1J5 Canada, phone (416)978-4871, founded 1970, editor Roger Greenwald, associate editor Richard Lush, is a "literary annual publishing new fiction, poetry, and translation of high quality; has room for unestablished writers." **No limitations on kind of poetry sought; new forms welcome. "Must show conscious and disciplined use of language."** They do not want to see "haiku, purely formal exercises, and poetry by people who don't bother reading." They have published poems by Rolf Jacobsen, Paavo Haavikko, Adelia Prado and J. Bernlef. As a sample the editor selected these lines from "Nineteen Poems" by Charles Douglas:

> *But even underground our journey will observe*
>
> *laws of topography, until an eruption*
> *becomes like a wart, a small disturbance*
> *of physiognomy, and each of our acts the weight*
>
> *of a stone on the hillside, under the freedom system.*

The magazine is 6×9, 96 pgs., flat-spined and sewn, professionally printed on heavy stock, matte card cover with color art. Circulation is 700, 125 subscriptions of which 75 are libraries, about 125 store and direct sales. **Sample postpaid: $7.50. Poems must be typed and easily legible, printouts as close to letter quality as possible. No simultaneous submissions. Reads submissions September 1 through April 30 only.** Editor "sometimes comments on rejections." **Reports in 2-3 months.** Acceptances appear in the next issue published. **Pays 2 copies and discount on bulk purchases. Buys first North American serial rights.** Staff reviews books of poetry. Send books— "but not self-published books"—for review consideration. The editor advises, "Read a copy of the magazine you're submitting to. Let this give you an idea of the quality we're looking for. But in the case of *WRIT*, don't assume we favor only the styles of the pieces we've already published (we can only print what we get and are open to all styles). Enclose phone number and SASE with Canadian stamps or SAE with International Reply Coupons."

THE WRITE WAY; TAKING CARE OF YOURSELF; ANN'S ENTERPRISES (I, IV-Themes), 810 Overhill Rd., Deland FL 32720, phone (904)734-1955, founded 1988, editor Ann Larberg. *TWW* is a quarterly using **poems of up to 30 lines on the theme of writing.** As a sample the editor selected "Limerick Lamentation" by Donna Bickley:

> *Composing a limerick's not easy*
> *Although my attempts make me queasy,*
> *I jot down a line, I stretch for a rhyme.*
> *Reaching as far as it pleases me.*

TWW is a 6-page newsletter with articles on writing and ads. Single copy: $3; subscription: $12. **Do not submit in summer. Reads submissions January 1 through June 30. Reports in 6 weeks. Pays 2 copies.** Open to unsolicited reviews. Poets may also send books for review consideration.

ALWAYS include a self-addressed, stamped envelope (SASE) when sending a ms or query to a publisher within your own country. When sending material to other countries, include a self-addressed envelope and International Reply Coupons (IRCs), available for purchase at most post offices.

They hold contests quarterly. *Taking Care of Yourself*, a newsletter of well-being, **accepts 2 poems/ issue on the theme of health. Sample free with SASE. Pays copies.**

THE WRITER; POET TO POET (I, II), 120 Boylston St., Boston MA 02116-4615, founded 1887, "Poet to Poet," column by Denise Dumars. This monthly magazine for writers has a quarterly instructional column to which poets may submit work for possible publication and comment by Denise Dumars. **Readers may find suggestions in the column for possible themes or types of poems.** As a sample the editor chose the opening lines of "Mallard" by Carol Diane Iversen:

> *For a moment, my lord, you are stilled*
> *in the water before me,*
> *your green head*
> *painted as finely as a decoy:*
> *I marvel at the beauty, clear*
> *engraving of each feather*
> *as you pose with your brown wife.*

Subscription: $27 (introductory offer: 5 issues for $10). Single copy: $3. **Submit no more than 3 poems, no longer than 30 lines each, not on onion skin or erasable bond, name and address on each page, one poem to a page. There is no pay and mss are not acknowledged or returned. Acquires first North American serial rights.**

WRITERS' CENTER PRESS; THE FLYING ISLAND; INDIANA CHAPBOOK POETRY CONTEST; WRITERS' CENTER OF INDIANAPOLIS (II, IV-Regional), P.O. Box 88386, Indianapolis IN 46208, founded 1979, executive director Jim Powell. Writers' Center Press publishes *The Flying Island*, a biannual of fiction, poetry, reviews and literary commentary by those **living in or connected to Indiana. They want poetry of high literary quality; no stylistic or thematic restrictions.** They have published poetry by Jared Carter, Alice Friman, Yusef Komunyakaa and Roger Mitchell. As a sample the editor selected these lines from "Snapshot: Father Washing the Dog" by Karen I. Jaquish:

> *The reek of Sergeant's Flea Soap stings.*
> *Our dog is lathered into placid acceptance.*
> *You glance up, toss that famous grin*
> *given to strangers and Kodak cameras.*

TFI, a 24-page tabloid, includes artwork, graphics and photography. They receive about 1,000 poems a year, accept approximately 5%. Press run is 1,000 for 500 subscribers. **Previously published poems OK, but not encouraged. Simultaneous submissions OK, if so advised. Brief bio required. Often comments on rejections. Send SASE for guidelines. Reports in 3-6 months. Pays $5 minimum for previously unpublished work. Buys first North American serial rights.** Staff reviews books of poetry. Send books for review consideration. The center sponsors frequent contests for members through its quarterly newsletter and open readings. They also hold the Indiana Chapbook Poetry Contest every other year (rotating with a short fiction contest). Prize is $150 and publication. They advise, "Balance solitary writing time by getting involved in a writing community. We frequently recommend rejected writers join a poetry workshop."

WRITER'S DIGEST (IV-Themes/writing, humor); WRITER'S DIGEST WRITING COMPETITION (II), 1507 Dana Ave., Cincinnati OH 45207, phone (513)531-2222, founded 1921, associate editor Angela Terez, is a monthly magazine for freelance writers—fiction, nonfiction, poetry and drama. "All editorial copy is aimed at helping writers to write better and become more successful. **Poetry is included in 'The Writing Life' section of *Writer's Digest* only. Preference is given to short, light verse concerning 'the writing life'**—the foibles, frenzies, delights and distractions inherent in being a writer. Serious verse is acceptable; however, no poetry unrelated to writing. We're looking for more serious poems on the joys and foibles of the writing life, but avoid the trite or maudlin." Preferred length: 4-20 lines. They have published poetry by Charles Ghigna. As a sample, the editors selected this poem, "Mixed Messages," by Lois McBride Terry:

> *"As a poet, you're no Poe."*
> *"At prose, you're certainly not a pro."*
> *"Your movie script is nondescript.*
> *(And sadder still, your comic strip.)"*
> *The only line they don't reject:*
> *"Enclosed is my subscription check."*

They use 2 short poems/issue, about 25/year of the 1,500+ submitted. *Writer's Digest* has a circulation of 225,000. Subscription: $21. **Sample postpaid: $3. Do not submit to Michael Bugeja, poetry columnist for the magazine. Submit to Angela Terez, associate editor, each poem on a separate page, no more than 8/submission. Previously published poems and simultaneous submissions OK if acknowledged in covering letter. Editor comments on rejections** "when we want to encourage or explain decision." **Send SASE for guidelines. Reports in 1-4 weeks. Pays**

CLOSE-UP

One Poet's Keys to Success

"At the old RKO"

In the warm forgiving dark
at the old RKO/Orpheum in Kansas City,
weeping into clean, carefully ironed hankies,
my chum, Betty Jo Newcomb (we had names like that
in the 30's), and I first tasted love
Romberg and Friml musical-comedy style.

And when Fred Astaire persuaded Ginger Rogers
to smile at last, we clung together
in brave, second-hand, ecstasies,
the passions spinning us unthinkable then.

On the swaying street-car going home,
we swore to be best friends forever.
Meanwhile, magic Austria, maybe all Europe,
waited out there for our sex lives to begin.

Judy Klare

Sometimes poets are so close to home that you pass them as you do strangers on the street or in the grocery store, unaware that you both share the same passion for verse. Such was the case with Judy Klare, a poet from Athens, Ohio, where I live and write my column for *Writer's Digest*.

I did not encounter Klare at the local Kroger's but in the top 100 winners in *WD's* annual writing competition. I noticed her name and hometown and telephoned her to convey my congratulations.

As it turns out, I should have noticed her name much earlier than I did because Klare had placed seven times in the magazine's top 100.

Klare, a licensed psychologist, began her career by teaching English and Social Studies in 1942 at the junior high school in Independence, Missouri. Later she worked as an editor and a consultant.

A seasoned poet years before I met her, Klare has recently placed work in such magazines as *Kentucky Poetry Review*, *Voices International*, *Piedmont Literary Review*, *Kansas Quarterly*, *Iowa Woman* and *Poetpourri*.

"My first publications came early," Klare says, "but then World War II, graduate school, raising a family and a part-time career meant that I could find little or no time to write."

Now retired, she can devote more time to writing—both nonfiction and poetry. She has placed two nonfiction books for teenage girls titled **Self-Esteem** and **Manners**, published in 1989 and 1990 respectively, by Rourke Publishing Group in Vero Beach, Florida. "Right now I'm doing a series of short bios for children (ages 11-14) on historic Native Americans like Red Cloud. I've been trying to work on a grammar book that also is humorous—i.e. 'interesting.'"

In between these projects she composes poems and enters some of them in contests. Klare says she usually sends work to contests sponsored by literary magazines where competition is often keen. "I think entering contests gives you a chance to discipline yourself—get something else out in the mail—and if you place, it gives you some idea of how you're doing."

Another key to her success is her belief in the value of writers' groups. "I currently belong to two," Klare says. "The local group is small—only seven members. We share information about marketing, contests and workshops at our monthly meetings. We also phone each other fairly regularly with pertinent tips or with news about acceptances or rejections.

"The other group is large—over 30 paying members. We meet twice monthly at 9:30 in the morning and read and critique until noon," she says. Then participants break for lunch to share marketing tips.

Belonging to a writer's group is important, but membership alone is not the only key to success as a poet, Klare says. "The chance to hear yourself aloud in front of other people is the best benefit." Reading poems in a room with other people sometimes helps a writer discover problems that she otherwise would have overlooked, she notes, "even before the audience does."

Klare also recommends writing workshops. "I attended the Appalachian Writers Workshop at Hindman, Kentucky," she says. "A poet on the faculty there encouraged me, among other counselings, to continue my interest in syllabic poetry"—poems whose line lengths are determined by the number of syllables.

But Klare had some misgivings about the form. While she thought it helped her tighten her poems, she also suspected that some editors were biased against syllabic verse. However, at the Kentucky workshop, the faculty poet did more than encourage her. Just as important, she says, "He gave me concrete ideas for markets for my work."

Finally, Klare says, attending literary festivals to hear and meet top poets can inspire work and lead to new contacts. "I am fortunate in that I live in a university town and can get to such festivals easily, but it's worth the time to find one." She suggests looking for festival listings in writers' magazines and newspapers.

As far as marketing poetry is concerned, Klare says, "The key words are: perseverance, perseverance and perseverance." She notes that directories like **Poet's Market** prove "there is an outlet for your best material. It's your job to find."

—*Michael J. Bugeja*

❝I think entering contests gives you a chance to discipline yourself—get something else out in the mail—and if you place, it gives you some idea of how you're doing.❞
—Judy Klare

$15-50/poem. Poetry up to 16 lines on any theme is eligible for the annual Writer's Digest Writing Competition. Watch magazine for rules and deadlines, or send SASE for a copy of the contest's rules. (Also see Writer's Digest Books under Publications Useful to Poets.)

WRITER'S EXCHANGE; R.S.V.P. PRESS (I, IV-Humor, themes/writing), Box 394, Society Hill SC 29593, phone (803)378-4556, founded 1983, editor Gene Boone, is a digest-sized newsletter of articles on any aspect of writing, poetry and artwork with a special emphasis on beginners. He wants **"poetry to 24 lines, any subject or style. I also consider short poems such as haiku, tanka, senryu and other fixed forms. I like writing that is upbeat, positive, enlightening or inspiring, especially humorous poetry. I will not consider material that is anti-religious, racist or obscene."** He has published poetry by Victor Chapman, Winnie E. Fitzpatrick, Violet Wilcox and Mary Ann Henn. As a sample he selected these lines (poet unidentified):

> *A hurried world, spinning too fast*
> *Modern technology replaces dreams*
> *With skyscraper nightmares*
> *God watches as we dance at Satan's feet.*

WE is 12-20 pgs., saddle-stitched, with a colored paper cover. It is published quarterly. He accepts about half or more of the poetry received. Press run is 150. Subscription: $10. **Sample postpaid: $2. "I prefer typed mss, one poem per page, readable. Poets should always proofread mss before sending them out. Errors can cause rejection."** No simultaneous submissions. Previously published poetry OK. **Cover letter required; list "prior credits, if any, and other details of writing background."** Send SASE for guidelines. **Responds in 2-4 weeks, usually 4 months until publication. Pays 1 copy. Acquires one-time rights.** Staff reviews books of poetry. Send books for review consideration. They offer cash awards for quarterly contests sponsored through the magazine. Send SASE for current rules. *Writer's Exchange* ranked #9 in the "New Poets" category of the June 1993 *Writer's Digest* Poetry 60 list. This category ranks those markets who often publish poets whose work is new to their publication. The editor says he comments on rejections, "if I feel it will benefit the poet in the long run, never anything too harsh or overly discouraging." His advice to poets: "Support the small press publications you read and enjoy. Without your support these publications will cease to exist. The small press has given many poets their start. In essence, the small press is where poetry lives!"

WRITERS' FORUM (II, IV-Regional), Dept. PM, University of Colorado, Colorado Springs CO 80933-7150, *Writers' Forum* founded 1974, Victoria McCabe is poetry editor. *Writers' Forum*, an annual, publishes both beginning and well-known writers, giving **"some emphasis to contemporary Western literature,** that is, to representation of living experience west of the 100th meridian in relation to place and culture. We collaborate with authors in the process of revision, reconsider and frequently publish revised work. We are open to **solidly crafted imaginative work that is verbally interesting and reveals authentic voice."** They have published poems by William Stafford, David Ray, Kenneth Fields, Harold Witt and Judson Crews. The annual is digest-sized, 225+ pgs., flat-spined, professionally printed with matte card cover, using 40-50 pgs. of poetry in each issue, circulation 800 with 100 subscriptions of which 25 are libraries. **The list price is $8.95 but they offer it at $5.95 to readers of *Writer's Digest*.** They use about 25 of 500 freelance submissions of poetry/year. **Simultaneous submissions OK if acknowledged. Send 3-5 poems. Reads submissions September 1 through March 15. Reports in 3 months. Pays 1 copy. Acquires all rights; returns rights.**

WRITERS FORUM; AND; KROKLOK (IV-Form), 89A Petherton Rd., London N5 2QT England, founded 1963, editor Bob Cobbing, is a small press publisher of experimental work with occasional issues of magazines dealing with sound and visual poetry in cards, leaflets, chapbooks, occasional paperbacks and magazines. **"Explorations of 'the limits of poetry'** including 'graphic' displays, notations for sound and performance, as well as semantic and syntactic developments, not to mention fun."** They have recently published poetry by Steve McCaffery, Dennis Barone, Virginia Firnberg, Harry Gilonis and Jennifer Pike. As a sample the editor selected these lines by jwcurry:

> mental
> while   anguishes
> waiting   languish
> weight   in the
> wage the   languages
>   lungs

The magazines are published "very irregularly" and use "very little unsolicited poetry; practically none." Press run "varies." **Payment "by arrangement." Work should generally be submitted camera-ready.** Under the imprint Writers Forum they publish 12-18 books a year averaging 28 pgs. **Samples and listing: $5. For book publication, query with 6 samples, bio, publications. Pays**

"by arrangement with author." The editor says, "We publish only that which surprises and excites us; poets who have a very individual voice and style."

WRITER'S GUIDELINES: A ROUNDTABLE FOR WRITERS AND EDITORS (I, IV-Themes), Box 608, Pittsburg MO 65724, founded 1988, poetry editor Susan Salaki, is "an open forum market news magazine, publishing down-to-earth comments and suggestions from editors and writers who want to help close the gap between these two professions, find less expensive ways of marketing work and help each other keep their fingers on the pulse of the buying markets. **Only poetry that can elicit strong emotions and vivid images from the reader is accepted. No vague, abstract poetry. All poetry must somehow pertain to publishing, editors or writing.**" They receive about 100 poems a year, accept 6. Sample postpaid: $4. No simultaneous submissions or previously published works. Send #10 SASE for guidelines, free Guideline List and Market Barometer, and brochure. **Reports in 1 week. Pays $1 or 1 copy. Acquires first rights.** The editor says, "If your poetry moves us emotionally, we'll buy it."

WRITER'S JOURNAL (I, II), incorporating *Minnesota Ink*, 27 Empire Dr., St. Paul MN 55103, phone (612)225-1306, *Writer's Journal* founded 1980, poetry editor Esther M. Leiper. *Writer's Journal* is a bimonthly magazine "for writers and poets that offers advice and guidance, motivation, inspiration, to the more serious and published writers and poets." Esther Leiper has 2 columns: "Esther Comments," which specifically critiques poems sent in by readers, and "Every Day with Poetry," which discusses a wide range of poetry topics, often—but not always—including readers' work. She says, "**I enjoy a variety of poetry: free verse, strict forms, concrete, Oriental. But we take nothing vulgar, preachy or sloppily written. Since we appeal to those of different skill levels, some poems are more sophisticated than others, but those accepted must move, intrigue or otherwise positively capture me.** 'Esther Comments' is never used as a negative force to put a poem or a poet down. Indeed, I focus on the best part of a given work and seek to suggest means of improvement on weaker aspects. **Short is best: 25-line limit, though *very* occasionally we use longer. 3-4 poems at a time is just right.**" They have published poetry by Lawrence Schug, Diana Sutliff and Eugene E. Grollmes. As a sample the editor selected these lines from "an unidentified author we'd love to hear from":

> I am with Haysie again on God's ranch,
> It is not yet dawn; we ride west
> over the mountains. His face is in shadow
> but I know it is Haysie because
> I have loved his shadow so.

The *Writer's Journal* is magazine-sized, professionally printed, 60 pgs. (including paper cover), using 4-5 pgs. of poetry in each issue, including columns. Press run is 45,000. They receive about 400 submissions/year of which they use 30-40 (including those used in Esther's column). **Sample postpaid: $4. No query. Reports in 4-5 months. Pays 25¢/line.** The section *Minnesota Ink* began as a separate magazine in 1987. "**We are open to style, prefer light-hearted pieces and of good taste.**" Payment varies. *Writer's Journal* has Spring and Fall poetry contests for previously unpublished poetry. Deadlines: April 15 and November 30. *Minnesota Ink* has summer and winter poetry contests. Deadlines: August 15 and February 28. Reading fee for each contest: $2 first poem, $1 each poem thereafter.

WRITER'S LIFELINE (I), P.O. Box 1641, Cornwall, Ontario K6H 5V6 Canada, phone (613)932-2135, fax (613)932-7735, founded 1974, editor Stephen Gill, published 3 times a year, containing articles and information useful to writers, **poetry** and book reviews. "**We prefer poems on social concerns. We avoid sex.**" As a sample the editor selected these lines from his poem, "Bigotry":

> It grows
> on the babel of confusion
> in the lap of
> the blinding dust of vanity
> by the arrogant prince of ignorance.

WL is digest-sized, 36-40 pgs., saddle-stitched with paper 2-color cover, printed in small type, poems sometimes in bold or italics. Circulation is 1,500. Subscription: $18. **Sample postpaid: $3. Send SASE for guidelines. Responds in 1 month. Pays 3 copies. Acquires first North American serial rights.** Reviews books of poetry in 500-1,500 words. "We need book reviews." Query if interested.

‡WRITING FOR OUR LIVES; RUNNING DEER PRESS (I, II, IV-Women), 647 N. Santa Cruz Ave., The Annex, Los Gatos CA 95030, phone (408)354-8604, founded 1991, editor/publisher Janet McEwan, appears twice a year. "*Writing For Our Lives* serves as a vessel for poems, short fiction, stories, letters, autobiographies and journal excerpts from the life stories, experiences and spiritual journeys of women." They want **poetry that is "personal, women's real life, life-saving, autobiographical, serious—**

but don't forget humorous, silence-breaking, many styles, many voices. Women writers only, please."
As a sample we selected these lines from "Sisters" by Rita A. White:

> Brought together in old age
> Friends and loved ones gone
> The same in many ways now
> Hands that tremble, legs that don't obey
> Cups of tea, nibbles of toast
> But still a difference.

Writing For Our Lives is 64-80 pgs., 5¼×8¼, printed on recycled paper and perfect-bound with matte card cover. They receive about 250 poems a year, accept approximately 15%. Press run is 1,000. Subscription: $11.50 individuals, $14 institutions. **Sample postpaid: $7. Submit typed poems with name and phone number at top of each page. Previously published poems ("sometimes") and simultaneous submissions OK. Include a self-addressed, stamped postcard "so I can promptly acknowledge receipt of your work."** A SASE should also be included for reply and return of ms. Closing dates are February 15 and August 15. "I read, make selections and send notification letters as soon as possible after the closing dates." Seldom comments on rejections. Send SASE for guidelines. Pays 2 copies, discount on additional copies and discount on 1-year subscription. Acquires first world-wide English language serial (or one-time reprint) rights. "Our contributors and circulation are international."

‡XANADU: A LITERARY JOURNAL (II), P.O. Box 773, Huntington NY 11743, founded 1979, editors Mildred Jeffrey, Barbara Lucas and Weslea Sidon, is an annual publishing "serious poems and one scholarly essay on contemporary poetry or critical theory." They want **well-crafted quality poems. Nothing inspirational, obscene or from beginners."** They have recently published poetry by Jill Bart, Diana Chang, Simon Perchik and Aaron Kramer. As a sample the editors selected these lines from "Sex, Genetics, The Sea" by Charles Entrekin:

> Like falling backwards in time
> toward something I don't comprehend,
> if I run forward, if I stand still,
> what I see has no name,
> slouches away if I look at it,
> yet feel in the touch of bones . . .

The editors describe the journal as 50-60 pgs., no ads, no graphics. Press run is 300 for 100 subscribers of which 5 are libraries. **Sample postpaid: $5. No previously published poems; simultaneous submissions OK. Poems must be typed.** Seldom comments on rejections. Send SASE for guidelines. Reports in 2 weeks to 3 months. Pays 1 copy. Acquires first North American serial rights.

XAVIER REVIEW (II), Box 110C, Xavier University, New Orleans LA 70125, phone (504)486-7411, founded 1961, editor Thomas Bonner, Jr., is a biannual that publishes poetry, fiction, nonfiction and reviews (contemporary literature) for professional writers, libraries, colleges and universities. Press run is 500. Subscription: $10. **Sample postpaid: $5. No submission information provided.**

XENOPHILIA; OMEGA CAT PRESS (II, IV-Themes), 904 Old Town Ct., Cupertino CA 95014, founded 1990, editor Joy Oestreicher. *Xenophilia* appears twice a year using **poetry on "geo-cultural topics; 'xenology'—alien or other cultures, or our society from other's view; exotic rituals, mythic traditions; surreal, beat, punk, fantasy/science fiction, humor and speculative works (to 20 pgs.). No forced rhymes, unfocused or pointless poems, limp endings."** They have published poetry by Denise Dumars, David Kopaska-Merkel, David Lincoln Fisher, Bruce Boston and Wendy Rathbone. As a sample the editor selected these lines from "In Chandris Valley" by Nancy Ellis Taylor:

> My children are born
> wet and pearly
> I wish they were
> green . . .

The magazine is digest-sized, 60+ pgs., saddle-stapled with glossy card cover, professionally printed. This small press product packs many poems (and punch) into each issue. Free verse is the norm. Subscription: $7. **Sample postpaid: $4. Send SASE for guidelines. Reports in 1 month, longer in December. Pays $5/page plus 1 copy. Buys first North American serial rights.** Editor comments on rejections "often. I occasionally ask for rewrites." Reviews books of poetry, 10-100 pages, single format. Query regarding reviews. Omega Cat Press publishes 1 chapbook/year. For their annual chapbook competition, submit 30-50 poems "about any national heritage or culture (not necessarily a real culture)—a people's customs, rites, typical social occasions, folkways, etc." **$5 reading fee/submission. Cover letter required. Deadline: December 1 for April publication.** Write for rules. All entrants receive a copy of the winning chapbook.

‡XIB; XIB PUBLICATIONS (I, II), P.O. Box 262112, San Diego CA 92126, phone (619)298-4927, founded 1990, editor tolek, appears irregularly, usually 2-3 times/year, publishing contemporary poetry, short fiction and b&w artwork and photos. They want **poetry of any form, length, subject, style or purpose. "Prefer to 'feel each other out' over many submissions those who don't hit the first time. No haiku or long poems and rhyming have less chance but not much. Quality can reign in any form."** They have recently published poetry by Robert Nagler, Lyn Lifshin and Jean Erhardt. As a sample the editor selected these lines from "Vehement Invocations" by John Graywood:

2

her body inscribed by the recognition of advancing woodsmoke

3

to describe her face, will begin with the trace of her breath
upon the mirror

xib is 50 pgs., 6½×8, photocopied on heavy bond, saddle-stapled, 10 pt. gloss mimeo cover, 40% illustrated with art and photos, some ads. They receive about 2,000 poems a year, use approximately 4%. Press run is 500 for 50 subscribers of which a third are libraries, 350 shelf sales. Subscription: $12 for 3 issues and a chapbook. **Sample postpaid: $4. Previously published poems and simultaneous submissions OK. Cover letter preferred. "Work sent without a cover letter will be read but may be returned without a reply." Often comments on rejections. "Guidelines available for SASE, but why waste a stamp? Just submit!" Reports in 1-3 weeks. Pays 1 copy. Acquires one-time rights.** xib publications publishes 1-2 chapbooks/year, **"irregularly and arbitrarily. Please do not query or submit with chapbook intent. Most chaps form out of friendly joint-efforts."** Press run for chapbooks is about 75-100. Authors receive half; the rest goes to subscribers, reviewers and trades.

XIQUAN PUBLISHING HOUSE; THE PARADOXIST LITERARY MOVEMENT JOURNAL; THE PARADOXIST MOVEMENT ASSOCIATION (IV-Form), P.O. Box 42561, Phoenix AZ 85080, founded 1990, editor Florentin Smarandache. *The Paradoxist Literary Movement Journal* is a biannual journal of "avant-garde poetry, experiments, poems without verses, literature beyond the words, anti-language, non-literature and its literature, as well as the sense of the non-sense; revolutionary forms of poetry." They want **"avant-garde poetry, 1-2 pages, any subject, any style (lyrical experiments). No classical, fixed forms."** They have published poetry by Teresinka Pereira, Paul Courget, Ion Rotaru, Michèle de LaPlante and Claude LeRoy. As a sample here is "Dear Deer" from **Nonpoems** by the editor:

- *Hear, here!*
  Buy, by
  our hour,
  four fore
  pears pairs!
- *Sun son,*
  no! Know
  two, too!
- *Hi! Hie!*

The editor says *TPLM* is 52 pgs., digest-sized, offset, soft cover. Press run is 500. "It is distributed to its collaborators." **No previously published poems or simultaneous submissions. Do not submit mss in the summer. "We do not return published or unpublished poems or notify the author of date of publication." Reports in 3-6 months. Pays 1-2 copies.** Xiquan Publishing House also publishes 2 paperbacks and **1-2 chapbooks/year, including translations. The poems must be unpublished and must meet the requirements of the Paradoxist Movement Association. Replies to queries in 1-2 months, to mss in 3-6 months. Pays 50 author's copies. Inquire about sample books.** They say, "We want anti-literature and its literature, style of the non-style, poems without poems, non-words and non-sentence poems, very upset free verse, intelligible unintelligible language, impersonal texts personalized, transformation of the abnormal to the normal. Make literature from everything; make literature from nothing!"

‡**THE YALE REVIEW (II)**, 1902 A Yale Station, New Haven CT 06520, phone (203)432-0499, founded 1911, editor J.D. McClatchy, is a "quarterly general magazine of intellectual distinction and literary excellence." It is known for publishing all forms and styles of poetry, and issues reviewed verify that fact. Both formal and free verse, marked by excellence, seems welcome. They have recently published poetry by John Ashbery, W.S. Merwin and Amy Clampitt. Press run is 6,000 for 2,000 subscribers of which 1,000 are libraries. Single copy: $7; subscription: $22. **No previously published poems or simultaneous submissions. Reads submissions September 1 through June 30 only.** Time between acceptance and publication is 9 months to 1 year. **Seldom comments on rejections. Reports within 2 months. Pays $100-300.** Staff reviews books of poetry in a regular column. Send books for review consideration. Poetry published in *The Yale Review* was also selected for inclusion in **Best American Poetry 1992.**

YALE UNIVERSITY PRESS; THE YALE SERIES OF YOUNGER POETS (III), 92A Yale Station, New Haven CT 06520, phone (203)432-0900, founded 1908, poetry editor (Yale University Press) Jonathan Brent. The Yale Series of Younger Poets is one of the most prestigious means available to launch a book publishing career. It is **open to poets under 40 who have not had a book previously published — a book ms of 48-64 pgs. Entry fee: $8. Submit February 1-28 each year. Send SASE for rules and guidelines.** Poets are not disqualified by previous publication of limited editions of no more than 300 copies or previously published poems in newspapers and periodicals, which may be used in the book ms if so identified. Previous winners include Richard Kenney, Julie Agoos, Pamela Alexander and George Bradley. Publication of the winning volume each year is on a standard royalty contract plus 10 author's copies, and the reputation of the contest guarantees more than the usual number of reviews.

YAMMERING TWITS (I, II), 62 W. Masem Square, E. Patchogue NY 11772, founded 1991, editor Tracey Erin Finnerty, is a quarterly, "a place for people to nurse their free verse hangovers. **Vivid imagery, under 30 lines, favored. I like poetry inspired by bars, rock-n-roll and other everyday heartbreaks. R.E.M. fans a plus. No sickly sweet love stuff, no cussing for sake of shock and no porking poetry without a payoff.**" She has recently published poetry by Dan Nielsen, Kyle Hogg and R.B. Weber. As a sample the editor selected these lines from "Background Notes" by Mike Costanzo:

> when we met
> there was a radio in the background
> set at random
> in the big chance love fishbowl
>
> as I talked
> you sang along,
> giving the night a soundtrack

YT is about 20 pgs., 8½×11, photocopied, stapled at top left corner, with b&w artwork. Single copy: $2; subscription: $5. **No previously published poems. Submit 1 poem/page on 8½×11 paper, "ready to be copied as is. Feelings are hurt without cover letter. No biographies ... tell me how your day went." Comments on rejections "if requested to do so." Reports in 1 month.** "Because I'll be doing this from college I ask for patience." **Pays 1 copy.** *Yammering Twits* ranked #9 in the "Nontraditional Verse" category of the June 1993 *Writer's Digest* Poetry 60 list. The editor says, "Read like machines and support the small press."

YANKEE MAGAZINE; YANKEE ANNUAL POETRY CONTEST (II), Main St., Dublin NH 03444, phone (603)563-8222, founded in 1935, poetry editor (since 1955) Jean Burden. Though it has a New England emphasis, the poetry is not necessarily about New England or by New Englanders, and it has a national distribution to more than a million subscribers. They want to see **"high quality contemporary poems in either free verse or traditional form. Does not have to be regional in theme. Any subject acceptable, provided it is in good taste. We look for originality in thought, imagery, insight — as well as technical control."** They do not want poetry that is "cliché-ridden, banal verse." They have published poetry by Maxine Kumin, Liz Rosenberg, Josephine Jacobsen, Nancy Willard, Linda Pastan, Paul Zimmer and Hayden Carruth. As a sample the editor selected these lines from "Waking" by Joan LaBombard:

> But blood's in thrall to the world
> and the body's bound
> by its clocks and invisible pulleys —
> sun plucking at bedclothes,
> a mockingbird's ultimatum.
> I reenter the world's cage, the house
> of my daylight body.
> My blood discovers its old riverbed,
> and my name remembers me.

The monthly is 6×9, 170+ pgs., saddle-stapled, professionally printed, using full-color and b&w ads and illustrations, with full-color glossy paper cover. They receive over 30,000 submissions a year, accept about 50-60 poems. Subscription: $22. **Submit poems up to 30 lines, free verse or traditional. Uses 4-5 poems/monthly issue. No simultaneous submissions or previously published poems. Submissions without SASE "are tossed." Editor comments on rejections "only if poem has so many good qualities it only needs minor revisions." Reports in 2-3 weeks.** Approximately 18-month backlog. **Pays $50/poem, all rights; $35, first magazine rights.** Sponsors an annual poetry contest judged by a prominent New England poet and published in the February issue, with awards of $150, $100 and $50 for the best 3 poems in the preceding year. *Yankee* ranked #9 in the "Top Pay" category of the June 1993 *Writer's Digest* Poetry 60 list. Jean Burden advises, "Study previous issues of *Yankee* to determine the kind of poetry we want. Get involved in poetry workshops at home. Read the best contemporary poetry you can find."

YARROW, A JOURNAL OF POETRY (II), English Dept., Lytle Hall, Kutztown State University, Kutztown PA 19530, founded 1981, editor Harry Humes, appears twice a year. They have published poetry by Gibbons Ruark, Jared Carter, William Pitt Root and Fleda Brown Jackson. It is 40 pgs., 6×9, offset. Press run is 350. Subscription: $5/2 years. **Reports in 1-2 months. Pays 2 copies plus 1-year subscription.** Poetry published in *Yarrow* was also selected for inclusion in a **Pushcart Prize** anthology.

YELLOW SILK: JOURNAL OF EROTIC ARTS, Verygraphics, P.O. Box 6374, Albany CA 94706. Prefers not to share information.

YESTERDAY'S MAGAZETTE (I, IV-Senior citizens), Independent Publishing Co., P.O. Box 15126, Sarasota FL 34277, editor and publisher Ned Burke, founded 1973. This bimonthly magazine is for "*all* nostalgia lovers. *YM* believes that everyone has a yesterday and everyone has a memory to share. Nothing fancy here . . . just 'plain folks' relating their individual life experiences. **We are always seeking new and innovative writers with imagination and promise, and we would like to see more 40s, 50s and 60s pieces.**" As a sample here are lines from "The Backyard Pump" by J.E. Coulbourn:

> *With two small hands you'd*
> *grasp the monster's tail*
> *And try to pump the water in the pail,*
> *But if his darned esophagus got dry*
> *No water came no matter how you'd try.*

YM is 22 pgs., magazine-sized, saddle-stapled, professionally printed on good stock with glossy color cover. A year's subscription is $12 or two years for $18. **Sample: $2. Submissions for "Quills, Quips, & Quotes" (their poetry page) should be "thoughtful, amusing, or just plain interesting for our 'plain folks' readers. No SASE is required as short items are generally not returned nor acknowledged, unless requested by the contributor." Pays copies.**

THE YOUNG CRUSADER (IV-Children, themes), National Woman's Christian Temperance Union, 1730 Chicago Ave., Evanston IL 60201, is a monthly publication for members of the Loyal Temperance Legion and young friends of their age — about 6-12 years. They want **"short poems appropriate for the temperance and high moral value and nature themes and their young audience."** It is a 12-page, digest-sized leaflet. **Pays 10¢/line for poetry.**

YOUNG VOICES MAGAZINE (IV-Children), P.O. Box 2321, Olympia WA 98507, phone (206)357-4683, founded 1988, publisher/editor Steve Charak, is "a magazine of **creative work of elementary through high school students. The age limit is rigid.**" It appears every other month. Press run 1,500 for 1,000 subscribers of which 40 are libraries. Subscription: $15 for 1 year, $28 for 2. **Sample postpaid: $4. Editor comments "definitely, on every piece of writing." Send SASE for guidelines. Pays $3/poem plus 1 copy (3 copies if you are a subscriber). Buys one-time rights.** He says, "Revise. Remember that in a poem, every word counts. Forget about the need to rhyme. Instead, put feeling into each word."

‡ZEITGEIST (II), P.O. Box 1006, Kalispell MT 59903, founded 1990, publisher/editor John S. Slack, appears 4 times/year. For poetry, **"best is 1 page or less dealing with personal relationships to world and others. Focused ideas. Disturbing or provocative imagery welcomed. No same old love-death-suicide stuff, graphic sex and/or gratuitous profanity. No blatantly didactic stuff."** They have recently published poetry by Adrian C. Louis, Gina Bergamino and Tom Caufield. As a sample the editor selected these lines by Pete Lee:

> *You bring it*
> *Back. It*
> *Never really*
> *Leaves you*
> *The habit*

Zeitgeist is 20-28 pgs., 8½×11, photocopied, edge-stapled. They accept about 10% of poems submitted. Press run is 50 for 40 subscribers of which 3 are libraries. Subscription: $10. **Sample postpaid: $3. Previously published poems and simultaneous submissions OK. "A 3-line bio would help us get a feel of who you are." Editor sometimes comments on rejections. Send SASE for guidelines. Reports in 1-4 months. Pays "each issue in which poet appears."** Open to unsolicited reviews. They offer free space for self-publishers. They also feature a poet in each issue with 5 poems. The editor says, "Write often. Sometimes raw is better. Keep your eyes, ears and nose open, along with your mind. Don't take rejection personally. Sometimes it takes a while to find your audience. We like 'in your face' poetry, but not for shock value only. Do have something worth saying."

‡ZEPHYR PRESS (III, IV-Translations), 13 Robinson St., Somerville MA 02145, founded 1980, editors Ed Hogan and Leora Zeitlin. "We accept about 1% or less of the mss we receive. **We are now publishing very little poetry, except some Russian and Eastern European poetry in translation.**" A recent publication is **The Complete Poems of Anna Akhmatova**, translations by Judith Hemschemeyer. Their catalog lists books of poetry by Sue Standing, Anne Valley Fox and Miriam Sagan. **Query with 5 sample poems. Simultaneous submissions OK. "We will respond only if interested." Pays 10% of print run or by royalty, depending upon the particular project.**

ZOLAND BOOKS INC. (III), 384 Huron Ave., Cambridge MA 02138, phone (617)864-6252, founded 1987, publisher Roland Pease, is a "literary press: fiction, poetry, photography, gift books, books of literary interest." They want **"high-quality" poetry, not sentimental.** They have published poetry by William Corbett, Karen Fiser, Marge Piercy, Patricia Smith and Gary Fincke. They publish 10-15 books a year, flat-spined, averaging 96 pgs. **Query with 5-10 sample poems, bio, publications. Editor does not comment on submissions. Pays 5-10% royalties plus 5 copies. Buys all rights.**

‡ZUZU'S PETALS QUARTERLY (II), P.O. Box 4476, Allentown PA 18105, phone (215)821-1324, founded 1992, editor T. Dunn. "We publish high quality fiction, essays, poetry and articles. As a journal of both the written and visual arts, we provide a home for outstanding work of postmodern creativity. Free verse, blank verse, experimental, etc. are all welcome here. We're looking for a freshness of language, new ideas and original expression. No 'June, moon and spoon' rhymed poetry. No light verse." They have recently published poetry by Max Greenberg, Gayle Elen Harvey, Jean Erhardt and Paul F. Thurn. As a sample the editor selected these lines (poet unidentified):

> Now I must learn to draw
> all over again
> struggle to lay claim
> to the perfect and last
> for all time depiction
> of your soft and faithful
> universal mouth

ZPQ is 50 pgs., 8½ × 11, side-stapled, matte card cover, b&w graphics and artwork throughout. They receive about 1,000 poems a year, accept approximately 10%. Press run is 300 for 200 subscribers. Subscription: $17. **Sample postpaid: $5. Previously published poems and simultaneous submissions OK. Seldom comments on rejections. Send SASE for guidelines. Reports in 2 weeks to 2 months. Pays 1 copy. Acquires one-time rights.** Staff reviews books of poetry and audiotapes of poetry readings in approximately 200 words. Send books for review consideration. They also sponsor quarterly poetry contests. Entry fee: $1/poem, any style, length or subject. Deadlines are the first of March, June, September and December. 40% of proceeds goes to prize winners: 25% to first prize, 10% to second, 5% to third. Free critiques to honorable mentions. The remaining 60% of proceeds goes toward the magazine. The editor says, "Read as much poetry as you can. Support the literary arts: Go to poetry readings, read chapbooks and collections of verse. Eat poetry for breakfast, cultivate a love of language, then write!"

Publishers of Poetry/'93-'94 Changes

Each year we contact all of the publishers listed in **Poet's Market** to request updated information for our next edition. The following magazine and book publishers were listed in the 1993 edition of **Poet's Market** but are not in the 1994 edition because either they did not respond to our request to update their listing (these names appear without further explanation) or their listing was deleted (for the reason indicated in parentheses).

While many of these publishers have ceased operation, the reasons some of them are not included this year are temporary (e.g., overstocked, temporarily suspending publication, etc.). *If you're interested in any of the following, first research the publisher and then write a brief letter (enclosing SASE) inquiring as to whether they are now interested in receiving submissions.*

Alta Napa Press
The Amaranth Review
American Association of Haikuists Newsletter
American Collegiate Poets
The And Review
Animal Tales (ceased publication)
Ant Farm (ceased publication)
Arizona Literary Review (ceased publication)
Ars Poetica Press
Atticus Review/Press
Auguries
Backyard Press
Bangtail
Beyond (suspended publication)
Blind Beggar Press
Blue Light Review
Bold Print (too many submissions)
Box Dog Press
Breitenbush Books, Inc. (ceased publication)
Caermaen Books
Callaloo Poetry Series
Canoe Press (asked to be deleted)
Carolina Quarterly
Carpenter Press
Ceilidh (ceased publication)
Chants
Charnel House (no longer publishes poetry)
Chastity & Holiness Magazine (unable to contact)
Chelsea
Children's Album (ceased publication)
Conditioned Response Press
Converging Paths (ceased publication)
Convictions (ceased publication)
Coop. Antigruppo Siciliano
Corona Publishing Co. (inactive at present)
Cramped and Wet
Crystal Rainbow (suspended publication)
Cyphers
The Dayspring Press
Deathrealm
Delaware Valley Poets
Delhi-London Poetry Quarterly
The Eleventh Muse
Emerald City Comix & Stories (temporarily suspended publication)
En Passant Poetry
Equilibrium
Equinox
Fennel Stalk (ceased publication)
Fleeting Monolith Enterprises
Forbidden Lines Magazine (no longer publishes much poetry)
Furry Chiclets
Galaxy Press
The Gamut (ceased publication)
The Gay Men's Press
Good Reading Magazine (suspended publication)
The Gopherwood Review (ceased publication)
Great Plains Canal and Avalon Dispatch (ceased publication)
The Greenfield Review Press (no longer publishes poetry)
Greyraven Press
Hammers
The Hampden-Sydney Poetry Review
Honeybrook Press (suspended publication)
Horses West
Insight Press
International Olympic Lifter
Inverted Ostrich (temporarily suspended publication)
University of Iowa Press
Iris
Jacaranda Review
Journal of Pan African Studies
Juniper Press (overstocked)
Just About Horses (overstocked)
Kairos
Katuah (ceased publication)
Kennebec (ceased publication)
Kentucky Writing
Kingfisher
Kings Review Magazine
La Nuez (suspending publication)
Lightworks
Lips
The Lithic Review (unable to contact)
Living Poets Society (AZ)
Living Streams (unable to contact)
Lollipops (uses very little poetry)
London Review of Books
Lost Magazine (ceased publication)
Lynx
Macmillan of Canada (no longer publishes poetry)
Mahogany & Molasses Family Reader
Manhattan Poetry Review
Manic D Press
Mark
Mattoid
The Mayberry Gazette (ceased publication)
Mid Coaster
Middle Eastern Dancer (attempting to sell publication)
Midland Review
Midmarch Arts Press
Mosaic Press (asked to be deleted)
MSS/New Myths
Nancy's Magazine (inappropriate submissions)
New Madrid (status uncertain)
New Methods
The New Renaissance
Next Exit (ceased publication)
The Nihilistic Review

North American Review
W.W. Norton & Company, Inc.
Nova SF
O-blek
Odyssey
One Meadway
Otis Rush
Out Magazine (unable to
  contact)
Oyez Review
Painted Bride Quarterly
Passaic Review
Pauper's Press
Peace and Freedom
Peacock Books
Pentagram Press
Phanes Press (asked to be
  deleted)
Philomel
Phoebe (VA)
Pie
Plainswoman (ceased
  publication)
Poet Gallery Press
Poetry Ireland Review
Poetry Magic Publications
  (temporarily suspending
  publication)
The Poetry Miscellany
Poetry Only (ceased
  publication)
The Poetry Peddler (ceased
  publication)
Poetry Review
Pogment Press (not accepting
  mss)
Poked with Sticks
Portland Review

Potes & Poets Press, Inc.
  (asked to be deleted)
The Prairie Journal
Primal Voices
Protea Poetry Journal
  (suspended publication)
Psych It (ceased publication)
The Pyramid
Recursive Angel (asked to be
  deleted)
Repository Press (no longer
  publishes poetry)
Resin
Rhyme Time (ceased
  publication)
Rienda Suelta/Free Rein
Rivelin Grapheme Press
River City
Scream of the Buddha
Seance
Seems
Sensations Magazine
Sideshow Magazine (ceased
  publication)
The Signal
The Single Scene (asked to be
  deleted)
Sinister Wisdom
Sisyphus (ceased publication)
Skaz
Some Bees Press
Soundings: A Newsletter for
  Survivors of Childhood
  Sexual Abuse
Soundings: Journal of the
  Living Arts (unable to
  contact)
South Head Press

Southern Review
Sunshine Magazine (suspended
  publication)
Swamp Root (unable to
  contact)
Tampa Bay Review
Toledo Poets Center Press
Tsunami
Untitled
Ver Poets Voices
Vigil
Vol. No. Magazine
Webber's
West (ceased publication)
Westenra (unable to contact)
Whispering Palm
Wildwood Journal
The Wishing Well
The Word Works
Wordsmith Publishing, Inc.
  (out of business)
Worldwide Poets' Circle
  (ceased publication)
The Write Technique
  (suspended publication)
Writers' Info (ceased
  publication)
Writers' Rendezvous
Writing (Australia, ceased
  publication)
Writing (Canada)
Wyrd
X-Press Productions
Zero Hour (no longer accepting
  poetry)
Zero One

State and Provincial Grants

Arts councils in the U.S. and Canada may provide assistance to artists (including poets) in the form of fellowships or grants. When offered, these grants can be substantial and confer prestige upon recipients; however, **only residents of the state or province are eligible.** Because deadlines for applications and the nature of available support vary annually, query first (with a SASE).

United States Art Agencies

Alabama State Council on the Arts
Barbara George, Programs Manager
1 Dexter Ave.
Montgomery AL 36130
(205)242-4076

Alaska State Council on the Arts
Jean Palmer, Grants Officer
Suite 1-E, 411 W. 4th Ave.
Anchorage AK 99501
(907)279-1558

Arizona Commission on the Arts
Tonda Gorton, Public Information Officer
417 W. Roosevelt
Phoenix AZ 85003
(602)255-5882

Arkansas Arts Council
Sally Williams, Artists Program Coordinator
1500 Tower Bldg., 323 Center St.
Little Rock AR 72201
(501)324-9150

California Arts Council
Carol Shiffman, Individual Fellowships
2411 Alhambra Blvd.
Sacramento CA 95817
(916)227-2550

Colorado Council on the Arts and Humanities
Daniel Salazar, Director
Individual Artists Program
750 Pennsylvania St.
Denver CO 80203-3699
(303)894-2619

Connecticut Commission on the Arts
Linda Dente, Grants Information
227 Lawrence St.
Hartford CT 06106
(203)566-7076

Delaware State Arts Council
Barbara King, Director
Individual Artist Category
State Office Building, 820 N. French St.
Wilmington DE 19801
(302)577-3540

District of Columbia Commission on the Arts and Humanities
Diem Jones, Literature Grants and Aid
5th Floor, Stables Art Center
410 Eighth St. NW
Washington DC 20004
(202)724-5613

Florida Arts Council
Valerie Ohlsson, Arts Consultant
Division of Cultural Affairs
Florida Department of State
The Capitol
Tallahassee FL 32399-0250
(904)487-2980

Georgia Council for the Arts
Ann Rivers, Manager
Community Arts Development
Suite 115, 530 Means St. NW
Atlanta GA 30318
(404)651-7920

Hawaii State Foundation on Culture & Arts
Wendell P.K. Silva, Executive Director
Room 202, 335 Merchant St.
Honolulu HI 96813
(808)586-0300

Idaho Commission on the Arts
Diane Josephy Peavey, Literature Director
304 W. State St.
Boise ID 83720
(208)334-2119

Illinois Arts Council
Richard Gage, Director
Communication Arts
Suite 10-500, 100 W. Randolph
Chicago IL 60601
(312)814-6750

Indiana Arts Commission
Tom Schorgl, Executive Director
Room 072, 402 W. Washington St.
Indianapolis IN 46204-2741
(317)232-1268

Iowa Arts Council
Julie Bailey, Grants Coordinator
State Capitol Complex, 1223 E. Court
Des Moines IA 50319
(515)281-4451

Kansas Arts Commission
Conchita Reyes, Program Coordinator
Jay Hawk Tower
Suite 1004, 700 Jackson
Topeka KS 66603
(913)296-3335

Kentucky Arts Council
Al Smith, Fellowship Program
31 Fountain Pl.
Frankfort KY 40601
(502)564-3757

Louisiana State Arts Council
Gerri Hobdy, Interim Director
P.O. Box 44247
Baton Rouge LA 70804
(504)342-8180

Maine State Arts Commission
Alden C. Wilson, Director
State House, Station 25
55 Capitol St.
Augusta ME 04333-0025
(207)289-2724

Maryland State Arts Council
Michele Moure, Program Director
601 N. Howard St.
Baltimore MD 21201
(410)333-8232

Massachusetts Cultural Council
Jim McCullough, Literature Coordinator
10th Floor, 80 Boylston St.
Boston MA 02116
(617)727-3668

Arts Foundation of Michigan
Ann Treadwell
Suite 2164, 645 Griswold
Detroit MI 48226
(313)964-2244

Minnesota State Arts Board
Karen Mueller, Program Associate
432 Summit Ave.
St. Paul MN 55102-2624
(612)297-2603

Mississippi Arts Commission
Cindy Harper, Program Director
Suite 207, 239 N. Lamar St.
Jackson MS 39201
(601)359-6030

Missouri Arts Council
Autry Jackson, Program Administrator
Wainwright State Office Complex
Suite 105, 111 N. 7th St.
St. Louis MO 63101
(314)340-6845

Montana Arts Council
Martha Sprague, Dir. of Art Services/Prog.
Suite 252, 316 N. Park Ave.
Helena MT 59620
(406)444-6430

Nebraska Arts Council
Nancy Quin, Grants Officer
3838 Davenport
Omaha NE 68131-2329
(402)595-2122

Nevada State Council on the Arts
William L. Fox, Director
329 Flint St.
Reno NV 89501
(702)688-1225

New Hampshire State Council on the Arts
Audrey Sylvester, Artists Services Coordinator
Phoenix Hall, 40 N. Main St.
Concord NH 03301
(603)271-2789

New Jersey State Council on the Arts
CN 306, 4 N. Broad St.
Trenton NJ 08625
(609)292-6130

New Mexico Arts Division
Randy Forrester, Operation Director
228 E. Palace Ave.
Santa Fe NM 87501
(505)827-6490

New York State Council on the Arts
Jewelle Gomez, Director, Literature Program
915 Broadway
New York NY 10010
(212)387-7020

North Carolina Arts Council
Deborah McGill, Literature Director
Department of Cultural Resources
221 E. Lane St.
Raleigh NC 27601-2807
(919)733-2111

North Dakota Council on the Arts
Mark Schultz, Arts Education, Artists Services
Suite 606, Black Bldg., 118 Broadway
Fargo ND 58102
(701)239-7150

Ohio Arts Council
Bob Fox, Literature Coordinator
727 E. Main St.
Columbus OH 43205
(614)466-2613

State Arts Council of Oklahoma
Betty Price, Executive Director
640 Jim Thorpe Bldg.
Oklahoma City OK 73105-4987
(405)521-2931

Oregon Arts Commission
Vincent Dunn, Assistant Director
550 Airport Rd. SE
Salem OR 97310
(503)378-3625

Pennsylvania Council on the Arts
Marsha Salvatore, Literature Program Director
Room 216, Finance Bldg.
Harrisburg PA 17120
(717)787-6883

Rhode Island State Council on the Arts
Iona B. Dobbins, Executive Director
Suite 103, 95 Cedar St.
Providence RI 02903
(401)277-3880

South Carolina Arts Commission
Steve Lewis, Literary Arts Director
1800 Gervais St.

Columbia SC 29201
(803)734-8696

South Dakota Arts Council
Dennis Holub, Director
Suite 204, 230 S. Phillips Ave.
Sioux Falls SD 57102
(605)339-6646

Tennessee Arts Commission
Alice Swanson, Director of Literary Arts
Suite 100, 320 6th Ave. N.
Nashville TN 37243-0780
(615)741-1701

Texas Commission on the Arts
Rita Starpattern, Program Director
Visual and Communication Arts
P.O. Box 13406, Capitol Station
Austin TX 78711-3406
(512)463-5535

Utah Arts Council
Karen Jorgensen, Individual Grants Coord.
617 E. South Temple St.
Salt Lake City UT 84102
(801)533-5895

Vermont Council on the Arts
Cornelia Carey, Grants Officer
Drawer 33, 136 State St.

Montpelier VT 05633-6001
(802)828-3291

Virginia Commission for the Arts
Susan FitzPatrick, Program Coordinator
223 Governor St.
Richmond VA 23219
(804)225-3132

Washington State Arts Commission
Artist Fellowship Awards in Literary Arts
110 9th and Columbia Bldg., P.O. Box 42675
Olympia WA 98504-2675
(206)753-3860

West Virginia Arts and Humanities Division
1900 Kanawha Blvd. E.
Charleston WV 23505
(304)558-0220

Wisconsin Arts Board
Beth Malner, Individual Artists Program Dir.
1st Floor, 101 E. Wilson St.
Madison WI 53702
(608)266-0190

Wyoming Council on the Arts
Michael Shay, Literary Arts Coordinator
2320 Capitol Ave.
Cheyenne WY 82002
(307)777-7742

Canadian Provinces Art Agencies

Alberta Community Development
Arts Branch
Clive Padfield, Director
3rd Floor, Beaver House, 10158 - 103 St.
Edmonton, Alberta T5J 0X6
(403)427-6315

British Columbia Arts Council
Cultural Services Branch
Walter Quan, Coord. of Arts Awards Prog.
5th Floor, 800 Johnson St.
Victoria, British Columbia V8V 1X4
(604)356-1728

Manitoba Arts Council
Gordon Shillingsford, Writing/Publishing Off.
525 - 93 Lombard Ave.
Winnipeg, Manitoba R3B 3B1
(204)945-0422

New Brunswick Department of Tourism, Recreation and Heritage
Arts Branch
Bruce Dennis, Program Officer
P.O. Box 6000
Fredericton, New Brunswick E3B 5H1
(506)453-2555

Newfoundland Department of Municipal and Provincial Affairs
Cultural Affairs Division
Elizabeth Batstone, Director of Cultural Affairs
P.O. Box 1854
St. John's, Newfoundland A1C 5P9
(709)729-3650

Nova Scotia Department of Tourism and Culture
Peggy Walt, Cultural Industries/Research Off.
P.O. Box 456
Halifax, Nova Scotia B3J 2R5
(902)424-5000

The Canada Council
General Information Officer
P.O. Box 1047, 99 Metcalfe St.
Ottawa, Ontario K1P 5V8
(613)598-4365

Ontario Arts Council
Lorraine Filyer, Literature Officer
Suite 500, 151 Bloor St. W.
Toronto, Ontario M5S 1T6
(416)961-1660

Prince Edward Island Council of the Arts
Judy McDonald, Executive Director
P.O. Box 2234
Charlottetown, Prince Edward Island C1A 8B9
(902)368-4410

Saskatchewan Arts Board
Gail Paul Armstrong, Literary Arts Prog. Dir.
3475 Albert St.
Regina, Saskatchewan S4S 6X6
(306)787-4056

Yukon Arts Council
Laurel Parry, Arts Coordinator
Box 2730
Whitehorse, Yukon Y1A 2C6
(403)668-6284

Contests and Awards

Though considerably smaller than the Publishers of Poetry section, this segment of **Poet's Market** also contains "markets" for your work. Here you will find various contests and awards whose prize offerings may include publication of your work in addition to their monetary awards. And even if publication is not included, the publicity generated upon winning some of these contests may make your name more familiar to editors.

Listed in this section is a wide range of competitions—everything from contests with modest prizes sponsored by state poetry societies, colleges or even cities to prestigious awards offered by private foundations. What you will not find, however, is any contest or award associated with publishers or organizations listed elsewhere in this directory. For those, you should refer to the list of Additional Contests and Awards at the end of this section and consult the listings mentioned there for specific information.

Selecting contests

Whether you're reading the listings in this section or referring to the listings in other sections, you should never submit to contests and awards blindly. Since many of them require entry fees, blind submissions will just waste your money. As in the Publishers of Poetry section, each listing here contains one or more Roman numerals in its heading. These "codes" will not only help you narrow down the list of contests and awards, but they should also help you evaluate your chances of winning (and recouping your expenses).

The I code, for instance, is given to contests that are very open to beginners. While these contests may require small fees, or membership in the sponsoring organization, they typically are not exploitive of poets, beginning or otherwise. Keep in mind, though, that if a contest charges a $5 entry fee and offers $75 in prizes, then the organizers only need 15 entries to cover the prizes. Even though fees may also go toward providing a small honorarium for the judge, 100 entries will surely net the organizers a neat profit—at the participating poets' expense. Be careful when deciding which of these contests are worth your money.

The II code follows the name of general literary contests, usually for poets with some experience. This code may follow awards for book-length manuscripts, such as the Capricorn Poetry Award for authors over 40, or previously published collections, such as The Poets' Prize, or fellowships which are designed for poets of "demonstrated ability," such as the Guggenheims. If you're just beginning, start building a reputation by having your work accepted by periodicals, then try your hand at these competitions.

Of all the codes, however, perhaps the most useful is **IV**, which designates specialized contests and awards. That is, you—or your poetry—must meet certain criteria to be eligible. Some contests, for instance, are regional, so only poets from a certain area may enter. Others are limited to certain groups, such as women or students. A few are for translations only. Still others are limited to poets writing in certain forms. If you write sonnets, for example, consider the Poets Club of Chicago International Shakespearean Sonnet Contest or the Salmon Arm Sonnet Contest. For those who have an interest in rhyme, there is the Rhyme International Competition for Rhyming Poetry, based out of England. Contests that primarily consider themselves specialized are often open to both beginning and established poets.

While most of the contests and awards in this section are open to entries, there are a few to which poets may not apply. These are coded **V**, indicating that the winners are chosen by nomination—often by an anonymous committee. See the listing for The Whiting Writers' Awards, for example. We include these and other such awards because winning one is a very prestigious honor and it is not only helpful to know that such awards exist, but it is also important to know that you should not attempt to apply for them.

Once you've narrowed down the contests and awards you want to enter, treat the submission process just as you would if you were submitting to a magazine: Always send a SASE for more information. Many contests want you to submit work along with their specific entry form or application. Others offer guidelines that spell out exactly how they want poetry submitted and you should follow such rules to the letter. Finally, deadlines are very important and often subject to change; if your work arrives after the deadline date, it may automatically be disqualified. For more detailed information about selecting contests, see page 18 of *The Business of Poetry* by Michael J. Bugeja.

AAA ANNUAL NATIONAL LITERARY CONTEST; ARIZONA LITERARY MAGAZINE (I), Suite 117-PM, 3509 Shea Blvd., Phoenix AZ 85028-3339, sponsoring organization Arizona Authors' Association, award director Gerry Benninger. 42 lines maximum, $5 entry fee, submit between January 1 and July 29. Prizes are $125, $75, $40, 6 honorable mentions $10 each. Include SASE with entry for contest results; no material will be returned. Winners are announced and prizes awarded in October. Winning entries are published in a special edition of *Arizona Literary Magazine*. Entries must be typed, double-spaced on 8½×11 paper. Write for more information and entry rules; enclose SASE.

MILTON ACORN POETRY AWARD; PRINCE EDWARD ISLAND LITERARY AWARDS (IV-Regional), The Prince Edward Island Council of the Arts, P.O. Box 2234, Charlottetown, Prince Edward Island C1A 8B9 Canada. Awards are given annually for short stories, poetry, children's literature, feature articles, children's creative writing and playwriting. Writers must have been resident at least 6 of the 12 months before the contest. Submit October 1 through February 15. For the Milton Acorn Poetry Award, participants may submit as many entries as they wish, each of no more than 10 pgs. Entry fee: $5. Prizes for '92-'93: A trip for 2 via Air Nova to New York, first prize; $200 and $100, second and third prizes.

‡ACTS INSTITUTE, INC. (II), #1201, 4550 Warwick Blvd., Kansas City MO 64111. This foundation offers money grants to those individuals/teams/groups accepted by artists/writers colonies who need financial assistance to be able to attend. Send SASE for 1994 application materials. Deadlines are June 1 for the following winter and December 1 for the following summer. An anthology of works created by former residents of artists/writers colonies—communities is targeted for publication in 1994. *Havens for Creatives*, 7th edition, is now available.

THE AIR CANADA AWARD (I, IV-Regional), % Canadian Authors Association, Suite 500, 275 Slater St., Ottawa, Ontario K1P 5H9 Canada. The Air Canada Award is an annual award of two tickets to any Air Canada destination, to a Canadian author, published or unpublished, under 30 who shows the most promise. Nominations are made before April 30 by Canadian Authors Association branches or other writers' organizations and the award is given at the CAA banquet in June.

AMERICAN-SCANDINAVIAN FOUNDATION TRANSLATION PRIZE; SCANDINAVIAN REVIEW (IV-Translation), 725 Park Ave., New York NY 10021, for the best translation into English of a work (which may be poetry) of a Scandinavian author after 1800, $2,000, publication in the *Scandinavian Review*, and a bronze medallion. To enter, first request rules. Deadline: June 1.

ARIZONA STATE POETRY SOCIETY ANNUAL CONTEST (I, II, IV), 2225 E. Dortha, Flagstaff AZ 86004, award director Trude Mullen. Contest for various poetry forms and subjects. Prizes range from $10-75; first, second and third place winners are published in the winter edition of *The Sandcutters*, the group's quarterly publication, and name and entries are listed for honorable mention winners. Contest information available for SASE. Fees vary. Deadline: August 31.

ARKANSAS POETRY DAY CONTEST; POETS' ROUNDTABLE OF ARKANSAS (I), over 25 categories, many open to all poets. Brochure available in June; deadline in September; awards given in October. For copy send SASE to Verna Lee Hinegardner, Apt. 109, 605 Higdon, Hot Springs AR 71913.

ARTIST TRUST; ARTIST TRUST GAP GRANTS; ARTIST TRUST FELLOWSHIPS (IV-Regional), Suite 415, 1402 Third Ave., Seattle WA 98101, phone (206)467-8734. Artist Trust is a nonprofit arts organization that provides grants to artists (including poets) who are residents of the state. It also publishes a 16-page quarterly tabloid of news about arts opportunities and cultural issues.

ATLANTIC WRITING COMPETITION; WRITERS' FEDERATION OF NOVA SCOTIA (IV-Regional), Suite 901, 1809 Barrington St., Halifax, Nova Scotia B3J 3K8 Canada, offers prizes of $150, $75 and $50 for 1-15 unpublished poems by residents of the Atlantic Provinces, entry fee $15, deadline August 27. Write for *mandatory* entry form.

BARNARD NEW WOMEN POETS PRIZE; WOMEN POETS AT BARNARD; BARNARD NEW WOMEN POETS SERIES; BEACON PRESS (IV-Women), Barnard College of Columbia University, 3009 Broadway, New York NY 10027-6598. Women Poets at Barnard holds open competition and annual series. The winner receives an award of $1,000 and publication in the Barnard New Women Poets Series, Beacon Press. The competition is open to any woman poet with a book-length ms who has not yet published a book (exclusive of chapbooks). Deadline: September 1. Submit two copies of ms with SASE, postcard for acknowledgement or receipt.

‡BAVARIAN ACADEMY OF FINE ARTS LITERATURE PRIZE (V), Max Josephplatz 3, 8 Munich 22, Germany. An award of DM 30,000 awarded annually to an author in the German language to honor a distinguished literary career—by nomination only.

GEORGE BENNETT FELLOWSHIP (II), Phillips Exeter Academy, Exeter NH 03833, provides a $5,000 fellowship plus room and board to a writer with a ms in progress. The Fellow's only official duties are to be in residence while the academy is in session and to be available to students interested in writing. The committee favors writers who have not yet published a book-length work with a major publisher. Send SASE for application materials. Deadline: December 1.

BOLLINGEN PRIZE (V), Beinecke Rare Book and Manuscript Library, Yale University, New Haven CT 06520, prize of $10,000 to an American poet for the best poetry collection published during the previous two years, or for a body of poetry written over several years. **By nomination only.** Judges change biennially. Announcements in January of odd-numbered years.

BP NICHOL CHAPBOOK AWARD (IV-Regional), 316 Dupont St., Toronto, Ontario M5R 1V9 Canada, $1,000 (Canadian) prize for the best poetry chapbook (10-48 pgs.) in English published in Canada in the preceding year. Submit 3 copies (not returnable). Entries close March 31.

BREAD LOAF WRITERS' CONFERENCE (II), Dept. PM, Middlebury College, Middlebury VT 05753, phone (802)388-3711, fellowships and scholarships. Candidates for fellowships must have book published. Candidates for scholarships must have published in major literary periodicals or newspapers. One letter of nomination required by March 1; applications and supporting materials due by April 1. Awards are announced in June for the conference in August.

BUCKNELL SEMINAR FOR YOUNGER POETS; STADLER SEMESTER FOR YOUNGER POETS (IV-Students), Bucknell University, Lewisburg PA 17837, phone (717)524-1853, director John Wheatcroft. In the spring of 1993, the Stadler Semester for Younger Poets was added to the Seminar for Younger Poets and the Poet-in-Residence Series. The Stadler Semester is distinctive in allowing undergraduate poets almost four months of concentrated work centered in poetry. Guided by practicing poets, the apprentice will write and read poetry and will receive critical response. The two Fellows selected will work with Bucknell's writing faculty. The visiting Poet-in-Residence also will participate in the program. Fellows will earn a semester of academic credit by taking four units of study: a tutorial or individual project with a mentor poet, a poetry-writing workshop, a literature course, and an elective. Undergraduates from four-year colleges with at least one course in poetry writing are eligible to apply; most applicants will be second-semester juniors. Send a 12-15 page portfolio and a letter of presentation (a brief autobiography that expresses commitment to writing poetry, cites relevant courses and lists any publications). Also include a transcript, two recommendations (at least one from a poetry-writing instructor), and a letter from the academic dean granting permission for the student to attend Bucknell for a semester. Application deadline for the Stadler Semester is November 1. Students chosen for the fellowhips will be notified by November 25. The Bucknell Seminar For Younger Poets is not a contest for poems but for 10 fellowships to the Bucknell Seminar, held for 4 weeks in June every year. Seniors and juniors from American colleges are eligible to compete for the ten fellowships, which consist of tuition, room, board, and spaces for writing. Application deadline for each year's seminar is March 10 of the previous year. Students chosen for fellowships will be notified on April 8.

THE BUNTING FELLOWSHIP PROGRAM (IV-Women), Radcliffe College, 34 Concord Ave., Cambridge MA 02138, phone (617)495-8212, supports women of exceptional promise and demonstrated accomplishment who want to pursue independent study in the creative arts (among other things). The stipend is $30,000 for a fellowship fulltime September 1-August 31, requiring residence in the Boston area. Applicants in creative arts should be at the equivalent stage in their careers as women who have received doctorates two years before applying. Deadline in early October.

BUSH ARTIST FELLOWSHIPS (IV-Regional), E-900 First National Bank Bldg., 332 Minnesota St., St. Paul MN 55101, are for South and North Dakota, western Wisconsin and Minnesota residents over 25 years of age to help published writers (poetry, fiction, literary nonfiction, playwriting and screenwriting), visual artists, choreographers and composers set aside time for work-in-progress or exploration of new directions. Maximum of 15 awards of a maximum of $26,000 (and up to $7,000 additional for production and traveling expenses) are awarded each year for 6-18 month fellowships. Deadline late October.

CALIFORNIA WRITERS' ROUNDTABLE POETRY CONTEST (I), under the auspices of the Los Angeles Chapter, Women's National Book Association, Lou Carter Keay, chairman, Suite 807, 11684 Ventura Blvd., Studio City CA 91614-2652. An annual contest with $50, $25 and $10 cash prizes for unpublished poems on any subject, in various forms, not more than 42 lines in length. WNBA members may submit free; nonmembers pay $3/poem entry fee. Send SASE for guidelines. Deadline is September 30.

CANADIAN AUTHORS ASSOCIATION LITERARY AWARDS; CANADIAN AUTHORS ASSOCIATION (IV-Regional), Suite 500, 275 Slater St., Ottawa, Ontario K1P 5H9 Canada, $5,000 in each of 4 categories (fiction, poetry, non-fiction, drama) to Canadian writers, for a published book in the year of publication (or, in the case of drama, first produced), deadline December 15. Nominations may be made by authors, publishers, agents, or others. (Also see The Air Canada Award in this section.)

CINTAS FELLOWSHIP PROGRAM (IV-Regional), Arts International, Institute of International Education, 809 United Nations Plaza, New York NY 10017, makes awards of $10,000 to young professional writers and artists of Cuban lineage living outside of Cuba. Call (212)984-5370 for applications and guidelines. Deadline for applications: March 1.

CLARK COLLEGE POETRY CONTEST (I), % Arlene Paul, 4312 NE 40th St., Vancouver WA 98661, jointly sponsored by Clark College, Oregon State Poetry Association and Washington Poetry Association. $3/poem entry fee (checks payable to Clark College Foundation), prizes of $50, $75 and $100, for poems up to 25 lines, unpublished, not having won another contest. Entries in triplicate, not identified. Type name, address and phone number on a 3×5 card, include title and first line on card. May purchase book of winners' poems for $3 postpaid. Deadline: February 15.

INA COOLBRITH CIRCLE ANNUAL POETRY CONTEST (IV-Regional), %Tom Berry, Treasurer, 761 Sequoia Woods Place, Concord CA 94518, has prizes of $10-50 in each of several categories for California residents only. Poems submitted in 3 copies, no names on copies. Enclose a 3×5 card with name, address, phone number, category, title, first line of poem and status as member or nonmember. Members of the Ina Coolbrith Circle pay no fee; others pay $5 for 3 poems (limit 3). Deadline in August. For further information contact Tom Berry.

COOS HEAD WRITERS POETRY CONTEST (I), P.O. Box 4022, Coos Bay OR 97420, director Mary Scheirman. Annual contest for poetry up to 1 page on any subject, with monetary prizes for 1st, 2nd and 3rd place and certificate for honorable mention. "For attendees category, writers have to attend the Coos Head Writer's workshop when annual one is held. Other category of Poets Choice does not require attendance of the annual workshop." Information available for SASE. Fees $3/2 poems; no limit on entries. Deadline: August 1.

ABBIE M. COPPS POETRY COMPETITION; GARFIELD LAKE REVIEW (I, II), contest chairperson Linda Jo Scott, Dept. of Humanities, Olivet College, Olivet MI 49076, phone (616)749-7683. Annual contest awarding $150 prize and publication in the *Garfield Lake Review*. $2/poem entry fee for unpublished poem up to 100 lines. Submit unsigned, typed poem, entrance fee, and name, address and phone number in a sealed envelope with the first line of the poem on the outside. Judge to be announced. Deadline: February 15.

CREATIVE ARTIST PROGRAM (IV-Regional), Cultural Arts Council of Houston, Suite 224, 1964 West Gray, Houston TX 77019-4808, phone (713)527-9330. Offers annual awards of $4,000 to Houston visual artists and writers. Unless funding prohibits, choreographers and composers are also included in the competition. Deadline for entry is in the fall.

DALY CITY POETRY AND SHORT STORY CONTEST (I), Daly City History, Arts & Science Commission, Serramonte Library, 40 Wembley Dr., Daly City CA 94015. Contest held annually, awarding prizes of $30, $25, $15 and $10 in various categories and $5 for honorable mention. Entry fee of $1/poem or $2/story. Stories must be unpublished. Send SASE for rules; attn: Ruth Hoppin, coordinator. Deadline: January 4.

BILLEE MURRAY DENNY POETRY AWARD (II), % Janet Overton, Lincoln College, Lincoln IL 62656. Annual award with prizes of $1,000, $500 and $250. Open to poets who have not previously published a book of poetry with a commercial or university press (except for chapbooks with a circulation of less than 250). Enter up to 3 poems, 100 lines/poem or less at $2/poem. Poems may be on any subject, using any style, but may not contain "any vulgar, obscene, suggestive or offensive word or phrase." Entry form and fees payable to Poetry Contest, Lincoln College, must be postmarked no later than May 31. Winning poems are published in **The Denny Poems**, a biennial anthology, available for $4 from Lincoln College. Send SASE for entry form.

MILTON DORFMAN NATIONAL POETRY PRIZE (II), Rome Art & Community Center, c/o Maureen Dunn Murphy, 308 W. Bloomfield St., Rome NY 13440. Annual award for unpublished poetry. Entry fee $3/poem (American funds only; $10 returned check penalty); checks made payable to: Rome Art & Community Center. Include name, address and phone on each entry. Poems are printed in Center's Newsletter. Contest opens July 1. Deadline: November 1.

ERGO!; BUMBERSHOOT (II), Box 9750-0750, Seattle WA 98109, phone (206)622-5123, founded 1973, producing director Louise DiLenge, an annual publication *ERGO!* is issued in conjunction with Bumbershoot, a multi-arts festival at the Seattle Center on Labor Day weekend. "Fifteen hundred will be published for distribution prior to and at the Festival. Included will be selected works by the Writers-in-Performance invitational participants and winners of the Written Works Competitions in addition to the official literary arts program schedule." Twenty-four honoraria will be awarded for written works. Considers simultaneous submissions. Deadline for application is mid-February. For application forms and further details write Bumbershoot at the address above. *ERGO!* **sample available for $9 postpaid. Competition guidelines available with a SASE.**

‡EUROPEAN POETRY LIBRARY; EUROPEAN POETRY TRANSLATION PRIZE; EUROPEAN COMPETITION FOR COMPOSITION IN MUSIC AND POETRY (IV-Translation, form, regional), European Poetry Library, P. Coutereelstraat 76, B-3000, Louvain, Belgium. Every third year the European Poetry Translation Prize of 5,000 ecus is awarded to a published book of translated poetry (second prize will be in 1995). Also every third year (next in 1994), there are prizes in several categories (40,000-50,000 BF) awarded to composers in the 12 member states of the European Community for setting to music published or unpublished poems in the language of one of those states. Both projects are supported by the European commission of the European communities.

FEDERATION INTERNATIONALE DES TRADUCTEURS; CARL-BERTIL NATHHORST TRANSLATION PRIZE; ASTRID LINDGREN TRANSLATION PRIZE (IV-Translation), Heiveldstraat 245, B-9040 Ghent, Belgium, or, for American applicants: American Translators Association, Suite 903, 1735 Jefferson Davis Highway, Arlington VA 22202. The Carl-Bertil Nathhorst prize is awarded once every 3 years for "promoting translation, improving the quality thereof and drawing attention to the role of the translator in bringing the people of the world together." The Astrid Lindgren Prize is awarded every 3 years for "promoting the translation of works written for children."

FLORIDA STATE WRITING COMPETITION; FLORIDA FREELANCE WRITERS ASSOCIATION (I), P.O. Box 9844, Fort Lauderdale FL 33310, is an annual contest with categories in free verse and traditional. Awards prizes up to $100 in each category. Entry fees are $2/poem for members of the FFWA, $2.50 for others. Guidelines available each fall through March for #10 SASE. Deadline: March 15.

FOSTER CITY WRITERS' CONTEST (II), F.C. Committee for the Arts, 650 Shell Blvd., Foster City CA 94404, phone (415)345-5731. Yearly competition for previously unpublished work in 5 categories: best fiction, best poem, best mystery story, best story for children, best science fiction. $10 entry fee, $250 prize in each category. Deadline: October 1. Send SASE for instructions.

GEORGIA STATE POETRY SOCIETY, INC.; BYRON HERBERT REECE AND EDWARD DAVIN VICKERS INTERNATIONAL AWARDS; THE REACH OF SONG ANNUAL ANTHOLOGY; ANNUAL CHAPBOOK COMPETITION (IV-Membership); GEORGIA STATE POETRY SOCIETY NEWSLETTER (I, IV-Anthologies, form), P.O. Box 120, Epworth GA 30541. The society sponsors a number of contests open to all poets, described in its quarterly *Newsletter* (membership $20/year). Sponsors an annual anthology, **The Reach of Song**, and an annual chapbook (for members only) competition. The Byron Herbert Reece and the Edward Davin Vickers International Awards have prizes of $250, $100, $50, $25, $15 and $10. Entry fee: $5, first poem, $1 each additional. Deadline: January 31, Reece Awards; April 30, Vickers Awards. SASE for guidelines. Sample newsletter $2; **Reach of Song**, $10.

‡JOHN GLASSCO TRANSLATION PRIZE (IV-Translation, regional), Literary Translators' Association of Canada, 3492, rue Laval, Montreal, Quebec H2X 3C8 Canada. $500 awarded annually for a translator's first book-length literary translation into French or English, published in Canada during the previous calendar year. The translator must be a Canadian citizen or landed immigrant. Eligible genres include fiction, creative nonfiction, poetry, published plays, children's books. Write for application form. Deadline: January 15.

GREEN RIVERS WRITERS' CONTESTS (I, IV-Themes, forms), Contest Chairman, 1043 Thornfield Lane, Cincinnati OH 45224, offers 8 contests for poetry on various themes and in various forms. Send SASE for rules. Entry fee $2/poem for nonmembers, $1 for members, prizes from $3-69. Deadline: November 1.

GROLIER POETRY PRIZE; ELLEN LA FORGE MEMORIAL POETRY FOUNDATION, INC. (II, IV-Themes), 6 Plympton St., Cambridge MA 02138. The Grolier Poetry Prize is open to all poets who have not published either a vanity, small press, trade or chapbook of poetry. Two poets receive an honorarium of $150 each. Four poems by each winner and 2 by each of 4 runners-up are chosen for publication in the *Grolier Poetry Prize Annual*. Opens January 15 of each year; deadline April 15. Submit 5 poems, not more than 10 double-spaced pages. Submit one ms in duplicate, without name of poet. On a separate sheet give name, address, phone and titles of poems. $5 entry fee, checks payable to the Ellen La Forge Memorial Poetry Foundation, Inc. Enclose self-addressed stamped postcard if acknowledgement of receipt is required. For update of rules, send SASE to Grolier Poetry Book Shop, Inc., before submitting mss. The Ellen La Forge Memorial Poetry Foundation sponsors intercollegiate poetry readings and a reading series, generally 5 per semester, held on the grounds of Harvard University. These are generally poets who have new collections of poetry available for sale at the Grolier Poetry Book Shop, Inc., which donates money toward costs (such as rental of the auditorium). They pay poets honoraria from $100-400 and occasionally provide overnight accommodations (but not transportation). Such poets as Mark Strand, Philip Levine, Robin Becker, Donald Hall and Bridget Pegeen Kelly have given readings under their auspices. The small foundation depends upon private gifts and support for its activities.

GUGGENHEIM FELLOWSHIPS (II), John Simon Guggenheim Memorial Foundation, 90 Park Ave., New York NY 10016. Approximately 145 Guggenheims are awarded each year to persons who have already demonstrated exceptional capacity for productive scholarship or exceptional creative ability in the arts. The amounts of the grants vary. The average grant is about $26,500. Application deadline: October 1.

HACKNEY LITERARY AWARDS; BIRMINGHAM-SOUTHERN COLLEGE WRITER'S CONFERENCE (II), Birmingham-Southern College, Box A-3, Birmingham AL 35254. This competition, sponsored by the Cecil Hackney family since 1969, offers $4,000 in prizes for novels, poetry and short stories as part of the annual Birmingham-Southern Writer's Conference. Poems must be postmarked by December 31. Send SASE for Hackney guidelines. Winners are announced at the conference, which is held in the spring.

THE HODDER FELLOWSHIP (II), The Council of the Humanities, 122 E. Pyne, Princeton University, Princeton NJ 08544. Write for details. Deadline: November 15.

HENRY HOYNS FELLOWSHIPS (II), Dept. of English, University of Virginia, Charlottesville VA 22903, are fellowships in poetry and fiction with stipends of varying amounts for candidates for the M.F.A. in creative writing. Sample poems/prose required with application. Deadline: February 15.

‡IRISH-AMERICAN CULTURAL INSTITUTE LITERARY AWARDS (IV-Ethnic/foreign language), Box 5026, 2115 Summit Ave., St. Paul MN 55105, for Irish writers who write in Irish or English, **resident in Ireland**, with published work. A total of $10,000 in prizes awarded every year.

JOHANN-HEINRICH-VOSS PRIZE FOR TRANSLATION (V), German Academy for Language and Literature, Alexandraweg 23, D-6100 Darmstadt, Germany, is an annual award of DM 20,000 for outstanding lifetime achievement for translating into German, by nomination only. 1992: Simon Wesle. 1993: Roswitha Matwin-Büsch-Mann.

THE CHESTER H. JONES FOUNDATION NATIONAL POETRY COMPETITION (II), P.O. Box 498, Chardon OH 44024, an annual competition for persons in the USA, Canadian and American citizens living abroad. Prizes: $1,000, $500, $250, and $50 honorable mentions. Winning poems plus others called "commendations" are published in a chapbook available for $3.50 from the foundation. Entry fee $2 for the first poem, $1 each for others, no more than 10 entries, no more than 32 lines each. Distinguished poets serve as judges. Deadline: March 31.

LAMPMAN AWARD (IV-Regional); OTTAWA INDEPENDENT WRITERS/LES ECRIVAINS INDE-PENDANTS D'OTTAWA, 922-2660 Norberry Crescent, Ottawa, Ontario K1V 6N2 Canada, phone (613)739-0626, is a $400 award for a published book of English-language poetry by writers in the National Capital region. Submit 3 copies of each title by February 28. Membership in Ottawa Independent Writers is $50/year, and offers their newsletter, programs, an entry in the OIW Directory and registration at reduced fees for their annual conference.

THE STEPHEN LEACOCK MEDAL FOR HUMOUR (IV-Humor, regional), Mrs. Jean Bradley Dickson, award chairman, Stephen Leacock Associates, P.O. Box 854, Orillia, Ontario L3V 3P4 Canada, phone (705)325-6546, for a book of humor, prose verse, drama or any book by a Canadian citizen. Submit 10 copies of book, 8×10 b&w photo, bio and $25 entry fee. Prize: Silver Leacock Medal for Humour and J.P. Wiser cash award of $3,500. Deadline: December 31. The committee also publishes *The Newspacket* 3 times/year.

‡THE LEAGUE OF MINNESOTA POETS CONTEST (I, IV-Members, students), % Pj Doyle, 4242 Stevens, Minneapolis MN 55400. Offers 15 different contests in a variety of categories and prizes of $5-75 for poems up to 55 lines, fees of $3 to enter all categories for members and $1/category for non-members. There is one category for students in grades 7 through 12 and one category for elementary students through grade 6. July 31 deadline. Winners are not published. Write for details.

LETRAS DE ORO SPANISH LITERARY PRIZES (IV-Foreign language), Iberian Studies Institute, North-South Center, University of Miami, P.O. Box 248123, Coral Gables FL 33124. Awards include a general prize of $2,500 and the publication of the book-length entry, plus an all expenses paid trip to Spain. For creative excellence in poetry written in the Spanish language. Contact for guidelines. Deadline: October 12.

AMY LOWELL POETRY TRAVELLING SCHOLARSHIP (II), Trust u/w/o Amy Lowell, Exchange Place, 35th Floor, Choate, Hall & Stewart, Boston MA 02109, award director F. Davis Dassori, Jr., Trustee, is an annual award of $29,000 (more-or-less: the amount varies annually), to an American-born "advanced" poet who agrees to live outside of North America for the year of the grant. Deadline for application: October 15.

MACARTHUR FELLOWS (V), John D. and Catherine T. MacArthur Foundation, Suite 1100, 140 S. Dearborn St., Chicago IL 60603. An anonymous committee selects individuals to whom the foundation awards large grants.

‡MASSACHUSETTS STATE POETRY SOCIETY NATIONAL POETRY DAY CONTEST; GERTRUDE DOLE MEMORIAL CONTEST (I), %Jeanette C. Maes, 64 Harrison Ave., Lynn MA 01905, both contests are open to all poets. The National Poetry Day Contest, with a September 1 deadline, offers prizes of $25, $15 and $10 for each of 12 or more categories; $3 fee for entire contest. The Gertrude Dole Memorial Contest, deadline March 28, offers prizes of $25, $15 and $10; $1 entry fee, one poem/poet. Send SASE for contest flyer.

MILFORD FINE ARTS COUNCIL POETRY CONTEST (I, II), 5 Broad St., Milford CT 06460. Open from September 15, 1993 to January 29, 1994. Send SASE for details.

MISSISSIPPI VALLEY POETRY CONTEST (I, II), sponsored by North American Literary Escadrille, P.O. Box 3188, Rock Island IL 61204, director S. Katz, annually offers prizes of approximately $1,200 for unpublished poems in categories for student (elementary, junior and senior high), adult, Mississippi Valley, senior citizens, jazz, religious, humorous, rhyming, haiku, ethnic and history. Fee: $5 for 1-5 poems; 50 lines/poem limit. Fee for children: $3 for 1-5 poems. Deadline: September 15. Professional readers read winning poems before a reception at an award evening each October.

MONEY FOR WOMEN (IV-Women/feminism), Barbara Deming Memorial Fund, Inc., Box 40-1043, Brooklyn NY 11240-1043, award director Pam McAllister, sponsors a semiannual contest with deadlines of December 31 and June 30 for small grants to feminists in the arts. Subjects include women, peace, justice issues. Send SASE for application form. Applicants must be citizens of US or Canada.

MONTANA INSTITUTE OF THE ARTS POETRY CONTEST; MARY BRENNEN CLAPP MEMORIAL AWARD (IV-Regional, membership), P.O. Box 1872, Bozeman MT 59771, annual contest with a March 31 deadline. Open to Montana poets only, for unpublished poems up to 100 lines, in a group of 3. No fee. Mary Brennen Clapp Memorial Award of $50 and prizes of $40, $30 and $20. Must submit 3 poems and cover letter. Send SASE for guidelines.

JENNY MCKEAN MOORE FUND FOR WRITERS, (II), Dept. of English, George Washington University, Washington DC 20052, provides for a visiting lecturer in creative writing for about $40,000 for 2 semesters. Apply by November 15 with resume and writing sample of 25 pgs. or less. Awarded to poets and fiction writers in alternating years.

NASHVILLE NEWSLETTER POETRY CONTEST (I), P.O. Box 60535, Nashville TN 37206-0535, Roger Dale Miller, editor/publisher. Founded 1977. Reporting time 6-10 weeks. Published quarterly. Sample copy $3. Any style or subject up to 40 lines. One unpublished poem to a page with name, address in upper left corner. Entry fee of $5 for up to 3 poems. Must be sent all at once. Prizes of $50, $25 and $10 with at least 50 Certificates of Merit.

NATIONAL ENDOWMENT FOR THE ARTS; FELLOWSHIPS FOR CREATIVE WRITERS; FELLOWSHIPS FOR TRANSLATORS (II), Literature Program, Room 722, Nancy Hanks Center, 1100 Pennsylvania Ave. NW, Washington DC 20506, phone (202)682-5451. Fellowships for Creative Writers is the largest program of individual grants for American writers of poetry, fiction and creative nonfiction. Awards of $20,000 are made each year to published writers. Applications are reviewed and recommendations for funding are made by an advisory panel composed of experts from the literature field. In reviewing applications, advisory panelists consider solely the literary quality of the manuscripts submitted. To be eligible, a poet must have in publication a volume of at least 48 pages, or 20 or more poems or pages of poetry in five or more literary publications. A limited number of $20,000 and $10,000 Fellowship grants are awarded to published translators of creative literature for translation projects from other languages into English. Matching grants are also available to nonprofit organizations for publishing and audience development projects, residencies and reading series, and services to writers and literary organizations. Phone or write for guidelines and application for ms.

NATIONAL POETRY SERIES ANNUAL OPEN COMPETITION (II), P.O. Box G, Hopewell NJ 08525, between January 1 and February 15 considers book-length (approximately 48-64 pgs.) mss. Entry fee $15. Manuscripts will not be returned. The 5 winners are published by participating small press, university press and trade publishers. Send SASE for complete submissions procedures.

NATIONAL WRITERS CLUB ANNUAL POETRY CONTEST (I), Suite 424, 1450 S. Havana, Aurora CO 80012, award director Sandy Whelchel, an annual contest with prizes of $100, $50 and $25. Entry fee $8/poem; additional fee charged if poem is longer than 40 lines. Deadline: November 1. All subjects and forms are acceptable.

‡**NATIONAL WRITERS' UNION ANNUAL NATIONAL POETRY COMPETITION (II)**, P.O. Box 2409, Aptos CA 95001, phone (408)457-7488. See National Writers' Union listing under Organizations. The Santa Cruz/Monterey Local 7 chapter at this address sponsors an annual competition with entry fee: $3/poem; prizes of $200, $100 and $50, with prominent poets as judges. Send SASE for rules beginning in April.

THE NATIONAL WRITTEN & ILLUSTRATED BY . . . AWARDS CONTEST FOR STUDENTS; LAND-MARK EDITIONS (IV-Students), P.O. Box 4469, Kansas City MO 64127, award director David Melton, is an annual contest for unpublished work for a book written and illustrated by a student. Three books published, one from each of 3 age categories (6-9; 10-13; 14-19). Send #10 SAE with 60¢ postage for rules.

NEUSTADT INTERNATIONAL PRIZE FOR LITERATURE; WORLD LITERATURE TODAY (V), University of Oklahoma, Room 110, 630 Parrington Oval, Norman OK 73019. Award of $40,000 given every other year in recognition of life achievement or to a writer whose work is still in progress; nominations from an international jury only.

NEW ENGLAND POETRY CLUB; DANIEL VAROUJAN AWARD; FIRMAN HOUGHTON AWARD; NORMA FARBER AWARD; BARBARA BRADLEY AWARD; ROSALIE BOYLE PRIZE; ERIKA MUM-FORD PRIZE (I), 2 Farrar St., Cambridge MA 02138. The contests sponsored by New England Poetry Club have a $2/poem fee for nonmembers (free to members), all with a June 30 deadline, all judged by well-known poets such as X.J. Kennedy and Peter Viereck. The Varoujan Award of $500 is for a poem "worthy of Daniel Varoujan, an Armenian poet killed by the Turks in 1915." The Firman Houghton Award is $250 (named for a former NEPC president); the Norma Farber Award is $75 for a sonnet or sonnet series; the Rosalie Boyle Prize of $75 is for a poem over 30 lines; the Erika Mumford Prize for a poem of exotic or faraway setting is $250; and the Barbara Bradley Award of $200 for a lyric poem under 21 lines written by a woman. Poems should be sent in duplicate with name of writer on one to NEPC Contests, Box 81275, Wellesley MA 02181, before June 30 annually.

NEW YORK FOUNDATION FOR THE ARTS (IV-Regional), 14th Floor, 155 Avenue of Americas, New York NY 10013, phone (212)366-6900, ext. 219, offers fellowships of $7,000 every other year for poets who are at least 18 and have resided in New York State for the 2 years prior to application. Submit up to 10 pages of poetry (at least 2 poems), 3 copies of a 1-page resume, and an application form. Call for deadline information and for application form.

NORDMANNS-FORBUNDET (NORSEMEN'S FEDERATION) (IV-Translation), Radhusgt. 23b, N-0158 Oslo 1, Norway, phone 22/42 75 14 or 22/42 23 76, fax 22/42 51 63, information officer Mrs. Dina Tolfsby. The Nordmanns-Forbundet, in its desire to make Norwegian culture known abroad, awards an annual grant (maximum 15,000 Norwegian crowns) to one or more publishing houses introducing Norwegian fiction or poetry in translation (preferably contemporary). Application deadline is March 1 of each calendar year with winners announced later in the spring. Payment is made at the time of publication.

THE NORTH CAROLINA POETRY SOCIETY ZOE KINCAID BROCKMAN MEMORIAL BOOK AWARD CONTEST (IV-Regional), % Robert Collins, president, 838 Everetts Creek Dr., Wilmington NC 28405, is an annual contest for a book of poetry (over 20 pages) by a North Carolina poet (native-born or current resident for 3 years). Send SASE for details. $100 cash prize and a Revere-style bowl awarded in 1992.

NORTHWEST POETS & ARTISTS CALENDAR (IV-Regional), Bainbridge Island Arts and Humanities Council, 261 Madison S., Bainbridge Island WA 98110, links literary visual work by contemporary NW artists. Each year 12 poets are selected by jury for inclusion in this full-color wall calendar and receive $50 awards. $6 fee for up to 6 poems, late January deadline. Send SASE in fall for required entry form.

OHIOANA BOOK AWARDS; OHIOANA KROUT MEMORIAL AWARD FOR POETRY; OHIOANA QUARTERLY; OHIOANA LIBRARY ASSOCIATION (IV-Regional), Ohioana Library Association, Room 1105, 65 S. Front St., Columbus OH 43215. Ohioana Book Awards given yearly to outstanding books published each year. Up to 6 awards may be given for books (including books of poetry) by authors born in Ohio or who have lived in Ohio for at least 5 years. The Ohioana Poetry Award of $1,000 (with the same residence requirements), made possible by a bequest of Helen Krout, is given yearly "to an individual whose body of work has made, and continues to make, a significant contribution to the poetry of Ohio, and through whose work as a writer, teacher, administrator, or in community service, interest in poetry has been developed." Nominations to be received by December 31. *Ohioana Quarterly* regularly reviews Ohio magazines and books by Ohio authors. It is available through membership in Ohioana Library Association ($20/year).

NATALIE ORNISH POETRY AWARD (IV-Regional); SOEURETTE DIEHL FRASER TRANSLATION AWARD (IV-Translations, regional); TEXAS INSTITUTE OF LETTERS, % James Hoggard, T.I.L., P.O. Box 9032, Wichita Falls TX 76308-9032. The Texas Institute of Letters gives annual awards for books by Texas authors in 8 categories, including the Natalie Ornish Poetry Award, a $1,000 award for best volume of poetry. Books must have been first published in the year in question, and entries may be made by authors or by their publishers. Deadline is January 4 of the following year. One copy of each entry must be mailed to each of three judges, with "information showing an author's Texas association . . . if it is not otherwise obvious." Poets must have lived in Texas for at least two consecutive years at some time or their work must reflect a notable concern with matters associated with the state. Soeurette Diehl Fraser Translation Award ($1,000) is given for best translation of a work into English. Same rules as those for Natalie Ornish poetry award. Write during the fall for complete instructions.

OTTAWA-CARLETON BOOK AWARD (IV-Regional), Carol Sage, Arts Advisory Board, Regional Municipality of Ottawa-Carleton, 111 Lisgar St., Ottawa, Ontario K2P 2L7 Canada, annual awards (1 for English, 1 for French) given to residents of the Ottawa-Carleton Region. Deadline: January 15.

OZARK CREATIVE WRITERS, INC. CONFERENCE AWARDS (IV-Membership), 6817 Gingerbread Lane, Little Rock AR 72204, conference director Peggy Vining. Registrants ($25 prior to September 1) for the annual writers' conference may enter various writing contests with prizes of $25, $15 and $10 ("some higher"). Deadline for entry is postmark date August 31. Conference is held in Eureka Springs, Arkansas, at the Inn of the Ozarks. Send SASE (#10 envelope) for brochure after April 1.

P.A.L.S. CLUB NEWSLETTER CONTESTS; POEM AND LETTER SOCIETY OF AMERICA (I), P.O. Box 60535, Nashville TN 37206-0535, founded 1988, offers 2-4 poetry contests per year, with $5 fee for nonmembers for up to 3 poems, prizes of at least $50, $25 and $10 and at least 50 Certificates of Merit. Membership is $20 a year. Members pay no entry fees for contests and receive the newsletter free.

PACIFIC NORTHWEST WRITERS CONFERENCE ADULT LITERARY CONTEST (I), Suite 804, 2033 Sixth Ave., Seattle WA 98121, phone (206)443-3807, contest for at least 1 but no more than 5 complete poems for a 5 page maximum length. Prizes: Distinguished, $300; Excellence, $200; Merit, $150 plus certificates of recognition. Fees are $20 for PNWC members, $30 for nonmembers.

PAUMANOK POETRY AWARD COMPETITION; THE VISITING WRITERS PROGRAM (II), SUNY College of Technology, Farmingdale NY 11735, phone (516)420-2031, director Dr. Charles Fishman. The Paumanok Poetry Award Competition offers a prize of $750 plus expenses for a reading in their 1994-95 series. Submit cover letter, 1 paragraph bio, 7-10 poems, published or unpublished, and $10 entry fee by September 15. Check payable to SUNY Farmingdale Visiting Writers Program (VWP). Poets who have read in their series include Hayden Carruth, Allen Ginsberg, Linda Pastan, Marge Piercy, Joyce Carol Oates, Louis Simpson, David Ignatow and many others.

PENNSYLVANIA POETRY SOCIETY ANNUAL CONTEST; WINE AND ROSES POETRY CONTEST; PEGASUS CONTEST FOR STUDENTS, 623 N. 4th St., Reading PA 19601, award director Dr. Dorman John Grace. The deadline for the society's annual contest, which has 11 categories open to nonmembers and 5 to members only, is January 15. Grand prize in category 1 (open) will be $100 in 1994; prizes in other categories range from $10-25, plus publication. Entry fees are $1.50/poem for nonmembers except for the grand prize, which requires an entry fee of $2/poem for everybody. For information regarding the Pennsylvania Poetry Society Contest contact Dr. Dorman John Grace, (215)374-5982. The Wine and Roses poetry contest, sponsored by the Wallace Stevens Chapter for unpublished poems in serious and light verse, has prizes of $50, $25, and $15 plus publication and telecast; entry fee $1/poem; deadline June 1; write to Dr. Dorman John Grace. For information about the Pegasus Contest for Students, write to Anne Pierre Spangler, contest chairman, 1685 Christian Dr., R.D. #2, Lebanon PA 17042. The Pennsylvania Poetry Society publishes a quarterly newsletter and an annual **Prize Poems** soft cover book, containing 69 prize and honorable mention award poems. Prize poems in the Wine and Roses and Pegasus contests are published in *PPS Newsletter*.

‡**RICHARD PHILLIPS POETRY PRIZE (II)**, 719 E. Delaware, Siloam Springs AR 72761, award director Richard Phillips, Jr. Poetry prize for book-length mss awarded 3 times/year. Submit 40-page ms, published or unpublished poems, 1 poem/page, any subject, any form. Include $10 reading fee/ms, payable to Richard Phillips Poetry Awards. Postmark deadlines for spring, summer and autumn prizes are April 30, July 30 and October 31. "Winner will be announced and check for $1000 presented May 25, August 25 and November 25." Publication is the following year. Mss are not returned.

POETIC PERSPECTIVE, INC. (I), 110 Onieda St., Waxahachie TX 75165, founded in 1989 by Pat Haley, editor. Presently sponsoring poetry contests through Poetry Society of Texas. Send SASE (#10 envelope) for themes and guidelines. Anthology published yearly.

THE POETRY CENTER BOOK AWARD (II), 1600 Holloway Ave., San Francisco CA 94132. Method for entering contest is to submit a published book and a $10 entry fee; book must be published and copyrighted during the year of the contest and submitted by December 31. "Beginners may enter but in the past winners have published several previous books." Translations are acceptable but "we cannot judge works that are not in English." Books should be by an individual living writer and must be entirely poetry. Prize (only one) is $500 and an invitation to read for the Poetry Center. No entry form is required.

POETRY OF HOPE AWARD (II, IV-Themes, young adult), P.O. Box 21077, Piedmont CA 94620, awarded annually, $200 first prize ($100 for junior division) for a poem up to 100 lines expressing "the spirit of hope" using inspirational themes. Themes should speak to the "healing" of social problems (i.e. war/peace, human rights, the homeless, the earth/ecology, etc.), hope for the highest good for all of creation. Application needed. No fee. Deadline: December 30. Send SASE.

‡**POETRY SOCIETY OF MICHIGAN ANNUAL CONTESTS; THE PSM OPEN; SCHNEIDER MEMORIAL NARRATIVE; MARGARET DRAKE ELLIOTT CONTEST; EDWARD VAN LEISHOUT MEMORIAL CONTEST; KENNETH HEAFIELD CONTEST FOR YOUNG ADULTS (I, IV-Children)**, 401 Cottage St., Olivet MI 49076; contest coordinator Ben Bohnhorst, 1051 Fox Hills Dr., East Lansing MI 48823. Sponsors 5 annual contests open to nonmembers: The PSM Open, any subject, form or length; Schneider Memorial Narrative, any form or length; Margaret Drake Elliott Contest, poetry for children, 20-line limit; Edward Van Leishout Memorial Contest, for poets age 16-25, 30-line limit; Kenneth Heafield Contest, for college students age 18-24, any subject or form, 60-line limit. Various entry fees. Prizes range from $5-100, some include publication. Also sponsors 10 contests for PSM members only. Deadline for all contests is November 15. Send SASE for guidelines on all contests and membership information.

POETRY SOCIETY OF TEXAS (I, IV-Membership), Asst. Corresponding Secretary Faye Carr Adams, 4244 Skillman, Dallas TX 75206, offers approximately 90 contests, prizes $25-350, some open to nonmembers for a fee of $2/poem. Awards given at an annual awards dinner in November. Send #10 SASE for rules booklet.

THE POETRY SOCIETY OF VIRGINIA ANNUAL CONTEST (IV-Forms), 2305 Maiden Lane SW, Roanoke VA 24015, phone (703)343-7790, contest chairperson Elisabeth Drewry. Offers 14 contests with 32 cash prizes for various categories including haiku, sonnet, limerick and popular song lyric. Contest information available for SASE. Fees: Adults, $2/poem; $1/high school entry; no fee for elementary school entries.

POETS CLUB OF CHICAGO INTERNATIONAL SHAKESPEAREAN SONNET CONTEST (II, IV-Form), chairman June Shipley, 2930 Franklin St., Highland IN 46322. Write for rules, include SASE, not earlier than March. No entry fee. Prizes of $50, $35 and $15. Deadline: September 1 (postmark).

POETS' DINNER CONTEST (IV-Regional), 2214 Derby St., Berkeley CA 94705. Since 1926 there has been an annual awards banquet sponsored by the ad hoc Poets' Dinner Committee, usually at Spenger's Fish Grotto (a Berkeley Landmark). Three typed copies of poems in not more than 3 of the 8 categories are submitted anonymously without fee (January 15 deadline), and the winning poems (grand prize, 1st, 2nd, 3rd) are read at the banquet and honorable mentions awarded. **Contestant must be present to win.** Prizes awarded cash; honorable mention, books. The event is nonprofit.

‡**POETS OF THE VINEYARD CONTEST (I)**, P.O. Box 12154, Santa Rosa CA 95406, an annual contest sponsored by the Sonoma County Chapter (PofV) of the California Federation of Chaparral Poets with entries in 7 categories. These include traditional forms, free verse, haiku/senryu and tanka and a themed category on grapes, vineyards, wine, viticulture. For a copy of the current contest rules send SASE. Prizes in each category are $20, $15 and $10, with a grand prize chosen from category winners

($50). Deadline March 1, entry fee $2/poem. Prize winning poems will be published in the annual anthology, **Vintage**.

THE POETS' PRIZE (II), The Poets' Prize Committee % the Nicholas Roerich Museum, 319 W. 107th St., New York NY 10025, phone (212)864-7752, award directors Robert McDowell, Frederick Morgan and Louis Simpson. Annual cash award of $3,000 given for a book of verse by an American poet published in the previous year. The poet must be an American citizen. Poets making inquiries will receive an explanation of procedures. Books may be sent to the committee members. A list of the members and their addresses will be sent upon request with SASE.

THE E.J. PRATT GOLD MEDAL AND PRIZE FOR POETRY (IV-Students), Admissions and Awards, University of Toronto, Toronto, Ontario M5S 1A3 Canada. Awarded to a full- or part-time graduate or undergraduate student for a poem or suite of poems of approximately 100 lines. Entries are submitted under a pseudonym with information on the poet's identity in a separate envelope. Deadline in February.

PRESIDIO LA BAHIA AWARD; SUMMERFIELD G. ROBERTS AWARD (IV-Regional), Sons of the Republic of Texas, Suite 222, 5942 Abrams Rd., Dallas TX 75231. Both may be awarded for poetry. The Presidio La Bahia Award is an annual award or awards (depending upon the number and quality of entries) for writing that promotes research into and preservation of the Spanish Colonial influence on Texas culture. $2,000 is available, with a minimum first prize of $1,200. Entries must be in quadruplicate and will not be returned. Deadline: September 30. The Summerfield G. Roberts Award, available to US citizens, is an annual award of $2,500 for a book or manuscript depicting or representing the Republic of Texas (1836-46), written or published during the calendar year for which the award is given. Entries must be submitted in quintuplicate and will not be returned. Deadline: January 15.

PULITZER PRIZE IN LETTERS (II), % The Pulitzer Prize Board, 702 Journalism, Columbia University, New York NY 10027, offers 5 prizes of $3,000 each year, including 1 in poetry, for books published in the calendar year preceding the award. Submit 4 copies of published books (or galley proofs if book is being published after November), photo, bio, entry form and $20 entry fee. July 1 deadline for books published between January 1 and June 30; November 1 deadline for books published between July 1 and December 30.

REDWOOD ACRES FAIR POETRY CONTEST (I), P.O. Box 6576, Eureka CA 95502, offers an annual contest with various categories for both juniors and seniors with entry fee of 50¢/poem for the junior contests and $1/poem for the senior contests. Deadline: May 19.

REGIONAL ARTISTS' PROJECTS GRANT (I, IV-Regional), Randolph Street Gallery, 756 N. Milwaukee Ave., Chicago IL 60622, phone (312)666-7737, RAP coordinator Kapra Fleming. Offers grants up to $4,000 maximum for regional artists working in interdisciplinary or innovative ways. Must be 1-year resident of Indiana, Illinois, Ohio, Missouri or Michigan. Deadline: March 1. Application available for SASE.

RHYME INTERNATIONAL COMPETITION FOR RHYMING POETRY (IV-Form), 199 The Long Shoot, Nuneaton, Warwickshire CV11 6JQ England, has 2 categories (open class, up to 50 lines, rhymed poetry; strict form class) with prizes averaging £400-500 in each class each year (at least 60% of fees received); minimum entry fee £5 (or $10). Ajudication takes place during a special workshop weekend in England under the supervision of a well-known poet. They claim to be "the only competition in the world exclusively for rhymed poetry." Write for entry form. Deadline: September 30.

MARY ROBERTS RINEHART FOUNDATION AWARD (II), Mary Roberts Rinehart Fund, English Dept., George Mason University, 4400 University Dr., Fairfax VA 22030-4444. Two grants are made annually to writers who need financial assistance "to complete work definitely projected." The amount of the award depends upon income the fund generates; the 1992 amount was approximately $950 in each category. Poets and fiction writers should submit work in odd numbered years, e.g., 1993, 1995. A writer's work must be nominated by an established author or editor; no written recommendations are necessary. Nominations must be accompanied by a sample of the nominee's work, up to 25 pgs. of poetry and 30 pgs. of fiction. Deadline: November 30.

THE ROBERTS FOUNDATION WRITING AWARDS (II, IV-Anthologies), Box 1868, Pittsburg KS 66762, an annual competition for poetry, short fiction and essays. The poetry prizes are $500, $200 and $100, fee $6 for up to 5 poems, $1 for each additional poem. Winners appear in an annual anthology that may be purchased for $4. Send SASE for guidelines and entry form. Deadline: September 15.

ANNA DAVIDSON ROSENBERG AWARD (IV-Ethnic), Judah L. Magnes Museum, 2911 Russell St., Berkeley CA 94705, offers prizes of $100, $50 and $25 (honorable mention) for up to 12 pgs. of 1-5 poems (in English) on the Jewish Experience. There is a Youth Commendation along with the prize if a winner is under 19, Senior Award if 65 or over. Do not send poems without entry form; write between April 1 and July 15 for entry form and guidelines (enclose SASE). Deadline: August 31 each year.

SALMON ARM SONNET CONTEST (IV-Form), Salmon Arm & Dist. Chamber of Commerce, Box 999, Salmon Arm, British Columbia V1E 4P2 Canada. An annual contest for unpublished sonnets. Prizes: $100-300 and books. Entry fee: $6/poem. Limit 2 entries. Deadline: May 1. Copies of winning entries will be sent to those requesting a copy.

‡SAN FRANCISCO FOUNDATION; JOSEPH HENRY JACKSON AWARD; JAMES D. PHELAN AWARD (IV-Regional), % Intersection for the Arts, 446 Valencia St., San Francisco CA 94103. The Jackson Award ($2,000) will be made to the author of an unpublished work-in-progress in the form of fiction (novel or short stories), non-fictional prose, or poetry. Applicants must be residents of northern California or Nevada for three consecutive years immediately prior to the deadline date of January 30, and must be between the ages of 20 through 35 as of the deadline. The Phelan Award ($2,000) will be made to the author of an unpublished work-in-progress in the form of fiction (novel or short stories), non-fictional prose, poetry or drama. Applicants must be California-born (although they may now reside outside of the state), and must be between the ages of 20 through 35 as of the January 30 deadline. Mss for both awards must be accompanied by an application form, which may be obtained by sending a SASE to the above address. Entries are accepted between November 15 and January 30.

CARL SANDBURG AWARDS (IV-Regional), sponsored by Friends of the Chicago Public Library, 9S-7, 400 S. State St., Chicago IL 60605, are given annually to native-born Chicago authors or present Chicago-area writers for new books in 4 categories, including poetry. Each author receives $1,000. Publisher or authors should submit 2 copies of books published between June 1 of one year and May 31 of the next. Deadline: September 1.

SASKATCHEWAN WRITERS GUILD ANNUAL LITERARY AWARDS; CITY OF REGINA WRITING AWARD (IV-Regional), SWG Literary Awards Convenor, Box 3986, Regina, Saskatchewan S4P 3R9 Canada, offers 3 prizes of $1,000 for long ms (every fourth year for poetry) and 3 prizes of $150 and $75 honorable mentions for 1 poem up to 100 lines. $15 entry fee for long mss, $4 for single poems. Deadline mid-June. (Contact for more details.) CRWA of $3,300 awarded annually to a writer living in Regina as of January 1 of the previous year to work for 3 months on a specific project. Deadline: March 15.

SCHOLASTIC WRITING AWARDS (IV-Teens), Dept. PM, Scholastic Inc., 730 Broadway, New York NY 10003, writing competition for grades 6-12. Categories include short story, essay, poetry, short short story, humor and dramatic script. Scholarships and prize money available. Write for entry information in September.

SOCIETY OF MIDLAND AUTHORS AWARD (IV-Regional), c/o Jim Bowman, 152 N. Scoville, Oak Park IL 60302, is for authors from Midland states: IL, IN, IA, KS, MI, MN, MO, NE, ND, SD, OH, WI. It is an annual award of $300 minimum and a plaque given at a dinner at the Drake Hotel in Chicago. Books in each calendar year are eligible, not self-published. Deadline January 15 of award year. Send SASE for entry form; books must be submitted to each of 3 judges, not to Jim Bowman.

‡SOUTH DAKOTA POETRY SOCIETY CONTESTS (I), Present Chairman of S.D. State Poetry Society Contests Audrae Visser, 710 Elk, Elkton SD 57026, 10 categories, August 31 deadline.

SPARROWGRASS POETRY FORUM (I), Dept. HM, 203 Diamond St., Box 193, Sistersville WV 26175, offers 6 annual free contests, each of which has $1,000 in prizes, including a $500 grand prize. Entrants are solicited to buy an anthology, but you do not have to buy the anthology to win. Contest deadlines are the last day of every other month. Send 1 original poem, no longer than 20 lines. Name and address at the top of the page. Any style, any subject.

SPRINGFEST AND WINTERFEST POETRY CONTESTS; MILE HIGH POETRY SOCIETY (I), P.O. Box 21116, Denver CO 80221, phone (303)426-8214, award director Jane C. Schaul. Each spring and fall they offer a contest with $300 1st prize, $100 2nd prize, and two 3rd prizes of $50 each for maximum 36-line poems. Entry fee $3/poem. Deadlines: May 31 and December 31.

WALLACE E. STEGNER FELLOWSHIPS (II), Creative Writing Program, Stanford University, Stanford CA 94305, 4 in poetry, $11,000 plus tuition of $4,000, for promising writers who can benefit from 2 years instruction and criticism at the Writing Center. Previous publication not required, though it can strengthen one's application. Deadline: Postmarked by the first working day after January 1.

TOWSON STATE UNIVERSITY PRIZE FOR LITERATURE; ALICE & FRANKLIN COOLEY ENDOW-MENT (IV-Regional), Towson State University, Towson MD 21204. Awards $1,000 for a book or book ms by a Maryland writer under 40. If published, the book must have appeared within 3 years of application. Award is on the basis of aesthetic excellence. Contact for guidelines. Deadline: May 1.

THE TRANSLATORS ASSOCIATION; JOHN FLORIO PRIZE; SCHLEGEL-TIECK PRIZE, SCOTT-MON-CRIEFF PRIZE; BERNARD SHAW PRIZE; PORTUGUESE TRANSLATION PRIZE (IV-Translation), 84 Drayton Gardens, London SW 10 9SB, England. The first three of these prizes are all for translation of 20th century literature published in the U.K. The John Florio Prize of £900 is for the best translation from Italian, awarded every other year. The annual Schlegel-Tieck Prize of £2,000 is for translation from German. The biannual Scott-Moncrieff Prize of £1,000 is for translation from French. The association also administers the Bernard Shaw Prize (£1,000 every 3 years), for translations from any period from Swedish into English and published in the UK, and the Portuguese Translation Prize (£3,000 every 3 years).

TRILLIUM BOOK AWARD; PRIX TRILLIUM (IV-Regional), Ministry of Culture and Communications, 77 Bloor St. W, 3rd Floor, Libraries Branch, Toronto, Ontario M7A 2R9 Canada, is given annually for a book by an Ontario author. Submissions of published books are by publishers. Deadline: December 31. Award given in April.

LAURA BOWER VAN NUYS CREATIVE WRITING CONTEST (I, II), Black Hills Writers Group, P.O. Box 1539, Rapid City SD 57709-1539. **"We will be holding the contest in even-numbered years only."** Professional and nonprofessional categories in fiction, articles and poetry. Guidelines available after January 1 of contest year.

THE VICTORIAN FELLOWSHIP OF AUSTRALIAN WRITERS; FAW AWARDS (IV-Regional, ethnic), 1/317 Barkers Rd., Kew 3101, Australia, all awards for Australian authors. The FAW Barbara Ramsden Award (plaques to author and publisher) is "the major literary award for a book of quality" (book of the year). The FAW Australian Natives Association Literature Award ($1,000) is for "a book of sustained quality and distinction with an Australian theme." The FAW Anne Elder Poetry Award (prizes of $1,000 and $500) is for a first published book of poetry. The FAW Christopher Brennan Award (known in its first years as the Robert Frost Award) is a bronze plaque to honor an Australian poet (entries not required; award by committee). FAW Alan Marshall Award ($500) is a manuscript award for fiction or a long poem with a strong narrative element. The FAW John Shaw Neilson Poetry Award ($600) is for an unpublished poem of at least 14 lines, December 31 deadline. The FAW Fedora Anderson Young Writers' Poetry Award ($100, $30, $20) is for unpublished poems by Australian writers 15-22 years old, January 31 deadline. The Patricia Weickhardt Award to an Aboriginal Writer is "to honour the achievement of Aboriginal writers (entries not required, award by committee)."

‡WESTERN HERITAGE AWARDS (IV-Themes), National Cowboy Hall of Fame and Western Heritage Center, 1700 NE 63rd St., Oklahoma City OK 73111. Since 1960, this national museum has awarded excellence in western literature, music, television and film. Principle creators of winning entries in 15 categories receive the bronze "Wrangler," an original sculpture by artist John Free, during special awards ceremonies held at the museum each March. The 1992 award for poetry went to Walter McDonald for his book **The Digs In Escondido Canyon,** published by Texas Tech University Press. Entry forms are mailed annually in October for works published between January 1 and December 31 of that year. Deadline for entries is December 31.

WESTERN STATES BOOK AWARDS; WESTERN STATES ARTS FEDERATION (IV-Regional), Dept. PM, 236 Montezuma Ave., Santa Fe NM 87501, presents annual book awards to outstanding authors and publishers. The awards include cash prizes, $5,000, for writers for their respective publishers. Mss must be written by an author living in Alaska, Arizona, California, Colorado, Idaho, Montana, Nevada, New Mexico, Oregon, Utah, Washington or Wyoming. Award given to books to be published in fall of 1994. Work must already have been accepted for publication by a publisher in one of these states. Work must be submitted by the publisher, submitted in ms form (not previously published in book form). Publisher must have published at least 3 books. Write for more information.

WFNB ANNUAL LITERARY CONTEST; THE ALFRED G. BAILEY AWARD; WRITERS' FEDERATION OF NEW BRUNSWICK (IV-Regional), P.O. Box 37, Station A, Fredericton, New Brunswick E3B 4Y2 Canada, offers prizes of $200, $100, $30, for unpublished poems of up to 100 lines (typed, double-spaced). The Alfred G. Bailey Award is given annually for poetry mss of 48 pgs. or more. May include some individual poems that have been published. $10 Canadian entry fee. Send SASE for guidelines. Deadline: February 14.

WHITE RABBIT POETRY CONTEST; THE HARBINGER (II), P.O. Box U-1030 USAL, Mobile AL 36688, is an annual, the winners and honorable mentions being virtually the only poetry published by *The Harbinger*. Awards are $100, $50 and $25. Send SASE for entry form, which must accompany submissions (2 copies, author's name on 1 only). Deadline: March 31.

WHITING WRITERS' AWARDS; MRS. GILES WHITING FOUNDATION (V), Room 3500, 30 Rockefeller Plaza, New York NY 10112, director Gerald Freund. The Foundation makes awards of $30,000 each to up to 10 writers of fiction, nonfiction, poetry and plays chosen by a selection committee drawn from a list of recognized writers, literary scholars and editors. Recipients of the award are selected from nominations made by writers, educators and editors from communities across the country whose experience and vocations bring them in contact with individuals of unusual talent. The nominators and selectors are appointed by the foundation and serve anonymously. **Direct applications and informal nominations are not accepted by the foundation.**

OSCAR WILLIAMS & GENE DERWOOD AWARD (V), Community Funds, Inc., 2 Park Ave., New York NY 10016, is an award given annually to nominees of the selection committee "to help needy or worthy artists or poets." Selection Committee for the award does not accept nominations. Amount varies from year to year.

WORLD ORDER OF NARRATIVE AND FORMALIST POETS (II, IV-Subscription, form), P.O. Box 174, Station A, Flushing NY 11358, contest chairman Dr. Alfred Dorn. This organization sponsors contests in at least 15 categories of traditional and contemporary poetic forms, including the sonnet, blank verse, ballade, villanelle, free verse and new contrapuntal forms created by Alfred Dorn. Prizes total at least $4,000 and range from $20 to $200. Only subscribers to *The Formalist* will be eligible for the competition, as explained in the complete guidelines available from the contest chairman. "We look for originality of thought, phrase and image, combined with masterful craftsmanship. Trite, trivial or technically inept work stands no chance." Postmark deadline for entries: May 26, 1994.

WORLD'S WORST POETRY CONTEST (IV-Regional), Pismo Beach Hardware and Nursery, 930 Price St., Pismo Beach CA 93449, award directors "Pismo Bob" Pringle and Rudy Natoli. Contest for "bad" poetry that mentions Pismo Beach. Vacations in Pismo Beach, California, and miscellaneous other awards. Deadline: June 15.

WRITERS' GUILD OF ALBERTA BOOK AWARD (IV-Regional), Writer's Guild, 10523 100th Ave., Edmonton, Alberta T5J 0A8 Canada, phone (403)426-5892, awarded in six categories, including poetry. Eligible books will have been published anywhere in the world between January 1 and December 31. Their authors will have been resident in Alberta for at least 12 of the 18 months prior to December 31. Contact the WGA head office for registry forms. Unpublished manuscripts are not eligible. Except in the drama category, anthologies are not eligible. Four copies of each book to be considered must be mailed to the WGA office no later than December 31. Submissions postmarked after this date will not be accepted. **Exceptions will be made for any books** *published* **between the 15th and 31st of December. These may be submitted by January 15.** Three copies will go to the three judges in that category; one will remain in the WGA library. Works may be submitted by authors, publishers, or any interested parties.

THE YORKSHIRE OPEN POETRY COMPETITION (II), Ilkley Literature Festival, 9A Leeds Rd., Ilkley, W. Yorkshire LS29 8DH England, award director P.A. Borthwick. Offers prizes of £150, £75, £30 and 10 prizes of £10 for any style of poetry. Fees are £2/poem, £5 for 3. Deadline: July 31.

Additional Contests and Awards

The following listings also contain information about contests and awards. See the General Index for page numbers, then read the listings and/or send SASEs for more details about their offerings.

Orbis: An International Quarterly of Poetry and Prose
Oregon State Poetry Association, The
Owl Creek Press
Oxalis
Painted Hills Review
Paisley Moon
Palanquin
Panhandler, The
Paper Salad Poetry Journal, The
Paris Review, The
Parnassus Literary Journal
Pasque Petals
Pearl
PEN American Center
Pendragon
Piedmont Literary Review
Pig Iron
Pikeville Review
Pitt Poetry Series
Plainsongs
Plowman, The
Poet
Poetic Page
Poetpourri
Poetry
Poetry & Audience
Poetry Break
Poetry Committee of the Greater Washington Area, The
Poetry Forum
Poetry Kanto
Poetry Nippon Press
Poetry Northwest
Poetry Nottingham
Poetry Society of America
Poets at Work
Poets House
Poet's Review
Poets' Roundtable
Potpourri
Prairie Schooner
Princeton University Press
Pudding House Publications
Purdue University Press
Pygmy Forest Press
Quarterly Review of Literature Poetry Series
Radcliffe Quarterly
Rainbow City Express
Rambunctious Press
Raven, The

Red Cedar Review
Renegade
Rhino
Rio Grande Press
Rockford Review, The
Salmon Run Publishers
San Diego Poet's Press
San Jose Studies
San Miguel Writer
Santa Barbara Writers' Conference
Saturday Press, Inc.
Scavenger's Newsletter
Secrets from the Orange Couch
Sewanee Review, The
Shawnee Hills Spring Poetry Workshop
Signpost Press, The
Silver Apples Press
Silver Wings
Silverfish Review
Sinipee Writers Workshop
Skoob Books Publishing Ltd.
Slate & Style
Slipstream
Smith Publisher, Gibbs
Snail's Pace Review, The
Society of American Poets, The
Songwriters and Poets Critique
Sonora Review
South Coast Poetry Journal
Southern California Anthology, The
Southern Humanities Review
Southern Poetry Association
Southern Poetry Review
Southwest Florida Writers' Conference
Southwest Review
Sow's Ear, The
Spitball
Staple
State of Maine Writers' Conference
State Street Press
Still Waters Press
Story Line Press
Studio, A Journal of Christians Writing
Sub-Terrain
Sucarnochee Review, The
Tails of Wonder
Taproot Literary Review
Tesseract Publications
Texas Tech University Press
Thorntree Press

Thumbprints
Tickled by Thunder: Writer's News & Roundtable
Trenton State College Writers Conference
University of Massachusetts Writers' Conference
Unterberg Poetry Center of the 92nd Street Y, The
Vegetarian Journal
Verve
Voices Israel
W.I.M. Publications (Woman in the Moon)
Washington Writers' Publishing House
Waterways: Poetry in the Mainstream
West Wind Review
Westerly
Weyfarers
Whetstone (Canada)
Whetstone (IL)
White Eagle Coffee Store Press
White Sands Poetry Review
Whitecrow Foundation, Tahana
Whitman Cultural Arts Center, Walt
Wild East
Willamette River Books
Willow Review
Willow Springs
Wind Publications
Wisconsin Press, University of
Wisconsin Regional Writers' Association
Woodley Memorial Press
Worcester Review
Wordsmith
World-wide Writers Service, Inc.
Wormwood Review Press
Write Way, The
Writers' Center at Chautauqua, The
Writers' Center Press
Writer's Digest
Writer's Exchange
Writer's Journal
Xenophilia
Yale University Press
Yankee Magazine
Zuzu's Petals Quarterly

Resources

Conferences and Workshops

Welcome to an entirely new section of **Poet's Market**! Since beginning this directory in 1986, it has become increasingly apparent that conferences and workshops have become valuable resources for many poets, especially those just beginning. A conference or workshop may serve as an opportunity to learn about specific aspects of the craft, gather feedback from other poets and writers, listen to submission tips from editors, and/or revel in a creative atmosphere that may stimulate one's muse.

We've added this section to help you locate conferences and workshops that meet your needs as you develop your craft and poetic career. Here you'll find a wide range of events. Some, such as the Catskill Poetry Workshop and the Festival of Poetry in Franconia, New Hampshire, are specifically geared to poets. Most, however, are more general conferences with offerings for a variety of writers, including poets.

A "typical" conference may have a number of workshop sessions, keynote speakers and perhaps even a panel or two. Topics may include everything from writing fiction, poetry and books for children to marketing one's work. Often a theme, which may change from year to year, will be the connecting factor. Other conferences and workshops cover the same topics but have an overriding focus. The Appalachian Writers Workshop, for instance, offers daily sessions on poetry but is designed to promote writers and writing of the Appalachian region. A few of the conferences and workshops gear themselves to women writers or Christian writers. And the Writing Workshop for People Over 57 is designed to aid older writers—in all areas of writing.

Despite different themes or focuses, each listing in this section details the offerings specifically available for poets. The listings also include information about other workshops, speakers and panels of interest. It is important to note, however, that some conference and workshop directors were still in the organizing stages when contacted. Consequently, some listings include information from last year's events simply to provide an idea of what to expect this year. For more up-to-date details, including current costs, send a SASE to the director in question a month or two before the date(s) listed.

Benefiting from conferences

For many poets, not just beginning ones, attending conferences and workshops is beneficial. First, these events provide poets with opportunities to learn more about their craft. Some even feature individual sessions with workshop leaders, allowing poets to specifically discuss their work with others. If these one-on-one sessions include critiques (generally for an additional fee), we've also included this information in listings.

Besides learning from workshop leaders, poets may also benefit from conversations with other attendees. Writers on all levels enjoy talking to and sharing insights with others. A conversation over lunch can reveal a new market for your work, or a casual chat while waiting for a session to begin can acquaint you with a new resource. If a conference or workshop includes time for open readings and you choose to participate, you may gain feedback from both workshop leaders and others in attendance.

Another reason poets find conferences and workshops worthwhile is the opportunity to meet editors and publishers who offer advice about marketing work. The availability of these folks, however, does not necessarily mean they will want to read your latest collection of poems (unless, of course, they are workshop leaders and you have an individual meeting scheduled with them). Though editors and publishers are glad to meet poets and writers, and occasionally discuss work in general terms, they cannot give personal attention to everyone they meet.

To make the most of your brief contact with editors and publishers, be courteous and friendly. Ask specific questions about their jobs or, better yet, some point of their presentations. Let the conversation turn toward your writing naturally. If your time is up before you get the chance to mention your craft, don't worry. You can follow up later with a letter making reference to having met at a certain conference.

Selecting a conference or workshop

When trying to select the right conference or workshop to attend, keep in mind your goals. If you want to learn how to improve your craft, for example, consider one of the events entirely devoted to poetry or locate a more general conference where one-on-one critique sessions are offered. If you're looking for more informal feedback, consider an event which includes open readings. If marketing your work seems like an ominous task, register for a conference that includes a session with editors. And if you have an interest in other forms of writing, an event covering a wide range of topics is a good bet.

Of course, you should always take into consideration your own resources. If both your time and funds are limited, search for a conference or workshop within your area—be it your city, state or province. Many events are held during weekends and may be close enough to allow you to commute. On the other hand, if you want to combine your vacation with time spent meeting other writers and working on your craft, consider events held in other states or workshops such as those sponsored by The Writers' Center at Chautauqua. In either case, it is important to at least consider the conference location and be aware of activities to enjoy in the area.

Still other factors may influence your decision when selecting a certain workshop or conference. For instance, events that sponsor contests allow poets and writers to gain recognition and recoup some of their expenses. Similarly, some conferences and workshops have financial assistance or scholarships available. Finally, many are associated with colleges and/or universities and may offer continuing education credits. You will find all of these options included in the listings here. Again, send a SASE for more details.

For further information about the wide range of conferences and workshops, consult **The Guide to Writers Conferences** (ShawGuides, Inc., Dept. 1406W, 625 Biltmore Way, Coral Gables FL 33134) and/or the May issue of *Writer's Digest* magazine (available on newsstands or by ordering directly from the publisher at 1507 Dana Ave., Cincinnati OH 45207). Another interesting source is **Author & Audience: A Readings and Workshops Guide**, available from Poets & Writers, Inc. (See the listing in Publications Useful to Poets.)

APPALACHIAN WRITERS CONFERENCE, Box 6935, Radford University, Radford VA 24142, phone (703)639-0812, AWA president Dr. R.P. Lanier. Annual 3-day event founded in 1980. 1994 dates: July 8-10. Location: "Radford University in Southwest Virginia, 40 miles from Roanoke in scenic New River Valley." Average attendance is 65 members. **Open to Appalachian writers. The conference's purpose is "to celebrate the successes, common bonds and concerns of writers in the Appalachian region." Theme for the 1994 conference is Appalachian Poetry: The Pastoral/Political Paradox.** Offerings specifically available for poets include workshop critiques, readings, book displays and market news. The featured guest speaker will be Bennie Lee Sinclair, poet laureate of South Carolina. Cost for 1993 conference was annual dues of $10; private room $48.50, double room $29.50. Accommodations are air-conditioned dormitory rooms with private baths. Poetry, fiction and essay contests sponsored as part of the conference. Send SASE for brochures and registration forms.

APPALACHIAN WRITERS WORKSHOP, Box 844, Hindman KY 41822, phone (606)785-5475, director Mike Mullins. Annual 5-day event founded 1977. 1994 dates: August 7-13; participants should plan to arrive on Sunday and depart the following Saturday. Location: Campus of Hindman Settlement School in Knott County, KY. "The campus is hilly and access for housing is limited for physically impaired, but workshop facilities are accessible." Average attendance is 60-70. **Open to "anyone regardless of sex, age or race." Conference is designed to promote writers and writing of the Appalachian region. It covers fiction, poetry, writing for children, dramatic work and nonfiction.** Offerings specifically available for poets include daily sessions on poetry, individual critique sessions and readings. All of the staff are featured readers, including James Still, Bobbie Ann Mason, Jim Wayne Miller, Chris Offutt, George Ella Lyon, Dick Hague, Lisa Koger and, in 1994, Robert Morgan and Lee Smith. Cost for workshop is approximately $300 for room, board and tuition; may be more for 1994. Information on overnight accommodations is available for registrants. Accommodations may include special rates at area hotels "once our facilities are filled." Submit mss for individual critiques in advance. Send SASE for brochures and registration forms. They recently published an anthology "of the best of the past 15 workshops." Write for information.

ARIZONA CHRISTIAN WRITERS CONFERENCE, P.O. Box 5168, Phoenix AZ 85010, phone (602)838-4919, director Reg Forder. Annual 3-day event founded in 1981. Usually held 2nd weekend in November at a Holiday Inn in Phoenix. Average attendance is 200. **Open to anyone. Conference covers fiction, poetry, writing for children.** Cost is $109, extra for beginning writers day; participants are responsible for their own meals. Accommodations include special rates at host hotel. Send SASE for brochures and registration forms.

ARKANSAS WRITERS' CONFERENCE, 1115 Gillette Dr., Little Rock AR 72207, phone (501)225-0166, director Clovita Rice. Annual 2-day event founded 1944. "In 1994 we are planning a bigger conference to celebrate our 50th anniversary." Always 1st weekend of June at the Holiday Inn West in Little Rock. Average attendance is 200. **Open to all writers. The conference is designed to "appeal both to beginning and already active writers with a varied program on improving their writing skills and marketing their work."** Offerings specifically available for poets include a poetry workshop offering critiques and poetry contests. In 1993, the guest speaker was Patricia Gallagher, author of **For All The Write Reasons**. Other special features include an awards luncheon (door prizes such as **Writer's Market** and **Poet's Market**) and banquet, and the announcement of the person selected for Arkansas Writers' Hall of Fame. Cost for 1993 conference was $10 registration for 2 days, $5 for 1 day. Five dollar fee to cover entry to 36 contests. Limousine service from airport to Holiday Inn West is provided. Accommodations include special rates at host hotel. Individual critiques are available. Bring one poem, 20-line limit, to workshop. Thirty-six contests (4 require attendance and 8 are limited to Arkansas residents) are sponsored as part of conference. Each contest has a chairman who will judge or secure a judge. Send SASE for brochures and registration forms after February 1 each year. Clovita Rice, conference director, is editor of *Voices International* (see listing in the Publishers of Poetry section).

AUTUMN AUTHORS' AFFAIR, 1507 Burnham Ave., Calumet City IL 60409, phone (708)862-9797, president Nancy McCann. Annual 3-day event founded 1983. Usually held during the 4th weekend in October at the Hyatt Lisle in Lisle, IL. Average attendance is 200-275. **Open to anyone. Conference covers fiction, but every year Professor Charles Tinkham of Purdue University, called "the poet of the people," gives a poetry workshop "covering the entire realm of writing poetry. We usually have between 40-75 published authors at the conference each year."** Cost for 1993 weekend, including meals, was $100, $75 for Saturday only. Information on overnight accommodations is available. Accommodations include special hotel rates. Send SASE for brochures and registration forms.

BAY AREA WRITERS WORKSHOP, P.O. Box 94062, Woodside CA 94602, phone (415)851-4568, fax (415)851-3279, codirector Laura Jason. Annual 2-day events founded in 1988. Usually held 4-5 summer weekends at various workshop settings. Average attendance is 15 for workshops. **Open to literary writers. Workshops cover poetry, novel and short story.** In 1993 the weekend intensive workshops were led by Carolyn Forche and Jack Gilbert. Cost for workshop is $250; participants are responsible for their own meals. Full scholarships are awarded to 10-15% of participants. Information on overnight accommodations and transportation is available for participants. Workshop evaluations are included. All participants receive manuscripts prior to weekend. Bay Area Writers also sponsor a biennial 1-day literary publishing conference for 300 participants. In 1992, the featured speaker was Diane Ackerman, author of **A Natural History of the Senses**. Cost of conference is $45. Send SASE for brochures and registration forms.

CAPE COD WRITERS CONFERENCE, c/o Cape Cod Conservatory, Rte. 132, West Barnstable MA 02668, phone (508)775-4811, director Marion Vuilleumier. Annual week-long event founded in 1963. Usually held the 3rd week of August at the Tabernacle, Craigville Conference Center. Average attendance is 150. **Open to everyone. Conference covers poetry, fiction, nonfiction, mystery/suspense and writing for children.** In 1993 the poetry teacher was Lance Hensen. Cost is $80 registration, $50 each course (full time); $25 registration, $20 each course (one day); 4 scholarships available. Participants are responsible for their own meals. "It is recommended that participants stay at the Craigville Conference Center (early registration necessary)." Other housing information available from Bed & Breakfast Cape Cod. Manuscript evaluations ($60) and personal conferences ($30) are also available. Send SASE for brochures and registration forms.

CAPE LITERARY ARTS WORKSHOPS, c/o Cape Cod Conservatory, Rte. 132, West Barnstable MA 02668, phone (508)775-4811, director Marion Vuilleumier. Annual week-long event founded 1985. Usually held the 2nd week of August at the South Congregational Parish House, Centerville. Average attendance is 10/workshop. **Open to everyone. Workshops cover poetry, fiction, script writing and children's book writing and illustration.** The 1993 poet was Carol Dine. Cost is $410; participants are responsible for meals although "plentiful snack spreads" are included. "Twenty hours of practically individual attention is given, including one personal critique." Private transportation recommended. Contact Bed & Breakfast Cape Cod for housing information or Centerville Corners Motor Lodge. Send SASE for brochures and registration forms.

CATSKILL POETRY WORKSHOP, c/o Office of Special Programs, Hartwick College, Oneonta NY 13820, phone (607)431-4415, fax (607)431-4318, program coordinator Gladys Freeland. Annual 8-day summer event founded 1988. Usually held at the beginning of August at Hartwick College's Pine Lake Environmental Center, "a 914-acre tract of ecologically diverse lands and various terrain. Located in northern foothills of Catskills, the center offers nature trails, flora and fauna for field work in biology and environmental studies, lodging, swimming and boating facilities, sauna, and the peace and quiet tranquility appropriate for contemplation and the imaginative work of the mind." Average attendance is 18-24 maximum. Workshop is **selective. Acceptance based on manuscript review of 5-7 poems. All applications are reviewed by the director of the workshop, Carol Frost. "Talented writers can apply themselves to the craft and art of poetry in a supportive atmosphere. The program includes workshops, classes on craft, evening readings by staff and guest writers, and individual instructional conferences."** Guest faculty for 1993 included Stephen Dobyns, Chase Twichell, Michael Waters, William Matthews, Sarah Gorham and Jeffrey Skinner. Costs for 1993 workshop were $625 (including tuition, room and board) and $425 (commuter rate, including tuition and lunch). An additional $75 is required if taken for ½ course unit undergraduate credit in English. College will provide local transportation from bus line in Oneonta to Pine Lake if needed. Arrangements must be made in advance. Room is provided at the lodge at Pine Lake or in cabins at the lake. Two individual manuscript conferences with workshop faculty and visitors are scheduled for each participant. Write for brochures and registration forms; SASE unnecessary.

FESTIVAL OF POETRY, Robert Frost Place, Franconia NH 03580, phone (603)823-5510, executive director Donald Sheehan. Annual week-long event founded in 1978. Usually held first week of August at Robert Frost's mountain farm (house and barn), made into a center for poetry and the arts. Average attendance is 50-55. **Open to poets only.** Recent faculty included Hayden Carruth, Amy Clampitt, Donald Hall, Brad Leithauger and Alicia Ostriker. Cost is $340-350 tuition, plus a $25 reading fee. "Room and board available locally; information sent upon acceptance to program." Application should be accompanied by 3 pages of poetry. Send SASE for brochures and registration forms.

THE FLIGHT OF THE MIND, WOMEN'S WRITING WORKSHOP, 622 SE 29th Ave., Portland OR 97214, phone (503)236-9862, director Judith Barrington. Annual event founded 1983. 1994 dates: June 19-July 1. Two workshops in summer for 6-11 days at "a rustic retreat center (Dominican owned) right on the wild McKenzie River in the foothills of the Oregon Cascades." Average attendance is 65 women/workshop in 5 different classes. **Open to women writers. Workshops cover fiction, poetry, essays, collaboration, special-topic classes (e.g. "landscape and memory") with a feminist philosophy.** In 1993 poetry workshop leaders were Naomi Shihab Nye, Judith Barrington and Elizabeth Woody. Cost for 1993 workshop (including tuition, all meals and room) was $550 and up depending on accommodations chosen. Scholarships available. Transportation to and from the event is provided. Participants are selected on the basis of work submitted. Peer critique groups form at workshop. "Competition is discouraged." Send first class stamp for brochures and registration forms.

HOFSTRA UNIVERSITY SUMMER WRITERS' CONFERENCE, 110 Hofstra University, Hempstead NY 11550, phone (516)463-5997, fax (516)564-0061, director Lewis Shena. Annual 10-day event founded 1972. Usually starts the Monday after July 4th. Location: Hofstra University. Average attendance is 50-60. **Open to all writers. Conference covers fiction, nonfiction, poetry, children's writing, stage/ screenwriting and one other area (science fiction, mystery, etc.). "Every year we offer a poetry workshop."** Guest speakers (other than the workshop leaders) "usually come from the world of publishing." There are also "readings galore and various special presentations." Cost for 1993 conference was $601 (non-credit). Additional fee of $275 for air-conditioned dorm room, one dinner and coffee/tea on a daily basis. For those seeking credit, other fees apply. Individual critiques are also available. "Each writer gets a half hour one-on-one with the poetry workshop leader." They do not sponsor a contest, but "we submit exceptional work to the *Paris Review*." Send SASE for brochures and registration forms (available as of April).

IOWA SUMMER WRITING FESTIVAL, University of Iowa, 116 International Center, Iowa City IA 52242, phone (319)335-2534, fax (319)335-2740, coordinators Karen Burgus Schootman and Peggy Houston. Annual event founded in 1987. Held each summer in June and July for six weeks, includes one week, two week and weekend workshops at the University of Iowa campus. Average attendance is 150/week. **Open to "anyone over 21 who has a desire to write." Conference offers courses in most all writing forms. In 1993, offerings available for poets included 14 poetry classes for all levels.** Speakers were Ethan Canin, Clark Blaise, Robert Waller, Gordon Mennenga, Gerald Stern and Kathleen Pierce. Cost for 1993 conference was $315 for 1 week and $150 for a weekend; discount available for early payment. Participants are responsible for their own meals. Accommodations available at the Campus Motel and Holiday Inn. Housing in residence hall costs about $23/night. Participants in week-long workshops will have private conference/critique with workshop leader. Send for brochures and registration forms.

THE IWWG SUMMER CONFERENCE, The International Women's Writing Guild, P.O. Box 810, Gracie Station, New York NY 10028, phone (212)737-7536, executive director Hannelore Hahn. Annual week-long event founded 1978. 1994 dates: August 12-19. Location: Skidmore College in Saratoga Springs, NY. Average attendance is 400. **Open to all women. Fifty-six workshops are offered. "At least four poetry workshops offered for full week."** Cost is $600 for conference program and room and board. "Critiquing available throughout the week." Send SASE for brochures and registration forms. The International Women's Writing Guild's bimonthly newsletter publishes and features hundreds of outlets for poets. See listing in Organizations Useful to Poets.

LIGONIER VALLEY WRITERS CONFERENCE, Box 8, RR 4, Ligonier PA 15658, phone (412)238-5749, fax (412)238-5190, president E. Kay Myers. Annual 3-day event founded in 1986. 1994 dates: July 8-10. "This is a relaxing, educational, inspirational conference in a scenic, small town." Average attendance is 80. **Open to anyone interested in writing. Conference covers fiction, creative nonfiction, poetry, writing for children and teaching children to write, and playwriting.** Poetry workshops each day. The 1993 speaker was Ralph Bennett, senior editor of *Reader's Digest.* Cost for conference is approximately $200, including some meals and picnic. Participants are responsible for their own dinners and lodging. Information on overnight accommodations is available for registrants. Individual critiques are also available. Must send samples in advance. Send SASE for brochures and registration forms. "We also publish *The Loyalhanna Review,* a literary journal, which is open to participants."

LITTLE SMOKIES OF OHIO FALL POETRY WORKSHOP, State Route 125, Friendship OH 45130, phone (614)858-6621 or contact D.H. Spears at (614)533-1081. Annual 3-day event founded 1992. Usually held during a weekend in September, beginning on Friday night with a campfire reading. Saturday morning is writing on the trails, Saturday afternoon includes time for editing workshops and Saturday evening is an awards banquet. Sunday morning is for evaluation and wrap-up. Average attendance is 22. **Open to anyone interested in the writing of poetry. The workshop "is designed to promote the writing of poetry and to celebrate the poetic achievements of the workshop participants.** The writing 'charge' changes each year and is kept secret until time to head for the trails." Cost is $12 registration; participants are responsible for their own meals and lodging. Information on overnight accommodations is available for registrants. Shawnee Lodge offers rooms that sleep 4; cost is $75/night. Cabins at Shawnee State Park sleep 6; cost is $99/night. A poetry contest is sponsored in conjunction with the workshop. Theme changes yearly. Deadline: August 31. Judge is Harding Stedler, workshop conductor. Send SASE for brochures and registration forms. The event is sponsored by the Phoenix Writers of Portsmouth, Ohio in affiliation with Shawnee State University.

MIDLAND WRITERS CONFERENCE, Grace A. Dow Memorial Library, 1710 W. St. Andrews, Midland MI 48640, phone (517)835-7151, fax (517)835-9791, conference co-chairs Margaret Allen and Eileen Finzel. Annual 1-day event founded 1979. Usually held the second weekend in June at the Grace A. Dow Memorial Library in Midland, MI. Average attendance is 100. **Open to any writer, published or unpublished. Conference usually includes six sessions that vary in content. "We always have one session on poetry and one session on writing for children. The other four sessions cover other subjects of interest to writers."** In 1993, Judith Kerman presented a session on "Writing Poetry From Both Sides of the Brain" and the keynote speaker was Judith Viorst. "We always have a well-known keynoter. In the past we have had Kurt Vonnegut, Andrew Greeley, Mary Higgins Clark and David McCullough." Cost for 1993 conference was $45 until 2 weeks prior to the event ($55 after that). For students, senior citizens and handicapped participants, cost was $35 until 2 weeks prior to the event ($45 after that). Information on overnight accommodations is available for registrants. Send SASE for brochures and registration forms.

MIDWEST WRITER'S CONFERENCE, 6000 Frank Ave., Canton OH 44720-7599, phone (216)499-9600, fax (216)494-6121, coordinator of continuing studies Debbie Ruhe. Annual weekend event founded 1968. 1994 dates: October 7-8. Location: Kent State University Stark Campus in Canton, Ohio. Average attendance is 250. **Open to aspiring writers in any category, but the writing contest is directed toward fiction, nonfiction, juvenile literature and poetry. "The conference provides an atmosphere in which aspiring writers can meet with and learn from experienced, established writers through lectures, workshops, competitive contests, personal interviews and informal group discussions."** Offerings specifically available for poets include a lecture session in the poetry area and a contest. Past panelists have included David Citino, Michael Heaton, Peter Miller and Kurt Vonnegut. One special feature of the conference is an all day book fair which includes several Ohio small presses. Cost for 1994 conference is $65 which covers conference registration, workshops, keynote address, lunch and ms entry fee. Contest entry fee exclusively is $40 for two mss and $10 for each additional ms. Participants are responsible for other meals. Information on overnight accommodations is available for registrants. Special conference rates are available through the Parke Hotel, and there is a special shuttle between the university and the hotel. Individual critiques are also available in the areas of poetry, fiction, nonfiction and juvenile literature. Submit one individual poem up to 200 lines. Contest sponsored as part of conference. "Work must be original, unpublished and not a winner in any contest at the time of entry." Judging is performed by local professionals in their appropriate categories. Send SASE for brochures and registration forms. Kent State University offers submissions to the annual publication of *Canto*. For more information, call (216)499-9600 ext. 365. Co-sponsor of the Midwest Writers' Conference is the Greater Canton Writers Guild, 919 Clinton Ave. SW, Canton OH 44706-5196.

MISSISSIPPI VALLEY WRITERS CONFERENCE, Augustana College, Rock Island IL 61201, phone (309)762-8985, founder/director David R. Collins. Annual week-long event founded in 1973. Usually held the second week in June at the Liberal Arts College of Augustana College. Average attendance is 80. **Open to all writers, "beginning beginners to polished professionals." Conference provides a general professional writing focus on many genres of writing. Offers week-long workshop in poetry.** Evening programs as well as daily workshops are included. Cost for 1993 conference was $25 registration, $35 one workshop, $60 two workshops, $30 each additional workshop. Conferees may stay on campus or off. Board and room accommodations are available at Westerlin Hall on Augustana campus, 15 meals and 6 nights lodging approximately $200. Individual critiques are also available. Submit up to 10 poems. Awards presented by workshop leaders. Send SASE for brochures and registration forms.

NAPA VALLEY WRITERS' CONFERENCE, 2277 Napa-Vallejo Highway, Napa CA 94558, phone (707)253-3070, fax (707)253-3015, managing director Sherri Hallgren. Annual week-long event founded 1981. Usually held the last week in July or first week in August on the grounds of Napa Valley College, 50 miles northeast of San Francisco. Average attendance is 36 in poetry and 36 in fiction. **"The conference has maintained its emphases on process and craft, featuring a faculty as renowned for the quality of their teaching as for their work. It has also remained small and personal, fostering an unusual rapport between faculty writers and conference participants. The poetry session provides the opportunity to work both on generating new poems and on revising previously written ones. Participants spend time with each of the staff poets in daily workshops that emphasize writing new poems - taking risks with new material and forms, pushing boundaries in the poetic process."** The 1993 poetry staff was Gerald Stern, Jane Hirshfield and Edward Hirsch. "Participants register for either the poetry or the fiction workshops, but panels and craft talks are open to all writers attending. Evenings feature readings by the faculty that are open to the public and hosted by Napa Valley wineries." Cost is $425, not including meals or housing. There are some limited partial scholarships, depending on donations. Shuttle service from the San Francisco Airport is available for a nominal fee. "Participants usually find it helpful to have a car during the week, but car pools can be arranged for those who need rides to conference events. A list of valley accommodations is mailed to applicants on acceptance and includes at least one reduced-rate package. Through the generosity of Napa residents, limited accommodations in local homes are available on a first-come, first-served basis." All applicants are asked to submit a qualifying ms with their registration (no more than 5 pages of poetry or 12 pages of fiction) as well as a brief description of their background as a writer. Send SASE for brochures and registration forms.

THE NAROPA INSTITUTE WRITING & POETICS SUMMER PROGRAM, 2130 Arapahoe Ave., Boulder CO 80302, phone (303)444-0202, director of writing & poetics Anne Waldman, assistant director Andrew Schelling. Annual month-long summer program founded in 1974. Usually held every July; participants may attend from 1-4 weeks. "We are located on 3.7 acres in the center of Boulder, Colorado. The campus houses a performing arts center, meditation hall, classrooms, offices and library. Many of the summer lectures are held under a huge tent on our back lawn." Average attendance is 100-120. **Open to anyone; students attending for credit must obtain department's permission. "It is a convocation of students, scholars, fiction writers, poets and translators. In dialogue with renown practitioners of verbal arts, students confront the composition of poetry and prose."** Theme for 1993 was Deeper into America, "a counter-celebration challenging the Euro-American way of life that has ignored and oppressed certain cultures and forms of life." Theme for 1994 is Beat Reunion, "a tribute to Allen Ginsberg." Offerings specifically available for poets include lectures, readings (both student and faculty), workshops and one-on-one interviews with guest faculty. Conference speakers include Allen Ginsberg, Anselm Hollo, Bobbie Louise Hawkins, Jack Collom, Bernadette Mayer, Michael McClure, Ron Silliman, Michael Ondaatje, Nathaniel Mackey and Eagle Cruz. Cost for 1 week is $375 (non credit), for 2 weeks $630 (non credit) and $750 (BA credit). Cost of 4 weeks is $1,260 (non credit), $1,500 (BA credit) and $2,000 (MFA credit). Lab fees are $10/week. Four scholarships are available for minority students. Participants are responsible for their own meals. "Student services can help find places to stay." Work to be critiqued does not need to be sent in advance. "During the weekly workshops and personal interviews, every writer will have a chance to be critiqued by professional poets/fiction writers." Send SASE for brochures and registration forms. "We also sponsor student readings and have an informal summer magazine and two other (more formal) school sponsored magazines, *Bombay Gin* and *Exit Zero.*"

OZARKS WRITERS CONFERENCE, Professional Writing Program, UMKC, 5100 Rockhill, Kansas City MO 64110, phone (816)235-1120, fax (816)235-2611, director James McKinley. Annual August event founded 1983. Usually held for 5-6 days around the first weekend in August. Location alternates between Branson, Missouri and Fayetteville, Arkansas. Average attendance is 50. **Open to everyone. Conference covers fiction, poetry, genre writing and creative nonfiction.** "One-third to one-half of sessions specifically devoted to poetry. All participants attend all sessions." Speakers have included Miller Williams, Eddy L. Harris, Crescent Dragowagon, Dan Jaffe, Donald Hayes, Paulette Jiles, James McKinley and Nancy Pickard. "Frequently we schedule specific 'extra day' topics, e.g. Ozarks history." Cost for 1993 conference was $280, including breakfast and lunch. Scholarships available. Information on overnight accommodations and transportation from Kansas City or Fayetteville airports is available through the Continuing Education Divisions of the University of Missouri at Kansas City's Arts and Science College and the University of Arkansas. "Special rates are secured for conference attendees." Individual critiques are also available for a fee. Mss should be submitted prior to conference. Send SASE for brochures and registration forms.

RAIN FOREST WRITERS, P.O. Box 22889, Juneau AK 99802, phone (907)789-8479, conference chair Stoney Compton. Annual 3-4 day event founded 1990. Usually held the 2nd or 3rd weekend of June at Centennial Hall Convention Center in downtown Juneau—"mountains, ocean, totem poles, and the friendliest folks you'll ever meet." Average attendance is 50-100. **Open to everyone. Conference is eclectic—fiction, nonfiction, poetry, juvenile literature, basics of writing and editors and agents. Includes at least 2 workshops in poetry and various panel discussions.** Cost for the 1993 conference, including a 1-year membership in Rain Forest Writers Inc., was $100 prior to April 30, $125 prior to May 31, $150 prior to June 6. Information on overnight accommodations is available to registrants. Basic housing available for free (bring a sleeping bag). Individual critiques of mss are also available. Send SASE for brochures and registration forms.

SANTA BARBARA WRITERS' CONFERENCE, P.O. Box 304, Carpinteria CA 93014, phone (805)684-2250, fax (805)684-2250 (after recorded message), conference director Barnaby Conrad. Annual week-long event founded in 1973. Held the last Friday to Friday in June at the Miramar Hotel in Montecito. 1994 dates: June 17-24. Average attendance is 350 people. **Open to everyone. Covers all genres of writing.** Workshops in poetry offered. In 1993, speakers included Sue Grafton, Ray Bradbury, Sol Stein, Perie Longo, W.R. Wilkins and Craig Broude. Cost for 1993 conference including all workshops and lectures, 2 al fresco dinners and room (no board), was $885 single, $660 double occupancy, $335 day students. Transportation to and from the event is provided. Individual critiques are also available. Submit 1 ms of no more than 3000 words in advance with SASE. Competitions with awards sponsored as part of conference. Send SASE for brochures and registration forms.

SEWANEE WRITERS' CONFERENCE, 310 St. Luke's Hall, Sewanee TN 37375, phone (615)598-1141, fax (615)598-1145, conference administrator Cheri B. Peters. Annual 12-day event founded 1990. Usually held the last 2 weeks in July at The University of the South ("dormitories for housing, Women's Center for public events, classrooms for workshops, student union building for dining, etc."). Attendance in 1993 was 105. **Open to poets, fiction writers and playwrights who submit their work for review in a competitive admissions process.** "We offer genre workshops (not thematic workshops) in each area." Poets on the 1993 faculty were Emily Grosholz, Mark Jarman, Maxine Kumin and Derek Walcott. Other speakers included editors who are also poets who read from their work and responded to questions on the editorial process. Readings were also given by Richard Wilbur and Anthony Hecht. Cost for 1993 conference was $1025, including room and board. Each year scholarships and fellowships based on merit are available on a competitive basis. "We provide bus transportation from the Nashville airport on the opening day of the conference and back to the airport on the closing day at no additional cost." Individual critiques are also available. "All poets admitted to the conference are entitled to a private, hour-long session with a member of the poetry faculty." A ms should be sent in advance after admission to the conference. Write for brochures and registrations forms. No SASE is necessary.

SHAWNEE HILLS SPRING POETRY WORKSHOP, HC 60, Box 562, Greenbo Lake State Park, Greenup KY 41144, phone (800)325-0083, contact D.H. Spears. Annual 3-day event founded 1983. Usually held during a weekend in April, beginning with a keynote speaker on Friday night. Saturday morning is for writing on the trails, Saturday afternoon includes editing workshops and Saturday evening is an awards banquet. Sunday morning is for evaluation and wrap-up. Average attendance is 40. **Open to practicing poets. The workshop is designed "to promote the writing of poetry and to celebrate the poetic achievements of workshop participants.** What varies from year to year are the keynote speaker and the writing 'charge' for going out on the trails. The 'charge' is kept secret until departure time." The speaker for 1993 was Robert L. Doty, professor of English at Campbellsville College. Cost is $12 registration; participants are responsible for their own meals and lodging. Information on overnight accommodations is available for registrants. The Jesse Stuart Lodge has 37 guest rooms, available at special rates. Rooms are also available at area hotels. The Phoenix Writers sponsor a poetry contest (32-line limit) in conjunction with the workshop. Theme changes yearly. Deadline: March 31. Judge is Harding Stedler, workshop conductor. 1st prize: $50, 2nd: $30, 3rd: $20. Send SASE for brochures and registration forms. For information about The Phoenix Writers, contact Harding Stedler, 307 Tanglewood Dr., Wheelersburg OH 45694. Also see the listing for Little Smokies of Ohio Fall Poetry Workshop.

SINIPEE WRITERS WORKSHOP, P.O. Box 902, Dubuque IA 52004-0902, phone (319)556-0366, director John Tigges. Annual 1-day event founded 1986. Usually held the 3rd or 4th Saturday in April on the campus of Clarke College, Dubuque, Iowa. Average attendance is 50-100. **Open to anyone, "professional or neophyte," who is interested in writing. Conference covers fiction, poetry and nonfiction.** As for offerings specifically available for poets, they say that in 1992, a poet gave an entire presentation in rhyme and in 1993 a poet demonstrated how to improve fiction using poetry devices. Other speakers in 1993 included Marshall Cook, author of half a dozen books on writing, and Kelly Foth, author of a book to familiarize the reader with manipulating the English language. Cost for 1993 workshop was $60 pre-registration, $65 at the door. Scholarships covering half of the cost are traditionally available to senior citizens and to full-time students, both college and high school. Cost included handouts, coffee and donut break, lunch, snacks in afternoon and book fair with authors in attendance available to autograph their books. Information on overnight accommodations is available for out-of-town registrants. Annual contest for both fiction and poetry sponsored as part of workshop. There is a $5 reading fee for each entry (short story of 1,500 words or poetry of 40 lines). Entrants in the contest may also ask for a written critique by a professional writer. The cost for critique is $10/ entry. Send SASE for brochures and registration forms.

SOUTHWEST FLORIDA WRITERS' CONFERENCE, P.O. Box 06210, Ft. Myers FL 33906-6210, phone (813)489-9226, fax (813)489-9127, director Joanne Hartke. Annual event founded 1980. Usually held the 4th Saturday in February, with an optional keynote address on Friday, on the campus of Edison Community College. Average attendance is 125-175. **Open to anyone interested in writing, including full-time high school and college students. "We cover many areas; in 1993 our offerings included true crime, science fiction, poetry and writing for children. Sessions are usually varied to provide something for both beginning and published writers."** The 1993 poetry session was "Living, Breathing, Walking, Talking Poetry" with Tommy Scott Young. Cost for the 1993 keynote/reception was $15; the Saturday conference was $49, including a continental breakfast and lunch. Limited scholarships are usually available and full-time students can attend the conference for only $15. "Though it is a one-day conference, we do arrange for a block of rooms at a local hotel. Rooms are available to conference attendees at a special rate. In 1993 it was $55 per night. We also provide a listing of several area hotels if the conference block is full or not their choice." An annual contest is sponsored as part of the conference. Judges are published authors and writers in the Ft. Myers community. Send SASE for brochures and registration forms.

STATE OF MAINE WRITERS' CONFERENCE, P.O. Box 296, Ocean Park ME 04063, phone (207)934-5034, fax (207)934-2823 (summer), phone (413)596-6734, fax (413)782-1746 (winter), director Dick Burns. Annual August event founded 1941. Usually runs from Tuesday evening to Friday noon. 1994 dates: August 16-19. Average attendance is 50-75. **Open to any interested person. Conference is "very eclectic, covers writing to publishing."** Every year there is a poetry tournament including a poetry booklet, Poems to be Put on Trees Contest and Beach Inspiration Poetry. Cost is $70, including Wednesday banquet only. Those 21 and under may attend at half price. Information on overnight accommodations is available for registrants. "Local accommodations are reasonable." There are many contests, 15-20/year. Separate contest announcement is available in advance to registrants. Send SASE for brochures and registration forms.

TRENTON STATE COLLEGE WRITERS CONFERENCE, Trenton State College, Hillwood Lakes CN 4700, Trenton NJ 08650, phone (609)771-3254, director Jean Hollander. Annual 1-day event founded 1981. Usually held the beginning of April at Trenton State College Campus. Average attendance is about 800. **Open to anyone. Conference covers all genres of writing. "We usually have a special presentation on breaking into print." Five to eight separate poetry workshops as well as readings are offered.** In 1993 the speakers were Edward Albee and Jamaica Kincaid. Cost in 1993 was $35 for day and evening sessions including coffee and donuts for breakfast. Discounts available for students. Information on overnight accommodations is available for registrants. Poets may submit ms to be critiqued in writing by workshop leaders. Send 1-2 poems and bring 10 copies of submitted poems to workshop. Contest sponsored as part of conference. 1st prize: $100; 2nd prize: $50. Judges are workshop leaders and a special panel from the English Dept. Send SASE for brochures and registration forms. In 1993, prize winners were published in *The Trenton Times*.

UNIVERSITY OF MASSACHUSETTS LOWELL WRITERS' CONFERENCE, 1 University Ave., Lowell MA 01854, phone (508)934-2405, fax (508)934-3008, special program coordinator John Hurtado. Annual event founded in 1988. Usually held the 1st weekend of March at Lowell Library Complex on the campus of the University of Massachusetts. Average attendance is 80. **Aimed at regional writers but open to everyone. Conference covers fiction, poetry, writing for children and publishing opportunities. Poetry workshops, readings and individual conferences are included.** In 1993 speakers included Askold Melnyczuk, a poet and founding editor of *The Agni Review*; Patricia Smith, author of the award-winning poetry volume **Life According to Motown**; and Paul Marion, founding editor of Loom Press and author of the poetry collection **Strong Place**. Cost for the 1993 conference was $140 2-day, $75 1-day; student/senior citizen: $75 2-day, $40 1-day. Information on overnight accommodations is available for registrants. Accommodations include special rates at area hotels and B&B's. Individual critiques are also available. Submit no more than 4 poems or 6 pages with $40 entry fee. In 1993, the UMass Lowell Literary Society sponsored a poetry and fiction contest for Writers' Conference participants. The winner was published in *The Lowell Pearl*. Send SASE for brochures and registration forms.

WILDACRES WRITERS WORKSHOP, c/o 233 S. Elm St., Greensboro NC 27401, phone and fax (919)273-4044, director Judith Hill. Annual week-long event founded 1983. Usually held the last week in June at "a beautiful retreat facility in the Blue Ridge Mountains of North Carolina." Average attendance is 100. **Open to all "serious adult writers." Conference covers fiction (including fiction for children), poetry, screen and play writing and nonfiction.** "We have two poetry workshops with a limit of twelve to a class. In total, we have eleven writers on staff who read and give programs. Plus we have an agent in residence." Cost is $360, including a double room, all meals and ms critique. Van transportation to and from the Asheville Airport is provided. Send SASE for brochures and registration forms. Some years they also publish *The Wildacres Review*.

WISCONSIN REGIONAL WRITERS' ASSOCIATION, 912 Cass St., Portage WI 53901, phone (608)742-2410, president Elayne Hanson. Biannual workshops founded in 1948. Usually held one Saturday in May and a full weekend in September at various hotel-conference centers around the state. Average attendance is 100-130. **Open to all writers, "aspiring, amateur or professional." All forms of writing/marketing rotated between conferences. "The purpose is to keep writers informed and prepared to express and market their writing in a proper format."** Poetry covered once a year. In 1993 speakers included Ellen Kort, poetry; Norbert Blei, nonfiction; Noreen Gilpatrick, fiction; and Mary Kay Croft, nostalgia. A book fair is held at both conferences where members can sell their published works. A banquet is held at the fall conference where writing contest winners receive awards. Spring conference is approximately $45, fall conference approximately $55. Spring conference includes coffee and sweet rolls, lunch and hors d'oeuvres at book fair. Fall conference also includes dinner and entertainment. Information about overnight accommodations is available for registrants. "Our organization 'blocks' rooms at a reduced rate." Sponsors 2 writing contests/year plus a "Yarns of Yesteryear" contest. Membership and small fee are required. Send SASE for brochures and registration forms. "We are affiliated with the Fellowship of Poets in cooperation, the Wisconsin Authors and Publishers Alliance and the Council of Wisconsin Writers. We also publish a newsletter four times a year for members."

THE WRITERS' CENTER AT CHAUTAUQUA, Box 408, Chautauqua NY 14722, phone (716)357-2445 (June-August) or (717)872-8337, director Mary Jean Irion. Annual event founded 1988. Usually held 9 weeks in summer from late June to late August. Participants may attend for one week or more. "We are an independent, cooperative association of writers located on the grounds of Chautauqua Institution." Average attendance is 30 for readings and speeches, 10 for workshops. **Readings and speeches are open to anyone; workshops are open to writers (or auditors). The purpose is "to make creative writing one of the serious arts in progress at Chautauqua; to provide a vacation opportunity for skilled artists and their guests (one each); and to help learning writers improve their skills and vision."** Poetry is available all nine weeks. Poetry Works meets two hours each day offering one hour of class for every hour of workshop. In 1993, speakers included Gerald Costanzo, Margaret Gibson and Carol Frost. Other special features include two speeches a week and one reading, usually done by the Writers-In-Residence. Cost is $50/week with price breaks for each additional week. Participants are responsible for gate fees, housing and meals. "A week's gate ticket to Chautauqua is $135 (less if ordered early); housing cost varies widely, but is not cheap; meals vary widely depending on accommodations—from fine restaurants to cooking in a shared kitchen." Access is best by car or plane to Jamestown, NY, where a limousine service is available for the 14 miles to Chautauqua ($18). Phone number for Accommodations Directory Service is available for registrants. Individual critiques are also usually available. Information published in spring mailing. The Director's Prize is given for the best poem handled in the workshops. Send SASE for brochures and registration forms.

WRITERS' FORUM, Community Education Dept., Pasadena City College, 1570 E. Colorado, Pasadena CA 91106-2003, phone (818)795-5592, fax (818)585-7910, contact Meredith Brucker. Annual 1-day event founded 1954. Usually held all day Saturday in mid-March at Pasadena City College. Average attendance is 200. **Open to all. Conference covers a wide variety of topics and always includes one poet.** Each year they end the day with a panel of book and magazine publishers or literary agents. In 1993, the speaker was poet Ron Koertge. In 1992 it was poet Jack Grapes, editor of *ONTHEBUS*. Cost for the 1993 conference was $72, including lunch. Write for brochures and registration forms. No SASE necessary.

WRITING WORKSHOP FOR PEOPLE OVER 57, % Donovan Scholars Program, University of Kentucky, Ligon House, 658 S. Limestone St., Lexington KY 40506-0442, phone (606)257-2657, fax (606)258-4940, director Roberta H. James. Annual event founded 1966. Usually held in June, the workshop runs from Sunday afternoon to Friday afternoon. Location: Carnahan House Conference Center, "a beautiful, restored mansion which sits on a former horse farm." Average attendance is 35-50 (maximum). **Open to "adults aged 57 or older who share an interest in writing and wish to learn more about how to express their thoughts in the written form. We offer classes in fiction, nonfiction, children's literature/juvenile novel and poetry."** Offerings specifically available for poets include "classes instructed by established writers in the field of poetry, whether local or elsewhere." Cost is $125/person. Information on overnight accommodations is available for registrants. "We offer four hotels, all within close proximity to Carnahan, and offer the hotel rates at a slight discount to workshop participants. Carnahan House itself offers a shuttle service to and from the various hotels." Writers may register as full-student status, which requires a ms to be submitted for critique, or as auditor status, which does not require a ms. Send SASE for brochures and registration forms. *Second Spring*, their yearly publication, contains the written work of past workshop participants.

YELLOW BAY WRITERS' WORKSHOP, Center for Continuing Education, The University of Montana, Missoula MT 59812, phone (406)243-6486, fax (406)243-2047, program manager Judy Jones. Annual week-long event founded 1988. Usually held during the third week of August at the University of Montana's biological research station which includes informal educational facilities and rustic cabin living on Flathead Lake in western Montana. Average attendance is 60. **Open to all writers. Conference offers two workshops in fiction, one in nonfiction and one in poetry.** In 1993, C. Michael Curtis, senior editor of *The Atlantic*, and Leonard Wallace Robinson, former managing editor of *Esquire*, joined the faculty for a panel on publishing. Cost for 1993 workshop was $425, commuter fee; $725, tuition and single lodging/meals; $695, tuition and double lodging/meals. Round-trip shuttle from Missoula to Yellow Bay (85 miles) is available for $40. Applicants must send a writing sample. Send SASE for brochures and registration forms.

Additional Conferences and Workshops

The following conferences and workshops either did not respond in time to receive a full listing in this section or their offerings for poets were more limited than those listed above. We have included contact names and addresses, however, so that you may write for details. Remember to always include a SASE with requests for information.

ANTIOCH WRITERS' WORKSHOP OF YELLOW SPRINGS, P.O. Box 494, Yellow Springs OH 45837, (513)767-7068, director Susan Carpenter. Conference held 2nd week in July.

AUSTIN WRITERS' LEAGUE SPRING AND FALL WORKSHOPS, Suite E-2, 1501 W. 5th, Austin TX 78703, (512)499-8914, executive director Angela Smith. Workshops held in spring and fall.

THE CHARLESTON WRITERS' CONFERENCE, College of Charleston, Charleston SC 29424, (803)792-5822, conference coordinator Judy Sawyer. Conference held in spring.

CHESAPEAKE WRITERS' CONFERENCE, P.O. Box 287, Glenns VA 23149, (804)758-5324, conference coordinator Jane Flower Deringer. Conference held 2nd Saturday in October.

CRAFT OF WRITING, Box 830688 CN 1.1, Richardson TX 75083, (214)690-2207, director Janet Harris. Conference held 3rd weekend in September.

DESERT WRITERS WORKSHOP, Canyonlands Field Institute, P.O. Box 68, Moab UT 84532, (801)259-7750, coordinator Linda Whitham. Usually held in fall.

FEMINIST WOMEN'S WRITING WORKSHOPS, INC., P.O. Box 6593, Ithaca NY 14851, directors Margo Gumosky and Mary Beth O'Connor. Conference held 2nd week of July.

HAYSTACK WRITING PROGRAM, Portland State University Summer Session, P.O. Box 751, Portland OR 97207, (503)725-4081, contact person Maggie Herrington. Six-week summer program with classes of 1-week duration scheduled throughout.

HIGHLIGHTS FOUNDATION WRITERS WORKSHOP AT CHAUTAUQUA, c/o 711 Court St., Honesdale PA 18431, (717)253-1192, director Jan Keen. Usually held 4th week of July.

MOUNT HERMON CHRISTIAN WRITERS CONFERENCE, P.O. Box 413, Mount Hermon CA 95041, (408)335-4466, director of public affairs David R. Talbott. Always held over Palm Sunday weekend.

NEBRASKA WRITERS GUILD SPRING/FALL CONFERENCE, 14824 Parker Place, Omaha NE 68154, program chair Diane Kirkle. One-day conferences held in spring and fall.

PENNWRITER CONFERENCE, Box 241, R.R. 2, Middlebury Center PA 16935, (717)376-2821, conference coordinator C.J. Houghtaling. Usually held 2nd weekend in May.

PORT TOWNSEND WRITERS' CONFERENCE, Box 1158, Port Townsend WA 98368, (206)385-0688, director Carol Jane Bangs. Conference begins 2nd week in July and runs for 10 days.

PROFESSIONALISM IN WRITING SCHOOL, Suite 701, 4308 S. Peoria, Tulsa OK 74105, (918)719-5588, coordinator Norma Jean Lutz. Usually held last weekend in March.

ST. DAVIDS CHRISTIAN WRITERS CONFERENCE, 1775 Eden Rd., Lancaster PA 17601-3523, (717)394-6758. Conference held 4th week in June.

SOUTHERN CALIFORNIA WRITERS CONFERENCE AT SAN DIEGO, 2596 Escondido Ave., San Diego CA 92123, (619)278-4099, codirector Michael Gregory. Four-day conference held 2nd week of September.

THUNDER BAY LITERARY CONFERENCE, 211 N. 1st Ave., Alpena MI 49707, project director Judi Stillion. Usually held 4th weekend in September.

UNIVERSITY OF WISCONSIN-MADISON'S SCHOOL OF THE ARTS AT RHINELANDER, 726 Lowell Hall, 610 Langdon St., Madison WI 53703, (608)263-3494, coordinator Kathy Berigan. Usually held last week in July.

WESLEYAN WRITERS CONFERENCE, Wesleyan University, Middletown CT 06457, (203)343-3938, director Anne Greene. Conference held last week in June.

WESTERN RESERVE WRITERS AND FREELANCE CONFERENCE, #110, 34200 Ridge Rd., Willoughby OH 44094, (216)943-3047, coordinator Lea Leever Oldham. Usually held 3rd Saturday in September.

WESTERN RESERVE WRITERS MINI CONFERENCE, #110, 34200 Ridge Rd., Willoughby OH 44094, (216)943-3047, coordinator Lee Leever Oldham. Usually held 3rd Saturday in March.

WRITING TODAY CONFERENCE, BSC A-3, Birmingham-Southern College, Birmingham AL 35254, (205)226-4921, director of special events Martha Andrews. Usually held 2nd weekend in April.

Writing Colonies

Writing colonies are places for writers (including poets) to find solitude and concentrated time to focus on their work. While a residency at a writing colony may offer participation in seminars, critiques and/or readings, the atmosphere of a writing colony or retreat is much more relaxed than that of a conference or workshop. Also, a writer's stay at a colony is typically anywhere from one to twelve weeks (sometimes longer), while time spent at a conference or workshop may run anywhere from one to fourteen days.

Like conferences and workshops, however, writing colonies and retreats span a wide range. Some, such as Yaddo, primarily offer residencies to writers "who have already achieved some recognition in their field." The Syvenna Foundation, on the other hand, awards residencies only to women writers "in the beginning and intermediate stages of development." And the Dobie-Paisano Project limits fellowships and residencies to writers with an identifiable Texas connection. Also, in addition to listings for colonies across the United States, this section contains listings that offer residencies in Alberta, Canada; Burgundy, France; Monaghan, Ireland; and the Italian Alps.

Despite different focuses and/or locations, all writing colonies and retreats have one thing in common: They are places where poets may work undisturbed, usually in very nature-oriented and secluded settings. A colony serves as a place for rejuvenation, a place where a poet may find new ideas for poems, rework old ones or put the finishing touches to a collection.

Selecting a writing colony

When selecting a colony or retreat, the primary consideration for many writers is cost, and you'll discover that the types of arrangements vary. The Millay Colony for the Arts, Inc., for instance, has no fee. Other colonies provide residences as well as stipends for personal expenses. Some suggest donations of a certain amount. And still others offer residencies for tidy sums but also have financial assistance available.

When investigating the various options, consider the meal and housing arrangements and your own family obligations. Some colonies provide meals for residents, for instance, while others require residents to pay for meals. Some colonies house writers in one main building; others provide separate cottages. (In both cases, residents are given private work space, although they usually must bring along their own reference materials and typewriter or personal computer.) A few writing colonies have provisions for spouses and/or families. The Cummington Community of the Arts, for example, runs a Summer Children's Program which offers supervised activity for children of artists-in-residence during July and August. Other colonies, however, prohibit families altogether.

Overall, residencies at writing colonies and retreats are competitive. Since only a handful of spots are available at each place, you must often apply months in advance for the time period desired. While a number of locations are open year-round, others are available only during certain seasons. Planning to go during the "off-season" may lessen your competition. In any case, be prepared to include a sample of your best work with your application. Also, have an idea of the project you'll work on while in residence, since many places request this information as well. (And have alternative projects in mind just in case the first one doesn't work out once you're there.)

Of course, before making your final selection, send a SASE to the writing colonies or retreats that interest you in order to receive the most up-to-date details. All of the above factors—particularly costs, application requirements and deadlines—are subject to change.

For other listings of writing colonies, see **The Guide to Writers Conferences** (available from ShawGuides, Inc., Dept. 1406W, 625 Biltmore Way, Coral Gables FL 33134), which not only provides information about conferences, workshops and seminars but also residencies, retreats and organizations. Another resource is *Havens for Creatives*, available from ACTS Institute, Inc. (see the listing in the Contests and Awards section).

THE EDWARD F. ALBEE FOUNDATION, INC.; THE WILLIAM FLANAGAN MEMORIAL CREATIVE PERSONS CENTER ("THE BARN"), 14 Harrison St., New York NY 10013, phone (212)226-2020, for information and application forms. The Albee Foundation maintains the center (better known as "The Barn") in Montauk, on Long Island, offering 1-month residencies for writers, painters, sculptors and composers, open June 1 through October 1, accommodating 6 persons at a time. Applications accepted at the Harrison Street address by regular mail only January 1-April 1. Fellowship announcements by May 15. "Located approximately 2 miles from the center of Montauk and the Atlantic Ocean, 'The Barn' rests in a secluded knoll that offers privacy and a peaceful atmosphere. The foundation expects all those accepted for residence to work seriously and to conduct themselves in such a manner as to aid fellow residents in their endeavors. The environment is simple and communal. Residents are expected to do their share in maintaining the condition of 'The Barn' as well as its peaceful environment."

ATLANTIC CENTER FOR THE ARTS, 1414 Art Center Ave., New Smyrna Beach FL 32168, phone (904)427-6975. The center was founded in 1979 by sculptor and painter Doris Leeper, who secured a seed grant from The Rockefeller Foundation. That same year the center was chartered by the state of Florida and building began on a 10-acre site. The center was officially opened in 1982. Since 1982, 51 Master Artists-in-Residence sessions have been held. At each of the 3-week sessions internationally known artists from different disciplines conduct interdisciplinary workshops, lecture and critique works in progress. They also give readings and recitals, exhibit their work and develop projects with their "associates"—mid-career artists who come from all over the US to work with the Masters. The center is run by an advisory council which chooses Masters for residencies, helps set policies and guides the center in its growth. The process of becoming an associate is different for each master artist. Recent poets in residence at the center include Ron Padgett (March-April 1990) and Amy Clampitt (January 1992).

BANFF CENTRE FOR THE ARTS MAY STUDIOS, Box 1020, 107 Tunnel Mountain Dr., Banff, Alberta T0L 0C0 Canada, offers 4-6 weeks of residence between May 1 and June 3 to writers "who already have a body of work (some of it preferably, but not necesssarily, published) attesting to their commitment and talent. Applicant should have a project in progress . . . . Enrollment is limited to 20 participants—10 in poetry, 10 in prose. Full scholarships for fee and room and board are offered to all successful candidates." Located in an inspirational mountain setting, The Banff Centre for the Arts is a unique Canadian institution. Participants are housed in single rooms that also serve as their private work spaces. Application deadline: mid-January.

BELLAGIO STUDY AND CONFERENCE CENTER, The Rockefeller Foundation, 1133 Avenue of the Americas, New York NY 10036, manager Susan Garfield. Offers 5-week residencies from January 20 through December 20 for artists and scholars. Applications are considered 4 times/year on a competitive basis. Approximately 145 residencies are awarded annually. The Center is located on Lake Como in the Italian Alps. Room available for spouses. Residents must pay their own travel costs. Write for application and guidelines.

CENTRUM, % Sarah Muirhead, coordinator, Residency Program, P.O. Box 1158, Port Townsend WA 98368, offers 1-month residencies, September through May, for architects, writers, musicians and printmakers. Centrum provides individual cottages, a stipend of $75/week and solitude. Families welcome. Located in Fort Worden State Park on the Strait of Juan de Fuca. Also sponsors the annual Port Townsend Writers' Conference held in July and other workshops and seminars. Contact Carol Jane Bangs, Literature Program Manager, for more information.

CHATEAU DE LESVAULT, 58370 Onlay, France, phone and fax (33)86-84-32-91. This French country residence is located in the national park "Le Morvan" of western Burgundy, halfway between Nevers and Autun and is surrounded by green hills and forests. The chateau accommodates 5 residents at a time in 5 large rooms with private baths, fully furnished and equipped for working. The facilities of the chateau are at the disposal of residents, including the salon, library and grounds. Requests for residencies from October through April should be made at least 3 months in advance. The cost is 4,500 FF per month for room, board (5 days a week) and utilities.

THE CLEARING, Box 65, Ellison Bay WI 54210, phone (414)854-4088, resident managers Donald and Louise Buchholz, "is first a school, then a place of self-discovery." Made up of cabins and lodges in a rustic setting overlooking Green Bay, it offers a variety of courses, including courses in writing and poetry, May-October. Fees include tuition, room (dormitory or twin-bedded room) and board.

COLONYHOUSE: OREGON WRITERS COLONY, c/o Rae Richen, P.O. Box 15200, Portland OR 97215, phone (503)771-0428, is a log cabin owned and operated by Oregon. It sleeps 8 and is available for weekly and weekend rentals at (Fall-Winter) $350/week, $150/weekend or (Spring-Summer) $450/week, $275/weekend. For colony members only. Membership is $20/year. Membership and newsletter information available through Robert Zimmer at the above address.

CUMMINGTON COMMUNITY OF THE ARTS, RR #1, Box 145, Cummington MA 01026, phone (413)634-2172, contact Rick Reiken. Offers residencies to artists in all disciplines from 2 weeks to 3 months. Living/studio spaces are in individual cabins or 2 main houses, on 110 acres in the Berkshires. During July and August, artists with children from age 5-12 are encouraged to apply. Cummington's Summer Children's Program offers supervised activity for children of artists-in-residence. Application deadlines: The first of the month 2 months prior to desired month of residency, except for July and August, when applications are due April 1.

DOBIE-PAISANO PROJECT, Attn: Audrey N. Slate, Main Building 101, The University of Texas, Austin TX 78712. Offers two annual fellowships of $7,200 and 6-month residency at Frank Dobie's ranch, Paisano, for Texans, Texas residents or writers whose work has been substantially identified with the state. Apply by January 29, 1994. Write for application and guidelines.

‡DORLAND MOUNTAIN ARTS COLONY, P.O. Box 6, Temecula CA 92593, established 1979. A 300-acre nature preserve which offers 2-week to 2-month residences for writers, visual artists and composers in a rustic environment with no elecricity, propane appliances (refrigerator, water heater, cooking stove, some lights), oil and Coleman lamps. Residents provide their own meals. A donation of $150/month is requested. Send SASE for application form and guidelines. Deadlines the first of September and March.

DORSET COLONY HOUSE RESIDENCIES; AMERICAN THEATRE WORKS, INC., Box 519, Dorset VT 05251, director John Nassivera. Residencies available to writers September-May for periods of 1 week-2 months for intensive work. Requested fee of $80 per week, but ability to pay is not a criterion in awarding residencies.

GREEN RIVER WRITERS RETREAT, Shelbyville Campus, University of Louisville, Green River Writers, 403 S. Sixth St., Ironton OH 45638, secretary D.H. Spears, phone (614)533-1081, provides a 2-day workshop, then 5-day retreat. Rooms are available at the conference center per night stayed plus registration fee. Beginning writers are furnished with advisors. Details available for SASE.

THE TYRONE GUTHRIE CENTRE, Annaghmakerrig, Newbliss, Co. Monaghan, Ireland, phone (353)47-54003, resident director Bernard Loughlin. Offers residencies, normally 3 weeks-3 months, for artists, including poets. "Each resident has a private apartment within the house . . . and all the centrally heated comfort an Irish Big House can afford. It is set on a wooded estate of 400 acres and overlooks a large lake. The house is surrounded by gardens and a working dairy farm. Couples or small groups of artists may stay for up to a year in Maggie's Farm, a cottage on the estate, and have use of studios at the Big House. Five newly built, self-contained farmyard cottages are also available for individuals and couples for longer stays. To qualify for residence it is necessary to show evidence of a significant level of achievement in the relevant field. Once accepted Irish artists are asked to contribute what they can afford toward the cost of their stay. Overseas artists are expected to pay the whole cost of a residency."

HAMBIDGE CENTER FOR CREATIVE ARTS AND SCIENCES, P.O. Box 339, Rabun Gap GA 30568, phone (706)746-5718. The center is located on 650 acres of unspoiled wooded slopes, mountain meadows and streams, near Dillard, Georgia. It is listed on the National Register of Historic Places. Resident Fellowships of 2 weeks-2 months are awarded to individuals engaged in all artistic disciplines for the purpose of solitude and the pursuit of creative excellence. Those accepted are given a private cottage equipped with a kitchen, living and studio/work space. Center is open from May-October with limited winter fellowships available. For more information and application forms send SASE. Application review begins in March.

HAWK, I'M YOUR SISTER; WOMEN'S WILDERNESS CANOE TRIPS; WRITING RETREATS, Beverly Antaeus, P.O. Box 9109, Santa Fe NM 87504. This organization offers wilderness retreats for women, many of them with writing themes, including A Writing Retreat with Sharon Olds in Baja California, Mexico. The canoe trips are held all over North America and typically last 8-10 days with fees $695-1,795. Write for annual listing of specific trips.

THE MACDOWELL COLONY, 100 High St., Peterborough NH 03458, founded 1907, offers residencies to established writers, composers, visual artists, filmmakers, architects and interdisciplinary artists. Over 3,000 artists have stayed there, many of them producing major works. Apply about 8 months before desired residency. Application deadlines: January 15 for May-August; April 15 for September-December; September 15 for January-April. Private studio, room and meals provided. Accepted artists are asked to contribute toward residency costs. Current application form is necessary; write address above or call (603)924-3886 or (212)966-4860. Average residency is 6 weeks. Professional work samples required with application.

THE MILLAY COLONY FOR THE ARTS, INC., Steepletop, P.O. Box 3, Austerlitz NY 12017-0003, founded in 1974, assistant director Gail Giles. Provides work space, meals and sleeping accommodations at no cost for a period of 1 month. Send SASE for brochure and application forms and apply with samples of your work before February 1 for June-September; before May 1 for October-January; before September 1 for February-May.

MONTALVO CENTER FOR THE ARTS; MONTALVO BIENNIAL POETRY COMPETITION, Box 158, Saratoga CA 95071, presents theatre, musical events and other artistic activities. They have an Artist-in-Residence program which has 5 apartments available for artists (including poets) for maximum 3-month periods. (No children or pets.) Limited financial assistance available. They offer a biennial poetry competition open to residents of Oregon, Nevada, Washington and California, with a prominent judge, with a first prize of $1,000 (and artist residency), other prizes of $500, $300 and 8 honorable mentions. Submit 3 poems in duplicate, entry fee $5, October 1, 1995, deadline. Send SASE for rules.

THE NORTHWOOD UNIVERSITY ALDEN B. DOW CREATIVITY CENTER, Midland MI 48640-2398, phone (517)837-4478, founded 1979, director Carol Coppage. Offers fellowships for 10-week summer residencies at the Northwood University Campus. Travel and all expenses are paid. No families/pets. Applicants can be undergraduates, graduates, or those without any academic or institutional affiliation, including citizens of other countries (if they can communicate in English). Projects may be in any field, but must be new and innovative. Write for application. Annual deadline December 31 for following summer.

PALENVILLE INTERARTS COLONY, 2 Bond St., New York NY 10012. Offers 1-8 week residencies in Palenville, New York, for seclusion or for interaction among artists of various disciplines in a relaxed and creative atmosphere. Fee (negotiable): $175 per week. Open June 1 to September 30. Application deadline is April 1.

PUDDING HOUSE PUBLICATIONS, 60 N. Main St., Johnstown OH 43031. See listing in Publishers of Poetry section.

RAGDALE FOUNDATION, 1260 N. Green Bay Rd., Lake Forest IL 60045, founded 1976, director Michael Wilkerson, provides a peaceful place and uninterrupted time for 12 writers, composers and artists. Meals, linen and laundry facilities are provided. Each resident is assigned private work space and sleeping accommodations. Couples are accepted if each qualifies independently. Residents may come for 2 weeks to 2 months. The fee is $70 per week. Some full and partial fee waivers available. The foundation also sponsors poetry readings, concerts, workshops and seminars in writing. Ragdale is open year-round except for June 15-30 and December 15-January 1. Apply by January 15 for residencies in May-August; April 15 for September-December; September 15 for January-April; $20 application fee.

THE ROCKY MOUNTAIN WOMEN'S INSTITUTE, 7150 Montview Blvd., Denver CO 80220, phone (303)871-6923, founded 1976, executive director Cynthia A. Stone, a nonprofit organization located at the University of Denver. Offers office or studio space, stipends and support services for one year for artists, writers and scholars chosen from applications. They also offer continuing support for former associates, and they sponsor exhibits, workshops, lectures and performances to highlight and promote the work of current and past associates. Terms begin each September. Applicants should have a specific project. Applications ($5 processing fee) are available beginning each January. Deadline: March 15. Write for further information.

SPLIT ROCK ARTS PROGRAM, University of Minnesota, 306 Wesbrook Hall, 77 Pleasant St. SE, Minneapolis MN 55455. The program is a summer series of week-long workshops in the visual and literary arts and in the nature and applications of creativity, on the Duluth campus of UM "in the green hills overlooking Lake Superior." The 1993 writing faculty included Lucille Clifton, Carolyn Forché, Sharon Doubiago, Michael Dennis Browne, Roberta Hill Whiteman, Jane Yolen, Paulette Bates Alden, Christina Baldwin, Carol Bly, David Bradley, Marisha Chamberlain, Phebe Hanson, Jim Heynen, Alexs Pate and Madelon Sprengnether. Tuition is $330 with an additional charge for graduate credit. Housing ranges from $160-230, depending on type of accommodation. Most students choose single or double rooms in 2-bedroom apartments on campus. Meals are in UMD's cafeteria, cooked by participants in their apartments, or in Duluth restaurants. Other housing options also available. Complete catalog available in March by mail or phone: (612)624-6800.

THE SYVENNA FOUNDATION, Rt. 1, Box 193, Linden TX 75563, phone (903)835-8252, associate director Barbara Carroll. The foundation has 2 cottages on forested land near the Texas-Arkansas border available to unestablished women writers for 3-month residencies. Pays $300/month stipend plus cottage and utilities. (The foundation's name is pronounced "Savannah.") Women writers of all ages in the beginning and intermediate stages of development as writers are welcome to apply any time of the year. Send SASE for application materials.

UCROSS FOUNDATION RESIDENCY PROGRAM, 2836 US Hwy. 14-16, Clearmont WY 82835, phone (307)737-2291, executive director Elizabeth Guheen. There are 8 concurrent positions open in various disciplines, including poetry, each extending from 2 weeks to 2 months. No charge for room, board or studio space, and they do not expect services or products from guests. Send SASE for information and application guidelines. Residents are selected from a rotating panel of professionals in the arts and humanities. Semiannual application deadlines are March 1 and October 1.

VERMONT STUDIO CENTER; VISUAL ARTISTS AND WRITERS RESIDENCIES, P.O. Box 613NW, Johnson VT 05656, phone (802)635-2727, founded 1984. Offers 2-week Writing Studio Sessions led by prominent writers/teachers focusing on the craft of writing. Independent Writers' Retreats for 2, 4 or more weeks are also available year-round for those wishing more solitude. Room, working studio and meals are included in all programs. Generous work-exchange Fellowships are available. Write or call for more information and application.

VIRGINIA CENTER FOR THE CREATIVE ARTS, Mt. San Angelo, Sweet Briar VA 24595, director William Smart. Provides residencies for 12 writers (and 9 visual artists and 3 composers) for 1-3 months at the 450-acre Mt. San Angelo estate. The normal fee is $20/day. Financial assistance is available.

‡**THE WRITERS COMMUNITY**, West Side YMCA Center for the Arts, New York NY 10023, phone (212)875-4124. Offers an advanced 3-month master writing program in poetry, October-December, March-May (application deadline mid-September, mid-January), working with a writer-in-residence. All members are asked to contribute $95 to the program, but there are no other fees. Submit biographical information and a minimum of 10 pgs. of poetry, which may be published material. All material should be typed or printed and copies should be retained. Mss cannot be returned. Call for application deadlines.

THE HELENE WURLITZER FOUNDATION OF NEW MEXICO, Box 545, Taos NM 87571. Offers residencies to creative, *not* interpretive, artists in all media, for varying periods of time, usually 3 months, from April 1 through September 30, annually. Rent free and utilities free. Residents are responsible for their food. No families. No deadlines on application.

YADDO, Box 395, Saratoga Springs NY 12866-0395, phone (518)584-0746, founded 1900, offers residencies to writers, visual artists, composers, choreographers, film/video artists and performance artists who have already achieved some recognition in their field and have new work under way. During the summer 35 guests can be accommodated, 14 during the winter, approximately 200 per year. The hours 9-4 are a quiet period reserved for work. There is no fixed charge for a guest stay, but voluntary payment in the suggested amount of $20/day to help defray costs of the program are accepted. However, no qualified artist is denied admission based on inability to pay. Write for applications to: Admissions, Yaddo, address above; enclose SASE. Application deadlines are January 15 and August 1. A $20 application fee is required.

Organizations Useful to Poets

The organizations listed in this section offer encouragement and support to poets and other writers through a wide variety of services. They may sponsor contests and awards, hold regular workshops or open readings, or release publications with details about new opportunities and/or area events. Many of these groups provide a combination of these services to members and others.

The PEN American Center, for example, holds public events, sponsors literary awards and offers grants and loans to writers in need—among other services. Those seeking financial assistance may also want to refer to the listing for the Authors League Fund or contact the arts council in their state or province (see the State and Provincial Grants section).

Many organizations provide opportunities to meet and discuss work with others. Those with access to computers and modems may connect with poets around the world through either CompuServe or GEnie. The National Federation of State Poetry Societies, Inc. and the Canadian Poetry Association are both national organizations with smaller affiliated groups which may meet in your state or province. And for those seeking gatherings more local or regional in focus, there are organizations such as The Lane Literary Guild and Burnaby Writers' Society.

For organizations even closer to home, you may want to check for information at your library or contact the local college English department. Better yet, if you are unable to find a local writer's group, consider starting one by placing an ad in your community newspaper or posting a notice on the library bulletin board. In fact, your library might even have space for your group to meet, and there are sure to be others in your area who would welcome the support.

To locate some of the larger organizations (or representative samples of smaller groups) that may fit your needs, read through the listings that follow and refer to the Additional Organizations Useful to Poets at the end of this section. Then send a SASE to those groups that interest you to receive more details about their services and/or membership fees.

THE ACADEMY OF AMERICAN POETS; FELLOWSHIP OF THE ACADEMY OF AMERICAN POETS; WALT WHITMAN AWARD; THE LAMONT POETRY SELECTION; HAROLD MORTON LANDON TRANSLATION AWARD; PETER I.B. LAVAN YOUNGER POET AWARDS, Suite 1208, 584 Broadway, New York NY 10012-3250, founded 1934, executive director William Wadsworth. Robert Penn Warren wrote in **Introduction to Fifty Years of American Poetry**, an anthology published in 1984 containing one poem from each of the 126 Chancellors, Fellows and Award Winners of the Academy: "What does the Academy do? According to its certificate of incorporation, its purpose is 'To encourage, stimulate and foster the production of American poetry. . . .' The responsibility for its activities lies with the Board of Directors and the Board of 12 Chancellors, which has included, over the years, such figures as Louise Bogan, W. H. Auden, Witter Bynner, Randall Jarrell, Robert Lowell, Robinson Jeffers, Marianne Moore, James Merrill, Robert Fitzgerald, F. O. Matthiessen and Archibald MacLeish—certainly not members of the same poetic church." They award fellowships, currently of $20,000 each, to distinguished American poets (no applications taken)—58 to date—and other annual awards. The Walt Whitman Award pays $1,000 plus publication of a poet's first book by a major publisher. Mss of 50-100 pgs. must be submitted between September 15 and November 15 with a $10 entry fee. Entry form required. Send SASE. The Lamont Poetry Selection, for a poet's second book, is again a prize of $1,000. Submissions must be made by a publisher, in mss form, prior to publication. The Academy distributes 2,000 copies to its members. Poets entering either contest must be American citizens. The Harold Morton Landon Translation Award is for translation of a book-length poem, a collection of poems or a verse-drama translated into English from any language. One award of $1,000 each year to a US citizen. Only publishers may submit the book. Write for guidelines. The Peter I.B. Lavan Younger Poet Awards of $1,000 each are given annually to three younger poets selected by Academy Chancellors (no applications taken). *Poetry Pilot* is an informative periodical sent to those who contribute $25 or more per year or who are members. Membership: $45/year. The Academy sponsors a national series of poetry readings and panel discussions.

ASSOCIATED WRITING PROGRAMS; AWP CHRONICLE; THE AWP AWARD SERIES, Old Dominion University, Norfolk VA 23529-0079, founded 1967. Offers a variety of services to the writing community, including information, job placement assistance, publishing opportunities, literary arts advocacy and forums. Annual individual membership is $45; placement service extra. For $18 you can subscribe to the *AWP Chronicle* (published 6 times/year), containing information about grants and awards, publishing opportunities, fellowships, and writing programs. They have a directory, **The Official Guide to Writing Programs**, of over 250 college and university writing programs for $17.95 (includes shipping). The AWP Award Series selects a volume of poetry (48 pg. minimum) each year ($10 entry fee) with an award of $1,500 and publication. Deadline: February 28. Send SASE for submission guidelines. Query after November. Their placement service helps writers find jobs in teaching, editing and other related fields.

THE AUTHORS GUILD, INC., 330 W. 42nd St., New York NY 10036, phone (212) 563-5904, executive director Helen A. Stephenson, "is an association of professional writers which focuses its efforts on the legal and business concerns of published authors in the areas of publishing contract terms, copyright, taxation and freedom of expression. We do not work in the area of marketing mss to publishers nor do we sponsor or participate in awards or prize selections." Send SASE for information on membership.

AUTHORS LEAGUE FUND, 234 W. 44th St., New York NY 10036. Makes interest-free loans to published authors in need of temporary help because of illness or an emergency. No grants.

BEYOND BAROQUE LITERARY/ARTS CENTER, 681 Venice Blvd., Venice CA 90291, phone (310)822-3006, director D.B. Finnegan. A nonprofit arts center established in 1968 that has been funded by the NEA, state and city arts councils and corporate donations. Members get a calendar of events, discounts on regularly scheduled programs, discounts in the bookstore, and borrowing privileges in the small press library of 3,000 volumes of poetry, fiction and reference materials, including audiotapes of Beyond Baroque readings. Beyond Baroque contains a bookstore open 5 days a week, including Friday evenings to coincide with regular weekly readings and performances. About 130 writers are invited to read each year; there are also open readings, poetry and fiction workshops.

BLACK CULTURAL CENTRE FOR NOVA SCOTIA, Box 2128, East Dartmouth, Nova Scotia B2W 3Y2 Canada, phone (902)434-6223, fax (902)434-2306. Founded in 1977 "to create among members of the black communities an awareness of their past, their heritage and their identity; to provide programs and activities for the general public to explore, learn about, understand and appreciate black history, black achievements and black experiences in the broad context of Canadian life. The centre houses a museum, reference library, archival area, small auditorium and studio workshops."

BURNABY WRITERS' SOCIETY, 6450 Deer Lake Ave., Burnaby, British Columbia V5G 2J3 Canada, contact person Eileen Kernaghan. Corresponding membership in the society, including a newsletter subscription, is open to anyone, anywhere. Yearly dues are $20. Sample newsletter in return for SASE with Canadian stamp. The society holds monthly meetings at The Burnaby Arts Centre (address at begining of listing), with a business meeting at 7:30 followed by a writing workshop or speaker. Members of the society stage regular public readings of their own work.

THE WITTER BYNNER FOUNDATION FOR POETRY, INC., Suite 118, 105 E. Marcy St., Santa Fe NM 87501, phone (505)988-3251. The foundation awards grants exclusively to nonprofit organizations for the support of poetry-related projects in the area of: 1) support of individual poets through existing nonprofit institutions; 2) developing the poetry audience; 3) poetry translation and the process of poetry translation; and 4) uses of poetry. The foundation "may consider the support of other creative and innovative projects in poetry." Grant applications must be received by February 1 each year; requests for application forms should be submitted to Steven Schwartz, executive director, at the address above.

THE CANADA COUNCIL; GOVERNOR GENERAL'S LITERARY AWARDS; INTERNATIONAL LITERARY PRIZES, P.O. Box 1047, 99 Metcalfe St., Ottawa, Ontario K1P 5V8 Canada, phone (613)598-4365/6. Established by Parliament in 1957, it "provides a wide range of grants and services to professional Canadian artists and art organizations in dance, media arts, music, opera, theater, writing, publishing and the visual arts." The Governor General's Literary Awards, valued at $10,000 (Canadian) each, are given annually for the best English-language and best French-language work in each of seven categories, including poetry. Books must be first-edition trade books written, translated or illustrated by Canadian citizens or permanent residents of Canada and published in Canada or abroad during the previous year (October 1 through September 30). In the case of translation, the original work must also be a Canadian-authored title. Books must be submitted by publishers with a Publisher's Submission Form, which is available from the Writing and Publishing Section. All books must be received at the Canada Council by September 30. The Canada Council administers four International Literary Prizes (Canada-Australia, Canada-French Community of Belgium, Canada-Switzerland) of $2,500-3,500 (Canadian and the Canada-Japan Book Award worth $10,000 Canadian). Winners are selected by juries. Except for the Canada-Japan Book Award, applications are not accepted.

CANADIAN CONFERENCE OF THE ARTS, Dept. PM, 189 Laurier Ave. E., Ottawa, Ontario K1N 6P1 Canada, phone (613)238-3561, fax (613)238-4849, was created for "the encouragement of the federal, provincial and municipal governments, as well as the corporate and private sector, to develop policies which will ensure the continued growth of the arts and the cultural industries in Canada." It supplies members with information on political issues affecting the daily lives of artists and writers. Members receive *Proscenium*, a news magazine published 4 times per year, and other information on cultural issues of the day; counseling, general representation and active support. They sponsor conferences such as taxation and the artist, and offer other services. Membership for individuals is $10 plus GST for students and senior citizens and $25 plus GST for others; organizational members is on a sliding scale (depending on the organization's budget) of $60-900 plus GST.

CANADIAN POETRY ASSOCIATION; POEMATA, 340 Station B, London, Ontario N6A 4W1 Canada. A broad based umbrella organization that aims to promote the reading, writing, publishing, purchasing and preservation of poetry in Canada through the individual and combined efforts of its members; to promote and encourage all forms and styles of poetry; to promote communication among poets, publishers and the general public; to promote the establishment and maintenance of poetry libraries and archives in educational institutions across Canada; and to develop an international connection for Canadian poets through *Poemata*, its quarterly newsletter, and events organized by independent, locally-run chapters. Through its 6 autonomous local chapters, CPA organizes poetry readings, literary and social events, and runs a book club. Membership is open to anyone with an interest in poetry, including other literary organizations, for $20 per year. Sample newsletter: $3.

CANADIAN SOCIETY OF CHILDREN'S AUTHORS, ILLUSTRATORS & PERFORMERS, P.O. Box 280, Station L, Toronto, Ontario M6E 4Z2 Canada, is a "society of professionals in the field of children's culture. Puts people into contact with publishers, offers advice to beginners, and generally provides a visible profile for members; 350 professional members and over 1,000 associates who are termed 'friends.' An annual conference in Toronto the last week of October provides workshops to people interested in writing, illustrating, and performing for children." Membership is $60 for professional members and $25 for associates/year, which includes a subscription to the quarterly *CANSCAIP News* and a free copy of the Membership Directory.

COMPUSERVE INFORMATION SERVICE, 5000 Arlington Centre Blvd., P.O. Box 20212, Columbus OH 43220, phone (800)848-8199 from outside Ohio or (614)457-0802 from within Ohio or outside the US. An international online information service available via modem from any computer. On CIS are many forums on specialized topics of interests, including Litforum. This has been described as a 24-hour nonalcoholic cocktail party: basically a bulletin board where various members post and respond to public messages (though you may communicate with them privately, too, either through the CompuServe Mail system or by leaving private messages in Litforum). It costs $49.95 to join CIS. When you join, you get a $25 online credit, so joining is practically free. Electronic mail is now included in the $7.95 monthly flat rate service fee. All CompuServe membership kits also contain the CompuServe Information Manager, customized software designed for IBM compatible, Mac and Windows platforms to make CompuServe easy to use. There are many services available through CIS (in addition to electronic mail), but most of the action is in the forums. In Litforum sometimes the talk is quite funny, often bawdy, and far-ranging, though there is a lot of practical, professional communication, too, and many people make contact via Litforum with agents, editors, other writers, researchers, and so on, that prove quite useful. You join Litforum (anyone can join; a number of the regulars are not even writers—just people interested in literature, writing, publication, chitchat), read the messages posted in some or all of the 17 sections (on such things as poetry and lyrics, fiction, nonfiction, speculative fiction, and so on), respond to any that you wish to, or just lurk. Each section has a library where you can post material you have written or download material by others, and comment if you wish. There is a workshop for which you can request admission (and you're in automatically) where each writer has a turn to have material criticized by the other workshop members.

COSMEP, THE INTERNATIONAL ASSOCIATION OF INDEPENDENT PUBLISHERS; COSMEP NEWS-LETTER, P.O. Box 420703, San Francisco CA 94142-0703. If you are starting a small press or magazine or are embarking on self-publication, you should know about the advantages of membership in COS-MEP. Write for information. It is the largest trade association for small press in the US. Included among membership benefits is the monthly *COSMEP Newsletter*, which prints news and commentary for small publishers. It also sponsors publishing conferences, stage exhibits at booksellers' and librarians' conventions and has insurance and cooperative advertising programs.

COUNCIL OF LITERARY MAGAZINES AND PRESSES; DIRECTORY OF LITERARY MAGAZINES, Suite 3-C, 154 Christopher St., New York NY 10014-2839. Publishes an annual directory useful to writers: The **Directory of Literary Magazines**, which has detailed descriptions of over 500 literary magazines, including type of work published, payment to contributors and circulation. The directory is $14.50 postage paid and may be ordered by sending a check to CLMP.

COWBOY POETRY GATHERING; COWBOY MUSIC GATHERING; WESTERN FOLKLIFE CENTER, 501 Railroad St., Elko NV 89801. Both of these gatherings are sponsored by Western Folklife Center, Box 888, Elko NV 89803, phone (702)738-7508, fax (702)738-2900. There is an annual 6-day January gathering of cowboy poets in Elko. The Cowboy Music Gathering will be held annually the last weekend in June. The Western Folklife Center publishes and distributes books and tapes of cowboy poetry and songs as well as other cowboy memorabilia. The well-established tradition of cowboy poetry is enjoying a renaissance, and thousands of cowboy poets participate in these activities. Catalog and brochure available by calling (800)748-4466.

FAIRBANKS ARTS ASSOCIATION; FAIRBANKS ARTS, P.O. Box 72786, Fairbanks AK 99707, phone (907)456-6485, fax (907)456-4112, editor Al Geist. FAA publishes a bimonthly magazine, *Fairbanks Arts*, which covers interior Alaskan arts and cultural events, organizations and people (artists, writers, musicians, actors, etc.), plus provides how-to information, market tips for Alaskan writers, humor and personal experiences pertaining to writing, marketing and lifestyles. Articles run 800-1,300 words. **Accepts all forms of poetry; limit submissions to 3 poems with maximum 40 lines each. Pays 5 contributor copies.** Subscription: $15. **Sample and guidelines: $3.** The FAA sponsors a Community Reading Series for Alaskan and visiting writers.

FEDERATION OF BRITISH COLUMBIA WRITERS, M.P.O. Box 2206, Vancouver, British Columbia V6B 3WC Canada, manager Corey Van't Haaff. The federation "is a nonprofit organization of professional and aspiring writers in all genres." They publish a newsletter of markets, political reports, awards and federation news, act as "a network centre for various other provincial writer's organizations; host, promote and organize workshops, public readings, literary competitions and social activities, publish directories which are distributed to schools, businesses, and organizations which may request the services of writers; and represent writers' interests on other professionally related organizations."

FESTIVAL OF POETS AND POETRY AT ST. MARY'S; EBENEZER COOKE POETRY FESTIVAL, St. Mary's College of Maryland, St. Mary's City MD 20686, phone (301)862-0239. An annual event held during the last two weekends in May of each year. Approximately 18 guest poets and artists participate in and lead workshops, seminars and readings. Concurrent with the festival, St. Mary's College offers an intensive 14-day poetry writing workshop. The Ebenezer Cooke Poetry Festival is now a biannual event in August of even numbered years, held in the name of the first Poet Laureate of Maryland.

Poets from Maryland and the surrouding areas are invited to give 5-minute readings, enjoy a crab feast and otherwise celebrate together.

‡GENIE SERVICE; WRITERS' INK, 401 N. Washington St., Rockville MD 20850, phone (800)638-9636, provides news, research information and entertainment to individuals throughout the US, Canada and numerous foreign countries. "There are dozens of areas of interest to poets, from workshops to an electronic encyclopedia. The heart of the writing community on GEnie is Writer's Ink, an electronic association of poets, authors, illustrators, screenwriters and others interested in all aspects of writing for enjoyment and/or publication. Members 'meet' using their computer and a modem (for most, it's a local phone call). The Writer's Ink Bulletin Board is filled with discussions and information on a wide variety of subjects—from publishing your first poem to working with imagery. Writers' Ink conducts frequent electronic meetings where people from all over the world can gather and discuss poetry and writing. There are also weekly online poetry readings where members share and discuss their work. Poets will find the Writers' Ink Libraries full of useful software, helpful articles and interviews as well as poems and stories by members. Poets can even find market information as well as tips for dealing with editors." Cost is $4.95/month. This fee includes electronic mail, an encyclopedia and access to many bulletin boards (including Writers' Ink). Other areas of GEnie are available for $6/hour (during non-prime time which is 6 p.m. to 8 a.m. local time).

‡INTERNATIONAL WOMEN'S WRITING GUILD, Box 810, Gracie Station, New York NY 10028, phone (212)737-7536, founded 1976, "a network for the personal and professional empowerment of women through writing." The Guild publishes a bimonthly 28-page newsletter which includes member's needs, achievements, contests, and publishing information. A manuscript referral service introduces members to literary agents. Other activities are 13 annual national and regional events, including a summer conference at Skidmore College; "regional clusters" (independent regional groups); job referrals; round robin manuscript exchanges; sponsorship of the "Artist of Life" award; group health and life insurance. Membership in the nonprofit Guild costs $35/year in the US and $45/year foreign.

JUST BUFFALO LITERARY CENTER, Dept. PM, 111 Elmwood Ave., Buffalo NY 14201, phone (716)885-6400, founded 1975 by Debora Ott, has executive director, 3 program directors, an office manager and a director of community relations. They offer readings, workshops, master classes, residencies, an annual Western New York Writers-in-Residence competition, an annual Labor in Literature competition open to WNY union members, Spoken Arts Radio broadcasts on National Public Radio affiliate WBFO, and Writers-in-Education in the Schools. Just Buffalo acts as a clearing house for literary events in the Greater Buffalo area and offers diverse services to writers and to the WNY region. "Although we are not accepting submissions for publication at this time, we will review works for possible readings."

THE LANE LITERARY GUILD, Lane Regional Arts Council, 411 High St., Eugene OR 97401. The guild is "a volunteer organization dedicated to encouraging and supporting poets and writers in Lane County, Oregon. We hold monthly readings featuring new and established poets and writers. Our readers are drawn from talent locally as well as from other cities and parts of the country. We also hold workshops, symposia and literary contests. Our funding comes from membership fees, donations at readings and from grant support by the Cultural Services Division of the City of Eugene, by the Oregon Arts Commission and by the National Endowment for the Arts. We are interested in hearing from poets and writers from around the country who will be in our neighborhood and might be interested in being one of our readers."

THE LEAGUE OF CANADIAN POETS; WHEN IS A POEM; WHO'S WHO IN THE LEAGUE OF CANADIAN POETS; HERE IS A POEM; POETRY MARKETS FOR CANADIANS; NATIONAL POETRY CONTEST; GERALD LAMPERT AWARD; PAT LOWTHER AWARD, Dept. PM, 24 Ryerson Ave., Toronto, Ontario M5T 2P3 Canada, phone (416)363-5047, founded 1966, information officer Clive Thompson. The league's aims are the advancement of poetry in Canada and promotion of the interests of professional, Canadian poets. Information on full and associate membership can be obtained by writing for the brochure, League of Canadian Poets: Services and Membership. The league publishes a biannual **Museletter** (magazine-sized, 30 pgs.) plus six 4-page issues; **When is a Poem**, on teaching poetry to children; a directory volume called **Who's Who in The League of Canadian Poets** that contains 1 page of information, including a picture, bio, publications and "what critics say" about each of the members; **Here is a Poem**, a companion anthology to **When Is a Poem**, featuring the work of Canadian poets; and **Poetry Markets for Canadians** which covers contracts, markets, agents and more. The league's members go on reading tours, and the league encourages them to speak on any facet of Canadian literature at schools and universities, libraries or organizations. The league has arranged "thousands of readings in every part of Canada"; they are now arranging exchange visits featuring the leading poets of such countries as Great Britain, Germany and the US. The league sponsors a National Poetry

Contest with prizes of $1,000, $750 and $500; the best 50 poems published in a book. Deadline: January 31. Entry fee $6/poem. Poems should be unpublished, under 75 lines and typed. Names and addresses should *not* appear on poems but on a separate covering sheet. Please send SASE for complete rules, info on judges, etc. Open to Canadian citizens or landed immigrants only. The Gerald Lampert Award of $1,000 is for a first book of poetry written by a Canadian, published professionally. The Pat Lowther Award of $1,000 is for a book of poetry written by a Canadian woman and published professionally. Write for entry forms. It is also the address of Writers Union of Canada which provides services and information to members, including a writer's guide to Canadian publishers ($3) and a variety of other publications to assist writers.

THE LOFT; LOFT-MCKNIGHT AWARDS, Pratt Community Center, 66 Malcolm Ave. SE, Minneapolis MN 55414, phone (612)379-0754, founded 1974, executive director Susan Broadhead. The Loft was begun by a group of poets looking for a place to give readings and conduct workshops and evolved into a sophisticated hub of activity for creative writing in all genres managed by an 19-member board of directors, and staff of 12. This past year 2,000 members contributed $30/year to the Loft; it was further supported by $56,000 from individuals, plus government, foundation and corporate grants. The Loft offers over 75 8-week courses each year, in addition to 30 workshops and panels. Its publication readings and emerging voices readings are meant for Minnesota writers whereas the Mentor Series and Creative Non-fiction residency feature nationally known writers. The Loft publishes a monthly newsletter called *A View from the Loft.* The Loft-McKnight Awards are offered annually to Minnesota writers: 8 awards of $7,500 each, 3 in poetry, 5 in creative prose; 2 Awards of Distinction, $10,500 each.

MAINE WRITERS & PUBLISHERS ALLIANCE; MAINE IN PRINT; MAINE WRITERS CENTER, 12 Pleasant St., Brunswick ME 04011-2201, phone (207)729-6333, founded 1975, membership coordinator Paul Doiron. This organization is "a nonprofit organization dedicated to promoting all aspects of writing, publishing, and the book arts. Our membership currently includes over 1,400 writers, publishers, librarians, teachers, booksellers and readers from across Maine and the nation. For an individual contribution of $25 per year members receive a range of benefits including *Maine in Print*, a monthly compilation of calendar events, updated markets, book reviews, grant information, interviews with Maine authors and publishers, articles about writing and more. The alliance distributes selected books about Maine and by Maine authors and publishers, and it maintains a bookstore, reference library, performance space and word processing station at the Maine Writers Center in Brunswick. MWPA regularly invites writers to read from their works and to conduct Saturday workshops." Reviews books of poetry only by Maine-based presses and poets. "We also have extensive on-going workshops in fiction and poetry and offer an annual fall writing retreat."

NATIONAL FEDERATION OF STATE POETRY SOCIETIES, INC., Membership Chairman: Barbara Stevens, 909 E. 34th St., Sioux Falls SD 57105; Contest Chairperson: Amy Jo Zook, 3520 State Route 56, Mechanicsburg OH 43044. "NFSPS is a nonprofit organization exclusively educational and literary. Its purpose is to recognize the importance of poetry with respect to national cultural heritage. It is dedicated solely to the furtherance of poetry on the national level and serves to unite poets in the bonds of fellowship and understanding." Any poetry group located in a state not already affiliated but interested in affiliating with NFSPS may contact the membership chairman. Canadian groups may also apply. "In a state where no valid group exists, help may also be obtained by individuals interested in organizing a poetry group for affiliation." Most reputable state poetry societies are members of the National Federation and advertise their various poetry contests through their quarterly bulletin, *Strophes*, available for SASE and $1, editor Kay Kinnaman, Route 3, Box 348, Alexandria IN 46001. Beware of organizations calling themselves state poetry societies (however named) that are not members of NFSPS, as such labels are sometimes used by vanity schemes trying to sound respectable. Others, such as the Oregon State Poetry Association, are quite reputable, but they don't belong to NFSPS. NFSPS holds an annual meeting in a different city each year with a large awards banquet, addressed by an honorary chairman. They sponsor 50 national contests in various categories each year, including the NFSPS Prize of $1,500 for first place; $500, second; $250, third; with entry fees ($3 for the entire contest for members, $5 for NFSPS Award; $1/poem for nonmembers and $5 for NFSPS award up to 4 poems per entry). All poems winning over $10 are published in an anthology. Rules for all contests are given in a brochure available from Kay Kinnaman at *Strophes* or Amy Jo Zook at the address above; you can also write for the address of your state poetry society. Scholarship information is available from Golda Walker, 915 Aberdeen Ave., Baton Rouge LA 70808 for a #10 SASE.

THE NATIONAL POETRY FOUNDATION; SAGETRIEB; PAIDEUMA, University of Maine, Orono ME 04469, Marie M. Alpert, publications coordinator. "The NPF is a nonprofit organization concerned with publishing scholarship on the work of 20th century poets, particularly Ezra Pound and those in the Imagist/Objectivist tradition. We publish *Paideuma*, a journal devoted to Ezra Pound scholarship, and *Sagetrieb*, a journal devoted to poets in the imagist/objectivist tradition, as well as one other journal of contemporary poetry and comment—*The New York Quarterly*. [See separate listing for *New York Quarterly*.] NPF conducts a conference each summer and celebrates the centennial of an individual 20th century poet." Sample copies: $8.95 for *Paideuma* or *Sagetrieb*; $6 for *New York Quarterly*.

NATIONAL WRITERS UNION, Second Floor, 873 Broadway, New York NY 10003. Offers members such services as contract bargaining, a grievance committee, contract guidelines, health insurance, press credentials, computer discounts, car rental discounts, and caucuses and trade groups for exchange of information about special markets. Members receive *The American Writer*, the organization's newsletter. Membership is $60 for those earning less than $5,000 per year; $105 for those earning $5,000-$25,000; and $150 for those earning more than $25,000.

NORTH CAROLINA WRITERS' NETWORK: THE NETWORK NEWS; HARPERPRINTS POETRY CHAPBOOK COMPETITION; THE RANDALL JARRELL POETRY PRIZE, P.O. Box 954, Carrboro NC 27510, established 1985. Supports the work of writers, writers' organizations and literary programming statewide. A $25 donation annually brings members *The Network News*, a 24-page bimonthly newsletter containing organizational news, national market information and other material of interest to writers, and access to the Resource Center, Writers' Exchange, Workshops, Literary Brokerage and Press Service. 1,500 members nationwide. Annual fall conference features nationally-known writers, publishers and editors. It is held in a different North Carolina location each year in November. Also sponsors competitions in short fiction, one-act plays and nonfiction essays for North Carolinians and members.

‡**THE OREGON STATE POETRY ASSOCIATION**, % Linda Smith, 471 NW Hemlock, Corvallis OR 97330, phone (503)267-7236; newsletter editor Elizabeth Bolton, P.O. Box 219006, Portland OR 97225. Founded in 1956 for "the promotion and creation of poetry," the association has over 400 members, $10 dues, publishes a quarterly *OSPA Newsletter*, and sponsors contests twice yearly, October and April, with total cash prizes of $300 each (no entry fee to members, $2/poem for non-members; out of state entries welcome). Themes and categories vary. For details write to Leona Ward, 1645 SE Spokane St., Portland OR 97202 after August 1 and February 15 each year. The association sponsors workshops, readings and seminars around the state.

PEN AMERICAN CENTER; PEN WRITERS FUND; PEN TRANSLATION PRIZE; RENATO POGGIOLI AWARD; PEN/REVSON FOUNDATION FELLOWSHIPS; GRANTS AND AWARDS, 568 Broadway, New York NY 10012, phone (212)334-1660, "is the largest of more than 100 centers which comprise International PEN, founded in London in 1921 by John Galsworthy to foster understanding among men and women of letters in all countries. Members of PEN work for freedom of expression wherever it has been endangered, and International PEN is the only worldwide organization of writers and the chief voice of the literary community." Its total membership on all continents is approximately 10,000. The 2,600 members of the American Center include poets, playwrights, essayists, editors, novelists (for the original letters in the acronym PEN), as well as translators and those editors and agents who have made a substantial contribution to the literary community. Membership in American PEN includes reciprocal privileges in foreign centers for those traveling abroad. Branch offices are located in Cambridge, Houston, Chicago, Portland/Seattle and San Francisco. Among PEN's various activities are public events and symposia, literary awards, assistance to writers in prison and to American writers in need (grants and loans up to $1,000 from PEN Writers Fund). Medical insurance for writers is available to members. The quarterly *PEN Newsletter* is sent to all members and is available to nonmembers by subscription. The PEN Translation prize, sponsored by the Book-of-the-Month Club, 1 each year of $3,000 for works published in the current calendar year. The Renato Poggioli Award, $3,000 annually, to encourage a promising translator from the Italian who has not yet been widely recognized. Candidates with a project in literary translation planning a journey to Italy will be favored. Submit resume, sample translation and description of project before January 15. The PEN/Revson Foundation Fellowships are $12,750 awarded in odd-numbered years to poets (and to writers of fiction in even-numbered years). A fellow writer or editor must nominate candidates age 35 or under by January 15 with three copies of no more than 50 pgs. of current work in progress, for someone whose "published work has not yet met with the recognition it merits." They publish **Grants and Awards** biennially, containing guidelines, deadlines, eligibility requirements and other information about hundreds of grants, awards and competitions for poets and other writers: $8 postpaid. Send SASE for booklet describing their activities and listing their publications, some of them available free.

PERSONAL POETS UNITED, 860 Armand Ct. NE, Atlanta GA 30324, % Jean Hesse, who started a business in 1980 writing poems for individuals for a fee (for greetings, special occasions, etc.). Others started similar businesses, after she began instructing them in the process, especially through a cassette tape training program and other training materials. She then organized a support group of poets around the country writing poetry-to-order, Personal Poets United. Send SASE for free brochure or $19.50 plus $4.50 postage and handling for training manual "How to Make Your Poems Pay."

PITTSBURGH POETRY EXCHANGE, P.O. Box 4279, Pittsburgh PA 15203, phone (412)481-POEM. Founded in 1974 as a community-based organization for local poets, it functions as a service organization and information exchange, conducting ongoing workshops, readings, forums and other special events. No dues or fees. "At our open workshop we each drop a dollar into the basket which we turn over to City Books as 'rent' for use of the space. Any other monetary contributions are voluntary, often from outside sources. We've managed not to let our reach exceed our grasp." Their readings programs are primarily committed to local and area poets, with honorariums of $25-60. They sponsor a minimum of three major events per year in addition to a monthly workshop. Some of these have been reading programs in conjunction with community arts festivals, such as the October South Side Poetry Smorgasbord—a series of readings throughout the evening at different shops (galleries, bookstores). Poets from out of town may contact the exchange for assistance in setting up readings at bookstores to help sell their books. Contact Michael Wurster at the above address or phone number.

THE POETRY COMMITTEE OF THE GREATER WASHINGTON AREA, % The Folger Shakespeare Library, 201 E. Capitol St. SE, Washington DC 20003, phone (202)544-7077, executive director Saskia Hamilton. Formed in the mid-70s at the invitation of the poetry coordinator of the Folger Library, meets informally 5 times a year. The membership (by invitation) consists of about 60 people who represent major and minor poetry organizations in the metropolitan area (a few from Baltimore also). Annual sponsors of Celebration of Washington Poetry, a reading and book sale highlighting area poets and presses, the Columbia Book Award for best book of poetry by Washington area poet within the past calendar year and the Columbia Merit Award for service to area poetry.

‡THE POETRY PROJECT AT ST. MARK'S CHURCH IN THE BOWERY, 131 E. 10th St., New York NY 10003, phone (212)674-0910, was established in 1966 by the US Dept. of H.E.W. in an effort to help wayward youths in the East Village. It is now funded by a variety of government and private sources. Artistic Director: Ed Friedman. Program Coordinator: Gillian McCain. From October through May the project offers workshops, talks, staged readings, performance poetry, lectures, an annual 4-day symposium, literary magazines and a series of featured writers who bring their books to sell at the readings. If the reading is a publication party, the publisher handles the sales.

POETRY RESOURCE CENTER OF MICHIGAN, Dept. PM, 111 E. Kirby, Detroit MI 48202, phone (313)754-9645, "is a nonprofit organization which exists through the generosity of poets, writers, teachers, publishers, printers, librarians and others dedicated to the reading and enjoyment of poetry in Michigan." The *PRC Newsletter* and *Calendar* is available by mail monthly for an annual membership donation of $20 or more, and is distributed free of charge at locations throughout the state. To obtain copies for distribution at poetry functions, contact the editor or any member of the PRC Board of Trustees.

POETRY SOCIETY OF AMERICA; POETRY SOCIETY OF AMERICA AWARDS, 15 Gramercy Park, New York NY 10003, phone (212)254-9628, is a nonprofit cultural organization in support of poetry and of poets, member and nonmember, young and established, which sponsors readings, lectures and workshops both in New York City and around the country. Their Peer Group Workshop is open to all members and meets on a weekly basis. They publish a newsletter of their activities and they sponsor a wide range of contests. The following are open to members only: Gordon Barber Memorial Award ($200); Gertrude B. Claytor Award ($250); Gustav Davidson Memorial Award ($500); Mary Carolyn Davies Memorial Award ($250); Alice Fay Di Castagnola Award ($2,000); *Writer Magazine*/Emily Dickinson Award ($100); Consuelo Ford Award ($250); Cecil Hemley Memorial Award ($300); Lucille Medwick Memorial Award ($500). Nonmembers may enter as many of the following contests as they wish, no more than 1 entry for each, for a $5 fee: Ruth Lake Award (III), $100 for a poem of retrospection any length or style; Elias Lieberman Student Poetry Award, $100 for students in grades 9-12; John Masefield Memorial Award (II) for a narrative poem in English up to 300 lines, $500, translations ineligible; Celia B. Wagner Award (II), $250 any form or length; George Bogin Memorial Award, $500 for a selection of 4 to 5 poems which take a stand against oppression; Robert H. Winner Memorial Award, $2,500 for a poem written by a poet over 40, still unpublished or with one book. (All have a deadline of December 31; awards are made at a ceremony and banquet in late spring.) The Society also has 3 book contests open to nonmembers, but publishers only may enter books. They must obtain an entry form, and there is a $10 fee for each book entered. Book awards are: Melville Cane Award (II), $500 in even-numbered years awarded to a book of poems, in odd years to prose work on poetry; Norma Farber Award (III), $1,000 for a first book; William Carlos Williams Award (III), $1,250 for a book of poetry published by a small press, nonprofit or university press, by a permanent resident of the US—translations not eligible. The Shelley Memorial Award of $4,000 is by nomination only. For necessary rules and guidelines for their various contests send SASE between August 1 and December 31. Membership: $40.

POETS & WRITERS, INC., See *Poets & Writers* under Publications Useful to Poets.

POETS' CORNER, THE CATHEDRAL CHURCH OF ST. JOHN THE DIVINE, Cathedral Heights, 1047 Amsterdam Ave. at 112 St., New York NY 10025, initiated in 1984 with memorials for Emily Dickinson, Walt Whitman, Washington Irving, Robert Frost, Herman Melville, Nathanial Hawthorne, Edgar Allen Poe, Henry James, Henry David Thoreau, Mark Twain, Ralph Waldo Emerson, William Faulkner, Wallace Stevens, Willa Cather, T.S. Eliot, Marianne Moore and Edwin Arlington Robinson. It is similar in concept to the British Poets' Corner in Westminster Abbey, and was established and dedicated to memorialize this country's greatest writers. A Board of Electors comprised of thirteen eminent poets and writers chooses two deceased authors each year for inclusion in The Poets' Corner.

POETS HOUSE; THE REED FOUNDATION LIBRARY; THE POETRY PUBLICATION SHOWCASE, 72 Spring St., New York NY 10012, phone (212)431-7920, founded 1985, Lee Ellen Briccetti, executive director, "is a poetry library, literary resource center and meeting place for poets and poetry readers from all parts of the aesthetic spectrum. Programs and events are designed to serve as a platform for discussions and emphasize cross-cultural and interdisciplinary exchange. The Reed Foundation Library is a non-circulating poetry collection open to the public and is comprised of 27,000 volumes, including books, journals, small press publications, a comprehensive audiotape archive and other fugitive poetry materials. Visits to the comfortable loftspace—as is membership—and donations to the library are welcomed." The Poetry Publication Showcase gathers all new poetry releases annually for exhibit and a festival of events. Poets House sponsors over 25 public events annually and offers a variety of programs for educators and students. These include a NY/NJ Teachers Conference; a conference for the chairpeople of high school English Departments; the Poetry Teacher of the Year Award, which divides a prize of $1,000 between a teacher and her/his school library; and in-house poetry workshops for visiting school classes.

POETS-IN-THE-SCHOOLS. Most states have PITS programs that send published poets into classrooms to teach students poetry writing. If you have published poetry widely and have a proven commitment to children, contact your state arts council, Arts-in-Education Dept., to see whether you qualify. Three of the biggest are Poets in Public Service (formerly NYSPITS), Suite 3B, 154 Christopher St., New York NY 10014, phone (212)206-9000; California Poets-in-the-Schools, 2845 24th St., San Francisco CA 94110, phone (415)695-7988; and COMPAS, Landmark Center, #308, 75 West 5th St., St. Paul MN 55102.

SCOTTISH POETRY LIBRARY; SCHOOL OF POETS; CRITICAL SERVICE, Tweeddale Court, 14 High St., Edinburgh EH1 1TE Scotland, phone (031)557-2876, director Tessa Ransford, librarian Penny Duce. It is a central information source and free lending library, also lending by post. The library has a computerized catalogue allowing subject-based searches. The collection has over 12,000 items and consists of Scottish and international poetry. The School of Poets is open to anyone; "at meetings members divide into small groups in which each participant reads a poem which is then analyzed and discussed." Meetings normally take place at 7:30 p.m. on the first Tuesday of each month at the library. They also offer a Critical Service in which groups of up to 6 poems, not exceeding 200 lines in all, are given critical comment by members of the School: £15 for each critique (with SAE).

THE SOCIETY OF AUTHORS, 84 Drayton Gardens, London SW10 9SB England. Advises members on business matters, takes up their complaints and institutes legal proceedings, sends them a quarterly journal, *The Author,* publishes guides regarding agents, copyright, income tax, contracts, etc., offers members retirement and medical insurance programs, administers trust funds as well as a number of literary awards, organizes special interest groups (e.g., broadcasters, children's writers, etc.), and pursues campaigns on behalf of the profession (e.g., for legislative changes).

SONGWRITERS AND POETS CRITIQUE, 11599 Coontz Rd., Orient OH 43146, founded in 1985 by Ellis Cordle, phone (614)877-1727. A nonprofit association whose purpose is to serve songwriters, poets and musicians in their area. The president of the organization says, "We have over 100 members from over 16 states at several levels of ability from novice to advanced, and try to help and support each other with the craft and the business of poetry and songs. We have published writers and recorded artists. We share information about how to pitch, send and package a demo and who to send it to. We have a songwriting contest for member writers." Annual dues are $20.

SOUTHERN POETRY ASSOCIATION; THE POET'S VOICE, P.O. Box 524, Pass Christian MS 39571, founded 1986, poetry editor Mildred Klyce. SPA offers networking, publishing, free critique service for members through Round Robin Groups, assistance in publishing chapbooks. $10 annual membership fee includes *The Poet's Voice* quarterly newsletter. The association sponsors a number of contests, including Voices of the South, Yarn Spinner, Poetry in Motion, Special People; some are for members only; some, such as the Voices of the South Contest, are open to all. Prizes total $200 with $3 entry fee/poem (28 line limit). June 1 deadline. High scoring poems are published in an anthology (which the poet is not required to purchase). Send 9×12 SAE with 58¢ postage for details. *The Poet's Voice* contains poetry book reviews, articles on great poets of the past, current activities and input from SPA members.

THE THURBER HOUSE; THE JAMES THURBER WRITER-IN-RESIDENCE, 77 Jefferson Ave., Columbus OH 43215, phone (614)464-1032, officially opened in 1985. Executive director Donn Vickers says that it is "one of the most diversely active of all restored writer's homes." The Thurber Center has a staff of 6 people plus over 30 volunteers and a 21-person Board of Trustees. Half of its budget comes from state, local and national arts councils; 35% from foundations; and the rest from sales. The house includes a bookstore which distributes the best small press books the Midwest has to offer. They sponsor a quarter-long writer-in-residence program, The James Thurber Writer-in-Residence, $5,000/ quarter plus living accommodations in Thurber's restored house, featuring playwrights, journalists and other writers (poetry and fiction). The house also includes performance spaces and offices. Local writers are invited to use the house as a place to "come together with others who care." They sponsor Evenings with Authors presenting major writers to the public, Literary Picnics on the lawn of Thurber House providing "convivial evenings in the company of both emerging and beloved authors, with delectable menus by some of Columbus's favorite chefs," and other activities.

THE UNTERBERG POETRY CENTER OF THE 92ND STREET Y; "DISCOVERY"/*THE NATION*** POETRY CONTEST**, (formerly The Poetry Center of the 92nd Street Y), 1395 Lexington Ave., New York NY 10128, phone (212)415-5760. Offers annual series of readings by major literary figures (36 readings September through May), writing workshops and lectures. You may join the center to participate in and be informed of these activities. Also co-sponsors the "Discovery"/*The Nation* Poetry Contest. Deadline early February. Send SASE for information.

‡**WELFARE STATE INTERNATIONAL**, The Ellers, Ulverston, Cumbria LA12 0AA England, phone 0229-581127/57146, fax 0229 581232, founded 1968, artistic director John Fox, is a "celebratory arts company of national and international status creating functional poetry both visual and verbal, for ceremonial occasions. Commissions range from small-scale domestic celebrations to city-scale spectaculars." They publish poster poems in limited editions, dramatic songs and interludes for performance works, and poetic masques.

WALT WHITMAN CULTURAL ARTS CENTER; CAMDEN POETRY AWARD, 2nd and Cooper St., Camden NJ 08102, executive director René L. Huggins, program coordinator Gustavo Paredes, phone (609)964-8300. A writers' center, founded 1975, it offers a variety of programs such as Notable Poets and Writers Series, Walt Whitman Poetry Series, school programs, adult and children's theater, musical presentations, Fine Art Exhibitions and the Camden Poetry Award. Their regular season runs September through May. During the summer months they provide a 4-week Creativity Camp and a children's theater series entitled "10 Fridays of Fun."

WOODLAND PATTERN, Box 92081, 720 E. Locust St., Milwaukee WI 53202, phone (414)263-5001. Executive director Anne Kingsbury calls it "a semi-glamorous literary and arts center." Kingsbury regards the center as a neighborhood organization; it includes a bookstore that concentrates on contemporary literature, much of it small press, much of it poetry and also on multicultural children's literature. It also incorporates a multipurpose gallery/performance/reading space, where exhibitions, readings, a lecture series, musical programs and a reading and study group are held. The *Woodland Pattern Newsletter*, mailed free to 1,900 people, contains an annotated calendar and pieces about visiting writers.

WORLD-WIDE WRITERS SERVICE, INC.; WRITERS INK; WRITERS INK PRESS; WRITERS UNLIMITED AGENCY, INC.; WESTHAMPTON WRITERS FESTIVAL; JEANNE VOEGE POETRY AWARDS, 186 N. Coleman Rd., Centereach NY 11720-3072, phone (516)736-6439, founded in 1976, Writers Ink Press founded 1978, director Suk-Hang Chin, poetry editor Dr. David B. Axelrod. "World-wide Writers Service is a literary and speakers' booking agency. With its not-for-profit affiliate, Writers Unlimited Agency, Inc., it presents literary workshops and performances, conferences and other literary services, and publishes through Writers Ink Press, chapbooks and small flat-spined books as well as arts editions. **We publish only by our specific invitation at this time.**" *Writers Ink* is "a sometimes newsletter of events on Long Island, now including programs of our conferences. We welcome news of other presses and poets' activities. Review books of poetry. We fund raise for nonprofit projects and are associates and sponsors of Westhampton Writers Festival and Jeanne Voege Poetry Awards. Arts

Editions are profit productions employing hand-made papers, bindings, etc. We have editorial services available at small fees ($50 minimum), but only after inquiry and if appropriate. We are currently concentrating on works in translation, particularly Chinese."

THE WRITER'S CENTER; CAROUSEL; POET LORE, 4508 Walsh St., Bethesda MD 20815, phone (301)654-8664, founder and artistic director Allan Lefcowitz, director Jane Fox. This is an outstanding resource for writers not only in Washington DC but in the wider area ranging from southern Pennsylvania to North Carolina and West Virginia. The center offers 200 multi-meeting workshops each year in writing, typesetting, word processing, and graphic arts, and provides a research library. It is open 7 days a week, 10 hours a day. Some 2,300 members support the center with $30 annual donations, which allows for 4 paid staff members. There is a book gallery at which publications of small presses are displayed and sold. The center's publication, *The Carousel*, is an 12-page tabloid that comes out 6 times a year. They also sponsor 40 annual performance events, which include presentations in poetry, fiction and theater. The center is now publisher of *Poet Lore* — 100 years old in 1989 (see listing in the Publishers of Poetry section).

THE WRITERS ROOM, 5th Floor, 153 Waverly Pl., New York NY 10014, phone (212)807-9519, provides a "home away from home" for any writer "with a serious commitment to writing," who needs a place to work. It is open 24 hours a day, 7 days a week, offering desks, storage space and "an alternative to isolation" for up to 150 writers. Space is allotted on a quarterly basis (which may be extended indefinitely) and costs $165 per quarter. "We now offer in-house scholarships for one-quarter year to writers in financial need." It is supported by the National Endowment for the Arts, the New York State Council on the Arts and other public and private sources, and it encourages applications. The Writers Room also offers monthly readings and workshops for its residents and has occasional exhibits on "writerly" subjects, such as revision.

Additional Organizations Useful to Poets

The following listings also contain information about organizations useful to poets. See the General Index for page numbers.

Publications Useful to Poets

The publications in this section are designed to help poets with all aspects of poetry writing and publishing. While few are actual markets for poetry, many of the publications detail new markets in addition to providing information on writing poetry, advice on marketing or interviews with poets and writers.

Poets & Writers Magazine, in fact, is one of the most useful resources for poets and fiction writers. In addition to informative articles and interviews, it includes calls for submissions and contests and awards. *Writer's Digest*, on the other hand, covers the entire field of writing and features a monthly poetry column by Michael J. Bugeja as well as various market listings. Both of these publications not only highlight new publishing opportunities, but they may also share information about publishers who have changed locations or gone out of business.

Other publications, such as *Dusty Dog Reviews*, *Small Press Review* and *Small Magazine Review*, include reviews of poetry books and chapbooks and/or reviews of small press magazines. These reviews may provide insight into the markets you may be considering. And for those interested in publishing their own poetry, this section also includes publishers that offer materials on self-publishing.

In addition to the listings that follow, you will find other useful publications, such as *New Writer's Magazine*, under Additional Publications Useful to Poets, located at the end of this section. To determine which of these publications may be most useful to you, read sample issues. Many of these books and periodicals may be found in your local library or located on newsstands or in bookstores. If you are unable to locate a certain magazine, order a sample copy directly from the publisher. For books, send a SASE with a request for the publisher's current catalog and/or further information.

AMERICAN POETS IN PROFILE SERIES; FORD-BROWN & CO., P.O. Box 2674, Boston MA 02208-2764, founded 1975 (in Birmingham AL), editor Steven Ford-Brown. Ford-Brown will consider prose submissions of critical profiles for its American Poets in Profile Series. Series includes book on Dave Smith, John Logan, Andrew Glaze, Vasser Miller, Carolyn Kizer and Fred Chappell. **Sample postpaid: $15.95. Pays advance and copies (amount "depends"). Reports on queries in 2 weeks. No simultaneous submissions.**

R.R. BOWKER; LITERARY MARKET PLACE; BOOKS IN PRINT, 121 Chanlon Rd., New Providence NJ 07974, phone (908)464-6800. **LMP** is the major trade directory of publishers and people involved in publishing books. It is available in most libraries, or individual copies may be purchased (appears in December each year; standing order price $158). **BIP** is another standard reference available in most libraries and bookstores. Bowker publishes a wide range of reference books pertaining to publishing. Write for their catalog.

CANADIAN POETRY, English Dept., University of Western Ontario, London, Ontario N6A 3K7 Canada, phone (519)661-3403, founded 1977, editor Prof. D.M.R. Bentley. A biannual journal of critical articles, reviews and historical documents (such as interviews). It is a professionally printed, scholarly edited, flat-spined, 100+ pg. journal which pays contributors in copies. Subscription: $15. **Sample: $7.50. Note that they publish no poetry except as quotations in articles.**

DUSTBOOKS; INTERNATIONAL DIRECTORY OF LITTLE MAGAZINES AND SMALL PRESSES; DIRECTORY OF POETRY PUBLISHERS; SMALL PRESS REVIEW; SMALL MAGAZINE REVIEW, P.O. Box 100, Paradise CA 95967. Dustbooks publishes a number of books useful to writers. Send SASE for catalog. Among their regular publications, **International Directory** is an annual directory of small presses and literary magazines, over 5,000 entries, a third being magazines, half being book publishers, and the rest being both. There is very detailed information about what these presses and magazines report to be their policies in regard to payment, copyright, format and publishing schedules. **Directory of Poetry Publishers** has similar information for 2,000 publishers of poetry. *Small Press Review* is a monthly magazine, newsprint, carrying current updating of listings in ID, small press needs, news, announcements and reviews—a valuable way to stay abreast of the literary marketplace. A new magazine, *Small Magazine Review*, began publication in June, 1993.

DUSTY DOG REVIEWS, 1904-A Gladden, Gallup NM 87301, phone (505)863-2398, founded 1990, editor/publisher John Pierce. *Dusty Dog Reviews* is a review magazine appearing 3 times/year, reviewing small press poetry books and chapbooks as well as poetry magazines, 60-80/issue, average length 200 words. Subscription: $4.50. Sample: $2. Open to unsolicited reviews. Poets may also send books for review consideration to Dave Castleman, 512 Tamalpais Dr., Mill Valley CA 94941. "All editors and publishers whose magazine issues and poetry books/chapbooks get reviewed will receive one copy of the issue in which the review appears." The editor advises, "Become very familiar with **Poet's Market** and what is said at the beginning of the book. The small press magazines are often 1 person staff and work very hard for you, the poet. Be patient with them, and support the magazines you like. If poets don't subscribe to the magazines that publish them, it is very hard for the magazine to continue publishing."

LAUGHING BEAR NEWSLETTER; LAUGHING BEAR PRESS (V), P.O. Box 36159, Bear Valley Station, Denver CO 80236, phone (303)744-3624, founded 1976, editor Tom Person. *LBN* is a monthly publication of small press information for writers and publishers containing articles, news and reviews; it was named one of the 9 best publishing and marketing newsletters in the 1992 *Small Press* Newsletter Awards. Cost: $10/year. *LBN* is interested in short (200- to 300-word) articles on self-publishing and small press. Payment in copies. Send SASE for sample copy. Laughing Bear Press publishes poetry books and cassette tapes of poetry but is not accepting unsolicited mss in 1994.

THE LETTER EXCHANGE, published by The Readers' League, % Stephen Sikora, P.O. Box 6218, Albany CA 94706. Published 3 times each year, *The Letter Exchange* is a digest-sized magazine, 36 pgs., that publishes 4 types of listings: regular (which are rather like personal classifieds); ghost letters, which contain lines like "Send news of the Entwives!"; amateur magazines, which publicizes readers' own publishing ventures; and sketch ads, in which readers who would rather draw than write can communicate in their chosen mode. All ads are coded, and readers respond through the code numbers. Subscription to *The Letter Exchange* is $20/year, and sample copies are $9 postpaid for current issue. Poets who are so inclined often exchange poems and criticism with each other through this medium.

LITERARY MAGAZINE REVIEW, English Dept., Kansas State University, Manhattan KS 66506, founded 1981, editor G.W. Clift. A quarterly magazine (digest-sized, perfect-bound, about 80 pgs.) that publishes critiques, 2-5 pgs. long, of various literary magazines, plus shorter "reviews" (about ½ page), directories of literary magazines (such as British publications) and descriptive listings of new journals during a particular year. Single copies are available for $4 or subscriptions for $12.50 year.

OPEN HORIZONS, (formerly Ad-Lib Publications), P.O. Box 205, Fairfield IA 52556, phone (515)472-6130 or (800)669-0773, publisher John Kremer, publishes how-to books about book publishing and self-publishing, such as **1001 Ways to Market Your Books, Directory of Book Printers**, and **Book Publishing Resource Guide** (also available on IBM PC or Macintosh disk as a database). Send SASE for catalog.

PARA PUBLISHING, Box 4232-880, Santa Barbara CA 93140-4232, phone (805)968-7277, orders (800)727-2782, fax (805)968-1379. Author-publisher Dan Poynter publishes how-to books on book publishing and self-publishing. **Is There a Book Inside You?** shows you how to get your book out. **The**

Self-Publishing Manual, How to Write, Print and Sell Your Own Book is all about book promotion. **Publishing Short-Run Books** shows you how to typeset and lay out your own book. Poynter also publishes **Publishing Contracts on Disk, Book Fairs** and 19 Special Reports on various aspects of book production, promotion, marketing and distribution. *Free* book publishing information kit.

POETRY BOOK SOCIETY, 10 Barley Mow Passage, London W4 4PH England. A book club with an annual subscription rate of £24, which covers 4 books of new poetry, the *PBS Bulletin*, the annual **Poetry Anthology**, a premium offer (for new members) and free surface postage and packing to anywhere in the world. The selectors also recommend other books of special merit, which are obtainable at a discount of 25%. The Poetry Book Society is subsidized by the Arts Council of Great Britain. Please write for details.

THE POETRY CONNECTION, 13455 SW 16 Court #F-405, Pembroke Pines FL 33027, phone (305)431-3016 (PM), editor/publisher Sylvia Shichman. *The Poetry Connection* provides information in flyer format. Poets, writers and songwriters receive information on how to sell their poetry/books and obtain assistance in chapbook publishing. *TPC* has information on writing for greeting card companies and songwriting directories. Sample issue: $5 plus 5 first class stamps.

POETRY EXCHANGE, P.O. Box 85477, Seattle WA 98145-1477. A monthly newsletter, circulation 1,600, $10/year, to which you may subscribe or in which you can buy ads. It has listings of workshops, "manuscripts wanted," and a calendar of regional poetic events. It is 4 to 8 magazine-sized pages.

POETS & WRITERS, INC.; A DIRECTORY OF AMERICAN POETS AND FICTION WRITERS; WRITER'S GUIDE TO COPYRIGHT; AUTHOR & AUDIENCE; LITERARY AGENTS; LITERARY BOOKSTORES; POETS & WRITERS MAGAZINE, 72 Spring St., New York NY 10012, phone (212)226-3586 or (800)666-2268 (California only), is our major support organization. Its many helpful publications include *Poets & Writers Magazine*, which appears 6 times a year ($18 or $3.95 for a single copy), magazine-sized, 72 pgs., offset, has been called *The Wall Street Journal* of our profession, and it is there that one most readily finds out about resources, current needs of magazines and presses, contests, awards, jobs and retreats for writers, and discussions of business, legal and other issues affecting writers. P&W also publishes a number of valuable directories such as its biennial **A Directory of American Poets and Fiction Writers** ($23.95 paperback), which editors, publishers, agents and sponsors of readings and workshops use to locate over 7,000 active writers in the country. (You may qualify for a listing if you have a number of publications.) They also publish **A Writer's Guide to Copyright; Author & Audience,** a list of over 400 organizations which sponsor readings and workshops involving poets and fiction writers, including a section on how to organize and present a reading or workshop; **Literary Agents: A Writer's Guide; Literary Bookstores: A Cross-Country Guide,** for people who travel; and many reprints of articles from *Poets & Writers Magazine*, such as "How to Give an Unsolicited Manuscript the Best Chance" and "On Cloud Nine: 24 Heavens for Writers" (information on writers' colonies).

POETS' AUDIO CENTER; THE WATERSHED FOUNDATION, P.O. Box 50145, Washington DC 20091. This is an international clearinghouse for ordering any poetry recording available, from both commercial and noncommercial producers. Catalog available free ("an introduction to our collection"); they stock over 500 titles. **Foundation not accepting applications at this time.**

BERN PORTER INTERNATIONAL, 22 Salmond Rd., Belfast ME 04915, founded 1911. A monthly journal that both reviews books of poetry and publishes poetry. Also provides sleeping bag space for poets and writers May 1 through November 1 for the cost or freewill contribution. No smoking. No drugs. No telephone.

PUSHCART PRESS, P.O. Box 380, Wainscott NY 11975. Publishes a number of books useful to writers, including the Pushcart Prize Series—annual anthologies representing the best small press publications, according to the judges; The Editors' Book Award Series, "to encourage the writing of distinguished books of uncertain financial value," The Original Publish-It-Yourself Handbook and the Literary Companion Series. Send SASE for catalog.

SIPAPU; KONOCTI BOOKS, 23311 County Rd. 88, Winters CA 95694, phone (916)662-3364, founded 1970, editor/publisher Noel Peattie. *Sipapu* consists of reviews of small press publications, interviews and conference news, but publishes no poetry. Konocti Books has published poetry but is now publishing by invitation only.

THE WASHINGTON INTERNATIONAL ARTS LETTER, P.O. Box 12010, Des Moines IA 50312, phone (515)255-5577. Appears 10 times/year, 6-8 pg. newsletter on grants and other forms of assistance for the arts and humanities—mostly lists various programs of support to artists including many for poets.

Reviews books of poetry. Subscription: $124 full rate; $55 for individuals; $82 for institutions.

‡**WORDWRIGHTS CANADA**, P.O. Box 456 Station O, Toronto, Ontario M4A 2P1 Canada, director Susan Ioannou, publishes "books on poetics in layman's, not academic terms, such as **Writing Reader-friendly Poems: Over 50 Rules of Thumb for Clearer Communication** and **Literary Markets that Pay.**" They consider manuscripts of such books for publication, paying $50 advance, 10% royalties and 5% of press run. They also conduct a "Manuscript Reading Service." Request order form to buy samples.

WRITER'S DIGEST BOOKS; WRITER'S DIGEST, 1507 Dana Ave., Cincinnati OH 45207, phone (800)289-0963 outside Ohio, or (513)531-2222. Writer's Digest Books publishes an array of books useful to poets, such as **The Poet's Handbook** by Judson Jerome, **Creating Poetry** by John Drury and **The Art and Craft of Poetry** by Michael J. Bugeja (available as of January, 1994). *Writer's Digest* is a monthly magazine about writing with frequent articles and much market news about poetry, in addition to a monthly poetry column. See entry in Publishers of Poetry section.

WRITERS NEWS; WRITERS LIBRARY, P.O. Box 4, Nairn, 1V12 4HU Scotland, phone 0667-54441, fax 0667-54401. The monthly magazine *Writer's News*, 48 pgs., is chock-full of announcements of markets, competitions, opportunities and news of the writing world. A regular feature is their Poetry Workshop, discussing the writing of poetry. Writers Library distributes books on writing, including many published by Writer's Digest Books. Subscription to the magazine: £38.90 or £33.90 if you pay by "direct debit" (charge card). Write for their book catalog.

WRITER'S N.W.; WRITERS NORTHWEST HANDBOOK; MEDIA WEAVERS, Blue Heron Publishing, Inc., 24450 NW Hansen Rd., Hillsboro OR 97124, phone (503)621-3911, is a professionally published tabloid quarterly giving market news, reviews of books of Northwest authors or presses, software reviews, literary activity, interviews, articles and other pertinent information for writers anywhere. Subscription: $10. **Writers NW Handbook** is a market directory for the Northwest (including British Columbia): $18.95 plus $2.50 postage and handling ($3 to Alaska, Hawaii and Canada).

Additional Publications Useful to Poets

The following listings also contain information about publications useful to poets. See the General Index for page numbers.

Academy of American Poets
Anterior Poetry Monthly
Artist Trust
Associated Writing Programs
Black Bear Publications
Black Buzzard Press
Borealis Press
Byline Magazine
Canadian Conference of the Arts
Canadian Poetry Association
Canadian Writer's Journal
Chips Off the Writer's Block
COSMEP, The International Association of Independent Publishers
Council of Literary Magazines and Presses
Emerald Coast Review
Fairbanks Arts Association
Federation of British Columbia Writers
Frank
International Women's Writing Guild
Julian Associates
Keystrokes
Laureate Letter, The
Leacock Medal for Humour, The Stephen
League of Canadian Poets, The

Ligonier Valley Writers Conference
Loft, The
Maine Writers & Publishers Alliance
Midwest Writer's Conference
My Legacy
Naropa Institute Writing & Poetics Summer Program
National Federation of State Poetry Societies, Inc.
National Poetry Foundation
National Writers Union
New Horizons Poetry Club
New Writer's Magazine
North Carolina Writers' Network
Northwoods Press
Oak, The
Oregon State Poetry Association, The
Parnassus: Poetry in Review
PEN American Center
Pequod: A Journal of Contemporary Literature and Literary Criticism
Piedmont Literary Review
Poetry Nippon Press
Poetry Plus Magazine
Poetry Resource Center of Michigan

Poetry Society of America
Poets' Roundtable
Quarry Magazine
Red Dancefloor
Rio Grande Press
Scavenger's Newsletter
Seneca Review
Small Press Writers & Artists Organization (SPWAO)
Smith, The
Society of Authors, The
Southern Poetry Association
Thumbprints
University of Massachusetts Writers' Conference
Verse
Wisconsin Regional Writers' Association
World-wide Writers Service
Write Way, The
Writer, The
Writer's Center, The
Writer's Exchange
Writers Forum (England)
Writer's Guidelines
Writer's Journal
Writer's Lifeline
Writing Workshop for People Over 57

Glossary

A3, A4, A5. Metric equivalents of 11¾ × 16½, 8¼ × 11¾ and 5⅞ × 8¼ respectively.

Bio. Some publishers ask you to send a short biographical paragraph with your submission; it is commonly called a "bio." They may also ask for your important previous publications or "credits."

Chapbook. A small book of approximately 20-25 pages of poetry. Such a book is less expensive to produce than a full-length book collection, though it is seldom noted by reviewers.

Cover letter. Letter accompanying a submission giving brief account of publishing credits and biographical information. See the advice and sample letter in The Business of Poetry article.

Digest-sized. Approximately 5½ × 8½, the size of a folded sheet of conventional typing paper.

Flat-spined. What many publishers call "perfect-bound," glued with a flat edge (usually permitting readable type on the spine).

Galleys. Typeset copies of your poem(s). You should proofread and correct any mistakes and return the galleys to editors within 48 hours of receipt.

IRC. International Reply Coupon, postage for return of submissions from another country. One IRC is sufficient for one ounce by *surface mail*. If you want an airmail return, you need one IRC for each half-ounce. Do not send checks or cash for postage to other countries: The exchange rates are so high it is not worthwhile for editors to bother with. (Exception: Many Canadian editors do not object to U.S. dollars; use IRCs the first time and inquire.)

Magazine-sized. Approximately 8½ × 11, the size of conventional typing paper unfolded.

ms, mss. Manuscript, manuscripts.

Multi-book review. Also known as an omnibus or essay review. A review of several books by the same author or by several authors. You might review four or five environmental poetry books for instance.

Multiple submission. Submission of more than one poem at a time; most poetry publishers *prefer* multiple submissions and specify how many should be in a packet. Some say a multiple submission means the poet has sent more than one manuscript to the same publication before receiving word on the first submission. See Multiple/Simultaneous Submissions in The Business of Poetry.

p. Abbreviation for pence.

pg., pgs. Page, pages.

Perfect-bound. See Flat-spined.

Query letter. Letter written to a publisher to elicit interest in a manuscript or to determine if submissions are acceptable.

Rights. See section in The Business of Poetry article. First North American serial rights means the publisher is acquiring the right to publish your poem first in a U.S. or Canadian periodical. All rights means the publisher is buying the poem outright. Selling all rights usually requires that you obtain permission to reprint your work, even in a book-length collection.

Saddle-stapled. What many publishers call "saddle-stitched," folded and stapled along the fold.

SAE. Self-addressed envelope.

SASE. Self-addressed, stamped envelope. *Every* publisher requires, with any submission, query, request for catalog or sample, a self-addressed, stamped envelope. This information is so basic it is excluded from the individual listings but repeated in bold type at the bottom of many pages throughout this book. The return envelope (usually folded for inclusion) should be large enough to hold the material submitted or requested, and the postage provided—stamps if the submission is within your own country, IRCs if it is to another country—should be sufficient for its return.

Simultaneous submission. Submission of the same manuscript to more than one publisher at a time. Most magazine editors *refuse to accept* simultaneous submissions. Some book and chapbook publishers do not object to simultaneous submissions. In all cases, notify them that the manuscript is being simultaneously submitted elsewhere if that is what you are doing.

Slush pile. Unsolicited manuscripts, usually hundreds each year, cluttering an editor's desk.

Status. The current situation concerning a particular manuscript: 1) The manuscript was never received. 2) We received the manuscript but cannot locate it. 3) We received and rejected said manuscript. 4) We are still considering it. 5) We are in the process of accepting your manuscript.

Subsidy press. See Vanity press.

Tabloid-sized. 11 × 15 or larger, the size of an ordinary newspaper folded and turned sideways.

Vanity press. A slang term for a publisher that requires the writer to pay publishing costs, especially one that flatters an author in order in order to generate business. These presses often use the term "subsidy" to describe themselves. Some presses, however, derive subsidies from other sources, such as government grants, and do not require author payment. These are not considered vanity presses.

Visual poetry. A combination of text and graphics usually only reproduced photographically.

Indexes

Chapbook Publishers

A chapbook is a slim volume of a poet's work, usually 20-25 pages (although page requirements vary greatly). Given the high cost of printing, a publisher is more apt to accept a chapbook than an entire book from an unproven poet.

Some chapbooks are published as inserts in magazines. Others are separate volumes. The quality of the product also varies. Whenever possible, request submission guidelines and samples.

You'll find many presses charge reading fees. Avoid any over $10. (Some go as high as $15 for book-length manuscripts, but chapbooks are much easier to process.)

If your chapbook is published, you may still participate in "first-book" competitions. Following are publishers who consider chapbook manuscripts. See the General Index for their specific page numbers.

North Dakota Quarterly
Nosukumo
Oasis Books
Occident Magazine
Ohio Review, The
ONTHEBUS
Outrider Press
Owl Creek Press
Palanquin
Panhandler, The
Parting Gifts
Pearl
Penumbra Press, The
Peregrine
Permeable Press
Petronium Press
Phase and Cycle
Phlebas Press, The
Phoenix Broadsheets
Pikestaff Forum, The
Pirate Writings
Plowman, The
Poet
Poetic License
Poetical Histories
Poetry Forum
Poetry Motel
Poets at Work
Poets. Painters. Composers.
Poets' Roundtable
Potato Eyes
Press of MacDonald & Rein-
    ecke, The
Printed Matter

Proof Rock Press
Prophetic Voices
Pudding House Pub.
Quarry Magazine
Rag Mag
Ranger Int. Prod.
Red Candle Press, The
Red Dancefloor
Red Herring Poets
Rose Shell Press
Runaway Spoon Press, The
St. Andrew Press
Score Magazine
Serpent & Eagle Press
Shamal Books
Ship of Fools
Signpost Press, The
Silver Apples Press
Silverfish Review
Slipstream
Small Press Writers & Artists
    Organization
Snail's Pace Review, The
Soleil Press
Sow's Ear, The
Spitball
Stand Magazine
Star Books, Inc.
State Street Press
Stevan Company, The
Still Waters Press
Stone Press
Stonevale Press
Stormline Press, Inc.

Sub-Terrain
Tak Tak Tak
Talisman Literary Research,
    Inc.
TapRoot
Textile Bridge Press
Third Half
Tightrope
Touchstone
Tower Poetry Society
Translucent Tendency
Trout Creek Press
2 AM Magazine
Underpass
Underwhich Editions
Viet Nam Generation
Village Idiot, The
W.I.M. Publications
Waterways
West of Boston
White Eagle Coffee Store
Whole Notes
Wild East
Willamette River Books
Wind Publications
Windless Orchard, The
Wineberry Press
WoRM fEASt!
Wormwood Review Press
Writers' Center Press
Writers Forum (England)
Xenophilia
xib
Xiquan Publishing House

Geographical Index

Use this index to locate small presses and magazines in your region. Much of the poetry published today reflects regional interests; also publishers often favor poets (and work) from their own areas. The listings are arranged alphabetically by state; refer to the General Index for specific page numbers. Also check your neighboring states for other opportunities.

The last sections are publishers in Canada, United Kingdom and other countries. Remember to always include a SAE with IRCs for replies from countries outside your own.

Alaska
Alaska Quarterly Review
Explorations
Intertext
Permafrost
Salmon Run Pub-
    lishers

Alabama
Alabama Literary Review
Aura Literary/Arts Mag.

Birmingham Poetry Review
Black Warrior Review, The
Catamount Press
Dreams and Nightmares
Druid Press
Elk River Review
Fighting Woman News
Laureate Letter, The
Minority Literary Expo
National Forum

Negative Capability
9th St. Laboratories
Poem
Southern Humanities
Sticks
Stohlmberg Publishers
Sucarnochee Review, The

Arkansas
Arkansas Press, The University
    of

Yale Review, The
Yale University Press

District of Columbia
Aerial
American Scholar, The
Dickinson Studies
Folio: A Literary Journal
G.W. Review
Middle East Report
New Republic, The
Plum Review, The
Sojourners
Three Continents Press Inc.
Washington Review
Washington Writers' Pub.
Wineberry Press

Delaware
Turbulence

Florida
Albatross
Anhinga Press
Anything That Moves
Apalachee Quarterly
Beer & Pub Poetry
Candlestones
Cathartic, The
Cats Magazine
Central Florida Contemporary
    Poetry Series, University of
Ediciones Universal
Emerald Coast Review
Florida Review, The
Gulf Stream Magazine
Half Tones to Jubilee
Harp-Strings
Human Quest, The
Kalliope
National Enquirer
New Collage Magazine
New Writer's Magazine
Onionhead
Panhandler, The
Pet Gazette, The
Poetry of the People
Runaway Spoon Press, The
Sun Dog
Tampa Review
Thematic Poetry Quarterly
Thoughts for All Seasons
Tiger Moon Press
White Sands Poetry Review
Write Way, The
Yesterday's Magazette
Abiko Quarterly Litter-ary Rag

Georgia
baby sue
Catalyst
Chattahoochee Review
Classical Outlook, The
Dickey Newsletter, James
Gaia
Georgia Journal
Georgia Press, University of
Georgia Review, The
Ice Cold Watermelon

Kennesaw Review
Linwood Publishers
Lullwater Review
Old Red Kimono, The
Parnassus Literary Journal
Pendragon
Poet's Review
Press of the Nightowl, The
Snake Nation Review
Society of American Poets
Twisted

Hawaii
Aloha
Chaminade
Hawaii Pacific Review
Hawai'i Review
Kaimana
Manoa
Pep Publishing
Petronium Press

Iowa
Ansuda Publications
Blue Light Press
Coe Review, The
Interstate Religious Writers
    Association
Iowa Review, The
Iowa Woman
Poet & Critic
Windhover Press, The

Idaho
Ahsahta Press
American Cowboy Poet
Boots
Confluence Press
Emshock Letter, The
Figment
Fugue
Limberlost Press
Paper Radio
Rocky Mountain Review
Science Fiction Poetry Associa-
    tion
Snake River Reflections
Trestle Creek Review
Village Idiot, The

Illinois
ACM (Another Chicago Maga-
    zine)
Aim Magazine
Anaconda Press
Ascent
Bagman Press
Black Books Bulletin
Brilliant Star
Chicago Review
Christian Century, The
Clockwatch Review
Cornerstone
Creative Woman, The
Cricket
Critic, The
Daughters of Sarah
Dream Int.
Farmer's Market

Gotta Write Network Litmag
Great Lakes Poetry Press
High/Coo Press
His Garden Magazine
Illinois Press, University of
Illinois Review, The
Insects Are People Too
International Black Writers
Journal of the American Medi-
    cal Association
Karamu
Kumquat Meringue
Lake Shore Publishing
Libido
Light
Magic Changes
Midwest Poetry Review
Mississippi Valley Review
Mystery Time
NCASA Journal
Night Roses
Nomos Press Inc.
Oak, The
Oblates
Outrider Press
Paper Bag, The
Path Press, Inc.
Pikestaff Forum, The
Poetic License
Poetry
Poetry East
Poetry Plus Magazine
Poets Pen Quarterly
Press of the Third Mind
Primavera
Rambunctious Press
Red Herring Poets
Rhino
Rockford Review, The
Shaw Publishers, Harold
Sou'Wester
Spoon River Poetry Review
Stormline Press, Inc.
Student Leadership Journal
Thorntree Press
Tia Chucha Press
TriQuarterly Magazine
2 AM Magazine
Whetstone (IL)
White Eagle Coffee Store
Willow Review
Young Crusader, The

Indiana
African American Review
Barnwood Press
Children's Better Health Insti-
    tute
Evangel
Explorer Magazine
Formalist, The
Hopewell Review
Indiana Review
Light and Life Magazine
Lines n' Rhymes
Once Upon A World
Pablo Lennis
Poets' Roundtable
Purdue University Press

Rag Mag
Sing Heavenly Muse!
Sisters Today
White Review, James
Writer's Journal

Missouri
Afro-Hispanic Review
Anterior Poetry Monthly
Big Now, The
Cape Rock, The
Cat's Ear
Chariton Review Press, The
Communications Publishing
  Group
Communities
Gospel Publishing House
Helicon Nine Editions
Laurel Review
manna
Metro Singles Lifestyles
Missouri Press, University of
Missouri Review
Nazarene Int. Hdq.
New Letters
Paintbrush
River Styx Magazine
Sharing the Victory
Timberline Press
Tornado Alley Quarterly
Unity
Webster Review
Writer's Guidelines

Mississippi
Bell's Letters Poet
Cross Roads
Mississippi Review

Montana
Corona
Council for Indian Education
Cutbank
Montana Poet Magazine
Perceptions
Portable Wall
Seven Buffaloes Press
Zeitgeist

Nebraska
American Dane
Beggar's Press
Climbing Art, The
Nebraska Review, The
Penumbra Press, The
Plainsongs
Prairie Schooner
Rock Falls Review

Nevada
Interim
Limited Editions Press
Pegasus
Sierra Nevada College Review

New Hampshire
Bauhan, Publisher, Wm. L.
Bone & Flesh Publications
Color Wheel

Golden Quill Press
Journeymen
Womenwise
Yankee Magazine

New Jersey
Africa World Press
Antaeus
Ararat
black bough
Blind Alleys
Chantry Press
Chimera Poetry Magazine for
  Children
Companion in Zeor, A
Exit 13
Fellowship in Prayer
First Hand
Footwork
Journal of New Jersey Poets
Kelsey Review
Lincoln Springs Press
Literary Review
Long Shot
Mixed Media
Ontario Review
Pegasus Review, The
Princeton University Press
Quarterly Review of Literature
  Poetry Series
Raritan Quarterly
Rose Shell Press
St. Joseph Messenger and Ad-
  vocate of the Blind
Saturday Press, Inc.
Silver Apples Press
Still Waters Press
Tails of Wonder
Talisman
US1 Worksheets
Warthog Press
Without Halos
Words of Wisdom

New Mexico
Duende Press
FishDrum
Frontiers
Katydid Books
New Mexico Humanities Re-
  view
Puerto Del Sol
Whole Notes

New York
Adrift
Advocate, The
Alms House Press
America
Amicus Journal, The
Antipodes
Art Times
Bacon Press, The
Bad Henry Review, The
Bank Street Press, The
Bantam Doubleday Dell
Belhue Press
Blue Ryder
Blueline

Boa Editions, Ltd.
Bomb Magazine
BOOG Literature
Braziller, Inc., George
Brooklyn Review
Buffalo Spree Magazine
C.L.A.S.S. Magazine
Camellia
Canal Lines
Columbia
Columbia University Transla-
  tion Center
Commonweal
Confrontation Magazine
Conjunctions
Cosmopolitan
Cover Magazine
Cross-Cultural Communica-
  tions
CWM
Dbqp
Different Drummer, A
Earth's Daughters
11th St. Ruse
ELF
Epoch
Essence
Farrar, Straus & Giroux
Feh!
Firebrand Books
For Poets Only
Free Focus
Frogpond
Futurific Magazine
Giants Play Well in the Drizzle
Giorno Poetry Systems Re-
  cords
Good Housekeeping
Graham House Review
Grand Street
Grove Atlantic
Grue Magazine
Hanging Loose Press
Heaven Bone Press
Helikon Press
Heresies
Holiday House, Inc.
Holt & Company, Henry
Home Planet News
Hudson Review, The
Hudson Valley Echoes
Iconoclast, The
Inky Blue
Israel Horizons
Italica Press
Jewish Currents
Journal of Poetry Therapy
Judi-isms
Keystrokes
Kiosk
Kitchen Table
Knopf, Alfred A.
Lactuca
Lang Publishing, Inc., Peter
Latest Jokes Newsletter
Ledge Poetry and Fiction
Lilith Magazine
Living Poets Society (NY)
Lodestar Books

Whitecrow Foundation
Wilderness
Willamette River Books

Pennsylvania
Absolute Interzone Bizarre
Aguilar Expression, The
Allegheny Review
Alpha Beat Soup
Alternative Press Magazine
American Poetry Review
American Writing
Anima
Apropos
Black Bear Publications
Bouillabaisse
Boulevard
Branch Redd Books
Carnegie Mellon Magazine
Cokefish
Collages & Bricolages
Cool Traveler, The
Country Journal
Creeping Bent
Dead Rebel News
Dust (From the Ego Trip)
Family Earth
Fat Tuesday
Feelings
5 AM
Flipside
Four Quarters
Friends Journal
Gettysburg Review, The
Ginger Hill
Green World Press
Guyasuta Publisher
Hellas
Highlights for Children
Hob-Nob
Journal of Asian Martial Arts
Lilliput Review
Mennonite Pub. House
Miraculous Medal, The
My Legacy
Other Side Magazine, The
Pennsylvania English
Pennsylvania Review, The
Phoenix Press
Pitt Poetry Series
Pittsburgh Quarterly, The
Poetry Forum
Poets at Work
Post-Industrial Press
Quick Brown Fox
Raw Dog Press
Reconstructionist
Rolling Coulter, The
Shooting Star Review
Singing Horse Press
Taproot Literary Review
Translucent Tendency
West Branch
Widener Review
Wordsong
Yarrow, A Journal of Poetry
Zuzu's Petals Quarterly

Rhode Island
Aldebaran
Copper Beech Press
Gávea-Brown Publications
Haunts
Hunted News, The
Italian Americana
Merlyn's Pen
Northeast Journal

South Carolina
Devil's Millhopper Press
Emrys Journal
Ninety-Six Press
Nostalgia
Palanquin
Raven, The
South Carolina Review
Writer's Exchange

South Dakota
Hen's Teeth
Pasque Petals
Prairie Winds
South Dakota Review
Tesseract Publications
Wicazo SA Review, The

Tennessee
Aethlon
alive now!
Baptist Sunday School Board
Co-Laborer Magazine
Cumberland Poetry Review
Four Directions, The
Mature Years
Nashville House
Now and Then
Old Hickory Review
RFD
Romantist, The
Rural Heritage
Sewanee Review, The
Southeastern FRONT
Sow's Ear, The

Texas
Aileron Press
American Atheist Press
American Literary Review
Analecta
Argonaut
Art-Core!
Arte Publico Press
Baby Connection News
Black Tie Press
Borderlands
Cochran's Corner
Concho River Review
Context South
Dagger of the Mind
Daily Meditation
Descant
Encodings
Experiment in Words
Grasslands Review
Gulf Coast
Gypsy
Inverted-A, Inc.

Julian Associates
Language Bridges
Literary Focus Poetry Publications
Maverick Press, The
North Texas Press, University of
Office Number One
Peace Farm Advocate, The
Prose Poem, The
REAL (Re Arts & Letters)
Red Rampan' Press
Rio Grande Press
Riverside Quarterly
Southwest Review
Stevan Company, The
Strain, The
Sulphur River Literary Review
Tangram Press
Texas Tech University Press
Touchstone
United Methodist Reporter

Utah
Dialogue
Ellipsis Magazine
International Poets of the Heart
Leading Edge, The
Literature and Belief
Magic Realism
Manna
New Era Magazine
Paper Salad Poetry Journal
Smith Publisher, Gibbs
Utah Holiday Magazine
Utah State University Press

Virginia
Black Buzzard Press
Bogg Publications
Brunswick Publishing
Chronicle of the Horse, The
Chrysalis
Dolphin Log
Dominion Review, The
Hollins Critic, The
Intro
Lintel
Lyric, The
Metropolitain
Miriam Press
New Virginia Review
Orchises Press
Piedmont Literary Review
Pocahontas Press, Inc.
Poetry Explosion
Proof Rock Press
Ranger Rick Magazine
Reflect
Roanoke Review
St. Andrew Press
Shenandoah
Vandeloecht's Fiction Magazine
Verse
Virginia Quarterly Review
William and Mary Review

Vermont
Awede Press
Green Mountains Review
Longhouse
New England Review
Threshold Books

Washington
Ag-Pilot Int. Magazine
Arnazella
Bad Haircut
Bear Tribe Publishing
Bellowing Ark Press
Brooding Heron Press
Brussels Sprout
Cleaning Business Magazine
Crab Creek Review
Dragongate Press
Duckabush Journal
Fine Madness
Fredrickson-Kloepfel
Graven Images
IHCUT
Jeopardy
L'Epervier Press
Lighthouse
Lockhart Press, The
Olympia Review
Open Hand Publishing Inc.
Orphic Lute
Owl Creek Press
Poetry Northwest
Poets. Painters. Composers.
Seattle Review
Signpost Press, The
Spindrift
Tapjoe
Twopenny Porringer, The
Willow Springs
Young Voices Magazine

Wisconsin
Abraxas Magazine
Blank Gun Silencer
Block's Poetry Collection
Caxton Ltd., Wm
Changing Men
Country Woman
Cream City Review
Dionysos
Fox Cry
Madison Review, The
Magazine of Speculative Poetry, The
Modern Haiku
Page 5
Peacemaking for Children
Ranger Int. Productions
Redneck Review of Literature, The
Touchstone
Wisconsin Academy Review
Wisconsin Press, University of
Wisconsin Restaurateur
Wisconsin Review

West Virginia
Aegina Press, Inc.

Wyoming
High Plains Press
Housewife-Writer's Forum

Puerto Rico
Revista/Review Interamericana

U.S. Virgin Islands
Caribbean Writer, The
Eastern Caribbean Institute

Canada
Aardvark Enterprises
Alchemist, The
Amber
Anjou
Antigonish Review, The
Arc
Ariel
Atlantis
Beneath the Surface
Borealis Press
Canadian Author
Canadian Dimension
Canadian Literature
Canadian Writer's Journal
Capers Aweigh Magazine
Carleton Arts Review
Carousel Magazine
Chalk Talk
Chickadee Magazine
Church-Wellesley Review, The
Coach House Press
Compenions
Cosmic Trend
Coteau Books
Dalhousie Review, The
Dance Connection
Dandelion
Descant
Ellipse
Event
Fiddlehead, The
Fireweed
Goose Lane Editions
Grain
Green's Magazine
Guernica Editions Inc.
Herspectives
Indigo Magazine
Inkstone
Legend
Malahat Review, The
Matrix
(m)öthêr TØñgués
Musicworks
New Quarterly, The
Nexus (Canada)
Our Family
Peckerwood
Plowman, The
Poetry WLU
Power Animal
Prairie Fire
Prairie Publishing

Presbyterian Record, The
Prism International
Quarry Magazine
Queen's Quarterly
Raddle Moon
Room of One's Own
Scat!
Secrets from the Orange Couch
Sister Vision Press
Sub-Terrain
Tessera
Thalia
Thistledown Press Ltd.
Tickled by Thunder
Tidepool
Tower Poetry Society
Townships Sun
Turnstone Press
Tyro Writers' Group
Underpass
Underwhich Editions
Unmuzzled Ox
Vehicule Press
Western Producer Pub.
Whetstone (Canada)
White Wall Review
Wild East
Windhorse Review, The
Windsor Review, University of
Wolsak and Wynn
Women's Education Des Femmes
Women's Press
Writ
Writer's Lifeline

United Kingdom
Acumen Magazine
Aireings
Allardyce, Barnett
Alphabox Press
Ambit
Aquarius
Calder Publications Ltd.
Chapman
Countryman, The
Crescent Moon
DAM
Diehard
Enitharmon Press
Envoi
Equinox Press
European Judaism
First Time
Foolscap
Forest Books
Frogmore Papers
Gairm
Global Tapestry Journal
Hangman Books
Hilltop Press
Hippopotamus Press
Honest Ulsterman
House of Moonlight
Hrafnhoh
Illuminations
Inkshed
Iota
Iron Press

Jackson's Arm
Joe Soap's Canoe
Kawabata Press
Krax
Lines Review
London Magazine
Mandeville Press, The
Memes
New Hope International
New Welsh Review
Nutshell
Oasis Books
One Earth
Orbis
Ore
Oriel Bookshop
Otter
Outreach
Paranoia Press
Pennine Ink
Pennine Platform
Phlebas Press, The
Phoenix Broadsheets
Plantagenet Productions
Poetical Histories
Poetry & Audience
Poetry Durham
Poetry Nottingham
Poetry Wales Press
Psychopoetica
Purple Patch
Quartos Magazine
Reality Streed Editions

Red Candle Press, The
Rialto, The
Scratch
Second Aeon Publications
Skoob Books Publishing
Smiths Knoll
Spectacular Diseases
Spokes
Stand Magazine
Staple
Stride Publications
Tak Tak Tak
Tears in the Fence
10th Muse
Third Half Literary Magazine, The
Times Literary Supplement
Weyfarers
Works Magazine
Writers Forum

Foreign
Abiko Quarterly Litter-ary Rag (Japan)
Carrefour Press, The (South Africa)
Doc(k)s (France)
Frank (France)
Going Down Swinging (Austra-lia)
Imago: New Writing (Austra-lia)
Improvijazzation Nation (Ko-rea)
International Poets Academy (India)

La Carta de Oliver (Argentina)
Landfall (New Zealand)
LiNQ (Australia)
Manushi (India)
Maroverlag (Germany)
New Cicada (Japan)
Northern Perspective (Austra-lia)
Nosukumo (Australia)
Paris/Atlantic (France)
Pinchgut Press (Australia)
Poetry Kanto (Japan)
Poetry Nippon Press (Japan)
Polyphonies (France)
Prakalpana Literature (India)
Printed Matter (Japan)
Rashi (New Zealand)
Renditions (Hong Kong)
San Miguel Writer (Mexico)
Sandberry Press (West Indies)
Scarp (Australia)
Studio (Australia)
Takahe (New Zealand)
Transnational Perspectives (Switzerland)
Vanitas Press, The (Sweden)
Verandah (Australia)
Voices Israel
Westerly (Australia)
Witwatersrand University Press (South Africa)

Subject Index

Use this index to save time in your search for the best market for your poem(s). The categories are listed alphabetically and contain the magazines, publishers, contests and awards that buy or accept poetry in these special categories. Most of these markets are coded **IV** in their listings.

Check through the index first to see the subjects. Then look at the listings in the subjects you're interested in. For example, if you're seeking a magazine or contest for your poem about homelessness, look at the listings under *Social Issues*. After you've selected a possible market, refer to the General Index for the page number. Then read the listing *carefully* for details on submission requirements.

In the section **Themes**, there are publishers and magazines which publish poetry on a particular theme or subject or publications directed to a special audience. The **Regional** section lists those outlets which publish poetry about or by poets from a special geographic area; and the category **Form/Style** contains those magazines and presses with a specific preference for haiku, sonnets, narrative poems or visual poetry, for example.

We do not recommend you use this index exclusively in your search for a market. Most magazines, publishers and contests listed in **Poet's Market** are very general in their specifications and don't choose to be listed by category. Also, many specialize in one subject but are open to others as well. Reading *all* the listings is still your best marketing strategy.

Anthology
Anthology of Magazine Verse & Yearbook of American Poetry
Ashland Poetry Press, The
Beer & Pub Poetry
Bellflower Press
Catamount Press
Crescent Moon
Cross-Cultural Communications
Fredrickson-Kloepfel
Georgia State Poetry Society, Inc.
Geppo Haiku Worksheet
Great Lakes Poetry Press
Guild Press
Gypsy
Helicon Nine Editions
Hen's Teeth
Illinois Press, University of
Judi-isms
Kawabata Press
Kitchen Table
Lake Shore Publishing
Literary Focus Poetry Pub.
Literary Olympics, Inc.
Lodestar Books
Nada Press
New Horizons Poetry Club
Night Roses
Northwoods Press
Papier-Mache Press
Penumbra Press, The
Plowman, The
Poetic Knight
Poetic Perspective, Inc.
Pudding House Pub.
Roberts Foundation Writing Awards, The
San Fernando Poetry Journal
Science Fiction Poetry Association
Seven Buffaloes Press
Shamal Books
Society of American Poets
Spirit That Moves Us, The
Summer Stream Press
Three Continents Press Inc.
Voices Israel
Waterways
West Wind Review
White Eagle Coffee Store
Wind Publications
Wineberry Press

Bilingual/Foreign Language
Atalantik (Bengali)
Bilingual Review Press (Spanish)
Cross-Cultural Communications
Doc(k)s (French)
Ediciones Universal (Spanish)
Ellipse (French)
Footwork (Spanish)
Gairm (Scottish Gaelic)
Gávea-Brown Publications (Portugese)
Indigo Magazine (French, Spanish)
Irish-American Cultural Institute Literary Awards
La Carta de Oliver (Spanish)
Language Bridges Quarterly (Polish)
Letras De Oro Spanish Literary Prizes
M.I.P. Company (Russian)
Maroverlag (German)
Nada Press (Spanish)
New Chicana/Chicano Writing (Spanish)
Osiris (French, Italian, Polish, Danish, German)
Prakalpana Literature (Bengali)
Princeton University Press
REAL (Re Arts & Letters)
Sachem Press (Spanish)
San Miguel Writer (Spanish)
Tessera (French)
Unmuzzled Ox (French)
Wake Forest University Press (Irish, French)
Witwatersrand University Press (African languages)
Women's Studies Quarterly (Spanish, French, Italian, German)

Children/Teen/Young Adult
Advocacy Press
alive now!
Brilliant Star
Broken Streets
Cat Fancy
Chalk Talk
Chickadee Magazine
Children's Better Health Institute
Chimera Poetry Magazine for Children
Clubhouse
College & Career Pub.
Communications Publishing
Coteau Books
Creative With Words Publications (C.W.W.)
Cricket

Dolphin Log
Farrar, Straus & Giroux
Gospel Publishing House
Hanging Loose Press
Hartland Poetry Quarterly
Highlights for Children
Holiday House, Inc.
Hopscotch
Kwibidi Publisher
Lighthouse
Lodestar Books
Louisville Review, The
Mennonite Publishing
Merlyn's Pen
Nazarene Int. Headquarters
New Era Magazine
Night Roses
Oak, The
Pandora
Peacemaking for Children
Pelican Publishing
Pikestaff Forum, The
Place in the Woods, The
Poetry Break
Poetry of Hope Award
Poetry Society of Michigan Annual Competitions
Poetry: USA Quarterly
Poets Pen Quarterly
Sandberry Press
Scholastic Writing Awards
Seventeen
Shofar
Sow's Ear, The
Stone Soup, The Magazine by Children
Straight
Team
Touch
Vanitas Press, The
Vegetarian Journal
Waterways
Whole Notes
Wordsong
Young Crusader, The
Young Voices Magazine

Ethnic/Nationality
Adrift (Irish, Irish-American)
Africa World Press (African, African-American, Caribbean and Latin-American)
African American Review
Afro-Hispanic Review
Aim Magazine
Alicejamesbooks (poets of color)
American Dane
Ararat (Armenian)
Arte Publico Press (US Hispanic)

Atalantik (Bengali)
Bear Tribe Publishing (Native American)
Bilingual Review Press (Hispanic)
Black Books Bulletin
Black Scholar, The
C.L.A.S.S. Magazine (Caribbean/American/African Third World)
Callaloo (North, South and Central American; European; African; Caribbean)
Carolina Wren Press (minorities)
Chapman (Scottish)
Communications Publishing (Asian-American, Black, Hispanic, Native American)
Council for Indian Education
Different Drummer, A
Eagle, The (Native American)
Ediciones Universal (Spanish, Cuban)
El Barrio (Latino)
El Tecolote (Latin American, US Latino)
Essence (African-American Women)
European Judaism
Firebrand Books
Four Directions, The (Native American)
Gairm (Scottish Gaelic)
Gávea-Brown Publications (Portugese-American)
Guernica Editions Inc. (Italian, Italian-Canadian, Italian American)
Guild Press (minorities)
Ice Cold Watermelon (African-American)
India Currents
International Black Writers
Irish-American Cultural Institute Literary Awards
Israel Horizons
Italian Americana
Japanophile
Judi-isms (Jewish)
Kitchen Table: Women of Color Press
Kwibidi Publisher (minorities)
La Bella Figura (Italian-American)
Language Bridges Quarterly (Polish)
L'Apache: An International Journal of Literature & Art
Lilith Magazine (Jewish)
Living Poets Society (NY)
Middle East Report
Midstream: A Monthly Jewish Review
Minority Literary Expo
Miorita: A Journal of Romanian Studies
New Chicana/Chicano Writing
New Welsh Review

Obsidian II: Black Literature in Review
Oracle Poetry (African)
Path Press, Inc. (African-American, Third World)
Poetry Wales Press (Welsh, Welsh-American)
Rarach Press (Czech)
Rashi (Jewish)
Reconstructionist (Jewish)
Response (Jewish)
Review: Latin American Literature and Arts
Revista/Review Interamericana (Puerto Rican, Caribbean, Hispanic American)
Rosenberg Award, Anna Davidson (Jewish)
Sandberry Press (Caribbean)
Shamal Books (African-American, Caribbean)
Shofar (American Jewish)
Shooting Star Review (African-American)
Sister Vision Press (Women of Color)
Soleil Press (Franco-American)
Stone Circle Press (Celtic)
Three Continents Press Inc. (non-Western; Asian/Pacific; Africa; Middle East; Caribbean)
Tia Chucha Press (African, Asian, Latin, Native American)
Victorian Fellowship of Australian Writers, The
Wake Forest University Press (Irish, French)
Whitecrow Foundation, Tahana (Native American)
Wicazo SA Review, The (Native American)
Witwatersrand University Press (African)

Form/Style

Alpha Beat Soup (Beat)
Amelia (all forms)
American Writing: A Magazine (experimental)
Asylum (prose poems)
Bennett & Kitchel
black bough
Bouillabaisse
Brussels Sprout (haiku, senryu, tanka)
Dbqp (short language, visual)
Duende Press (avant-garde Earth poems)
Equinox Press (haiku, senryu)
European Poetry Library
Experimental (Basement) Press (visual, conceptual, language)
Formalist, The (metrical)
Frank: An International Jour-

nal of Contemporary Writing and Art
Free Focus
Frogpond: Biannual Haiku Journal
Generator (language, concrete, visual)
Georgia State Poetry Society, Inc.
Geppo Haiku Worksheet
Green Rivers Writers' Contests
Haiku Headlines: A Monthly Newsletter of Haiku and Senryu
Hellas: A Journal of Poetry and the Humanities
High/Coo Press (haiku)
Hippopotamus Press
Hrafnhoh (metrical Christian)
Inkstone: A Magazine of Haiku
Lilliput Review (no longer than 10 lines)
Los Hombres Press (haiku)
Luna Bisonte Prods (experimental, visual, collaboration)
Lyric, The (traditional)
M.A.F. Press (13 lines only)
Malahat Review, The (long poems)
Mirrors (haiku)
Modern Haiku
New Cicada (haiku)
9th St. Laboratories (experimental, graphic)
North Carolina Haiku Society Press, The
Paper Radio (up to 100 lines)
Piedmont Literary Review (oriental, haiku)
Plains Poetry Journal (rhyme, meter)
Poetry Nippon Press (tanka, haiku, one-line poems)
Poetry Society of Virginia Annual Contest, The (haiku, sonnet, limerick, popular song lyric)
Poets Club of Chicago International Shakespearean Sonnet Contest
Point Judith Light (haiku, senryu)
Prakalpana Literature (experimental, avant-garde)
Press of the Third Mind, The (concrete, collaborative)
Prose Poem, The
Raddle Moon (language-centered, new lyric)
Red Candle Press, The
Red Rampan' Press (long poems)
Reflect (spiral poetry)
Rhyme International Competition for Rhyming Poetry
Runaway Spoon Press, The (visual, textual)
Salmon Arm Sonnet Contest

Regional

Above the Bridge Magazine (Upper Peninsula, MI)

Acorn Poetry Award, Milton (PEI, Canada)

Ahsahta Press (American West)

Air Canada Award, The

Alicejamesbooks (New England)

Aloha, The Magazine of Hawaii and the Pacific

Antietam Review (DC, DE, MD, PA, VA, WV)

Antipodes (Australia)

Appalachian Heritage (Southern Appalachia)

Artist Trust (WA)

Atlantic Writing Competition (Atlantic provinces)

Blueline (Adirondacks)

Borderlands: Texas Poetry Review

BP Nichol Chapbook Award (Canada)

Bush Artist Fellowships (SD, ND, western WI, MN)

C.L.A.S.S. Magazine (Caribbean, American, African Third World)

Canadian Authors Association Literary Awards

Canadian Literature

Canal Lines (New England, upstate NY)

Capers Aweigh Magazine (Cape Breton, Nova Scotia, Canada)

Caribbean Writer, The

Caxton Ltd., Wm (northern Midwest)

Chaminade Literary Review (HI)

Cincinnati Poetry Review

Cintas Fellowship Program

Coach House Press

Concho River Review (TX)

Confluence Press (northwestern US)

Coolbrith Circle Annual Poetry Contest, Ina (CA)

Coteau Books (Canada)

Cottonwood (KS, Midwest)

Coyote Chronicles: Notes from the Southwest

Creative Artist Program (Houston)

Cross Roads: A Journal of Southern Culture

Dandelion (Alberta, Canada)

Descant (Canada)

Dolphin-Moon Press (MD)

Eastern Caribbean Institute

Ediciones Universal (Cuba)

El Barrio (SW Detroit)

Emerald Coast Review (Gulf Coast)

European Poetry Library (European Community)

Farmer's Market (Midwest)

Fiddlehead, The (Canada, Atlantic)

Fireweed: Poetry of Western Oregon

FishDrum (West Coast)

Footwork: The Paterson Literary Review (Passaic County, NJ)

Georgia Journal

Glassco Translation Prize, John (Canada)

Goose Lane Editions (Canada)

Guernica Editions Inc. (Canada)

Hangman Books (England)

High Plains Press (WY, US West)

Honest Ulsterman (Northern Ireland)

Hopewell Review (Indiana)

Imago: New Writing (Queensland, Australia)

India Currents

Journal of New Jersey Poets

Kaimana: Literary Arts Hawaii (Pacific)

Kansas Quarterly

Kelsey Review

Lampman Award (Ottawa)

Landfall (New Zealand)

Leacock Medal for Humour, The Stephen (Canada)

LiNQ (North Queensland, Australia)

Long Island Quarterly

Loonfeather

Louisiana Literature

Matrix (Canada)

Maverick Press, The (TX)

Mayapple Press (Great Lakes)

Metropolitain

Middle East Report

Midwest Villages & Voices

Minority Literary Expo (AL)

Montana Institute of the Arts Poetry Contest

Montana Poet Magazine, The

New Mexico Humanities Review

New Quarterly, The (Canada)

New Rivers Press (IA, MN, ND, SD, WI)

New York Foundation for the Arts

Ninety-Six Press (SC)

North Carolina Poetry Society Zoe Kincaid Brockman Memorial Book Award Contest, The

North Texas Press, University of

Northeast Journal (RI)

Northwest Poets & Artists Calendar

Now and Then (Appalachia)

Ohioana Book Awards

Oregon East

Oriel Bookshop (Wales)

Ornish Poetry Award, Natalie (TX)

Ottawa-Carleton Book Award

Otter (Devon, England)

Out Loud: The Monthly of Los Angeles Area Poetry Events

Painted Hills Review (West Coast)

Paranoia Press (Cleveland, UK)

Pasque Petals (SD)

Pelican Publishing Company (Southern US)

Permafrost (AK)

Petronium Press (HI)

Pinchgut Press (Australia)

Poetical Histories (England)

Poets' Dinner Contest (Berkeley, CA)

Potato Eyes (Appalachian Chain)

Prairie Publishing Company, The (Manitoba, Canada)

Presidio La Bahia Award (TX)

Puckerbrush Press, The (ME)

Pueblo Poetry Project

Puerto Del Sol (US Southwest)

Quarry Magazine (Canada)

Queen's Quarterly: A Canadian Review

Rambunctious Press (Chicago)

Redneck Review of Literature, The (US West)

Regional Artists' Projects Grant

Review: Latin American Literature and Arts

Revista/Review Interamericana

Ridge Review Magazine (northern CA)

Riverwind (Appalachia)

San Francisco Foundation

Sandberry Press (Caribbean)

Sandburg Awards, Carl (Chicago)

Saskatchewan Writers Guild Annual Literary Awards (Regina, Saskatchewan)

Scat! (Canada)

Scop Publications, Inc. (MD)

Seven Buffaloes Press (US West, CA, southern Appalachia)

Society of Midland Authors Award (IL, IN, IA, KS, MI, MN, MO, NE, ND, SD, OH, WI)

Solo Flyer (OH)

South Dakota Review (US West)

Sow's Ear, The (Appalachia)

Spectrum/Old Times (CO)

Spoon River Poetry Review, The (IL)

Tessera (Canada)

Thistledown Press Ltd. (Canada)

Thumbprints (MI)

Radcliffe Quarterly (alumnae)
Slate & Style (blind writers)
Vanitas Press, The (children's)

Spirituality/Inspirational
Anima
Capper's
Chrysalis
Color Wheel
Crescent Moon
Explorer Magazine
Heaven Bone Press
His Garden Magazine
Moksha Journal
New Earth Publications
Oblates
One Earth
Poetry Break
Presbyterian Record, The
Rainbow City Express
Sharing the Victory
Silver Wings
Star Books, Inc.
Studio
TAL
Threshold Books

Sports
Aethlon
Sharing the Victory
Spitball

Students
Allegheny Review
Analecta
Bucknell Seminar for Younger
   Poets
College & Career
Dream Shop, The
Fiddlehead, The
Hanging Loose Press
League of Minnesota Poets
   Contest, The
Lyric, The
Merlyn's Pen
Modern Haiku
National Written & Illustrated
   By . . . Awards Contest for
   Students
Night Roses
Pratt Gold Medal and Prize
Rackham Journal of the Arts
   and Humanities
Response
Student Leadership Journal

Themes
alive now! (children's religious)
American Atheist Press
American Cowboy Poet Maga-
   zine, The
American Tolkien Society
Apalachee Quarterly (as an-
   nounced)
Ashland Poetry Press, The (as
   announced)
Atlantean Press Review, The
   (human value)
Baker Street Publications (hor-

ror, mystery, science fiction,
   fantasy, western, literary)
Bear Tribe Publishing (earth
   awareness, self-sufficiency,
   sacred places, native peo-
   ple)
Beer & Pub Poetry
Bellflower Press (societal val-
   ues)
Bishop Publishing Co. (folk-
   lore)
Black Mountain Review (as an-
   nounced)
Bloodreams: A Magazine of
   Vampires & Werewolves
Boots
Byline Magazine (writing)
Canadian Writer's Journal
Cat Fancy
Catalyst
Cats Magazine
Chips Off the Writer's Block
Chronicle of the Horse, The
Chrysalis: Journal of the Swe-
   denborg Foundation
Classical Outlook, The
Cleaning Business Magazine
Climbing Art, The
Colorado Review
Communications Publishing
   (college preparation, career
   planning, life skills)
Cool Traveler, The
Cosmic Trend (new age)
Council for Indian Education
Cowboy Magazine
Coyote Chronicles: Notes from
   the Southwest
Creative With Words Publica-
   tions (C.W.W.)
Creative Woman, The
CWM (as announced)
Cyanosis (provocative topics)
DAM (Disability Arts Maga-
   zine)
Dance Connection
Daughters of Sarah (feminist
   Christian philosophy)
Different Drummer, A (urban)
Dionysos: The Literature and
   Addiction TriQuarterly
Dolphin Log (ecology, environ-
   ment)
Dream International Quarterly
Dry Crik Review (cowboys, cat-
   tle business)
Dust (autobiographical)
Earth's Daughters: A Feminist
   Arts Periodical
Event (as announced)
Feh! A Journal of Odious Po-
   etry
Fighting Woman News (women
   in martial arts)
Five Fingers Review
Fredrickson-Kloepfel (as an-
   nounced)
Friends Journal (Quakerism)
Futurific Magazine

Green Rivers Writers' Contests
   (as announced)
Grolier Poetry Prize
Hartland Poetry Quarterly, The
Heresies
Indigo Magazine: The Spanish-
   Canadian Presence in the
   Arts
Insects Are People Too
Journal of Asian Martial Arts
Journal of Poetry Therapy
Journal of the American Medi-
   cal Association
Judi-isms
Juggler's World
Julian Associates (living by
   night, writing)
Kaleidoscope: International
   Magazine of Literature,
   Fine Arts, and Disability
Kalliope
Kansas Quarterly (mid-
   America)
Keystrokes (writing, comput-
   ers)
Luna Ventures
Magic Changes (as announced)
Middle East Report
Midwifery Today
Miriam Press (women in crisis)
Musicworks
My Legacy
Mystery Time
Nada Press (objectivist-based)
Nashville House
NCASA Journal (Newsletter of
   the National Coalition
   Against Sexual Assault)
New Writer's Magazine
Now and Then (as announced)
Ore (Arthurian legend)
Papier-Mache Press (women's
   experience)
Partisan Review
Passager: A Journal of Remem-
   brance and Discovery
Peacemaking for Children
Pegasus Review, The (as an-
   nounced)
Penumbra Press, The
Pep Publishing (group mar-
   riage)
Pet Gazette, The
Pig Iron (as announced)
Pipe Smoker's Ephemeris
Poetry New York: A Journal of
   Poetry and Translation
Poetry of the People
Poetry of Hope Award
Poetry: USA Quarterly
Poets On: (as announced)
Psychopoetica
Queen's Mystery Magazine, El-
   lery
Rackham Journal of the Arts
   and Humanities
Rio Grande Press (la vie)
Rohwedder: International
   Journal of Literature & Art

General Index

Can't find a poetry publisher's listing? Check pages 447-448 at the end of the Publishers of Poetry section for Other Poetry Publishers.

Other Books of Interest

Poetry Books
Creating Poetry, by John Drury $18.95
The Poet's Handbook, by Judson Jerome (paper) $12.95

General Writing Books
Freeing Your Creativity, by Marshall Cook $17.95
30 Steps to Becoming a Writer, by Scott Edelstein $16.95
The 28 Biggest Writing Blunders. by William Noble $12.95
The Writer's Essential Desk Reference, edited by Glenda Neff $19.95
Writing as a Road to Self-Discovery, by Barry Lane $16.95

Nonfiction Writing
How to do Leaflets, Newsletter, & Newspapers, by Lisa Collier Cool (paper) $10.95
The Complete Guide to Magazine Article Writing, by John M. Wilson $17.95
Writing Articles From the Heart: How to Write & Sell Your Life Experiences, by Marjorie Holmes $16.95

Fiction Writing
Characters & Viewpoint, by Orson Scott Card $13.95
Creating Characters: How to Build Story People, by Dwight V. Swain $16.95
Dialogue, by Lewis Turco $13.95
Manuscript Submission, by Scott Edelsteinn $13.95
Plot, by Ansen Dibell $13.95
Scene and Structure, by Jack Bickham $14.95
Theme and Strategy, by Ronald B. Tobias $13.95

The Writing Business
The Complete Guide to Self-Publishing, by Tom & Marilyn Ross (paper) $18.95
This Business of Writing, by Gregg Levoy $19.95

To order directly from the publisher, include $3.00 postage and handling for 1 book and $1.00 for each additional book. Allow 30 days for delivery.

Notes

Notes

Notes

Notes

A Poetry Marketing Plan

Market Categories:

Look for these important codes in the listings to help you decide where to submit your poetry.

I Beginning: *Very open to beginners' submissions, often encourage and offer advice to new writers. May require fees, purchase of publication or membership in an organization.*

II General: *Usually accept 10% or less of poems received, but in this category a poet developing a list of publication credits will find many names respected in the literary world.*

III Limited: *Typically overstocked; do not encourage widespread submissions from poets who have not published elsewhere, although on occasion they publish relatively new and/or little-known poets.*

IV Specialized: *Publications which encourage contributors from a specific geographical area or a specific group (by age, ethnic background, etc.), or which accept poems in specific forms (e.g., haiku) or on specific themes.*

V Closed: *Listings which do not accept unsolicited manuscripts; you cannot submit without specific permission to do so.*